6-26-65

1965-66 $20.52

PLANT PHYSIOLOGY

A TREATISE

Plant
Physiology

Volume III: Inorganic Nutritio
of Plants

Plant Physiology

A TREATISE

EDITED BY
F. C. STEWARD

Department of Botany
Cornell University, Ithaca, New York

Volume III: Inorganic Nutrition
of Plants

1963

 ACADEMIC PRESS, *New York and London*

PRINTED IN THE UNITED STATES OF AMERICA

CONTRIBUTORS TO VOLUME III

C. BOULD, *Fruit Nutrition Section, Long Ashton Research Station, University of Bristol, England*

E. J. HEWITT, *Department of Plant Physiology, Long Ashton Research Station, University of Bristol, England*

WILLIAM D. McELROY, *McCollum-Pratt Institute, The Johns Hopkins University, Baltimore, Maryland*

JORMA K. MIETTINEN, *Biochemical Institute, Helsinki, Finland*

ALVIN NASON, *McCollum-Pratt Institute, The Johns Hopkins University, Baltimore, Maryland*

D. J. D. NICHOLAS, *Long Ashton Research Station, University of Bristol, England*

J. H. QUASTEL, *McGill University, Montreal, Canada*

ARTTURI I. VIRTANEN, *Biochemical Institute, Helsinki, Finland*

PREFACE TO VOLUME III

With Volume III, on mineral nutrition, the Treatise on Plant Physiology enters upon its second section, which deals with the nutrition and metabolism of plants.

In Volume II plants were considered in their general relation to water and to solutes. Photosynthesis and respiration, starting from and returning to carbon dioxide and water, have been discussed in Volumes IA and IB, and the manifold processes of intermediary metabolism will be taken up in Volume IV. Therefore, Volume III is now concerned solely with the role of those elements of the periodic table, other than carbon, hydrogen, and oxygen, which are essential to, or used by, plants in their vital processes.

In the subject of mineral nutrition, plant physiology bears a close relationship to agriculture. The practical importance of the mineral nutrition of plants, through manurial practices or fertilizer programs, gave to the emerging science of plant physiology much of its early impetus; this debt to agriculture has been amply repaid. This volume, then, briefly traces the history of mineral nutrition of plants, and, as it summarizes the present status of knowledge, the intention is that it will also point to the challenge of the future.

The plan of the treatise remains as previously announced, and its aims and general style have not changed. Again the subject matter could only be covered by a selected group of authors, each an authority in his own field. While each chapter of Volume III is complete in itself, the volume as a whole should present a philosophy of plant nutrition. In the difficult attainment of these ends, the individual authors have rightly exercised a large measure of discretion in their respective chapters, and the value of the volume thus rests upon their scholarly work. To all these contributors the editor is greatly indebted.

Although the various chapters in this volume are conveniently grouped together, this is nevertheless a somewhat arbitrary device, for, in their role, the mineral elements also touch all aspects of plant behavior. Thus hardly a physiological topic can be considered without at some point disclosing a connection with, or a decisive role for, some essential inorganic element. In fact, it is these interactions that give much of the current impetus to the subject of mineral nutrition.

The now familiar form of the indexes is preserved in this volume of the treatise. Subject and Author Indexes and an Index of Plant Names are again included. In the over-all plan of the entire treatise the same conventions concerning the use of plant names are applied in this as in the previous volumes, and the application of these conventions has again been supervised by Dr. W. J. Dress, who has also prepared the Index of Plant Names. The Subject Index for Volume III was compiled by Mr. Richard D. Holsten. For all this help the editor is also grateful.

Since the authors completed their manuscripts for this volume, the rules on nomenclature of enzymes and coenzymes have been reviewed by a Commission of the International Union of Biochemistry. The recommendations of this commission are summarized in *Science* (1962) **137**, 405–408. According to these recommendations, such time-honored names as cozymase; coenzyme I (Co I); coenzyme II (Co II); diphosphopyridine nucleotide (DPN); triphosphopyridine nucleotide (TPN) should no longer be used, although, for lack of a suitable alternative, coenzyme A (CoA) is still permissible! Therefore, in this volume the older and well understood practices have of necessity been retained, although it is apparent that plant physiologists must now learn to recognize these familiar enzymes and coenzymes under their new and approved names.

Wherever possible, the text is illustrated by figures and tables which are reproduced from original sources. The purpose of this is to present enough of both the evidence and the analysis of it to reduce the need continually to consult the original sources, which are also cited. Each author has obtained prior permission to include in his chapter the previously published material which he has used, and the form of citation in the text and in the bibliography is held to convey the acknowledgments and the thanks of both authors and editor for the use of these materials. To list separately all such cases in a work of this sort would be a formidable task indeed.

Finally, the editor again wishes to acknowledge the very real help he has received from the personnel of Academic Press.

F. C. Steward

Ithaca, New York
February, 1963

PLANT PHYSIOLOGY

The Plan of the Treatise

The treatise is planned in three main sections, as follows:

Section on *Cell Physiology and Problems Relating to Water and Solutes*

The purpose of this section is to present the properties of cells, their energy relations (Volume I) and behavior toward water and solutes with the closely related problems of the movement of solutes within the plant body and the economy of water in plants (Volume II).

The underlying theme of Volumes I and II is the basis of plant physiology in cell physiology.

Section on *Nutrition and Metabolism*

In this section the detailed facts and knowledge of nutrition and metabolism are presented, first with reference to the need for, and utilization of, inorganic nutrients (Volume III), and second with respect to the processes of organic nutrition (Volume IV). The treatment of organic nutrition leads to a reconsideration of photosynthesis and respiration at the level of organs and organisms. Volume IV describes the intermediary metabolism of carbon and nitrogenous compounds and presents a brief comparison of plants in health and in disease.

The main theme of Volumes III and IV is the nutrition, organic and inorganic, of plants and the biochemical steps by which these processes are achieved.

Section on *Growth and Development*

The purpose of the last section is to present the problems of plant physiology as seen through the analysis of growth and development, mainly with reference to flowering plants. This entails (Volume V) a reappraisal of the main events of growth and development from the standpoint of morphology and leads to a consideration of growth of cells and of organs. Tropisms and the role of hormones and the effects of synthetic growth regulators are discussed. In Volume VI the attention is focused upon the quantitative analysis of growth and development, the physiology of reproduction, the development of fruits and seeds, the problems of dormancy and perennation. The role of environmental factors in the control of growth and development merits separate treatment. Finally the problems of growth and development are examined from the standpoint of genetic control and from the interpretation of abnormal growth as seen in the formation of tumors. Throughout this treatment the controlling mechanisms of growth are evaluated.

Thus the last section of the work provides a synthesis of knowledge about plants since all their physiological processes converge upon growth and development.

The fulfillment of these objectives is possible only through the co-operation of many authors. The scope and treatment of individual chapters reflects the special interests of the contributors. While each volume is a complete unit, with its own table of contents and indexes, it is also an integral part of the whole plan.

Outline of the Plan

Section on *Cell Physiology and Problems Relating to Water and Solutes*

        Volume IA. Cellular Organization and Respiration
        Volume IB. Photosynthesis and Chemosynthesis
        Volume II. Plants in Relation to Water and Solutes

Section on *Nutrition and Metabolism*

        Volume III. Inorganic Nutrition of Plants
        Volume IV. Organic Nutrition and Metabolism

Section on *Growth and Development*

        Volume V. Analysis of Growth
        Volume VI. The Physiology of Development

NOTE ON THE USE OF PLANT NAMES

The policy has been to identify by its scientific name, whenever possible, any plant mentioned by a vernacular name by the contributors to this work. In general, this has been done on the first occasion in each chapter when a vernacular name has been used. Particular care was taken to ensure the correct designation of plants mentioned in tables and figures which record actual observations. Sometimes, when reference has been made by an author to work done by others, it has not been possible to ascertain the exact identity of the plant material originally used, because the original workers did not identify their material except by generic or common name.

It should be unnecessary to state that the precise identification of plant material used in experimental work is as important for the enduring value of the work as the precise definition of any other variables in the work. "Warm" or "cold" would not usually be considered an acceptable substitute for a precisely stated temperature, nor could a general designation of "sugar" take the place of the precise molecular configuration of the substance used; "sunflower" and *Helianthus* are no more acceptable as plant names, considering how many diverse species are covered by either designation. Plant physiologists are becoming increasingly aware that different species of one genus (even different varieties or cultivars of one species) may differ in their physiological responses as well as in their external morphology, and that experimental plants should therefore be identified as precisely as possible if the observations made are to be verified by others.

On the assumption that such common names as lettuce and bean are well understood, it may appear pedantic to append the scientific names to them—but such an assumption cannot safely be made. Workers in the United States who use the unmodified word "bean" almost invariably are referring to some form of *Phaseolus vulgaris;* whereas in Britain *Vicia faba*, a plant of another genus entirely, might be implied. "Artichoke" is another such name that comes to mind, sometimes used for *Helianthus tuberosus* (properly, the Jerusalem artichoke), though the true artichoke is *Cynara scolymus*.

By the frequent interpolation of scientific names, consideration has also been given to the difficulties that any vernacular English name alone may present to a reader whose native tongue is not English. Even some American and most British botanists would be led into a misinterpretation of the identity of "yellow poplar," for instance, if this vernacular American name were not supplemented by its scientific equivalent *Liriodendron tulipifera*, for this is not a species of *Populus* as might be expected, but a member of the quite unrelated magnolia family.

When reference has been made to the work of another investigator who, in his published papers, has used a plant name not now accepted by the nomenclatural authorities followed in the present work, that name ordinarily has been included in parentheses, as a synonym, immediately after the accepted name. In a few instances, when it seemed expedient to employ a plant name as it was used by an original author, even though that name is not now recognized as the valid one, the valid name, preceded by the sign =, has been supplied in parentheses: e.g., *Betula verrucosa* (= *B. pendula*). Synonyms have occasionally been added elsewhere also, as in the case of a plant known and frequently reported upon in the literature under more than one name: e.g., *Pseudotsuga menziesii* (*P. taxifolia*); species of *Elodea* (*Anacharis*).

Having adopted these conventions, their implementation rested first with each contributor to this work; but all outstanding problems of nomenclature have been referred to Dr. W. J. Dress of the Bailey Hortorium, Cornell University. The authorities for the nomenclature employed in this work have been Bailey's *Hortus Second* and Bailey's *Manual of Cultivated Plants* for cultivated plants. For bacteria Bergey's *Manual of Determinative Bacteriology*, for fungi Ainsworth and Bisbee's *Dictionary of the Fungi* have been used as reference sources; other names have been checked where necessary against Engler's *Syllabus der Pflanzenfamilien*. Recent taxonomic monographs and floras have been consulted where necessary. Dr. Dress' work in ensuring consistency and accuracy in the use of plant names is deeply appreciated.

THE EDITOR

CONTENTS

CHAPTER THREE

Inorganic Nutrient Nutrition of Microorganisms *by* D. J. D.
NICHOLAS 363

CHAPTER FOUR

Modes of Action of the Essential Mineral Elements *by* ALVIN
NASON AND WILLIAM D. MCELROY 451

CHAPTER FIVE

Biological Nitrogen Fixation *by* ARTTURI I. VIRTANEN AND
JORMA K. MIETTINEN 539

CHAPTER SIX

Microbial Activities of Soil as They Affect Plant Nutrition *by*
J. H. QUASTEL

CONTENTS OF VOLUMES IA, IB, AND II

Trends in the Inorganic Nutrition of Plants

F. C. Steward

Autotrophic plants can survive in an inorganic world. Indeed, the ability of plants to subsist on inorganic sources of nitrogen (nitrate or ammonia) is at least one of their distinguishing characteristics. The ability to utilize even elementary nitrogen, by biological nitrogen fixation (which is somewhat more widely dispersed through the plant kingdom than used to be thought) represents the highest degree of autotrophy for nitrogen. From this point of view certain blue-green algae that can both fix nitrogen and carry on photosynthesis are perhaps the most autotrophic organisms which are known. This may be part of their survival value and their role as early colonists of naked surfaces, which are otherwise free of organic matter, surfaces which range from volcanic laval slopes to the raised muds of salt marshes.

Essential and Dispensable Elements

When one considers the surprisingly small number of elements of the periodic table with which nature has elaborated the form and substance of plants, the elements of water and of carbon dioxide may be, and usually are, treated separately. The remaining elements are distinctively of mineral origin. Water is not usually considered to be a nutrient. However, water is by far the most abundant molecular species in cells and organisms. It may be calculated, for example, that a carrot root cell may contain about 10^{17} water molecules and about 10^8 protein molecules of an assumed, but probable, average molecular weight. A nutrient is that which nourishes and out of which the substance of plants is built; in this sense water certainly performs an essentially nutritional role. In fact, so high is the percentage of water that one may say that the minute amount of mineral matter and the larger, but still small, amount of organic matter which constitute the organization of plants is what imparts to the mass of water they contain the distinctive properties by which the organisms are recognized. A medusa in the sea may be almost entirely composed of water, but its relatively minute amount of salts and organic matter impart to this mass of water the organization which makes it the distinctive creature that it is.

1

Thus, although not commonly regarded as an inorganic nutrient, water nevertheless enters into all aspects of the physiology of plants as the essential medium in which biological reactions occur, the essential and most abundant stuff of which plants are made and, through hydrogen bonding, water is also an essential part of the architecture of the complex substances and large molecules so important in the microscopic and submicroscopic morphology of living things. Water is also the molecule from which hydrogen is transferred to cause reduction, and to which it is restored in the essential step of transfer to oxygen, as in the terminal oxidative step of respiration. Thus water is the essential basis of so many of the energy exchanges in cells. Being composed of very small atoms, and by reason also of its molecular asymmetry, water packs a large amount of matter in the minimum of space and its physical properties (specific heat, latent heats of fusion and of vaporization, dielectric constant, surface tension) are unique among liquids at the prevailing temperatures of this earth. Therefore, one can as little conceive of life, as we know it, without the properties of water as one can conceive of it without the distinctive properties of carbon and of that element's ability to combine with itself to form the rings, chains, films, fibrils, and lamellae and the large molecules out of which the form of cells and organisms is so largely built. Thus, although commonly they are considered separately, the elements C, H, and O have their premier place in the list of essential elements.

The rich variety of the plant kingdom, from the thallophytes to the angiosperms, and the range and complexity of the physiological functions and biochemical reactions of plants are achieved by utilizing the chemical properties of only a very few of the total chemical elements of the periodic table. Though it is a long way from the "Earth, Air, Fire, and Water" of Aristotelian doctrine to modern knowledge of the ten essential macronutrient elements (C, H, O, N, P, S, K, Ca, Mg, Fe), to the five well-established micronutrient elements for angiosperms (B, Mn, Cu, Zn, and Mo) and to the more recently established elements which are either generally essential or beneficial in certain situations (Cl, Na, Si, and V), it is still surprising how dispensable are so many of the chemical elements, even those that are most abundant in the earth's surface.

The elements most utilized by plants are certainly not those which are the most common. Despite the abundance of sodium, it is so dispensable and so unable to replace the essential role of potassium that only recently has it been added to the list of elements that are essential for certain land plants (cf. Chapter 2). However, one cannot conceive of sea water and of marine plants apart from the properties of sodium.

Aluminum and silicon are also among the most abundant chemical elements in the earth's crust, but again, apart from certain special situations in which they may contribute to the skeletal substances of plants (as for example silicon in diatoms and in certain plant cell walls), these elements also are essentially dispensable. But aluminum and silicon, like carbon, enter into chemical configurations which permit almost indefinitely repeating patterns in space. However, carbon, by its small size and its ability to combine directly with itself, can form such repeating patterns alone, whereas other elements (oxygen, aluminum, boron, etc.) must be interposed in the case of silicon. Thus, while carbon forms the essential skeleton of many large molecules important in nature and together with nitrogen and phosphorus forms the essential structure of proteins and nucleoproteins, without which terrestrial biology could not exist, the large molecules which are built from silicon, with aluminum and oxygen, etc., provide the repeating patterns in space, which are the basis of much inorganic form in minerals and in soils. But for all practical purposes the elements silicon and aluminum are dispensable by plants.

It is almost essential to believe that primeval life utilized the minimum number of elements and, as morphological specialization developed, its requirements became more exacting, and life adapted to and utilized the special properties of an increasing range of substances. In this way the properties of a given chemical element could be used in a given molecular situation. The highly specialized molecular situations in which micronutrient or trace elements form part of specific enzymes are obvious examples here. The more advanced and specialized cells and organisms become, the more prescribed are their nutritional requirements. (Calcium is not commonly required by bacteria and fungi, and there is little or no evidence of boron requirement for these organisms.) In fact, it is still a puzzle why such elaborate molecules had to be developed to permit an inorganic element to perform what often seems to be a simple function. For example, the oxygen-carrying properties of iron in hemoglobin or myoglobin is but one of many similar examples in both plants and animals. Despite the complexity of some of these relationships (as for example iron to cytochromes), it is surprising how generally distributed they now are and how little evidence one can see of what may be called a progressive biochemical evolution parallel to the morphological evidence.

Some Historical Landmarks

From their early origins in Aristotelian doctrine, the primitive concepts of mineral nutrition of plants advanced but slowly, or not at all, through the Middle Ages. Van Helmont, and later others who resorted to experiment, ushered in the modern period in which the mineral nutrition of plants was to be based on a rational system of chemistry. With Théodore de Saussure's well-known book of 1804, entitled "Recherches chimiques sur la végétation," this trend was firmly established; and by the end of the nineteenth century the ideas of mineral nutrition had reached such a level that, although details were still to be added, the essential structure did not need to be changed.

The nineteenth century saw very rapid advances to knowledge of plant nutrition; this is ably summarized in many available sources, such as E. J. Russell's "Soil Conditions and Plant Growth," Sach's "History of Botany to 1860" and its companion volume by Reynolds Green for the period to 1900. (A work which is quite different in style and scope by Th. Weavers also treats the first half of the twentieth century.) However, scientific discovery is not made only at the volition of the investigator and the research worker, for it is also a product of the intellectual climate of the day, and it requires a setting which is necessary for successful advances to be made and to be applied. The course of mineral nutrition since the seventeenth century is interesting in this connection.

The great wave of progress, virtually nonexistent through the Middle Ages, acquired a slow start with Van Helmont. Van Helmont's classical experiment, in the early seventeenth century, with the growth of a willow twig may have been anticipated by Nicholas of Cusa in the fifteenth century, even as it was repeated by Robert Boyle later in the seventeenth century. Through the observations of John Woodward (1699) and others, progress gathered pace especially in the early nineteenth century, and it has continued ever since. (A short but useful account of early 18th century plant nutrition and agriculture by G. E. Fussell is to be found in the *Proceedings of the Chemical Society* for June 1960, pages 193–198.)

However, the time was especially ripe for developments in plant nutrition to occur in western Europe after the Napoleonic wars. During the Napoleonic wars the prices of grain soared so that borderline lands were brought into cultivation. In the depression that followed, the impoverished economy and unbalanced agriculture of western Europe was revived by the birth of the fertilizer industry and by the marriage of the science of chemistry with agriculture. The population increase, which was to be stimulated by the Industrial Revolution, placed even greater demands on agriculture. Boussingault in France, Liebig in Germany, Lawes and Gilbert in Britain, all were influenced by the nineteenth century trend toward, and the search for, a more efficient agriculture through a knowledge of the manurial and crop rotation practices that would give the best response in terms of plant growth. The role of nitrogen in manurial practice, the importance of legumes in a plan of crop rotation, the paramount importance of N, P, K in artificial ferti- lizers and the foundations of soil microbiology were all to be well ap- preciated by the end of that century. Boussingault's quantitative field experiments, Liebig's ill-fated artificial fertilizer, were as much in tune with the needs of the times as Lawes' more successful venture into the solubilization of rock phosphate as superphosphate of lime. The cele- brated partnership of Lawes and Gilbert was to study the application of the new chemistry to agriculture. But it was Sir John Lawes, using his family estate and the income from the new fertilizer industry, who far-sightedly installed, in perpetuity, the Lawes plots at Rothamsted to demonstrate the responses of the growth of plants to specified manurial practices.

It has been said, however, that part of the pressure that prompted this development by Lawes and Gilbert was a new imbalance in a long established economy between London and its agricultural environs. This economy stressed sheep as the source of meat and root crops to feed the sheep over the winter. Farm produce reached the city in horse- drawn carts, and the predominantly horse-drawn transport of the city furnished return loads of stable manure to fertilize the fields. With the rise of population in the vicinity of London, this precarious balance be- came disturbed, and alternative means to stimulate the growth of crops needed to be sought. It was in this atmosphere that the contributions of Lawes and Gilbert were to be made. With the later use of sand and nutrient solution techniques, the elaboration of the ten essential ele- ments, well known by the turn of the century, and with the furnishing of these elements in the simplest mixtures of salts (calcium nitrate, potassium dihydrogen phosphate, magnesium sulfate, with a little iron) science seemed to have largely closed the book of plant nutrition by the end of the nineteenth century and the first decade of the twentieth.

However, during and after the First World War, plant nutrition profited from the great stimulus to chemistry which that scientific pe- riod fostered. When Germany was cut off by sea power from Chilean sources of nitrate, her agriculture was maintained by chemical fixation of atmospheric nitrogen by the Haber process, which received its first great impetus at this time. Indeed, it was in this postwar period that the knowledge of trace elements [that is nutrient elements needed in such small amount that, as foreshadowed by Mazé (1914), they had been overlooked in the erstwhile list of ten essential elements] became known. In the period after the Second World War plant physiology responded to the stimulus from physics and physical chemistry, which was to be a distinctive feature of that time. The search for sources of power and of energy was now paramount. Wars and the needs of industry had plundered the fossil fuels or stored products of the photosynthesis of bygone days, and the so-called population explosion called in question the ability of conventional agriculture to feed the world population. In plant physiology at this time there was a heavy preoccupation with the need to understand photosynthesis as the means by which plants utilize the energy of the sun and also to understand the way that energy, once stored, is applied to biological work of all kinds. The recognized importance of the expanse of the oceans in the total fixation of solar energy led to such ideas as those of "farming of the seas" as sources of food to meet man's needs. Also, in this productive period the now available radioactive isotopes soon penetrated into all branches of nutritional and metabolic study.

Thus, plant physiology and the study of plant nutrition has repeatedly responded to the trend of the time. Its progress has likewise interacted with the fluctuating balance between agriculture and industry, between urban and rural societies and with the onset of population pressures. These more general implications merit some further comment below.

Inorganic Plant Nutrition: Its Place in the Economy of Nature and of Man

Plants are still the ultimate source of organic nitrogen for both man and beast. Agriculture—i.e., plant and animal husbandry—turns inorganic nitrogen into usable protein. Thus the inorganic nutrition of crop plants has been dominated by nitrogen, though even today—despite the efficiency of agriculture and of artificial nitrogen fertilizers—much of the world's population is protein poor. Despite all man-made means to refurnish nitrogen in forms chemically fixed from the air, the biological means of returning plant and animal waste through the nitrogen cycle and the biological means of nitrogen fixation are by far the most important. In this respect the standards of Western urban civilization, which returns so much nutritional wastes eventually to the sea, presents a constant drain upon the nitrogenous reserves of the soil. Since an acre of shallow sea may furnish annually amounts of organic matter which are the rough equivalent of that produced by an acre of arable land and, since the seas occupy so much of the earth's surface, thought is now being given to the seas as the solution of man's food problems. Phosphate and nitrate, replenished by the rising currents from great depths, are often in limitingly low concentrations in the shallow seas, and ideas of "farming the sea" in landlocked shallow bays are perhaps no more visionary than those of hydroponics and of large scale algal culture. None of these ideas, which contemplate the large-scale growth of food plants in water and which have been prominently suggested in the twentieth century, would have seemed either feasible or necessary in an earlier day. But there was then less awareness than now that man's reproduction may soon tax the earth's resources and that also man may shortly venture into space. Thus plant physiology and the inorganic nutrition of plants is fraught with intensely practical applications which are closely bound up with the destiny of man.

Additional to the large area of the earth's surface (approximately four-fifths) which is occupied by sea and to that which is limited for conventional agriculture either because it is desert, or too cold or too mountainous, there are still vast areas which are occupied by forest. Indeed, forest trees may compose about 80% of the living matter on land. Prior to man's intervention, a large part of the North Temperate Zone was in fact occupied by a climax forest vegetation. From the early exploitation of the oak forests in Britain for shipbuilding (to furnish Britain's traditional "wooden-walls") and for the later smelting of iron ore, to the wholesale cutting of the North American forests in this century, the balanced nutrition of the climax forest has been disturbed, and one may note that the timber industry removes at one harvest even more of the accumulated fertility of the forest than a conventional annual agricultural crop would do. Whereas planned rotational and fertilizer practices in food crop production are ancient, the knowledge and the economical practice of the nutrition of forest trees are still relatively immature. Thus, in the full use of the energy of the sun to meet man's needs, the nutrition of forest trees has a role which is still to be perfected. Indeed, the same is also true of the full use of vast areas of tropical land. In both these great areas—the nutrition of forest trees and of tropical plants and vegetation—knowledge is still meager.

The balance between agriculture, as the source of food, and industry as the means of satisfying man's technological needs has loomed large in human affairs ever since the Middle Ages. This and the prevailing standards of urban and rural civilization have had their implications in relation to plant nutrition. In the fifteenth and sixteenth centuries the open fields gave place to inclosures and, because of the wealth in wool, the landlords of Britain gave over their land largely to sheep, so that measures were enforced to curb the conversion of arable land to grazing for sheep. "By the 39th year of the reign of Elizabeth (1597) arable land made pasture since 1st Elizabeth (1558) shall be again turned into tillage, and what is arable shall not be converted into pasture." This quotation shows an early attempt to stem the inroads of technology upon the food of man and to balance agriculture and industry in the economy. The first references to the fattening of sheep on turnips in winter and to the beneficial effects of animal dung to improve the efficiency of food production occurred toward the end of the seventeenth century. Clover and probably also turnips were introduced to Britain from Holland about 1652 by a Sir Richard Weston to increase the efficiency of agricultural operations, and he is said to have described, with startling accuracy in the light of modern knowledge, how to grow a stand of clover on a light heath soil after it was cleared, burnt, and lime was added to the ashes. After several years of cropping the clover, the land would then yield well in wheat for several years more! The balance between industrial and agricultural technology has now swung far in the other direction since, particularly in the United States, efficient control of nutrient supply—particularly of nitrogen—and an efficient mechanized agriculture permit a very small fraction of the population to produce food in sufficient, even excessive, quantities for the whole population.

But as Britain became ever more intensely industrialized it became less and less self-sufficient until, prior to the First and Second World Wars, Britain depended more upon its permanently established grass lands than upon its arable lands. In such a situation the imported fertility from other lands, in the form of grain, supported both man and beast; the latter were fattened and fed to convert much imported plant protein, somewhat inefficiently (about 15%), into animal protein; and, after human consumption, much of this fertility was destined for the sea under Western systems of sanitation and hygiene. Such an expensive agricultural practice and imbalanced economy can be supported only by a rich community which is able to export the product of its industry. However, experiments made in Germany in the immediate postwar period showed that certain plant sources of protein were entirely adequate as a substitute for milk in the feeding of infants, especially if it is fortified by the addition of methionine and lysine. Moreover, the postwar trend even in Britain has been to replace much of the imported grain for livestock by high protein grass, harvested early and kept well nourished directly by the use of nitrate and phosphate and lime under a so-called "ley-farming" system. Thus the maximum use may now be made of well-nourished pasture which is grown especially for its high content of leaf protein. Work is also under way to make, from the harvested foliage, a nutritionally effective source of leaf protein even for humans which, if necessary, may be supplemented by the critically limiting amino acids such as methionine and lysine. Although this is a still somewhat visionary possibility of solving the food problems of large populations, nevertheless the inefficient conversion of leaf protein to animal protein for human nutrition might eventually be circumvented in this way. Thus we can see that the food chain links the fertility factors that determine the growth of plants, as regulated by supplies of inorganic nutrients, to the state of balance or imbalance between agricultural and industrial production and to the nutritional status of Western urban communities with their high protein requirements.

Certain regions of southwest England—for long thought to be unsuited to cattle—are now known to produce pasture which is toxically rich in molybdenum, a condition which is paradoxically aggravated by "improving" the pasture with clover but which may be alleviated by the use of ammonium sulfate to discourage the clover and to foster the growth of grasses. Also, large areas of Australian pasture, hitherto deficient in traces of molybdenum, have been brought into more efficient production by supplying this essential nutrient. Thus, the late discovery of the role of minute amounts of molybdenum in plant nutrition, which may seem academically remote from the considerations that determine the complex balance between an industrial population and its food supply, nevertheless plays a part in the over-all dependence of man and his society on the nutrition and growth of plants.

Thus science has come a long way from John Woodward's (1699) insistence that some sort of terrestrial matter determined the growth of mint sprigs! But as man embarks upon the space age, his nutritional problems are once again being posed in unfamiliar terms; these problems may be left to the future to solve. However, for any kind of continuously balanced system of men in missiles, or on space platforms, the inorganic nutrition of plants in all its ramifications will be needed to harness light energy to make carbohydrates and thence to convert inorganic nitrate into protein.

Some Modern Concepts and Future Trends

In the nineteenth century the cell doctrine and the study of cells and organisms—with the impending rise of genetics—produced unifying concepts that permeated the whole of biology. Some now familiar aphorisms gave expression to essential truths, as it was seen that all cells came from preceding cells, all nuclei from preceding nuclei, etc.; and that self-duplication is an inherent characteristic of the way cells grow and divide. While cell biology in general profited greatly from these broad generalizations, the students of plant nutrition, for a while, seemed to become bogged down in a search for a fastidiously prescribed "best" nutrient solution for this or that plant. Indeed, long before the full range of variables and parameters was properly realized, there was a somewhat sterile attempt to control the osmotic pressure of nutrient solutions and to vary only the relative proportions of those three known main constituents of culture solutions, namely the salts calcium nitrate, potassium dihydrogen phosphate, and magnesium sulfate, to which a small amount of an iron salt was added. In retrospect this approach monopolized far too much time and effort, until by the greater use of statistical methods it was shown about 1921 that many of the supposed differences between the growth in the different solutions were often not statistically significant.

For the next great wave of development the science of plant nutrition was to be enriched by the stimulus of enzymology and by concurrent developments in genetics. The gene-enzyme hypothesis of Beadle and Tatum; the accumulated knowledge of proteins as enzymes and of their regulatory role in metabolism; the purification and crystallization of enzyme proteins, all consolidated the view that certain metals, known to be essential in trace quantities for the growth of plants, could owe their essentiality to their role in metalloproteins which also function as enzymes concerned with some reaction which is essential for growth or metabolism—so much so that a new metal, found to be essential for growth, now leads almost inevitably to the first presumption that it may function by virtue of its relation to an enzyme. Nevertheless, despite the stimulus of this modern approach, there are still trace elements whose essential role is not yet adequately explained—for example, boron.

But some developments that may well determine much of the future trend of research were slow, and still are slow, to come about. For a long time the inorganic nutrition of plants seemed to require rather fixed nutrients in fixed amounts, at least above some ill-defined minimum. The idea that there is no universally applicable nutrient requirement to cover all environmental conditions and all phases of plant development was seemingly slow to emerge. Also, the need to see the importance of the nutrient elements not merely in terms of their individual and separate actions, but also in terms of their interactions with each other and with climatic and environmental conditions, is a still emerging but potentially very important concept. Interactions among potassium, nitrogen, and light were prominently noted years ago (1935); and interactions among nitrogen, phosphorus, and respiration were also seen in the same general period. For one reason or another, such pairs of factors as calcium and boron; copper and molybdenum; iron and manganese; zinc and insolation; need to be considered together, because they have interacting effects which suggest that they impinge ultimately upon the same site of metabolic action.

But why was it ever supposed that the inorganic nutrient requirements of plants and of their constituent cells are fixed irrespective of the conditions that affect their growth and development? Nutrient requirements are commonly held to begin with the seed, but does not this neglect the all-important development of the zygote in the ovule and its consequential dependence on its parent sporophyte? Why should all cells of the plant body, despite their variety of form and function, be assumed to require the same essential nutrients as the whole plant? Do such morphologically distinct plants as a long- or a short-day plant, as a high- or a low-night temperature plant, require the same nutrients in the same concentrations? Why indeed should nutrition have ever been regarded as a requirement which is fixed throughout development? To the extent that these problems become obtrusive, questions of the mobilization of specific nutrients in the different regions and organs of the plant body also arise; this also involves those problems of uptake and accumulation of particular ions by cells, as well as the mechanism of their transport, which are dealt with in Volume II. Thus there is still much room for new work and new discovery, but work in this field poses some especially difficult logistic problems.

Even after the problem of interacting effects is recognized and it is also granted that the criteria of nutrient action should be extended to include the full range of developmental and metabolic processes that may be affected by nutrition (even when visible symptoms of abnormality are not apparent), there is still a real dilemma. How should one design the experiments, collect all the necessary data, and then interpret them in such a way that due weight is given to all the parameters of this complex system and to the factors which interact with each other? The use of statistics and the design of experiments which will permit subsequent statistical analysis of the data are now conspicuous features of the current scene. These were largely stimulated, initially, by R. A. Fisher and by those in plant nutrition, notably by F. G. Gregory and his school, who seized upon the significance of Fisher's monumental work. But, nevertheless, the full complexity of the task that faces those who would make even further contributions to plant nutritional knowledge may, even yet, not be widely or fully appreciated. As growth-controlling installations and climate-controlling devices come into general use in plant physiology, the problems of the complex design in experiments which require a team approach to the problems of nutrition will need to be faced and, no doubt, modern computing machines will also be needed to analyze and formulate what all the data mean. Indeed, if the science of plant nutrition were ever to be complete, would it not then be feasible, in advance, to prescribe all the requirements and the responses of a given fertilized egg, or of a spore, throughout its subsequent growth under all conditions?

An astonishing amount of current plant nutritional knowledge derives from but a few economically important plants. In fact, the essentiality of trace elements has been largely demonstrated for crop plants which are often grown in habitats which are very different from those to which the plants were first adapted. Thus, crop plants will often show field symptoms of nutritional disorders when the adjacent native plants, or even the trees, show no such signs. This observation leads to the following considerations.

The inorganic nutrition of plants is essentially a function of the environment during their growth, even as it is of the plant in question. It is also beginning to appear as a function of the genetic constitution of the plants involved. As recently as 1953 Pope and Munger found inorganic nutrition to be governed by a single gene which regulated the requirement of celery plants for boron, while another gene determined the requirement for magnesium. Such genetically determined mineral requirements and genetically determined nutritional levels mean that constant watch should now be kept upon inorganic nutrition from this point of view. By mutation, or by the work of plant breeders, new nutritional disorders that can be corrected only by the intervention of specific chemical elements may even be created. It would be interesting, for example, to re-examine the required trace element nutrition of a wild, still uncultivated species compared with the derived varieties and strains that have been bred from it to fit them for practical use.

Inorganic plant nutrition, therefore, now impinges upon all other branches of plant science, and the book of plant nutrition that seemed about to be closed at the turn of this century now presents as much challenge to the investigator, or rather to the team of investigators, as at any period in the history of plant science.

PREAMBLE TO CHAPTER 1

It is appropriate to begin the inorganic nutrition of plants by reference to the media from which they draw their nutrients (cf. also Volume II, Chapter 4). For land plants—whether natural vegetation, agricultural crops, or forest trees—this concerns the soil; for aquatic plants and many microorganisms it is an ambient solution; and for experimental plants it is often an artificial culture medium.

The plant nutritional considerations that flow from the study of the soil are first historical, for it was here that the subject began; they are physical and physicochemical because the soil is a complex system in which the structure and properties of its minerals and organic matter determine its supplying powers for ions; they are biological because in the intimate association of soil and root, i.e., the rhizosphere, and in its support of the soil flora the soil is a complex biological and microbiological system. (Soil microbiological aspects of mineral nutrition are also taken up in Chapters 5 and 6.) Statistical considerations also arise, because the investigation of growth and nutrition of plants in the field only became precise through special field plot design and through the application of statistical methods to the interpretation of the data. These various concepts, which form the basis of an understanding of plant and soil interrelationships, are, therefore, appropriately introduced in Part 1 of Chapter 1 in their special relation to plant physiology; they may, of course, be pursued much further with respect to crop plants through the literature of agronomy and in relation to natural vegetation through the study of ecology.

Although the soil looms large in the nutrition of plants in their natural environment, the understanding of inorganic plant nutrition as a branch of plant physiology awaited the means by which it could be investigated without the complications which growth of plants in the field or in soil so obviously presents. This area of plant physiology also presents its own special considerations. Even the first experimental usage of plants with their roots out of contact with soil yielded a major but first level of new knowledge, notably the nineteenth century discovery of the ten essential, or so-called macronutrient, elements. However, an understanding of the scope of inorganic plant nutrition necessarily awaited the recognition that even the culture methods were not as simple as at first supposed, and an awareness of the role of the essential micronutrients in plant nutrition. It is, therefore, appropriate also to develop the general considerations which flow from the growth of plants in culture media as Part 2 of Chapter 1.

Although this division of Chapter 1 between growth in soil and growth in defined culture media is convenient, a philosophy of plant nutrition combines all points of view; this is implied by their organization as parts of a single introductory chapter. Significantly, therefore, Part 2 which deals with soil-free culture media contains references to edaphic factors even as Part 1, which deals primarily with soil, concludes by reference to the direct supply of plant nutrients through foliage applications.

CHAPTER ONE

Mineral Nutrition of Plants in Soils and in Culture Media

C. Bould and E. J. Hewitt

PART 1. MINERAL NUTRITION OF PLANTS IN SOILS *by* C. BOULD

1. Historical: Soils and Plant Nutrition

A. EARLY DEVELOPMENTS

Speculation on the factors that control plant growth can be traced to Roman times and earlier. Cato (234–149 B.C.) was one of the earliest Roman agricultural writers. He considered that good ploughing was more important than manuring but urged careful conservation of manure. Among the practices advocated by the Romans may be listed the following: (1) thorough tillage, (2) green manuring, (3) crop rotation, (4) use of lime, (5) application of manure, and (6) growth of legumes for soil improvement. With the fall of the Roman Empire, agriculture, as well as other forms of civilization, lost ground for many years. The historical account by Russell (205) traces the gradual emergence of rational ideas of plant nutrition until, in the nineteenth century, they could be based on an adequate knowledge of chemistry.

The period between 1630 and 1750 was taken up with a search for "the principle of vegetation" when, from time to time, any one of the five "elements," fire, water, air, earth, and niter, was considered to be the active ingredient of vegetable matter. It was during this period that Van Helmont (1577–1644) conducted his classic experiment with a willow (*Salix* sp.) tree, although it is thought that he was preceded in this type of experiment by Nicholas of Cusa (1401–1446) (see Harvard Case Histories No. 5, 1952). Van Helmont placed 200 pounds of oven-dried soil in a pot, moistened it with rain water, and planted in it a willow shoot weighing 5 pounds; this he allowed to grow for a period of five years. At the end of this period he weighed the tree and found it to weigh 169 pounds and about 3 ounces. The tree had received nothing but rain water, and the soil was covered with a sheet to exclude dust. At the end of the experiment the soil weighed 200 pounds less about 2 ounces. Van Helmont concluded, therefore, that the additional 164 pounds of wood, bark, and root arose from the water alone. The experiment was simple and convincing and satisfied another eminent chemist, Robert Boyle, who repeated the experiment with "squash" (*Cucurbita* sp.) and obtained similar results. Both experimenters concluded that the substance of the plant was, in each instance, produced from water. Nevertheless, the conclusion which then appeared sound is entirely wrong because they both overlooked the part played by air and the missing 2 ounces of soil (205).

Glauber, in 1656, obtained saltpeter from cattle manure and found that it had great stimulating effect on plant growth. He concluded that fertility of the soil and the value of manures are entirely due to saltpeter. This view was supported by John Mayow, who estimated the amount of niter in the soil at different times of the year. He showed that it occurs in greatest quantity in the spring when plants are just beginning to grow, but that it is not to be found "in soil on which plants grow abundantly, the reason being that all the niter of the soil is sucked out by the plants."

John Woodward (283) published the results of an interesting experiment in 1699. He grew spearmint (*Mentha* sp.) in (a) rain water, (b) water from the river Thames, (c) effluent from Hyde Park conduit, and (d) effluent plus garden mold. At the end of 77 days the plants were weighed; the weights were found to be in ascending order from (a) to (d). Since all plants had an abundance of water, the growth must have been related to the amount of sediment. Woodward concluded, therefore, that water could not be the principle of growth. He ascribed growth to absorption of a "certain peculiar terrestial matter." For many years no outstanding advance was made, except that by Stephen Hales (ca. 1727), who showed that air is "wrought into the composition" of plants (205).

Advances, however, were being made in agricultural practice, owing largely to the writings from 1731 onward of Jethro Tull, an Englishman. He held that: (a) all plants live on the same food, namely, fine soil particles; (b) pressure caused by the swelling of the roots forced minute soil particles through the "lacteal mouths of the roots" and hence to enter the circulatory system; (c) cultivation of the soil increased its fineness and thus the feeding opportunity of plants; (d) a rotation of crops is a convenience but not a necessity; (e) any soil will nourish any plant if temperature and moisture supply are in proper adjustment; (f) applications of manure were effective because they brought about a fine, crumbly soil condition. The position about this time can be summed up in Tull's own words: "It is agreed that the following materials contribute in some manner to the increase of plants, but it is disputed which of them is that very increase or food: (1) niter, (2) water, (3) air, (4) fire, (5) earth" (205).

During the latter half of the eighteenth century great interest was taken in agriculture. Beginning in 1755 Home, an English chemist, made pot experiments to determine the effect of various substances on plant growth. He found that saltpeter, Epsom salts, and potassium sulfate all lead to increased growth, yet they are three distinct salts. This was a big advance because it showed that plant nutrition depends on several factors. Home also established two methods for studying plant nutrition, namely, pot culture and plant analyses.

Between 1770 and 1800 work was done on the effects of vegetation on air. Joseph Priestley, in 1775, investigated the effects of sprigs of mint (*Mentha* sp.) on vitiated air. He found that the mint made the air purer, and concluded "that plants, instead of affecting the air in the same manner as animal respiration, reverse the effects of breathing, and tend to keep the atmosphere pure and wholesome." But he had not yet discovered oxygen and so could not interpret his discovery. It was left to Ingen-Housz, in 1779, to show that purification goes on in light only, whereas vitiation takes place in darkness and plants had then the same effect on air as did animals. Jean Senebier, of Geneva, went further and showed that plants extract something from the air which he designated as "fixed air." Furthermore he explained the growth of Van Helmont's willow tree on the basis of the absorption of this fixed air (205).

B. Period of Rapid Scientific Development

During this period (1800–1880) much progress was made in the knowledge of chemistry, and the information obtained was applied to the study of soils and plant growth, in particular by de Saussure and Liebig. The initiation of modern experimental methods in plant nutrition is largely due to de Saussure. He showed: (a) that the elements of water are fixed in the plant at the same time as the carbon; (b) that there is no normal nutrition of the plant without the uptake of nitrates and mineral matter; (c) that the nitrogen in the plant comes, not from the air as advocated by Liebig, but from the soil. Further, he showed that the root is not a mere filter; it takes in water more readily than dissolved matter, and it absorbs nonnutrient elements. He showed that the composition of plant ash is not constant, but varies with the nature of the soil and with the age of the plant. Unfortunately de Saussure's discoveries were not accepted by his contemporaries, who adopted the prevailing view that plants draw their carbon and other nutrients from soil humus (195).

This latter view was ridiculed by Liebig (146) in a report which he prepared for the British Association for the Advancement of Science in 1840, in which he summarized the state of knowledge at that time. Contrary to general opinion at the time, he stated quite categorically "that humus in the form in which it exists in the soil does not yield the smallest nourishment to plants." This was a reference to humus as a direct source of plant carbon, a view currently held by plant physiologists. He went on to argue "that carbon must be derived from other sources; and as soil does not yield it, it can only be extracted from the atmosphere." He argued that because the quantities of carbonic acid and oxygen in the atmosphere remain unchanged "a cause must exist which prevents the increase of carbonic acid by removing that which is constantly forming, and there must be some means of replacing the oxygen. Both these causes are united in the processes of vegetable life." He held, incorrectly, that humus nourishes plants "by presenting a slow and lasting source of carbonic acid which is absorbed by the roots, and is the principal nutriment of young plants at a time when, being destitute of leaves, they are unable to extract food from the atmosphere." He maintained that all the hydrogen necessary for the formation of organic compounds is derived from water and that nitrogen is taken from the air, or soil, as ammonia. With regard to mineral nutrition he thought that "all substances in solution in a soil are absorbed by the roots of plants, exactly as a sponge inbibes a liquid, and all that it contains, without selection." Magnesium and phosphate were necessary for seed formation; alkalis were needed to neutralize organic acids, and common salt, sulfate of potash, chloride of potassium, and other matters were necessary constituents of many plants. In order to maintain soil fertility he maintained that all those substances removed by crops must be returned to the soil. He predicted that "a time will come when fields will be manured with a solution of glass (silicate of potash), with the ashes of burnt straw and with salts of phosphoric acid." Acting on this last conclusion Liebig made up a mineral fertilizer and placed it on the market. However, it failed because the minerals were first rendered insoluble by fusion.

Liebig's report attracted a great deal of attention and finally killed the humus theory, i.e., as a direct source of plant carbon. Later he developed his mineral theory of nutrition and gave it a quantitative form: "The crops on a field diminish or increase in exact proportion to the diminution or increase of the mineral substances conveyed to it in manure," and still later he added what became known as the law of the minimum: "By the deficiency or absence of one necessary constituent, all the others being present, the soil is rendered barren for all

those crops to the life of which that one constituent is indispensable."
Liebig's insistence that plants derive their nitrogen from ammonia in
the atmosphere and that the low content of phosphorus in the ash of
turnip proved that the turnip had a low phosphorus requirement, were
shown to be erroneous by Lawes and Gilbert, who started their famous
field experiments at Rothamsted, England, in 1843. These experiments
were conducted on the same general lines as those of Boussingault in
Alsace. By 1855, the following points had been definitely settled: (a)
crops require phosphates and salts of the alkalis, but the composition
of plant ash does not afford reliable information as to the amounts of
each needed; (b) nonleguminous crops require a supply of some
nitrogenous compound, nitrates and ammonium salts being equally
good; (c) soil fertility may be maintained for some years at least by
means of artificial manures; and (d) the beneficial effect of fallowing
lies in the increase brought about in the available nitrogen compounds
in the soil (205).

At about this time Way (273) carried out his important investigation on the base-exchange properties of soil, the results of which will
be described in Section IV, B. Way noted that the active ingredient
in soil was clay and that the exchangeable bases were associated with
the clay fraction.

The nitrogen nutrition of plants remained a controversial problem
for many years. Liebig held that ammonia, but not gaseous nitrogen,
was taken up by plants, a view confirmed by Lawes, Gilbert, and Pugh
(142) in 1861. Leguminous plants, however, still puzzled the investigators. Lachmann, 1858, first noted the presence of organisms in
the nodules of leguminous plants, but his paper attracted little attention.
In 1885, Berthelot showed that certain soil microorganisms could fix
atmospheric nitrogen, and in the following year Hellriegel and Wilfarth established the relationship between the root nodule organisms
and the power of leguminous plants to fix nitrogen. Beijerinck, 1888,
isolated the organism; thus another landmark in the nutrition of plants
in soils had been established.

By 1880 the following facts concerning the nutrition of plants had
been established: (a) soils have the ability to support vegetation for
an undetermined time; (b) soils are derived from rocks, yet pulverized
rock is not soil; (c) weathering has produced important changes in the
chemistry of the derived soils; (d) mineral constituents are necessary
for plants; (e) mineral constituents are obtained from the soil; (f) the
mineral constituents absorbed by plants come chiefly from a fraction
of the soil; (g) the osmotic properties of the contents of root cells are
related to their ability to absorb water from the soil; (h) the ratio of
the mineral constituents absorbed by the plant differs from the ratio

existing in the soil; (i) plant growth is related intimately to rainfall and temperature; and (j) soil amendments sometimes increase plant growth (195).

In the early part of the twentieth century considerable attention was paid to the soil solution, in particular by King and his co-workers at Wisconsin, and by Whitney and Cameron, of the United States Department of Agriculture. Cameron developed (54) the fundamental ideas of the soil solution considered as a liquid phase, wherein the roots find ions which they may absorb. He showed that the commonly occurring minerals in the soil are far more soluble than had been assumed and that the dissolved substances reach a more or less constant concentration. He held that no soil is ever in a state of final equilibrium, because of the effects of manifold physical and chemical factors. Later Burd introduced (49) the concept of the "supplying power" of the soil. A very dilute solution, accordingly, could afford enough nutrients, if the supplying power were adequate. For example, the absolute amounts of potassium or phosphate might not be adequate at any one moment, yet they could suffice if the rate of release to the soil solution was sufficient to maintain a fairly constant concentration. The formulation of the concept of the soil as a dynamic system took place early in the twentieth century and liberated soil science from the domination of Liebig.

The work of Way on base exchange in the previous century, although creating a marked impression at the time, was not followed up until Gedroiz, in 1918, discovered that there are differences in the readiness with which soils absorb different ions (130). For example, the potassium ion is a somewhat more powerful replacer than the sodium ion and is more readily adsorbed by the clay. The state of knowledge in 1924 concerning base exchange was summarized by Hissink (107) as follows: "The exchangeable bases are located on the surface of the soil particles; in other words they occur in the adsorbed condition. The cause of this adsorption is to be sought in the chemical attraction between the bases and the soil acids (clay and humus acids). When the soil is treated with water, a soil suspension is formed. A part of the surface molecules then become ionized, forming around the surface of the absorbing clay and humus particles an electrical double layer. In the inner part of this double layer are found the anions of the soil acids, in the outer part the cations; H^+, Mg^{++}, Ca^{++}, K^+, Na^+." Hissink also postulated the presence of free ions in true solution. Shortly afterward it was shown by Ross and Shannon, by Hendricks and Fry, and by others, that clays are composed of crystalline minerals having a lattice structure (see Section IV, A, 1). This enabled Kelley et al. (131) in 1931 to advance the idea that easily replaceable ions, like calcium, are held on the outside of the crystal lattice of the clay particles and hence are readily exchangeable. Others, like magnesium and potassium, are held to some extent on the inside of the lattice and hence are not so readily exchangeable unless the lattice is broken by grinding; some magnesium and potassium is, however, easily exchangeable and readily available for plant nutrition.

The discovery of the crystalline lattice structure of clay minerals was an important landmark in soil science and has helped in solving many problems concerned with the fixation of plant nutrients in soil. These problems will be dealt with in later sections.

II. Factors in the Occurrence and Distribution of Mineral Nutrients in the Soil

A. Geochemistry

Early in the evolution of the earth, a condensation of matter from a hot gaseous stage to liquid and solid phases must have taken place. Goldschmidt (83) advances the hypothesis that equilibria in the partition of elements among metallic, semimetallic, and silicate phases have been responsible for the distribution and more or less effective elimination of certain elements from the material of the earth's crust. The distribution of the elements was essentially controlled by their chemical affinities for oxygen and sulfur. As a suitable measure of these affinities one can take the free energy of oxidation per gram atom of oxygen. Elements that have a higher free energy of oxidation than iron, e.g., silicon, aluminum, alkali, and alkaline earth metals, may be expected to concentrate in the silicate crust during primordial differentiation. Elements with a lower free energy of oxidation, e.g., nickel and cobalt, are associated with metallic iron.

The second step involves redistribution during crystallization from liquid magmas and the building up of space lattices of atoms, or ions, depending on their atomic or ionic radii. Into such a lattice only those particles can enter which are of a size appropriate to the lattice spacings. Therefore the crystals act as a kind of sorting or sieving mechanism allowing certain particles to enter and excluding others of unsuitable size. Radii and valency thus regulate the distribution of elements in the primary magmatic rocks and in minerals derived from them. Generally the possibility of large-scale isomorphous substitution in minerals (see Section IV, A, 1) will be limited to such pairs of ions, the radii of which agree within a tolerance of 10–15% of the larger radius of the pair. For instance, magnesium (0.78 A) and ferrous iron (0.83 A) freely replace each other in ionic crystals, but not magnesium and calcium (1.06 A).

The third stage, i.e., the distribution of elements in sedimentary formations is regulated by the ionic potential (the quotient between ionic charge and ionic radius). Substances with low ionic potential (large ions with small charge), such as sodium, potassium, calcium, and magnesium, remain in solution or may be adsorbed during the process

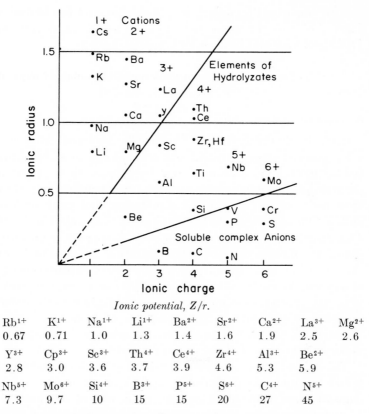

Ionic potential, Z/r.

Cs^{1+}	Rb^{1+}	K^{1+}	Na^{1+}	Li^{1+}	Ba^{2+}	Sr^{2+}	Ca^{2+}	La^{3+}	Mg^{2+}
0.61	0.67	0.71	1.0	1.3	1.4	1.6	1.9	2.5	2.6

Sm^{3+}	Y^{3+}	Cp^{3+}	Sc^{3+}	Th^{4+}	Ce^{4+}	Zr^{4+}	Al^{3+}	Be^{2+}
2.7	2.8	3.0	3.6	3.7	3.9	4.6	5.3	5.9

Ti^{4+}	Nb^{5+}	Mo^{6+}	Si^{4+}	B^{3+}	P^{5+}	S^{6+}	C^{4+}	N^{5+}
6.3	7.3	9.7	10	15	15	20	27	45

Fig. 1. Distribution of elements in sedimentary formations in relation to ionic potential. From Goldschmidt (83).

of weathering and transportation, those with intermediate ionic potentials (between 2 and 12) are precipitated by hydrolysis, and those with still higher ionic potentials (above 12) form anions with oxygen (Fig. 1). Goldschmidt (84) likens the process of weathering and the cycle of formation of sedimentary rocks to that of a gigantic semi-quantitative chemical analysis in which the following products are separated:

1. Insoluble residues such as sand or sandstone, with such resistant minerals as quartz and zircon
2. Hydrolyzates, such as bauxite, clay, and shales, with hydrated oxides and hydrosilicates of aluminum
3. Oxidates such as many sedimentary iron and manganese ores
4. Reducents such as coal, bituminous sediments, sedimentary sulfides and sulfur
5. Carbonates, such as limestone and dolomite
6. Evaporates containing such salts as chlorides, sulfates, and borates of alkali and alkaline earth metals.

The effect of this separation on the distribution of major and trace elements is shown in Table I.

TABLE I

DEPOSITION OF SEDIMENTARY ROCKS WITH
THEIR ASSOCIATED MAJOR AND TRACE ELEMENTS[a]

Process of sedimentation	Major constituents	Type of product	Main rock types	Associated trace constituents
⟶	Si ⟶	Resistates	Sandstones	Zr, Ti, Sn, rare earths Th, Au, Pt, etc.
⟶	Al ⟶ Si K	Hydrolyzates	Shales and bituminous shales	V, U, As, Sb, Mo, Cu, Ni, Co, Cd, Ag, Au, Pt, B, Se
			Bauxites	Be, Ga, Nb, Ti
⟶	Fe ⟶ Mn	Oxidates	Iron ores	V, P, As, Sb, Se
			Manganese ores	Li, K, Ba, B, Ti, W, Co, Ni, Cu, Zn, Pb
⟶	Cu ⟶ Mg Fe	Carbonates	Limestones, dolomites	Ba, Sr, Pb, Mn
⟶	K ⟶ Na Ca Mg	Evaporates	Salt deposits	B, I

[a] From Mitchell (168).

The distribution of many minor elements depends very much on their stage of oxidation. Iron, manganese, and cobalt are often immobilized as a result of processes of oxidation; sulfur, selenium, arsenic, vanadium, chromium and molybdenum may be mobilized by oxidation to readily soluble complex anions, in accordance with the rules of ionic potential. In the processes of oxidation and reduction important biochemical reactions participate and often predominate.

The fourth stage in distribution of elements is represented by bio-logical accumulation, as illustrated by the accumulation of elements under forest covers. The elements are then dissolved in the soil solution, taken up by the roots, translocated to the leaves which in turn fall on to the soil surface. Here, during the process of decomposition, the soluble nutrients are leached out and the insoluble elements remain in the surface layer. Elements accumulated in this manner include boron, manganese, nickel, and cobalt.

B. PEDOLOGY

Pedology originated in Russia with the classic researches of Doku-chaev (1877 and thereafter) and his pupils (124). Like other natural sciences pedology started out with the descriptive phase. The soil body was cut open vertically and the exposed surfaces were described. In a mature state, the soil body revealed a definite construction consisting of distinct layers, known as horizons, which are specific in their morphological characters irrespective of the geographic position of the soil and of the underlying geological formation, provided it is located in identical climatic zones. The genetically related exposed horizons of a vertical cut in the soil body, taken as a unit, comprise what is known as the soil profile. Pedology begins, therefore, with a profile study of the soil body and aims to unravel the fundamental laws which govern the processes of soil formation in relation to weathering, one of the primary physicochemical forces of nature responsible for the genesis of the soil. A knowledge of these laws of soil formation enables one to predict the geographical distribution of soils. Thus the zone of the podsol soils is typical of the temperate humid regions; the chernozem is found in less humid regions, such as the steppes of Russia; the lateritic soils are typical of the tropics. One of the fundamental laws of pedology, formulated by Dokuchaev is "the law of the adaptability of soil types of the globe to natural (primarily climatic) conditions" (124).

The factors concerned in soil formation are parent material, topog-raphy (the configuration of the soil surface), climate, and organisms. Soil is an independent, dynamic body of nature that acquires properties in accordance with the forces which act upon it. It may be defined as that material which occupies the outermost part of the earth's crust and the character of which varies from the surface to the parent ma-terial (see Fig. 2).

One of the most important changes in the minerals of the parent material during soil development is their diminution in particle size. This in turn leads to greater chemical activity, since most of the chemi-cal reactions involve primarily the unit cells exposed at the surface of

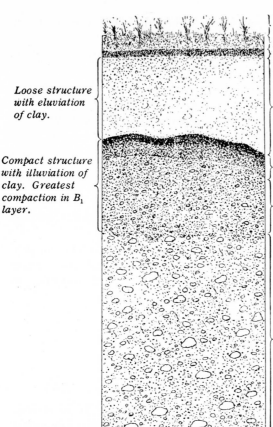

Vegetation

Raw humus layer (A_0)
Humus layer (A_1)

Ashen gray or light gray
layer (A_2), leached of
humus and sesquioxides.
Bleached sand grains,
stones, and gravel.

Black to dark brown layer of
humus accumulation (B_1). Black
staining on stones and gravel.

Brown to orange-brown layer of
sesquioxide accumulation (B_2).
Brown iron staining on stones
and gravel.

Gray or brownish gray
parent material (C).

Loose structure
with eluviation
of clay.

Compact structure
with illuviation of
clay. Greatest
compaction in B_1
layer.

Fig. 2. Diagrammatic representation of a podsol profile, showing soil horizons. From Robinson (204).

a crystal particle. The reactions that lead to changes in composition and availability of nutrients include: ion exchange, hydrolysis, solution, diffusion, oxidation-reduction, and adsorption and swelling due to hydration. Water is essential in all these reactions. One of the most important soil reactions is illustrated by the loss of K^+ from biotite, which may be considered as an exchange reaction, thus:

$$K \text{ biotite} + H^+ \rightarrow H \text{ biotite} + K^+$$

or as the result of a hydrolysis reaction, thus:

$$K \text{ biotite} + H_2O \rightarrow H \text{ biotite} + K^+ + OH^-$$

but since part of the biotite goes into solution, the reaction may also be viewed as solution.

These three reactions, exchange, hydrolysis, and solution, constitute the primary loss of bases from minerals.

Diffusion of cations into and out of the interior of crystal particles is responsible for converting one type of mineral to another type.

Oxidation reactions are of primary importance in minerals that contain ferrous iron. Because the electrostatic neutrality of a crystal structure must be maintained, oxidation of ferrous to ferric iron brings about the expulsion of some other cation. Such departures leave empty positions, which cause the structure to become unstable, thereby accelerating weathering.

Adsorption of water, H^+ or OH^-, is termed hydration, and is the first step in the release of oxides from crystal particles (18).

The adsorption of organic substances, such as amino acids and proteins, within the spacings between successive layers of clay causes large particles to disintegrate, besides giving a degree of protection to the organic substance from microbiological decomposition.

III. Nature and Content of Soil Nutrients

A. MACRONUTRIENT ELEMENTS

1. Nitrogen

Nitrogen occurs primarily in organic combination. It is present partly in the form of original nitrogenous plant constituents, somewhat modified, and partly as microbial cells. Free amino acids have also been isolated from certain soils. Much of the so-called "humus" consists of a lignin-protein complex which on acid hydrolysis gives approximately one-third of the total nitrogen as α-amino acids. From this it is deduced that at least one-third, or more, of soil organic nitrogen is in protein form (44). In addition to amino acids, soils contain amino sugars. There is also some evidence for the occurrence of nucleic acids (27).

Complex organic nitrogen compounds must first be mineralized before the nitrogen can be utilized by plants. The biological transformation occurs thus: organic nitrogen → ammonium → nitrite → nitrate, the amount of nitrate finally produced depending on the relative amounts of easily decomposable carbonaceous materials present (224). If the carbon:nitrogen ratio is high little, if any, nitrogen will appear as nitrate, the intermediate compounds being utilized by microorganisms for further decomposition of organic substances. The mineralization and immobilization of nitrogen in soil has been reviewed recently by Winsor (279). Inorganic nitrogen occurs in soils as nitrous and nitric oxides, ammonium, nitrite, and nitrate. The first two are gases and are present only in trace amounts. Ammonium ion is usually adsorbed on the soil colloids, but it is now known that, like potassium ions, it may be fixed in the expanding crystal lattices of clay minerals such as illite, vermiculite, and montmorillonite. Recent studies have shown that 3–8% of the total nitrogen in surface soils, and 9–44% of the nitrogen in subsoils, was in the form of fixed ammonium (45). Nitrite is present only in trace amounts as a transition compound, and practically all the nitrate is present in the soil solution.

The surface layer of cultivated soils contains between 0.02 and 0.4% nitrogen, the amount depending largely on soil type, temperature, and rainfall. Climate plays a dominant part in determining the nitrogen status of soils. Within belts of uniform moisture conditions and comparable vegetation, the average nitrogen and organic matter contents of the soil decrease exponentially as the annual temperature rises (120).

Some of the earliest work on the absorption of nitrogen by plants was carried out by Boussingault, and by Ville from 1837 onward (195), but the source of plant nitrogen was probably first demonstrated by John Lawes of Rothamsted about 1840. He collected rain and determined its nitrogen content. Since this amounted only to 3–5 pounds per acre annually he assumed that plants obtained the remainder from the soil. He then tried applying mineral forms of nitrogen to his wheat (*Triticum*) crops. The enhanced growth and increased yield resulting from the minerals demonstrated that crops derive most of their nitrogen from the soil (142).

2. Phosphorus

Soil phosphorus may be divided into two primary classes, organic and inorganic. Organic phosphorus occurs in the form of phospholipids, nucleic acids and inositol phosphates. Phospholipid phosphorus seldom exceeds 3 parts per million (ppm), but values as high as 34 ppm have been reported (27). Values that range from 17 to 58% have been found for nucleic acid phosphorus, and in certain Iowa soils from 41 to 49% of the organic phosphorus was present in the form of phytin and lower phosphoric acid esters of inositol. Organic phosphorus, expressed as a percentage of total phosphorus, may range from 2.6 to 75%. It would appear that the phosphorus in these organic compounds must first be mineralized before it can be absorbed by plants.

Inorganic phosphorus occurs in many forms, the nature and extent depending largely on soil pH. A small fraction, normally less than 1 ppm, is present in the soil solution and is in equilibrium with adsorbed phosphorus. In acid soils, most of the inorganic phosphorus is associated with iron and aluminum compounds and to a lesser degree with clay minerals, such as dufrenite, vivianite, and wavelite. Recently the presence of certain dihydroxy-dihydrogen phosphates of iron and aluminum, known as strengite [$Fe(OH)_2H_2PO_4$] and variscite [$Al(OH)_2$-H_2PO_4], have been identified (138, 143). In alkaline and calcareous soils phosphorus is present largely as apatite, hydroxyapatite, and carbonatoapatite.

The total phosphorus content of the lithosphere (outer crust of the earth) averages 0.28% P_2O_5, but most surface soils contain from 0.022 to 0.083% of phosphorus. Total phosphorus values are of little use in predicting the response to phosphatic fertilizer. For the purpose of estimating "available" phosphorus, a number of chemical (278) and biological tests (257) have been devised. Chemical methods involve the use of dilute organic and mineral acids, and biological methods include the Neubauer, Mitscherlich, and *Aspergillus niger* tests (see Section VI, B).

Liebig, in 1840, and Way, in 1850, were among the first investigators to observe that phosphate was retained by soils. Lawes and Gilbert (1843–1855) demonstrated the response of field crops to soluble phosphates and thus laid the foundation of the phosphatic fertilizer industry. Ville, 1861, appears to have been one of the first investigators to show that phosphorus is necessary for all plant growth. He also showed that, in order to serve as a plant nutrient, the phosphorus must be in the form of phosphate (195).

3. Potassium

Potassium occurs as primary and weathered minerals, and in non-exchangeable, exchangeable, and water-soluble forms. The most important potassium-containing minerals are orthoclase and microcline feldspar ($KAlSi_3O_8$), muscovite [$K(AlSi_3O_{10})Al_2(OH,F)_2$], biotite [$K(AlSi_3O_{10})Mg_3(OH,F)_2$], and the clay mineral, illite. The nature of these soil minerals has been changed somewhat from the original; they have lost some interlayer potassium and gained some water of hydration.

For plant nutrition the exchangeable and water-soluble forms are the most readily available, the nonexchangeable potassium acting as a reserve. The upper lithosphere contains 2.59% potassium (85). Bear *et al.* (19) found the average distribution of potassium in 20 New Jersey soils as follows: exchangeable, 0.2 meq; nonexchangeable 46.3 meq; total, 46.5 meq/100 gm soil.

It has been shown by a number of studies that exchangeable and "available" potassium are by no means identical. As much as 50% of the total potassium absorbed by crops may come from the nonexchangeable fraction. Exchangeable potassium may be determined by leaching the soil with neutral salts. "Available" potassium may be determined by extraction with 1% citric acid, neutral normal ammonium acetate, sodium acetate-acetic acid buffer solution (Morgan's reagent), or by biological tests (Neubauer).

Although Birner and Lucanus, 1866, experimenting with oats in water culture, gave the first proof that potassium is essential for flowering plants, potassium deficiency in field crops was first described by Wilfarth and Wimmer in 1902 (154), and for fruit crops by Wallace (265) in 1921.

4. Calcium

The most important primary calcium minerals in the soil are anorthite $(CaAl_2Si_2O_8)$ and pyroxenes of the type $CaMg(SiO_3)_2$. In addition, small amounts of calcium may be present as borosilicates. Calcite $(CaCO_3)$ may be the dominant source in some soils, and dolomite $[CaMg(CO_3)_2]$ in others. A variety of calcium phosphates generally occur in soil. The most important are apatites, $Ca_5(PO_4)_3F$ and $Ca_5(PO_4)_3Cl$, and hydroxyapatite, $Ca_5(OH)(PO_4)_3$. Calcium sulfate, or gypsum, may be present in surface soils or subsoils to some extent.

The black earth soils, including chernozems (black earth soils of Russia) and rendzinas (humus soils arising from limestone or gypsum), are very high in calcium carbonate, reaching values of 40–50%.

The calcium most readily available for plant nutrition includes the water-soluble and exchangeable fractions. In fertile soils the exchangeable calcium should constitute from 70 to 80% of the total exchangeable bases. It is usually determined by leaching the soil with neutral salts.

Calcium deficiency is usually associated with acidity effects, and it is often difficult to differentiate one from the other (100). The effects of calcium deficiency on tobacco under field conditions and solution culture are identical (154). Stohman, 1862, concluded that calcium was necessary for green plants, and Wolf, 1864, appears to have discovered that calcium had a stimulating effect on root growth (195).

Excess calcium, associated with alkaline pH, may lead to deficiencies of iron, manganese, copper, boron, and zinc.

5. Magnesium

Magnesium is present in soil as water-soluble, exchangeable, fixed and primary mineral forms. It is found chiefly in the commonly occurring aluminosilicate minerals, such as biotite, augite, hornblende, and montmorillonite. In regions of limited rainfall, dolomite [MgCa $(CO_3)_2$], magnesite ($MgCO_3$), and epsomite ($MgSO_4 \cdot 7H_2O$) may constitute appreciable sources of this element.

The lithosphere contains an average of 2.68% of magnesium. Soils vary considerably in their magnesium content according to their geological origin. Jacob (116) gives the range of magnesium in soils from European countries as 0.006 to 1.0% of MgO. The total magnesium content of a soil is not necessarily a reliable guide to its availability. This may be determined by biological or chemical methods. The availability of magnesium depends not only on the total amount present, but on the amount in relation to the exchange capacity of the soil colloids, and on the nature of the complementary ions. According to Prince *et al.* (191), if magnesium constitutes less than 6% of the exchange cations of the soil, crops growing on that soil are likely to respond to applications of magnesium. The ideal amount of magnesium is believed to be about 10% of the total exchange capacity of the soil. Furthermore the ratio K:Mg should not greatly exceed 2:1.

Although the researches of Willstätter, 1906, had shown the presence of magnesium in chlorophyll, magnesium deficiency in plants in the field was not diagnosed until Garner *et al.* (81) showed it to be responsible for the condition known as "sand drown" in tobacco (*Nicotiana tabacum*). The symptoms of magnesium deficiency in a wide range of crops are described by Jacob (116) and Wallace (266). Deficiency is clearly linked with soil type: it occurs mainly on podsolic soils but is not to be expected on black earths.

6. Sulfur

Sulfur is present in soils in both inorganic and organic forms. In humid soils the bulk is present as pyrite (FeS_2), sphalerite (ZnS), chalcopyrite ($CuFeS_2$), cobaltite (CoAsS), and varying amounts of gypsum and epsomite. Field soils of humid temperature regions have 50–500 ppm of sulfate soluble in water or weak acids. The total sulfur in these soils ranges from 0.01 to 0.15%. In arid and semiarid soils much of the total sulfur is present as soluble sulfates of calcium, magnesium, potassium, and sodium. In glasshouse soils accumulation of soluble sulfates may cause root injury and depression of plant growth. From the time of Liebig it has been known that sulfates are necessary for plant growth.

Sulfur deficiency is very rare in industrial countries. The so-called "yellows" disease of tea (*Camellia sinensis* [*Thea sinensis*]) has been reported by Storey and Leach (238) to be due to sulfur deficiency. Under field conditions it has also been reported in tobacco (*Nicotiana tabacum*), sugar cane (*Saccharum officinarum*), soybean (*Glycine max*), citrus (*Citrus* spp.) and subterranean clover (*Trifolium subterraneum*).

B. MICRONUTRIENT ELEMENTS

1. Iron

Iron is present in appreciable amounts in minerals, hydrated oxides similar to goethite and limonite, and as the sulfide. It is also present in organic complexes. The total Fe_2O_3 content of soils varies from about 2–6% in normal temperate soils to as much as 60% in the ferruginous latosols (tropical soils).

It would appear that the ferrous form is most available for plant nutrition. As the soil becomes more alkaline the iron becomes oxidized to the ferric form, which is relatively unavailable to plants. Under alkaline soil conditions plants may suffer from iron deficiency often referred to as lime-induced iron deficiency. Heavy metals when present in excess amounts may also induce iron deficiency. Until recently heavy metal-induced iron deficiency was difficult to control under field conditions, but with the introduction of synthetic iron chelates, such as iron ethylenediaminetetraacetic acid (Fe-EDTA), the control of metal toxicity under acid soil conditions is now possible. This was first demonstrated by Stewart and Leonard (234).

The first nutrient deficiency ever to be reported, by Gris in 1844, appears to be that of iron (90). Excess manganese is reported to induce iron deficiency in pineapple (*Ananas comosus*), and excess copper causes chlorosis of citrus in Florida. Bennett (20) was the first to treat lime-induced chlorosis in fruit trees by trunk injection of iron salts. This method has been superseded by the use of soil dressings and foliar sprays of iron chelates, the most successful being iron-ethylenediamine bis (*o*-hydroxyphenylacetic acid).

2. Copper

Chalcopyrite ($CuFeS_2$) is the most important copper compound in primary rocks, and natural deposits of copper sulfide have probably originated from it. Field experiments have shown that copper sulfide acts as a source of copper for plant growth.

The average copper content of the lithosphere is 70 ppm (241). The total copper content of soils ranges from 2 to 100 ppm of which about 1 ppm may be extracted by dilute hydrochloric acid. Availability depends on the relative amounts of copper in the exchangeable, mineral, and organically complexed form. It is assessed by extraction in dilute mineral acids, by buffered salt solutions, or biologically using the fungus *Aspergillus niger* (see Section VI, B). Extraction of Danish soils with HCl at pH 2 gave values varying from <0.05 to >1 ppm, organic soils generally giving low values. The earliest instances of copper deficiency under field conditions occurred in citrus in Florida in 1875 (235). The deficiency gave rise to symptoms known as "exanthema" or die-back. Copper deficiency in other fruit trees was recorded in the United States in 1928, and Sjollema in 1933 attributed the "reclamation" disease of cereals, and other crops, to a deficiency of copper. Excess copper induces iron deficiency, as noted by Reuther and Smith (197) in citrus.

3. Zinc

Zinc occurs in ferromagnesian minerals, magnetite, biotite, and hornblende. Most zinc-bearing minerals are readily weathered, the zinc so released is probably adsorbed onto colloids as a divalent cation or is complexed by organic matter. Nelson and Melsted (172) investigated the fate of zinc added to neutral and acid soils. With an acid soil, practically all the zinc could be replaced by ammonium acetate, whereas with a calcium soil part of the zinc could be recovered only by repeated leachings with dilute hydrochloric acid. This acid-soluble zinc did not occupy exchange sites because there was no reduction in the exchange capacity of the soil.

Swaine (241) gives the abundance in the lithosphere as 80 ppm. Normal soils contain 10–300 ppm of total zinc. Total zinc content of soils is not necessarily related to availability. Tucker and Kurtz (254) compared several methods of extracting available zinc and found that the bioassay, dithizone, and 0.1 N HCl procedures were the most satisfactory. Dilute acids, such as 0.5 N acetic acid, may remove up to 30 ppm, and neutral normal ammonium acetate <10 ppm. By the *Aspergillus niger* method it was found that normal soils contained >10 ppm and deficient soils <2 ppm Zn (34).

Little leaf, and rosetting of fruit trees, were the first field symptoms to be related to zinc deficiency. Pecan (*Carya illinoinensis*) rosette was recognized by growers as early as 1900, although it was not diagnosed as zinc deficiency till 1932. White bud of maize (*Zea mays*), and mottle leaf, or frenching, of citrus are other field disorders known to be due to zinc deficiency (235).

4. Manganese

Soil manganese can be divided into the bivalent ion—existing in the soil solution, or as an exchangeable ion, or in a nonexchangeable form— and the insoluble higher oxides, minerals, and organically combined forms, all of which are in dynamic equilibrium with one another (144). The average content in the lithosphere is 1000 ppm, and the total amount in soils varies from 200 to 3000 ppm (241). Exchangeable manganese is usually determined by extraction with neutral salt solutions, values <2 ppm being regarded as indicative of deficiency. A value which is marginal or low for a soil with a pH of 7 becomes satisfactory if the pH is lowered to 6. The manganic forms act as a reserve; the ease with which they can be reduced to the manganous state varies considerably. The quinol-soluble manganese is taken as an index of potential availability: in normal soils it should exceed 100 ppm.

The main soil factors that determine availability are pH and the oxidation-reduction conditions. pH values around 6–6.5 appear to be critical, lower values favoring reduction and higher values, oxidation. Quastel (192) believes that organisms are mainly responsible for oxidation from pH 6 to 7.9 pH and that nonbiological oxidation is marked only above pH 8. He suggests that when biological oxidation takes place in neutral or slightly acid soils, tervalent manganese is formed. This in turn dismutes forming manganese dioxide and bivalent manganese, which undergoes biological oxidation once more (cf. Chapter 6).

"Gray speck" disease of oats (*Avena sativa*) has been known for many years and could be controlled by treatment with manganese salts, but the proof that "gray speck" was actually related to manganese deficiency was provided by Samuel and Piper in 1928 (209). Marsh spot of peas (*Pisum sativum*), pahala blight of sugar cane (*Saccharum officinarum*), speckled yellows of sugar beet (*Beta vulgaris*), and frenching of tung (*Aleurites fordii*) trees are other common field disorders caused by manganese deficiency.

5. Boron

Boron occurs as tourmaline, a very insoluble fluorine-containing borosilicate, as calcium and magnesium borates, and as iron and aluminum complexes (168). Total boron ranges from 2 to 100 ppm. The boron status of plants is related to the amount of boron removed from soil by extraction with boiling water. The amounts range from <0.05 to >50 ppm, the majority of soils having values >3 ppm. The deficiency level depends on conditions of extraction, pH, and organic matter status. A limiting value would be in the region of 0.5 ppm air-dry soil.

The sunflower (*Helianthus annuus*) is very sensitive to boron deficiency and has been used by Stephenson and Schuster and by Colwell for determining plant-available boron (257).

Light, acid soils in humid regions are likely to be deficient in available boron because of the ease with which boron is leached. Higher amounts of boron are found in organic soils. Plant uptake of boron is reduced by increasing the soil pH by liming. Colwell and Cummings (59) have drawn attention to the possible significance, in this respect, of the differences in molecular structure between calcium metaborate and the corresponding sodium and potassium salts.

Boron toxicity can arise in arid areas in which sodium and calcium borates accumulate in the surface soils. Irrigation waters containing >2 ppm of boron are reported to be undesirable (168).

According to Miller (166), Agulhon (1), in 1910, was the first to recognize the essential nature of boron in plant life, but his work was not generally accepted until Warington's (272) work on the bean (*Phaseolus vulgaris*) was published. Since then a voluminous literature on boron in relation to plant growth has developed. Heart rot of sugar beet, mangolds (*Beta vulgaris*) and other root crops, browning of cauliflower (*Brassica oleracea* var. *botrytis*), cracked stem of celery (*Apium graveolens* var. *dulce*), lucerne (*Medicago sativa*), yellows, top sickness of tobacco (*Nicotiana tabacum*), and internal cork of apples (*Malus sylvestris*) are but a few of the economic diseases associated with boron deficiency.

6. Molybdenum

Molybdenum occurs in igneous rocks as molybdenite, MoS_2, and as the primary molybdates powellite, $CaMoO_4$, and wulfenite, $PbMoO_4$. The average content of molybdenum in the lithosphere is 2.3 ppm (85). Total molybdenum in soils varies from 0.2 to 5 ppm the average value is about 2 ppm. Dilute acids or neutral normal ammonium acetate usually extract <0.2 ppm.

Davies (63) classifies soil molybdenum as follows: unavailable, held within the crystal lattice of primary and secondary minerals; conditionally available, retained as the MoO_4 anion by clay minerals and available to a greater or lesser degree depending on pH and phosphate status; in organic form; and water soluble. Up to 90% of the total molybdenum may occur in the unavailable category. Available molybdenum may be assessed by analysis of indicator plants such as sweet vernal grass (*Anthoxanthum odoratum*), by bioassay using *Aspergillus niger*, and by chemical extractants such as neutral normal ammonium acetate and Tamm's acid oxalate, pH 3.3. Using acid oxalate, Davies (63) found that a fair prediction of response could be made if interpretation was modified according to soil pH. At pH 5 the response level was 0.2 ppm and at pH 6.5, 0.05 ppm molybdenum.

Two field disorders, whiptail of cauliflower and broccoli (two forms of *Brassica oleracea* var. *botrytis*) and yellow spot of citrus, were described about 30 to 45 years before the responsibility for the disorders were attributed to a molybdenum deficiency by Mitchell and by Davies in 1945 for brassicae, and by Stewart and Leonard in 1952 for citrus (101). The first instance of molybdenum deficiency in higher plants growing in the field in the United States was recorded by Walker in 1948 (101).

Excess molybdenum in soils was first investigated by Ferguson, Lewis, and Watson (72) in relation to a cattle disease known locally in southwest England as "teart" and characterized by extreme diarrhea. This condition is favored by alkaline soils and high phosphate status. Deficiency is usually associated with acid soils. Heavy liming and molybdate application frequently bring about equal improvement in yield. Plant (188) showed that 5 tons of crushed limestone per acre and 4 pounds of ammonium molybdate were equally effective in controlling "whiptail" in cauliflower in English soils, but in New Zealand absolute deficiency may respond only to dressings of molybdate.

7. Other Elements of Biological Interest

Although not essential for the growth of higher plants, cobalt is essential for animals and for some symbiotic nitrogen-fixing microorganisms and vanadium is essential for certain microorganisms. In addition, iodine and fluorine are concerned with animal health; arsenic and selenium may be toxic to animals, and nickel and chromium to plants. Sodium is beneficial to some plants but not to others, and chlorine deficiency has not been observed under field conditions. All these elements occur in soils to varying extents.

In ruminant animals, the production of vitamin B_{12} necessitates adequate supplies of cobalt for rumen bacteria. Many instances of cobalt deficiency have been reported on soils of diverse character in Australia, New Zealand, Great Britain, Norway, the United States, Canada, and other countries. The largest areas probably occur on sandstones, and symptoms are particularly pronounced if the sandstones are calcareous. In deficient soils there is generally an inherently low content of cobalt, total contents of $<0.5–3$ ppm being commonly reported whereas contents of up to 30 ppm are usual in soils which support healthy stock (168). Owing to differences in availability from soil to soil, no direct correlation is noted between total cobalt content of the soils and of the herbage. In soils, cobalt may occur in an available or extractable form as adsorbed Co in the exchange complex, as phosphate, or as sulfate. The amount of cobalt extracted from Scottish arable soils by 2.5% acetic acid varies from <0.05 ppm in very deficient sands to >1 ppm in many soils derived from basic igneous rocks. In cultivated mineral soils with moderate acidity (pH 5.6), the deficiency level is in the region of 0.25 ppm of acetic-soluble cobalt (168), or 5 ppm of total cobalt (285).

Vanadium occurs in greatest amount in shales and the less basic igneous rocks. The total contents of eight Scottish soils varied from 20 to 250 ppm (168). Impeded drainage results in increased amounts of vanadium which is soluble in acetic acid. Bertrand (21) determined the vanadium content of sixty-two plant materials and found a range of 0.27 to 4.2 ppm in dry matter. Seeds of legumes were particularly poor in vanadium. The gallium content of twenty soils ranged from 0.4 to 6 ppm (22).

Fluorine is much more abundant than iodine in soils. The bulk of the fluorine occurs in the crystal lattices of silicates and phosphate minerals. The total content of fluorine in soils ranges from about 10 to 1000 ppm, whereas the range for iodine is about 0.6 to 8 ppm with exceptional values up to 70 ppm, most of which is water soluble (168). Fluorine toxicity sometimes occurs in the neighborhood of smelting works.

Arsenic occurs naturally in most soils in amounts between 1 and 70 ppm (241). In fruit orchards it may accumulate in the surface soil; Greaves (88) found values ranging from 7.2 to 367 pounds per acre-foot of soil. Water-soluble arsenic is not related to total content. Fortunately plant growth appears to be restricted before amounts dangerous to animals are absorbed.

Many soils are seleniferous and thus bear crops injurious to animals. The first account of a disease of horses, now known to be due to selenium poisoning, was given in 1857. Crops which accumulate selenium include species of *Astragalus, Machaeranthera* (*Xylorrhiza*), *Haplopappus* (*Oonopsis*), and *Stanleya*. In seleniferous areas, Cretaceous shales and other sedimentary rocks contain abnormally high amounts of selenium varying from 1 to 10 ppm. An area of seleniferous soils in Ireland contains 30–300 ppm selenium, and herbage contents up to 500 ppm have been reported (271). Soils from healthy areas contained <2 ppm selenium. The average selenium content of accumulator plants was found by Trelease (249) to be 500 ppm, and the highest recorded is 15,000 ppm.

Of the remaining elements that occur in toxic amounts, nickel is the most important. Contents of up to 8000 ppm total nickel and 100 ppm nickel soluble in acetic acid have been recorded in Scotland in poorly drained soils derived from ultrabasic rocks (168).

There are many well-authenticated cases in which additions of sodium salts have increased the yield of, or otherwise improved, various

crops. Nevertheless the evidence is not sufficient to prove that the element is essential for normal growth of plants. Crops which respond well to applications of sodium salts include celery, mangold, sugar beet, table beet, and turnip. Sodium, like potassium, is present as an exchangeable cation in normal soils and ranges in amount from 100 to 200 pounds per acre (6-inch surface layer). It is present as sodium carbonate in alkali soils.

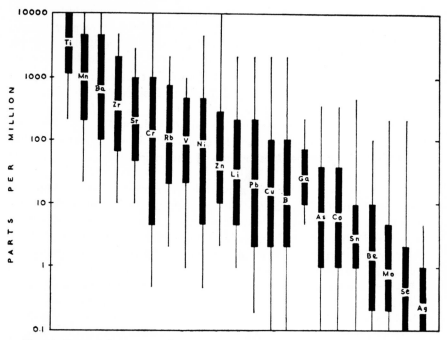

Fig. 3. Range of contents of some trace elements commonly found in mineral soils. Thin lines indicate more unusual values; certain extremely high contents reported from abnormal localities influenced, for instance, by ore deposits have been ignored. From Mitchell (168).

Normal soils contain many other elements which may have a beneficial effect on plant growth, but their essentiality has not yet been established (see Fig. 3).

IV. Factors in the Retention and Availability of Nutrients

A. NATURE OF THE SOIL COLLOIDS

The colloidal fraction of soils is partly inorganic (clay) and partly organic (humus), the two forming in most soils a clay-humus complex.

Knowledge of the nature and properties of soil colloids is essential if one is to understand the part they play in plant nutrition. Colloidal surfaces have the property of adsorbing ions: this adsorption may be designated as positive (cations), negative (anions), or chemical.

1. Clay

The clay fraction of soils includes all inorganic particles with a diameter of <2 μ; those particles <1 μ are termed colloidal clay and consist mainly of weathered minerals. The nature of these materials has given rise to a great deal of speculation. The earliest theory regarded kaolinite as the essential mineral of clay, this being formed from orthoclase felspar according to the equation

$$K_2O \cdot Al_2O_3 \cdot 6SiO_2 + 3H_2O = Al_2O_3 \cdot 2SiO_2 \cdot 2H_2O + 2KOH + 4SiO_2$$

Kaolinite does not possess all the properties inherent in clay, and it is now known to be only one of a number of clay minerals. Later, workers tried to characterize clays by their solubility in hot mineral acids and placed them in categories according to their SiO_2/Al_2O_3 ratios.

Van Bemmelen, 1888, and later Stremme, 1911, divided their colloidal fraction into two parts. One part, which was soluble in hydrochloric acid, they called allophaneton, and a second part not soluble in hydrochloric acid but soluble in hot concentrated sulfuric acid came to be called kaolinton. Attempts were made to classify clay materials on the basis of their kaolinton and allophaneton content. Wiegner, 1936, considered the colloidal exchange material as being made up of three parts: (a) a kernel, (b) a layer of adsorbed anions external to the kernel but lying in contact with it, (c) exchangeable cations attracted to the particle by the adsorbed anions. The kernel was considered to be a hydrous compound chiefly of alumina and silica of variable composition and of unknown structural attributes. Mattson, 1938, regarded the colloidal complex as a crystalline kernel covered with an amorphous heterogeneous coating which lacks a definite composition and is not identical with the nucleus (89).

For many years it had been suggested that clay materials were composed of extremely small particles of a limited number of crystalline minerals, but prior to about 1920 there were no adequate research tools to provide the positive evidence. In 1923, Hadding in Sweden, and in 1924 Rinne in Germany, working quite independently, published the first X-ray diffraction analyses of clay minerals. Both these workers found crystalline material in the finest fraction of a series of clays. About 1924, Ross and his colleagues, in America, on the basis of work with the petrographic microscope, also showed that clay minerals were largely crystalline and were limited in number. They confirmed these findings later by means of X-ray analysis (89).

By the early 1930's what has come to be known as the clay-mineral concept became firmly established. According to this concept, clays generally are composed of extremely small crystalline particles of one or more members of a small group of minerals. The clay minerals are essentially hydrous aluminum silicates with magnesium or iron substituting wholly or in part for the aluminum in some minerals, and with alkalis or alkaline earths present as essential constituents in some of them. The classic investigation of Pauling in 1930 provided the basic ideas which permitted the elaboration of the structure of the layer clay minerals (89).

Two structural units are involved in the atomic lattices of most of the clay minerals. One unit consists of two sheets of closely packed

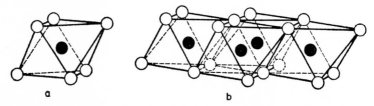

FIG. 4. Diagrammatic sketch showing (a) single octahedral unit and (b) the sheet structure of the octahedral units. Open circles, hydroxyls; filled circles, aluminums, magnesiums, etc. From Grim (89).

oxygens or hydroxyls in which aluminum, iron, or magnesium atoms are embedded in octahedral coordination, so that they are equidistant from six oxygens or hydroxyls (Fig. 4). When aluminum is present, only two-thirds of the possible positions are filled to balance the structure, which is the gibbsite structure and has the formula $Al_2(OH)_6$. When magnesium is present, all the positions are filled to balance the structure, which is the brucite structure and has the formula $Mg_3(OH)_6$.

The second unit is built of silica tetrahedrons. In each tetrahedron a silicon atom is equidistant from four oxygen, or hydroxyls if needed to balance the structure, arranged in the form of a tetrahedron with a silicon atom at the center. The silica tetrahedral groups are arranged to form a hexagonal network, which is repeated indefinitely to form a sheet of composition $Si_4O_6(OH)_4$ (Fig. 5). The terahedrons are so arranged that their tips all point in the same direction, and their bases are all in the same plane. Combination of these two units, with modifications and substitutions, give rise to the lattice structure of clay minerals (89). Those clay minerals usually found in soils include kaolinite, halloysite, montmorillonite, illite, chlorite, and vermiculite.

The clay minerals can be classified according to their lattice structure, of which there are two basic types. Kaolinite has a 1:1 lattice and may be described as a single silica tetrahedral sheet topped by a slightly distorted gibbsite sheet, both being joined by condensation and

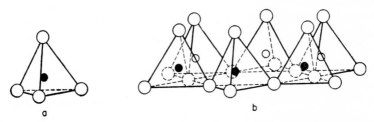

Fig. 5. Diagrammatic sketch showing (a) single silica tetrahedron and (b) sheet structure of silica tetrahedrons arranged in a hexagonal network. Larger circles, oxygens; smaller circles, silicons. From Grim (89).

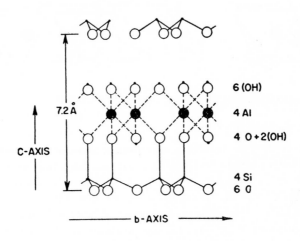

KAOLINITE $(OH)_8Al_4Si_4O_{10}$

Fig. 6. Schematic diagram of the crystal structure of kaolinite. Courtesy of J. W. Grüner and Akademische Verlagsgesellschaft Geest and Portig K.-G. (publishers of Z. Krist.). From Toth (247).

splitting off of water (Fig. 6). Lattice substitution for all practical purposes does not exist. Montmorillonite has a 2:1 lattice and consists of a single gibbsite sheet between two sheets of silica tetrahedrons (Fig. 7). Lattice substitutions include Al and P for Si, and Mg, Fe, Ni, and Li for Al. Because of these lattice substitutions, the atomic charges within the lattice are unbalanced. Compensation for the unbalance includes substitution of OH for O in the octahedral layer, and adsorption of exchangeable cations. In kaolinitic types, broken bonds around the edges of the silica-alumina sheets are largely responsible for their cation exchange capacity (247).

It should be pointed out that clay minerals seldom occur in a pure state but are contaminated with inorganic amorphous isoelectric precipitates and organic matter. The inorganic contaminants make little

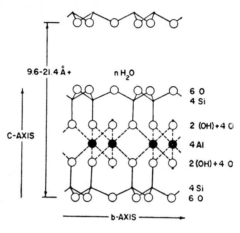

FIG. 7. Schematic diagram of the crystal structure of montmorillonite. Courtesy of V. Hofmann *et al.* and Akademische Verlagsgesellschaft Geest and Portig K.-G. (publishers of *Z. Krist.*). From Toth (247).

contribution to the cation exchange capacity of soils but are responsible for a considerable proportion of the anion exchange capacity.

2. Organic Matter

Soil organic matter consists of plant residues together with the products of decomposition, the excretions from soil microorganisms and microbial cells. That part which has undergone advanced change and lost its original structure is referred to as humus. The term humus however has no precise chemical definition. The earlier soil chemists attempted to separate and fractionate humus by the use of solvents. To some of these fractions they gave the names fulvic acid, hematomelanic acid, and humic acid (see Scheme I). Later, workers showed that these fractions were not chemical entities. Waksman (262) and his co-workers applied a new technique in which they fractionated organic matter into known biochemical constituents. By this means they were able to account for more than 90% of the total matter in humus.

In the process of biological decomposition the chemical and physical nature of organic matter is changed, and it acquires certain colloidal properties which play an important part in plant nutrition. Carbohydrates are decomposed with the formation of CO_2 and H_2O and the synthesis by the microorganisms of polyuronides, substances which have an important bearing on soil structure. During the partial decomposition of lignins the cation exchange capacity increases, owing to the formation of phenolic and carboxylic groups. Organic matter is dealt with in somewhat more detail by Quastel (see Chapter 6).

SCHEME I

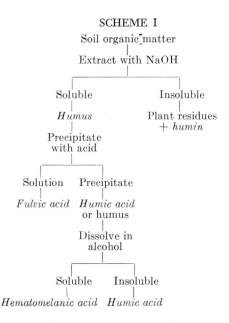

Proteins undergo biological decomposition with the liberation of ammonia, which is oxidized to nitrate. At the same time new nitrogenous compounds are synthesized. These include chitin, amino sugars, and proteins.

Organic matter in loam soils is intimately mixed with the clay fraction and in clays with a 2:1 lattice structure part of the organic molecule may penetrate into the spacings between successive layers of clay. In this manner it is protected from further biological decomposition (247).

The importance of the organic content of soils is indicated by the fact that the cation exchange capacity may be reduced by as much as 20–50% by its removal, even though it constitutes normally only 3–5% of the total soil mass. The cation exchange capacity of soil organic colloids ranges from 250 to 450 meq per 100 gm dry weight.

B. CATION AND ANION EXCHANGE

Although it was known for many centuries that soil had the power to decolorize and deodorize liquid manure it was not until about 1850 that these soil properties were investigated scientifically by Thompson, Way and Forschamer. Thompson analyzed the leachates obtained by percolating water, to which ammonium sulfate or ammonium carbonate had been added, through a short column of sandy loam soil. He showed that all the ammonium was absorbed by the soil, and calcium sulfate appeared in the leachate. According to Kelley (130), Thompson discussed his results with Way, who carried out a more thorough investigation. In his first paper, published in 1850, Way (273) arrived at the following conclusions:

1. The cations of a neutral salt solution are "absorbed"* by the soil, and this is accomplished by the displacement of an equivalent amount of calcium from the soil, but the anion of the salt remains in solution provided an insoluble calcium salt is not formed.

2. The absorption is caused not by sand, organic matter, calcium carbonate, or free alumina but by the clay fraction of the soil.

3. The absorptive power of the soil may be reduced by preheating the sample, but is not completely destroyed unless it is heated to a high temperature.

4. The rate of absorption is rapid, like the reaction between an acid and an alkali.

5. Ammonium hydroxide and ammonium carbonate are absorbed by the soil in their entirety, practically no exchange of cation taking place.

6. The base-exchange power of the soil is not restricted to ammonium but includes potassium, sodium, and magnesium. However, if any of these is applied as the hydroxide or carbonate, the base is absorbed without change.

7. Calcium added as a solution of the sulfate, chloride, or nitrate passes through the soil unchanged, but calcium hydroxide and bicarbonate are absorbed in their entirety.

8. The ammonium-absorbing power of the soil increases with the concentration of the solution, and also as the ratio of solution to soil is increased.

9. The base absorptive power of the soil is irreversible.

Among Way's conclusions nos. 1, 3, 4, and 8 have stood the test of time, and a substantial part of 2 and 6 have been verified by soil scientists. On the other hand conclusions 5, 7, and 9 were for the most part erroneous. At the time of Way's investigations the fact that hydro-

* Where Way used the terms "absorbed" or "absorption," which are here retained, we would now use the terms adsorbed and adsorption. (Ed.)

gen ions can take part in exchange reactions was not known, and this accounts for his conclusion that alkaline compounds are absorbed without exchange. His greatest error was the conclusion that the exchange of cation was irreversible.

After Way's work further important contributions were made by Peters, 1860; Van Bemmelen, 1878; Gedroiz, 1912–1925; Wiegner, 1931; and Mattson, 1929–1947 (130).

1. The Modern Concept of Cation and Anion Exchange

Ion exchange is the reversible process by which cations and anions are exchanged between solid and liquid phases, and between solid phases if in close contact with each other. The ion exchange property of a soil is due almost entirely to the clay fraction and the organic matter. Soil colloids are amphoteric, as evidenced by their power to bind both cations and anions. In general they carry a net negative charge. This charge arises essentially in two ways: first, by isomorphous ion substitution, and secondly by ionization of hydroxyl groups attached to silicon of broken tetrahedron planes in the clay lattice. The negative charges created in the former way are more uniformly distributed in the clay particles, whereas those created in the latter way are at corners and along the edges. In addition, negative charges may arise from humic, phosphoric, and silicic acids constituting an integral part of the clay particle surface.

The positive charges may originate from hydrous oxides of iron, aluminum and manganese, and from exposed octahedral groups. The electric charge, and the surface charge density, are not constant but vary with pH. The negative charge increases, and the positive charge decreases, with rising pH (275).

The electric charge on the soil particles is neutralized by an equivalent amount of oppositely charged ions. The bonding energy is dependent in part on the position of the adsorbed cation on the clay mineral unit. Thus cations between the basal plane surfaces (held by forces due to isomorphous ion substitution) are likely to be held more strongly than those around the edges of the units. The most common cations are Ca^{++}, Mg^{++}, H^+, K^+, Na^+, and NH_4^+. In very acid soils Al^{+++} may constitute a considerable part of the exchangeable cations, whereas in neutral soils Ca^{++} is the dominant cation.

The cation exchange capacity, C_7, is defined as the amount (in milliequivalents) of a cation species adsorbed at pH 7 by 100 gm dry soil. It may vary from 2–5 meq for a kaolinitic type of clay to 80–120 meq for a montmorillonitic type.

Because of thermal motion, the exchangeable ions are distributed within a certain space, forming a diffuse layer, or ion swarm, around the colloidal particles. The exchangeable ions are themselves surrounded by water molecules and may thus be considered as forming an inner solution, in distinction to the outer solution of free electrolytes. The thickness of the diffuse layer decreases, with increasing valency of the ions and with increasing concentration of electrolyte.

Anion exchange in soils has received less attention than cation exchange.

There appear to be two, and possibly three, types of anion exchange in the clay minerals:

1. Replacement of OH ions, as has been suggested by many authors for the phosphate adsorption by kaolinite. The extent of this reaction depends on the accessibility of the OH ions, and in general the only factor which prevents complete substitution is the fact that many OH ions are within the lattice and, therefore, not accessible.

2. The geometry of the anion in relation to the geometry of the clay-mineral structure units. Anions such as phosphate, arsenate, and borate, which have about the same size and geometry as the silica tetrahedron, may be adsorbed by fitting onto the edges of the silica tetrahedral sheets and growing as extensions of these sheets. Other anions such as sulfate, chloride, and nitrate, because their geometry does not fit that of the tetrahedral sheets, cannot be so adsorbed.

In both cases anion exchange would take place around the edges of the clay minerals.

Schofield has suggested a third manner of anion exchange, namely that the clay minerals may have anion exchange spots on basal plane surfaces. Such active anion exchange spots would be due to unbalanced charges within the lattice, e.g., an excess of aluminum in the octahedral positions (89).

The capacity of soils for adsorbing anions increases with acidity. Lowering of pH induces the activation of the basic groups by increased acceptance of protons

$$R\!-\!OH \;+ H^+Cl^- = R\!-\!OH_2{}^+Cl^-$$
$$R\!-\!NH_2 + H^+Cl^- = R\!-\!NH_3{}^+Cl^-$$

Cl^- may then be replaced by other anions.

In the neutral regions Cl^-, $NO_3{}^-$, and $SO_4{}^{--}$ are adsorbed very slightly, or not at all, hence these anions are easily lost by leaching. With increase in acidity the adsorption affinity of a kaolinitic type of soil is in the order: $Cl^- < SO_4{}^{--} << PO_4{}^{---}$. Adsorption of Cl and $PO_4{}^{---}$ by a montmorillonitic type of soil is similar at low pH, but adsorption of Cl^- does not occur above pH 3.2. For a more detailed discussion on exchange phenomena, see Wiklander (275).

C. FIXATION OF PLANT NUTRIENTS

Fixation is the process by which soluble plant nutrients are changed to less soluble forms by reaction with inorganic or organic soil constituents, or by biological activity.

1. *Phosphorus*

Three general reactions account for the loss of solubility of applied phosphate; adsorption, isomorphous replacement, and double decomposition. If a soil, low in calcium, is equilibrated with a phosphate solution at a neutral pH the first reaction is one of adsorption of phosphate on the colloid surfaces. With increased time of contact further reactions take place that lead to fixation of phosphate. This second reaction may be due to isomorphous substitution of phosphate for hydroxyl or silicate ions in the crystal lattice. The amount of substitution that can take place without causing instability of the lattice is, however, limited.

The double-decomposition reactions fall into two categories, those that involve iron and aluminum with the formation of compounds of the type $M(H_2O)_3(OH)_2H_2PO_4$, and those that involve calcium. The aluminosilicates and free sesquioxides may be regarded as the primary source of aluminum. Since the availability of Al^{+++} and Fe^{+++} for reaction with phosphate is controlled by the hydroxyl ion concentration, phosphorus fixation by these two elements can be decreased by raising the soil pH. However, with increase in pH and the presence of calcium carbonate, hydroxyapatite and carbonatoapatite may be formed, both of which are very insoluble. Thus Ca^{++} concentration and pH are the controlling factors in phosphate fixation. For a detailed review of inorganic phosphorus in acid and neutral soils, Kurtz (138) and Hemwall (96) may be consulted.

Organic matter affects most of the reactions involving phosphate fixation. The effects are as follows:

1. In adsorption reactions the organic compounds, being anionic in character, would be expected to compete with the phosphate ion in polar adsorption phenomena and hence decrease fixation.

2. With respect to isomorphous replacement it is highly improbable that the organic anions would fit into the clay mineral lattices.

3. In double decomposition reactions involving iron and aluminum, the acids produced in organic matter transformations could decrease the pH and thus increase fixation by solubilizing iron and aluminum. On the other hand, hydroxy acids such as tartaric, citric, malonic, and

malic are known to be formed in soils, and such acids can chelate iron and aluminum and prevent them from reacting with phosphate (129).

In general, the over-all effect of the organic phase in soils is to decrease phosphate fixation. Biological activity, on the other hand, can temporarily lock up a considerable fraction of the soil phosphorus in organic form.

2. Cations

Cation fixation in soils occurs when exchangeable and water-soluble forms are converted into a state whereby they cannot be readily extracted with a neutral salt solution. As long ago as 1894, Dyer, at Rothamsted, found that the potash removed by crops and that remaining soluble in 1% citric acid accounted for only about one-half of the amount applied as fertilizer, the remainder having either been lost by leaching or converted into difficultly soluble forms (70). About 25 years later Frear and Erb (77), working in Pennsylvania, determined the potash content of control plots, one of which had received 200 pounds per acre of potassium chloride biennially for 36 years, making in all a total of 1800 pounds per acre of potash. Here again, they could only account for about one-half of the potash—that removed by the crops or remaining in the soil in readily available forms. They concluded that "much of the potash applied as fertilizer remains in the surface soil in a state highly available to crops; that most of it remains there in a condition of lower availability, and that losses by drainage have probably not been great."

Volk (259) made a detailed study of potassium fixation in soils. He showed that: (a) alternate wetting and drying of soils treated with soluble salts caused rapid fixation of potassium in a nonreplaceable form. When these soils were kept continuously moist very little fixation of this kind took place; (b) fixation is dependent on the nature of the colloids as well as the quantity; (c) X-ray analysis indicated that a portion of the potassium had reacted with colloidal silicates and become fixed in the form of muscovite, thus converting added available potassium into difficultly available form; and (d) for practical reasons it would seem to be advisable to make frequent moderate applications of potash fertilizer rather than less frequent large applications, and at a greater depth to lessen the influence of alternate wetting and drying. Localized application would also tend to reduce fixation.

Volk also studied the effect of concentration of soluble potassium on fixation. He treated 20-gm. portions of soil with potassium bicarbonate at rates varying from 0 to 120,000 pounds per acre. The contents of each tube were then wetted and dried ten times at 70°C. The samples were leached with neutral normal ammonium acetate to remove exchangeable potassium. The results are shown graphically in Fig. 8. From these results it appears that under the conditions of the experiment a soil will fix a maximum of potassium in a very short time.

Ammonium fixation by soil was discovered by McBeth (151), who reported that it was impossible to remove more than 81% of the NH_4^+ ions added to a Californian soil, even after prolonged extraction with 10% HCl.

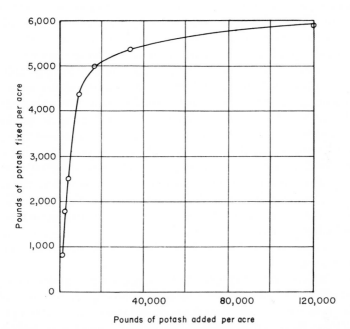

Fig. 8. Effect of the concentration of soluble potash on the amount fixed by Miami silt loam when treated with varying quantities of potassium bicarbonate and then alternately wetted and dried ten times at 70°C. From Volk (259).

Chaminade, in 1936, related potassium fixation to the exchange capacity of soils. He found that maximum fixation resulted if more than 4% of the exchange capacity was occupied by potassium. Chaminade and Drouineau (55) showed that NH_4^+ and Mg^{++} could also be fixed but Ca^{++} and Na^+ could not. They suggested that the fixation resulted from a diffusion of the cations into the crystal lattice of the soil colloids. This theory was further elaborated by Page and Baver (181), who suggested that ions whose diameter allows them to fit snugly into the lattice "holes" should be strongly fixed. The essential features of their theory were as follows:

1. The exposed surface layers of the 2:1 expanding lattice clays, such as montmorillonite, consists of a sheet of oxygen ions arranged hexagonally, the opening within the hexagon being 2.8 A in diameter.

2. As the clay is dehydrated, the layers contract and the adsorbed ions lose their hulls of oriented water molecules, approaching the unhydrated ionic diameter in size.

3. Ions, such as potassium, whose diameter (2.66 A) allows them to fit closely into the lattice "holes" should be held very tightly because

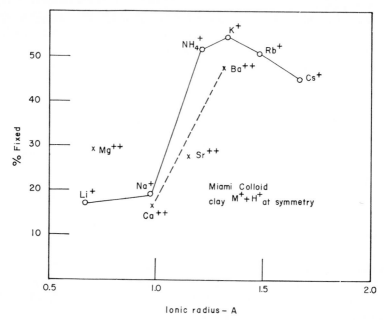

Fig. 9. The relation of ionic size to cation fixation by colloidal clay. From Page and Baver (181).

they are closer to the negative electrical charges within the crystal. Larger cations that could not enter the "holes" would remain more loosely held *between* the layers rather than *within* the layer and would be more accessible for rehydration. Smaller cations would be able to enter the "holes," but they would be too small to contact and bind the two layers together and upon rehydration should have room to assume a water hull, or for exchanging ions to replace them.

Figure 9 shows the relationship between ionic *radius* and percentage fixation in a 2:1 lattice type clay. The data support the concept that ionic size is of great importance in fixation.

Later work has shown that the spacing between the clay lattice crystals is also important in fixation. If, on dehydration, the contraction is prevented by the presence of large cations, then the fixation of potassium is reduced (129).

D. Soil pH and Acidity Complex

Acidity is associated with the presence of hydrogen ions, and probably aluminum ions, in exchangeable form. A soil is said to be acid when the activity of the hydrogen ions exceeds that of the hydroxyl ions. Because of other indirect effects, it is often referred to as the "soil acidity complex."

In practice, soil pH is measured potentiometrically using a glass electrode and a soil:water ratio of 1:2.5. The pH value of soils is not a constant: it varies with the soil:water ratio and the salt concentration. Lowering the amount of water and increasing the salt concentration

TABLE II

pH Values of a Soil Measured under Different Conditions[a]

Conditions	Supernatant liquid	Suspension	Sediment
Natural soil	6.2	5.8	4.7
Leached soil	6.5	5.9	5.2
Soil in N KCl	5.1	5.1	5.1

[a] From Coleman et al. (58).

both decrease the observed pH value. To eliminate variation in observed pH due to salt concentration the values are sometimes determined in N KCl or 0.01 M $CaCl_2$. Table II illustrates the variation in pH of the same soil under different conditions of measurement.

The factors that contribute to the "soil acidity complex" are summarized by Hewitt (100) thus:

1. Direct injury by hydrogen ions
2. Indirect effects of low pH
   a. Physiologically impaired absorption of calcium, magnesium, and phosphorus
   b. Increased solubility, to a toxic extent, of aluminum, manganese, and possibly iron and heavy metals
   c. Reduced availability of phosphorus, partly by interaction with aluminum or iron, possibly after absorption by the plant
   d. Reduced availability of molybdenum
3. Low base status
   a. Calcium deficiency
   b. Deficiencies of magnesium and potassium

4. Abnormal biotic factors
   a. Impaired nitrogen cycle and nitrogen fixation
   b. Impaired mycorrhizal activity
   c. Increased attack by certain soil pathogens
5. Accumulation of soil organic acids or other toxic compounds owing to unfavorable oxidation-reduction conditions or pH that limits microorganisms.

Arnon and Johnson (14) have shown that acidity per se is not necessarily injurious to plants and that growth between pH 4 and 8 is unaffected provided an adequate supply of plant nutrients is maintained.

Aluminum probably acts as a toxin in certain acid soils. Concentrations of aluminum in displaced soil solutions of strongly acid soils are equal to, or greater than, those required to produce detrimental effects. It has been shown that 1 ppm of aluminum in culture solution may have a significant depressing effect on the growth of corn and barley. This value is often exceeded in soil solutions having pH values <4.5.

Evidence for the toxicity of manganese in acid soils has been provided by Wallace *et al.* (268) and Morris (170). Morris found that the amounts of water-soluble manganese in a 1:2 soil:water extract from 25 acid soils ranged from 0 to 6.3 ppm, and the exchangeable manganese from 1.2 to 638 ppm. Judged by the toxicity of manganese in culture solutions, the manganese content of many of the soils would be toxic to plant growth.

There is some evidence that calcium deficiency in crops grown on acid soils may occur under conditions of low calcium supply combined with a high crop requirement, or low calcium supply combined with a high proportion of other exchangeable cations (4).

The availability to plants of soil phosphorus tends to be greater in neutral than in acid soils. Application of limestone thus may have an effect similar to that of an application of phosphatic fertilizer.

Of the trace elements that are affected by soil acidity, molybdenum appears to be the only one that behaves like phosphorus. Availability of molybdenum is increased when acid soils are limed (252).

The general relationship between soil pH and availability of plant nutrients is shown in Fig. 10.

V. Nutrient Uptake from Soil

There are three possible sources from which roots can extract their nutrients: the soil solution, the exchangeable ions, and the readily decomposable minerals.

A. Soil Solution

The soil moisture with the salts and gases dissolved in it is commonly considered to be the soil solution. Sometimes reference is made to the "inner" and "outer" soil solution. The term inner solution refers to the moisture in intimate contact with the colloidal soil particles, in which the concentration and composition of the solutes are in equilibrium with the solid phase. By the outer solution is meant the liquid in the

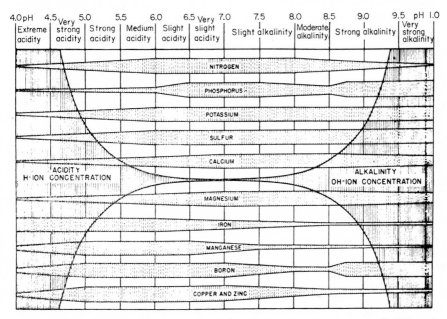

Fig. 10. Chart showing general trend of relation of reaction to availability of plant nutrients. From Truog (252).

larger capillary spaces, which is considered to be much more dilute than that in close contact with the colloidal particles.

Schloesing, in 1866, was the first to use a displacement method for collecting soil solutions. He used water colored with carmine as the displacing solution. Ischerekov, in 1907, used ethyl alcohol as the displacing liquid and obtained results which indicated that the displaced liquid was the true solution in an unaltered condition. Moist soil was packed in a glass tube which had a piece of linen tied over the bottom. After alcohol had been placed on top of the soil column the soil solution soon began to drop from the bottom of the tube. Ischerekov found that successive portions of the displaced solution were of the same composition, and that the concentration of the soil solution was inversely proportional to the moisture content of the soil. Van Suchtelen, 1912, modified Ischerekov's method by using paraffin oil as a displacing liquid and by applying suction to hasten displacement. Morgan, 1916, used a combination of pressure and displacement methods, in which a heavy oil was used as the displacing liquid and an applied pressure of about 500 pounds per square inch was used to force the oil into the packed soil. Several methods have been suggested for determining the concentration of the soil solution directly in the soil: these include electrical conductance and freezing point depression methods (182).

Parker (182) compared the displacement, water extraction, and freezing point methods for determining the concentration and composition of the soil solution from a number of soils. Some of the more important conclusions derived from his results are given below:

1. Ethyl alcohol was found to be more satisfactory as a displacing liquid than water, methyl alcohol, acetone, or liquids immiscible with water.

2. The composition of the soil solution obtained by displacement was not influenced by the displacing liquid used.

3. Successive portions of the displaced solution gave the same freezing point depression and contained the same amount of total salts.

4. The concentration of the displaced solution was found to be inversely proportional to the moisture content of the soil.

5. The displacement method gave the same amount of nitrate nitrogen and approximately the same amount of total salts as a 1:5 water extraction of the soil.

6. The freezing point method does not give a measure of the concentration of the soil solution directly in the soil at ordinary moisture contents.

Burd and Martin (50) have pointed out that a soil's effective solution may attain a relatively constant total concentration, as measured by freezing point depression or conductivity, while undergoing large changes in the concentration of its solutes, notably in its bicarbonate and nitrate content.

It may be asked whether, in general, the concentration and composition of soil solutions from productive soils are of such a nature as to be adequate when apart from the solid phase of the soil. Hoagland (109) made such a comparison by growing barley plants in artificial solutions side by side with plants grown in soils; he came to the conclusion that when used in sufficient amounts they were adequate for supporting normal growth.

Burd and Martin (51) used a water displacement method to obtain the soil solutions from cropped, fallowed, and stored soils and concluded that continuous cropping invariably decreases the concentration of the solutions. On the other hand, fallowing increases the concentration. This is clearly illustrated in Table III. The quantitative composition of the soil solution in soils under crop is continuously changing (Table IV). Burd and Martin (51) point out that nutrient solutions made up in imitation of the soil solution as it exists at the beginning of the

TABLE III

Average Composition of Displaced Soil Solutions from Cropped (A), Fallowed (B), and Stored (C) Soils after 8 Years[a]

		Anions (meq)					Cations (meq)				Total ions
Soils	%	NO$_3$	HCO$_3$	Cl	SO$_4$	PO$_4$	SiO$_3$	Ca	Mg	Na	K	(meq)
A	12.6	3.72	1.84	0.00	12.53	0.08	1.61	10.14	7.10	1.84	0.68	39.54
B	16.3	29.56	1.02	1.44	9.66	0.07	1.48	27.88	10.99	2.77	1.61	86.49
C	16.2	18.36	1.31	8.10	5.43	0.19	1.38	19.02	8.80	5.04	1.92	69.56

[a] From Burd and Martin (51).

TABLE IV

Seasonal Changes in the Composition of Displaced Soil Solutions from Cropped Soils[a]

Soil no.	Date	Moisture	pH	Parts per million of displaced solution							
				NO$_3$	HCO$_3$	SO$_4$	PO$_4$	Ca	Mg	Na	K
7	April 30, 1923	10.7	7.4	174	83	655	1.1	283	106	49	24
	Sept. 4, 1923	12.5	7.6	58	155	432	0.6	193	47	40	9
8	April 30, 1923	9.6	7.4	274	93	633	2.5	267	93	31	20
	Sept. 4, 1923	8.4	7.6	88	143	275	1.4	153	56	28	11

[a] From Burd and Martin (51).

season cannot represent soil solutions during the later stages of the growth of crops. With the exception of bicarbonate ion, all other determined ions decrease between April and September.

Because nitrate is entirely contained in the soil solution, and is rapidly absorbed by plants, the rate at which it is replenished is more important than the total amount of nitrate nitrogen present in the soil.

Concentrations of phosphate in the soil solution are low—of the order of 1 ppm of solution. In order to maintain the phosphate supply to growing plants it is necessary to postulate complete renewal of the soil solution phosphate at least ten times daily.

Studies with solution potassium and plant uptake indicate that water-soluble potassium alone is insufficient for maintenance of adequate plant growth.

B. Exchangeable Cations

The relative quantities, as milligram equivalents, of the major exchangeable bases in soils follow the order, calcium > magnesium > potassium. The content of exchangeable sodium may be either larger or smaller than that of potassium. This is shown in Table V, which gives a summary of results of different investigators. Soils of humid regions may contain substantial quantities of exchangeable hydrogen and aluminum, so that the degree of base saturation is less than 100%.

TABLE V

Exchangeable Bases in Milligram Equivalents in Typical Soils[a]

Soils	Ca	Mg	K	Na	Authority
25 Dutch soils	30	5.0	0.8	2.5	D. J. Hissink
17 Scottish soils	9.95	0.78	0.24	0.27	A. M. Smith
7 Neutral soils, U.S.A.	13.92	4.83	0.75	1.48	W. P. Kelley and S. M. Brown
5 Alkali soils, U.S.A.	0.0	0.80	1.65	6.88	W. P. Kelley and S. M. Brown
6 Acid soils, U.S.A.	1.06	0.68	0.13	0.51	W. P. Kelley and S. M. Brown

[a] From Robinson (204).

As exchangeable bases are released to the soil solution, and removed by plant uptake, they are continually being replenished from nonexchangeable sources and minerals. Illite and montmorillonite clays contain nonexchangeable magnesium, and illite contains nonexchangeable potassium. Kaolinite is of no value as a source of these nutrients. The ease with which a particular cation is released to the soil solution depends upon the nature of the complementary ions present on the colloid. The behavior of the individual cations in this respect is described by the complementary-ion principle, which may be stated as follows: "The proportionate release of a given cation from the exchangeable form to the solution in an incomplete exchange reaction increases with the increasing strength of bonding of the complementary exchangeable cations" (26).

The effect of complementary ions on the release of a given ion is illustrated in Table VI from data of Jarusov (118). In this experiment 5 meq of ammonium chloride was added to soils, each sample of which contained 0.5 meq of exchangeable calcium and 0.5 meq of a complementary ion. The displacement of the exchangeable calcium was greatest with hydrogen, intermediate with magnesium, and least with sodium as the complementary ion. By inference, hydrogen was attached most strongly and sodium least strongly.

The over-all complementary ion effects in natural soils that contain a variety of cations may be summarized by the series $Na > K > Mg > Ca$, where sodium is released most readily and calcium least readily in

TABLE VI

Influence of the Complementary Ion on the Release of Exchangeable Calcium from a Chernozem Soil[a]

Exchangeable cations in soil sample (meq)	Amount of calcium displaced from soil	
	Milligram equivalents	Per cent of total
0.5 Ca + 0.5 H	0.30	60
0.5 Ca + 0.5 Mg	0.18	36
0.5 Ca + 0.5 Na	0.09	19

[a] From Jarusov (118).

TABLE VII

Calcium Content of Wheat Seedlings Grown on Soil Saturated with Calcium or with Calcium and Different Complementary Ions

Exchangeable cations in soil sample	Calcium in seedlings (mg)
100% Ca	9.7
60% Ca + 40% H	8.6
60% Ca + 40% Mg	8.1
60% Ca + 40% Na	5.2
Control (sand without soil)	5.2

[a] After Black (26) from data of Ratner.

an incomplete exchange. Thus sodium is released more readily if it is accompanied by a high proportion of calcium than by a high proportion of potassium; magnesium is released more readily if it is accompanied by a high proportion of calcium than of potassium. This explains in part the effect of high exchangeable K:Mg soil ratios on the inducement of magnesium deficiency in crops.

Table VII shows the uptake of calcium by plants from soil in which a fixed quantity of exchangeable calcium was accompanied by different complementary ions. The uptake of calcium was greater with hydrogen than with magnesium as the complementary cation, and greater with magnesium than with sodium.

Many attempts have been made to relate the exchangeable cations in soils to their uptake by crops, and to the response by crops of further additions of cations as fertilizers. Bray (42) studied the quantitative relation of exchangeable potassium to crop yields and of crop response to potash additions. The potassium extraction technique consisted of shaking 5 gm of soil with 10 ml of either 22% $NaClO_4$ or $NaNO_3$ in water for 1 minute, followed by filtration. He found only a fair correlation between the increase in corn (*Zea mays*) yield obtained with potash fertilizers and the total exchangeable potassium in the surface soil, expressed in pounds per 2,000,000 pounds of soil. If, however, the yields from the nonfertilized plots, expressed as a percentage of the yields from the fertilized plots, were plotted against the exchangeable potassium, a better correlation was obtained. The curve could be expressed by a modified Mitscherlich equation

$$\text{Log } (A - y) = \text{Log } A - c_1 b_1$$

where c_1 = the proportionality constant, b_1 = amount of nutrient in the surface soil as measured by the soil test, A = yield when potash is not deficient, y = yield when no potash is added.

The above relationship holds with approximately the same value for c_1 where many physical and chemical soil properties vary within a rather wide range and where the ultimate yields under full treatment also vary considerably.

Harding (94) studied the relationship between exchangeable K, Na, Mg, and Ca in the soils of California orange (*Citrus sinensis*) orchards, and in leaf composition. A better correlation was found between percentage saturation of K, Na, and Mg in the soil colloids than between the actual concentrations in the soil, expressed as milligram equivalents, and the respective concentrations in the leaf tissue (see Table VIII).

The most extensive work on predicting the proportionate content of bases in plants from measurements on soils has been done by Mehlich and his co-workers in North Carolina (162). They showed that the cation content of plants is related to: (a) the concentration of metal cations in the exchange complex, (b) the distribution of cations present, (c) the relative energy with which the cations are retained, and (d) the total and proportionate cation requirement of different plant species. The cation content of plants should be predictable if the characteristics of (d) are known and the soil properties under (a) to (c) are determined. They tested out their concepts with *Crotalaria striata* grown on five soils, of varying cation exchange capacity, type of colloid, and

Ca:Mg and Ca:K ratios. The proportionate content of the various bases in *Crotalaria* were estimated from the soil measurements by means of an equation, which may be simplified to the following form for calcium (26):

$$\frac{Ca_{plant}}{Ca_{plant} + Mg_{plant} + K_{plant}} = \frac{Ca_{HCl}}{Ca_{HCl} + \alpha Mg_{HCl} + \beta K_{HCl}}$$

where Ca_{plant}, Mg_{plant}, and K_{plant} represent the milligram equivalents of the respective bases per 100 gm of plant material; where Ca_{HCl}, Mg_{HCl}, and K_{HCl} represent the milligram equivalents of the respective

TABLE VIII

CORRELATION BETWEEN CATION CONTENT OF LEAVES AND OF SOIL FROM
72 CALIFORNIAN ORANGE ORCHARDS[a]

| | | Soil | | |
| | | --- | --- | --- |
Cations in leaves	Cation	Determination	Depth (inches)	Correlation coefficient (r)
K	K	% Saturation	0–6	+0.669[b]
K	K	% Saturation	6–18	+0.710[b]
K	K	meq/100 gm	6–18	+0.183
Na	Na	% Saturation	0–6	+0.566[b]
Na	Na	% Saturation	6–18	+0.734[b]
Na	Na	meq/100 gm	6–18	+0.513[b]
Mg	Mg	% Saturation	6–18	+0.493[b]
Mg	Mg	meq/100 gm	6–18	+0.337[b]
Ca	Ca	% Saturation	6–18	−0.035[b]

[a] From Harding (94).
[b] Significant at 0.1% level.

bases in the extract by shaking 100 gm soil for 15 minutes with 500 ml of water containing 1 meq of hydrochloric acid; and where α and β are constants. An analogous equation was used to estimate the proportionate content of the other bases in the plants. A high correlation for Ca ($r = 0.98$) and Mg ($r = 0.98$) between calculated and determined values was obtained. The calculated and determined values for Ca and Mg failed to agree whenever the percentage Ca saturation was too low for optimum plant growth.

It is generally recognized that the exchangeable cations act as a source of readily available plant nutrients, but there is some difference of opinion as to their mode of transfer from the soil colloids to the root surfaces. The early workers regarded the exchangeable bases as being in equilibrium with the soil solution: as nutrients were withdrawn from the soil solution by plant roots, the equilibrium was restored by exchangeable ions going into solution. Jenny and Overstreet (122) questioned this concept of nutrition in soils. They pointed out that the cations on the surface of clays are not held rigidly. As a result of thermal agitation they oscillate and at times may be at a considerable distance from the surface, but they remain in the field of force emanating from the colloid. Although the ions are surrounded by water molecules, they are not in solution in the sense that they can diffuse freely. Jenny and Overstreet postulated that when a root surface makes intimate contact with soil colloids, interchange of ions takes place by contact exchange, i.e., without the ions necessarily going into solution. Hydrogen ions on the root surface are exchanged for cations on the soil colloid. Jenny (121) quotes evidence showing that the uptake of radioactive sodium,

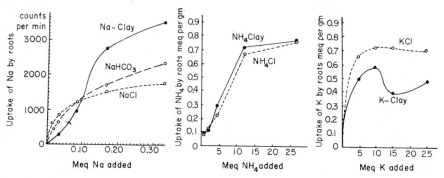

Fig. 11. Comparison of cation uptake by roots from clay suspensions and salt solutions having equal cation content. From Jenny (121).

at higher concentrations, is decidedly greater in clay suspensions than in chloride or bicarbonate solutions of equal concentrations. The uptake of ammonium by the roots is nearly the same for the two systems, but potassium chloride provides a better source of potassium than potassium clay (see Fig. 11).

In a recent paper, Olsen and Peech (180) described experiments which cast doubt on the validity of the contact theory. They tested the significance of the suspension effect (greater cation concentrations or activity in the soil suspension than in the equilibrium dialyzate) in determining the uptake of cations by plant roots by comparing the rate of uptake of Rb^+ and Ca^{++} by excised roots of barley (*Hordeum vulgare*) and mung beans (*Phaseolus aureus*) from a suspension of clay, or cation exchange resin, with that from the corresponding equilibrium dialyzate. They found that although the cation concentration of the clay, or resin suspension, greatly exceeded that of the corresponding equilibrium dialyzate, the rate of uptake of Rb^+ and Ca^{++} by the roots was exactly the same from both the suspension and dialyzate. The results for Ca^{++} are given in Table IX. These results are at variance with the prediction of the contact-exchange theory. Olsen and Peech concluded that the composition of the soil solution, or the equilibrium dialyzate, should completely characterize the ionic environment of plant roots in soil-water systems. This conclusion does not necessarily minimize the value of assessing the exchangeable cations in soil, for they constitute the immediate reserve supply and determine to what

TABLE IX

The Absorption of Ca^{++} by Excised Mung Bean (*Phaseolus aureus*) Roots from Clay and Resin Suspensions and the Equilibrium Dialyzate[a]

| Suspension | Concentration of Ca^{++} in | | Concentration ratio[b] | Relative uptake of Ca^{++} by roots[c] |
	Dialyzate (mg/liter)	Suspension (mg/liter)		
2% Kaolinite	0.60	32	53	0.94
2% Montmorillonite	0.60	400	670	1.06
2% Amberlite IR-120	0.60	660	1100	1.03
2% Amberlite IRC-50	0.60	3960	6300	1.26

[a] From Olsen and Peech (180).
[b] Ratio of concentration of Ca^{++} in the suspension to that in the dialyzate.
[c] The amount of Ca^{++} absorbed by roots from the suspension divided by the Ca^{++} absorbed from the dialyzate.

extent the low concentration in the soil solution will be replenished and maintained upon removal by the plant roots.

C. Cation Exchange Properties of Roots

The French chemist Devaux, 1916 (163), was the first to report the existence of root cation exchange properties; he attributed it to the presence of pectose in the walls of the root hairs. More recently, cation exchange capacities have been measured by a number of different techniques (277). In general, the cation exchange values are much higher for dicotyledons than for monocotyledons (see Table X). Values ranging from 9 meq for wheat to 94 meq per 100 gm dry matter for larkspur have been recorded by Mehlich and Drake (163). Roots with high exchange values have been shown to have bonding energies for calcium that are more than double the bonding energy for potassium. The higher the exchange capacity of roots, the greater is the relative adsorption of calcium over potassium. The root colloid and the soil colloid compete for cations, and the cation uptake by the plant depends partly upon the relative exchange capacities of the root and soil colloid (71).

The valency effect can be nullified by greatly increasing the cation concentration of the solution and enhanced by dilution. Schuffelen (211) demonstrated the valency and dilution effect in relation to the uptake of potassium and magnesium by fruit trees. In a wet spring magnesium deficiency is greater than in a dry spring. According to the

TABLE X

The Cation Exchange Capacity of Plant Roots in Milliequivalents
per 100 gm Dry Matter[a]

Dicotyledons	Cation exchange capacity	Monocotyledons	Cation exchange capacity
Larkspur, *Delphinium ajacis*	94.0	Orchard grass, *Dactylis glomerata*	24.9
Lettuce, *Lactuca sativa*	65.1	Timothy, *Phleum pratense*	22.6
Soybean, *Glycine max*	65.1	Oats, *Avena sativa*	22.8
Blue lupin, *Lupinus angustifolius*	53.3	Red top, *Agrostis alba*	17.3
Carrot, *Daucus carota* var. *sativa*	51.7	Rosen rye, *Secale cereale*	15.1
Red clover, *Trifolium pratense*	47.5	Barley, *Hordeum vulgare*	12.3
Buckwheat, *Fagopyrum esculentum*	39.6	Millet, *Panicum miliaceum*	12.2
Tomato, *Lycopersicon esculentum*	34.6	Winter wheat, *Triticum vulgare*	9.0

[a] From Mehlich and Drake (163).

TABLE XI

The Effects of Moisture Content on the Ratio
of K:Mg in the Soil Solution[a]

Sandy soil		Clay soil	
Moisture content	K:Mg	Moisture content	K:Mg
15%	0.50	11	0.21
30	1.45	17	0.20
60	1.69	22	0.42
		28	0.45

[a] From Schuffelen (211).

Donnan rule the ratio of K:Mg in the soil solution should be higher in a wet soil than in a dry soil of the same composition. This was confirmed experimentally (Table XI). A similar effect is noted with "sand drown," a magnesium deficiency of tobacco on light soils.

Cation uptake by plants from nutrient solutions is not subject to this important competition of soil colloid with plant root colloid for adsorbed cations.

D. Bonding Energy of Clays

It has been shown that a specific cation on a given clay mineral can be held with a wide range of bonding energies (157) (see Fig. 12). Although the activity of Ca^{++} in a H^+-Ca^{++} montmorillonite clay changes very little from 30 to 70% saturation, it almost triples as the calcium

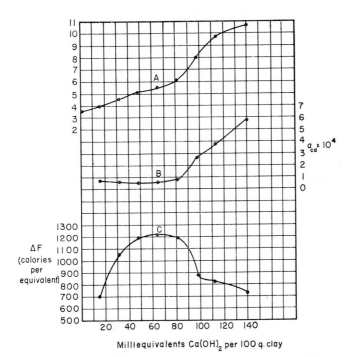

Fig. 12. Clay titration curves for 1.07% Wyoming bentonite with calcium hydroxide. A, pH titration curve. B, Calcium ion activity plotted against base added. C, Mean free energy of calcium ions (per equivalent) plotted against base added. From Marshall (157).

saturation increases from 70 to 90%. A given clay, such as montmorillonite, has different bonding energies for different cations, and different clays have widely different bonding energies for the same cation. Furthermore the complementary ion has an important effect on bonding energies (163).

E. Phosphorus Nutrition

The phosphorus nutrition of plants in soil has been studied intensively (64). Studies using culture solutions have shown that plant growth is retarded with solution concentrations of 0.1 ppm phosphorus or less. On the other hand, crops appear to grow normally on soils where the concentration of phosphorus in the soil solution is less than 0.1 ppm. This may be due to one or more reasons: (a) The displaced solution is not the true solution. (b) The plant roots exert a solvent action on the soil particles and thus bring more phosphorus into solution. (c) There is a higher concentration of phosphorus at the solid-solution interphase than in the displaced soil solution.

Fried and Shapiro (79) consider that the uptake of phosphorus by plants from a soil system may be divided into four stages: first, the release of the phosphate ion from the solid phase into the soil solution; second, the movement of the phosphate ion from any point in the soil solution to the vicinity of the root; third, the movement of the ion from the vicinity of the root into the root; and fourth, the movement of the phosphate ion to the top of the plant. Each of these steps involves rate constants, and the over-all process may be rate-limiting at any of the transfer points. The soil solution phosphorus in agricultural soils must be renewed many times per day by the solid phase in order to give the total uptake of phosphorus noted in plants. This ability to renew the phosphorus in solution is a capacity factor. The relationship between the intensity factor (concentration in the soil solution) and the capacity factor, and the level of these factors, distinguishes the phosphorus system in one soil from the phosphorus system in another. Shapiro and Fried (212) developed a relationship between the phosphorus capacity factor (soil-P) and the phosphorus intensity factor (P) as shown in the equation

$$\text{Soil-P} = -K \frac{\text{soil-P}}{\text{P}} + \sum \text{soil}$$

where K = an apparent dissociation constant for the system at the particular pH specified; $\sum$ soil = amount of phosphorus adsorbed per gram of soil when all the adsorption sites are saturated with P; and soil-P = amount of phosphorus adsorbed per gram of soil. $\sum$ soil and K characterize the soil and permit the calculation of changes in phosphorus concentration when the soil phosphorus system is placed under stress.

It has been shown that organic acids such as citric, oxalic, tartaric, malic, malonic, and galacturonic acids are highly effective in solubilizing phosphate and that one or more of these acids may be produced by microorganisms in the rhizosphere. Chelation of calcium, from insoluble calcium phosphates, is also an important factor. It has been shown recently that 2-ketogluconic acid is formed by certain organisms in the rhizosphere (67). This acid is very effective in chelating calcium, thereby also liberating phosphorus.

Plant roots that possess high bonding energies for calcium, high cation exchange capacities, and high acid dissociation would be expected to obtain more phosphorus from insoluble forms than would those roots low in these properties.

F. ION UPTAKE

Uptake of ions by plant roots has been shown to consist of two phases, adsorption and accumulation. Adsorption is a physiochemical phenomenon: it is nonmetabolic and is predominantly concerned with cations. It is considered to be an exchange process, hydrogen ions generated by respiration being released into the culture medium in exchange for cations. Accumulation, however, is dependent on respiration and is concerned with the active uptake of both cations and anions. In the interpretation of active uptake of ions, specific carrier compounds or sites have been invoked, but their nature is still unknown, although various suggestions have been made, such as phosphorylated energy-rich nitrogen compounds and ribonucleoproteins. To what extent accumulation is dependent on adsorption is not certain, but according to Laties (141), adsorption exchange as we know it has little or nothing to do with accumulation. This general subject is dealt with in detail by Steward and Sutcliffe (Vol. II, Chapter 4) (231).

VI. Methods for Determining the Nutrient Requirement of Crops in the Field

There are three recognized ways of determining crop nutrient requirements under field conditions: (a) by manurial experiments, (b) by soil analysis and (c) by chemical analysis of selected plant organs.

A. MANURIAL EXPERIMENTS

Fussell (80) has traced the development of the technique of field experiments from its primitive beginnings to a period of great activity in the middle of the nineteenth century. The early experiments were essentially qualitative; a single area was treated in some special way and judged in terms of profit or by general experience. The stimulus to experimentation was provided by the introduction of artificial fertilizers. Before spending money on costly fertilizers it appeared perfectly reasonable to make comparisons by treating halves or quarters of a field in two or four different ways and harvesting their produce separately. Indeed, Arthur Young, a celebrated English farmer wrote in 1805, "Every farmer should have an experimental field on which experimental plots should be laid out for trying new ideas, seeds and manures, etc., in small before taking them on a commercial scale."

The most important experiments undertaken during the nineteenth century were those of Boussingault, in Alsace in 1834, Georges Ville in France, and John Bennett Lawes, at Rothamsted in 1843, who broke away from normal commercial practice and set up continuous plots of the main farm crops. Originally, Lawes and Gilbert used long narrow strips, one for each kind of manuring; later their plots were arranged in rectangular form with strips of different mineral manures in one direction combined with strips of nitrogenous fertilizers running at right angles. Occasionally two unmanured plots were included, in a single experiment, but otherwise Lawes and Gilbert were not concerned by irregularities in soil fertility.

The publication in 1849 of James F. W. Johnston's book on "Experimental Agriculture, being the Results of Past and Suggestions for Future Experiments in Scientific and Practical Agriculture" was a most important landmark in the history of field experimentation. Fussell states that it marked the beginning of the modern scientific field experimental technique. Some of the recommendations made by Johnston are listed below.

1. Everything should be done by weight and measure.

2. Both the chemical composition and physical qualities or condition of all substances used should be accurately ascertained and recorded.

3. Two experiments of the same kind, one to check the other, should always be made. In field experiments the two plots devoted to the same treatment should be as far removed from each other as convenient.

4. Land experimented upon ought to be in a uniform, natural, and well-understood condition.

5. A second experiment must not be made on the same spot until several years have elapsed.

6. All experiments ought to be contrived and executed with a definite object.

7. All experiments must be comparative.

In the absence of replication, Johnston considered it wise to regard all differences of between 5 and 10% as within the limits of natural variation. Johnston's requirements appear to have proved too stringent for most of his contemporaries.

The experimenters in the second half of the nineteenth century were not seriously concerned with soils as such and do not appear to have contemplated the possibility that soil might profoundly modify the action of certain fertilizers or that the relative value of two kinds of fertilizers might vary greatly with type of soil. Furthermore, the early enthusiasm for field experimentation seems to have been damped by the uncertainty of single-plot experiments.

Early in the twentieth century, stimulated by variety yield trials, large numbers of very small plots were enclosed in wire cages in so-called "chessboard plots." For large-scale trials comparing two varieties Beaven in 1920, introduced his well-known "half-drill, strip method" in which the two varieties (A and B) were drilled simultaneously from two halves of the seed drill so as to produce a series of long narrow strips running across the field in the order AB/BA/AB/BA, etc. In this way the comparisons were made on closely adjacent strips (61).

The first mathematical treatment of the errors in yield trials was made by Wood and Stratton (282) in 1909, using a formula based on the theory of probability, the essential feature being to use not the deviations from the mean, but the squares of these quantities.

$$\text{Probable error (P.E.)} = \sqrt{\frac{d^2}{n - 1}}$$

where d = deviation from the mean and n = number of results. The probable error thus determined is a measure of the reliability of any one result.

Mercer and Hall (164) harvested an acre of wheat in plots of one five-hundredth acre and showed that the yields followed very closely a normal distribution curve. From this and other experiments they concluded that for practical purposes each unit of comparison (variety, method of manuring, etc.) should be given five plots of one-fortieth acre each, systematically distributed within the experimental area.

The next important advance in the mathematical treatment of field experiments was made by R. A. Fisher, at Rothamsted, England. He developed rigid methods of testing the significance of differences between means from a small number of plots, and he elaborated a formal method for analyzing the results known as "the analysis of variance." This method of analysis reveals directly the contributions of the various controlled factors and the uncontrolled ones to the total variation in the experiment, and the effects of any one of the factors may be compared with those which, being beyond control, are conventionally termed "error." The magnitude of these latter is expressed as a "standard error," and a statement of mean yields with their standard errors contains all the information needed for a sound comparison.

$$\text{Standard error of mean (S.E.)} = \sqrt{\frac{d^2}{n(n - 1)}}$$

where d = deviation from the mean and n = number of results. The basis and application of the analysis of variance are fully treated in Fisher's well-known "Statistical Methods for Research Workers" (74).

Following on the new mathematical approach to field experimentation, two new designs of field plots were devised: (a) the randomized block and (b) the Latin square. These are the simplest arrangements that fulfill the conditions necessary to a valid estimate of error and at the same time possess the advantage of eliminating a substantial part of the soil heterogeneity. In the randomized block design the positions of the treatments, or varieties, are chosen at random for each block, a treatment occurring once only per block. The advantage of the randomized block is that replication is secured and at the same time it is easy to distinguish the variation within the blocks from that between different blocks. The design is robust, and if one block has to be eliminated for some reason the precision of the experiment is reduced but the analysis is not affected.

In the Latin square two restrictions are made. There are as many replicates of each treatment as there are treatments, the plots being arranged in a square, with as many rows as columns, so that each treatment occurs once in each column and once in each row of the square. This provides for a double elimination, in two directions at right angles to one another, of soil differences.

Fisher also developed Johnston's proposal, that two or more fertilizers should always be tested not merely alone but in combination, into a general treatment of factorial experiments. A comprehensive account of the design and analysis of factorial experiments has been given by Yates (284).

Experiments with large numbers of treatments lead to large blocks; several methods have been devised to avoid this difficulty, one of which is the "split-plot" technique. In this design large plots are used to test treatments that require a fair amount of land, such as irrigation, cultivation, cover crops, etc. The large plots are then subdivided for the subsidiary treatments for which it forms a block. Different factors are thus replicated to unequal extents and comparisons are made with varying degrees of accuracy.

The design, analysis, and interpretation of a modern factorial manurial experiment on black currants (*Ribes nigrum*) is given below; for the statistical analysis of the experiment the author is indebted to G. M. Clarke.*

The experiment illustrated in Fig. 13 was carried out on two varieties planted in adjacent rows; experimental plots thus consisted of seven

* Statistics section, Long Ashton Research Station, Bristol, England.

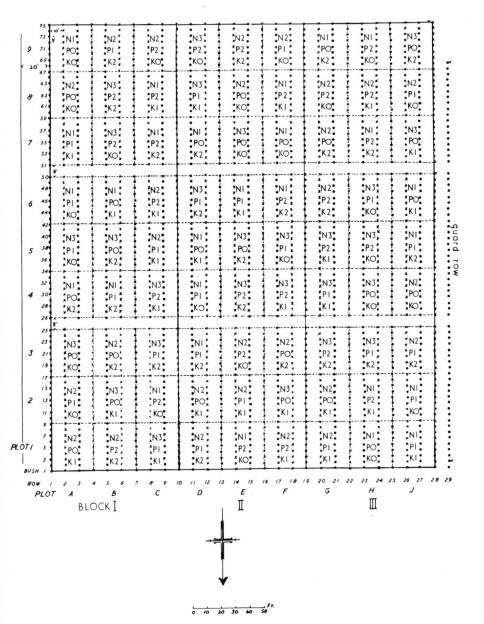

Fig. 13. Showing field layout of a modern factorial manurial experiment with black currant (*Ribes nigrum*). Three factors, N (ammonium sulfate), K (potassium sulfate), P (superphosphate), were used each at three levels, given in hundred-weights (cwt, 112 pounds) per acre: N1, 3 cwt; N2, 6 cwt; N3, 9 cwt; K0, 0 cwt; K1, 1 cwt; K2, 2 cwt; P0, 0 cwt; P1, 3 cwt; P2, 6 cwt. Varieties: •, Baldwin; ×, Mendip Cross; planted 10 × 4 feet apart. From Bould (32).

bushes of each variety and were surrounded by guard rows (dotted lines in figure) to reduce errors due to drifting of fertilizers during application and cultural operations, and to root spread. Three factors N, P, K, each at three levels (detailed below figure) were used, giving 27 experimental treatments in all; these were replicated three times to make 81 plots in the complete trial. This type of layout is *factorial* in the sense that it allows the experimenter to examine (a) the *main effect* of each factor, that is, whether there is a dominant response to that factor irrespective of the levels of other factors, and (b) *interactions* between factors, that is, whether the response to one factor varies according to

TABLE XII

ANALYSIS OF VARIANCE OF CROP WEIGHTS VAR. BALDWIN, 1955

Source of variation	Degrees of freedom	Sum of squares	Mean square	Variance ratio
Blocks	2	338.5425	169.2713	$F_{(2,52)} = 15.76^a$
N	2	36.6269	18.3135	$F_{(2,52)} = 1.71$
P	2	76.5499	38.2750	$F_{(2,52)} = 3.56^b$
K	2	22.7484	11.3742	$F_{(2,52)} = 1.06$
NP	4	50.9612	12.7403	$F_{(4,52)} = 1.19$
NK	4	118.4449	29.6112	$F_{(4,52)} = 2.76^c$
PK	4	21.0731	5.2683	$F_{(4,52)} < 1$
NPK	8	60.5936	7.5742	$F_{(8,52)} < 1$
Error	52	558.3442	10.7374	
Total	80	1283.8847		

[a] = statistically significant at the 0.1% level.
[b] = statistically significant at the 5% level.
[c] = statistically significant at the 5% level.

the level of application of other factors. The field results were analyzed separately for each variety; the crop weights per plot of seven 'Baldwin' bushes in the experiment's first year, 1955, gave the analysis of variance of Table XII. The total variation among the 81 plots has 80 degrees of freedom assigned to it; this can be partitioned into 2 degrees of freedom for variations between the 3 blocks, 2 for each of N, P, K (at 3 levels each), $2 \times 2 = 4$ for the interaction between N and P, and so on. After the partitioning has been carried out in the manner detailed in statistical textbooks (57), the variance ratio test shows which of the sources of variation are large enough not to be due entirely to natural variation (experimental error) among the bushes. The block variation was so large as to be very unlikely (statistically only once in 1000 by chance) to be natural, due to the bushes, and is interpreted as due to real differences in soil fertility from east to west; block I consists of rows 2–9, block II rows 11–18, block III rows 20–27. Examination of the block totals showed: block III, 559 > block II, 479 > block I, 425.

There is a main effect of P (statistically significant at the 5%, or 1 in 20 level): for any given combination of N and K the plots containing P_2 show higher yield than P_1 or P_0 with the same N and K. The mean yields (averaged over all N, K combinations) are 17.89 pounds per plot for P_0, 16.99 for P_1, 19.34 for P_2, and statistical t tests show P_1 and P_2 significantly different at the 5% level, i.e., there is only one chance in 20 that we would not be correct in asserting a real difference in response to P_1 and P_2. P_0 falls between these and is not significantly different from either; a little deeper analysis would help in deciding whether the apparent trough of the response at P_1 were real. The analysis of variance also revealed an interaction between N and K; this

TABLE XIII

MEANS (AVERAGED OVER ALL P LEVELS) OF COMBINATIONS OF N AND K

–	K_0	K_1	K_2
N_1	17.37	18.86	20.16
N_2	19.13	**14.82**	17.57
N_3	17.03	19.02	18.69

indicates that there will be at least one NK mean which stands out as aberrant from the general pattern of Table XIII. The t test shows that there is no statistical difference between any two means in this table unless they differ numerically by 3.10 pounds per plot. N_2K_1 is significantly less than N_1K_1 and N_3K_1, signifying a trough in the N response when K is applied at level 1; this is true for any of the levels of P included in this experiment. N_2K_1 is less than some other means in this table also, in fact most of them, signifying it to be a poor combination by any standards. The N response under K_0 appears to have a peak at N_2, though this cannot be stated decisively on these figures and would need more sensitive experimentation to be confirmed. Since no NPK interaction appeared in the analysis of Table XII, we can explain the results for P and for NK separately, without needing to examine individual mean yields for every combination N, P, K. For a detailed account of modern experimental designs and their statistical analysis, see Cochran and Cox (57).

Field experiments, as a method for determining the nutrient requirements of crops, have certain limitations. If the general nutritional status of the crop is such that the leaf concentration of all essential elements exceeds the critical, or sufficiency, values (see Section VI, C), then there will be no response to applied fertilizers. If the response is negative the experimenter cannot be sure whether the fertilizer failed to reach the rooting zone, owing to fixation or faulty placement, or whether the crop is already amply supplied with nutrients. This can be determined only by leaf analysis. A clear example of this is illustrated in the data from the black currant experiment described in Fig. 13, and from a similar experiment on a different site. Table XIV shows the yield of fruit in pounds per plot and the leaf composition of bushes grown on the Efford site. There was an immediate response to applied phosphate, due to an initial low leaf-phosphorus concentration, and a delayed response to applied potash correlated with the fall in leaf potassium. Table XV shows the data from an experiment, of similar layout and the same fertilizer treatments, on a different site. In this manurial experiment there was no response to applied fertilizer, the reason being that the concentration of leaf N, P, and K, throughout the duration of the experiment was adequate.

Field experiments, therefore, may indicate only whether or not the crop is adequately supplied with the fertilizer under test, and the results apply to that site only. If there is no response, one can never be certain whether this lack of response is due to an adequate supply of the nutrient in the soil, the presence of some other limiting factor, or failure of the applied nutrient to be absorbed by the test crop.

B. SOIL ANALYSIS

The development of soil analysis as a tool for assessing the nutrient status of soils in relation to crop requirement has proceeded for little more than a century and historically can be divided into three imperfectly defined periods (7). The first, from 1845 to 1906, deals essentially with the work of four authors: Daubeny, Liebig, Hilgard, and Dyer. During the second period, roughly 1906 to 1925, emphasis was placed on the fundamental chemical composition of soils as related to crop production. The third period, from 1925 to 1952, with ramifications extending to the present time, was concerned with a search for methods that were universally applicable.

One of the first records of quick soil tests for an assay of soil fertility is that of Daubeny in England in 1845. He suggested the terms "active" and "dormant" to express the more or less soluble nutrient constituents of a soil, respectively. The solvent used for extracting the active portion was carbonated water. Owing to analytical difficulties little further progress was made for a quarter of a century when soil testing was revived by the German chemist Liebig, in 1872. Liebig extracted soils

TABLE XIV

Effect of Fertilizers on Yield of Black Currants (*Ribes nigrum*) in Relation to Leaf Nutrient Concentration at Efford, 1954–1958[a]

Fertilizer:	Nitrogen				Phosphorus				Potassium			
Rate:	N_1	N_2	N_3	F[d] Sig.	P_0	P_1	P_2	F Sig.	K_0	K_1	K_2	F Sig.
Yield[b]												
1955	—	—	—	N.S.	17.0	17.9	19.3	5%	—	—	—	N.S.
1956	30.8	28.4	26.6	0.1%	26.8	26.7	32.3	0.1%	—	—	—	N.S.
1957	—	—	—	N.S.	28.4	25.7	32.1	0.1%	27.3	27.8	31.1	5%
1958	—	—	—	N.S.	26.1	28.3	29.2	5%	25.1	29.2	29.3	0.1%
Nutrient[c] 9/7/54	2.73	2.86	2.86	1%	0.240	0.232	0.228	N.S.	1.61	1.57	1.70	N.S.
10/7/57	2.74	2.82	2.86	1%	0.241	0.262	0.253	1%	0.67	0.85	1.07	0.1%

[a] From Bould (32).
[b] Mean yield in pounds per plot of 7 bushels.
[c] Nutrients as per cent leaf dry matter.
[d] F = Variance ratio; N.S. = not significant.

TABLE XV

Effect of Fertilizers on Yield of Black Currants (*Ribes nigrum*) in Relation to Leaf Nutrient Concentration at Luddington, 1953–1958[a]

Fertilizer: Rate:	Nitrogen				Phosphorus				Potassium			
	N_1	N_2	N_3	F[d] Sig.	P_0	P_1	P_2	F Sig.	K_0	K_1	K_2	F Sig.
Yield[b] 1954	22.9	24.2	24.2	N.S.	—	—	—	N.S.	—	—	—	N.S.
1955	31.4	31.6	30.1	N.S.	—	—	—	N.S.	—	—	—	N.S.
1957	28.4	29.0	25.4	N.S.	—	—	—	N.S.	—	—	—	N.S.
1958	46.8	51.9	50.3	N.S.	—	—	—	N.S.	—	—	—	N.S.
Nutrient[c] 24/6/53	2.61	2.74	2.80	0.1%	0.300	0.315	0.315	N.S.	1.58	1.66	1.58	N.S.
15/7/55	2.75	2.89	2.96	0.1%	0.345	0.361	0.397	0.1%	2.02	2.05	2.11	N.S.

[a] From Bould (32).
[b] Mean yield in pounds per plot of 7 bushes.
[c] Nutrients as per cent leaf dry matter.
[d] F = Variance ratio; N.S. = not significant.

74

with dilute solutions of hydrochloric, nitric, and acetic acids. The soils used by him were from the Rothamsted Experiment Station, where fertilizer histories had been known for nearly thirty years.

The first really modern approach to soil testing as a guide for fertilizer practice was made by Dyer (70) in 1894. On the basis of his knowledge of the acidity of plant cell sap, and the earlier work of Stutzer in 1884, Dyer chose 1% citric acid as the solvent for extracting soil nutrients. He found that the phosphorus dissolved by 1% citric acid was more closely related to crop production than was the total quantity of phosphorus present (Table XVI). His conclusions, from a careful consideration of the whole of his studies with phosphorus, led him to suggest that "when a soil contains as little as 0.01 per cent of phosphoric

TABLE XVI

Barley (*Hordeum vulgare*) Yields, Total and 1% Citric Acid-Soluble P_2O_5
Contents of Soil from Hoos Field, Rothamsted[a]

Average yields over 38 years (bushels/acre)	Total P_2O_5 in soil	P_2O_5 soluble in 1% citric acid
28.5	0.102	0.0063
30.5	0.108	0.0094
39.5	0.180	0.0498
38.9	0.175	0.0428

[a] From Dyer (70).

acid (P_2O_5) soluble in one per cent citric acid, it would be justifiable to assume that it stands in immediate need of phosphatic manure." He was less definite about soil potassium but said that "probably this value lies below 0.005 per cent K_2O." Later, when it was shown that carbon dioxide was the main excretory product of plant roots that could be assumed to have any solvent action on the soil, weak acid digestion methods fell into more or less disrepute, although Dyer's method has continued in use to the present time.

It was thought, in this period, that the available nutrients were present in the soil in two well-defined forms, namely, the primary minerals that had not undergone decomposition, and the zeolites, or secondary minerals. On the assumption that zeolites were present in soils, and that they were the main source of available mineral nutrients, it seemed desirable to increase the strength of the acid employed in soil digestion. Accordingly E. W. Hilgard, of California, proposed the use of constant-boiling hydrochloric acid, S.G. 1.115. Later the American Association of Official Agricultural Chemists made this solvent and concentration, with certain arbitrarily chosen time and temperature requirements, "official." Thus early American soil literature was filled with data obtained by what was known as the "strong acid digestion method." As a result of his work on the total nutrient contents of Mississippi soils, Hilgard (106) suggested that the critical level of phosphorus in soils below which they respond to phosphatic fertilizer was about 0.1% P_2O_5. The corresponding value for total potassium was 0.25% K_2O. The assumption on which this method of extraction was based, however, was later shown to have little foundation.

The second period, defined by Anderson, was concerned with fundamental chemical data on soils, with which the names of C. G. Hopkins of Illinois and M. Whitney of the federal Bureau of Soils are best known. Hopkins decided to make a survey of the total contents of nutrient elements in soils and plants, whereas Whitney and his associates concentrated on the soil solution.

In the third period a search was made for extractants that would characterize available plant nutrients in the soil. Strong mineral acids were used in concentrations varying from 0.02 N to 0.3 N, sometimes in conjunction with buffered salt solutions. This period also saw the development of rapid soil tests, a comparison of which has been made by Anderson and Noble (8). Truog (251) used a solvent consisting of 0.002 N sulfuric acid neutralized to pH 3.0 after addition of 3 gm of ammonium sulfate per liter; Bray (43), a mixture of 0.03 N ammonium fluoride in 0.1 N hydrochloric acid; and Morgan (169), 0.5 N acetic acid solution buffered at pH 4.8 with sodium acetate. Morgan's reagent has been widely used for quick soil tests (183) and plant tissue testing by a number of extraction procedures. The most successful one, according to Morgan, on sandy and loam soils involves direct extraction of the soil by percolation of the soil mass in a folded filter paper cone. A series of color tests are then made on the filtrate and compared with color charts covering the range very low to very high. Other workers have used dilute lactic and acetic acids, sodium bicarbonate, and water.

A completely new method of measuring available soil nutrients was proposed by Fried and Dean (78), based on the principle of isotopic dilution, and the concept that a plant having two sources of a nutrient will absorb it from each of these sources in direct proportion to the amounts available. The quantity of available nutrient in a soil can be determined in terms of a standard, provided the proportion of the nutrient in the plant derived from this standard is determined. This is made possible by the use of radioactive isotopes. The mathematical expression of this relationship, proposed by Fried and Dean, is

$$A = \frac{B(1 - y)}{y}$$

where A = amount of nutrient available in the soil; B = amount of nutrient in the standard, and γ = proportion of the nutrient in the plant derived from the standard.

A similar method of determining available soil phosphorus, based on isotopic dilution, was proposed by Larson (140). By determining the ratio of P^{32} in fertilizer and plant phosphorus after more than 7 weeks, the content of exchangeable phosphate in the soil could be calculated from the formula

$$y = \left(\frac{C_0}{C} - 1\right) x$$

where y = amount of exchangeable soil phosphate; x = amount of soluble phosphate added to the soil; C_0 = content of radiophosphorus in the added fertilizer, and C = the content of radiophosphorus in the plant grown in the treated soil. The values for y were found to be independent of the amount of phosphate added to the soil, providing it was soluble.

A detailed account of modern methods of soil chemical analysis is given by Jackson (115).

Although chemical methods of determining available plant nutrients in the soil correlate reasonably well with plant growth and response to fertilizers, they are arbitrary and do not simulate the feeding power of plant roots. For this reason attempts have been made to use biological methods, employing higher plants and microorganisms, to assess the availability of soil nutrients. The two principal methods in which specific higher plants are used are the pot culture technique, originally proposed by Mitscherlich in 1909, and the seedling method developed by Neubauer in 1923. The principal methods in which bacteria and fungi serve as the test organisms are the *Azotobacter* soil-plaque technique suggested by Winogradsky in 1927 and the *Aspergillus niger* method developed by Benecke and Söding in 1928. Numerous modifications of these four principal techniques have been proposed and used by various investigators. These are described and discussed in detail by Vandecaveye (257).

The Mitscherlich method is based on his theory that the addition of each successive equal increment (Baule unit*) of a nutrient gives just one-half as much increase in crop growth as was obtained by the preceding increment. For example, if the addition of one Baule of P_2O_5 increased the yield of a crop by 100 pounds, the addition of another equal increment of P_2O_5 would give an additional increment of only 50 pounds, and a third increment of only 25 pounds. Results from

* A Baule unit is the quantity of any growth factor which will produce one-half of the theoretical highest yield = A in Mitscherlich's equation.

a large number of field and pot experiments in Germany support this observation. A "theoretical highest possible yield" is assumed for each set of growth conditions. This yield, designated as A, will vary with the supply of other nutrients, climatic conditions, systems of cultivation, etc. The equation proposed by Mitscherlich to express this relationship of yield to growth factors is

$$\log (A - y) = \log A - c(x + b)$$

where A = maximum yield; y = actual yield; x = quantity of applied nutrient; b = quantity of nutrient in the soil in an available form, and c = an effectiveness factor. The effectiveness factor c, which is specific for each growth factor, was determined by a great deal of experimental work and was found to be independent of the kind of plant involved.

TABLE XVII
NEUBAUER "LIMIT VALUES"[a,b]

Nutrient	Barley	Oats	Rye	Wheat	Turnips	Potatoes	Sugar beet
P_2O_5	6	6	5	5	7	6	6
K_2O	24	21	17	20	39	37	25

[a] From Vandecaveye (257).
[b] Values in milligrams per 100 gm of soil.

The effectiveness factor c, in terms of pounds per acre, for N = 0.00135; for P_2O_5 = 0.00664, and for K_2O = 0.00442. The Baule units for N, P_2O_5, and K_2O in pounds per acre are 220.4, 44.6, and 66.9, respectively. These values include the amounts of available nutrients in the soil in addition to any that are supplied in fertilizers (165).

The Neubauer method is based on the principle of intensive uptake of plant nutrients by a large number of seedlings grown on a small quantity of soil. One hundred rye (*Secale cereale*) seedlings are grown in 100 gm of soil diluted with nutrient-free sand in a glass container for a period of 14–18 days at a constant temperature. The roots and shoots of the seedlings are harvested, washed free from soil, and analyzed for total phosphorus and potassium. The difference in nutrient content between controls (sand only) and soil-grown seedlings gives the amount of nutrients taken up from the soil. The Neubauer "limit values," i.e., the minimum values for satisfactory yields of the crops indicated, are given in Table XVII. Neubauer found that the phosphorus and potassium taken up by the seedlings is dependent on the soil and appears to be a constant value for each sample of the same soil under a standard technique. The technique has since been extended to estimate available calcium and several minor elements.

Nicholas and Fielding (176) developed the *Aspergillus niger* (M) test for the determination of available magnesium, zinc, copper, and molybdenum in soils. The extreme sensitivity of the bioassay method is shown by the following effective nutrient ranges in micrograms per 50 ml of culture solution. Mg, 25–500; Cu, 0.05–2; Zn, 0.1–5; Fe, 0.1–20; Mn, 0.01–10; Mo, 0.00005–0.02. Dry-weight yields of fungus and intensity of sporulation are used in complementary roles for the determination of a response to a nutrient under test. This bioassay method is based on the fact that the fungus will not complete its life cycle unless certain mineral nutrients are present in the culture solution, viz. the macronutrients nitrogen, phosphorus, potassium, magnesium, and sulfur and the micronutrients zinc, copper, iron, manganese, molybdenum, and possibly gallium and vanadium. Moreover, the response to the addition of an essential element, from deficiency to sufficiency levels, when others are present in adequate supply, is specific and quantitative. Thus for bioassay work, a known amount of the material for test is added to a culture solution containing all the mineral elements other than the one to be determined. The growth of the fungus under these conditions thus depends on the amount of mineral nutrient present in the added material. This can be determined by reference to the growth of fungus in standard series.

Tchan (243) has recently described a new biological soil test in which a mixed culture of algae is used. Algae and higher plants show similar growth responses in the presence of different quantities of nutrients. The test involves adding 5–10 gm of air-dry soil to 50 ml of complete nutrient solution (minus the nutrient under test). The pH of the medium is adjusted to that of the soil. A mixed culture of algae is then added and the flasks are incubated under conditions of constant light and temperature for 2–3 weeks. The culture is then filtered and the chlorophyl extracted with ethanol, the intensity of the extract being compared with extracts from a standard series. The method does not claim to give quantitative estimations of nutrient elements; it aims rather at predicting the response by plants when fertilizer is supplied to a particular soil.

C. PLANT ANALYSIS

1. Full Chemical Analysis

Chemical analysis for available soil nutrients is based on the assumption that plant roots will extract nutrients from the soil in a manner comparable to chemical soil extractants and that there is a relationship between the extractable ions in the soil and their uptake by plants.

Although this may be true for some nutrients and crops, it is not universally true. Routine soil analysis for advisory purposes does not take into account the relative bonding power of different soil colloids for mono- and divalent ions, the effect of complementary ions, ion antagonism, or the differential feeding power of plant roots. These limitations have been recognized by soil chemists and from time to time attempts have been made to use plant analysis, either of the whole plant or of selected organs, to characterize soil fertility. Liebig, in 1840, was the first to associate the composition of plants with soil fertility, and he put forward the view that if soil fertility were to be maintained the quantities of nutrients removed from the soil in crops would need to be restored to it in the form of manures and fertilizers ("law of restitution"). Heinrich, 1882, objected to the use of whole plants for analysis and, as a result of experimental work on different plant parts, concluded "that the roots are the most appropriate organ for comparative investigations involving the determination of nutritional conditions in the soil." He propounded a "law of the minimum," to the effect that when the supply of a nutrient is limiting growth its concentration in the root tissue will decline to a minimum value. Von Dikow, 1891, suggested that this law should be supplemented by a "law of the maximum": until this maximum mineral content is attained, fertilizer applications will not have their maximum effect on plant growth. Mitscherlich, 1909, proposed a different law of the minimum which states that the increase in yield per unit of limiting nutrient applied is directly proportional to the decrement from the maximum yield (86).

Hall (92) in 1905 carried out a series of experiments to see whether he could assess the fertility of the soil by means of the plant. His scheme was to take a particular plant grown upon the soil in question and to determine in its ash the proportions of constituents like phosphoric acid and potash. Any deviations from the normal in these proportions were taken as indicating deficiency, or excess, of the same constituents in the soil, and therefore the need or otherwise of specific manuring in that direction. His theory was based on two assumptions, first that each plant had a typical ash composition, and secondly that the variations in the proportions of a constituent, such as phosphoric acid, will reflect the amount of that plant nutrient available in the soil. The crops used were oats, wheat, barley, potatoes, swedes, and mangolds. His general conclusions follow:

1. The proportions of phosphoric acid and of potash in the ash of any given plant varies with the amount of these substances available in the soil, as measured by the response of the crops to phosphatic or potassic manures.

2. The extent of variation due to this cause is limited; it is often no greater than the variations due to season.

3. The fluctuations in the composition of the ash are reduced to a minimum in the case of the organs of the plants, like the grain of cereals or the tubers of potatoes.

4. The composition of the ash of cereals is less affected by changes in the composition of the soil than is that of root crops.

5. Pending the determination of phosphoric acid and potash "constants" for some test plant occurring naturally on unmanured land, the interpretation of soil conditions from analysis of plant ash is not a practical method by which chemical analysis of the soil can be displaced.

Hall's paper appears to have had a discouraging effect on plant analysis as a diagnostic procedure, and only very limited work was carried out during the next two decades. Probably the development of improved methods of soil analysis was also in part responsible.

The early workers used plant analysis as a biological method for assessing soil fertility, but the present trend is to use leaf analysis as a guide to the nutritional status of the plant—first to establish threshold levels for nutrients below which plants show deficiency symptoms, and secondly to establish nutrient values associated with optimum growth, or yield of fruit. Lagatu and Maume (139) were the first to adopt this new approach, to which they gave the name "foliar diagnosis," in their nutritional studies with vine.

Macy (155) introduced the concept of "critical nutrient percentages" in leaf dry matter. He held that for any given plant there exists a fixed "critical percentage" for each nutrient: amounts in excess of this percentage represent "luxury consumption," and amounts below represent a "poverty adjustment range" that finally reaches a "minimal percentage." The critical percentage is thought of as an "ideal," subject perhaps to some slight variation depending upon other growth factors, but it is regarded essentially as a fixed value characteristic for a given plant of a given age. Macy thus visualized three ranges, or portions of a curve, relating plant response to percentage concentration: (a) a narrow minimal percentage range where response may increase but internal concentration remains constant; (b) a poverty adjustment range where both response and internal concentration rise; and (c) a luxury consumption range in which response remains constant but concentration increases.

Macy's theory was based largely on the relationship between leaf nitrogen and yield in cereals (Fig. 14).

Thomas (245) put forward the idea of (a) *quantity* or intensity of

nutrition and (b) *quality* of nutrition, or the ratio of the dominant elements to one another, as being inherent in foliar diagnosis.

Ulrich (255) defines "critical nutrient level" as that range of concentrations at which growth of the plant is restricted in comparison to
that of plants at a higher nutrient level. Evidence shows that plants
with widely different nutrient composition give similar yields so long
as these nutrient concentrations are well above the critical level. However, when one or more of the nutrients reaches the critical level, i.e.,
it becomes limiting, any change in the nutrient balance will affect the
growth of the plant.

Shear *et al.* (213) maintain that plant growth is a function of two
variables of nutrition, intensity and balance, as they are reflected in the

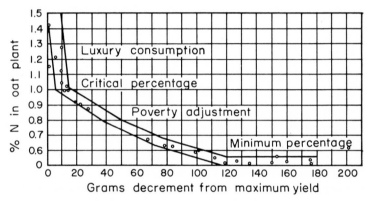

Fig. 14. The relation between percentage nitrogen content and nitrogen response
of the oat (*Avena sativa*) plant at the milk stage. After Macy (155) from data
of Pfeiffer *et al.*

composition of the leaves when the plants are in the same stages of
growth or development. At any level of nutritional intensity (total
equivalent concentration of all functional nutrient elements in the leaf)
a multiplicity of ratios may exist between these elements. Maximum
growth and yield occur only upon the coincidence of optimum intensity
and balance. When the concentration of any element is substantially
different from that at its optimum intensity, the maximum growth possible within the new limits of supply of that element can result only
when the concentration of all other elements has been brought into
balance at the new level of intensity. These authors believe that leaf
composition is the only valid criterion of the nutritional status of the
plant, provided that due consideration is given to time of sampling
and to the position of the leaves on the shoot and that the factors affect-

ing the accumulation of the nutrients in the leaves are taken into consideration.

Goodall and Gregory (86), in a most comprehensive account of the chemical composition of plants as an index of their nutritional status, consider that plant growth is conditioned by two sets of factors: (a) the external factors such as light, temperature, water, and nutrient supply and (2) internal factors, mainly nutritive but also hormonal. For each factor there is an optimum intensity level: growth will be increased if the intensity is brought up to this level and decreased if it is raised further. These optima are not fixed, but depend on all factors simultaneously: nevertheless in theory one may postulate an optimal concatenation of factors at which development of the plant would be maximal.

Lundegårdh (150) maintains that there is always for each factor a range of S values [S (Spiegelwerten) = mg-atoms per 100 gm. of dry matter] in which a strong positive correlation exists between S values and growth. Thus growth is primarily correlated with concentration, not with absolute quantities. He emphasizes however, that if nitrogen is limiting, the plants grow slowly and the organs remain small in relation to the absorptive area of the roots; even with low concentrations of potassium and phosphorus in the soil these nutrients reach high S values in the leaves. When the conditions of growth are not known, as will be the case in practical leaf analysis, low N-index values provide sufficient warning against overvaluation of the K and P values.

Steenbjerg (226) stresses the importance of studying the yield curve in plant nutrition studies. If the yield curve is S-shaped, then the percentage content of those nutrients not present in limiting amounts will on the whole show a constant decrease with increasing weight of dry matter produced. On the other hand, the nutrient present in limiting concentration shows first a decrease, and then an increase, in percentage concentration with increasing weight of dry matter production as a result of treatment with increasing amounts of the limiting nutrient. This is illustrated in Fig. 15. In the concave region of the S-shaped yield curve Steenbjerg advocates caution in the use of chemical analysis of plant material as a criterion of nutrient deficiency.

The choice of leaf and time of sampling are most important in using leaf analysis as a guide to nutritional status (33). Steenbjerg (226) states that care must be taken to choose such organs of the plants that the differences in the analytical results will be as great as possible, and that the sampling should be carried out during that part of the growing season when differences in the analytical results will be greatest. Figure 16 shows how the nitrogen and calcium concentrations of black

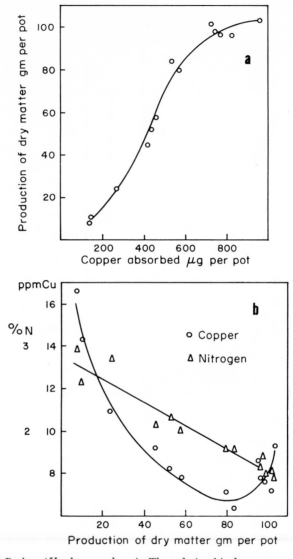

Fig. 15. a. Barley (*Hordeum vulgare*). The relationship between copper absorbed and the production of dry matter. Leaves and straw. Copenhagen, 1939–1941. b. The relationship between the production of dry matter and the relative content of copper (ppm) and nitrogen (%). Dry matter basis. Leaves and straw. Copenhagen, 1939–1941. From Steenbjerg (226).

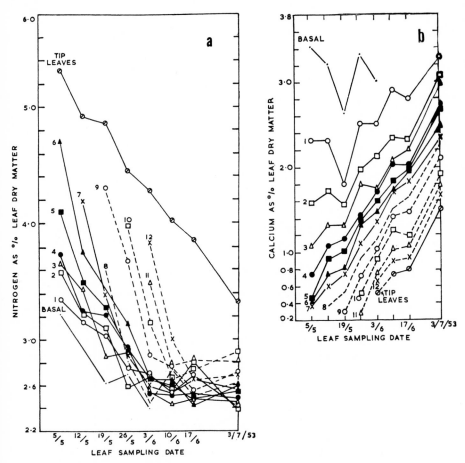

FIG. 16. a. Effect of position and time of sampling on nitrogen status of black currant (*Ribes nigrum* var. Mendip Cross) leaves. b. Effect of position and time of sampling on calcium status of black currant (*Ribes nigrum* var. Mendip Cross) leaves. From Bould *et al.* (33).

currant (*Ribes nigrum*) leaves change with position and time of sampling. From these and other studies Bould (31) concluded that for diagnostic and nutritional studies leaves should be taken from the middle third region of extension shoots just prior to fruit picking. Generally speaking, leaf-nutrient differences between normal and deficient plants are greatest at about the time of fruit ripening.

Having decided on the type of leaf, size of sample, and time of sampling it is then necessary to determine, for each crop, the concentration of leaf nutrients associated with deficiency, sufficiency, and excess.

This can be done by taking leaf samples at the appropriate stage from factorial field and pot culture experiments and carrying out a full chemical analysis. In fact, leaf analysis offers the only means of applying directly to field work the results of sand- and solution-culture experiments, since the interpretation of nutritional status on the basis of leaf composition is not concerned with the means by which that composition was obtained, but only with the effect on growth of changes in leaf composition. This has been done for a number of crops: the results of Reuther and Smith (198) for orange (*Citrus sinensis*) are given in Table XVIII. The leaf standards presented in Table XVIII and their interpretation all presume that the root system of the trees sampled are not handicapped or damaged by poor aeration, fungus diseases, pests, or other causes. The authors emphasize that conclusions based on leaf analysis alone can lead to an erroneous diagnosis of a problem unless disease, pests, soil tilth, and soil drainage factors are competently evaluated.

Plant analysis as a guide to fertilizing crops has its limitations. It cannot tell the grower how much fertilizer to apply to overcome the deficiency, but once the fertilizers have been applied the adequacy, or inadequacy, can be determined by analysis of leaf samples taken later in the season, or during the following year. The fertilizer program can then be modified in the light of these results by reference to the standard leaf-nutrient values. Leaf analysis is also invaluable for confirmation of a diagnosis by visual symptoms.

2. Tissue Testing

This method of diagnosing the nutritional status of crops is based on the detection and assessment of unelaborated plant nutrients during the process of translocation, the test normally being made on the stems and petioles of plants. If a plant is amply supplied with nutrients these can be detected and assayed prior to metabolism by rapid semiquantitative tissue tests. If the supply of nutrients to the roots is limited, then the effect on the concentration of soluble nutrients in transit in the plant may be detected before the effects on growth and visual symptoms become apparent. It is sometimes possible, therefore, to apply the appropriate fertilizer treatment in time to prevent the occurrence of deficiency in the crop.

Much of the early work on chemical tissue tests was carried out in the United States. Hoffer (111) showed by a qualitative staining technique that iron accumulated in the nodes of maize (*Zea mays*) when potassium was deficient. A later development was the analysis of ex-

TABLE XVIII

TENTATIVE STANDARDS FOR CLASSIFICATION OF THE NUTRIENT STATUS OF ORANGE (*Citrus sinensis*) TREES BASED ON CONCENTRATION OF MINERAL ELEMENTS IN 4- TO 7-MONTH-OLD, SPRING-CYCLE LEAVES FROM NONFRUITING TERMINALS[a]

Element and chemical symbol	Dry matter basis	Deficient, less than	Low range	Optimum range	High range	Excess, more than
Nitrogen (N)	%	2.0	2.1 to 2.3	2.4 to 2.9	3.0 to 3.5	3.6
Phosphorus (P)	%	0.08	0.09 to 0.11	0.12 to 0.16	0.17 to 0.29	0.3?
Potassium (K)	%	0.6	0.7 to 1.1	1.2 to 1.7	1.8 to 2.3	2.4
Calcium (Ca)	%	1.5 ?	1.6 to 2.9	3.0 to 5.5	5.6 to 6.9	7.0?
Magnesium (Mg)	%	0.15	0.16 to 0.29	0.3 to 0.6	0.7 to 1.1	1.2?
Sulfur (S)	%	0.13	0.14 to 0.19	0.2 to 0.3	0.4 to 0.5 ?	0.6?
Boron (B)	ppm	20	21 to 40	50 to 150	160 to 260	270
Iron (Fe)	ppm	35	36 to 59	60 to 120	130 to 200 ?	250 ?
Manganese (Mn)	ppm	15	16 to 24	25 to 200 ?	300 to 500 ?	1000 ?
Zinc (Zn)	ppm	15	16 to 24	25 to 100 ?	110 to 200 ?	300 ?
Copper (Cu)	ppm	4.0	4.1 to 5.9	6 to 16?	17 to 22 ?	23 ?
Molybdenum (Mo)	ppm	0.05	0.06 to 0.09	0.10 to 0.29?	0.3 to 0.4 ?	?

[a] From Reuther and Smith (198).

pressed sap for nitrate, phosphate, and potassium. Gilbert and Hardin (82) studied the composition of the expressed solution of lettuce, cabbage, beet, and celery in relation to fertilizer treatment. They concluded that it may not always be possible to choose arbitrary values which indicate critical nutrient situations, but suggested the following tentative critical concentrations: potassium, roots or tops, 3000 ppm; phosphate phosphorus, roots, 20 ppm; nitrate nitrogen, blades of leaves, 300 ppm.

These quick tests were improved by Thornton *et al.* (246) and extended to include other nutrients. The extraction of nutrients by the Purdue method, devised by Thornton and associates, is made by the chemicals used for detecting the nutrients themselves, e.g., cobaltinitrite for potassium, ammonium molybdate for phosphate, and diphenylamine in sulfuric acid for nitrates. Different parts of plants give different results, and some are more reliable indicators of fertilizer needs than others. Thornton and co-workers found that in general tests for phosphorus should be made on main stems, or leaf petioles, from actively growing portions of the plant. For potassium, with grasses and cereals, tests should be made on the base of the leaf near the middle of the stem; and for other plants, the main stems or leaf petioles. Their results were reported in four categories, viz, very high, high, medium, and low. This method has been used by numerous workers for the diagnosis of mineral deficiencies in crop plants (136).

A number of solvents have been used in tissue testing to extract soluble nutrients from plants; these include water, dilute organic and mineral acids, and buffered acids such as Morgan's reagent. Nicholas (173) has given a comprehensive account of tissue testing, based on extraction with Morgan's reagent. The tests are carried out on small petiole portions taken from numerous leaves approximately half way between leaf attachment and base of the lamina. In the cauliflower, midrib portions of comparable girth near the tip of the lamina are taken. About 4 gm. of finely chopped tissue are immersed in 40 ml of Morgan's reagent for 15 minutes and filtered through a plug of cotton wool in a filter funnel. If colored compounds are present these are removed by the addition of 0.2 gm. of purified carbon per 25 ml of extract, stirring, and filtering through a No. 41 Whatman paper. For the detection of deficiency levels of manganese in crop plants a purified Morgan's reagent is used. The chemical tests used are given in Table XIX. It is necessary to fix values for each nutrient in each crop corresponding to high, medium, and low levels, at different stages of growth. A close correlation was found between the data of tissue tests and those of full chemical analysis over the range of values for the

TABLE XIX

Chemical Tests
Using Morgan's Reagent as the Extracting Solution[a]

Cations or anions tested	Reagents used	Coloration or turbidity ranges	
		Minimum	Maximum
Potassium (K)	0.2 ml 35% sodium cobalti- nitrite 1 ml 50% glycerin 2 ml isopropyl alcohol	Clear reddish brown solu- tion	Deep canary yellow tur- bidity
Calcium (Ca)	2 ml 50% glycerin 5 ml saturated solution of ammonium oxalate	Colorless solution	Grayish white turbidity
Magnesium (Mg)	0.2 ml 0.15% Titan yellow[b] 0.5 ml 2% hydroxylamine hydrochloride 0.5 ml 5% sucrose 2 ml 10% sodium hydroxide	Straw-yellow solution	Salmon pink color
Manganese (Mn) (present in excess)	0.5 ml 10% trioxymethylene sulfate 2 ml 10% sodium hydroxide	Colorless solution	Deep cherry color
Manganese (Mn) (sensitive test for deficiency levels)	2 ml potassium periodate[b] (saturated solution) 0.4 ml 1% tetramethyldia- minodiphenylmethane[b]	Pale blue color	Deep blue color
Nitrate (NO_3)	2 ml 25% w/v phenoldisulfonic acid in sulfuric acid 5 ml H_2O 10 ml 30% ammonia until alkaline	Colorless	Deep buff color
Phosphate (PO_4)	2 ml 4% ammonium molybdate 1 ml 1% hydroquinone 2 ml {26% potassium carbonate / 5% sodium sulfite}	Faint blue color	Deep Mediter- ranean blue color
Chloride (Cl)	2 ml $N/50$ silver nitrate 3 drops HNO_3 (conc.)	Colorless solution	White turbid- ity

[a] From Nicholas (173).
[b] Should be recrystallized and standardized before use.

diagnosis of deficiencies. This is shown in Tables XX and XXI. For potassium, the tissue test results are significantly correlated with total amounts irrespective of crop, variety, extracting solution, sampling, or season. For magnesium the tissue tests are significantly correlated with

TABLE XX

CORRELATION COEFFICIENTS BETWEEN TOTAL ANALYSIS AND TISSUE TEST
DATA FOR POTATO (*Solanum tuberosum*)[a,b]

Season:	1952				1953	
Variety:	Kerr's Pink		Dunbar Standard		Kerr's Pink	
Extracting solution:	Acetate	Citrate	Acetate	Citrate	Malonate	Succinate
Element K	0.97***	0.93***	0.93***	0.98***	0.98***	0.98***
Element Mg	0.94**	0.96***	0.91**	0.93**	0.76*	0.79**
Element Ca	0.93**	0.98***	0.79*	0.16	0.72	0.62
Element N	0.96***	0.95***	0.86**	0.95***	0.85**	0.66
Element P	—	—	—	—	0.78**	0.85**

[a] From Nicholas (175).
[b] Level of significance: * = 5%; ** = 1%; *** = 0.1%.

TABLE XXI

CORRELATION COEFFICIENTS BETWEEN TOTAL ANALYSIS AND TISSUE TEST DATA
FOR CAULIFLOWER[a,b]

Plant portion:	Leaf lamina		Midrib	
Extraction solution:	Malonate	Succinate	Malonate	Succinate
Element K	0.87**	0.97***	0.97***	0.93***
Element Mg	0.71	0.26	0.85	0.75
Element Ca	0.85*	0.86*	0.30	0.28
Element N	0.92**	0.47	—	—
Element P	0.82**	0.91**	0.74	0.97***

[a] From Nicholas (175).
[b] Level of significance: * = 5%; ** = 1%; *** = 0.1%.

total amounts for potato (*Solanum tuberosum*), but not for cauliflower. For the other nutrients the correlation depends upon extracting solvent.

Nicholas (175) warns that often the apparent simplicity of chemical tissue tests is misleading. The techniques described, including the sampling of *fresh* plant material, preparation of test samples, extraction, chemical testing, and interpretation of the results need great care and all the necessary precautions at each stage. Although differences in nutrient status of extracts of normal and deficient plant tissue may give a clue to the limiting nutrient, it is only by an intensive study of crops grown in a number of long-term manurial experiments located on various soil types, that standards for normal and deficiency status can be determined. The extraction of fresh leaf tissue with acetate buffer in a blendor apparatus is recommended as the best rapid method for determining the K, Mg, Ca, P, and nitrate N status of most agricultural and horticultural crops.

VII. Foliar Nutrition

The concept that leaves and other aerial plant parts may function as nutrient absorbing organs of sufficient importance to alter markedly the nutrient status of a plant is still held in reservation by some plant physiologists. Yet the absorption of nutrients from sprays by above-ground plant parts has been known and accepted, and the principle has been utilized in a limited way in practical crop production for many decades, one of the earliest records being that of Forsyth in 1803 (280). Ballard and Volk, in 1914, used winter sprays of sodium nitrate on dormant apple trees, and Lewis (145), in 1936, published a note on the absorption of phosphate by lettuce leaves.

In recent years it has become increasingly popular to apply nutrients as foliar sprays (37, 281). The usefulness of foliar application of nutrients depends on the following circumstances: (a) the existence of special problems that may not be coped with as well by application of the fertilizer to the soil or by soil management; (b) satisfactory response to the nutrient sprays; and (3) economical materials and methods of application.

Foliar sprays of iron, zinc, manganese, and copper compounds are used in preference to soil applications because of fixation problems. Another special problem is slow response to soil application and need for a temporary control method in the period before the soil treatment takes effect. This is the main reason for using foliar sprays of Epsom salts on apple trees. Magnesium deficiency in fruit crops is often induced by high potash manuring, which results in a high soil K:Mg ratio. Under these circumstances it takes several years, and heavy soil dressings, to correct the deficiency by soil treatment, whereas three to four foliar sprays of 2% Epsom salts will raise the leaf magnesium level from deficiency to sufficiency in one season (35). This is clearly illustrated in Table XXII. With regard to response, Bukovac and Wittwer (48) have studied the absorption, transport, and mobility of foliar-applied isotopes of rubidium, sodium, potassium, phosphorus, chlorine, sulfur, zinc, copper, manganese, iron, molybdenum, calcium, strontium, and barium with bean as the test crop. Using as a criterion the percentage of the foliar-applied radioactive isotope which is recovered in non-treated plant parts, and autoradiography to portray gross distribution in the plant, it was found that rubidium, sodium, and potassium were the most readily absorbed and most highly mobile. Calcium, strontium, and barium although absorbed by the leaf were not exported from the leaf and were considered immobile. Phosphorus, chlorine, sulfur, zinc, copper, manganese, iron, and molybdenum were intermediate with

TABLE XXII

EFFECT OF FOLIAR SPRAYS OF 2% EPSOM SALTS ON THE MAGNESIUM STATUS OF APPLE LEAVES[a]

| | MgO as % dry matter | | | |
Treatments	Before treatment, May 19, 1948	After treatment, Aug. 30, 1948	Response to treatment	Increase over control
Control, no spray	0.252	0.202	−0.050	—
1 Foliage spray[b]	0.287	0.302	+0.015	0.100
2 Foliage sprays	0.273	0.343	+0.070	0.141
3 Foliage sprays	0.260	0.493	+0.233	0.291
4 Foliage sprays	0.262	0.800	+0.538	0.598

[a] From Bould and Tolhurst (35).
[b] Applied at fortnightly intervals beginning at petal fall.

decreasing mobility in the order given. The economics of foliar sprays versus soil dressings can be illustrated by the use of iron chelates for the control of lime-induced chlorosis in fruit trees. Whereas it takes from $\frac{1}{2}$ to 1 pound of ferric ethylenediaminetetraacetic acid (Fe-EDTA), applied as a soil dressing to a single mature apple (*Malus sylvestris*) or pear (*Pyrus communis*) tree, to control lime-induced chlorosis, 1 pound of Fe-EDTA will make 100 gal of foliar spray. This will allow many more trees to be treated, assuming 3 to 4 annual sprays as being necessary for a seasonal control of chlorosis.

A. FACTORS THAT AFFECT THE ABSORPTION OF FOLIAR-APPLIED NUTRIENTS

Reference may here be made to Part III of the Chapter by Steward and Sutcliffe in Vol. II of this treatise (231).

It has been shown by Cook and Boynton (60) that lower leaf surfaces of apple absorb more urea than upper surfaces; that lower surfaces of leaves which were grown under high nitrogen conditions were more efficient in absorption than were low nitrogen leaves, and that the lower surfaces of basal leaves were less efficient than were lower surfaces of terminal leaves. Different areas of the same leaf may have varying absorption rates (see Table XXIII). As a possible explanation for differences in the rates of foliar absorption among species, Gustafson (91) has suggested that stomatal pores function as the primary sites of entry into the leaf. There is, however, considerable controversy on this point. Experiments, using species where the stomatal number on the lower leaf surface greatly exceeded that on the upper

TABLE XXIII

ABSORPTION AND TRANSPORT OF P^{32}-LABELED O-PHOSPHORIC ACID BY
DIFFERENT REGIONS OF BEAN LEAVES[a,b]

	Surface of leaf	
Position of leaf	Upper	Lower
Tip	0.104	0.062
Margin	0.130	0.102
Midrib	0.148	0.104
Base	0.206	0.090

[a] After Wittwer (280) from data of Tukey et al.
[b] Values = micrograms in roots 2 hours after treatment.

surface, showed that both sides of the leaf blade functioned equally well in the absorption of urea (260). Damaging the epidermal hairs by gentle brushing increased absorption of urea tenfold. Furthermore, absorption was three to ten times greater during the night than during the day, and three times greater in the morning than in the afternoon. This suggests that internal factors in the leaf, which undergo diurnal fluctuations, may play an important role in foliar absorption of urea. Oland and Opland (179), studying the uptake of magnesium by apple leaves, found that young leaves absorb magnesium readily, whereas old leaves absorb very little or none if they are sprayed during the day. When sprayed in the evening, just before darkness, old leaves absorb large amounts of magnesium. This effect of the time of spraying could be related to humidity and the nature of the salt used in addition to diurnal changes in internal composition. Allen (5) has shown that when attached leaves of apple rootstocks were momentarily dipped in a solution of the appropriate salt, magnesium was taken up by leaves more rapidly from the chloride or nitrate than from the sulfate. The amount of magnesium initially retained on the surfaces of leaves which were dipped in a 0.1 M solution was independent of the salt used. The differential uptake was due to the relative humidity and the behavior of the salts in relation to it. At 20°C, the relative humidity of air in equilibrium with saturated solutions of magnesium sulfate, acetate, nitrate, and chloride is 82, 65, 55, and 33%, respectively. Therefore at 20°C, a relative humidity of 32% would cause solutions of all four salts to crystallize out, and a relative humidity of 60% would cause the sulfate and acetate to crystallize out, but would allow the nitrate and chloride to remain in solution. Thus, assuming that magnesium can enter the leaf only from solutions, differences in behavior of the three salts can be accounted for on the basis of the different conditions under which their solutions dry out on the leaf surface, i.e., relative humidity.

It was thought at one time that the outer epidermal cell walls of apple leaves were covered with a continuous layer of cutin. Roberts et al. (203) have since shown the presence of pectinaceous substances which form a continuous path reaching from the outside of the leaf and extending to the walls of the vein extensions. The epidermal cell walls of the apple leaf, therefore, can no longer be considered as covered with a continuous cuticle which prevents the absorption of water and salts. The amount and location of the pectinaceous substances present in the leaves may account for the entrance of water-soluble materials such as nutrients, hormones, and fungicides.

The widespread occurrence of epidermal plasmodesma (strands of protoplasm) may provide the most probable exchange sites and the pathway for entry of nutrients through leaf surfaces. They increase in frequency as the young leaf develops, until a maximum is reached in vigorous bright green leaves, and they decline as the leaf yellows. Skoss, according to Wittwer (280), has reported that intracellular plasmodesma may even penetrate the cuticle.

It is known that different plant species, and different varieties of the same species, vary as regards their ease of wetting. This is due to the chemical and physical nature of the leaf cuticle and the degree of pubescence. The addition of surfactants (wetting agents) to foliar sprays may increase or decrease the absorption of foliar-applied nutrients. Cook and Boynton (60), working with McIntosh apple leaves found that the absorption of urea solutions by lower leaf surfaces in

4-hour periods was increased, on the average, more than 100% by the addition of Tween 80 (a sorbitan mono-oleate polyoxyalkylene derivative) at 0.1% or by Tween 20 (a sorbitan monolaurate polyoxyalkylene derivative) at 0.01%. The effect of the wetting agent in increasing absorption was apparent only when the leaves had not been sprayed previously with solutions containing wetting agents or oils. On the other hand, Teubner *et al.* (244) tested the effect of a number of surfactants on the absorption of phosphate by bean leaves, as measured by the percentage of applied P^{32} recovered in nontreated

TABLE XXIV

Total Absorption from Foliar Sprays as Percentages of Amounts of Isotopically Labeled Nutrient Applied[a]

Nutrient	Plant treated	Approximate absorption (%)	Absorption time	Authority
Phosphorus	Apple	32–48	7 Days	Fisher and Walker (1955)
	Apple	75–100	30 Days	Eggert et al. (1952)
	Bean and squash	40–50	6 Days	Mayberry (1951)
	Swede	50	10–12 Days	Thorne (1955)
Nitrogen (as urea)	Tobacco	25	6 Hours	Volk and McAuliffe (1954)
	Cucumber, bean, tomato, corn	100	3–12 Hours	Hinsvark et al. (1953)
Potassium	Bean and squash	25–35	72 Hours	Mayberry (1951)

[a] From Wittwer (280).

plant parts, and with one exception all additives up to a concentration of 1.0% reduced absorption. Similar results were obtained by Koontz and Biddulph (135) with red kidney bean (*Phaseolus vulgaris*) using nonionic and cationic surface active agents, but Fisher and Walker (73) more than doubled the absorption of P^{32} labeled monopotassium phosphate (0.2%) by adding glycerine (1 or 2%) or Triton X-100 (an alkyl aryl polyether alcohol) to the spray solution applied to apple leaves. Generally speaking, the addition of wetting agents to nutrient foliage sprays enhances the uptake of the nutrient, particularly cations. The percentage absorption of some foliar-applied nutrients is given in Table XXIV, and the rate of absorption of foliar-applied nitrogen as urea, phosphorus as KH_2PO_4, and magnesium as $MgSO_4 \cdot 7H_2O$ is shown in Fig. 17.

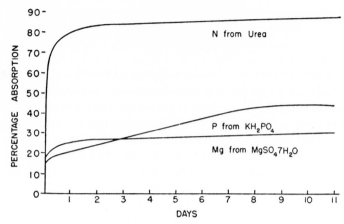

Fig. 17. The rate of absorption of nitrogen, phosphorus, and magnesium from sprays applied to the lower surface of McIntosh apple leaves. From Fisher and Walker (73).

Not only are nutrients taken up from foliage sprays, but they may also be lost by leaching during rainfall (62, 156) (see Table XXV). Long *et al.* (149) grew plants in solutions labeled with P^{32} and K^{42}. The plants were then leached with a mist of distilled water for 4–48 hours and the runoff was collected and analyzed. Intact plants lost no

TABLE XXV

Amount of Leaf Components Leached from Apple Trees by Rain during 1954, Calculated per Hectare of Tree-Covered Area

Variety	K (kg)	Na (kg)	Ca (kg)	Organic constituents
Bramley seedling	30.0	9.0	10.5	7.4
Cox's orange	25.0	9.0	—	—
Rain water	1.7	4.5	3.8	4.0

a From Dalbro (62).

phosphate, but cuttings lost from 1.5 to 12.8% of the absorbed P^{32}. After 12 hours of root absorption in the dark, subsequent leaching for 4 hours removed up to 71% of the previously absorbed K^{42}. Analysis of the leachates also indicated the presence of amino acids and reducing substances. It would appear that potassium is the nutrient most readily lost by leaching.

PART 2. MINERAL NUTRITION OF PLANTS IN CULTURE MEDIA

by E. J. HEWITT

VIII. Early Experiments and the Development of Nutrient Culture Methods

The study of problems concerned with the ways in which plants derive nutrients from the media with which their roots are in contact represents some of the first aspects of quantitative plant physiology which received the attention of botanists. In this Part, therefore, attention will be focused on developments which were made possible as the need to grow plants in soil could be circumvented, thus evading many of the complications which have been dealt with above in Part 1. Useful reviews of the history of this subject have been given by Tottingham (248), Pfeffer (184), Shive (216), Reed (195), Stiles (235), and Johnson and Woodman (126). Van Helmont (1577–1644) is frequently credited with having performed one of the first experiments in an attempt to discover the origin of increase in fresh weight of a willow (*Salix* sp.) cutting (cf. Section I, A). Perhaps the most interesting point for present-day students is his appreciation of the possibilities of nutrients being provided by atmospheric dust. This source may in fact be a major difficulty to be considered in the continuing search for evidence of essentiality of mineral elements for plants.

Probably the earliest water culture experiment without a solid root medium was made by Woodward (283) in 1699 (cf. Section I, A). However, Woodward also grew potato (*Solanum tuberosum*), vetch (*Vicia* sp.) in addition to mint (*Mentha* sp.) in water of various origins including rainwater, spring water, river water, and distilled water. He concluded that water functioned "only as a carrier of terrestrial matter." This experiment was probably the first to test the effects of distilled water in plant nutrition. Duhamel du Monceau in 1758 (68) grew oak (*Quercus* sp.), almond (*Prunus amygdalus*), chestnut (*Castanea sativa*), walnut (*Juglans regia*) trees and beans in filtered water obtained from the river Seine, but he did not produce any important conclusions.

In 1804, de Saussure (66) made one of the first attempts to analyze the factors involved in nutrient culture of plants. He grew *Bidens cannabina* and *Polygonum persicaria* in distilled water and in dilute salt solutions. This work established the need to provide nitrate in the culture solution. He concluded that roots are not selective between the uptake of beneficial and toxic compounds and that the required amount of different salts could be absorbed from very dilute solutions. Wiegman and Polstorff (274) concluded that plants derived all their mineral requirements by absorption through the roots, except for a contribution made from the seed. This was the first recognition of the importance of the seed as a source of essential nutrients. Sprengel (223) was, according to Shive (216) the first to determine the essential nature of the major nutrients for plants. The importance of iron was recognized soon afterward by Gris (90), who observed the response of chlorotic plants in the field to application of iron compounds.

Boussingault (ca. 1851–1856) (36) introduced the idea of growing plants in sand culture. This method was extended by Salm-Horstmar (207, 208), whose work may be regarded as the beginning of modern experimentation on micronutrient problems. He introduced novel ideas, such as wax coatings for glass containers, acid extraction of sand, the use of quartz or charcoal as rooting media, and then he devised the method of testing deficiency treatments whereby various elements in turn were omitted from a complex "complete" nutrient solution. This work demonstrated the effects on oats (*Avena sativa*) of deficiencies of nitrogen, phosphorus, sulfur, potassium, calcium, magnesium, and iron. His efforts were also sufficiently successful to produce the symptoms now known as "gray speck" caused by manganese deficiency.

Modern methods for use of water cultures are based on these experiments and on those introduced twenty years later at the Tharandt School of Forestry by Sachs (206). Sachs appreciated the desirability of eliminating sand as a potential source of impurities in experiments that were intended to establish the identity of essential mineral elements. Sachs developed a standardized and simple formula for providing all the elements then thought to be required, and he included manganese in the formula, which was prepared by mixing two basic stock solutions. Sachs also tested the effects of ammonium compounds as sources of nitrogen. The need to change nutrient solutions at regular intervals and to limit the number of plants in relation to the capacity of the culture jars was also recognized.

Knop (132–134), at about the same time, published results of experiments on effects of nutrient composition on growth and introduced a simplified and widely used nutrient solution based upon molar ratios (134). He also recognized the importance of providing conditions for the production of uniform seedlings by the since widely used method of germinating them on a muslin gauze stretched over dilute nutrient solution. Tottingham (248) and Shive (214, 215), further simplified the composition of nutrient solutions used to provide major elements and established some relationships between growth and the total concentration of salts in terms of osmotic pressures of the solutions and the proportions of the individual ions. A very large number of complex and simple nutrient solution formulas have since been devised, and these are fully reviewed elsewhere (99). An early type of solution of great importance and success, especially in water culture, was that described by Van der Crone (258). This is still in use today and is based on the use of sparingly soluble salts such as ferrous phosphate and calcium phosphate and sulfate. Essential micronutrients are provided according to choice. Hoagland (108) attempted to provide the nutrients in amounts which resembled those in the soil solution. A widely used solution in common use today was described by Hoagland and Snyder (110). A later development was the nutrient formula devised by Arnon and Hoagland (12), which provided a balanced formula related to the amounts absorbed by tomato plants and with trace elements. Hoagland and Snyder's solution was one of the first to include molybdenum before the essential nature of that element for higher plants was known. Chlorine was however given in the formulas of Mazé (159), Sommer (220), Hoagland and Snyder (110) many years before the conclusive proof of its importance was obtained, and cobalt was first specified in the formulas of Sommer (221), Hoagland and Snyder (110), and Hewitt (99). The discovery of the importance of each of these elements is described below. A nutrient solution formula which is used to grow a wide range of species in sand cultures with excellent results at Long Ashton is shown in Table XXVI, together with others which have already been noted and one which is adopted for use with gymnosperms by Swan (242). Mitchell (167) also has developed a formula for similar purposes.

IX. The Essential Plant Micronutrients

A. TERMINOLOGY

The requirements by plants, microorganisms, and animals for mineral elements in small amounts has been accepted as likely for nearly as long as the subject of mineral nutrition has been studied. Numerous terms that have been used to describe such elements include minor element, trace element, *Spurenelement*, oligo-element. Such terms have certain disadvantages because they may imply either secondary importance or rarity, and this may be misleading. Arnon (11a) introduced the term micronutrient element (abbreviated to micronutrient). This does not have some of the limitations mentioned and is still descriptive. The term is now widely used and is adopted here and in Chapter 2.

B. DISCOVERIES OF ESSENTIAL MICRONUTRIENTS

The introduction of nutrient solutions containing the minimum number of salts which would provide the elements known at the time to be essential thus prepared the way for more systematic studies on the

TABLE XXVI
Examples of the Composition of Nutrient Solutions

1. Knop 1865 (134)

	gm/l
KNO_3	0.2
$Ca(NO_3)_2$	0.8
KH_2PO_4	0.2
$MgSO_47H_2O$	0.2
$FePO_4$	0.1

2. Van der Crone 1904 (258)

	gm/l
KNO_3	1.0
$Ca_3(PO_4)_2$	0.25
$CaSO_4$	0.25
$Fe_3(PO_4)_27H_2O$	0.25
$MgSO_47H_2O$	0.25

3. Hoagland and Snyder 1933 (110)

	gm/l
KNO_3	0.51
$Ca(NO_3)_2$	0.82
$MgSO_47H_2O$	0.49
KH_2PO_4	0.136

Iron as 0.5% iron tartrate at rate of 1 ml per liter when required Supplements A and
B (1 ml/l of each) containing in 18 liters the weights (grams) shown:

  A. $(Al)_2(SO_4)_3$, 1.0; KI, 0.5; KBr, 0.5; TiO_2, 1.0; $SnCl_22H_2O$, 0.5; LiCl, 0.5;
  $MnCl_24H_2O$, 7.0; H_3BO_3, 11.0; $ZnSO_47H_2O$, 1.0; $CuSO_45H_2O$, 1.0;
  $NiSO_46H_2O$, 1.0; $Co(NO_3)_26H_2O$, 1.0

  B. As_2O_3, 0.1; $BaCl_2$, 0.5; $CdCl_2$, 0.1; $Bi(NO_3)_2$, 0.1; Rb_2SO_4, 0.1; K_2CrO_4,
  0.5; KF, 0.1; $PbCl_2$, 0.1; $HgCl_2$, 0.1; MoO_3, 0.425; H_2SeO_4, 0.1; $SrSO_4$,
  0.5; VCl_3, 0.1

4. Arnon and Hoagland 1940 (12)

	gm/l
KNO_3	1.02
$Ca(NO_3)_2$	0.492
$NH_4H_2PO_4$	0.23
$MgSO_47H_2O$	0.49
	mg/l
H_3BO_3	2.86
$MnCl_24H_2O$	1.81
$CuSO_45H_2O$	0.08
$ZnSO_47H_2O$	0.22
$H_2MoO_4H_2O$	0.09
$FeSO_47H_2O$ 0.5% ⎱	0.6 ml/l 3 × weekly
Tartaric acid 0.4% ⎰	

TABLE XXVI (*Continued*)

5. Nutrient solution suitable for several coniferous species from sowing to sapling stages. Swan (242). (pH 5.0)

	mM/l	Parts per million
$Ca(NO_3)_2$	3	Ca, 120; N, 84
KNO_3	2	K, 78; N, 28
NH_4Cl	2	Cl, 71; N, 28
$MgSO_47H_2O$	2	Mg, 48; S, 64
$NaH_2PO_42H_2O$	0.2	Na, 4.6; P, 6.2
Fe as ferric sodium ethylenediamine di(O-hydroxyphenylacetate)	5.0	
Mn as $MnCl_24H_2O$	0.22	
Zn as $ZnCl_2$	0.048	
Cu as $CuCl_22H_2O$	0.018	
B as H_3BO_3	0.44	
Mo as MoO_3	0.033	

6. Long Ashton formula, modified from Hewitt (99)

	gm/l	ppm	mM/l
KNO_3	0.505	K, 195; N, 70	5
$Ca(NO_3)_3$	0.820	Ca, 200; N, 140	5
$NaH_2PO_42H_2O$	0.208	P, 41	1.33
$MgSO_47H_2O$	0.369	Mg, 24	3
Ferric citrate	0.0245	Fe, 5.6	0.1

or at 2.8 ppm (0.05 mM/l) as ferric potassium ethylenediaminetetra acetate prepared as given by Jacobsen (117)

$MnSO_4$	0.00223	Mn, 0.55	0.01
$CuSO_45H_2O$	0.000240	Cu, 0.064	0.001
$ZnSO_47H_2O$	0.000296	Zn, 0.065	0.001
H_3BO_3	0.00186	B, 0.37	0.033
$(NH_4)_6Mo_7O_24H_2O$	0.000035	Mo, 0.019	0.0002
$CoSO_47H_2O$	0.000028	Co, 0.006	0.0001
$NaCl$	0.00585	Cl, 3.55	0.1

essential nature of other elements. There were, however, numerous reports of additional requirements during a period of seventy-five years after the early work of Salm-Horstmar. The first major event in this period was the observation of the essential nature of manganese for *Aspergillus niger* by Raulin (194). This was confirmed by Bertrand and Javillier (23, 24, 25). Javillier (119) showed the importance of zinc for fungi and these observations were extended by Bertrand and Javillier (23a). Confirmation of the importance of manganese for higher plants represented by oat (*Avena sativa*), soybean (*Glycine max*), pea (*Pisum sativum*), cowpea (*Vigna* sp.), tomato and other species was obtained by McHargue (152, 153). Conclusive experiments on "gray speck" of oats and on "marsh spot" of peas by Samuel and Piper (209, 210) and by Piper (186) showed that manganese deficiency is the cause of these disorders.

The importance of zinc for higher plants represented by maize (*Zea mays*), was indicated by Mazé (159) and confirmed in a spectacular manner for several species, including barley (*Hordeum vulgare*), sunflower (*Helianthus annuus*), buckwheat (*Fagopyrum esculentum*), broad bean (*Vicia faba*), kidney bean (*Phaseolus vulgaris*), by Sommer and Lipman (222) and Sommer (220). Copper was the next element for which essential requirements were shown in simultaneous and independent experiments by Sommer (221) and by Lipman and McKinney (148) on barley, flax (*Linum usitatissimum*), sunflower, and tomato. Further work to confirm the general importance of copper for higher plants was carried out by Piper (187) in studies with pea, lucerne (*Medicago sativa*), subterranean clover (*Trifolium subterraneum*), tomato, wheat (*Triticum aestivum*), *Lolium subulatum*, *Phalaris tuberosa*, and flax.

The essential nature of boron was first suggested from the work of Aghulon (1) and shortly after by Mazé (160, 161) for maize. This discovery was confirmed beyond any doubt for broad bean (*Vicia faba*) by the thorough work of Warington (272).

The importance of molybdenum was recognized first for microorganisms by Bortels (29, 30), who found that *Azotobacter vinelandii* and *A. chroococcum* required molybdenum for maximal rates of nitrogen fixation. Bortels also showed that molybdenum could be partially replaced in these species by vanadium with a reduced effectiveness of about 60% of that of molybdenum for nitrogen fixation. Hoagland and Snyder (110) concluded that a nutrient supplement (A-Z solution) which provided twenty-two elements in addition to the known nutrients including boron, manganese, zinc, and copper, produced additional growth in strawberry (*Fragaria*) plants in water culture. Later Arnon (9) similarly observed unexplained improvements in growth of barley (*Hordeum vulgare*) with ammonium sulfate when given chromium, molybdenum, and nickel in addition to known nutrients. Arnon (10) then found that the growth of lettuce and asparagus (*Asparagus officinalis*) in water culture was stimulated by a group of seven elements which he grouped together as A7: namely, molybdenum, vanadium, chromium, nickel, cobalt, tungsten, and titanium. The addition of thirteen others (A13) comprising aluminum, arsenic, cadmium, beryllium, fluorine, bromine, iodine, selenium, strontium, lithium, rubidium, lead, and mercury, produced no further effect.

The unequivocal demonstration of the essential nature of molyb-

denum for higher plants nevertheless occurred unexpectedly. Stout and
Arnon (239) had recently described improved techniques based on the
earlier methods of Steinberg (227, 228) for the removal of manganese,
iron, copper, and zinc from stock solutions of nutrient reagents and for
the elimination of contamination by these elements in other culture materials. In some experiments with tomato plants grown by these methods
but given all the essential elements then known, Arnon and Stout (16)
observed striking leaf symptoms of mottling and necrosis caused by a
physiological disorder not previously recorded. These symptoms were
cured when the B7 solution of Arnon (10) was added. The whole effect
of this solution could be obtained by adding one component alone,
namely molybdenum at 0.01 ppm, whereupon growth was rapidly
restored to normal. Although Arnon and Stout (16) attributed the discovery to the purification method adopted, it is not generally accepted
[Hewitt (99), Piper (185)] that the methods in question, namely the
precipitation of heavy metals with phosphates adsorbed at an alkaline
pH on calcium carbonate and phosphate is particularly effective for the
removal of molybdenum, and it is not now recommended for this purpose. It is likely that the discovery of molybdenum deficiency in this
work was mainly due to the use of reagents exceptionally free from this
element, and in combination with other effective precautions (239),
which excluded its presence from water and containers. This work was
closely followed independently by that of Piper (185) with Algerian
oats. Hewitt and Jones (105) extended the investigations to include
brassica crops and mustard (*Sinapis alba*) and reproduced for the first
time experimentally the field disorder of cauliflower widely and long
known as "whiptail," which had been described in 1924 by Clayton
(56). The significance of this problem is discussed in Chapter 2 and
elsewhere (102). It is interesting to note that "yellow leaf spot" of
citrus described by Floyd in 1908 (75, 76) was identified as long as
fifty years later by Stewart and Leonard (232, 233) as a disorder
caused by molybdenum deficiency. Both problems are associated with
acid soil conditions, but whiptail also occurs in neutral soils when they
are severely molybdenum deficient.

The history of investigations on the essential nature of chlorine is
also interesting. About a hundred years ago, Nobbe and Siegert (177,
178) concluded that chlorine was required by buckwheat (*Fagopyrum
esculentum*); since then several attempts, notably by Mazé (160, 161)
and by Lipman (147), have produced strong indications that chlorine
might be an essential element for higher plants.

Although these specific attempts had been made to ascertain whether
plants require chlorine, the results which led to the conclusion that it

is important for tomato were obtained by Broyer, Carlton, Johnson, and
Stout (47) unexpectedly in the course of experiments designed to test
whether cobalt is required. Precautions were directed to eliminating
cobalt from water, containers, and nutrient reagents. The method of
nutrient purification which was used involved the coprecipitation of
cobalt as a sulfide with silver as a collector. The silver also combined
with halides and thereby removed a substantial part of these impurities.
Later work showed that recrystallization was more effective than precipitation by silver for removal of chloride and bromide from nutrient
reagents. Tomato plants grown in these experiments developed a browning and necrosis of the leaves which had not previously been recorded.
A marked response was observed in growth when increasing amounts of
cobalt chloride were given, but these supplements appeared to exceed
in quantity what might be expected to be adequate for a micronutrient,
when such elaborate precautions were necessary to demonstrate the
requirement in the first place. Reinvestigation of the stimulation produced by some of the unpurified nutrient reagents and by the chloride
anion provided by cobalt chloride, revealed that the deficient element
was chlorine and not cobalt. Further work by Johnson, Stout, Broyer,
and Carlton (125) with several crops showed marked responses with
lettuce, lucerne, and brassicas. Ulrich and Ohki (256) extended the list
to include sugar beet. The substitution of chlorine by bromine was also
shown in the work of Johnson *et al.* (125) and of Ulrich and Ohki
(256).

Sodium has long been known to have beneficial effects upon higher
plants when deficient in potassium, and investigations on possible
sodium requirements for plants have been numerous since the time of
Hellriegel and Willfarth (95). This aspect of sodium nutrition is discussed in Chapter 2. There is however evidence that sodium may be
essential for both higher plants and microorganisms. Brownell and
Wood (46) concluded that sodium is specifically required in the presence of potassium by *Atriplex vesicaria* when grown in water cultures
with special precautions to eliminate sodium. As little as 2.3 ppm appeared to be adequate. Allen and Arnon (6) found that sodium was
necessary in addition to potassium for the growth of *Anabaena
cylindrica*.

The importance of cobalt has been recognized for microorganisms,
especially *Lactobacillus lactis* (217) for several years in relation to its
presence in cyanocobalamin compounds of the B_{12} group, and more
recently in its elemental form or as B_{12} by some blue-green algae including *Nostoc muscorum* studied by Holme-Hansen, Gerloff, and
Skoog (112). Hutner, Provasoli, Schatz, and Haskins (113) concluded

that *Euglena* was relatively sensitive in showing a requirement for cobalt. The question whether cobalt is required by higher plants is undecided in spite of the careful work of Broyer *et al.* (47). Symptoms of an apparent cobalt deficiency were described for cocoa (*Theobroma cacao*) by Maskell, Evans, and Murray (158). Bolle-Jones and Mallikarjuneswara (28) concluded that cobalt stimulated the growth of rubber (*Hevea brasiliensis*) seedlings. More recently Ahmed and Evans (2, 3, 3a), Reisenauer (196) Delwiche, Johnson, and Reisenauer (65), and Hallsworth, Wilson, and Greenwood (93) independently found that cobalt stimulated and was clearly required for the growth of nodulated soybean (*Glycine max*) and alfalfa (*Medicago sativa*) and subterranean clover (*Trifolium subterraneum*) plants when dependent on atmospheric nitrogen fixation. This effect may reflect a cobalt requirement by the rhizobia or for the symbiosis rather than for the host plant since Ahmed and Evans (3a) were able to reduce yields to less than one-tenth that of controls by omission of cobalt when nitrogen fixation was involved but could not observe the slightest effect of cobalt when nitrate was given in the same experiments with soybean. It is not clear whether the response to cobalt, which leads to greatly increased vitamin B_{12} production, is due to the formation of leghemoglobin; although the increase in hemoglobin content of nodules was clearly related to cobalt supply it was small in proportion to the increased growth and nitrogen fixation and the B_{12} production that occurred over the same range of added cobalt. The first direct effect of cobalt appeared to be on nitrogen fixation rather than on the growth of *Rhizobium* according to Delwiche, Johnson, and Reisenauer (65); these authors found that the fixation process could be detected in 2 hours in excised nodules on giving cobalt whereas growth of *Rhizobium* was not affected under these conditions.

The discovery of Arnon and Wessel (17) that vanadium is required by *Scenedesmus obliquus* was also, as described for chlorine, the result of experiments intended to investigate other problems: in this instance, the interrelationships between iron supply and growth. Arnon and Wessel observed that increasing amounts of iron, in the presence of other known micronutrients, produced a stimulation in growth which was apparent for a more extended range of iron concentrations than would be expected. The major nutrient reagents were purified by a sulfide coprecipitation method (99, 240), and they were relatively free from vanadium as well as from molybdenum. The ferric chloride was not however purified, and the presence of an unidentified micronutrient was suspected. When ferric chloride, purified by extraction with ether in the presence of 6 *N* hydrochloric acid (99, 186, 187), was substituted for the unpurified compound the growth stimulation was greatly decreased. It could, however, be replaced by vanadium alone. No stimulation was obtained with nickel or cobalt. The optimum concentration was about 20 μg/liter, which is probably twenty times the optimum for molybdenum.

The specific requirement for vanadium by the green alga *Scenedesmus obliquus* is additional to its already established requirement for molybdenum. Arnon and Wessel (17) forecast that vanadium might be required by green plants in general, but vanadium has not so far been shown to have any essential or even clearly established beneficial effect on higher plants.

Claims have been made since the early work by Mazé (159, 160, 161) that aluminum, silicon, and iodine may be essential for higher plants (147, 193, 219, 237, 261). The early work of Sommer (219) was unusually interesting in that millet (*Pennisetum* sp.) plants raised from seed produced by plants grown in the absence or the presence of aluminum in the previous generation, showed a permanent differential and beneficial effect when sown and raised in a single container to which no aluminum was given. A repetition of this curious experiment would be of interest.

There are also reports that strontium may partially substitute for calcium in higher plants (270) as it does in some microorganisms (263) and rubidium can certainly partially replace potassium as clearly shown by Richards (199–201) for barley. Selenium may be beneficial (249) for certain accumulator species such as *Astragalus bisulcatus* according to Trelease and Trelease (250). Other reports of interest indicating as yet unproved requirements for trace elements include the stimulating effect of nickel on oats, as recorded by Roach and Barclay (202), and the occasionally beneficial effects of arsenic, iodine, and other elements noted by Stiles (236).

C. Criteria for the Determination of Essential Nutrient Requirements

The investigation of the essential nature of mineral nutrients involves several problems with respect to both the technique and the standards by which essential status may be determined. This second point is considered first.

The progress of the nutritional investigation here reviewed shows that the apparently essential nature of many elements including those regarded as "trace elements," had been discovered and accepted by 1931. The logical approach to such studies was, however, put on a firm basis by Arnon and Stout (15), Arnon (11) by the introduction of *criteria of essentiality* by which the status of an element might be judged.

These criteria were outlined as follows: (a) The element must be essential for normal growth, or reproduction, which cannot proceed in its absence. (b) The requirement for the element must be specific and not replaceable by another. (c) The requirement must be direct, not a manifestation of indirect effects such as antagonism of a toxic effect.

At the time of their proposal these criteria seemed adequate and unambiguous, but since then it has become necessary to take account of some other ideas which may sometimes qualify their application.

The first criterion would appear unequivocal. If apparently stimulatory effects of certain elements occur at low levels, but no abnormality or serious restriction of growth can be detected when attempts are made to exclude all traces of such elements, the exact interpretation or application of the first criterion becomes problematic. The question is considered below in relation to the "beneficial" elements.

It is clear that vanadium can replace molybdenum at comparable or decreased efficiency in certain species of *Azotobacter* [Burk (52), Bortels (29, 30)] or in *Clostridium butyricum* [Jensen and Spencer (123)]. Similarly strontium can replace calcium in *Azotobacter* [Burk and Lineweaver (53)] or in *Chlorella pyrenoidosa* [Walker (263)]. It follows that if replacement is complete, essential requirements for either one of the pair cannot be demonstrated if the other element is present, and in the absence of both, either can be shown to be apparently essential.

It is conceivable that if an element is required for a single specific role which can be made superflous by altering some other aspect of nutrition, e.g., nitrogen supply or possibly a change from autotrophic to partially heterotrophic nutrition, the particular element might no longer be essential. This situation appears to occur with the molybdenum requirement by *Scenedesmus obliquus*, when nitrate is replaced by urea or ammonium carbonate according to very careful work by Ichioka and Arnon (114). The question of essentiality of molybdenum for other organisms under similar circumstances is discussed in Chapter 2 and elsewhere (102).

The presence or absence of certain elements may influence the course of metabolism so that tissue composition or enzyme activity are materially altered. Plants, however, appear to tolerate large differences in their composition with respect to certain major metabolic constituents including amino acids, sugars, phosphate esters, and organic acids, and they may yield widely differing enzyme activities *in vitro* with normal external appearance. Such an element would not thereby qualify as essential in spite of its capacity to influence metabolism. The formation of selenomethionine under conditions of selenium nutrition might provide an example of such a relationship.

The problem of apparently beneficial elements discussed at length in Chapter 2 must be considered. It is well known that some reports of beneficial effects of an element were due to failure to decrease the threshold levels of the element to a point where severe deficiency effects were produced. It is conceivable, however, as outlined in Chapter 2, that one element (A) may replace another (B) at greater efficiency in a certain role (bi) but may be unable to fulfill some other function (bii) for which B is essential and is not replaced by A. Element A would then fulfill a beneficial but not essential role. The quantitative relationships would determine whether the effect was barely perceptible or was tantamount to a quasi-essential function. Beneficial elements include also those which may partially substitute for an essential element under deficiency conditions. Sodium and potassium comprise the best-known example of this relationship, as discussed in Chapter 2.

The question whether an element is essential cannot be answered in a negative sense. Stout and Arnon (239), who developed greatly improved methods for the study of nutrient requirements of plants, emphasized that when attempts to show a requirement for a particular element yielded negative results it was possible only to say that, if required, the necessary concentration of the element was below the limits of the methods used to eliminate that element or to detect its presence. It is, however, equally important to recognize the possibility that not all the chemical elements in the periodic table are in fact essential to all, or even to any, living cells and the negative results may reflect a nonessential character even though this cannot be proved. The requirements of various organisms are clearly diverse, and it is not justifiable at present to argue from the particular to the general by suggesting that the observation of essential requirements for a certain element by one organism, e.g., for vanadium by *Scenedesmus* (17), make a requirement likely for green plants as a group, as Arnon and Wessel suggest. The requirement for individual elements may differ qualitatively for different organisms and what is essential for one may not be required by another, particularly as evolution of protein specificity may change the extent to which a particular element can serve as a prosthetic group.

In spite of the earlier emphasis on the difficulty of interpreting negative results, i.e., of proving that an element is not required, Ichioka and Arnon (114) definitely concluded that for *Scenedesmus*, molybdenum was not required at all when the alga was grown with urea or ammonium carbonate. Critical inspection of their data does in fact show no response whatsoever to molybdenum under these conditions; if it is required, the concentration must be two or three orders lower than concentrations that produce detectable effects with all other organisms that have been tested under similar conditions of nitrogen supply. Arnon and associates (13) concluded that, in the presence of nitrate, the molybdenum level was 1.5×10^3 atoms per cell when deficiency effects were seen. Taking into consideration the experience gained from a great many experiments with different organisms by several workers and from prolonged studies with higher plants at Long Ashton as described in Chapter 2, it may be concluded that if molybdenum is required by *Scenedesmus* in the presence of urea or ammonium carbonate, the level at which a deficiency would be observed might well be only about 15 atoms per cell. The question is therefore still open, but the conclusion of Ishioka and Arnon (114) appears reasonable and may be correct.

X. Experimental Methods for the Study of Micronutrient Requirements

The quantitative requirements of plants for micronutrients are often so low that special methods are necessary to reduce their levels to values in the range where deficiency effects can be detected. The concentrations (as parts per million) suitable for many plants grown in culture solutions have been fully reviewed elsewhere (99); they usually lie within the following ranges: Fe 0.5–5.0, Mn 0.1–0.5, B 0.1–1.0, Zn 0.02–0.2, Cu 0.01–0.05, Mo 0.01–0.05. Deficiency effects may be severe at one-tenth to one-hundredth of these concentrations or even at much lower ones. These small amounts are often provided as impurities from incidental sources. The sources of contamination which require attention are the containers, the rooting medium, water, nutrient reagents, cutting, seed or spore, and the atmosphere. Many of the problems associated with these sources have been discussed in great detail elsewhere (99) in relation to the sources of impurities and to specific methods for eliminating contamination and for controlling the levels of micronutrients given in culture solutions. Only a brief outline of the basic methods will be attempted here, with inclusion of more recent developments of special interest.

A. Culture Containers

The culture vessels except possibly for experiments with boron deficiency, are commonly of borosilicate glass, which appears to be extremely inert with respect to iron, manganese (209, 210), copper, zinc (239), molybdenum (99), vanadium (17), chlorine (125), and cobalt (2,

3). Natural polyethylene containers such as buckets also appear suitable for the work with the lowest attainable levels of all the micronutrients (unpublished work at Long Ashton), but the possible use of molybdenum and cobalt catalysts in the manufacture of high density Polythene (225) and of zinc stearate as an extrusion lubricant must be recognized as potential sources of contamination. Compounds of zinc, copper, cobalt, molybdenum, and titanium are used for pigmenting or "filling" commercial plastic ware. Tubing made of polyvinylchloride may sometimes contain several metals, but black Polythene is inert. Polytetrafluorethylene (Teflon) may also prove to be suitable for making inert containers, or for other purposes. It is however expensive and has not yet been tested. Silica containers have been used on occasions, but they may not present any great advantage over borosilicate glass (except where boron requirement is in question).

B. Rooting Media

Solid rooting media, where used, require purification. High purity silica sand or crushed quartz are most suitable, and it is possible to attain very low levels of available micronutrients (99, 103). When sand is suitably treated, in an apparatus described elsewhere, with steam and a mixture of hydrochloric and oxalic acids (99), deficiency symptoms comparable in severity to those produced in water culture can be produced on a large scale. The available molybdenuum content should be reduced to 0.00001 ppm as estimated with *Aspergillus niger* (103). The advantages and problems of using a solid rooting medium have been discussed elsewhere (99). Briefly, solid culture media are easier to manage and less prone to iron deficiency, but they involve the labor of purification.

C. Water

Water supplies have in the past composed an important source of impurities. Distillation from metal stills was often unsatisfactory as a means for removing copper, zinc, and molybdenum, and for work with these elements single or double redistillation from stills made entirely from borosilicate glass or provided with a borosilicate condensing surface was found to be necessary to obtain water of suitable quality (187, 239). Recently ion exchange resins have been used to purify either distilled water or rain water (99, 104). When rain water is passed through two pairs of single-bed anion and cation resins, then through a mixed-bed resin, it is comparable to water twice distilled from glass stills with respect to the known micronutrients, including molybdenum, as shown from tests carried out with several plant species over the last fifteen years at Long Ashton. The total heavy-metal content of water treated in this way is less than 0.00001 ppm, and the molybdenum concentration may be less than 0.000003 ppm (103).

D. Nutrient Reagents

The reagents that are used to supply the major elements are usually serious sources of several impurities (99). The presence of undetected micronutrient impurities in major salts has often prevented the succesful production of deficiency effects. In several experiments, however, such effects have been observed when solutions prepared with unpurified reagents were used. The occurrence of different micronutrient impurities is often unpredictable and inconsistent. For this reason it is essential, in order to obtain reproducible results under the most severe deficiency conditions, that the major salts should be appropriately purified. This requires the use of specific and highly efficient methods to deal with amounts of the order of a few micrograms per liter present in molar stock solutions of each reagent. The principles involved in nutrient purification have been described elsewhere (99) and the most important procedures are also given.

Early attempts to purify reagents were described by Salm-Horstmar (208) in 1851. One of the earliest principles to be generally adopted and still used in various forms at present is the use of coprecipitation or adsorption by calcium carbonate, introduced by Javillier (119) to remove zinc. The use of calcium carbonate in conjunction with autoclaving was introduced by Steinberg and developed to a reproducible and highly effective procedure (227, 228) for removal of metals such as iron, manganese, zinc, and copper. It was extended to include an alkaline phosphate and a soluble calcium salt independently by Stout and Arnon (239) and by Piper (187). Further improvements were made by including sodium bicarbonate, which leads to precipitation of calcium carbonate in a more active form during autoclaving (99). Munns and Johnson (171) found that coprecipitation with an alkaline solution of magnesium hydroxide was an effective procedure for the removal of cobalt, but measurements with radioactive cobalt indicated that the process was not always complete. Complete removal of copper and zinc is generally achieved by extraction with diphenylthiocarbazone in chloroform or carbon tetrachloride (187). Other extraction methods including the use of 8-hydroxyquinoline for the removal of zinc, iron, and manganese are reviewed elsewhere (99).

Recrystallization has been used in several experiments, but the method suffers from several limitations and may be wholly ineffective when isomorphous compounds are present. Recrystallization was, however, shown to be the simplest way to remove boron compounds from major salts (99) and is also the better method for removal of chlorides [Johnson et al. (125)] when compared with the use of precipitation by silver nitrate. The addition of ethanol improves yields and facilitates crystal formation with some salts. Repeated evaporation with concentrated nitric acid has been tested by Munns and Johnson (171) as an efficient method for the removal of halides.

The early observations on molybdenum requirements (16, 185) were not striking by present standards and were in some degree fortunate since the methods used to purify nutrient salts were not particularly effective for the removal of molybdenum. The first specifically suitable method was that using coprecipitation with 8-hydroxyquinoline and iron introduced for nutrient culture purposes by Hewitt and Jones (105) and was used to reproduce the "whiptail" symptoms in cauliflower for the first time in plants grown in sand culture. Molybdenum as sulfide is readily coprecipitated by other metal sulfides, especially those of copper or lead, and this was applied by Meagher [cf. Stout and Meagher (240)] for the removal of molybdenum from stock solutions. The method was critically evaluated by Hewitt and Hallas (103) using an Aspergillus niger assay technique. The efficiency of the method for removal of molybdenum, as standardized at Long Ashton, was found to exceed 99.9% of amounts of the order of 1 μg per liter. Delwiche, Johnson, and Reisenauer (65) applied the 8-hydroxyquinoline method of Hewitt and Jones (105) in the purification of some of the nutrient reagents in a successful study of effects of cobalt on nitrogen fixation by root nodules of Medicago sativa. Bolle-Jones and Mallikarjuneswara (28) used α-nitroso-β naphthol extraction to remove cobalt, and this method was followed by Ahmed and Evans (2, 3). Extraction with dithizone was used to remove cobalt from magnesium sulfate and ether-6 N hydrochloric acid extraction removed cobalt from ferric chloride (65, 87).

Iron compounds are important sources of micronutrient impurities especially Cu, Zn, Mn, Co, V, and Mo, and normal supplements of iron frequently introduce sufficient of these elements to prevent the production of deficiency effects, as already noted. Ferric chloride is readily extracted into ether in the presence of 6 N hydrochloric acid whereas salts of Cu, Zn, Mn, Co, and Ni are not extracted. The method was introduced by Piper (186, 187) for purification of nutrient salts and was tested for efficiency by Grahame and Seaborg (87), who used radioactive cobalt as an indicator. The purified ferric chloride supplied in the experiments on vanadium by Arnon and Wessel (17) was prepared by the ether-extraction method. Tetravalent vanadium compounds are not extracted by this method, but pentavalent compounds are; peroxide-free ether must therefore be used for this method when freedom from vanadium is required. Compounds of molybdenum and gallium are extracted along with ferric chloride into the ether phase, but, as ferrous iron compounds are not so extracted, a separation can be achieved in this way. Treatment of ferrous sulfate with copper and hydrogen sulfide is, however, more convenient and probably more efficient for the removal of molybdenum. Sodium or potassium Versenate are also purified in this way at Long Ashton (E. J. Hewitt *et al.*, unpublished work) before mixing to prepare ferric Versenate as described by Jacobsen (117). Other micronutrient salts are not usually purified, and the use of spectrographically pure compounds is usually an adequate precaution.

E. Cell Nutrient Reserves

It is probable that all cells of a normal plant contain adequate amounts of each essential element. It therefore follows that the seeds or any parts used to propagate the plants must provide an initial supply of any essential element. This source may be significant either in attempts to produce deficiency effects of a known micronutrient or to demonstrate requirements for an element where its status as an essential nutrient has not been determined. The importance of nutrient reserves in seeds has been shown especially in experiments on molybdenum and copper deficiencies by Hewitt, Bolle-Jones, and Miles (104). Seeds of large-seeded species such as beans and pea may contain sufficient molybdenum to provide for normal growth of the plant and may even support limited growth in the next generation. In these circumstances it is necessary to deplete the seed reserves by growing the plants under deficiency conditions in order to obtain seed that will permit of the demonstration of deficiency effects. Some examples are shown in Chapter 2, Fig. 45.

F. Atmospheric Sources of Nutrients

Atmospheric sources may provide significant amounts of several micronutrients both as volatile compounds or in precipitation. The amount of the latter may be judged from data obtained by exposing glass slides to a greenhouse atmosphere (99). Deposits as milligrams per square meter per month were as follows: Fe, 11; Cu, Zn, Mn, 2–3; B, 6; Mo, 0.1–0.3. Spectrographic analysis of greenhouse dusts by Dr. R. L. Mitchell at the Macaulay Institute showed the presence of 24 elements in addition to the major nutrients, including 30 ppm cobalt and 150 ppm vanadium but only 10 ppm molybdenum. Johnson, Stout,

Broyer, and Carlton (125) found that filtration of the air through activated charcoal decreased chlorine contamination in the air from which plants were able to absorb appreciable amounts through the leaves. Further examples are given elsewhere (99).

G. Problems in the Exclusion of Specific Elements

The sources of micronutrient contamination are sometimes difficult to identify. Unpublished work at Long Ashton with E. W. Bolle-Jones and A. J. Abbott over a period of four years involved elaborate precautions in attempts to exclude impurities from nutrient cultures. Water was double distilled from Pyrex glass stills after treatment with several ion exchange resins; Pyrex glass containers were boiled in acid and steamed: nutrient reagents were processed by a series of methods, repeated in different order, including recrystallization in the presence of EDTA; extraction with various chelating agents including dithizone, 8-hydroxyquinoline, and cupferron in immiscible solvents; alkaline phosphate-carbonate adsorption; acid and alkaline metal sulfide coprecipitation. Acid-cleaned polyethylene covers and plant supports were used, and in one experiment plants in the greenhouse were further protected in a chamber covered by plastic sheeting. In spite of these precautions, attempts to exclude cobalt, nickel, vanadium, chromium, and other elements did not prevent the uptake of spectrographically detectable amounts of these elements in roots and often into leaves of tomato plants. There were also unexpectedly notable amounts of strontium, barium, titanium, and other elements not given in the nutrient solutions, and these, as well as vanadium, accumulated, especially in the roots. The sources of these elements were not determined. Cobalt was below the limits of detection in the concentrated stock reagent solutions prepared in some years, but could still be detected at other times. Vanadium was detected in one stock solution and would have provided 0.00001 ppm in the nutrient solution, but appreciable amounts of nickel and chromium were present, corresponding to 0.0001 ppm in the dilute nutrient. A cobalt need has since been shown for *Alnus*.*

The example described above and the data of Munns and Johnson (171) illustrate the problems involved in attempts to discover whether a particular element is an essential micronutrient. Environmental conditions undoubtedly affect nutrient requirements, as noted in Chapter 2. The need to use a controlled environment in work of this type has been underlined in the experiments of Steward and his collaborators (230) in studies on the amino acid content of plants. The use of a small plant capable of indefinite vegetative subculture under controlled sterile

* See paper by G. Bond and E. J. Hewitt, *Nature* 195, 94–95 (1962).

conditions is also advantageous and was pointed out by Steinberg (229) in studies with *Lemna minor*. There is still abundant scope for further investigation and improvement in this field.

H. Tests for Contamination and for Evaluation of Results

It is desirable to apply tests to discover whether nutrient equipment and reagents have been adequately processed and to test the efficiency of specific methods. Stout and Arnon (239) described the use of diphenylthiocarbazone for testing water and solutions of purified salts with respect to "heavy metal" content, particularly copper, zinc, and lead. The test as described will detect 1 μg per liter (0.001 ppm) total heavy metals. The test does not, however, detect manganese, molybdenum, or vanadium, but it is more sensitive than spectrographic methods for zinc or lead. Manganese is conveniently detected down to limits of about 1 μg per liter with periodate and tetramethyldiaminodiphenylmethane (tetrabase) (99). Spectrographic methods are useful for the assessment of contamination in nutrient reagents and other materials and are especially sensitive for copper and cobalt. The sensitivity of spectrographic detection of molybdenum is, however, inadequate for the most critical experiments, and biological assay with *Aspergillus niger* as described by Hewitt and Hallas (103) and by Nicholas (174, 176) is the accepted method for assay of molybdenum contamination in nutrients, water, and other materials. The method will detect and measure Mo at a concentration of 0.0001 μg Mo in 50 ml (0.000002 ppm).

The detection of cobalt and vanadium in culture materials is not easy at present, and suitably sensitive assay methods are required. Activation analysis by irradiation may prove to be suitable, but preliminary trials have not been entirely satisfactory. The efficiency of removal of elements for which adequate chemical or biological assays are not available can sometimes be assessed by using radioactive isotopes. This approach was used in measuring the separation of cobalt from iron compounds by ether extraction in the work of Grahame and Seaborg (87), the removal of cobalt from major nutrient stock solutions by sulfide coprecipitation in the experiments described by Johnson, Stout, Broyer, and Carlton (125), in the procedure employing alkaline magnesia treatment devised by Munns and Johnson (171).

In general it may be noted that the biological test, especially when carried out with the organisms or plants for which the requirement is already known, e.g., the test by *A. niger* (103, 174, 176) or by sensitive indicators such as tomato or cauliflower or lettuce (99, 101, 104) for molybdenum contamination, is the best method of discovering whether methods for elimination of impurities have been effective.

Scenedesmus obliquus might provide a suitable test organism for vanadium (17), though the concentration reported to be needed appears rather high for sensitive assay purposes. *Euglena* (113) or *Nostoc muscorum* (112) might be applied for bioassay of cobalt. The requirement for cobalt in organic combination as vitamin B_{12} described by Shorb (217) was applied in a test of effects of inorganic cobalt supply to *A. niger*, which was found by Nicholas (174) to produce a B_{12} active compound in relation to the cobalt supply. A combination of chemical and spectrographic methods, activation analysis and biological assay, and analysis of the plants grown in the experiments represents the best approach when attempting to establish an essential requirement. Negative results can be interpreted only as described earlier, namely, that if present, the amounts are below those which can be detected by the available methods and that, if required, the minimum concentrations are also below the levels which can be eliminated by the methods employed.

In a positive sense, it is desirable to include in all nutrient media known amounts of all recognized micronutrients since it is always possible that unusually pure materials may result in accidental deficiencies such as those that led to the discovery of the essential nature of several of the known micronutrients. The discovery of other essential micronutrients may occur in the same way in the future, and any unusual observation suggestive of an unsuspected nutrient deficiency may provide the next clue in the continuing search.

XI. The Application of Culture Methods in the Study of Edaphic Factors

The relationships between ecological distribution of species and soil pH are well known and were described by Small (218). The precise causes of such observed distribution and the strict applicability of the terms "calcicole" and "calcifuge" are perhaps less well established than may be generally accepted. The factors associated with change in soil pH from low to high values have been enumerated earlier in this chapter and include transitions from injurious effects of excess of H^+ ions, manganese, or aluminum, immobilization of phosphorus, and deficiencies of major bases or molybdenum deficiency under acid conditions, to insufficient availability of phosphorus and iron, manganese and other micronutrient elements at alkaline pH values. This relationship is illustrated in Fig. 10 of this chapter.

Some recent work has been aimed to identify the possible soil factors mainly concerned with limitations to the growth or distribution of different species and varieties in natural ecological communities and wider practical agricultural conditions. The basic approach has involved the application of culture techniques for growing the plants in such a way that each factor can be tested separately without interference by the complicating effects of the others and without limitations on availability caused by changes in soil pH.

A. SOIL ACIDITY AND CROP PRODUCTION

The elucidation of factors causing injury to crop plants grown in acid soils has been studied with the use of sand cultures in several experiments by Hewitt (97, 98, 100), Morris (170), Wallace, Hewitt, and Nicholas (268), and in parallel field studies described by Plant (188–190). This work showed that different factors were separately and sometimes jointly responsible for failure or injury in different crop species. Thus sugar beet, celery, and barley are unable to tolerate aluminum, whereas marrowstem kale (*Brassica oleracea* var. *acephala*), cauliflower, swede (*Brassica napobrassica*), and French beans are particularly sensitive to excess of manganese. However, whereas sugar beet will tolerate quite high levels of manganese, barley will not. Kale and swede and several brassicas are relatively insensitive to aluminum, but the effect of this element on dwarf French beans differs greatly with closely related varieties. Although the potato is commonly thought to be an acid-tolerant plant, several failures in acid upland soils were observed when potatoes were planted after first ploughing; the cause was found to be due to complex interactions (269) and often to severe calcium deficiency (267). Molybdenum deficiency is a common cause of failure in broccoli and cauliflower in acid soils (189, 190), and this causes the appearance of "whiptail." On acid greensand soils, however, continued cultivation and decrease in organic matter may result in the later appearance of manganese toxicity as a main symptom of injury (190) and molybdenum deficiency may be masked. The application of the method of visual diagnosis by Wallace (266), using the symptoms of deficiencies and excesses of elements produced in sand cultures (97, 98, 189), has revealed that in the same area of acid soil, oats may show magnesium deficiency; kale, manganese toxicity; barley, aluminum toxicity; broccoli, molybdenum deficiency; and potatoes, calcium deficiency.

B. ADAPTATION TO EDAPHIC FACTORS

The method of using culture techniques has also been applied with interesting results by Bradshaw, Lodge, Jowett, and Chadwick (39, 40) to the elucidation of the reasons for distribution of natural ecotypes; by Bradshaw and Snaydon (41) to the identification of edaphic ecotypes with respect to nutrient requirements within a species population, and by Bradshaw (38), Kruckeberg (137), Walker, Walker, and Ashworth (264), and Jowett (127, 128) to the demonstration of adaptation to specific soil conditions of mineral toxicity. Willis and Yemm (278a) have used techniques of nutrient purification (99) and indicator crop responses (266) to elucidate the edaphic nutritional factors concerned in the ecology of dune soils. It was shown by a comparison between growth of tomato in sand cultures and in the dune soils where different elements were omitted separately, that no appreciable limitation by any micronutrient deficiencies was a factor in the nutrient status of the dune soils. The nitrogen, phosphorus, and potassium contents were, however, of great importance. Restoration of these elements together to turf transplants resulted in rapid increase in *Agrostis stolonifera, Festuca rubra, Poa pratensis* subsp. *subcaerulea*. When nitrogen only was given, *Carex flacca* became dominant, and growth of the grasses was limited by phosphorus.

Bradshaw *et al.* (39, 40) pointed out the importance of small differences in determining the effects of nutrient supply on the distribution of a species. Of four grass species examined, *Cynosurus cristatus* showed the largest response to calcium. This was positive and was greater at pH 6.5 than at pH 5.5. *Nardus stricta* appeared to be a true calcifuge and grew best at low calcium levels. When the pH was maintained at 4.0 the optimum calcium level was 20 ppm. At pH 5.5, 5 ppm calcium produced the best growth; there was a negligible response to calcium at pH 6.5. Growth of *Agrostis tenuis* was not affected by calcium level at low pH values of 4.0 and 5.5 but responded in a markedly positive way at the higher pH of 6.5. *Lolium perenne* grew best at pH 5.5 and the response to calcium level was similar to that of *Agrostis stolonifera*, being very great over the range 5–15 ppm and continuing up to 200 ppm.

Bradshaw and Snaydon (41) observed a highly significant interaction between edaphic ecotypes of *Festuca ovina* and calcium supply. Plants taken from an acid upland peat soil showed optimum growth at 20 ppm of calcium with a depression at 100 ppm whereas plants from a chalk soil showed a progressive increase in growth up to 100 ppm, where yields exceeded those of the peat strain. *Agrostis tenuis*, however, did not show any interaction on growth between origin of the population and effect of calcium supply, or soil type; in plants from populations from all soils the acid soil produced the better growth in contrast with the interaction between origin and soil medium observed with *Festuca*.

Adaptation to unfavorable conditions has been observed by Bradshaw (38) and Jowett (127, 128) in relation to the presence of high concen-

trations of lead, copper, nickel, and zinc in soils contaminated by lead
ore grinding or of mineral outcrops. This response or selection has
therefore occurred in a relatively short period of evolution. Plants taken
from nearby pastures, which were unable to tolerate lead, showed much
larger responses to calcium and phosphorus than the lead-tolerant
strain (128). *Agrostis tenuis* was reported to have shown evidence of
adaptation to excesses of other elements including copper and nickel.
The reasons for such adaptive differences in tolerance have not been
elucidated. Jowett (127) examined five strains of *Agrostis tenuis* and
three other *Agrostis* spp. and found remarkable differences in tolerance
to copper, nickel, lead, and zinc according to their origin. Strains that
were tolerant in terms of root growth to nickel were not so tolerant as
others to copper or zinc, and vice versa, and provided evidence of selection in response to edaphic conditions, especially when obtained from
areas where soil toxicities were known to occur.

Wilkins (276) tested the individuals of several populations of *Festuca
ovina* with respect to their tolerance to lead nitrate when measured by
its effects on root growth of clones obtained as tillers. It was found that
most individuals were highly sensitive to lead, but tillers from plants
growing on lead mine tips showed outstanding tolerance to lead nitrate.
It appeared that three groups, namely, tolerant, semitolerant, and nontolerant plants could be distinguished. Genetic crosses in all combinations showed the lead-tolerant strains to be dominant. Diploid and
tetraploid representatives of tolerant strains were found in some areas.
It was also found that some lead-tolerant strains failed to flourish in a
normal garden soil and the possibility that the metalliferrous habitat
was associated with some other requirement was recognized. Kruckeberg
(137) found tolerant and nontolerant strains of *Streptanthus glandulo-
sus* to serpentine soils. This species is almost endemic on serpentine
soils where excesses of magnesium, chromium, and nickel occur, but
Gilia capitata and *Achillea borealis* (*A. millefolium* var. *borealis*)
which occur in nonserpentine areas also could be resolved into tolerant
and intolerant strains.

The importance of calcium and magnesium in the structure of ribonucleoprotein particles and in chromosome integrity, noted in Chapter
2 in the sections on calcium and magnesium, would indicate a possible basis for nutritional selection in relation to the available calcium
and magnesium status of soils. Acid soils might, therefore, be associated
with higher rates of mutation. The observations reported by Durrant
and Tyson (69) of stable mutations in flax having persisted through
four generations, apparently induced experimentally by differential
phosphorus treatment (NPK and NK), might also reflect an effect

either of phosphorus supply, or of calcium in superphosphate on gene production, in terms of increased numbers of allelomorphic genes and associated production of deoxyribonucleic acid. Lead and other heavy metals, including chromium and nickel, which might be present in mine waste tips and which are also known to be concentrated in the ribonucleoprotein fractions, might, in an analogous way, affect the structure or reactivity of deoxyribonucleic acid and consequently of chromosomes and their genes.

REFERENCES FOR PARTS 1 AND 2

1. Aghulon, H. Recherches sur la présence et le rôle du bore chez les végétaux. Thesis, University of Paris, 1910. (Not seen.) Quoted by Miller (166).
2. Ahmed, S., and Evans, H. J. Effect of cobalt on the growth of soybeans in the absence of supplied nitrogen. *Biochem. Biophys. Research Communs.* 1, 271–275 (1959).
3. Ahmed, S., and Evans, H. J. Cobalt: a micronutrient element for the growth of soybean plants under symbiotic conditions. *Soil Sci.* 90, 205–210 (1960).
3a. Ahmed, S., and Evans, H. J. The essentiality of cobalt for soybean plants grown under symbiotic conditions. *Proc. Natl. Acad. Sci. U.S.* 47, 24–36 (1961).
4. Albrecht, W. A., and Smith, C. E. Soil acidity as calcium deficiency. *Intern. Soc. Soil Sci. Trans. Dublin 1952,* 1, 119–135 (1953).
5. Alles, M. B., The uptake of metallic ions by leaves of apple trees. II. The influence of certain anions on uptake from magnesium salts. *J. Hort. Sci.* 35, 127–135 (1960).
6. Allen, M. B., and Arnon, D. I. Studies on nitrogen fixing bacteria. II. The sodium requirement of *Anabaena cylindrica. Physiol Plantarum* 8, 653–660 (1955).
7. Anderson, M. S. History and development of soil testing. *Agr. and Food Chem.* 8, 84–87 (1960).
8. Anderson, M. S., and Noble, W. M. Comparison of various chemical quick tests on different soils. *U.S. Dept. Agr. Misc. Publ. No.* 259, 1937.
9. Arnon, D. I. Ammonium and nitrate nitrogen nutrition of barley at different seasons in relation to hydrogen ion concentration, manganese, copper and oxygen supply. *Soil Sci.* 44, 91–113 (1937).
10. Arnon, D. I. Microelements in culture solution experiments with higher plants. *Am. J. Botany* 25, 322–325 (1938).
11. Arnon, D. I. Criteria of essentiality of inorganic nutrients for plants with special reference to molybdenum. *Lotsya* 3, 31–38 (1950).
11a. Arnon, D. I. A memorandum regarding nomenclature. *Lotsya* 3, 40 (1950).
12. Arnon, D. I., and Hoagland, D. R. Crop production in artificial solutions and in soils with special reference to factors influencing yields and absorption of inorganic nutrients. *Soil Sci.* 50, 463–484 (1940).
13. Arnon, D. I., Ichioka, P. S., Wessel, G., Fujiwara, A., and Woolley, J. T. Molybdenum in relation to nitrogen metabolism. I. Assimilation of nitrogen by *Scenedesmus. Physiol. Plantarum* 8, 538–551 (1955).
14. Arnon, D. I., and Johnson, C. M. Influence of hydrogen ion on the growth of higher plants under controlled conditions. *Plant Physiol.* 17, 525–539 (1942).

15. Arnon, D. I., and Stout, P. R. The essentiality of certain elements in minute quantity for plants with special reference to copper. *Plant Physiol.* **14**, 371–375 (1939).
16. Arnon, D. I., and Stout, P. R. Molybdenum as an essential element for higher plants. *Plant Physiol.* **14**, 599–602 (1939).
17. Arnon, D. I., and Wessel, G. Vanadium as an essential element for green plants. *Nature* **172**, 1039–1041 (1953).
18. Barshad, I. Soil development. *In* "Chemistry of the Soil" (F. E. Bear, ed.), pp. 1–52. Reinhold, New York, 1955.
19. Bear, F. E., Prince, A. L., and Malcolm, J. L. Potassium needs of New Jersey soils. *New Jersey Agr. Expt. Sta. Bull. No.* **721** (1945).
20. Bennett, J. P. The treatment of lime induced chlorosis with iron salts. *Calif. Agr. Expt. Sta. Circ. No.* **321** (1931).
21. Bertrand, D. Distribution of vanadium in plants. *Compt. rend. acad. sci.* **212**, 1170–1172 (1941).
22. Bertrand, D. The gallium content of arable soils. *Compt. rend. acad. sci.* **237**, 578–580 (1953).
23. Bertrand, G., and Javillier, M. Influence du manganèse sur le développement de l'*Aspergillus niger*. *Compt. rend. acad. sci.* **152**, 225–228 (1911).
23a. Betrand, G., and Javillier, M. Influence combinée du manganèse et du zinc sur le développement et la composition minérale de l'*Aspergillus niger*. *Compt. rend. acad. sci.* **152**, 900–903 (1911).
24. Bertrand, G., and Javillier, M. Action du manganèse sur le développement de l'*Aspergillus niger*. *Bull. soc. chim. France* [IV] **11**, 212–221 (1912).
25. Bertrand, G., and Javillier, M. Action du manganèse sur le développement de l'*Aspergillus niger*. *Ann. inst. Pasteur* **26**, 241–249 (1912).
26. Black, C. A. "Soil-Plant Relationships." Chapman and Hall, London, 1957.
27. Black, C. A., and Goring, C. A. I. Organic phosphorus in soils. *In* "Soil and Fertilizer Phosphorus in Crop Nutrition" (W. H. Pierre and A. G. Norman, eds.), pp. 123–152. Academic Press, New York, 1953.
28. Bolle-Jones, E. W., and Mallikarjuneswara, V. R. A beneficial effect of cobalt on the growth of *Hevea brasiliensis*. *Nature* **179**, 738–739 (1957).
29. Bortels, H. Molybdän als Katalysator bei der biologischen Stickstoffbindung. *Arch. Mikrobiol.* **1**, 333–342 (1930).
30. Bortels, H. Weitere Untersuchungen über die Bedeutung von Molybdän, Vanadium, Wolfram und anderen Erdaschenstaffen für Stickstoffnerbindende und andere Mikroorganismen. *Zentr. Bakteriol. Parasitenk. Abt. II*, **95**, 193–218 (1936).
31. Bould, C. Seasonal changes in the major nutrients of black currant leaves. *J. Hort. Sci.* **30**, 188–196 (1955).
32. Bould, C. Manurial experiments with fruit. III. *Ann. Rept. Agr. Hort. Research Sta. Long Ashton Bristol*, pp. 84–92 (1959).
33. Bould, C., Bradfield, E. G., and Clarke, G. M. Leaf analysis as a guide to the nutrition of fruit crops. 1. General principles, sampling techniques and analytical methods. *J. Sci. Food Agr.* **11**, 229–242 (1960).
34. Bould, C., Nicholas, D. J. D., Tolhurst, J. A. H., and Potter, J. M. S. Zinc deficiency of fruit trees in Great Britain. *J. Hort. Sci.* **28**, 260–267 (1953).
35. Bould, C., and Tolhurst, J. Report on the use of foliage sprays for the control of magnesium deficiency in apples. *Ann. Rept. Agr. Hort. Research Sta.* Long Ashton Bristol, pp. 51–58 (1948).

36. Boussingault, J. B. "Recherches sur la végétation." Agronomie, chimie agricole et physiologie, Mallet-Bachelier, 3rd ed. Paris, 1886–1891.

37. Boynton, D. Nutrition by foliar application. *Ann. Rev. Plant Physiol.* **5**, 31–54 (1954).

38. Bradshaw, A. D. Populations of *Agrostis tenuis* resistant to lead and zinc poisoning. *Nature* **169**, 1098 (1952).

39. Bradshaw, A. D., Lodge, R. W., Jowett, D., and Chadwick, M. J. Experimental investigations into the mineral nutrition of several grass species. I. Calcium level. *J. Ecol.* **46**, 749–757 (1958).

40. Bradshaw, A. D., Lodge, R. W., Jowett, D., and Chadwick, M. J. Experimental investigations into the mineral nutrition of several grass species. Part II. pH and calcium level. *J. Ecol.* **48**, 143–150 (1960).

41. Bradshaw, A. D., and Snaydon, R. W. Population differentiation within plant species in response to soil factors. *Nature* **183**, 129–130 (1959).

42. Bray, R. H. Soil plant relations: I. The quantitative relation of exchangeable potassium to crop yields and to crop response to potash additions. *Soil Sci.* **58**, 305–324 (1944)

43. Bray, R. H. Correlation of soil tests with crop response to added fertilizers and with fertilizer. *In* "Diagnostic Techniques for Soils and Crops" (H. B. Kitchen, ed.), pp. 53–86. American Potash Institute, Washington, D.C., 1948.

44. Bremner, J. M. Studies on soil organic matter. I. The chemical nature of soil organic nitrogen. *J. Agr. Sci.* **39**, 183–193 (1949).

45. Bremner, J. M. Determination of fixed ammonium in soil. *J. Agr. Sci.* **52**, 147–160 (1959).

46. Brownell, P. F., and Wood, J. G. Sodium as an essential micronutrient element for *Atriplex vesicaria*, Heward. *Nature* **179**, 635–636 (1957).

47. Broyer, T. C., Carlton, A. B., Johnson, C. M., and Stout, P. R. Chlorine, a micronutrient element for higher plants. *Plant Physiol.* **29**, 526–532 (1954).

48. Bukovac, M. J., and Wittwer, S. H. Absorption and mobility of foliar applied minerals. *Plant Physiol.* **32**, 428–435 (1957).

49. Burd, J. S. Water extraction of soils as criteria of their crop producing power. *J. Agr. Research* **12**, 297–309 (1918).

50. Burd, J. S., and Martin, J. C. Water displacement of soils and the soil solution. *J. Agr. Sci.* **13**, 265–295 (1923).

51. Burd, J. S., and Martin, J. C. Secular and seasonal changes in the soil solution. *Soil Sci.* **18**, 151–167 (1924).

52. Burk, D. Azotase and nitrogenase in *Azotobacter. Ergebn. Enzymforsch.* **3**, 23–57 (1934).

53. Burk, D., and Lineweaver, H. The influence of calcium and strontium on the catalysis of nitrogen fixation by *Azotobacter. Arch. Mikrobiol.* **2**, 155–186 (1931).

54. Cameron, F. K. "The Soil Solution." Chemical Publ. Co., Easton, Pennsylvania, 1911.

55. Chaminade, R., and Drouineau, G. Researches on the chemical mechanics of exchangeable cations. *Ann. Agron.* **6**, 677–690 (1936).

56. Clayton, E. E. Investigations of cauliflower diseases on Long Island. *N. Y. State Agr. Expt. Sta. (Geneva, N.Y.) Bull. No.* 506 (1924).

57. Cochran, W. G., and Cox, G. M. "Experimental Designs." Wiley, New York, 1958.

58. Coleman, N. T., Williams, D. E., Nielsen, T. R., and Jenny, H. On the validity

of interpretation of potentiometrically measured soil pH. *Soil Sci. Soc. Am. Proc.* **15**, 106–110 (1950).

59. Colwell, W. E., and Cummings, R. W. Chemical and biological studies on aqueous solutions of boric acid and of calcium, sodium and potassium metaborates. *Soil. Sci.* **57**, 37–49 (1944).

60. Cook, J. A., and Boynton, D. Some factors affecting the absorption of urea by McIntosh apple leaves. *Proc. Am. Soc. Hort. Sci.* **59**, 82–90 (1952).

61. Crowther, E. M. The technique of modern field experiments. *J. Roy. Agr. Soc.* **97**, 1–28 (1936).

62. Dalbro, S. Leaching of apple foliage by rain. *Proc. 14th Intern. Hort. Congr.* **1**, 770–778 (1955).

63. Davies, E. B. Factors affecting molybdenum availability in soils. *Soil Sci.* **81**, 209–221 (1956).

64. Dean, L. A., and Fried, M. Soil-plant relationships in the phosphorus nutrition of plants. *In* "Soil and Fertilizer Phosphorus in Crop Nutrition" (W. H. Pierre and A. G. Norman, eds.), pp. 43–58. Academic Press, New York, 1953.

65. Delwiche, C. C., Johnson, C. M., and Reisenauer, H. M. Influence of cobalt on nitrogen fixation of Medicago. *Plant Physiol.* **36**, 73–78 (1961).

66. de Saussure, Th. "Recherches chimiques sur la végétation," Nyon, Paris, 1804.

66a. Dorph-Petersen, K., and Steenbjerg, F. Investigations of the effect of fertilizer containing sodium. *Plant and Soil* **2**, 283–300 (1950).

67. Duff, R. B., and Webley, D. W. 2-Ketogluconic acid as a natural chelator. *Chem. & Ind.* (London), pp. 1376–1377 (1959).

68. Duhamel du Monceau, H. L. "La physique des arbres." Guerin & Delatour, Paris (1758).

69. Durrant, A., and Tyson, H. Conditioned lines of flax. *Nature* **185**, 60 (1960).

70. Dyer, B. On the analytical determination of probable available mineral plant food in soils. *J. Chem. Soc.* (*London*) **65**, 115–167 (1894).

71. Elgababy, H. M., and Wiklander, L. Effect of exchange capacity of clay mineral and acidoid content of plant on uptake of sodium and calcium by excised barley and pea roots. *Soil Sci.* **67**, 419–424 (1949).

72. Ferguson, W. S., Lewis, A. H., and Watson, S. J. Action of molybdenum in nutrition of milking cattle. *Nature* **141**, 553 (1938).

73. Fisher, E. G., and Walker, D. R. The apparent absorption of phosphorus and magnesium from sprays applied to the lower surface of McIntosh apple leaves. *Proc. Am. Soc. Hort. Sci.* **65**, 17–24 (1955).

74. Fisher, R. A. "Statistical Methods for Research Workers," 7th ed. Oliver and Boyd, London, 1938.

75. Floyd, B. F. Leaf spotting of citrus. *Florida Agr. Expt. Sta. Ann. Rept. No.* **91** (1908).

76. Floyd, B. F. Yellow spotting of citrus. *Florida Agr. Expt. Sta. Ann. Rept. No.* **86** (1909).

77. Frear, W., and Erb, E. S. Condition of fertilizer potash residues in Hagerstown silt loam soil. *J. Agr. Research* **15**, 59–81 (1918).

78. Fried, M., and Dean, L. A. A concept concerning the measurement of available soil nutrients. *Soil Sci.* **73**, 263–271 (1952).

79. Fried, M., and Shapiro, R. E. Soil-plant relations in phosphorus uptake. *Soil Sci.* **90**, 69–76 (1960).

80. Fussell, G. E. The technique of early field experiments. *J. Roy. Agr. Soc. Engl.* **96**, 78–88 (1935).

81. Garner, W., McMurtrey, J., Bacon, C., and Moss, E. G. Sand drown, a chlorosis of tobacco due to magnesium deficiency, and the relation of sulphates and chlorides to the disease. *J. Agr. Research* **23**, 27–40 (1923).
82. Gilbert, B. E., and Hardin, L. J. The current mineral nutrient content of the plant solution as a possible means of chemical control of optimum fertilization. *J. Agr. Research* **35**, 185–192 (1927).
83. Goldschmidt, V. M. The principles of distribution of chemical elements in minerals and rocks. *J. Chem. Soc. Part 1*, 655–673 (1937).
84. Goldschmidt, V. M. The geochemical background of minor-element distribution. *Soil Sci.* **60**, 1–7 (1945).
85. Goldschmidt, V. M. "Geochemistry" (A. Muir, ed.). Oxford Univ. Press, London and New York, 1954.
86. Goodall, D. W., and Gregory, F. G. "Chemical Composition of Plants as an Index of their Nutritional Status." *Imp. Bur. Hort. Plantation Crops Tech. Commun. No.* **17**. Imperial Agricultural Bureaux, Aberystwyth, Wales, 1947.
87. Grahame, D. C., and Seaborg, G. T. The distribution of minute amounts of material between liquid phases. *J. Am. Chem. Soc.* **60**, 2524–2528 (1938).
88. Greaves, J. E. The arsenic content of soils. *Soil Sci.* **38**, 355–362 (1934).
89. Grim, R. "Clay Mineralogy." McGraw-Hill, New York, 1953.
90. Gris, E. Nouvelles expériences sur l'action de composés ferrugineux solubles appliqué à la végétation et spécialement en traitement de la chlorose et de la débilité des plantes. *Compt. rend. acad. sci.* **19**, 1118–1119 (1844).
91. Gustafson, F. G. Absorption of Co^{60} by leaves of young plants and its translocation through the plant. *Am. J. Botany* **43**, 157–160 (1956).
92. Hall, A. D. The analysis of the soil by means of the plant. *J. Agr. Sci.* **1**, 65–88 (1905).
93. Hallsworth, E. G., Wilson, S. B., and Greenwood, E. A. N. Copper and cobalt in nitrogen fixation. *Nature* **187**, 79–80 (1959).
94. Harding, R. B. Exchangeable cations in soils of California orange orchards in relation to yield and size of fruit and leaf composition. *Soil Sci.* **77**, 119–127 (1954).
95. Hellriegel, H., and Wilfarth, H. Vegetationsversuche über den Kalibedarf einiger Pflanzen. *Arb. deut. Landw Ges.* **34** (1898). Cited by Dorph-Petersen and Steenbjerg (66a).
96. Hemwall, J. B. The fixation of phosphorus in soils. *Advances in Agron.* **9**, 95–112 (1957).
97. Hewitt, E. J. The resolution of the factors in soil acidity. Some effects of manganese toxicity. *Ann. Rept. Agr. Hort. Research Sta. Long Ashton Bristol, 1945*, 50–61 (1946).
98. Hewitt, E. J. The resolution of the factors in soil acidity. The relative effects of aluminum and manganese toxicities on farm and market garden crops. *Ann. Rept. Agr. Hort. Research Sta. Long Ashton Bristol, 1946*, 82–96 (1947); ibid. *1947*, 58–65 (1948).
99. Hewitt, E. J. "Sand and water culture methods used in the study of plant nutrition." *Commonw. Bur. Hort. Plantation Crops (Gt. Brit.) Tech. Commun. No.* 22 (1952).
100. Hewitt, E. J. A biological approach to the problem of soil acidity. *Intern. Soc. Soil Sci. Trans. Dublin 1952*, **1**, 119–135 (1953).
101. Hewitt, E. J. Symptoms of molybdenum deficiency in plants. *Soil Sci.* **81**, 159–171 (1956).

102. Hewitt, E. J. The metabolism of micronutrient elements in plants. *Biol. Revs. Cambridge Phil. Soc.* **74**, 333–377 (1959).
103. Hewitt, E. J., and Hallas, D. G. The use of *Aspergillus niger* (Van Tiegh.) M strain as a test organism in the study of molybdenum as a plant nutrient. *Plant and Soil* **3**, 366–408 (1951).
104. Hewitt, E. J. Bolle-Jones, E. W., and Miles P. The production of copper, zinc and molybdenum deficiencies in crop plants with special reference to some effects of water supply and seed reserves. *Plant and Soil* **5**, 205–222 (1954).
105. Hewitt, E. J., and Jones, E. W. The production of molybdenum deficiency in plants in sand culture with special reference to tomato and *Brassica* crops. *J. Hort. Sci.* **23**, 254–262 (1947).
106. Hilgard, E. W. "Soils." Macmillan, London, 1912.
107. Hissink, D. J. *In* "Base Exchange in Soils," pp. 551–566. The Faraday Society, London, 1924.
108. Hoagland, D. R. Relation of concentration and reaction of the nutrient medium to the growth and absorption of the plant. *J. Agr. Research*, **18**, 73–117 (1919).
109. Hoagland, D. R. Physiological aspects of soil solution investigations. *Hilgardia* **1**, 227–257 (1925).
110. Hoagland, D. R., and Snyder, W. C. Nutrition of strawberry plant under controlled conditions. (a) Effects of deficiencies of boron and certain other elements, (b) susceptibility to injury from sodium salts. *Proc. Am. Soc. Hort. Sci.* **30**, 288–294 (1933).
111. Hoffer, G. N. Testing corn stalks chemically to aid in determining their plant food needs. *Bull. Indiana Agr. Expt. Sta.* **298**, 1–31 (1926).
112. Holme-Hansen, O., Gerloff, G. C., and Skoog, F. Cobalt as an essential element for blue-green algae. *Physiol. Plantarum* **7**, 665–675 (1954).
113. Hutner, S. H., Provasoli, L., Schatz, A., and Haskins, C. P. Some approaches to the study of the role of metals in the metabolism of microorganisms. *Proc. Am. Phil. Soc.* **94**, 152–170 (1950).
114. Ichioka, P. S., and Arnon, D. I. Molybdenum in relation to nitrogen metabolism. II. Assimilation of ammonium and urea without molybdenum by *Scenedesmus*. *Physiol. Plantarum* **8**, 552–560 (1955).
115. Jackson, M. L. "Soil Chemical Analysis." Constable, London, 1958.
116. Jacob, A. "Magnesium, the Fifth Major Plant Nutrient." Staples Press, London, 1958.
117. Jacobsen, L. Maintenance of iron supply in nutrient solutions by a single addition of ferric potassium ethylenediamine-tetra acetate. *Plant Physiol.* **26**, 411–413 (1951).
118. Jarusov, S. S. On the mobility of exchangeable cations in the soil. *Soil Sci.* **43**, 285–303 (1937).
119. Javillier, M. Sur l'influence favorable de petites doses de zinc sur la végétation du *Sterigmatocystis nigra* (Van Tiegh). *Compt. rend. acad. sci.* **145**, 1212–1215 (1907).
120. Jenny, H. "Factors of Soil Formation." McGraw-Hill, New York, 1941.
121. Jenny, H. Contact phenomena between adsorbents and their significance in plant nutrition. *In* "Mineral Nutrition of Plants" (E. Truog, ed.), pp. 107–132. Univ. of Wisconsin Press, Madison, 1951.
122. Jenny, H., and Overstreet, R. Cation interchange between plant roots and soil colloids. *Soil Sci.* **47**, 257–272 (1939).
123. Jensen, H. L., and Spencer, D. The influence of molybdenum and vanadium on

nitrogen fixation by *Clostridium butyricum* and related organisms. *Proc. Linnean Soc. N. S. Wales* **72**, 73–86 (1947).

124. Joffe, J. A. "Pedology." Rutgers Univ. Press, New Brunswick, New Jersey, 1936.

125. Johnson, C. M., Stout, P. R., Broyer, T. C., and Carlton, A. B. Comparative chlorine requirements of different plant species. *Plant and Soil* **8**, 337–353 (1957).

126. Johnson, D. A., and Woodman, R. M. Plant growth with nutrient solutions. I. A brief review of existing work. *J. Agr. Sci.* **36**, 69–79 (1946).

127. Jowett, D. Populations of *Agrostis* spp. tolerant of heavy metals. *Nature* **182**, 816–817 (1958).

128. Jowett, D. Adaptation of a lead-tolerant population of *Agrostis tenuis* to low soil fertility. *Nature* **184**, 43 (1959).

129. Kardos, L. T. Soil fixation of plant nutrients. *In* "Chemistry of the Soil" (F. E. Bear, ed.), pp. 177–199. Reinhold, New York, 1955.

130. Kelley, W. P. "Cation Exchange in Soils." Reinhold, New York, 1948.

131. Kelley, W. P., Dore, W. H., and Brown, S. M. The nature of the base exchange material of bentonite soils and zeolites, as revealed by chemical investigations and X-ray analysis. *Soil Sci.* **31**, 25–55 (1931).

132. Knop, W. Über die Ernährung der Pflanzen durch wasserige Lösungen bei Auschluss des Bodens. *Landwirtsch. Vers.-Sta.* **2**, 65–99 (1860).

133. Knop, W. Quantitative analytische Arbeiten über den Ernährungsprocess der Pflanzen. *Landwirtsch. Vers.-Sta.* **3**, 295–324 (1861).

134. Knop, W. Quantitative Untersuchung über die Ernährungsprocess der Pflanzen. *Landwirtsch. Vers.-Sta.* **7**, 93–107 (1865).

135. Koontz, H., and Biddulph, O. Factors affecting absorption and translocation of foliar applied phosphorus. *Plant Physiol.* **32**, 463–470 (1957).

136. Krantz, B. A., Nelson, W. L., and Burkhart, L. F. Plant tissue tests as a tool in agronomic research. *In* "Diagnostic Techniques for Soils and Crops" (H. B. Kitchen, ed.), pp. 137–155. American Potash Institute, Washington, D.C., 1948.

137. Kruckeberg, A. R. Intra specific variability in the response of certain native plant species to serpentine soil. *Am. J. Botany* **38**, 408–419 (1951).

138. Kurtz, L. T. Inorganic phosphorus in, acid and neutral soils. *In* "Soil and Fertilizer Phosphorus in Crop Nutrition" (W. H. Pierre and A. G. Norman, eds.), pp. 59–88. Academic Press, New York, 1953.

139. Lagatu, H., and Maume, L. Évolution remarquablement régulière de certains rapports physiologiques (chaux, magnésie, potasse) dans les feuilles de la vigne bien alimentée. *Compt. rend. acad. sci.* **179**, 782–785 (1924).

140. Larson, S. The use of ^{32}P in studies on the uptake of phosphorus by plants. *Plant and Soil* **4**, 1–10 (1952).

141. Laties, G. G. Active transport of salt into plant tissue. *Ann. Rev. Plant Physiol.* **10**, 87–112 (1959).

142. Lawes, J. B., Gilbert, J. H., and Pugh, E. On the sources of the nitrogen of vegetation, with special reference to the question whether plants assimilate free or uncombined nitrogen. *Phil. Trans. Roy. Soc. London* **151**, 431–577 (1861).

143. Lawton, K. Chemical composition of soils. *In* "Chemistry of the Soil" (F. E. Bear, ed.), pp. 53–84. Reinhold, New York, 1955.

144. Leeper, G. W. The forms and reactions of manganese in the soil. *Soil Sci.* **63**, 79–94 (1947).

145. Lewis, D. A note on the absorption of solutes by leaves. *J. Pomol. Hort. Sci.* **14**, 391 (1936).
146. Liebig, J. "Organic Chemistry in its Applications to Agriculture and Physiology" (L. Playfair, ed.). Taylor and Walton, London, 1840.
147. Lipman, C. B. The importance of silicon, aluminium and chlorine for higher plants. *Soil Sci.* **45**, 189–198 (1938).
148. Lipman, C. B., and McKinney, G. Proof of the essential nature of copper for higher green plants. *Plant Physiol.* **6**, 593–599 (1931).
149. Long, W. G., Sweet, D. V., and Tukey, H. B. Loss of nutrients from plant foliage by leaching as indicated by radioisotopes. *Science* **123**, 1039–1040 (1956).
150. Lundegårdh, H. "Leaf Analysis." Hilger and Watts, London, 1951.
151. McBeth, I. G. Fixation of ammonia in soils. *J. Agr. Research* **9**, 141–155 (1917).
152. McHargue, J. S. The role of manganese in plants. *J. Am. Chem. Soc.* **44**, 1592–1598 (1922).
153. McHargue, J. S. Effect of different concentrations of manganese sulphate on the growth of plants in acid and neutral soils, and the necessity of manganese as a plant nutrient. *J. Agr. Research* **24**, 781–794 (1923).
154. McMurtrey, J. E. Visual symptoms of malnutrition in crops. *In* "Diagnostic Techniques for Soils and Crops" (H. B. Kitchen, ed.), pp. 231–289. American Potash Institute, Washington, D.C., 1948.
155. Macy, P. The quantitative mineral nutrient requirement of plants. *Plant Physiol.* **11**, 749–764 (1936).
156. Mann, C. E. T., and Wallace, T. The effects of leaching with cold water on the foliage of the apple. *J. Pomol. Hort. Sci.* **4**, 146–161 (1925).
157. Marshall, C. E. The activities of cations held by soil colloids and the chemical environment of plant roots. *In* "Mineral Nutrition of Plants" (E. Truog, ed.), pp. 57–77. Univ. of Wisconsin Press, Madison, 1951.
158. Maskell, E. J., Evans, H., and Murray, D. B. Report of Cocoa Research 1945–1951, pp. 53–64. *Imp. Coll. Trop. Agr. Trinidad* (1953).
159. Mazé, P. Recherche de physiologie végétale. Influence respective des éléments de la solution minerale sur le développement du maïs. *Ann. inst. Pasteur* **28**, 21–68 (1914).
160. Mazé, P. Détermination des éléments minéraux rares nécessaires aux développement du maïs. *Compt. rend. acad. sci.* **160**, 211–214 (1915).
161. Mazé, P. Recherche d'une solution purement minérale capable d'assurer l'évolution complète du maïs cultivé a l'abri des microbes. *Ann. inst. Pasteur* **33**, 139–173 (1919).
162. Mehlich, A., and Coleman, N. T. Type of soil colloid and the mineral nutrition of plants. *Advances in Agron.* **4**, 67–99 (1952).
163. Mehlich, A., and Drake, M. Soil chemistry and plant nutrition. *In* "Chemistry of the Soil" (F. E. Bear, ed.), pp. 286–327. Reinhold, New York, 1955.
164. Mercer, W. B., and Hall, A. D. The experimental error of field trials. *J. Agr. Sci.* **4**, 107–132, (1911).
165. Millar, C. E. "Soil Fertility." Chapman and Hall, London, 1955.
166. Miller, E. C. "Plant Physiology," 2nd ed. McGraw-Hill, New York, 1938.
167. Mitchell, H. L. Growth and nutrition of *Pinus strobus* seedlings in cultures with varying N, P, K and Ca. *Black Rock Forest Bull. No. 9* (1939).
168. Mitchell, R. L. Trace Elements. *In* "Chemistry of the Soil" (F. E. Bear, ed.), pp. 253–285. Reinhold, New York, 1955.
169. Morgan, M. F. Chemical soil diagnosis by the universal soil testing system. *Conn. Agr. Expt. Sta. Bull. No. 450*, 1941.

170. Morris, H. D. The soluble manganese content of acid soils and its relation to the growth and manganese content of sweet clover and lespedeza. *Soil Sci. Soc. Am. Proc.* **13**, 362–371 (1949).

171. Munns, D. N., and Johnson, C. M. Removal of heavy metal and halide contamination from macronutrient salts. *Plant Physiol.* **35**, 978–981 (1960).

172. Nelson, J. L., and Melsted, S. W. The chemistry of zinc added to soils and clays. *Soil Sci. Soc. Am. Proc.* **19**, 439–443 (1955).

173. Nicholas, D. J. D. The application of rapid chemical tests to the diagnosis of mineral deficiencies in horticultural crops. 1. Crops grown on a manurial trial. *J. Hort. Sci.* **24**, 72–105 (1948).

174. Nicholas, D. J. D. The use of fungi for determining trace metals in biological materials. *Analyst* **77**, 629–642 (1952).

175. Nicholas, D. J. D. An appraisal of the use of chemical tissue tests for determining the mineral status of crop plants. *In* "Plant Analysis and Fertilizer Problems" (P. Prevot., ed.), pp. 119–139. Institut de Recherches pour les Huiles et Oléagineux (I.R.H.O.) I.R.H.O., Paris, 1956.

176. Nicholas, D. J. D., and Fielding, A. H. The use of *Aspergillus niger* (M) for the determination of magnesium, zinc, copper and molybdenum in soils and crop plants. *J. Hort. Sci.* **26**, 125–147 (1951).

177. Nobbe, F., and Siegert, T. Über das Chlor als spezifischer Nährstoff der Buchweizenpflanze. *Landwirtsch. Vers.-Sta.* **4**, 318–340 (1862). Cited by Stiles (236).

178. Nobbe, F., and Siegert, T. Über das Chlor als spezifischer Nährstoff der Buchweizenpflanze. *Landwirtsch. Vers.-Sta.* **5**, 116–136 (1863). Cited by Stiles (236).

179. Oland, K., and Opland, T. B. Uptake of magnesium by apple leaves. *Physiol. Plantarum* **9**, 401–411 (1956).

180. Olsen, R. A., and Peech, M. The significance of the suspension effect in the uptake of cations by plants from soil-water systems. *Soil Sci. Soc. Am. Proc.* **24**, 257–260 (1960).

181. Page, J. B., and Baver, L. D. Ionic size in relation to fixation of cations by colloidal clay. *Soil Sci. Soc. Am. Proc.* **4**, 150–155 (1940).

182. Parker, F. W. Methods of studying the concentration and composition of the soil solution. *Soil Sci.* **2**, 209–232 (1921).

183. Peech, M., and English, L. Rapid microchemical soil tests. *Soil Sci.* **57**, 167–195 (1944).

184. Pfeffer, W. "Die Vegetationsversuche." Berlin, 1918.

185. Piper, C. S. Molybdenum as an essential element for plant growth. *J. Australian Inst. Agr. Sci.* **6**, 112–114 (1940).

186. Piper, C. S. Marsh spot of peas. A manganese deficiency disease. *J. Agr. Sci.* **31**, 448–453 (1941).

187. Piper, C. S. Investigations on copper deficiency in plants. *J. Agr. Sci.* **32**, 143–178 (1942).

188. Plant, W. The control of "Whiptail" in broccoli and cauliflower. *J. Hort. Sci.* **26**, 109–117 (1951).

189. Plant, W. An analysis of the acid soil complex by the use of indicator plants. *Plant and Soil* **5**, 54–66 (1953).

190. Plant, W. The effects of molybdenum deficiency and mineral toxicities on crops in acid soils. *J. Hort. Sci.* **31**, 163–176 (1956).

191. Prince, A. L., Zimmerman, M., and Bear, F. E. The magnesium-supplying powers of 20 New Jersey soils. *Soil Sci.* **63**, 69–78 (1947).

192. Quastel, J. H. Lecture on soil metabolism. *Roy. Inst. Chem. (London) Lectures, Monographs, Reports,* 1946.

193. Raleigh, G. J. Evidence for the essentiality of silicon for the growth of the beet plant. *Plant Physiol.* **14**, 823–828 (1939).

194. Raulin, J. Études chimiques sur la végétation des Mucedinées particulièrement de l'*Ascophora nigrans*. *Compt. rend, acad. sci.* **57**, 228–230 (1863).

195. Reed, H. S. "A Short History of the Plant Sciences." Chronica Botanica, Waltham, Massachusetts, 1942.

196. Reisenauer, H. M. Cobalt in nitrogen fixation by a legume. *Nature* **186**, 375–376 (1960).

197. Reuther, W., and Smith, P. F. Effects of high copper content of sandy soil on growth of citrus seedlings. *Soil Sci.* **75**, 219–224 (1953).

198. Reuther, W., and Smith, P. F. Leaf analysis in citrus. *In* "Fruit Nutrition" (N. F. Childers, ed.), pp. 257–294. Somerset Press, Somerville, New Jersey, 1954.

199. Richards, F. J. Physiological studies in plant nutrition. XI. The effects on growth of rubidium with low potassium supply and identification of the effect by other nutrients. Part 1. The effect on total dry weight. *Ann. Botany (London)* [N.S.] **5**, 263–296 (1941).

200. Richards, F. J. Physiological studies in plant nutrition. XI. The effects on growth of rubidium with low potassium supply and identification of the effect by other nutrients. Part 2. The effect on dry weight distribution, net assimilation rate, tillering, fertility, etc. *Ann. Botany (London)* **8**, 323–356 (1944).

201. Richards, F. J., and Berner, E. Physiological studies in plant nutrition. XVII. A general survey of the free amino acids of barley as affected by mineral nutrition with special reference to potassium supply. *Ann. Botany (London)* **18**, 15–33 (1954).

202. Roach, W. A., and Barclay, C. Nickel and multiple trace elements in agricultural crops. *Nature* **157**, 696–697 (1946).

203. Roberts, E. A., Southwick, M. D., and Palmiter, D. H. A microchemical examination of McIntosh apple leaves showing relationship of cell wall constituents to penetration of spray solutions. *Plant Physiol.* **23**, 557–559 (1948).

204. Robinson, G. W. "Soils: Their Origin and Constitution," 3rd ed. Thomas Murby, London, 1949.

205. Russell, E. J. (revised by Russell, E. W.). "Soil Conditions and Plant Growth," 8th ed. Longmans, Green, London, 1950.

206. Sachs, J., von. Berichte über die physiologische Thätigheit an der Versuchsstation in Tharandt. IV. Vegetations-versuche mit Ausschluss des Bodens über die Nährstoffe und sonstigen Ernährungsbedingungen von Mais, Bohner und anderen Pflanzen. *Landwirtsch. Vers.-Sta.* **2**, 219–268 (1860).

207. Salm-Horstmar, F. Zu. Versuche über die nothwendigen Aschenbestandtheile einer Pflanzen-species. *J. prakt. Chem.* **46**, 193–211 (1849).

208. Salm-Horstmar, F. Zu. Recherches sur la nutrition de l'avoine, particulièrement en ce qui concerne les matières qui sont nécessaires à cette nutrition. *Ann. chim. et phys.* **33**, 461–509 (1851).

209. Samuel, G., and Piper, C. S. Grey speck (manganese deficiency) disease of oats. *J. Dept. Agr. S. Australia* **31**, 696–700 (1928).

210. Samuel, G., and Piper, C. S. Manganese as an essential element for plants. *Ann. Appl. Biol.* **16**, 493–524 (1929).

211. Schuffelen, A. C. The absorption of potassium by the plant. *In* "Potassium Symposium," pp. 169–181. International Potash Institute, Bern, 1954.

212. Shapiro, R. E., and Fried, M. Relative release and retentiveness of soil phosphates. *Am. Soc. Soil Sci. Proc.* **23**, 195–198 (1959).

213. Shear, C. B., Crane, H. L., and Myers, A. T. Nutrient element balance: a fundamental concept in plant nutrition. *Proc. Am. Soc. Hort. Sci.* **47**, 239–248 (1946).

214. Shive, J. W. A study of physiological balance in nutrient media. *Physiol. Researches* **1**, 327–399 (1915).

215. Shive, J. W. A three-salt nutrient for plants. *Am. J. Botany* **2**, 157–160 (1915).

216. Shive, J. W. Sketch of the development of the water culture method of growing plants. *Sci. Monthly* **51**, 233 (1940).

217. Shorb, M. S. Activity of vitamin B_{12} for the growth of *Lactobacillus lactis*. *Science* **107**, 397–398 (1948).

218. Small, J. "pH and plants." Ballière, Tyndall and Cox, London, 1946.

219. Sommer, A. L. Studies concerning the essential nature of aluminum and silicon for plant growth. *Univ. Calif. (Berkeley) Publs. Agr. Sci.* **5**, 57–81 (1926).

220. Sommer, A. L. Further evidence of the essential nature of zinc for the growth of higher green plants. *Plant Physiol.* **3**, 217–221 (1928).

221. Sommer, A. L. Copper as an essential element for plant growth. *Plant Physiol.* **6**, 339–345 (1931).

222. Sommer, A. L., and Lipman, C. B. Evidence of the indispensable nature of zinc and boron for higher green plants. *Plant Physiol.* **1**, 231–249 (1926).

223. Sprengel, C. "Die Lehre vom Dunger." Leipzig, 1839. Cited by Shive (216).

224. Stanford, G., and Hanway, J. Predicting nitrogen fertilizer needs of Iowa soils: II. A simplified technique for determining nitrate production of soils. *Am. Soc. Soil Sci. Proc.* **19**, 74–77 (1955).

225. Steadman, F. Raw materials and manufacturing processes. *In* "Polythene, the Technology and Uses of Ethylene Polymers" (A. Renfrew, and P. Morgan, eds.), Chapter 2, pp. 11–19. Iliffe, London, 1957.

226. Steenbjerg, F. Manuring, plant production, and the chemical composition of plants. *Plant and Soil* **5**, 226–242 (1954).

227. Steinberg, R. A. A study of some factors in the chemical stimulation of the growth of *Aspergillus niger*. *Am. J. Botany* **6**, 330–336 (1919).

228. Steinberg, R. A. Nutrient solution purification for the removal of heavy metals in deficiency investigations with *Aspergillus niger*. *J. Agr. Research* **51**, 413–424 (1935).

229. Steinberg, R. A. Mineral requirements of *Lemna minor*. *Plant Physiol.* **21**, 42–48 (1946).

230. Steward, F. C., Crane, F., Millar, K., Zacharias, R. M., Rabson, R., and Margolis, D. Nutritional and environmental effects on the nitrogen metabolism of plants. *Symposia Soc. Exptl. Biol. No.* **13**, 148–176 (1959).

231. Steward, F. C., and Sutcliffe, J. F. Plants in relation to inorganic salts. *In* "Plant Physiology" (F. C. Steward, ed.), Vol. II, pp. 253–478. Academic Press New York, 1959.

232. Stewart, I., and Leonard, C. D. Molybdenum deficiency in Florida citrus. *Nature* **170**, 714–715 (1952).

233. Stewart, I., and Leonard, C. D. Correction of molybdenum deficiency in Florida citrus. *Proc. Am. Soc. Hort. Sci.* **62**, 111–115 (1953).

234. Stewart, I., and Leonard, C. D. Chelated metals for growing plants. *In* "Fruit Nutrition" (N. F. Childers, ed.), pp. 775–809. Somerset Press, Somerville, New Jersey, 1954.

235. Stiles, W. "Trace Elements in Plants and Animals," 1st ed. Cambridge Univ. Press, London and New York, 1946.

236. Stiles, W. Essential micro-(trace)elements. *In* "Handbuch der Pflanzen-physiologie—Encyclopedia of Plant Physiology" (W. Ruhland, ed.), Vol. 4, pp. 558–598. Springer, Berlin, 1958.

237. Stoklasa, J. "Über die Verbreitung des Aluminiums in der Natur und seine Bedeutung beim Bau- und Betriebsstoffwechsel der Pflanzen." Fischer, Jena, 1922.

238. Storey, H. H., and Leach, R. A sulphur deficiency disease of the tea bush. *Ann. Appl. Biol.* **20**, 23–56 (1933).

239. Stout, P. R., and Arnon, D. I. Experimental methods for the study of the role of copper, manganese and zinc in the nutrition of higher plants. *Am. J. Botany* **26**, 144–149 (1939).

240. Stout, P. R., and Meagher, W. R. Studies of the molybdenum nutrition of plants with radioactive molybdenum. *Science* **108**, 471–473 (1948).

241. Swaine, D. J. The trace element content of soils. *Commonwealth Bur. Soil Sci. (Gt. Brit.) Tech. Common. No. 48* (1955).

242. Swan, H. S. D. The mineral nutrition of Canadian pulp wood species. I. The influence of nitrogen, phosphorus, potassium and magnesium deficiencies on the growth and development of white spruce, black spruce, jack pine and western hemlock seedlings grown in a controlled environment. Woodlands Research Index No. 116. *Pulp and Paper Research Inst. Tech. Rept.* (Montreal) **168**, (1960).

243. Tchan, Y. T. Study of soil algae. III. Bioassay of soil fertility by algae. *Plant and Soil* **10**, 220–232 (1959).

244. Teubner, F. G., Wittwer, S. H., Long, W. G., and Tukey, H. B. Some factors affecting absorption and transport of foliar-applied nutrients as revealed by radioactive isotopes. *Mich. State Univ. Agr. Expt. Sta. Quart. Bull.* **39**, 398–415 (1957).

245. Thomas, W. Foliar diagnosis: principles and practice. *Plant Physiol.* **12**, 571–599 (1937).

246. Thornton, S. F., Conner, S. D., and Fraser, R. R. The use of rapid chemical tests on soils and plants as aids in determining fertilizer needs. *Purdue Univ. Agr. Expt. Sta. Circ. No.* **204** (1939) (revised).

247. Toth, S. J. Colloid chemistry of soils. *In* "Chemistry of the Soil" (F. E. Bear, ed.), pp. 85–106. Reinhold, New York, 1955.

248. Tottingham, W. E. A quantitative chemical and physiological study of nutrient solutions for plant cultures. *Physiol. Researches* **1**, 133–245 (1914).

249. Trelease, S. F. Selenium in soils, plants, and animals. *Soil Sci.* **60**, 125–131 (1945).

250. Trelease, S. F., and Trelease, H. M. Selenium as a stimulating and possibly essential element for indicator plants. *Am. J. Botany* **25**, 372–380 (1938).

251. Truog, E. The determination of the readily available phosphorus of soils. *J. Am. Soc. Agron.* **23**, 874–882 (1930).

252. Truog, E. Lime in relation to availability of plant nutrients. *Soil Sci.* **65**, 1–7 (1948).

253. Truog, E. Soil as a medium for plant growth. *In* "Mineral Nutrition of Plants" (E. Truog, ed.), pp. 23–55. Univ. of Wisconsin Press, Madison, 1951.

254. Tucker, T. C., and Kurtz, L. T. A comparison of several chemical methods with the bioassay procedure for extracting zinc from soils. *Am. Soc. Soil Sci. Proc.* **19**, 477–481 (1955).

255. Ulrich, A. Plant analysis, methods and interpretation of results. *In* "Diagnostic

Techniques for Soils and Crops" (H. B. Kitchen, ed.), pp. 157–198. American Potash Institute, Washington, D.C., 1948.

256. Ulrich, A., and Ohki, K. Chlorine, bromine and sodium as nutrients for sugar beet plants. *Plant Physiol.* **31**, 171–181 (1956).

257. Vandecaveye, S. C. Biological methods of determining nutrients in soil. *In* "Diagnostic Techniques for Soils and Crops" (H. B. Kitchen, ed.), pp. 199–230. American Potash Institute, Washington, D.C., 1948.

258. Van der Crone, G. Ergebuisse von Untersuchung über die Wirkung der Phosphorsäure auf die höheren Pflanzen und eine neue Nährlosung. Dissertation, University of Bonn, Germany 1904. (Not seen.)

259. Volk, N. J. The fixation of potash in difficultly available form in soils. *Soil Sci.* **37**, 267–287 (1934).

260. Volk, R., and McAuliffe, C. Factors affecting the foliar absorption of N^{15} labelled urea by tobacco. *Am. Soc. Soil Sci. Proc.* **18**, 308–312 (1954).

261. Wagner, F. Bedeutung der Kieselsäure für das Wachstum einiger Kulturpflanzen, ihren Nährstoffhaushalt und ihre Aufälligkeit gegen echte Meltaupilze. *Phytopathol. Z.* **12**, 427–479 (1940).

262. Waksman, S. A. "Humus: Origin, Chemical Composition and Importance in Nature," 2nd ed., Williams & Wilkins, Baltimore, Maryland, 1938.

263. Walker, J. B. Inorganic micronutrient requirements of *Chlorella.* I. Requirement for calcium (or strontium), copper and molybdenum. *Arch. Biochem.* **46**, 1–11 (1953).

264. Walker, R. B., Walker, H. M., and Ashworth, P. R. Calcium-magnesium nutrition with special reference to serpentine soils. *Plant Physiol.* **30**, 214–221 (1955).

265. Wallace, T. Pot experiments on the manuring of fruit crops. I. *Ann. Rept. Agr. Hort. Research Sta. Long Ashton Bristol,* pp. 42–57 (1921).

266. Wallace, T. "The Diagnosis of Mineral Deficiencies in Plants by Visual Symptoms." A Colour Atlas and Guide. H. M. Stat. Office, London, 1951.

267. Wallace, T., and Hewitt, E. J. Effects of calcium deficiency on potato sets in acid soils. *Nature* **161**, 28–29 (1948).

268. Wallace, T., Hewitt, E. J., and Nicholas, D. J. D. Determination of factors injurious to plants in acid soils. *Nature* **156**, 778–779 (1945).

269. Wallace, T., Morley-Davies, W., Hewitt, E. J., and Nicholas, D. J. D. Some effects of lime and fertilizers on potatoes on a strongly acid sandy soil as determined by visual symptoms and chemical tests. *Ann. Rept. Agr. Hort. Research Sta. Long Ashton Bristol 1946,* 61–66 (1947).

270. Walsh, T. The effect on plant growth of substituting strontium for calcium in acid soils. *Proc. Roy. Irish Acad.* **B150**, 287–294 (1945).

271. Walsh, T., and Fleming, G. A. Selenium levels in rocks, soils and herbage from a high selenium locality in Ireland. *Intern. Soc. Soil Sci. Trans. Dublin 1952,* **2**, 178–183 (1953).

272. Warington, K. The effect of boric acid on the broad bean and certain other plants. *Ann. Botany (London)* **37**, 629–672 (1923).

273. Way, J. F. On the power of soils to absorb manure. *J. Roy. Agr. Soc. Engl.* **11**, 313–379 (1850).

274. Wiegman, A. F. J., and Polstorff, A. L. Cited by Reed (195) p. 242.

275. Wiklander, L. Cation and anion exchange phenomena. *In* "Chemistry of the Soil" (F. E. Bear, ed.), pp. 107–148. Reinhold, New York, 1955.

276. Wilkins, D. A. Recognizing adaptive variants. *Proc. Linnean Soc. London,* **171**, Pt. 1, 122–126 (1960).

277. Williams, D. E., and Coleman, N. T. Cation exchange properties of plant root surfaces. *Plant and Soil* **2**, 243–256 (1950).
278. Williams, E. G. Evaluating the phosphorus status of soils. *Intern. Soc. Soil Sci. Trans. Dublin 1952*, **1**, 31–47 (1953).
278a. Willis, A. J., and Yemm, E. W. Braunton Burrows: Mineral nutrient status of the dune soils. *J. Ecol.* **49**, 377–390 (1961).
279. Winsor, G. W. Mineralisation and immobilisation of nitrogen in soil. *J. Sci. Food Agr.* **9**, 792–801 (1958).
280. Wittwer, S. H. Nutrient uptake and foliar absorption. *In* "Atomic Energy and Agriculture," pp. 139–164. American Association for the Advancement of Science, Washington, D.C., 1957.
281. Wittwer, S. H., and Teubner, F. G. Foliar absorption of mineral nutrients. *Ann. Rev. Plant Physiol.* **10**, 13–32 (1959).
282. Wood, T. B., and Stratton, F. J. M. The interpretation of experimental results. *J. Agr. Sci.* **3**, 417–440 (1910).
283. Woodward, J. Thoughts and experiments on vegetation. *Phil. Trans. Roy. Soc. London* **21**, 382–398 (1699).
284. Yates, F. "The Design and Analysis of Factorial Experiments." *Imp. Bur. Soil Sci. Tech. Commun. No.* **35**. Harpenden, England, 1937.
285. Young, R. S. Solubility of cobalt in soil. *J. Soil Sci.* **6**, 233–240 (1955).

PREAMBLE TO CHAPTER 2

Chapter 1, Part 2, outlined some general considerations which flow from the growth of seed plants in soil-free culture media. Chapter 2 is focused upon the requirements for specific elements, the symptoms incurred by their deficient supply, and the evidence that a given element is to be considered to be an essential one. Although at first the criteria upon which these judgments were based were, and often still are, visual, the trend is now increasingly toward the additional use of metabolic criteria to characterize the plants which are grown at different levels of nutrient supply.

It will be evident from Chapter 2 that still further discoveries on the role of mineral nutrients and of the essential elements are fraught with increasing difficulty; they require ever more fastidious control over the chemical environment in which the plants are grown, and they involve an ever wider recognition of the interactions of nutrient elements with each other and with features of the environment during the growth of the plants. Thus to comprehend all the possible effects of nutrient supply, or deficiency, and to assess the specific effects of any or all of the prospective essential nutrients and their interactions may require information so detailed that it may become tantamount to understanding growth and metabolism in all its aspects.

This clearly raises the question, what does normal nutrition really mean? How far is the maximum growth best determined by the exogenous nutrient supply, and how far is it preconditioned by endogenous genetic factors? These considerations are necessary in the interpretation of what determines the *maximum* yield of agricultural plants. The essential first step, however, is to know which elements are necessary for the growth of plants and which, by lack, cause abnormalities. Chapter 2 furnishes this information in detail.

CHAPTER TWO

The Essential Nutrient Elements:
Requirements and Interactions in Plants

E. J. HEWITT

I. Introduction

Investigations that lead to the recognition of the essential macro- and micronutrient mineral elements for higher plants have been described in Chapter 1, in which the criteria of their essentiality and problems in the determination of essential nutrient status were discussed. The chemical functions of mineral elements in enzyme systems are also described in Chapter 4 by Nason and McElroy, and the nutrition of microorganisms is dealt with by Nicholas, Chapter 3.

The action of the essential elements in the growth processes of higher plants has sometimes been revealed by a study of the visible or anatomical effects that result from mineral deficiencies or by the effects of controlled levels of these elements on the chemical composition of the plants affected. Often, however, the characteristic symptoms or chemical changes associated with mineral deficiency or excess in one plant may differ, apparently fundamentally, from those observed in another. It is necessary to recognize, therefore, that direct manifestations of the specific functions of mineral elements in different plants may be masked or complicated by differences in the indirect or secondary effects of abnormal mineral concentrations on metabolism as a whole. This is understandable. Quantitative and qualitative differences in the activity and distribution of sequentially dependent enzyme systems—and possibly quantitative differences in the subsequent or prior metabolism of cell constituents that may either accumulate or be depleted as a result of such differences in enzyme activity, such as occurs with the amino acids (Section II, C)—would exert different effects on growth. The integrated effects of such variations in metabolic activity might provide very numerous variations in the over-all behavior, which is revealed in visible, anatomical, or chemical characteristics. These over-all effects are nevertheless individually recognizable, and it may be concluded that although distinct in their characteristics they are the outcome of reproducible and presumably specific metabolic states. Thus the slight or severe deficiency of a given element might, through a defection in the same basic function, produce apparently quite different chemical or anatomical responses in different plants which have different quantitative requirements for that element, different quantitative activities in sequential enzyme systems, and different qualitative capacities to metabolize the intermediate products of the normal or deficient systems (e.g., the factors responsible for putrescine formation in relation to potassium deficiency, which are described later).

Although this view may explain the diverse characteristics associated with a mineral deficiency or excess in different plants, it also emphasizes that caution is needed in drawing conclusions in regard to function from a specific set of chemical or anatomical symptoms observed in a single plant, even when these symptoms appear to be readily interpreted.

Thus, and for this reason, confusion may exist regarding the apparent roles of certain mineral nutrients. The diversity of the effects of some mineral deficiencies also justifies the need to specify the relevant plant species and even the variety concerned in the observation. This is particularly so when detailed records, such as those required for diagnostic purposes, are concerned. The records of visible symptoms have often provided the first indication of other problems, including such effects as ion antagonism, differential distribution, interaction with environment, metabolic interrelationships with other elements, and chemical or physiological action, as, for example, the role of molybdenum in nitrate assimilation.

The roles of mineral elements, especially the micronutrients, in specific enzyme activities necessarily comprise the main basis for their effects on growth, morphology, cell composition, and physiological activities. Discussion of such specific functions in enzyme systems is presented separately by Nason and McElroy (Chapter 4); they are therefore excluded from this chapter. There are, however, many aspects of nutrition—such as the over-all effects of mineral deficiencies and excesses on changes in morphology or composition, e.g., in carbohydrate or amino acid concentrations, or on such activities as photosynthesis, respiration, and protein synthesis—which probably reflect the interaction of several factors, and these can be described only as physiological responses until more is known regarding their exact derivation. Interrelationships between different elements, between environment and nutrient status, and between development and nutrient requirement also occur and modify the effects of deficiency, or excess, as described later.

II. Morphological, Anatomical, Chemical, and Physiological Effects of Mineral Disorders and Nutrient Interactions

The visible features described here are not intended for diagnostic purposes; for such purposes the reader is referred to books by Wallace (553) and Hambidge (177), and to comprehensive papers by McMurtrey (337a) and Piper (407, 408), where extensive references to the literature on this subject are also given. Effects of micronutrients on plant growth and function are also dealt with by Stiles (512), who lists in comprehensive manner the initial records of the evidence for essential micronutrients in many higher plants. This is also given in the historical sections of Chapter 1. Independent reviews of micronutrient problems have also been given by Hewitt (198, 206, 207, 209), Mulder (365), Stiles (513, 513a), and Pirson (411, 412), and of macronutrients by Baumeister (28a).

A. Macronutrient Elements

1. Nitrogen

Nitrogen is included here as it may be classed as a mineral element with regard to its availability to many plants and to the effects of deficiency levels on the visible symptoms and nutrient interrelationships to be described below. Nitrogen metabolism is excluded from this account (see Volume IV).

a. Deficiency symptoms. A characteristic feature in many plants is the decrease in angle between stem and leaf. Leaves become more erect than normal, especially in cereals, grasses, potato (*Solanum tuberosum*), tomato (*Lycopersicon esculentum*), and flax (*Linum usitatissimum*). Lateral buds often remain dormant. This results in the absence of tillering in cereals which may have single shoots; many plants, e.g., flax, potato, tomato, clovers (*Trifolium* spp.), have a thin or spindly habit due to the reduced growth of lateral buds. Tuber formation in potatoes is decreased in number as well as size of the tubers.

Dormancy is often prolonged and normal swelling and opening of buds is delayed, especially in many fruit crops (550a). Delayed dormancy is often accompanied by early senescence. This is seen generally in premature leaf fall, and also in premature maturation of stem tissues in flax. Both these responses would result from early differentiation of meristematic tissues—the first response as a result of differentiation of abscission layers; and the second, of xylem and parenchyma tissues.

Nitrogen deficiency causes marked decreases in chlorophyll content and leaves are pale green. Older leaves become yellow-green and often completely yellow, a condition associated with severe proteolysis without concurrent synthesis. Many plants, however, produce other pigments when they lack nitrogen. In *Brassica* plants the pigments occur first in the mesophyll areas of the upper surface whereas in tomato the dark purple tint is present particularly in petioles and veins. This pigment appears first in veins on the underside of the leaf and later occurs between veins on both surfaces, in addition to yellowing following the loss of chlorophyll. Stems and leaf bases of cereals and stems of flax and fruit trees produce bright red or purple tints. Apples become highly colored especially under conditions of high light intensity. The anthocyanin formation may be suppressed under greenhouse conditions (550a). Slight restriction of nitrogen supply is sometimes used to produce fruit of attractive appearance.

b. Effects on growth. Bosemark (41) described effects of nitrogen supplied as nitrate on the growth of wheat (*Triticum aestivum*) roots in a controlled environment. Nitrogen deficiency, produced by decreasing the nitrogen supply to 10^{-4} M sodium nitrate, resulted in elongated roots which extended 137 mm in 10 days compared with those grown at 10^{-3} to 10^{-2} M concentration, which extended 105 mm. There was a progressive increase in cell length from 188 to 324 μ with decreasing nitrogen, a condition which accounted mainly for the effects on root length. Effects of nitrogen level on cell numbers, calculated as "relative cell number," were not consistent. In the first experiment there was initially a decrease followed by a marked increase in cell numbers with increasing nitrogen supply up to the highest nitrogen level. In a second experiment increasing nitrogen from 10^{-4} to 10^{-2} M nitrate sharply decreased cell numbers. In a third test, in which seeds were removed at 4 days, there was a large decrease in cell numbers when nitrate was increased from 10^{-4} to 10^{-3} M and a further decrease at 10^{-2} M. Bosemark concluded that high nitrogen supplies inhibited cell multiplication as well as cell elongation. There appeared to be about three times as much total and insoluble nitrogen in the inhibited cells as in those of the low nitrogen treatments. Interpretation of these results is complicated, however, by two factors. The basal nutrient solutions were very dilute by normal standards and provided only 10^{-3} M Mg^{++}, 10^{-4} M Ca^{++}, 10^{-3} M PO_4^{---}, and no specified potassium compounds. The increases in sodium up to 10^{-2} M (i.e., at 100:1 sodium:calcium ratio, which might well have been toxic to cell growth) and great increases in sodium:potassium ratios might also depress cell expansion. It would appear desirable to extend these observations to account for the possible effects of the other ions and to use higher levels of the other essential nutrients. Tören (524a) also observed hypertrophy of cells in excised carrot tissue when deficient in nitrogen.

Lutman (309) observed that nitrogen deficiency was associated with small nuclei in normal-sized cells in the undifferentiated regions of Japanese millet (*Setaria italica*) root tips but caused small cells in buckwheat (*Fagopyrum esculentum*) root tip and premature vacuolation in rape (*Brassica napus*), where this change could be interpreted as early senescence. Leaf epidermal cells were notably smaller in millet and buckwheat, but not in rape. The outer walls and cuticle were obviously thin in millet. Leaf palisade cells in potato were relatively slender and separated by large intercellular spaces when nitrogen deficient. Chloroplasts were decreased both in size and number in millet, but in potato, higher nitrogen produced small chloroplasts with abundant starch in contrast to large chloroplasts in millet.

Njoku (386) observed that high, as compared with low, nitrogen supply increased both the mean size and the total number of leaf epidermal cells in *Ipomoea caerulea*. In older leaves, which would have been formed when nitrogen supplies were less limiting on growth, total cell numbers were about 50% greater and the size (as reciprocal of numbers per square millimeter) was about 30% greater with high, than with low, nitrogen. These differences together accounted for double the leaf area. In the youngest leaf, developed after a longer period of low or high nitrogen supply, the high nitrogen treatment produced two and a half times as many cells, which were 20% greater in surface area, than in the low nitrogen treatment; together these differences accounted for a threefold range in leaf area. Related observations of Morton and Watson (361) for effects of nitrogen on beet (*Beta vulgaris*) are discussed in Section II, A, 7, b.

Cytological changes in cauliflower chloroplasts and leaf cells have been studied by D. P. Hucklesby and E. J. Hewitt (unpublished work).

The uniform chlorosis commencing in the oldest leaves of cauliflower (*Brassica oleracea* var. *botrytis*) resulted from a progressive enlargement of the chloroplast starch grains and the concomitant reduction of the lipoprotein structure of the plastid, which remained around the mass of starch grains only as a thin skin. The ribonucleic acid (RNA) staining was similarly reduced. Breakdown followed; it was characterized by the gathering of the lipoprotein portion into intensely golden yellow globules which lay at random on the surface of the starch grains or extended in strings along the starch grain interfaces. These globules eventually separated from the starch grains, where they tended to fuse, becoming progressively larger and fewer. Rapid lysis of starch grains followed, accompanied by the accumulation of anthocyanin pigments in the vacuoles of the epidermal and first subepidermal layers of cells. After the completion of starch lysis, the anthocyanin disappeared, and the mesophyll cells contained, apart from the cytoplasm and nuclei, one or two large globules formed from the chloroplast structure, and many small colorless cytoplasmic lipid droplets.

The over-all effects of nitrogen deficiency are first to decrease the rate and extent of protein synthesis by direct limitation of nitrogen supply. This naturally limits cell expansion and still more, cell division. Similarly the lack of tillering probably reflects the decreased production of new meristems rather than excessive apical dominance. The second effect of nitrogen deficiency is indirect and is due to the corresponding tendency for carbohydrates to accumulate during the early stages of the deficiency. Chloroplasts are, therefore, initially heavily packed with starch grains. Cell sap osmotic pressures are also often high owing to the high sugar contents.

2. Phosphorus

a. Deficiency symptoms. Wallace (553) has pointed out that many of the visible effects of phosphorus deficiency resemble those which are caused by lack of nitrogen. The similarities apply to such effects as acute leaf angles and lack of tillering, as shown in flax (Fig. 1), pro-

Fig. 1. Phosphorus deficiency in flax (*Linum usitatissimum*); single stems, small leaves with narrow leaf angles.

longed dormancy of lateral buds, premature leaf fall, decreased size and number of flower primordia, delay or suppression of flowering, and few, small fruits or seeds. Exceptions occur, however, since leaf angles in tomato become very wide and leaves curve downward (190). Leaf proportions may be altered and tobacco leaves (*Nicotiana tabacum*) are narrower in relation to length when they are phosphorus deficient (337).

Foliage often lacks the normal luster and the leaf surfaces appear dull by reflected light. Leaf color is often abnormal: it may be initially dark green or olive green as in French beans (*Phaseolus vulgaris*), blue green as in tomato and some brassicas and clovers and cereals, or merely dull pale green as in lettuce (*Lactuca sativa*) and pea (*Pisum sativum*). In the oldest leaves, faded yellow-green or brown colors appear. Additional pigments are often produced. These are usually deep purple as in tomato, apple (*Malus sylvestris*), and maize (*Zea mays*), or red and purple as in oat (*Avena sativa*), swede (*Brassica rapa*), rape, in brassicas generally, and in oat and barley (*Hordeum vulgare*). Pigments are sometimes practically absent as in wheat, sugar beet (*Beta vulgaris*), potato, celery (*Apium graveolens* var. *dulce*). Bronzing due to a brown coloration, which develops in very small necrotic areas or groups of cells, is also common in many plants, e.g., celery, hop (*Humulus lupulus*), French beans. Larger areas of necrosis, leading to marginal scorch, also occur in potato and hop. Red clover (*Trifolium pratense*) leaflets develop purple-brown tinted necrotic spots. Sugar beet shows dark brown marginal scorch and potato leaflets develop upcurled scorched margins. Stem bases of cereals and leaf petioles of many plants, e.g., carrot (*Daucus carota* var. *sativa*), tomato, clovers, are also strongly pigmented. Leaf symptoms usually appear first in the older leaves and progress to younger leaves owing to the translocation of phosphorus from the older to the younger parts (189, 190, 192). In most plants the fading and tinting effects are distributed fairly evenly on the leaf surface between, or including, the major veins, and pronounced interveinal patterns may not appear. In cocoa (*Theobroma cacao*) (324) symptoms of chlorosis immediately adjacent to major veins, as observed in some virus diseases, may occur together with leaf asymmetry, sometimes leading to mild "sickle leaf" effects similar to those that are associated with zinc deficiency (164, 165); stipules remain green and attached to stems from which the leaves have fallen. Zinc and phosphorus deficiencies are also similar in some respects for maize, peas, and some other plants (218, 221).

Top:root ratios may be decreased as in nitrogen deficiency; this was observed in subterranean clover (*Trifolium subterraneum*) (356).

Phosphorus interacts with calcium, and a marked example of this effect was observed in subterranean clover by Greenwood and Hallsworth (163). The phosphorus level of 40 ppm, which gives good growth with many plants (200), was found to be toxic at a low calcium level of 8 ppm, but it was beneficial, or not depressive, at a high calcium level of 64 ppm if the nitrogen supply was also high. With low nitrogen supply, when plants were dependent on nitrogen fixation by root nodules, an increase in phosphorus level from 8 to 40 ppm caused a marked depression with 64 ppm calcium (Table XIII). High phosphorus supply also greatly depressed nodulation and the total nitrogen content of the plants. This effect might reflect an induced calcium deficiency since the calcium requirement for nodule formation exceeds considerably that required for the growth of the host plant when fixed nitrogen is provided (302, 303). The data are given in Table XIII in relation to copper requirements.

b. *Anatomical and histological effects.* Lyon and Garcia (310) observed that phosphorus deficiency in tomato resulted in necrosis of thin-walled central pith cells of the stem and production of abnormally large intercellular spaces. The pericycle cells and xylem elements were also thin walled. Phloem was greatly decreased in amount and appeared mainly as undifferentiated parenchyma. The chlorenchyma tissues were reduced to a few layers and were mainly disintegrated.

c. *Effects of phosphorus supply on composition.* Eaton (125, 126, 128) studied the effects of phosphorus supply on the carbohydrate and nitrogen fractions in three plants. Phosphorus deficiency in sunflower (*Helianthus annuus*) (Table I) caused increased concentrations of total sugars, reducing sugars, sucrose, and starch in young plants, but in old plants there were either no effects or effects the reverse of those stated above. In soybean (*Glycine max*) (Table II) phosphorus deficiency increased the concentrations of all the carbohydrate fractions, and in black mustard (*Brassica nigra*) there were increases in total and reducing sugars and sucrose, but not in starch. Haas (171) observed, however, that increasing phosphorus in lemon cuttings (*Citrus limonia*) caused increases in total and reducing sugars. The latter were maximal at 1–10 ppm whereas nonreducing sugars increased up to 100 ppm phosphorus.

Although the effects of phosphorus deficiency on the carbohydrates observed by Eaton were fairly similar for different crops, they were variable for the nitrogen fractions in the three plants. In sunflower, phosphorus deficiency resulted in decreased concentrations of soluble and insoluble nitrogen fractions (Table I). In soybean however there were increases in concentrations of total soluble, insoluble, amide, and ammonia nitrogen fractions (Table III). Increases in amino nitrogen could therefore be expected, although this was not estimated separately There was a gradient of increasing amide concentration in leaves from the apex to mid-stem with low phosphorus and from basal to apical leaves with adequate phosphorus. Eaton suggested that phosphorus deficiency resulted in proteolysis in the lower leaves and impaired resynthesis. In black mustard there were only slight increases in amide concentrations.

Ergle and Eaton (135) found that the total phosphorus content of cotton (*Gossypium* sp.) was decreased, but the proportion of organic phosphorus was increased, by phosphorus deficiency. Phosphorylated sugars were decreased, and starch and reducing sugars were greatly in-

TABLE I

Effects of Phosphorus Supply on Some Carbohydrate and Nitrogen Fractions (As % Dry Weight) in Sunflower (*Helianthus annuus*)[a]

Stem level	Total sugars		Reducing sugars		Sucrose		Starch		70% Alcohol-soluble N		70% Alcohol-insoluble N	
	Minus P	Plus P	Minus P	Plus P	Minus P	Plus P	Minus P	Plus P	Minus P	Plus P	Minus P	Plus P
First harvest
Upper	7.74	0.83	5.83	0.82	1.90	0.01	0.86	0.61	2.05	3.79	1.22	1.82
Middle	7.78	0.41	4.41	0.25	3.39	0.16	0.99	0.50	2.35	4.04	0.74	1.03
Lower	3.94	0.29	2.77	0.21	1.17	0.08	0.81	0.34	2.35	3.60	0.71	0.97
Second harvest
Upper	18.97	11.03	16.72	8.67	2.26	2.36	1.04	1.20	1.34	2.77	0.81	1.48
Middle	15.98	5.20	12.45	4.50	3.53	0.71	1.02	0.87	1.31	3.31	0.45	0.86
Lower	10.50	2.96	7.96	2.34	2.55	0.62	1.00	0.80	1.34	2.76	0.42	0.88
Third harvest
Upper	11.91	21.53	10.37	20.05	1.54	1.48	0.87	1.04	1.35	1.88	0.68	1.05
Middle	13.15	13.60	11.19	12.86	1.96	0.75	0.58	0.64	1.08	1.96	0.36	0.61
Lower	9.39	6.80	7.84	5.90	1.55	0.90	0.68	0.43	0.98	1.72	0.32	0.57

[a] From Eaton (125).

TABLE II
Effects of Phosphorus Supply on Some Carbohydrate Fractions
(as % Dry Weight) in Soybean (*Glycine max*)[a]

Stem level	Total sugars		Reducing sugars		Sucrose		Starch	
	Minus P	Plus P	Minus P	Plus P	Minus P	Plus P	Minus P	Plus P
First harvest								
Upper	4.41	2.09	3.52	1.84	0.89	0.25	2.25	1.44
Middle	1.34	0.65	0.43	0.32	0.91	0.33	3.34	0.47
Lower	1.59	0.47	0.48	0.24	1.11	0.23	5.52	0.41
Second harvest								
Upper	2.65	3.36	1.36	2.51	1.29	0.85	4.64	0.94
Middle	1.63	0.93	0.37	0.32	1.26	0.61	7.29	0.59
Lower	1.69	0.83	0.53	0.34	1.16	0.49	8.19	0.52
Third harvest								
Upper	2.13	3.34	1.11	2.54	1.02	0.80	6.11	1.19
Middle	1.01	1.28	0.29	0.42	0.72	0.86	9.27	0.95
Lower	1.14	1.36	0.24	0.38	0.90	0.98	7.96	0.90

[a] From Eaton (126).

TABLE III
Effects of Phosphorus Supply on Some Nitrogen Fractions
(as % Dry Weight) in Soybean (*Glycine max*)[a]

Stem level	70% Alcohol-soluble solids		Total N		70% Alcohol-soluble N		70% Alcohol-insoluble N	
	Minus P	Plus P	Minus P	Plus P	Minus P	Plus P	Minus P	Plus P
Upper	24.6	29.9	2.28	2.34	1.41	1.16	0.87	1.18
Middle	19.3	19.2	3.12	1.73	2.08	0.91	1.04	0.82
Lower	19.5	15.4	3.20	1.16	2.15	0.34	1.05	0.82

	Ammonia N		Amide N		Nitrate N	
	Minus P	Plus P	Minus P	Plus P	Minus P	Plus P
Upper	0.030	0.005	0.372	0.298	0.176	0.363
Middle	0.028	0.000	0.516	0.179	0.182	0.434
Lower	0.051	0.000	0.496	0.059	0.262	0.172

[a] From Eaton (126).

creased, in deficient plants, but sucrose and hemicellulose showed little change. Detailed studies by Gregory and Richards and others on effects due to interactions of phosphorus with other major elements in barley (*Hordeum vulgare*) are described later (Section II, A, 7), and inter-relationships among potassium, iron, and phosphorus are described in Section II, B, 2, b.

The subject of phosphorus metabolism is beyond the scope of this chapter. It may be noted, however, that phosphorus as adenosine triphosphate (ATP) and numerous phosphorylated products is involved in practically every synthetic reaction of the cell. The primary formation of adenosine triphosphate and of other phosphorylated compounds whether derived from photosynthetic or oxidative phosphorylation will naturally be depressed with inadequate phosphorus supply. Decreased phosphorus also results often in increased nitrogen uptake. Under these circumstances increased accumulation of free amino acids as described in Section II, C would be expected, because amino acid activation as adenosyl derivatives, which are essential to protein synthesis and to ribonucleic acid production and upon which this process is also dependent, would most probably be depressed. Changes in concentrations of amides and peptides, the synthesis of which is also dependent on ATP, would be decreased for similar reasons, but failure to convert amino acids to protein would have a compensating effect in increased amide formation. For these reasons changes in amides and peptides might occur in either direction depending on several factors, such as relative effects on nitrogen uptake and on amino acid activation, etc.

Thus in Eaton's comparative studies amide accumulation was considerable in soybean (Table III) but it was insignificant in sunflower (Table I) and black mustard.

Hewitt and Tatham (225) found that acid phosphatase activity in leaves of tomato plants was increased over tenfold by phosphorus deficiency (Table IV). This may be a response to a decreased inorganic phosphate level, which inhibits phosphatase activity; if so, the effect must be on the synthesis of the enzyme during growth, but not by direct inhibition *in vitro* (225). It cannot be said at present whether such increased activity is significant *in vivo* nor whether, if it is, its effects are useful or harmful, since remobilization of inorganic phosphorus for use in younger tissues and destruction of phosphate ester bonds might be either desirable or unfavorable activities according to the circumstances and the location.

It would be expected that phosphorus deficiency would decrease deoxyribonucleic acid synthesis as well as that of ribonucleic acid. Such an effect would chiefly restrict nuclear division or might cause defects

TABLE IV

Effects of Macronutrient Deficiencies on Acid Phosphatase Activity
in Tomato (*Lycopersicon esculentum*) Leaf Tissues[a]

Nitrogen source	Control	Minus Mg	Minus K	Minus P	Means
A. On fresh weight basis[b]					
NO$_3$	8.80	8.38	13.25	71.30	22.93
NO$_2$	8.93	8.13	13.43	83.38	28.46
NH$_4$	9.33	7.25	12.95	105.28	33.70
Means	9.02	7.92	13.21	83.32	—
LSD Separate treatments	5%, 16.15		Nitrogen sources (means)		5%, 8.08
LSD Separate treatments	0.1%, 28.71		Nitrogen sources (means)		1%, 10.85
B. On protein basis[c]					
NO$_3$	0.234	0.293	0.452	2.177	0.789
NO$_2$	0.221	0.221	0.404	2.688	0.884
NH$_4$	0.230	0.256	0.367	4.198	1.263
Means	0.228	0.257	0.408	3.021	—
LSD Separate treatments	5%, 0.666		Nitrogen sources (means)		5%, 0.333
LSD Separate treatments	0.1%, 1.222		Nitrogen sources (means)		1%, 0.453

[a] From Hewitt and Tatham (225).
[b] μM Phenolphthalein phosphate hydrolyzed per 100 mg. tissue in 20 minutes.
[c] μM Phenolphthalein phosphate hydrolyzed per 100 mg. tissue per minute.

in parts of chromosomes or gene suppression. These possibilities merit further investigation (see Chapter 1, p. 119, and ref. 69).

3. Sulfur

a. Morphological and visible effects. Plants deprived of sulfur show some visible effects which resemble those caused by nitrogen deficiency. These effects may include marked decrease in leaf size, with general paling and development of orange, red, or purple pigments, for example, in gooseberry (*Ribes grossularia*), strawberry (*Fragaria chiloensis* var. *ananassa*), and apple (550a).

A point of difference, however, is that young leaves which are sulfur deficient are usually affected more than, or before, old ones. This happens in tobacco (337), tea (*Camellia sinensis*), and tomato, in which foliage is markedly pale green and tips of leaves are characteristically turned downward. In cocoa (324) the young leaves of each flush of growth are chlorotic and chlorophyll production is delayed. Other plants in which young leaves are affected first or more severely include *Calceolaria rugosa* (337a), soybean (121), pecan (*Carya illinoinensis* [*C. pecan*]) (337a), *Antirrhinum* (337a), sugar cane (*Saccharum officinarum*) (337a), cotton (*Gossypium* sp.) (134), and citrus species (72).

Sulfur deficiency in tea was identified by Storey and Leach (515) as the cause of "tea yellows." Plants have very chlorotic, ultimately yellow, young leaves which are drastically decreased in size when severely affected. Margins and tips of young leaves become necrotic and rolled. Defoliation is severe and rapid, and the stem apex is killed. Internodes are much shortened, lateral buds develop prematurely with small yellow leaves, and shoots die back, producing multiple branches with dead tips. The symptoms in citrus (72) are similar in several respects. Stems may be abnormally stiff and woody as in tomato (385), and lateral bud development may be suppressed in contrast to tea. Stem and root diameter may be greatly decreased, as in soybean and tomato plants. Internode distances in young stem regions of tomato may be increased in contrast with tea. Flowering is reduced, but fruit formation that occurs is premature. General aspects of sulfur nutrition are reviewed by Gilbert (154).

b. Anatomical and cytological effects. Anatomical changes reported (310) in sulfur-deficient tomato plants included a marked increase in the thickness of cell walls of stems, especially in fiber, xylem, and collenchyma cells, which were all increased greatly in proportion to the other tissues. Phloem area decreased more than other regions and pith increased. Wedin and Struckmeyer (576) found that tobacco stem diameter was decreased from 20 to 12 mm. This was associated with decreased cell sizes in transverse section. Cell walls especially in xylem were much thinner. Epidermal, cortical, and pith parenchyma cells were rounded. Cambial tissues were decreased from six to three layers of cells. Phloem cells were also smaller, and phloem fiber cells were lacking. There were no marked necrotic lesions, but phloem cells collapsed. In leaves the cells were less compactly arranged and leaves were thicker than normal. With high sulfate levels leaf cell walls were thinner than usual, but increased parenchyma produced thicker leaves with enlarged and rounded cells.

Cell division may become abnormal in sulfur-deficient plants. Steffensen (499) observed that sulfur deficiency in *Tradescantia paludosa* resulted in the failure of bivalent chromosomes to separate at the first anaphase of meiosis, and they formed micronuclei. In some instances micronuclei comprised single pairs of bivalent chomosomes. Abnormal formation of tripolar spindles also occurred. In less acute deficiency there was unequal, or delayed, separation of the chromosomes. Root tips of sulfur-deficient plants also contained micronuclei, owing to the failure of chromosome separation, and delayed mitosis occurred. Steffensen referred to examples of abnormal meiosis in other plants caused by sulfur deficiency. As deoxyribonucleic acid does not contain sulfur, it may be supposed that protein synthesis is here abnormal owing to the insufficient supply of the sulfur-containing amino acids. It is also possible that spindle movements and mechanism depend on the presence of thiol groupings which form cross linkages by oxidation and disulfide formation. The appearance of micronuclei, with chromosomes which are defective in deoxyribonucleic acid, implies that their production may be dependent on specific sulfur-containing proteins at some stage in the cell division process.

c. Effects on composition. Eaton (121, 123, 124, 127) described effects of sulfur on the composition of tomato, soybean, sunflower, and black mustard (*Brassica nigra*) plants. Sulfur deficiency in soybean decreased the content of total and reducing sugars but increased those of starch and crude hemicellulose fractions (Table V). Effects on total carbohydrates and sucrose were not consistent. The maximum effects of sulfur deficiency on sugars occurred in stems; effects were large also in roots compared with leaves. Sulfur deficiency increased sucrose and starch but decreased reducing sugars in tomato and black mustard. The ratio reducing sugar:sucrose was decreased from about 6 to 1.5 by prolonged sulfur deficiency in tomato (Table VI) and from 10 to about 0.6 in black mustard (Table VII). Starch was also increased in sunflower, and total sugars were decreased (Table VIII). In general there were decreases in reducing sugars and increases in total carbohydrates.

Sulfur deficiency had fairly consistant effects on the major nitrogen fractions. Insoluble nitrogen, which probably reflected protein nitrogen, was decreased in all species whereas soluble organic nitrogen, amides, amino and ammonia nitrogen, and nitrate were increased by sulfur deficiency. It was concluded that protein synthesis was markedly impaired, and rapid proteolysis was inferred.

Eaton (124) found that sulfur deficiency led to high concentrations of soluble organic sulfur compounds in mustard. Contrary to Eaton's findings, earlier work by Nightingale, Schermerhorn, and Robbins (385) indicated increases in concentrations of reducing sugars and sucrose as well as of polysaccharides in sulfur-deficient tomato plants. There were also deposits apparently of calcium oxalate. Nightingale *et al.* (385) examined also the effects of sulfur deficiency on sulfur and nitrogen fractions in tomato plants, previously raised in a potting

TABLE V

EFFECTS OF SULFUR DEFICIENCY ON CONCENTRATIONS OF CARBOHYDRATE
FRACTIONS (AS % DRY WEIGHT) IN SOYBEAN (*Glycine max*)[a]

Carbohydrate fraction and plant part	Samples taken					
	April 22, 1933		May 5, 1933		April 21, 1934	
	Plus S	Minus S	Plus S	Minus S	Plus S	Minus S
Total sugars						
Leaves	3.792	4.479	3.091	2.676	1.688	1.544
Stems	3.218	1.580	2.692	1.070	2.3084	0.862
Roots	3.084	2.588	3.412	2.461	1.822	1.315
Reducing sugars						
Leaves	1.245	1.174	1.109	0.930	0.682	0.481
Stems	1.411	0.411	1.653	0.300	1.704	0.404
Roots	1.461	0.872	1.562	1.048	1.263	0.712
Sucrose						
Leaves	2.419	3.139	1.883	1.659	0.955	1.012
Stems	1.717	1.110	0.986	0.732	0.487	0.440
Roots	1.343	1.630	1.757	1.341	0.530	0.572
Starch						
Leaves	10.564	14.140	7.560	7.067	2.324	2.338
Stems	8.586	10.677	3.894	8.386	1.896	2.318
Roots	2.740	2.614	2.071	3.334	1.835	1.811
Hemicelluloses						
Leaves	4.784	5.227	4.706	7.047	4.790	5.046
Stems	9.686	10.173	11.878	11.767	12.073	11.612
Roots	9.480	9.228	8.644	8.888	7.578	8.718
Total carbohydrates						
Leaves	19.140	23.846	15.357	16.890	8.802	8.928
Stems	21.490	22.430	18.464	21.224	16.277	14.792
Roots	15.304	14.430	14.127	15.474	11.235	11.844
Total carbohydrates	18.651	21.431	16.236	18.000	12.354	11.869

[a] From Eaton (121).

compost, after 8 weeks with or without sulfur. As compared with the initial composition, sulfur deficiency markedly decreased free sulfate, sulfur in proteins, and total sulfhydryl groups. There was by contrast a great increase in the unidentified nonprotein sulfur, other than sulfate. Sulfur deficiency greatly increased total nitrogen, nitrate nitrogen, free amino nitrogen, and soluble nitrogen other than nitrate,

TABLE VI

Effects of Sulfur Nutrition on Carbohydrate and Nitrogen Fractions (as % Dry Weight) in Tomato (*Lycopersicon esculentum*)[a]

Solution	Total sugars	Reducing sugars	Sucrose	Starch	Total N	70% Alcohol-soluble N	70% Alcohol-insoluble N	Ammonia	Amides	Nitrates
First harvest										
Minus S	1.74	1.12	0.62	0.79	3.72	2.44	1.28	0.056	0.099	1.904
Plus S	2.03	1.44	0.59	0.60	3.70	2.49	1.21	0.028	0.081	1.874
Second harvest										
Minus S	6.17	3.67	2.50	2.56	3.17	2.44	0.73	0.361	0.180	0.945
Plus S	13.27	11.33	1.94	0.99	2.22	1.29	0.93	0.049	0.066	0.716

[a] From Eaton (127).

153

TABLE VII
EFFECTS OF SULFUR DEFICIENCY ON CARBOHYDRATE AND NITROGEN FRACTIONS
(AS % FRESH AND DRY WEIGHTS) IN BLACK MUSTARD (*Brassica nigra*)[a]

Solution	Dry matter	Green matter	Dry matter	Green matter	Dry matter	Green matter	Dry matter	Green matter
	Reducing sugars		Sucrose		Starch		Acid-hydrolyzable carbohydrates	
Minus S	0.318	0.023	0.549	0.040	2.404	0.175	10.495	0.764
Plus S	2.303	0.114	0.230	0.011	0.608	0.030	9.657	0.478
	Total N		Total organic N		70% Alcohol-soluble N		70% Alcohol-insoluble N	
Minus S	6.112	0.445	2.996	0.218	4.520	0.329	1.592	0.116
Plus S	6.143	0.304	2.285	0.113	4.391	0.217	1.752	0.087
	Ammonia N		Amino N		Amide N		Nitrate N	
Minus S	0.237	0.0172	0.452	0.034	0.219	0.016	3.116	0.227
Plus S	0.077	0.004	0.114	0.006	0.106	0.005	3.858	0.191

[a] From Eaton (124).

TABLE VIII
EFFECTS OF SULFUR DEFICIENCY ON CARBOHYDRATE AND NITROGEN FRACTIONS
(AS % DRY WEIGHT) IN SUNFLOWER (*Helianthus annuus*)[a]

Stem level	Minus S	Plus S	Minus S	Plus S	Minus S	Plus S	Minus S	Plus S
	Reducing sugars		Sucrose		Starch		Acid-hydrolyzable carbohydrates	
Upper	5.005	19.592	0.365	2.472	1.296	0.725	0.516	0.323
Middle	3.660	16.767	0.900	2.480	0.735	0.537	0.972	0.512
Lower	2.246	10.730	0.747	1.738	0.315	0.098	1.305	1.095
	Total N		Total organic N		70% Alcohol-soluble N		70% Alcohol-insoluble N	
Upper	5.526	3.824	3.188	1.717	4.537	2.656	0.989	1.168
Middle	4.673	2.968	2.431	1.112	4.145	2.221	0.528	0.747
Lower	2.397	1.801	1.231	0.766	1.971	1.249	9.426	0.552
	Ammonia N		Amino N		Amide N		Nitrate N	
Upper	0.163	0.022	0.798	0.185	0.192	0.004	2.339	2.107
Middle	0.092	0.011	0.625	0.115	0.156	0.004	2.243	1.856
Lower	0.035	0.002	0.233	0.085	0.071	0.000	1.166	1.035

[a] From Eaton (123).

and also increased sucrose and reducing sugar levels, compared with levels in plants given sulfur.

Ergle (133, 134) observed that sulfur deficiency in cotton decreased protein and protein-bound sulfur and soluble sulfur compounds. There were increased concentrations of amides and amino nitrogen compounds. Sulfur of chloroplast protein was also decreased but to a lesser degree than in leaves as a whole. Sulfur deficiency caused nitrate accumulation. It was concluded that sulfur released during proteolysis in apical tissues when sulfur deficient, was not reutilized in protein synthesis.

Biddulph (34) found that trifoliate leaves and roots of kidney bean plants (*Phaseolus vulgaris*) contained more sulfur than stems and prophylls. Part only of the total sulfur was freely mobile in the plant. The rate of movement of sulfur in the phloem was similar to that of sucrose or phosphorus, in contrast to that of calcium, which was apparently nil. Part of the sulfur in seeds was translocated to roots, where it remained immobile until sulfur was absorbed by roots from the external medium.

Sulfur is essential for the conversion of nitrogen fixed from atmospheric nitrogen by legume root nodules into protein nitrogen. Anderson and Spencer (11) concluded that, although sulfur deficiency limited the nodulation of subterranean clover, this effect was indirect and was due to a limiting effect of sulfur on the nutrition of the host plant. Sulfur deficiency, unlike molybdenum deficiency (10), did not prevent nitrogen fixation by nodules, where present, but prevented the conversion of nitrogen into protein. In the absence of molybdenum, however, sulfur had no effect on the efficiency per unit weight of the increased nodule mass.

Effects of sulfur deficiency on sulfur-containing and other amino acids are described in Section II, C below. The discussion of the role of sulfur and the intermediary metabolism of sulfur-containing compounds in plants is beyond the scope of this chapter.

4. Calcium

a. Visible effects of deficiency. i. Leaves and stems. The characteristic effects of calcium deficiency may occur in many parts of a plant, and the susceptibility of different tissues differs in various species. In many plants with entire broad leaves, the first indication of calcium deficiency is a slight paling of a limited region of the leaf margin, some distance behind the leaf apex. Leaf growth becomes uneven and the leaf breadth is restricted so that the marginal outline is perceptibly concave in the chlorotic regions (Fig. 2). Successively younger leaves

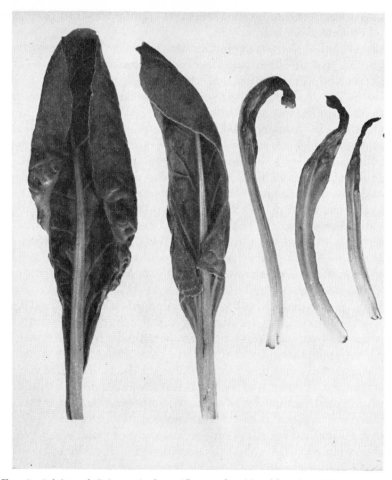

Fig. 2. Calcium deficiency in beet (*Beta vulgaris*); chlorotic and restricted marginal growth about mid-marginal region initially (left hand leaves) and progressing nearer to leaf apex to produce backward hooking of leaf tip (center) and black necrosis of leaf tip (right).

show more pronounced chlorosis and marginal curvature, which occurs nearer the leaf tip with decreasing age of the leaf. Ultimately the leaf apex is included and is killed. On subsequent expansion the leaves develop a sharply pointed, truncated, lamina behind the growing tip which is often surrounded by scorched or blackened tissues. In the older leaves the areas of restricted marginal growth become scorched and they tear, whereas in the youngest leaves only the petiole may develop with a blackened tip and no lamina at all (189, 190, 192).

Many plants, including beet (*Beta vulgaris*), brassicas, e.g., cauliflower (*Brassica oleracea* var. *botrytis*), tobacco (147, 337), and cocoa (324), that produce these symptoms often show a characteristic "hooking" of the leaf tip. This arises because the differential growth of the marginal and central regions of the leaf causes strain and consequential change in leaf shape. The hooking may occur in either direction but is usually backward.

In cauliflower and in kale (*Brassica oleracea* var. *acephala*), extensive interveinal necrotic spotting may appear in median parts of partly expanded leaves. The necrosis may be preceded by gray tinting; it occurs in a well-defined zone within the margins. In these circumstances the "tip hooking" effects occur later in the younger leaves. In tomato, margins of terminal and then lateral leaflets on recently expanded leaves become purple tinted. Central interveinal areas are chlorotic, develop orange tints, and then become necrotic and scorched. These symptoms precede effects in the young leaves, in which leaflets remain folded, become chlorotic at their margins, and finally necrotic and withered. The youngest leaves become necrotic and die without expanding; the shoot apex withers. Lateral buds tend to remain dormant, unlike those in boron-deficient plants, but side shoots that have commenced expansion may show similar symptoms after the death of the main axis.

In potato the first symptoms on the aerial parts of plants that have already made substantial growth occur in the young leaves. The leaflets remain folded, become chlorotic at the margins, and develop small black necrotic spots just within the margins. Leaflets shrivel and the stem apex dies and withers. Black streaks and lesions occur in the stems a little way below the apex. When calcium deficiency is very severe, the shoots produced from tubers may die soon after they begin to extend (555). Stem growth is not injured in this way when tubers are maintained under "sprouting" conditions, in which roots are unable to absorb nutrients and stems may attain 20 cm or more without evidence of the injury produced when plants are rooting in a calcium-deficient nutrient. Root development is initially vigorous also when tubers are set in calcium-deficient sand cultures. It appears, therefore, that stem growth of the potato is more sensitive than root growth when stems are attached to tubers and that stem tissues are injured when their roots develop in a calcium-deficient medium, but not when their roots are suppressed by sprouting tubers in the open air.

Under slight to moderate conditions of calcium deficiency, aerial stem growth may appear normal or exhibit only a slight marginal paling of young leaflets. The tubers from such plants, however, are usually severely malformed (Fig. 3), numerous, and much smaller than normal. Tubers are frequently branched or multiple in appearance, and the surface may be concave. The effect on tubers is the most sensitive response and may be the only symptom to occur with slight deficiency of calcium. Internally such tubers may show a breakdown which resembles the medullary necrosis reported by Van Schreven (535) and Bolle-Jones (36) or a vascular necrosis with production of excessive corky periderm.

Calcium deficiency is often associated with wilting symptoms, which appear in two ways that may be related. In partly expanded leaves of

Fig. 3. Calcium deficiency in potato (*Solanum tuberosum*) tubers; diminutive size, with severe malformation and production of numerous "satellite" tubers.

cauliflower, rape, kale, swede, radish (*Raphanus sativus*), parsnips (*Pastinaca sativa*) (190, 192) and peach (*Prunus persica*) wilting occurs in the central interveinal areas of the leaf (92). Major veins, midribs, and petioles may become involved successively, and the leaf falls over (Fig. 22). Wilting also occurs in leaf petioles, pedicels, and parts of stems in calcium-deficient plants, often during, or just prior to, flowering (192) and may occur in the elongating flower stems of biennials which have shown only slight leaf symptoms the previous year; in general it appears to be associated with moderate, rather than severe, deficiency. It occurs in rape, kale, radish, tulip (*Tulipa gesneriana*, Rose Copland) (224), pea, clovers (111, 190), lucerne, flax; in this plant the field condition is called "wither tip" (351, 355).

The leaf symptoms in cereals, such as barley, wheat, oats, include gray tinting followed by total white chlorosis of leaf tips of young leaves, which remain rolled. A constriction occurs in the rolled leaf about 3–5 cm behind the tip. The leaf wilts at this point and the tip portion later withers. These symptoms may closely resemble those caused by copper deficiency described later (189, 190, 192). Maize leaves become gelatinous at the tips. These dry out and adhere to each other (337a) and this effect resembles that of boron deficiency (130).

Death of the stem apex is characteristic of calcium deficiency in many plants. In slight or moderate deficiency, the number of shoots may be increased, as in flax or potato, producing a markedly bushy habit. A possibly related effect is the tendency for calcium-deficient oat plants to produce lateral shoots from nodes along the prostrate main stem. In timothy grass (*Phleum pratense*), the stem nodes produce adventitious roots. Proteolysis associated with prolonged darkness leads to liberation of calcium from older tissues (383).[1]

ii. Roots. Calcium deficiency often has especially serious growth effects on roots, and this is reflected in the fact that the top:root ratio in subterranean clover, for example (356), may be increased by calcium deficiency instead of showing the usual decrease caused by many disorders. Roots of barley, oats, wheat, etc., are particularly sensitive to calcium deficiency. They become stunted or die back from the apex. Adventitious roots from the first node may die when only 2.5–5 mm long. Mustard roots become gray and translucent. Similar translucence and gelatinization occurs in a few days when the roots of citrus species are immersed in calcium-deficient salt solutions (436a). In apple and peach (92) and tomato (383) the roots become bulbous and proliferate just behind the primary root tip, which dies back.

Sorokin and Sommer (491, 492) examined the effects of calcium deficiency over a range of controlled calcium levels on the growth of pea roots. Their methods were similar to those used for the study of boron deficiency (490), and very low calcium levels were achieved. The roots were clearly far more sensitive than the aerial parts to the first effects of calcium deficiency when the plants were transferred to calcium-free solution after a few days' growth with complete nutrient. Within 2 or 3 days the apex of the main root appeared translucent; the root sometimes appeared to be constricted about 2–4 mm from the apex. Further apical growth then ceased. With 0.06 ppm calcium there were more lateral primordia, most of which failed to develop; some of these at the base of the main root, however, elongated slightly. Increasing calcium up to 0.25 ppm produced mainly increased lateral root development with restricted main roots. Main root elongation was normal in the presence of a saturated solution of calcium sulfate. Histological effects are described later.

[1] Effects of lack of calcium and other elements are now being observed at the submicroscopic level and in the growing points (cf. Marinos, *Amer. J. Bot.*, **49**, No. 8, 1962; and other papers in *Proc. 5th Int. Cong. Electron Microscopy*, Philadelphia, 1962). This is a welcome trend. (Ed.)

The growth of root hairs as related to calcium supply has been reviewed by Cormack (84, 85). He concluded from his own and other work that root hair cell walls comprise an inner elastic layer of cellulose surrounded by a harder layer of calcium pectate except at the softer tip area, where either pectic acid or a modified calcium pectate is said to be present. When adequate calcium is present this softer area is small and root hairs are elongated. With low calcium levels the soft area is enlarged and the root hair tip swells to a bulbous state. The formation of root hairs in cabbage roots was thought to reflect the extent to which external calcium would combine with the pectic acid of the cell wall. Some cells had a low internal pH and did not readily form root hairs whereas others had a higher pH and proceeded to form elongated root hairs and to produce calcium pectate, the formation of which Cormack found to be in accordance with the effect of pH on the ease of combination of calcium and pectic acid *in vitro*. The extension of the root hair cell from the tip was considered to reflect the increasing hardening of calcium pectate in the basal regions. These views regarding the effect of calcium on cell wall plasticity would be in agreement with those of Burström given below. Cormack later concluded that an external supply of calcium was required for formation of root hairs initially. The mechanism was thought to depend on internal water pressure forcing out the cell wall at the weakest point left during the hardening of the remaining area by calcium pectate. Excessive calcium and alkaline conditions lead to such rapid calcification over all the surface that root hair formation would then be suppressed. With calcium deficiency and low pH, lack of hardening of the wall results in gross expansion of the weak walls with consequent swelling, branching, and other abnormalities. Recovery is possible only in regions which are able to resume growth; abnormal hair cells do not change.

Loneragen and Dowling (303), and Loneragen (302), have shown that the calcium requirement for root nodule formation by subterranean clover is about tenfold greater than the amount needed for the growth of the host plant when nitrate is the nitrogen source. On the other hand the calcium requirement, if any, for the growth of the *Rhizobium* bacteria, was extremely low, less than 0.1 μM. Effects of pH were more critical for the rhizobia than for the production of nodules, regardless of calcium supply above the critical values of 0.1 M calcium or pH 4.5 where increase in the level of the one could offset an unfavorable effect of the other.

Burström (59, 60) described effects of calcium and hydrogen ion concentration on the growth of wheat roots in water cultures using a continuous flow of dilute nutrient solution. At concentrations of 10^{-6} and

10^{-8} M calcium there was an optimum effect of pH around pH 5–6.0. As the calcium level was progressively increased to 10^{-3} M, increasing pH values produced increased growth in length up to pH 7 or above. Analysis of these effects in terms of cell elongation or cell multiplication produced different effects. Cell multiplication was slightly depressed at 10^{-3} and 10^{-8} M Ca^{++} and at pH values up to 6.0, compared with intermediate calcium levels of 10^{-6} to 10^{-4} M. There was little or no effect of pH above pH 5.5, but a very great decrease in cell numbers at pH 4. Cell elongation, however, was markedly increased by increasing calcium from 10^{-8} to 10^{-6} M to 10^{-4} at pH 6 or 7; 10^{-3} M calcium appeared to be above the optimum for cell multiplication, but not for cell elongation. Low values (about pH 4.4) were associated with abnormally elongated cells, especially at the higher calcium levels. Burström advanced the suggestion that calcium exerts its effect by "hardening" the cell walls and that it thus counteracts the effect of auxin in softening, or increasing the elasticity, of cell walls.

In a later experiment Burström (60) found that cell multiplication was increased by calcium between 10^{-6} and 10^{-5} M when iron was also given, in accordance with observations of Brown and Possingham (52). The low pH optimum possibly reflects some effect on the availability of iron. Calcium requirements for cell division therefore appear to be about one-tenth or one-hundredth of those that are optimal for cell expansion. (This is consistent with the very low calcium requirements for growth of bacteria.)

Increasing calcium from 10^{-6} to 10^{-4} M progressively increased protein content and fresh weight but did not greatly affect dry weight, a finding from which Burström concluded that the increased cell elongation was due to increased water uptake. The increased protein was apparently related to increased nitrate uptake. Calcium appeared to be necessary for the development of the elastic properties of the cell walls but did not affect their plasticity. Burström suggested that calcium functioned during the growth of the cell wall by intussusception by promoting the formation of an elastic structure and also by increasing the uptake of nitrate required for protein synthesis. From the results obtained by Florell (141, 142), it would appear that the effect of calcium on nitrate uptake was closely related to its effect on mitochondrial formation. Subsequent experiments by Burström and Tullin (61) confirmed the effect of calcium on cell elongation. This was not inhibited by ethylenediaminetetraacetic acid (EDTA) 10^{-5} M, but cell multiplication was. This inhibition was reversed by 10^{-5} M calcium or manganese, but not by ferrous ions.

Carr and Ng (65) suggested that the stimulation of coleoptile elongation in the presence of a citrate-containing buffer at pH 5 can be explained by the sequestration of calcium, which is present in all walls of wheat coleoptiles to the extent of 0.1% of their dry weight. EDTA was unable to exert such effects [Ng and Carr (376)], and this result was not considered to support the view of Bennet-Clark (32), noted later, that stimulation of cell expansion by EDTA in *Avena* coleoptile is due to chelation of calcium present as calcium pectate. In excised carrot root tissues, calcium deficiency resulted in the disappearance of cambial tissues (524a).

iii. Flowers and fruits. Calcium deficiency severely limits seed production even when flower formation is otherwise normal. Grain formation is often totally suppressed in cereals; barley and wheat bear empty glumes though the foliage symptoms may have been slight. Flowers fall prematurely during blossoming in broad bean (*Vicia faba*), French beans, clovers, lucerne, and mustard. When organs such as pods are formed, the developing ovules abort at an early stage. Broad bean pods may show black lesions along their dorsal and ventral sutures and over the sides. The spongy uneven surface becomes black around the attachment of the ovule. The ovule remains small, the integuments turn brown irregularly, and the ovule becomes limp and finally shrivels. The radicle of the embryo and the tissue attaching it to the cotyledons may also blacken. These symptoms may occur even in externally normal pods. A similar collapse of the ovule, with irregular necrosis of the embryonic cotyledons and shrinkage within the integuments, which remain bladder-like, also occurs in pea and in dwarf and climbing French beans (189, 190, 192). This necrosis in embryonic tissues may be analogous to the effects of calcium deficiency on the gynophore of *Arachis*, which is described below.

"Blossom-end rot" of tomato fruit is readily induced by calcium deficiency. The symptoms commence either as a sunken region a few millimeters in width, near the distal end of the youngest fruit on the truss, or as dark-colored areas beneath the surface of a fruit; these are caused by woody tissue surrounded by green tissues in the otherwise orange-colored flesh of the ovary wall. Mucilage is often lacking and ovules may be absent. Fruit are progressively affected from the apex to the base of the truss with increasing severity. Spurr (497) has reviewed the problem in general and has described a detailed anatomical study of the effects of calcium on the incidence of "blossom-end rot." Proteinaceous inclusions develop in necrotic epidermal cells and in deeper layers of the distal region of the pericarp. Calcium deficiency rather than water shortage was regarded as the primary cause of the disorder. The incidence of "blossom-end rot" under conditions of high salt nutrition may reflect induced calcium deficiency.

The role of calcium in the growth of the peanut (*Arachis hypogaea*) fruit is another example of the differential requirements for calcium at different stages of development. Brady (43) has shown that the gynophore requires an independent calcium supply so that the fruit can develop. The calcium supply is critical during a period of 15–35 days after the gynophore reaches the ground, and calcium that is absorbed by the roots cannot be utilized for this stage of development; a supply of calcium for 18 days over the critical period permits nearly 80% fruit development. Bledsoe, Comar, and Harris (35) demonstrated this point by giving radioactive calcium to the plant rooting medium or the gynophore rooting medium in separate compartments. Only a trace of calcium given to the roots was recovered in the seed, and only 1%, or less, of that taken up by the roots was found in the gynophore.

   b. *Anatomical and histological effects.* Florell (141, 142) studied the formation of mitochondria in wheat roots and concluded that calcium was necessary for this activity. Increasing calcium from nil or 10^{-7} M to 10^{-4} M increased mitochondrial weight by 54% and increased their protein content by 39%. There was no effect on mitochondrial respiration, and he concluded that the effect of calcium was on "cytoplasmic organization." Effects of calcium on mitochondrial formation were 50% greater than those observed for root elongation. Florell (142) concluded that calcium had a beneficial effect in promoting anion uptake by increasing mitochondrial formation since mitochondria may be partly involved in this process.

   The histological changes in root cells of pea, due to calcium deficiency, were described by Sorokin and Sommer (491, 492) using cytological methods available between 1929 and 1940. Earlier records were also reviewed. Complete absence of calcium appeared to result in profound changes in cell behavior (Fig. 4). The translucent extension of the root apex comprised small isodiametric cells which remained undifferentiated and were unable to differentiate. Normal mitoses were absent but pseudomitoses, or amitosis involving the separation of nuclei into two parts, was observed. Mitotic failure occurred about 4 days after transfer to a calcium-free solution. The nuclei showed many stages between normal mitosis and amitosis including intermediate stages of partial spindle formation, incomplete separation of chromosomes, and aggregation of chromatin into granules or lumps. Some nuclei contained two nucleoli. Some cells failed to produce new cell walls after division, and binucleate cells were observed. This occurred when cells appeared to have lost most of their cytoplasmic contents. Amitotically produced nuclei sometimes appeared to remain connected by cytoplasmic connections, and some nuclei appeared large and possibly polyploid. The biochemical significance of calcium in DNA and microsomal particle organization is discussed below. In most cases

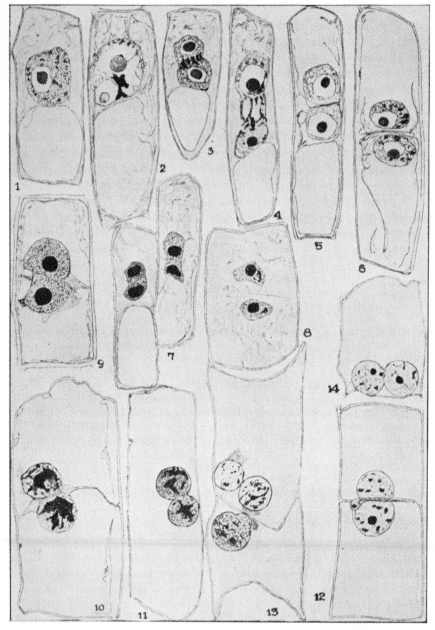

FIG. 4. Effects of calcium deficiency on the cytology of pea (*Pisum sativum*) roots. Reproduced from Sorokin and Sommer (491).

All drawings were made with the aid of an Abbé camera lucida, with Zeiss

normal cell walls were observed by Sorokin and Sommer to be present after irregular mitosis had occurred, and no specific effect on cell wall formation was inferred. The cells in these mitotic stages were abnormally vacuolated, and the vacuoles often occupied much of the cell. Cells produced in this way appeared to be very susceptible to bacterial invasion followed by dissolution of the cell contents. With 0.06 ppm calcium, mitosis was practically normal within the cells of the main root. The axis of cell division, however, was abnormal, and many divisions had horizontal or oblique axes which resulted in an increase of root diameter instead of elongation. Prolonged deficiency at 0.06 ppm caused the appearance of abnormal mitoses in lateral primordia, which resembled those described for absence of calcium in the main axis. With 0.125 ppm the meristematic region appeared enlarged and mitoses extended into the differentiated region of the endodermis. After 20 days, however, the mitoses were often abnormal

---

apochromatic objective 3 mm, 1.30 N.A., compensating ocular $\times$ 12. The plate was not reduced in reproduction. The drawings were made from the meristematic cells of root tips grown in solutions in the absence of calcium (1–6), in the absence of calcium and boron (7–9), and in the absence of calcium and magnesium (10–14).

1. A cell with the nucleus in a resting stage, chromatin material distinctly granular. A large vacuole is present in the cytoplasm.

2. Beginning of pseudoamitosis. Two nucleoli, each surrounded by a clear area. Chromatin material is accumulated into large clumps.

3. Further stage of pseudoamitosis. Chromatin material arranged in a plane, individual chromosomes not distinct.

4. Rudimentary spindles formed. Bridges of chromatin material distinct.

5. A division of the nucleus without the formation of a rudimentary spindle.

6. Formation of a cell plate by strands of cytoplasm which extend from the parietal layer and separate the daughter nuclei.

7. Pseudoamitosis in a portion of the root, where cells are dividing very frequently. Chromatin material and nucleoli clumped together. The nucleus is dividing by constriction.

8. From the same preparation as drawing 7. Formation of a cell plate by cytoplasm.

9. Pseudoamitosis followed by cytokinesis. Cytoplasm is accumulated at the place of constriction of the nucleus and begins to form a cell plate.

10. A pseudoamitosis in the absence of calcium and magnesium. Cytoplasm forms the cell plate.

11. Amitosis not followed by cytokinesis. Cytoplasm almost entirely absent.

12. Stage somewhat similar to that shown in drawing 10. The chromatic elements resolved into granules.

13. Upper cell binucleate, lower cell has one nucleus. Both have very little cytoplasm.

14. A binucleate cell almost without cytoplasm.

in these cells, and constricted nuclei and the binucleate condition were observed. With 0.25 ppm mitosis appeared normal but many cells had quadriploid nuclei when seen at metaphase after 20 days.

The effects of restoring the calcium supply on the recovery of injured roots was observed. The abnormal tissues produced by irregular mitosis, which had remained undifferentiated, were found to be incapable of recovery or further development on addition of calcium. Cells produced before calcium deficiency had become acute and formed by a normal mitotic process were, however, able to resume growth immediately. Day (94) found that calcium deficiency in pea did not affect mature structures already formed. According to early observations of Reed (426), calcium deficiency did not prevent mitosis in *Spirogyra* or maize, but it suppressed new cell wall formation owing, it was thought, to failure to form the cell plate on which the middle lamella was laid. Reed (426) concluded that calcium deficiency in *Spirogyra* caused a narrowing of the spiral chloroplast, which also lost the characteristic lobes.

Davis (93) described effects of calcium deficiency on the histology of *Pinus taeda*. In the apical meristem of the stem, the normally isodiametric cells of the tunica became longitudinally extended and mitosis was suppressed. The apical dome was narrow and more pointed. In the central region or medulla, the mother cells were enlarged radially and were prematurely vacuolated; they differentiated earlier than in normal meristems. The mass of xylem and phloem tissue was markedly decreased, but cell walls were thicker in tissues of the hypodermis. In the root meristem, cells were greatly enlarged, especially just behind the apex, and were irregularly shaped. The root cap was short and rounded instead of pointed and long. Early differentiation occurred in cells forming tracheids; there was also either proliferation of central cells of the vascular region or decreased cell numbers with large cells and premature differentiation (Fig. 5).

Lyon and Garcia (310) observed that increase of the calcium supply increased both cell numbers and cell wall thickness in tomato collenchyma. Pericycle cells were also decreased in size but increased in wall thickness. Millikan (355) observed that calcium deficiency inhibited fiber-cell formation in flax. Cell walls were unlignified in the pericycle region whereas cuticle and epidermal walls appeared to be thicker. Much early work on the effects of calcium deficiency was reviewed by Bamford (27), who also described effects on the growth of wheat and maize roots. A marked effect of magnesium was observed regarding the calcium level at which injury occurred, but magnesium had no effect if calcium comprised over 2.5% of the total salts present.

Bamford found that root tip cells undergoing mitosis at the time of transfer to a calcium-deficient solution were liable to become binucleate with small disorganized nuclei. Kalra (260) presented a review of many anatomical effects of calcium deficiency and described results of calcium deficiency in tomato. Calcium deficiency caused a marked increase in the size of chromatin granules in nuclei in the region of the nucleolar membrane, as observed by Sommer and Sorokin. Nuclear size in stem apices was decreased more than cell size, but nuclei were always present. Nuclei tended to be located against cell walls. The outer layers of cells in the apical meristem were often fused and indistinguishable while mitosis could still be observed in deep layers. Calcium deficiency led to premature vacuolation and cell maturity and tended to suppress mitosis in less active meristems. In root apices the dermatogen was first affected and then the procambium. Nuclear size appeared to be decreased within 4 hours of transfer from normal to calcium-deficient solutions. In leaves, chloroplasts were enlarged when plants were transferred from normal to calcium-deficient treatments. Dense staining of vacuolated undifferentiated cells was characteristic of calcium deficiency. There was no evidence of dissolution of cell walls, but these were usually fragile to sectioning.

c. *The functions of calcium with particular reference to cell structure.* The functions of calcium in plant growth appear to be manifested in several ways, and it is unlikely that a single role is involved. Requirements by different plants appears to vary greatly. Thus brassicas, legumes such as beans, pea, and clovers, tomato, celery, potato, and beet varieties readily show calcium deficiency whereas many cereals, especially oat and rye (*Secale cereale*), appear much more tolerant of low calcium levels, around 1 ppm or less. Mevius (343, 344) recorded that *Pinus pinaster* had extremely low calcium requirements in comparison with those of *Onobrychis sativa* and several species of lupines. Maize was intermediate, but requirements were as low as for *Pinus pinaster* when the roots were maintained at 16°C as compared with 30°C when high requirements, which could be partially replaced by strontium, were observed. The partial replacement of calcium by strontium in the high requirement group including *Onobrychis* and *Lupinus* was not observed at 30°C.

i. *Calcium in cell walls.* The function of calcium as a constituent of cell walls in the form of calcium pectate in the middle lamella was commonly accepted from the early work of Mangin (319) and Hansteen (179) and of others reviewed by Molisch (359a) and True (527). Reed (426) attributed the original hypothesis of calcium pectate in the middle lamella to Payen in 1846. The observation by Bennet-Clark

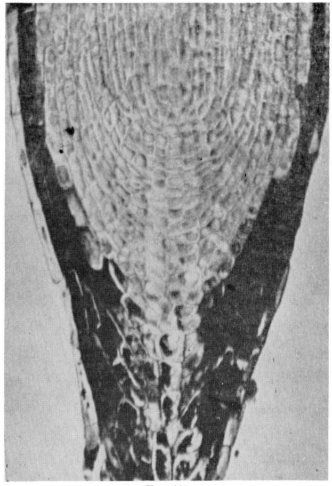

FIG. 5A

FIG. 5. Normal (A) and calcium-deficient (B) root tips of *Pinus taeda* showing decreased number of enlarged cells, bifurcation of apex, absence of root cap, and early initiation of tracheids. From Davis (93).

(32) that ethylenediamine tetraacetate (EDTA) has stimulating effects on the growth of *Avena* coleoptile is explained by assuming that EDTA chelates calcium bound as pectate and permits cell wall extension as a result of the increased plasticity produced. Support for this view was also provided by the fact that ammonium oxalate, but not ammonium chloride, encouraged cell wall extension. Results also show that trivalent ions, such as praseodymium, had markedly inhibitory effects on *Avena*

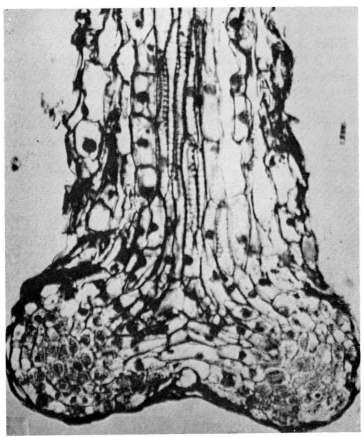

Fig. 5B

cell wall extension at concentrations well below those at which osmotic effects could have been implicated. The plasticity of the cell wall was considered to be maximal when pectins were fully methylated, intermediate when free carbonyl groups provided some measure of hydrogen bonding, and minimal when calcium, or possibly other multivalent ions, were able to provide electrovalent binding of adjacent polygalacturonide chains. The use of EDTA alone (Letham, 293), or with protein- and lipid-dissolving reagents as recommended by Ginsburg (157) to promote tissue maceration, is additional evidence for the presence of calcium and possibly other metals in the pectic structure of the middle lamella, which may also contain protein between the adjacent primary walls. Ginsburg (157a) obtained experimental evidence for the cementing effect of calcium and other metal cations on the binding of cell walls. Combinations of calcium, magnesium, iron, and copper were more effective than one or two of these metals.

ii. Calcium in cell membranes and lipid structures. The minute amounts of calcium that are required to produce normal mitosis, as described earlier, suggest that calcium has a specific function in the organization of chromatin, or of the mitotic spindle. Premature differentiation and premature vacuolation could be secondary effects due to suppression of mitosis. Reed (426) observed that severe calcium deficiency in *Spirogyra* caused the appearance around the nuclei of a substance resembling lecithin, and Florell (141) found decreased numbers of mitochondria in calcium-deficient roots of wheat. Both these effects could result from defects in membrane formation or organization in which lipids such as lecithin might be involved as calcium salts. Abnormal mitosis might also be related to failure to utilize lipid components in a membrane. The suggested defective cell plate formation proposed by Reed (426) could also result from failure to lay down a membrane across the separate protoplasts produced after mitosis. This would then account for the binucleate cells, as recorded by Sorokin and Sommer (492). Bennet-Clark (32) drew attention to the widespread distribution of the enzyme lecithinase D in plants. This enzyme hydrolyzes lecithin to choline and phosphatidic acid, and he pointed out that the lecithins form lipid-soluble salts with divalent ions which could provide a means of conveying inorganic salts across semipermeable membranes by means of a lecithin cycle. Two other possibly significant points may be noted here. Maizel and Benson (316) found that phosphorylcholine constituted a major organic phosphorus compound in shoots and might comprise up to 20% of the total soluble phosphorus. Davidson and Long (91) found that calcium, which was partly replaceable by strontium or barium, activated cabbage leaf phospholipase, which hydrolyzes ovolecithin D and related compounds, and that it had a high optimum concentration of 0.01 *M in vitro*. This enzyme is widespread and very active in brassicas where calcium requirements are known to be high; it occurs in both soluble and particulate fractions. This enzyme, and therefore calcium, may have a role in the transport of ions across mitochondrial or nuclear membranes. Equally probable, calcium salts of lecithin-like compounds may be essential components of such membranes. The observation of Pearsall and Hanby (401) that excess calcium led to thick cuticle formation in *Potamogeton* was interpreted by them as indicating a role of calcium in lipid metabolism. The association between calcium and so-called "protoplasmic permeability" discussed by Heilbrunn (186) would also be consistent with the requirement for calcium in a membrane surface either at the cell surface, or around the vacuole, or both.

iii. Calcium in the nucleic acid structure of chromosomes. The formation of compounds between deoxyribonucleic acids (DNA) and divalent metals has recently been described by Kirby (278). The ability of DNA to form complexes with divalent metals is probably directly related to the cytological observations of Steffensen (500, 501), Mazia (327), Levine (294), Eversole and Tatum (137), and Hyde and Paliwal (236). A close relationship between calcium deficiency and chromosome abnormality has been found. Suitable treatment with EDTA in media of low ionic strength, or alternate treatment by citrate and water, causes dispersion of the chromosomes due, it is thought, to dissolution of ionic bridges. EDTA also caused increased chiasma frequency in *Drosophila*. Calcium deficiency caused great increases in chromosomal aberrations in *Tradescantia* pollen cells (500). Increased chiasma frequency in *Plantago ovata* and chromosome abnormalities in *Tradescantia* occurred when calcium-deficient plants were irradiated. It is suggested here that calcium is directly involved in chromosome stability and is a constituent of the chromosome structure. It is interesting to recall that a direct role of calcium on nuclear organization has been postulated from quite early work, reviewed by Sorokin and Sommer (491). The biochemical basis for these observations, which have been relatively neglected, is now apparent. The possibility that mutation rates may be higher in calcium-deficient organisms or on plants grown in acid soils merits consideration. The effect of magnesium, noted later, on microsomal particles is probably analogous.

iv. Other functions. Joham (251) concluded from studies with cotton that calcium has an effect on translocation of carbohydrates in a manner analogous to that which is postulated for boron. Calcium probably has a role in providing a major component of the bases required to provide the optimum salt-hydrogen ion environment in the cell. It is clear from the work of Richards and others, to be described later, that calcium-sodium-potassium interactions have important effects on cell hydration. For this reason probably, if for no other, not all the base requirements of the cells can be provided as calcium, and conversely a substantial proportion must be present as such. The presence of calcium oxalate crystals in cells, which is reviewed by Olsen (392), might be regarded as a special case of calcium acting as a base for the removal of high concentrations of oxalate. Burström (59, 60) also regarded the effect of calcium, in the counteracting of injury to root elongation at low pH at concentrations above those required for cell expansion and division, as a specific function.

It might be concluded that calcium is required simultaneously at different concentrations for cell division and chromosome stability, cell expansion and middle lamella structure, mitochondrial production, cell hydration, as a cell base component, for activation of phospholipase D, and possibly in determination of membrane structure, stability, or ionic permeability.

5. Magnesium

a. Visible symptoms. The importance of magnesium as a plant nutrient is discussed by Jacob (242) in a recent book. The function of magnesium as a constituent of chlorophylls a and b naturally determines some of the most important effects caused by deficiency of this element. All green plants show some type of chlorosis due to lack of magnesium, and the symptoms are practically always more severe, or are first seen, in the older leaves. Exceptionally the oldest leaves of some plants, e.g., tomato, may remain green after chlorosis has developed in other mature leaves. This effect has been noted also in a few instances for potassium deficiency and molybdenum deficiency, although plants usually show the first symptoms of these deficiencies in the oldest leaves.

In spite of the general effect of chlorosis, the details of magnesium deficiency symptoms may vary considerably in individual plants. Certain features however, are especially frequent. Loss of chlorophyll is often followed by the appearance of other pigments. In some plants, including most brassicas, sugar beet, radish, and lettuce, chlorosis usually commences as a marked interveinal yellow-green mottling or blotching that is distributed uniformly over most of the older leaves, while most vascular tissues remain green. In tobacco (146, 337), celery, and parsnip, the margins and/or leaf tip are first affected. In many plants, however, including certain varieties of apple, cherry, tomato, some varieties of potato, citrus, pea, broad bean, red clover (*Trifolium pratense*), white clovers (*Trifolium repens, T. hybridum*), and lucerne, the chlorosis often occurs first in interveinal areas within clearly defined green margins. The margins frequently become brilliantly tinted with yellow, orange, red, or purple colors. Production of brilliant tints is the most characteristic symptom of magnesium deficiency in most plants in addition to the chlorotic pattern (189, 190, 192, 550a–553). Tinting other than bright yellow may however, be practically absent in lettuce, citrus species (62), tomato and pear (*Pyrus communis*). The last is in striking contrast to the effects of nitrogen deficiency (550a, 553). Pigmentation may precede appreciable chlorosis, as in cotton (83), subterranean clover (356), gooseberry, and black currant (*Ribes nigrum*) (553). In some plants, e.g., clovers, the green margins are the regions ultimately to show most red or purple pigmentation.

Necrosis often follows chlorosis and pigmentation; it may occur in margins that were formerly green and later pigmented, as in clovers, or it may develop in the centrally chlorotic areas, as in potato 'Majestic' and in many apple varieties. Regular central, interveinal, oval necrotic areas which are associated with red and purple tints within green margins, produce a striking pattern in sweet cherry (*Prunus avium*) (Fig. 6). The pattern of chlorosis shown with magnesium deficiency reflects the distribution of the element in the leaf (276).

In dwarf French beans the first symptom of magnesium deficiency is a purple-brown spotting which is regularly arranged in interveinal

FIG. 6. Magnesium deficiency in sweet cherry (*Prunus avium*): chlorotic interveinal areas within green leaf margins are bordered by purple-tinted areas (left). This condition is followed by bleaching (right) of most of lamina except for deep purple margins and "yellow-green" areas of original centers of chlorosis.

areas close to the midrib and major lateral veins and which radiates outward from the basal regions of the leaflets on older leaves. The veins are bordered by a pale green region which encloses the pigmented spot. Later the leaves show bright yellow-green interveinal chlorosis and profuse fine necrotic spotting. There is considerable resemblance between this symptom produced by magnesium deficiency and that resulting from manganese deficiency, except that in the latter, the regularly arranged purple or brown necrotic spots appear in the young leaves. The interchangeability of magnesium and manganese in many enzyme systems, as described in Chapter 4, may be related to this particular similarity in their deficiency symptoms. The difference in the distribu-

tion of the symptoms may reflect differences in retranslocation of the
two elements, or in the dissociation constants or optimal activating
concentrations, or the developmental stages at which the relevant
enzymes are produced. Maize shows bright yellow-green or orange
interveinal striping of old leaves followed by white necrotic lesions.
In barley the leaf margins and tips are first affected and become deep
yellow or orange. Magnesium deficiency in oat begins as light and
dark green "beading" between the veins along the older leaves (Fig.
7). Irregular areas become chlorotic and are ivory, or pale orange,
in color. These areas become necrotic.

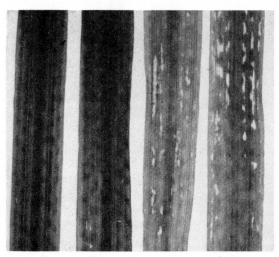

Fig. 7. Magnesium deficiency in oats (*Avena sativa*): initial chlorotic pattern
of interveinal striping with small "islands" of greener tissues in beaded chains is
followed by ivory-tinted necrotic flecking and striping of old leaves.

Tomato fruits which lack magnesium are notably lacking in red pigment and may be pale orange; the flesh is "woolly" and lacks mucilage.
Other symptoms of magnesium deficiency in various plants are described in books by Wallace (553) and by Jacob (242).

b. *Anatomical and cytochemical effects of magnesium.* Lyon and Garcia (311) found that a high magnesium supply appeared to depress the
development of internal or primary phloem tissues of tomato stems. Magnesium deficiency led to small pith cells and chlorenchyma was densely
packed with chloroplasts; a high magnesium supply produced the maximum size and smallest numbers of chlorenchyma cells.

A possible cytochemical role of magnesium has been described by
Ts'o (529) and Ts'o, Bonner, and Vinograd (529a). Microsomal par-

ticles, containing ribonucleic acid (RNA) and protein, from pea stems appear to consist of submicrosomal particles which are considered to be bound together by magnesium ions combined with the phosphate radicals of RNA. The particles may be dissociated into two subparticles by increased pH or phosphate content of the medium and they are reversibly associated at a critical magnesium concentration of $5 \times 10^{-4} M$. Addition of EDTA also causes dissociation into three subparticles, all of which comprise ribonucleoprotein structures. These particles contain magnesium and also about one-sixth as much calcium. Most of the magnesium appears to be combined with nucleic acid phosphate radicals to the extent of about one-half of their combining capacity.

Zillig *et al.* (593) inferred a direct role of magnesium in protein synthesis in *Escherichia coli* at the stage of binding RNA with large polypeptide structures of molecular weight about 17,000. This conclusion was based on the evidence that ethylenediaminetetraacetic acid splits these compounds by chelation with magnesium. It must follow that, if the ribosomes are specific sites for protein synthesis, magnesium deficiency should have a direct effect upon protein synthesis. This effect might be masked by carbohydrate deficiency because of effects of chlorosis, but it should be detectable in nonchlorophyllous tissues, e.g., roots with adequate carbohydrate supply. The complexity of ribonucleoprotein particles is further illustrated by the requirement for manganese also (312), which is described later.

Chloroplast breakdown in cauliflower (Hewitt and Hucklesby, unpublished) was preceded by extreme starch accumulation. The course of events was almost identical with that described for nitrogen deficiency, although tests for protein and RNA have not been carried out. Epidermal pigments were formed only in local patches, however, and the lipid globules formed from chloroplast breakdown were not colored golden yellow.

c. Effects on composition. Early accounts, reviewed by Jacob (242), of the role of magnesium were often directed to the idea that magnesium is a "carrier" of phosphorus in plants, and this was investigated by Truog *et al.* (528). Peas grown in water culture contained more phosphorus in the seed with increasing magnesium levels, regardless of the wide range over which phosphorus was supplied. In spite of such results as this, however, it is probable that the apparent role of magnesium as a phosphorus "carrier" is due mainly to the almost universal importance of magnesium in the enzyme systems which are involved in all aspects of phosphorus metabolism (207). It would be expected that the response to phosphorus would be limited if the enzyme systems mediating its metabolism were limited by magnesium supply. The uptake of phosphorus into organic combination, which is especially dependent on magnesium, would also favor transport of inorganic phosphorus to sites of its assimilation.

The role of magnesium in one or more reactions of photosynthetic phosphorylation (17) naturally implies a profound effect of magnesium on composition. Williams (582) observed that, in tomato, magnesium deficiency decreased malic acid by 20% but decreased citric acid by 85% compared with normal plants. The effects of magnesium on amino acid composition are described in Section II, C.

6. Potassium

a. Visual symptoms of deficiency. Symptoms of potassium deficiency show a number of features that are clearly analogous in many plants, but different in detail. Marked changes in growth habit are produced by potassium deficiency. Plants, such as beet, celery, carrot (*Daucus carota* var. *sativa*), and parsnip (*Pastinaca sativa*), that normally grow from a crown without an extended stem, develop an acute rosette habit when they are deficient in potassium. Marked shortening of the internodes occurs in many plants, including broad bean (*Vicia faba*), pea, mustard (*Brassica hirta* [*Sinapis alba*]), flax, cereals, tomato, and potato. The internode shortening appears to be related to light intensity (or length of day): it is more marked when plants, e.g., broad beans, are exposed to full light intensities, and it may be absent, or even reversed, in mustard during winter greenhouse conditions. Stem diameter may be increased in mustard when it is potassium deficient and the stem tissues may be more succulent. The shoot:root ratio is significantly decreased in subterranean clover (356).

Potassium deficiency appears to result in decrease of apical dominance since some plants—e.g., flax and cereals, particularly barley—develop a bushy habit due to the extension of numerous axillary shoots, usually near the base of the plants. Multiple, weak axillary shoots develop from axillary buds along the length of branches of many citrus species when they are severely deficient in potassium (62). The tillers in barley may be nearly prostrate, and this also indicates a possible change in some hormone activity. The loss of apical dominance often occurs before the death of the apical bud. Death of the terminal bud and the terminal lateral buds does, however, occur in severe conditions, and the "dieback" so produced is followed by regeneration from the basal regions to produce a stunted, bushy habit. Richards and Shih (447, 448) attributed the increase of tillering in potassium-deficient barley to an interaction with the high level of sodium which was a necessary concomitant of this response.

Some form of leaf tissue collapse is always associated with potassium deficiency when it is sufficiently severe. In many plants, e.g., brassicas, apple (548, 549), currants (*Ribes* spp.) cocoa, hop, beet, broad bean, this collapse occurs as a clearly defined marginal scorch that extends with the age of the plant and the severity of the deficiency to inter-veinal regions until it may involve practically the whole of the lamina before leaf fall (189, 190, 553). Tissue collapse may commence at the leaf tip as in flax, barley, or leek (*Allium porrum*). In other plants, e.g., potato, French beans, citrus species, parsnip, the necrosis may oc-cur at random, either as numerous small necrotic spots, or as variously sized areas of irregular scorch. In potato, the necrotic spots are black or dark brown (Fig. 17a, c): they appear first on the lower surface of the leaf, often in vascular tissues. Necrotic areas usually enlarge and fuse into a general scorching of much of the leaf. The blackening in potato tissues probably relates to the abnormally high tyrosinase activity which develops under these conditions (364, 367). In peas, the old leaves often show regular scorching whereas younger leaves show irregular necrotic spotting and marginal cupping, or folding, of leaflets. The puckering, or "tucking," of interveinal areas of potassium-deficient orange (*Citrus aurantium*) leaves may be analogous (62). In tomato, either well-defined pale brown marginal scorch, commencing from tips of leaf segments, or irregular black necrotic areas close to or along leaf veins may occur. The conditions that determine the type of symptoms produced have not been elucidated. In clover and lucerne (alfalfa), necrosis also begins in small areas but appears as a regular pattern of spotting or interveinal "hatching" close to, but often within, margins which may remain green for a longer period.

In subterranean clover (*Trifolium subterraneum*) varieties the necro-sis may take several forms in one plant (356). Thus the Dwalganup variety first shows small red-brown spots in the upper surface, close to the margins. Later, purple necrotic areas appear around margins of leaflets that do not show the first symptom. In extreme cases gray-purple col-lapsed spots may appear in the distal part of leaflets that do not show the other symptoms.

Although symptoms of leaf scorch are always produced, other symp-toms may precede, or accompany, their appearance in potassium-de-ficient plants. Irregular fading of chlorophyll and production of gum spots in leaves occurs in citrus (62). Foliage of potatoes is initially dark blue-green and shiny before necrotic spotting appears. Foliage of celery, parsnip, carrot, barley, and other cereals may also be initially darker green, or blue green, whereas leaves of beans, lucerne, clovers, tomato, brassicas, mustard, some apple varieties, and grasses are markedly pale prior to the appearance of necrosis, or scorch. In cereals the blue-green color fades to pale green. It is evident that effects of potassium deficiency on chlorophyll content, or stability, vary with the action of other undefined factors in different plants.

It would be of interest to examine whether these apparently distinct ways in which initial tissue breakdown occurs reflect either the distribution of the element as suggested by the leaf ash pattern for potassium and magnesium deficiencies, as observed by Kidson (276), or whether anatomical features and irregularly distributed water tensions are associated with the pattern of necrosis. It is also difficult to distinguish between a necrosis which is caused by cell death due to dehydration and that which is due to the accumulation of toxic constituents. Thus the necrotic lesions which develop in potassium-deficient barley, especially when it is grown with high calcium-low sodium nutrients, or on chalkland soils, are due to, or associated with, accumulation of putrescine (78, 79, 445, 446). Putrescine also accumulates in clovers and wheat, but not in flax. The effects of putrescine as a means for simulating potassium deficiency symptoms in clovers and wheat or other plants have not been reported. Clovers contain amine oxidase (267) which may yield hydrogen peroxide as a toxic factor, but the enzyme is not reported in the cereals. The necrotic areas are often pale brown or white in clovers, pea, and French bean, whereas in broad bean and potato they are dark brown or black. These differences might be related to differences in polyphenolase activity, which is extensive in potato and in broad bean and in the presence or absence of substances that may be transformed into melanin pigments, e.g., tyrosine or polyphenols (364).

Under most conditions, leaf symptoms of potassium deficiency occur first in the oldest leaves and later in the younger leaves. Occasionally in tomato, the oldest leaves remain apparently normal for some days after marked scorching has appeared in slightly younger leaves, then severe general scorch may occur suddenly. It is also found that, whereas marginal paling may precede scorching in old leaves, the young leaves develop marginal scorch without previous marginal paling. The effects of iron supply on the distribution of potassium deficiency symptoms are described later, and this factor might account for differences of the type just noted above.

Early symptoms of potassium deficiency are often associated with a tendency for the leaves to curve downward, or outward, from the crown of the plant. The leaf lamina may become markedly convex on the upper side as in French bean and potato. The marginal regions however, often roll inwards toward the upper surface when scorching occurs.

Petioles may show independent symptoms in some plants. Elongated dark brown, or black lesions, which tend to be watersoaked, develop in the upper surface regions in petioles of sugar beet, and these collapse and shrivel when potassium deficiency is very severe; petiole collapse is also common in celery.

In some plants, including maize, (230) potato (37, 217), oats (554), flax, some grasses (192), and cocoa (164, 165), there are interactions with iron or phosphorus supply which are discussed later. A detailed investigation of these effects is described by Bolle-Jones (37). In these plants and possibly others, initial leaf paling may be due to an induced iron deficiency condition. Another important factor, which may modify the effects of potassium deficiency, is the supply of other elements including calcium and sodium or other monovalent ions. The distribution of potassium deficiency symptoms reflects the retranslocation of the element from old to young tissues, where concentrations tend to be higher (384, 402) in stem and root apices, cambia, and abscission layers of several plants. These points are discussed in later sections.

b. Anatomical and histological effects. Nightingale, Schermerhorn, and Robbins (384) studied histological and chemical effects of potassium deficiency in tomato. Early effects due to lack of potassium included loss of cambial activity except at the stem apex. Lignification was increased, pericycle and collenchyma cell walls were thicker. As the deficiency progressed there was a marked change in anatomy. Pericycle and lignified walls became very thin. Collenchyma decreased, and xylem became parenchymatous. The importance of potassium in cambial and meristematic activity was also indicated by the continued presence of potassium in cambial cells of deficient tomato stems and its disappearance from most other tissues, except the stem apex, as observed by Penston (402) and Janssen and Bartholemew (247). The high rate of protein synthesis in meristematic cells and their sensitivity to potassium has generally implicated potassium in protein synthesis [cf. Webster (573)].

In subterranean clover (356) the necrotic areas develop initially in cells of the palisade tissues. These show strong affinity for safranine staining but they do not collapse immediately so that the epidermis does not become sunken at the earliest stage, as in manganese deficiency (356). Spongy parenchyma is affected later, and the necrotic areas shrink and dry out. Millikan (356) cited earlier work by Lindenbein showing a similar sequence.

Lyon and Garcia (311) described anatomical effects of different combinations of potassium with calcium or magnesium levels given to tomato plants. Decreasing the potassium supply appeared to cause increased formation of secondary phloem, especially sieve tubes, which were derived from phloem parenchyma. With low potassium and low calcium, but high magnesium, levels there was an extensive development of phloem parenchyma with isolated groups of sieve tubes whereas with low potassium, low magnesium, and high calcium levels the phloem tissue was dense, highly organized with numerous sieve tubes and a minimum of parenchyma. Potassium deficiency generally resulted in the smallest sizes of phloem cells. By contrast with external secondary phloem, increase in potassium and a corresponding decrease in calcium resulted in an increased development of internal, or primary, phloem tissues. Pith cells disintegrated under conditions of potassium deficiency. High potassium levels produced the smallest numbers of cells and thinnest walls in the collenchyma. Tören (524a) observed that omission of potassium from cultures of excised carrot tissues resulted in decreased lignification of tracheids, loss of meristematic activity, and production of giant thin-walled parenchyma cells. By contrast, calcium deficiency caused the production of large numbers of relatively small cells. White (579b) found that potassium deficiency suppressed lateral root formation in excised tomato roots without preventing their elongation.

   c. *Effects on composition.* Some aspects of the effects of potassium supply on composition are discussed in Section II, A, 7. Other work is considered here. Nightingale *et al.* (384) observed at first an accumulation of starch in phloem, cortex, medullary rays, and pith of tomato stems when deficient in potassium. Later stages of the deficiency led to a disappearance of starch. These changes probably corresponded to the multiple and interacting effects of potassium deficiency on decreased protein content and on decreased assimilation as elucidated by Gregory and Richards and their collaborators, to be described later. There is general agreement between results of Eaton (129) with sunflower, Hartt (183) with sugar cane, Cooil and Slattery (82) with guayule (*Parthenium argentatum*), and the very thorough work on barley by Gregory, Richards, and their collaborators described in Section II, A, 7, that potassium deficiency causes marked increases in amide and in α-amino nitrogen fractions. Total and insoluble (protein) nitrogen fractions may change variously according to age, to the tissue analyzed, plant species, or other factors.

   Hartt (183) found with sugar cane (*Saccharum officinarum*) and Cooil and Slattery (82) with guayule, that potassium deficiency led to increased proportions of reducing sugars (Table IX). In sugar cane sucrose levels were decreased, and in guayule, polysaccharides of the levulin and inulin type were decreased, when potassium was deficient.

Cooil and Slattery observed that the ratio K:Ca was highly correlated with the ratio levulin + inulin to reducing sugars. They suggested that potassium promoted fructosan formation, possibly indirectly, through an effect—since shown to occur in plants (329, 349)—on the pyruvic kinase or pyruvic phosphotransferase system, in which calcium was

TABLE IX

CARBOHYDRATE CONTENT OF GUAYULE (*Parthenium argentatum*) PLANTS GROWN WITH AND WITHOUT POTASSIUM[a,b]

Treatment	Total carbohydrates[c] (% dry wt.)	Inulin (% dry wt.)	Levulin (% dry wt.)	Reducing sugars (% dry wt.)	Reducing sugars as % of total carbohydrates
Expanding leaves					
Minus K	1.79	0.10	0.40	1.29	72.1
Plus K	1.22	0.26	0.42	0.54	44.3
Mature leaves					
Minus K	3.50	0.08	0.74	2.69	76.9
Plus K	1.42	0.09	0.55	0.79	55.6
Young stems					
Minus K	3.39	0.02	1.79	1.59	46.9
Plus K	3.11	0.11	2.54	0.46	14.8
Old stems					
Minus K	1.59	0.25	0.89	0.44	27.7
Plus K	2.53	0.31	1.76	0.46	18.2
Roots					
Minus K	1.88	0.32	1.01	0.55	29.3
Plus K	2.77	0.08	2.20	0.49	17.7
Flowers and fruits					
Minus K	4.57	0.03	0.93	3.62	79.2
Plus K	5.11	0.08	1.04	4.00	78.3

[a] From Cooil and Slattery (82).
[b] Seventeen-month nursery plants received nutrient treatments from December 23, 1944, to April 24, 1945.
[c] Inulin plus levulins plus reducing sugars.

considered to be inhibitory (183) and thereby accounted for the importance of the K:Ca ratio. Potassium deficiency also increased the proportion of reducing sugars to total carbohydrate. Eaton (129) observed that potassium deficiency in sunflower decreased total and reducing sugars in leaves and increased sucrose in stems (Table X). These results generally are in agreement with those of Gregory, with Baptiste (167), and with Sen (169), for barley. It is evident that the effects of potassium on relative concentrations of carbohydrate fractions are complex and probably differ according to the species, possibly owing to multiple functions of the element, as well as being determined by the actual levels of potassium used in different experiments. The plant age or severity of the symptoms also determine the nature of the changes, as seen in Eaton's work (Table X).

TABLE X

EFFECTS OF POTASSIUM SUPPLY ON CARBOHYDRATE FRACTIONS (AS % DRY WEIGHT) IN SUNFLOWER (*Helianthus annuus*)[a]

Plant part	Total sugars		Reducing sugars		Sucrose		Sucrose percentage of total sugars		Starch	
	Minus K	Plus K	Minus K	Plus K	Minus K	Plus K	Minus K	Plus K	Minus K	Plus K
First harvest (24-day-old plants)										
Leaves	4.39	1.34	3.57	1.01	0.82	0.33	18.67	24.75	0.52	0.52
Upper stems	12.65	8.48	10.87	7.49	1.78	0.99	14.06	11.65	1.22	1.17
Middle stems	7.44	4.79	5.55	4.04	1.89	0.75	25.39	15.60	0.85	0.84
Lower stems	4.01	2.83	2.81	2.04	1.20	0.79	29.98	27.92	0.68	0.84
Second harvest (31-day-old plants)										
Leaves	6.84	1.23	4.41	0.77	2.43	0.47	35.47	37.81	0.67	0.41
Upper stems	6.56	7.78	4.34	6.61	2.22	1.17	33.86	15.04	1.01	1.09
Middle stems	4.22	3.60	2.73	2.71	1.50	0.88	35.42	25.54	0.74	0.77
Lower stems	2.08	2.65	1.12	1.80	0.96	0.85	46.26	32.13	0.67	0.66
Third harvest (42-day-old plants)										
Leaves	5.24	3.48	3.50	2.94	1.74	0.55	33.23	15.74	0.59	0.51
Upper stems	5.84	21.23	3.23	20.11	2.61	1.12	44.61	5.26	0.82	0.82
Middle stems	3.02	12.65	1.44	11.83	1.58	0.82	52.44	6.46	0.53	0.61
Lower stems	1.56	6.92	0.83	6.24	0.74	0.68	47.12	9.88	0.56	0.56

[a] From Eaton (129).

An additional complication is that potassium deficiency may interfere with translocation, as suggested by Hartt (182) from observations on phloem necrosis in sieve tubes and companion cells of sugar cane stem, and by Gregory and Sen (169) for barley. Eaton (129) reviewed the controversial observations regarding effects of potassium deficiency on carbohydrate status. He concluded that carbohydrates often accumulated during the early stages of potassium deficiency and reflected the predominating effect of decreased potassium supply on impaired protein synthesis at this stage. More severe deficiency, or prolonged effects of moderate deficiency, and consequent protein breakdown would lead to loss of chloroplast activity, to depressed photosynthesis and, together with increased respiration, to decreased carbohydrate content as recorded by Gregory and Richards and their associates (see Section II, A, 7). The data of Table X for sunflower show the reversal in the effects of potassium deficiency on sugar content and on sucrose : total sugar ratios as the plants became older and more deficient. Leaves and stems also showed different trends with increasing age.

Cooil (81) also observed effects of potassium on the organic acid content of guayule. There was a general correlation between cations and the total organic acids. High potassium levels led to high concentrations of unidentified organic acids. Citric acid was maximal at an intermediate potassium level. High potassium levels depressed malic acid concentrations, apparently through the depressive effect of potassium on calcium, since calcium level was positively and closely correlated with malic acid level. This point is considered below (Section II, B, 2, a) in relation to lime-induced chlorosis.

7. Interrelationships among Nitrogen, Phosphorus, Potassium, Calcium, and Sodium in Water Content, Dry Matter, Growth, Assimilation Rates, and Respiration

The discussion of the significance of tissue hydration, water content, or succulence is beyond the scope of this chapter. The estimation of water content has however been frequently adopted in nutritional studies, especially in relation to some of the macronutrients in experiments that have reported various growth measurements. It is convenient, therefore, to describe under one heading the effects and interactions of some macronutrient elements on water content, on relative growth changes, and on assimilation and respiration rates.

a. Water content. Richards and Shih (447, 448) carried out experiments to resolve the apparently contradictory results reviewed by Richards and other workers regarding the effects of potassium and its interactions with other elements on water content. Barley was used in this work and the levels of magnesium and chloride were maintained constant, while sulfate was allowed to vary. Decreasing potassium increased water content, or succulence. Decreasing sodium decreased succulence. Decreasing phosphorus only slightly decreased succulence. The effects of phosphorus were dependent on the levels of sodium, potassium, and calcium. There were also interactions between effects of potassium and the age of the plants. Analysis of the plants showed, however, that in spite of the effect of potassium treatment, there was no correlation between potassium content and succulence. In fact, when partial correlations with sodium, calcium, and phosphorus were eliminated, there was a small but significantly negative correlation between potassium status and succulence. The correlation between sodium content and succulence was very high, and that between phosphorus content and succulence was also high. It was concluded, therefore, that the effects of potassium treatment were indirect through changes in sodium content. The contradictory results reported by others were explained in part by the varied effects of potassium on carbohydrate content and in part by the sodium-calcium balance in the nutrients supplied. Nitrogen had inconsistent effects on water content. There was no interaction between nitrogen and potassium, contrary to the marked effects of nitrogen supply on potassium deficiency often observed in other respects and under field conditions. At the lowest phosphorus levels nitrogen had little effect on succulence, but at the highest phosphorus level, increasing nitrogen at first increased, and then decreased, water content. At the medium phosphorus levels, increasing the nitrogen mainly decreased succulence. Goodall *et al.* (160) found that the water content of the aerial parts of lettuce was consistently increased, and often doubled, by increase in levels of phosphorus, regardless of the prevailing nitrogen or potassium levels or of the time of sampling. There were, however, interactions between phosphorus and potassium levels. The effect of phosphorus was much greater at low than at high potassium levels. Increasing potassium generally increased slightly the low water content of plants grown with the lowest phosphorus level, though minima sometimes occurred at intermediate potassium levels and markedly decreased succulence at intermediate and sometimes at high phosphorus levels.

b. Leaf and stem growth. The effects of nutrition, and more especially of the interactions of macronutrients on leaf growth, have been reviewed by Ashby (22) and further information has been assembled by Njoku (386). Early observations by Pearsall and Hanby (401) on *Potamogeton* had shown that high Ca:K ratios, as contrasted with high K:Ca ratios, led to broad leaves with short internodes and increased the development of minor leaf veins. Differential supply of calcium and potassium to roots or foliage showed the calcium effect to be dominant. Cell counts indicated that excess calcium increased cell numbers 2.5 times relative to excess potassium, but the latter produced larger cells with greater elongation, as would be expected from the discussion on the role of calcium. Pearsall and Hanby suggested that calcium impaired, whereas potassium enhanced, cell wall plasticity. On the other hand, excess calcium was thought to lead to larger leaf primordia attributable to increased cell division.

Njoku (386) grew *Ipomoea caerulea* in sand cultures with low and high levels of nitrogen, phosphorus, and potassium (N, P, K) in eight factorial combinations. The low levels did not produce deficiency symptoms but were low enough to limit maximum growth. Osmotic concentrations were maintained constant by the use of sodium chloride so that chloride replaced nitrate or phosphate and sodium replaced potassium. With these experimental restrictions the following effects of the N, P, and K levels were inferred.

Increased nitrogen, potassium, or phosphorus, in general, increased the rate of leaf production as judged by visible leaves and reduced the degree of lobing of the leaves. There was a highly significant negative correlation between the degree of lobing and the apparent rate of leaf production. The greatest effects occurred with additional nitrogen and decreased in the order of phosphorus and potassium. The effects of phosphorus or potassium were marked only in the presence of nitrogen. Increased potassium increased lobing and decreased leaf production in the presence of high phosphorus with low, but not with high, nitrogen; the interaction between potassium and phosphorus was significant. The high NPK treatment gave the greatest rate of leaf production and the minimum lobing, whereas the PK (low N) treatment gave the opposite extremes with a twofold range. Njoku (386) concluded from a review of the literature on heteroblastic leaf development, that the degree of lobing was an inverse function of the rate of leaf production, regardless of the cause of the latter, and that it reflected the effects of the ratio of mature to immature leaves produced at a given stage of growth.

Morton and Watson (361) found that high nitrogen supplies increased by about 20% the rate of leaf production by beet, and increased the total number of leaf cells to about double the number produced in the low nitrogen treatment. The effect was greater for the fifteenth, than for the first or fifth, leaves, as would be expected for the progressive effects of nitrogen shortage. An approximate estimate of cell sizes in the fully expanded leaves showed that nitrogen had a slight negative effect in the first leaf and consistent, progressively increasing, positive effects on cell size in the fifth, tenth, fifteenth, and twentieth leaves; in the latter the cells were 50% larger in apparent area and therefore about double the volume of those in expanded leaves produced during the low nitrogen treatment. Total leaf areas were progressively increased with high nitrogen from the first to the twentieth leaf, with ratios of high to low nitrogen of 1.1 to 5.4 in the low salt series. Salt had little effect on cell size or total numbers of leaf cells.

Schwabe (460) described in detail the interrelationships between potassium and phosphorus under different conditions of sodium, calcium, and nitrogen supply on the characteristics of the growth and on the assimilation rate of bracken fern (*Pteridium aquilinum*). The interactions were complex and can be summarized only in part. Phosphorus deficiency depressed the total dry weight under high potassium nutrition and the effects of increasing potassium were observed at increasingly high levels of this element with increasing phosphorus supply. In spite of the frequently reported beneficial effects of sodium, the "high calcium-no sodium" type of nutrient was clearly superior to the "low calcium-with sodium" nutrient for potassium deficiency treatments. The distribution of dry weight among root, rhizome, and leaf was changed by the nutrient treatment. Mean leaf area was greatest for high potassium and phosphorus levels with ammonium nitrogen in the presence of high calcium and low sodium. Decreasing potassium decreased leaf area most under these conditions and least when phosphorus was also low. The relative effects on leaf area, of solutions of the calcium, sodium, and ammonium types were reversed for high and low phosphorus levels, and the ammonium nitrogen-low sodium nutrient was very unfavorable with low phosphorus. This would be expected from the role of potassium or sodium in ATP synthesis and the role of ATP in the utilization of ammonia. The variations in water content were affected by highly significant third-order interactions among nutrients. Phosphorus supply had an outstanding effect on water content, which was decreased by low phosphorus treatments. Effects of potassium were more complex. Water contents were increased by increasing potassium in the calcium type nutrients, at low or high phosphorus levels, and, decreased in the "low calcium-with sodium" types when phosphorus level was high. With two exceptions, low phosphorus supply markedly decreased net assimilation rates for all potassium levels and nutrient type combinations. Decreasing potassium decreased net assimilation rate only at the lowest level with the low sodium, or with the ammonium-with high calcium, types of solutions.

c. Assimilation, respiration, nitrogen and carbohydrate metabolism. Nightingale, Schermerhorn, and Robbins (384) reviewed the effects of potassium on sugar accumulation and pointed out the complexity of the relationships involved. Early work by Janssen and Bartholemew (247, 248) indicated that maximum carbohydrate production, or accumulation, occurred in tomato at intermediate levels of potassium supply between deficiency and luxury consumption levels in the absence of added sodium.

Gregory and Richards and their collaborators have described several experiments with a pure line of barley which they have used to study the interaction of macronutrients on growth and on carbon and nitrogen metabolism. Only the main effects of this extensive work can be summarized here.

Gregory and Richards (168) and Richards (442) found that potassium deficiency produced a low net assimilation rate in accordance with the low photosynthesis rates recorded by Briggs (47) and high respiration rates. Phosphorus deficiency did not markedly affect respiration, but it slightly increased the net assimilation rate. Nitrogen deficiency decreased respiration rate and produced a normal net assimilation rate at low light intensity, and a relatively low rate at high light intensity. A very low potassium level decreased the respiration rate relative to a moderate potassium deficiency. This effect was attributed to severe carbohydrate shortage. The leaf position which showed maximal respiration rate differed for different levels of potassium supply. Net assimilation rate (NAR) may be markedly affected by water content or supply. Thus Morton and Watson (361) found that transfer of plants grown with high nitrogen treatments from a low to a high water regime resulted in a large increase in NAR. These plants had previously accumulated relatively high internal nitrogen concentrations.

Richards and Templeman (449) extended studies on NPK interactions to changes in nitrogen fractions. Phosphorus deficiency had an early effect in decreasing leaf protein. There was a corresponding increase in amino, and especially in amide, nitrogen so that the amide:amino nitrogen ratio was also increased. Potassium deficiency permitted normal protein formation in the young leaves. There was an increase in both amide and amino nitrogen, but no change in their ratio. The first sign of potassium deficiency was the increased level of amino nitrogen, but protein synthesis in the meristem continued. Richards and Templeman suggested that the function of potassium was to maintain the protoplasmic complex in an organized state rather than to be involved directly in protein synthesis. When potassium was withdrawn from leaves under deficiency conditions, proteolysis was inferred to result. Webster (573), however, found that potassium was required for protein synthesis in pea microsomes. The potassium requirement in peptide synthesis, and in particular that for formation of glutathione from cysteine (574, 575), may be of significance in the maintenance of protoplasmic organization, if this is at all dependent on a steady production of glutathione as the functional source, rather than cysteine, for maintenance of sulfhydryl groups in the cell.

Gregory and Baptiste (167) and Gregory and Sen (169) investigated the interrelationships between supplies of nitrogen, phosphorus, and potassium in barley and carbohydrate and nitrogen metabolism, with special reference to the utilization of sugars in respiration and protein synthesis. Nitrogen deficiency increased total sugars but did not have a consistent effect on free reducing sugars. Phosphorus deficiency increased free reducing sugars, but had only a slight positive effect on total sugars. Potassium deficiency decreased both total and reducing sugars and the concentrations fell with increasing leaf age throughout growth for all leaves. The ratio of sucrose to reducing sugars was relatively high, nitrogen being especially deficient in the sixth leaf; the ratio was low with potassium deficiency, particularly in the first and tenth leaves.

The production and utilization of sugars under different nutritional conditions was discussed. Photosynthesis was apparently similar and uniform at full leaf emergence for both full nutrient and nitrogen-deficient treatments. With potassium deficiency there was a progressive decline in photosynthesis up to the eighth leaf, followed by a recovery. Phosphorus deficiency caused a decline in photosynthesis after the fifth leaf until the ninth leaf, followed by a recovery. It was concluded that the low sugar content of potassium-deficient plants was the result of a direct effect of potassium supply on photosynthesis whereas the high content in nitrogen-deficient plants was indirect. Latzko (282) has concluded that potassium is directly involved in photosynthetic phosphorylation. This function might be that shown to exist for the pyruvic kinase system and would account for the direct effects of potassium on assimilation. Calculations by Gregory et al. of differences among sugars in the leaves of plants given different treatments, and of the expected values from assimilation rates, were related to the production of tillers. This production was very low with nitrogen and phosphorus deficiencies, and slightly higher than normal with potassium deficiency. Losses calculated from respiration data of Gregory and Richards were considered to be small relative to the sugar content found. Translocation effects were calculated in terms of the ratio of dry weights stem and root to leaves. High sugar content was related to a high level of translocation under nitrogen deficiency, and low sugar content was related to low translocation with potassium deficiency.

Protein synthesis was calculated on a carbon basis from the data of Richards and Templeman (449). There was an evident correlation between the high levels of sugars and low protein carbon with nitrogen deficiency. Potassium deficiency, which was not associated with a low protein content in the experiments of Gregory and Sen (169), produced on the contrary a low sugar content due to the dominating effects of low assimilation and high respiration rates.

There was a marked inverse relationship between total and reducing sugars on the one hand and amino nitrogen on the other, with decreasing potassium supply but no change in protein. This relationship was associated with a maximum respiration rate for the intermediate

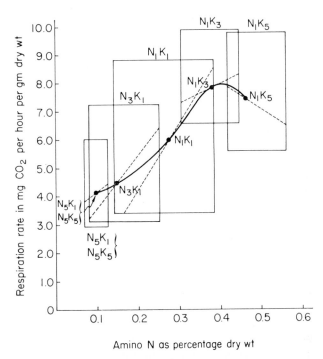

Fig. 8. Relationships between nitrogen and potassium supply on respiration in barley (*Hordeum vulgare*) leaves in the various manurial series. The rectangles enclose the values for the successive leaves in each manurial series. The regression of respiration on amino nitrogen is shown as a dotted line for each manurial series. The mean values for each series are marked on the regression lines. Reproduced from Gregory and Sen (169).

potassium level where sugars were adequate but amino nitrogen was already high (Fig. 8). Potassium appeared to exert two opposed effects on respiration: namely, to increase it in relation to increasing amino nitrogen, and to decrease it by limiting sucrose at extreme deficiency. It appeared that a low sucrose content was the limiting factor in respiration under extreme potassium deficiency, whereas sugar content was not correlated with respiration rate in the low nitrogen series (Fig. 9).

A rapid fall in the respiration rate of detached leaves over a period of 36 hours was observed with potassium deficiency. There was a similar decrease in full-nutrient leaves and a minimum change in nitrogen-deficient leaves, in which the steady respiration rate in the dark was characteristic. The complex interactions between potassium or nitrogen treatments and the relationships between respiration and amino nitro-

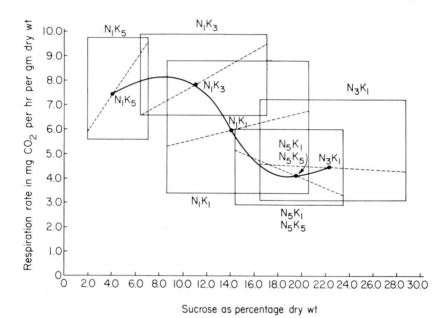

Fɪɢ. 9. Relationships between nitrogen and potassium status, respiration rate, and sucrose content in barley (*Hordeum vulgare*) leaves in the various manurial series. The rectangles enclose the values for the successive leaves in each manurial series. The regression of respiration on sucrose is shown as a dotted line for each manurial series. The mean values for each series are marked on the regression lines. Reproduced from Gregory and Sen (169).

gen or sucrose concentrations for barley are illustrated in Figs. 8 and 9. The values for K_1, K_3, and K_5 or N_1, N_3, and N_5 were in threefold decreasing progression of concentration, i.e., $K_5 =$ one-ninth of K_1.

A final and still more penetrating analysis of the interactions of nitrogen, potassium, and phosphorus in respiration, nitrogen, and carbohydrate metabolism was given by Richards (442a). Maximum respiration rates at fully expanded leaf stages were observed with maximum phosphorus and low potassium supply; the minimum rate occurred under the opposite conditions.

Extreme nitrogen deficiency eliminated the effect of phosphorus. Phosphorus deficiency decreased protein and increased amino nitrogen in a highly significant manner. These effects were, respectively, highly correlated positively and negatively with respiration, regardless of potassium supply. Effects of potassium were more complex and depended partly on leaf position. The effects of potassium on respiration were positively highly correlated at normal phosphorus level with amino nitrogen, which increased with decreasing potassium supply.

Sucrose content and respiration, sucrose content and protein, and protein and respiration were also positively correlated, whereas reducing sugars were negatively correlated with protein. Richards concluded that phosphorus deficiency led to high amide and high reducing sugar levels as well as to low protein. There was a high correlation between the level of reducing sugars and respiration at extreme phosphorus deficiency level. The poor correlation between respiration and protein at low phosphorus levels was explained by the high values for reducing sugars which were thought to be direct respiratory substrates. At normal and moderately deficient phosphorus levels, correlation between respiration and protein was good; when the effects of reducing sugars were eliminated statistically, the correlation was good also at the lowest phosphorus level. In contrast to the good correlation between respiration and reducing sugars at normal phosphorus levels, there was no correlation between sucrose and respiration at the lowest phosphorus level. Richards concluded, however, that the correlation between sucrose content and respiration, which was observed at normal phosphorus levels, was fortuitous. It was suggested that both reducing sugar content and phosphorus level were factors in respiration rate at low phosphorus supply, but that reducing sugar levels played comparatively little part in determining respiration at normal phosphorus level.

Respiration was therefore positively correlated with amino nitrogen at normal phosphorus level with respect to effects of variations in potassium, and with reducing sugars at low phosphorus supply. There was a correlation with protein in all treatments. Calculations from data in previous experiments showed that respiration as CO_2 production *per unit of protein* was increased with nitrogen deficiency and with moderate potassium deficiency. Respiration rate was, however, proportional to protein content for a wide range of phosphorus levels. Therefore decrease in phosphorus depressed respiration and protein equally without changing their ratio. Richards concluded that phosphorus deficiency decreased protein because it depressed respiration. This conclusion is adequately justified, for nonphotosynthetic tissues, in the light of recent work on the fundamental role of adenosine triphosphate (ATP) and other nucleotide triphosphates in protein synthesis. In photosynthetic tissues a deficiency of inorganic phosphorus would directly restrict ATP production by photosynthetic phosphorylation. Malnutrition led either to high respiration:protein ratios (deficiencies of nitrogen or potassium) or to low protein and low respiration (deficiency of phosphorus). Optimum nutrition was associated with maximum protein and minimum respiration:protein ratio.

B. Micronutrient or Trace Elements

1. Iron

a. Symptoms of iron deficiency. The most characteristic effect of iron deficiency is the failure to produce chlorophyll in young leaves. Leaves that have obtained adequate iron during their full period of expansion seldom develop chlorosis, even when the deficiency is subsequently so severe as to cause complete chlorosis and necrosis of the younger leaves. Chlorosis may be confined to only a few of the youngest leaves, or it may be more general and less severe in many partly expanded leaves. The distinction probably reflects the extent to which expansion of individual leaves, or growth of their chloroplasts, has occurred in relation to the level of iron supply over the period of growth, or it is related to the time at which the supply was decreased. Chlorotic leaves sometimes show little or no recovery when expansion has ceased, should there be a renewal of the iron supply to the developing plant, but rapidly expanding leaves usually recover within 5 days if iron is given to the roots, and they may respond to foliar applications in 2–5 days. The capacity for response is probably related to renewed chloroplast development, which may be impossible after a certain stage of leaf growth.

In most plants the chlorosis is initially interveinal and tissues immediately adjacent to all veins, including the very small ones, remain relatively green. This produces a fine reticulate pattern in partially expanded leaves. In cereals the symptoms usually consist of bright yellow-green or yellow chlorosis in regular longitudinal stripes between the veins of younger leaves, which are finally completely yellow or ivory in color (Fig. 10). The pattern reflects the distribution of limited amounts of iron, as shown by the radioautographs obtained by De Kock (96).

Necrosis is often absent from the interveinal areas even when chlorosis has become pure yellow, ivory, or even white. When the deficiency becomes more severe or progresses with successive production of younger leaves, these may be more severely chlorotic; tissues between tertiary and many secondary veins of broad-leaved plants also become totally chlorotic. The basal regions of major lateral veins and tissues adjacent to the leaf midrib are usually the last to become chlorotic, and veins are always sharply outlined by very narrow green borders un-

FIG. 10. Iron deficiency in maize (ᴜea mays). Ivory-tinted interveinal chlorosis.

til they have become completely chlorotic. In tomato, however (Fig. 11), the central basal areas of leaflets may be the first to show chlorosis. The sharp pale green outline of minor and major veins is often an important point of distinction between iron and manganese deficiency, as described below. Necrosis of interveinal areas may appear at any stage, but it is usually delayed until practically all chlorophyll has gone in many plants, e.g., beet, tomato, brassicas, potato. The delayed incidence of necrosis is also an important point of distinction from the effects of manganese deficiency. General papery collapse of leaf margins or whole leaves may follow total bleaching in severe conditions of iron deficiency. In a few plants, e.g., tomato, purple pigments appear in the petioles and veins of chlorotic young leaves and in the epidermis of young stems. Bright purple-brown mottling of stems and petioles, which also make very acute angles, occurs in cocoa (165).

Fruits of tomato become silvery-green and are orange rather than red when ripe (190). Presumably, decreased chlorophyll or chloroplast activity in the fruit has an effect on other pigment formation. Apple and pear fruits become chlorotic and brightly tinted with

Fig. 11. Iron deficiency in tomato (*Lycopersicon esculentum*). Note interveinal finely patterned chlorosis, more pronounced in basal and central regions of leaflets, and absence of necrotic areas.

a red or orange flush due to production of anthocyanin rather than of plastid pigments (553). Glumes of oats may become chlorotic even when the subtending leaf is only slightly affected (190, 553).

b. Effects on growth. Brown and Possingham (51, 52) (Figs. 12–16) observed that iron deficiency caused an abrupt cessation of cell division in the apical meristem of excised pea roots after 7 days without iron (Fig. 12). Cell expansion and protein synthesis appeared to be continuing at the time cell division ceased (Fig. 13). Protein content per cell therefore increased in the iron-deficient roots (Fig. 14). The concentration of iron required for cell division therefore exceeded that which was necessary for cell expansion. Restoration of the iron supply resulted in the immediate resumption of cell division in the original meristematic group. It was suggested that a cyanide-sensitive cytochrome oxidase system was specifically necessary for cell division but that other respiratory pathways, which developed after 3 days, were able to support protein synthesis and to maintain an adequate respiration rate. The depressed rates of respiration on a root and on a protein basis are shown in Figs. 15 and 16, respectively. Possingham and Brown (418) found that radioactive iron was localized in the nuclei of root meristems during prophase but was not seen in mitotic figures. Iron deficiency caused an abrupt end to production of leaf primordia in tomato stem apex but the central dome of the apex remained normal.

  c. *Effects on chloroplasts.* Chloroplasts are decreased in size by iron deficiency. Jacobsen and Oertli (245) concluded that where chlorotic leaves failed to respond to iron sprays the injury to the chloroplasts was irreversible. Changes produced in chloroplasts of cauliflower have also been studied by E. J. Hewitt and D. P. Hucklesby (unpublished work).

  Breakdown of the chloroplasts, which was associated with chlorosis of young leaves, occurred by spreading of the structure into the cytoplasm with early lysis of the starch grains, in contrast with effects of magnesium deficiency. Vacuolation of the chloroplasts was occasionally observed. The disintegrating chloroplast material usually broke up into portions that agglutinated and stained deeply with methyl violet, without the formation of the lipid globules produced with magnesium and nitrogen deficiencies. Loss of chlorophyll occurred at the same time as plastid breakdown and did not precede it.

  d. *Effects on respiration.* Glenister (159) showed that iron deficiency in sunflower produced no difference in the respiration rate of old leaves which remained green. Young chlorotic leaves had a respiration rate, in terms of CO_2 output, of less than half that of corresponding leaves of plants given iron. Maximum respiration rate occurred in young leaves of normal plants and in mid-stem leaves of chlorotic plants. The effects of iron deficiency on enzyme activity, reviewed elsewhere (207), are also described by Nason and McElroy (Chapter 4) in relation to the role of iron in enzyme systems. It is, however, pertinent that iron deficiency in tobacco was found by Welkie and Miller (579) to produce large increases in the content of free riboflavin and riboflavin phosphate (FMN), which attained over ten times the concentration found in normal plants, while flavin adenine dinucleotide was slightly decreased in amount. Neither cytochrome reductase nor nitrate reductase activities were appreciably changed under these conditions of decreased iron supply. It is possible that diaphorase

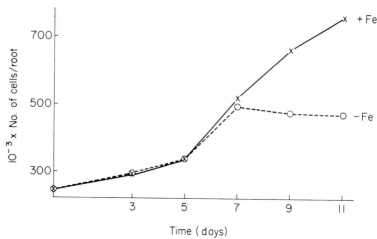

Figs. 12–16. Effects of iron supply on growth of excised pea (*Pisum sativum*) roots. From Brown and Possingham (52).

Fig. 12. Change in numbers of cells in whole roots cultured in the presence and in the absence of iron. Treatment difference at day 7, not significant; day 9, significant at $P < 0.001$; day 11, significant at $P < 0.001$.

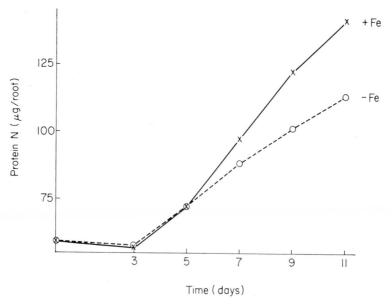

Fig. 13. Change in protein nitrogen content of whole roots, cultured in the presence and in the absence of iron. Treatment difference at day 7, significant at $P < 0.05$; day 9, significant at $P < 0.01$; day 11, significant at $P < 0.001$.

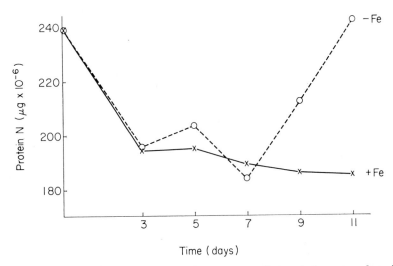

Fig. 14. Change in average protein nitrogen per cell in whole roots cultured in the presence and absence of iron. Treatment difference at day 7, not significant; day 9, significant at $P < 0.05$; day 11, significant at $P < 0.05$.

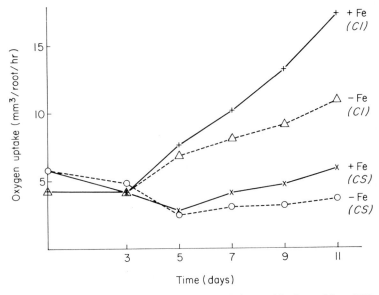

Fig. 15. Change in cyanide sensitive (CS) and cyanide insensitive (CI) rates of oxygen absorption by whole roots in the presence and absence of iron. Difference between day 7 and day 11, significant at $P < 0.05$ in $+Fe(CI)$, $-Fe(CI)$ and $+Fe(CS)$; not significant, $-Fe(CS)$.

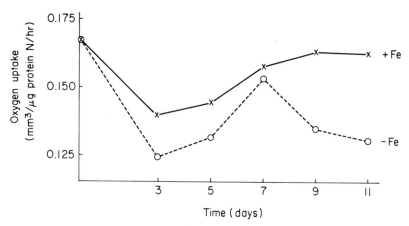

Fig. 16. Change in the rate of oxygen absorption per unit protein nitrogen in whole roots cultured in the presence and absence of iron.

systems, or other flavoprotein enzymes involving electron transport, increased adaptivity, as has been observed in microorganisms when deficient in iron [Lenhoff *et al.* (292)]. It may be concluded that under normal conditions iron is the principal metal in the respiratory chain and that the cytochrome system, terminating in cytochrome oxidase, is the normal respiratory pathway (cf. Chapter 3, Vol. IA); it may be noted also that Webster (572) demonstrated the existence of cytochrome oxidase in particulate preparations from each of the 50 species he examined.

2. Relationships between Iron and Other Elements

Iron deficiency may occur in plants grown under several different conditions, which were reviewed by Bennett (31) and Wallace and Hewitt (554), in addition to actual lack of the element. These conditions include the presence of calcium or magnesium carbonates; deficiencies of potassium or calcium; excess of phosphorus or of several metals including cobalt, nickel, chromium, cadmium, copper, zinc, manganese, molybdenum, and vanadium; bicarbonate ions and high pH values also induce iron deficiency.

a. Lime-induced chlorosis and related effects. The well-known field condition known as lime-induced chlorosis seriously affects trees and soft fruits in particular, but it may occur also in brassicas, beet, spinach, flax, and cereals. The problem has been discussed in detail in different contexts by Wallace (550), Lindner and Harley (297), Thorne and Wallace (523), Guest (170), McGeorge (332), and De Kock (96). Plants grown with their roots in contact with finely divided calcium or magnesium carbonates often become acutely chlorotic. The symptoms appear to be identical with those of severe iron deficiency and are usually cured, or decreased, by applications of more iron to the plant. These applications may be made either as a foliage spray or by an increased concentration of iron around the roots, sometimes in chelated form (41a) or as a solid, such as magnetite, in the rooting medium (170, 196).

Analyses have often failed to show consistent trends in the total iron content of the foliage. Various attempts by Oserkowsky (394), Bennett (31), Jacobson (244), and Bolle-Jones (37) to identify a fraction corresponding to "active" iron in the tissues of green leaves revealed that iron fractions soluble in dilute acid, which comprised only a limited proportion of the total iron, were relatively well correlated with chlorophyll content of green or chlorotic leaves. Experiments by De Kock (96), using radioactive iron, showed that whereas green leaves of mustard contained far more iron in the interveinal areas than in the vascular tissues, those of chlorotic leaves contained little iron in the interveinal areas and much greater amounts in the vascular tissues. The chlorotic pattern, therefore, reflects iron status rather than effectiveness in this example.

A notably consistent feature of plants which are affected by lime-induced chlorosis is the increase in the potassium:calcium ratio in the chlorotic, as compared with the green, foliage; this was first observed by Wallace (550) and has been noted by many others since. This relationship may not occur in similar plants when chlorosis is directly due to insufficient iron, according to Lindner and Harley (297). This relationship is discussed below in connection with the effects of deficiency of potassium.

b. Relation of iron nutrition to potassium and phosphorus. Wallace and Hewitt (554) pointed out that deficiencies of potassium, phosphorus, or calcium are possible causes of apparent iron deficiency in plants. One of the earliest observations of iron deficiency that was induced by potassium deficiency was made by Hoffer (230), who found that chlorosis in the leaves of potassium-deficient maize plants was associated with an accumulation of iron in the stem nodes. Hartt (182) observed a similar accumulation of iron in the nodes of sugar cane. Olsen was one of the first to note the association between iron chlorosis and phosphorus supply in maize. Sayre (454a) observed that iron accumulation in maize stems varied greatly but was always located in the bundle sheath and vascular pith of the nodal plate.

The interrelationships among iron, potassium, and phosphorus have been studied in detail, in the potato, at Long Ashton in collaboration with Bolle-Jones (37, 217). The main observations and conclusions are given here and are illustrated in Fig. 17, A–D.

B

A

200

C   D

FIG. 17. Fe:K:P balance in potato (*Solanum tuberosum*).

FIG. 17A. Left: low Fe, high K, high P. Center: low Fe, low K, high P. Right: high Fe, low K, high P; early stage showing iron and potassium deficiencies in same plant (center) and no symptoms in upper or lower parts (right) but general pale foliage (left).

FIG. 17B. Later stage in growth showing chlorosis in young, and potassium deficiency in old, leaves of low iron, low potassium, high phosphorus (left), and much more severe effects of potassium deficiency and collapse of young leaves of high iron, low potassium, high phosphorus (right).

FIG. 17C. Left: Low iron, low potassium, high phosphorus: symptoms of severe chlorosis and potassium deficiency. Right: Low iron, low potassium, low phosphorus: no chlorosis and only slight symptoms of potassium deficiency are apparent.

FIG. 17D. High iron, low potassium, low phosphorus: a plant of the same age as that shown in Fig. 17C shows no effects of potassium deficiency, but severe symptoms of phosphorus deficiency.

Potato plants grown with low iron levels show iron deficiency symptoms earlier and more severely in the apical leaves when they are grown at low, rather than high potassium levels. With adequate potassium, iron deficiency chlorosis not only is much less severe, but is more evenly distributed and mature leaves may be more chlorotic than young ones. Symptoms of potassium deficiency appear several days earlier in iron-deficient plants than in those given adequate iron (Fig. 17, A, B). Increased iron however, causes more severe effects of potassium deficiency at a later stage and the symptoms develop more rapidly in the young leaves than at a low iron level. Death of the shoot apex occurs in "high iron-low potassium" plants whereas the apex is still functional in iron-deficient plants given the same potassium level. Increasing the iron supplied, decreased the accumulation of potassium in the young over the older leaves [cf. Bolle-Jones (37)]. High phosphorus levels greatly accentuate the symptoms of iron and potassium deficiencies. Plants grown with low iron and low potassium levels show acute apical chlorosis and severe potassium deficiency in old leaves when given a high phosphorus level, but they may be merely slightly pale green and show slight potassium deficiency when given a low phosphorus level (cf. Fig. 17, C). Plants given low potassium and low phosphorus levels show acute phosphorus deficiency when given a high iron supply (Fig. 17, D). Therefore, it is evident that the iron level given to the plants deficient in both potassium and phosphorus can determine which of these two may appear to be limiting. At combined low iron and low potassium levels, phosphorus supply has a dominating and similar effect on the severity of both potassium and iron deficiencies. At normal phosphorus levels, the incidence of iron deficiency is determined mainly by potassium supply.

It was found that chlorotic leaves contained a higher K:Ca ratio (reciprocal Ca:K ratio) than green leaves in the low potassium treatments, but there was no significant relationship between the K:Ca ratio and chlorophyll content in the presence of adequate potassium. This result was obtained both in the absence and presence of added calcium carbonate, which greatly accentuated chlorosis in potassium-deficient plants. It was concluded, therefore, that the high K:Ca ratio in chlorotic leaves found in these experiments and in plants showing lime-induced chlorosis reflects a condition of acute or incipient potassium deficiency. The change in the K:Ca ratio was associated with the fact that under conditions of potassium deficiency the migration of potassium from old to young leaves was greater in iron-deficient plants than in those given iron. This is consistent with the effects of iron supply, already noted, on the distribution and time of appearance of potassium deficiency symptoms, and it suggests that changes in the K:Ca ratio are not causal, but result from a disturbance in the iron and potassium nutrition.

There was also a fairly close correlation between the ratio of total phosphorus:total iron and the chlorophyll content in potato leaves (37, 217). This ratio was markedly decreased by increased potassium supply. Potassium also exerted an independent effect on the ratio of inorganic to total phosphorus which was greater in potassium-deficient plants (Table XI). It may be concluded that the effect of potassium

TABLE XI

Effect of Potassium and Iron Supplies on the Proportions of Inorganic and Organic Phosphorus Fractions in Potato (*Solanum tuberosum*) Leaves[a]

Treatment	First sampling					Second sampling				
	Inorg. P	Org. P	$\frac{\text{Inorg.,}}{\text{total}}$	$\frac{\text{Org.,}}{\text{total}}$	$\frac{\text{Inorg.,}}{\text{org.}}$	Inorg. P	Org. P	$\frac{\text{Inorg.,}}{\text{total}}$	$\frac{\text{Org.,}}{\text{total}}$	$\frac{\text{Inorg.,}}{\text{org.}}$
$Fe_1K_1P_3$	7.11	1.88	0.79	0.21	3.78	6.23	6.23	0.50	0.50	1.00
$Fe_1K_2P_3$	5.54	1.56	0.78	0.22	3.55	3.99	5.88	0.40	0.60	0.68
$Fe_1K_3P_3$	1.90	2.05	0.48	0.52	0.93	2.12	4.59	0.32	0.68	0.46
$Fe_3K_3P_3$	3.72	3.02	0.55	0.45	1.23	3.33	4.19	0.44	0.56	0.80

[a] From Bolle-Jones (37).

supply on iron deficiency symptoms are due to a complex response to several effects. These include the effect of potassium (a) in decreasing inorganic phosphorus concentration by promoting phosphorylation in phosphokinase systems (226, 329, 349), (b) in decreasing phosphorus uptake, though organic phosphorus is not affected to the same extent, and (c) in increasing the translocation to foliage of iron from roots, where it was possibly immobilized by phosphate (37, 391a). In contrast, an increased phosphorus level tended to immobilize iron in the roots and in the younger leaves.

The ratio of chlorophyll to iron in young leaves was markedly increased by increased potassium supply, a finding that showed that potassium increased the efficiency of iron utilization in chlorophyll production. This relationship was illustrated by Bolle-Jones, who showed [cf. Figs. 5 and 6 in ref. (37)] that "soluble" iron, extracted by 0.1 N HCl saturated with ether, was closely related to total potassium content and that the chlorophyll content was correlated with "soluble" iron. De Kock and Hall (98) found that chlorotic leaves, or parts of leaves, from genetically variegated plants had substantially higher ratios of

phosphorus to iron and also high potassium:calcium ratios. They concluded that these ratios might be related to the proportions of un-
specified organic acids determined by the iron supply available for
cellular oxidation. De Kock and co-workers (96, 97, 98, 99) have gen-
eralized the idea on iron:phosphorus ratios to cover many conditions of
chlorosis, but it is not clear that their conclusion is generally applicable
and the importance of other factors should not be overlooked (554).

De Kock *et al.* (99) carried out an experiment with mustard plants
which was similar in many respects to those described for potato
(37, 217). Iron was given at three levels as chloride, or chelated with
ethylenediamine tetraacetate (EDTA) or with *N,N'*-ethylenebis-
(2-o-hydroxyphenyl)glycine in factorial combination with four levels
of potassium and two of phosphorus. Marked chlorosis developed with
ferric chloride; this development was intensified with increasing potassium, which depressed the iron content in both the chloride and
EDTA series and had no significant effect (though in fact apparently
a reverse effect) on iron content in the hydroxyphenylglycine series.
Increasing the iron supply increased the K:Ca ratio mainly because
iron appeared to depress calcium content. De Kock *et al.* considered that
the antagonism between iron and potassium observed by them was not
inconsistent with the synergistic effect found for potato (37, 217) since
the latter results were, according to De Kock *et al.* (99), explicable
by a translocation of potassium from the old to the young leaves. In
fact, this interpretation is not acceptable because increasing the potassium supply in potato increased the iron content in young and old
leaves, and increasing iron caused a relative retention of potassium in
old leaves, resulting initially in delayed symptoms of potassium deficiency and later in more general symptoms in upper leaves, as indicated in Fig. 17, A, B. It must be concluded at present that mustard and
potato react differently to the effects of iron and potassium on the
uptake of these elements and to relationships between the utilization
of iron in chlorophyll production and the changes in the K:Ca ratio.

c. *Relationships with organic acid and bicarbonate metabolism.* De
Kock and Morrison (101) concluded that iron deficiency which caused
chlorosis in mustard led to a 50% decrease in malic and citric acid concentrations in the leaves. When nickel toxicity was the cause of
chlorosis, malic acid decreased but citric acid increased. The ratio of
citric to malic acid was considered to be positively correlated with the
ratios P:Fe and K:Ca. On the other hand, Williams (582) reported
that phosphorus deficiency in tomato doubled the citric:malic acid
ratio. Rhoads and Wallace (440a) observed that in bush beans
(*Phaseolus vulgaris*) chlorosis induced by high calcium carbonate

content in the soil was associated with a high concentration of citric acid and a great increase in oxalic acid but no decrease in malic acid. The citric:malic ratio therefore increased as reported by De Kock and Morrison (101), but for a different reason. Chlorosis was also related to increased malonic acid concentration. The high oxalic acid content was thought possibly to explain the high K:Ca ratio commonly observed.

The problem of lime-induced chlorosis has been considered in relation to organic acid metabolism by Iljin (237, 239) and McGeorge (332). Iljin found between four and twenty times as much citric acid in chlorotic foliage as compared with normal foliage of several species. There was no correlation between malic acid levels and chlorosis; earlier work cited suggested, however, a general relationship between citric acid and chlorosis in dicotyledonous species, but not in monocotyledonous species. Chlorotic foliage contained less oxalic acid than normal foliage. Increased citrate in iron-deficient plants therefore seems to be of general occurrence, but the direct causal relationship is still obscure.

The presence of bicarbonate ions may also induce chlorosis. Wadleigh and Brown (543) studied this effect with *Phaseolus vulgaris* and also reviewed other work on the subject. Bicarbonate-induced chlorosis was reversed by iron-containing foliage sprays. Bicarbonate tended to decrease calcium and increase potassium content of chlorotic leaves thus producing the high K:Ca ratio familiar in chlorotic foliage. The total iron content varied erratically, but iron soluble in 1 N hydrochloric acid was decreased. Bicarbonate also decreased the total phosphate content and increased the concentrations of citric and malic acids in the trifoliate leaves. De Kock (96) observed that bicarbonate ions induced chlorosis in mustard. Lime-induced chlorosis may possibly be due to effects of bicarbonate rather than of calcium or of pH only.

Miller and Evans (347, 348) concluded that bicarbonate ions had a markedly inhibitory effect on cytochrome oxidase activity in roots of soybean and other plants. A recent symposium [Bear (30)] reviews several effects of bicarbonate ions on plant growth and especially on relationships between iron and phosphorus supply. A general conclusion seems to be that bicarbonate accentuates chlorosis indirectly through an effect on phosphorus availability and increased phosphorus uptake. Brown (49) working with soybean, Goss (161) with *Phaseolus vulgaris*, and Olsen *et al.* (393) using an inorganic solution of calcium phosphate without plants, all concluded that bicarbonate exerts at least one effect by increasing phosphate uptake or solubility. Hale and Wallace (175) obtained evidence that phosphate or bicarbonate competitively inhibit iron accumulation when iron is given in chelated form, possibly because the anions competed with the anionic chelate for adsorption on to a specific site.

d. *Metal-induced iron deficiency.* Excesses of several metals, including manganese, chromium, copper, zinc, cobalt, nickel, and cadmium, may induce symptoms apparently identical with those of iron deficiency in some plants. Circumstances in which these metals may act have been reviewed by Wallace and Hewitt (554), Hewitt (196, 197, 198, 202), Millikan (352, 353), Twyman (531a, 532), De Kock (97), Vergnano and Hunter (540), Nicholas (378), Nicholas and Thomas (381, 382), and Nicholas and Forster (379). Interest in this prob-problem dates from early investigations by Kelley (263), McGeorge (331), and Johnson (254, 255) on effects of manganiferous soils on pineapple (*Ananas comosus*) and of Hopkins *et al.* (233) on beans (*Phaseolus vulgaris*), which appear also to be especially sensitive to this effect of manganese.

The activity of manganese in inducing iron deficiency symptoms was given a novel interpretation from work on soybean by Shive and his associates (473, 486, 487), who proposed a theory which has stimulated much discussion and investigation. It was maintained that iron deficiency and manganese excess could be identified with each other as relative terms for the same physiological disorder caused by too high a manganese:iron ratio in the plant, so that manganese deficiency was suggested as being possibly synonymous with iron excess. The mechanism invoked was that manganese, owing to the high value of the redox potential for the divalent-trivalent system $Mn^{++} \rightarrow Mn^{+++} + e^-$ ($E_0 =$ 1.51 volts) was able to cause the oxidation of most of the ferrous iron of the cell to the ferric state. Ferrous iron was assumed to be the "active" form, presumably as regards its role in chlorophyll formation; the ferric form was thought to be precipitated as a complex with phosphate in organic combination, possibly as envisaged by Noack and Liebick (387) in chloroplasts in combination with phosphoprotein. Iron phosphoprotein compounds, such as ferritin, may contain up to 23% of iron [Granick (162)]. Such a hypothesis would be consistent with the phosphate immobilization mechanism postulated by De Kock for many aspects of iron deficiency. The hypothesis of Shive and his associates required that divalent manganese ions should be oxidized *in vivo* to the trivalent or a higher oxidation state, but no mechanism for this was known at the time. Kenten and Mann (265, 266, 269, 271, 272) have now established the biochemical basis for a mechanism whereby divalent manganese can be oxidized to the trivalent state by peroxidase systems in the presence of hydrogen peroxide, generated by amine oxidase (268) or other oxidase systems, and a monophenol cofactor such as *p*-cresol. Trivalent manganese is normally too reactive to persist long and is rapidly reduced by *o*-diphenols such as catechol or by polyphenols such as pyrogallol, guaiacol, and caffeic acid. Chelating agents such as pyrophosphate, however, can stabilize trivalent manganese, and natural chelating agents might also achieve this. The oxidation of manganese has been achieved in the presence of illuminated chloroplasts *in vitro* (271) and has been observed to occur *in vivo* in pea plants given high levels of manganese (272). The reactions may be represented as follows:

Peroxidase (Per) $+ H_2O_2 \rightarrow$ Per I $+ H^+$ (nomenclature of George (150)

Per I $+$ ROH (monophenol or resorcinol) $\rightarrow RO^\bullet$ (free radical) $+$ Per II $+ H_2O$

Per II $+$ ROH $\rightarrow RO^\bullet + OH^- +$ Per (Per $H_2O_2 + 2ROH \rightarrow$ Per $+ 2RO^\bullet + 2H_2O$)

$2RO^\bullet + 2Mn^{++} + 2H^+ \rightarrow 2ROH + 2Mn^{+++}$

$n\ RO^\bullet \rightarrow (RO)_n$ (inactive polymer which brings chain reaction to an end)

$2Mn^{+++} + HOOH \rightarrow 2Mn^{++} + O_2 + 2H^+$ (decomposition of hydrogen peroxide by Mn^{+++})

$Mn^{+++} + P_2O_7^{----} \rightarrow$ stable Mn^{+++} chelate

$2Mn^{+++} + R(OH)_2 \rightarrow 2Mn^{++} + R(O)_2 + 2H^+$ (Reduction of Mn^{+++} by *o*- or *p*-diphenol)

Although a possible mechanism for manganese-induced iron deficiency has now been demonstrated, it was pointed out by Hewitt (197, 198) that manganese and cobalt are not alone in inducing iron deficiency. It was shown that zinc (196, 202) and especially cadmium (202) (Table XII) were active in this respect although neither metal

TABLE XII

Effects of Metal Toxicities, Molybdenum and Nitrogen Supplies on Chlorophyll Content[a] of Young Sugar Beet (*Beta vulgaris*) Leaves[b]

Metal treatments	Nitrate N		Urea N	
	Normal Mo	High Mo	Normal Mo	High Mo
Basal	158	151	110	100
CrO_4^{--}	71	137	18	14
Cr^{+++}	146	95	84	32
Mn^{++}	139	53	78	20
Co^{++}	8	10	10	9
Cu^{++}	28	10	11	14
Zn^{++}	104	47	94	34
Cd^{++}	6	14	4	4

[a] Results given in milligrams chlorophyll per 100 gm fresh weight. Significant difference at 5% level = 15.

[b] Hewitt (197a, 203).

can undergo a valency change, which was a requirement postulated by Shive and his associates. Hypotheses based on the relative oxidation-reduction potentials of metals which are able to induce iron deficiency were shown also to be inconsistent with the numerical values of oxidation-reduction potentials of couples involving the simple ions. Independent investigations of the problem of soil acidity by Hewitt (193–195) showed, moreover, that symptoms of manganese toxicity were often entirely distinct from those of iron deficiency and often did not occur under the same conditions. Furthermore Nicholas (377) found no relationship between iron and manganese status in several crops growing under field conditions.

Comparative studies of the effects of copper, cobalt, nickel, manganese, chromium, zinc, cadmium, and other metals on beet and other plants in sand cultures (196, 202, 203) showed that the relative activity of these metals in inducing chlorosis in beet resembled the order of stability of metal-chelate compounds (240, 317, 340, 340a). The relative stability of metal-organic complexes is almost independent of the ligand and is given generally as $Cu^{++} > Ni^{++} > Fe^{+++} > Zn^{++} > Cd^{++} > Fe^{++} > Mn^{++} > Mg^{++}$. Metallo-organic complex formation was suggested as a probable explanation of metal-induced iron deficiency in beet (198, 202).

Later work with oats by Hunter and Vergnano (235) produced further evidence to support this hypothesis. Certain discrepancies were recorded between results obtained for beet and oats, and the position of cadmium is anomalous (202) (Table XII), but the suggestion merits consideration as a working hypothesis. Sideris and Young (474) suggested a replacement of iron by manganese in a protoporphyrin IX complex but without evidence for such a reaction. The hypothesis of metal-organic complex formation as a cause of metal-induced iron deficiency implies that the metals compete with iron at some stage of chlorophyll formation at a site which is normally occupied by iron. The data on metal-chelate stabilities favor the view that ferrous iron occupies the catalytic site since ferric complexes would be very stable and unlikely to be suppressed by other metals.

Twyman (532) suggested that the effect of manganese in causing iron deficiency might be explained by competition between iron and manganese for a primary iron-acceptor site in the plant, and that when the acceptor was not combined with iron at the stage of the production of the acceptor in the cell, it could be converted irreversibly to a form which combined more firmly with iron subsequently introduced. This would account for the observation of high concentrations of iron in chlorotic tissues when induced iron deficiency is involved (554). This hypothesis is not inconsistent with others dependent on relative stability of metallo-organic complexes. A compound resembling ferritin could account for the observed immobilization of iron in the ferric form. The autoxidation of ferrous bicarbonate to produce ferric iron, which then combines with ferritin [Bayer (29)] would also suggest a possible analogy for an explanation of bicarbonate-induced chlorosis. The observation by Brown et al. (49a), that efficient uptake of ferric iron by roots of soybean plants is related to their capacity to reduce ferric iron at the surface of the roots and is genetically controlled, may be relevant to Twyman's hypothesis. It may also be relevant that Schmid and Gerloff (454b) have obtained evidence for the existence of a natural iron chelate in anionic form in xylem fluid with a high stability constant of log $K_1 = 17–20$.

Labbe and Hubbard (280) have described an enzyme from rat liver which is considered to be responsible for the insertion of iron into the protoporphyrin chelate to give heme. This mechanism might be of universal significance and, if so, could be involved in chlorophyll synthesis, if ferrous protoporphyrin is a precursor of the magnesium compound. Metal toxicity might result from competition between the metals and ferrous iron at the enzyme site. Bicarbonate-induced chlorosis might also occur in a similar manner if autoxidized iron in ferric form was irreversibly held at the active site on the enzyme.

Nicholas and Thomas (381, 382) studied the effects of cobalt and nickel excess in tomato plants grown in soil. Both metals caused chlorosis and stem and petiole lesions that were due to collapse of the cortex in plants given nickel. The toxic effects of cobalt and nickel on histology in oats were described by Vergnano and Hunter (540) and compared with iron deficiency. Nickel caused agglutination of chloroplasts followed by cell rupture and lysis of contents. Collapse of epidermal cells and phloem necrosis followed. Cobalt had similar effects but did not cause epidermal collapse or phloem necrosis. There was less epidermal cell collapse and cell rupture. Iron deficiency caused swelling of epidermal cells and often of cells in other tissues. There were large plastids heavily stained by hematoxylin and heavily stained phloem with many cell inclusions. Hewitt (202), and Hunter and Vergnano (234) described symptoms of nickel toxicity in several plants. Crooke, Hunter, and Vergnano (87) and Crooke (86) concluded that the degree of chlorosis associated with induced iron deficiency in oats given various levels of iron and nickel was essentially determined by the nickel:iron ratio and was severe at values above 6 and usually negligible with values below 1. Crooke and Inkson (88) concluded that, whereas calcium, magnesium, potassium, and nitrogen decreased toxic effects of nickel, phosphorus increased it and caused increased initial uptake. Crooke and Knight (89) found that the necrotic and chlorotic areas of leaves of oat plants given excess nickel contained less iron than the green ones. Symptoms of nickel toxicity induced in sand cultures resemble effects produced under field conditions due to nickel excess in serpentine soils.

The effects of various metals on apparent iron status is further complicated by other factors. Millikan (351, 352, 354) described experiments, with flax grown in water culture, which showed that iron deficiency and specific toxicity symptoms induced by manganese, zinc, copper, nickel, and cobalt were decreased in severity by high levels of molybdenum. Similar experiments by Hewitt (197, 202) with beet grown in sand culture produced opposite results. Extra molybdenum intensified the chlorosis caused by several metals tested by Millikan. Hunter and Vergnano (235) reported results in agreement with those of Hewitt. Warington (566–568) studied interactions among iron, manganese, vanadium, and molybdenum; she also failed to confirm Millikan's results and found that molybdenum accentuated manganese-induced chlorosis in soybean and flax, whereas vanadium had inconsistent effects. The effects of molybdenum appeared to be related to pH (569). Hewitt concluded that induced iron deficiency, chlorosis of young leaves of beet plants, and specific toxic effects of several metals were greater when nitrogen was given as ammonium nitrate or urea than as nitrate (197a, 203; Table XII). Millikan (354) found that manganese toxicity in flax was more severe when nitrogen was given as nitrate or urea than as ammonia. Molybdenum excess effects were least marked with nitrate or urea and most severe with ammonia. The effects of molybdenum on chromium-induced chlorosis are in opposite directions for Cr^{+++} and CrO_4^{--} treatments (197a) (Table XII). Effects of molybdenum interactions with manganese are shown in Figs. 18 and 19.

Zinc, cobalt, and nickel toxicities may be interrelated with the functions of manganese. Thus Hewitt (196) observed apparent manganese deficiency symptoms in beet given excess zinc, and possible manganese deficiency in potato leaflets in the presence of excess nickel (202). Tomato plants given excess cobalt and nickel also showed possible manganese deficiency symptoms (202). Ahmed and Twyman (5) found a reciprocal antagonism between cobalt and manganese toxicities in tomato plants, in which small additions of cobalt decreased manganese toxicity and extra manganese decreased cobalt toxicity.

Heavy metal-induced iron deficiency may also affect magnesium fractions (203). There were accumulations of acetone-soluble magnesium compounds in leaves of beet grown with excess manganese or zinc, although chlorophyll concentration was decreased by both metals and total magnesium also was decreased by zinc. The significance

FIGS. 18 and 19. Interaction between excess manganese and molybdenum in sugar beet (*Beta vulgaris*).

FIG. 18 (*Above*). Left: Basal treatment. Right: Basal manganese with high molybdenum level.

FIG. 19. Left: High manganese level. Right: High manganese and high molybdenum levels; note severe induced iron deficiency chlorosis.

of these changes was not elucidated, but the existence of ether-soluble magnesium compounds other than chlorophyll is known (482), and these may include chlorophyll precursors (162a) or products of diverted metabolic activity. De Kock *et al.* (97a) similarly observed differential effects of induced iron deficiency with respect to changes in catalase and peroxidase. Whereas simple iron deficiency decreased both, but catalase more than peroxidase, nickel toxicity depressed catalase only slightly and increased peroxidase activity markedly in extracts of mustard leaves, but decreased both chlorophyll and total hematin.

Weinstein and Robbins (578) concluded that interaction of iron and manganese determined to some extent the apparent activity of catalase and cytochrome oxidase in sunflower. Anderson and Evans (13) found that the iron-manganese balance markedly affected the activity of malic and isocitric dehydrogenases in bean (*Phaseolus vulgaris*) roots and leaves in a complex manner.

3. Manganese

a. Visible effects of deficiency or excess. i. Deficiency. The visible effects of a deficiency of manganese are more diverse than of those of many other mineral elements. The symptoms may occur first in young or in old leaves and may comprise a wide variety of chlorotic patterns and necrotic spotting. Named field disorders such as "gray speck" of oats (452, 453), "marsh spot" of peas (409), "speckled yellows" of beet (553) are caused by manganese deficiency.

The younger leaves are initially and principally affected in flax, potato, subterranean clover (356), tobacco (337), cotton (83), citrus (62) and cocoa (164, 324). Older leaves are usually first to show symptoms in tomato, cereals, brassicas, lettuce, parsnip, beet, spinach (*Spinacia oleracea*), plum (*Prunus domestica*), and raspberry (*Rubus idaeus*) (190, 192, 553).

Many plants, such as apple, pear, cherry, parsnip, and cocoa, show a "bold' chlorotic pattern in which the midrib and major veins only, or sometimes these with a few secondary veins, are surrounded by a relatively broad zone of dark green tissue; most of the remaining interveinal area is markedly chlorotic, but does not readily develop necrosis, except in cocoa (164, 324). In tomato, orange-yellow mottling over the tip and later the whole leaflet between dark green minor veins is rapidly followed, or may be preceded, by profuse small, dark brown necrotic spots that perforate the leaf (Fig. 20). Leaflets of very young leaves become totally chlorotic. Their shape is altered and the lamina is decreased in width relative to length. Sugar beet shows diffuse, blotchy, dull yellow interveinal mottling followed rapidly by necrotic patterns that perforate. This appearance contrasts with the bright pale-yellow or ivory color, clear-cut "fine" pattern of minor veins, and freedom from necrosis in iron deficiency.

In potato, black, rounded necrotic spots occur close to the midrib and in single rows along either side of major veins of young expanding leaflets; the spots precede appreciable chlorosis. Profuse necrotic spotting in chlorotic leaflets occurs in subterranean clover (356). In dwarf French beans, bright yellow-green interveinal chlorosis of most leaves, and finally total bleaching of young leaves, is frequently preceded or associated with fine, brown- or purple-tinted necrotic spots arranged in regular rows adjacent to major veins. The resemblance of this

Fig. 20. Manganese deficiency in tomato (*Lycopersicon esculentum*). Orange-yellow chlorotic mottling with early development of profuse brown necrotic spotting.

symptom to effects of magnesium deficiency in old leaves of dwarf bean (*Phaseolus vulgaris*) has been noted.

Manganese deficiency causes chocolate-brown lesions in barley, white necrotic streaks in wheat or rye, and "gray speck" in oats (553). These "gray speck" symptoms begin between veins near the base of an old, pale green leaf. The spot becomes necrotic and dries out with a pale, blue-green or gray-green "halo" around it. Successive spots coalesce across the width of the leaf, which collapses. Successive leaves have more numerous necrotic areas. These occur nearer the leaf tip and also on leaf bases around the stem. Leaves and stems are limp, and tillering is greatly reduced. Ear formation may be suppressed or glumes are withered and devoid of grain.

Manganese deficiency causes a characteristic sunken brown necrosis of the center of the cotyledons of pea (409), broad bean and climbing French bean (*Phaseolus multiflorus*) (191), and haricot bean (*Phaseolus vulgaris*) (553) (Fig. 21). Dwarf French beans (*P. multiflorus*) show these symptoms only very rarely, in spite of great susceptibility in terms of leaf symptoms (553), whereas peas, which are the

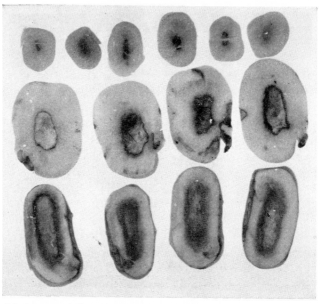

FIG. 21. Manganese deficiency in legume seeds. "Marsh spot" necrotic collapse of cotyledons, and browning of radicle or plumule. Upper row, peas (*Pisum sativum*). Middle row, broad beans (*Vicia faba*). Lower row, climbing French beans (*Phaseolus multiflorus*).

most susceptible, may show no leaf symptoms or only slight paling and small necrotic areas. In haricot bean the brown necrosis may occur in the cotyledons, the radicle or plumule of the embryo or in two or all of these sites. Necrosis of the embryonic prophylls also occurs, though less often in the other species. An unusual effect caused by dual deficiency of manganese and iron, or high pH conditions, was observed by Greenwood and Posnette (166) for cacao. Leaves became changed in morphology and developed deeply lobed margins at the leaf apex under these conditions. Dual deficiencies of iron and magnesium or calcium (324) may produce similar effects.

Manganese requirements are affected by light intensity, but unlike those for zinc, they are decreased in some plants at high light intensity. This phenomenon is apparently related to the fact that manganese uptake is stimulated by light, as shown by McCool (329a) and more recently by Sutton and Hallsworth (520), who found that manganese toxicity in lucerne was accentuated by high light intensity.

ii. Manganese excess. The effects of manganese excess on plants may be revealed in two, apparently quite distinct, ways. These are described here as manganese-induced iron deficiency and direct manganese toxicity. The first is discussed in Section II, B, 2, d. Direct manganese toxicity has been shown in sand culture experiments to be a major factor responsible for the injurious effects of many acid soils (193–195, 199, 300, 301, 556).

Different plants vary greatly in their susceptibility to manganese toxicity. Highly susceptible types include French beans, marrowstem kale (*Brassica oleracea* var. *ramosa*), swede, and many other brassicas, but not rape or thousandhead kale (*B. oleracea* var. *acephala*).

Relatively tolerant types include sugar beet, oat, rye, celery, broad bean. Barley, potato, tomato, red clover, and tobacco are intermediate in tolerance. The differences in tolerance are partly related to relative uptake of manganese, which is relatively low in beet and oats, and partly to actual differences in tolerance.

Symptoms of manganese toxicity also show considerable variety. Many brassicas, particularly Savoy cabbage (*B. oleracea* var. *capitata*), kale, Brussels sprouts (*B. oleracea* var. *gemmifera*), swede, and cauliflower, show pronounced forward marginal cupping of the leaves due to restricted marginal growth compared with that of the central parts (Fig. 22). There is often a white or yellow-green chlorosis of the leaf margin, especially in Savoy cabbage and Brussels sprouts or alternatively marginal and interveinal mottling as in kale and swede. Dark brown, or purple, necrotic spots occur in the marginal area in cauliflower, swede, and kale and may become more general. Interveinal areas perforate, and leaf distortions may be severe. The marginal effects are associated with marked accumulation of manganese. Concentrations may be as much as ten times greater in the chlorotic, or cupped, margins as in interveinal areas near the midrib (193). Severe manganese toxicity causes purple lesions and necrosis of epidermal and other tissues in midrib and petioles.

In potato, early symptoms include profuse distribution of minute black necrotic spots over petioles, on undersides of leaf veins, and along stems. The necrotic spots later coalesce on stems and produce a stem streak necrosis. Petioles collapse, leaves wilt and hang down, and symptoms resemble stem speck virus infection. Tomato plants show brown or sunken necrosis of stems, especially in the region of leaf bases, and basal leaflets collapse at the petiole and hang down. Chocolate-brown lesions occur in leaves of barley and are similar to those observed with manganese deficiency.

Fig. 22. Manganese toxicity in cauliflower (*Brassica oleracea* var. *botrytis*). Interveinal chlorosis, forward cupping of leaf margins, and dark brown or indigo-colored necrotic spotting in marginal tissues; younger leaves have collapsed owing to calcium deficiency.

In French beans the symptoms begin as faint, diffuse, whitish blotches between the veins of older leaves. These become more chlorotic. In young leaves acute chlorosis with interveinal necrotic spots and dark green veins may be confused with iron deficiency. Leaflets also show marginal waving and interveinal distortion. Profuse black spotting occurs along the petioles but is absent from the pulvinus region (Fig. 23). It is possible that in some cases the dark-brown or black necrotic areas contain an accumulation of a higher oxide of manganese. Kenten and Mann (272) have identified the production of trivalent manganese compounds *in vivo* in peas grown in water cultures with excess manganese, but other species, which also show dark necrotic spots, did not apparently accumulate trivalent manganese compounds.

Löhnis (301) found that magnesium, as well as calcium, antagonized the uptake of manganese at toxic levels by some crops. The effect of magnesium in solution cultures was great with beans and potato, less

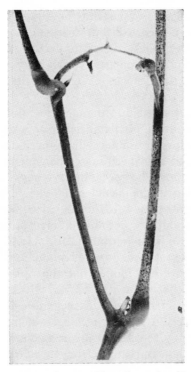

Fig. 23. Manganese toxicity in beans (*Phaseolus vulgaris*) showing black necrotic specking of petioles except for pulvinus regions at base of petioles, which remain green.

with some brassica crops, and was not observed with lucerne. Hannay *et al.* (178) observed a clear magnesium-manganese interaction in growth of excised tomato roots. The optimum levels of one element were affected by concentrations of the other.

b. Cytological effects. Eltinge (131) observed that chloroplasts were the first cell components to be affected by manganese deficiency in tomato. Loss of chlorophyll was associated with loss of the starch grain. Chloroplasts became vacuolated and contents appeared coarsely granular. They then disintegrated and were also immediately lysed by diluted soap solution. Epidermal cells over the palisade were often hyper-trophied. Xylem tissue was reduced in amount and xylem elements were plugged by insoluble materials. There was an accumulation of fats and of calcium oxalate crystals in leaf cells indicative of abnormal car-boxylic acid metabolism. Silver nitrate reduction in chloroplasts was also decreased. Plastid disintegration also occurs in subterranean clover (356), where palisade cells show the first necrosis and collapse be-neath the still-normal upper epidermis.

Brown *et al.* (54) reported that manganese deficiency in *Elodea canadensis* and *Lemna minor* caused the frequent appearance of paired or tetrad groupings of chloroplasts, which they suggested was due to interference in the final stages of chloroplast division under these conditions.

Lyttleton (312) observed that manganese fulfilled a specific role in the stability, or association, of ribonucleoprotein molecules in ribosomes of wheat embryo. Similar functions have been shown for magnesium and calcium, as noted elsewhere in sections on these elements. In the wheat embryo ribosomes, however, dialysis against magnesium failed to preserve the identity of the particles that were dissociated. Manganese (0.2 mM) mainly suppressed this dissociation, but the full stabilizing effect was produced only by a combination of manganese (0.2 mM), calcium (1.5 mM), and magnesium (1.0 mM). Calcium could not be replaced by magnesium, and other divalent ions were only slightly effective. Bowen (42a) has found that the nutrient status of tomato seeds significantly affects the extent to which irradiation induces hereditable mutations. Irradiation of maganese-deficient seed resulted in a significant increase in the numbers of pale green cotyledons whereas zinc deficiency resulted in a correspondingly notable decrease in the number of these mutants. Deficiencies of boron, calcium, and phosphorus also resulted in significant, but less striking, decreases in the proportions of this type of seedling. Lethal mutations were in-creased with deficiencies of nitrogen or copper and decreased by deficiency of magnesium.

c. Physiological effects of manganese. That the effects of manganese are complex and multiple is evident from recent reviews by McElroy and Nason (330) and by Hewitt (207, 209). It is to be expected, there-fore, that the effects of manganese on such processes as respiration and photosynthesis are sometimes apparently contradictory or difficult to interpret, as, for example, when manganese deficiency may cause both nitrate (58, 228, 283) and amino acids (222) to accumulate.

Gerretsen (151) concluded that manganese deficiency decreased photosynthesis per unit area by detached oat leaves under conditions where chlorophyll content was not appreciably different in the two manganese treatments.

In the experiments of Reuther and Burrows (440) with tung (*Aleurites fordii*) the application of manganese to isolated leaves apparently caused an increase in carbon assimilation only by young leaves but had no net effect with older leaves. Portsmouth (414), using attached potato leaves, found a negative effect of manganese on net assimilation rate of manganese-deficient plants, but it was not possible to eliminate possible simultaneous effects on increased respiration, which may have exceeded those on photosynthesis. Ruck and Bolas (451) used rooted, detached potato leaves from normal and manganese-deficient plants to reinvestigate the problem. The leaves were selected for comparable chlorophyll contents. Net assimilation rates of manganese-deficient leaves were usually less than half those observed in normal leaves. Leaves initially grown with low manganese and then transferred to a normal manganese level did not, however, show any increase in assimilation rate over a 3-week period, and they appeared to have been permanently impaired in this respect, possibly in respect of the chloroplasts. In another experiment using rooted leaves there was an increased net assimilation rate in rooted shoots when they were tested 8 days after they had been transferred from low to normal manganese.

Ruck and Bolas (451) found that manganese also significantly stimulated respiration, measured as carbon dioxide production, by rooted leaves, but the effect was only of the order of 10–20%. In rooted shoots no effect of manganese could be detected. In earlier experiments Lundegårdh (308) found that manganese stimulated oxygen uptake by manganese-deficient roots. The increase was between two- and fivefold when excised roots were used, but only up to twofold when the leaves remained attached. Gerretsen (151) observed that manganese-deficient oat leaves produced about 30% less carbon dioxide than normal leaves in the dark. It is difficult to interpret these results owing to the complexity of the functions of manganese. Stimulation of several reactions in the carboxylic acid cycle and in decarboxylation reactions would, however, stimulate carbon dioxide production and by regenerating reduced pyridine nucleotides would also favor oxygen uptake. It is possible that manganese-catalyzed peroxidation reactions (265, 266, 270) would also be stimulated.

Pirson (413) concluded that in green algae manganese deficiency sharply depressed photosynthesis under autotrophic conditions but that it had no effect on respiration in the dark in the presence of glucose. Pirson (411) has also suggested that the somewhat contradictory results produced by manganese deficiency may reflect the age and type of tissue used. This is most likely when the complex nature of the enzyme systems dependent on manganese and the differential activity of these systems in different tissues are considered (198, 207, 209).

Gerretsen (152) reported effects of manganese on the oxidation-reduction potentials of oat leaf chloroplast suspensions. Manganese stimulated the increase in oxidation-reduction potential during illumination of both normal and manganese-deficient suspensions. His interpretation was that manganese reacted with ·OH radicals and thereby prevented their recombination with hydrogen atoms produced during the photolysis of water.

Kenten and Mann (271) have shown, however, that illuminated chloroplast suspensions catalyze the oxidation of Mn^{++} to Mn^{+++} when stabilized by a chelating agent, e.g., pyrophosphate. This would be expected to lead to a rise in oxidation-reduction potential on illumination.

Mehler (338, 339) described a Hill reaction in which manganese was required for the utilization of oxygen as a Hill reagent, with the production of hydrogen peroxide. This was detected and removed by coupled oxidation of alcohol to acetaldehyde in the presence of catalase. The Mehler reaction comprises the following intermediate reactions:

$$4H_2O \rightarrow 4H + 4OH: \text{photolysis of water} \tag{1}$$
$$4OH \rightarrow 2H_2O + O_2: \text{oxygen evolution} \tag{2}$$
$$4H + 2O_2 \rightarrow 2H_2O_2: \text{oxygen uptake} \tag{3}$$

$$\text{net reaction } 2H_2O + O_2 \rightarrow 2H_2O_2 \tag{4}$$

In the presence of catalase (either endogenous or added) and ethanol, the peroxide is used to oxidize the ethanol and a net oxygen uptake results. If ethanol is omitted there is no net change, as the peroxide is decomposed to yield oxygen and water.

The source of hydrogen cannot be reduced pyridine nucleotides, since these are not autoxidizable; reduced riboflavin phosphates, however, are:

$$FMNH_2 + O_2 \rightarrow FMN + H_2O_2$$

Habermann (174) found that, in the chloroplasts from *Phytolacca americana* (pokeweed), manganese catalytically stimulated both oxygen evolution and oxygen uptake, as revealed by using O^{18} to distinguish the two processes. During oxygen evolution, manganese mediated the formation of peroxide. This might, however, arise in a secondary manner from oxidation of reduced flavins (15). It is possible that this reaction then leads to the oxidation of manganese in the presence of pyrophosphate and illuminated chloroplasts in the Kenten and Mann system (271) and could also account for oxygen uptake by chloroplast suspensions when illuminated (153). Practically all work on the role of manganese as a catalyst in photosynthesis has been done with green algae, but Brown *et al.* (54) reported a 40% recovery of Hill reaction capacity in washed, or EDTA-treated, chloroplasts of *Phytolacca americana, Spinacia oleracea,* and *Gleditsia triacanthos* (honey locust) when manganese was restored. Effects reported with green algae are much greater (54, 273, 274, 413). Manganese is apparently essential for both the Hill reaction and photosynthesis at levels or times when chlorophyll content is not a factor (see also, Chapter 4, Volume IB). Pirson (413) considered whether the effects of manganese on photosynthesis in higher plants were similar, or not, to those more clearly shown for algae; he concluded that a different behavior must still be considered a possibility, especially in view of the participation of hydrogenase in some algae, although oxygen evolution is inhibited by manganese deficiency when photoreduction is unaffected.

The significance of manganese in photosynthesis is, however, unexplained. The fact that manganese can participate in photochemical oxidation-reduction reactions *in vitro*—such as the Kenten and Mann (265, 266, 269) system or as postulated by Andreae (15), where autoxidation of a photochemically reduced flavin leads to peroxide formation, which in turn oxidizes manganese—does not necessarily explain its role in photosynthesis.

The Mehler reaction (cf. Chapter 4, Volume IB, p. 196) does not result in net oxygen uptake unless a peroxide trapping system is present. Pirson (413) suggested that manganese was involved in the formation of a peroxide intermediate postulated by Kessler (275, 275a) as being derived from the primary reduced Hill oxidant. Habermann (174) found that the stimulating effect of manganese on oxygen uptake was greater, when measured as a ratio to control values, than its effect on oxygen production by chloroplasts of *Phytolacca americana.* Moreover the presence of quinone (a Hill reagent) masked, or eliminated, the effect of manganese on oxygen uptake; and oxygen evolution in normal Hill reaction conditions does not appear to depend on manganese. For these reasons it seems possible that manganese is involved in more than one reaction system. The relative stimulation in the two reactions produced over a range of manganese concentrations should provide a more critical test of this point. Alternatively, as Habermann (174) considers, manganese may stimulate peroxidase formation as an alternative pathway in oxygen evolution. Kessler (273–275) has shown that manganese is almost certainly involved in the process but the significance of various mechanisms postulated *in vitro* may be different *in vivo* in the absence of Hill reagents or the Mehler reaction. Under these circumstances the effect of manganese on oxygen uptake would be expected, as is observed, to be greater than on oxygen evolution, which would be partly independent of manganese supply. Kessler (274, 275), Pirson (413), and Habermann (174), however, all consider that manganese is primarily concerned in some aspect of the oxygen-evolving process, but the nature of the reaction and its significance in photosynthesis remains obscure.

4. Copper

a. *Visible effects of deficiency.* Copper deficiency is well known, particularly in deciduous fruit trees (14), tung (362), cereals, herbage legumes and in many other plants grown in culture experiments. The condition is often known as "exanthema" and has been described in citrus (62, 173), French prune (*Prunus domestica*) and Japanese plum (*Prunus salicina*) (485), pear (395), olive (*Olea europaea*) (485) and in apple (117), where it is also known as "summer dieback." Leaves are often initially dark green, though sometimes twisted and may be borne on abnormally vigorous "water shoots," which in citrus become curved or S shaped. Terminal leaves of citrus (542) and stone fruit (14) may later show interveinal chlorotic mottling. Leaves become necrotic, sometimes beginning with death of the leaf tip in cocoa (324) and in pear (14), where the margins also scorch. Characteristic orange-brown striations may occur parallel to the margins (395). Bark of apple, pear, citrus, plum, becomes roughened owing to raised blisters, and deep splits occur from which gum exudes and gives the condition called "exanthema." Brown stains may develop in leaves and bark in citrus. This stage is followed by dieback of the shoot and by the production of characteristic multiple buds. There may be 10–20 small weak buds clustered in the place of each of the usual auxillary buds near the apex of the shoot in citrus (62, 542), and they are also common in stone fruit (14). Extension of these buds leads to numerous weak shoots causing a "witch's broom" habit. These secondary shoots may die back and repeat the process of multiple bud production. Multiple bud development due to death of successive growing points was observed in rubber (*Hevea brasiliensis*) (38).

Symptoms of copper deficiency appear in young leaves of many plants including those of the trees already mentioned and also those of tomato, cereals (410), broad bean, pea, lucerne (218, 410), subterranean clover (357), and flax (355, 410). Necrosis and withering appear first in old leaves of tomato (428) and sugar beet. In French beans necrosis comprises fairly regular rows of necrotic spots, situated close to the major veins near the bases of the leaflets. Foliage is at first abnormally dark blue-green in tomato, potato, lucerne and subterranean clover, though fading or chlorosis may follow; in cereals, dwarf bean, pea, flax, and sugar beet the foliage is initially gray green or chlorotic. Curling or rolling of leaves, which may be markedly twisted, is often characteristic as in tomato (Fig. 24) (410, 428), flax (355), citrus, oat, and especially wheat, of which leaves become coiled into a tight spiral

Fig. 24. Copper deficiency in tomato (*Lycopersicon esculentum*) plants. Left, two plants showing inrolled leaflets; right, a leaf from a normal plant of the same age.

which sometimes reverses its direction (Fig. 25). Marked epinastic curvatures of petioles of leaflets occurs in lucerne (410).

In the "white tip" or "reclamation disease" of cereals, caused by copper deficiency in peat soils, the young leaves become limp and chlorotic and remain tightly rolled. Leaves become white from the tip; constrictions occur a few centimeters behind the tip, which collapses. The tips of younger emerging leaves tend to remain trapped within the rolled part of the subtending leaves, and this causes a characteristic loop. The growing point is killed and ear formation is suppressed (410). Copper deficiency in Sitka spruce (*Picea sitchensis*) (33) also causes spiral twisting of the needles and ring-shaped necrotic lesions.

Excessive production of weak tillers is common in cereals and may be analogous to multiple bud formation in trees. If so, it is possible that copper deficiency causes some disturbances in auxin (indoleacetic acid) metabolism and loss of apical dominance.

Flowers of broad bean lose their dark purple-brown pigment on the keel, which becomes pale brown when copper deficient (Fig. 26). This suggests that a copper oxidase is responsible for this localized pigmentation. The pigment in the central region of subterranean clover leaflets

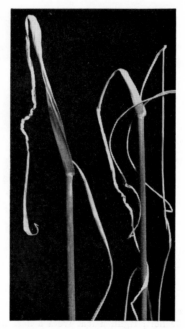

Fig. 25. Copper deficiency in wheat (*Triticum*). Closely rolled totally chlorotic leaf tip of young leaves; constrictions at intervals along length and spiral distortion of leaves.

may also disappear when copper is deficient (410). Dark-colored *Iris* and *Dahlia* flowers are reported by Sarata (454) to contain more copper than pale ones. The copper supply available to plants during the vegetative period materially affects the copper status of the seed (218). The pale flower color of the broad bean plants shown in Fig. 26 were observed only in flowers produced by plants grown from copper-deficient seed and deprived of copper in the following generation also. The phenolic substrates which may be involved in tyrosinase activity have been summarized by Mallette (318). Another example of seed reserves affecting growth response to copper supply is shown in Fig. 27 for broad beans.

b. Effects on histology. Histological studies by Reed (428) on tomato leaves showed that the first changes appeared in the palisade cells. These cells separated beneath the stomata and caused the appearance of large cavities (Fig. 28). Separation was often complete and

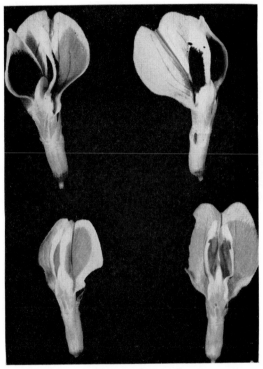

Fig. 26. Copper deficiency in broad bean (*Vicia faba*) showing loss of chocolate-brown pigment in "keel" of flowers in lower pair produced by plants grown from copper-deficient seed in absence of copper. Upper pair of flowers produced by plants grown from normal seed in absence of added copper.

was followed by shrinkage of the separated cells and finally by lysis of the contents, producing a columnar structure. Necrosis began in palisade cells. Plastids were initially large and numerous and later became clumped together. Chlorophyll became distributed discontinuously in the plastids and collected into droplets that were dispersed into a uniform phase in the cytoplasm on treatment with sodium oleate.

c. Effects of copper on nitrogen and carbon metabolism. Apart from causing simultaneous increases and decreases in enzyme activity, described in Chapter 4, copper deficiency also caused marked changes in the amino acid pattern observed by Possingham (416) and Steinberg (506). In tomato (416), the total amino nitrogen content was greatly increased owing to lack of copper; the changes were mainly in amounts of aspartic acid, glutamic acid, asparagine, β-alanine, arginine, and proline. There were significant decreases in the amounts of histidine, lysine, and phenylalanine; the last was a particularly notable difference. The amides were practically unaffected by copper supply. These changes are described in more detail in Section II, C. Leaves of copper-deficient tung contained higher protein-nitrogen contents than normal plants and decreased oil, starch, and reducing sugars, according to Gilbert (155) and his collaborators (156). High nitrogen status accentuated copper deficiency symptoms (504a). Higher protein contents were also reported by Lucas (307) in several copper-deficient plants, especially in carrot roots. Wood and Womersley (590) found high protein contents in different parts of copper-deficient oat plants. Copper requirements for barley in water cultures were accentuated by inadequate aeration or by the use of ammonium nitrogen according to Arnon (16). Loustalot *et al.* (305) observed a sharp decrease in carbon dioxide absorption during photosynthesis of young tung trees when they were deficient in copper. Trees given no copper showed a decrease to half the normal rates when still free from visible

Fig. 27. Effect of copper status of seed on growth of bean (*Vicia faba*) in absence of copper. Front: plant produced by seed saved from copper-deficient plant. Rear: plant produced from normal seed and showing symptoms of deficiency late in development.

symptoms and a decrease to one-fifth the normal when symptoms were apparent. This observation may be related to the recent discovery of Katoh (261), Katoh and Takamiya (262), of a blue copper protein in chloroplasts of *Chlorella* and of higher plants, which is reduced by light in the presence of chloroplast grana and functions as a natural Hill reagent for oxygen evolution. This discovery gives a new interest

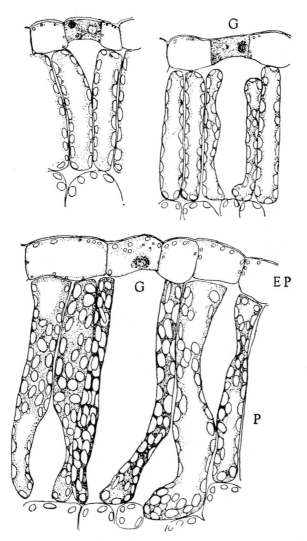

Fig. 28. Effects of copper deficiency on leaf structure of tomato (*Lycopersicon esculentum*). Palisade parenchyma of tomato leaves to show successive stages in the formation of lacunae in copper-deficient plants. Drawings from fixed material stained with acid fuchsin and methyl green. The upper diagrams represent conditions in younger leaflets. The lower diagram represents a condition characteristic of older leaflets. *EP*, epidermis; *G*, guard cell; *P*, palisade. From Reed (428).

in the role of copper, which is more general than that of the copper-containing oxidases, whose physiological functions are still obscure (318, 375).

d. *Interactions between copper and other elements in clover.* Greenwood and Hallsworth (163) described a study of complex interactions shown by subterranean clover to variation in the supply of copper, molybdenum, calcium, phosphorus, and nitrogen (Table XIII). As

TABLE XIII

Interactions among Copper, Calcium, and Phosphorus in Nitrogen
Nutrition of Subterranean Clover (*Trifolium subterraneum*)[a]

	Variables[b]		% N		Mg N/plant		Yield (gm)	
			Cu 0.064	Cu 0.0064	Cu 0.064	Cu 0.0064	Cu 0.064	Cu 0.0064
N224	Ca64	P40	2.97 → 3.29		382 ← 264↑		12.9	8.0
		P8	2.82 → 3.41		376 ← 222		13.3	6.5
	Ca8	P40	3.53	3.40	103	58	2.9	1.7
		P8	3.63 ← 3.25		211	102↓	5.8	3.1
N12	Ca64	P40	3.15 ← 2.73↑		79	60	2.5	2.2
		P8	2.86 ← 2.43		192 ←	68	6.7	2.8
	Ca8	P40	1.96	1.92↑	26	26	1.3	1.4
		P8	1.78	1.64	32	18	1.8	1.1

[a] From Greenwood and Hallsworth (163).

[b] The arrows in the table indicate the change in a positive direction as a result of the change in treatment where the differences were significant.

some of the more important effects concerned interactions with copper the work is considered in this context.

Calcium, copper, and molybdenum interacted in their effects on yield in one experiment in a significant but unexplained manner. With adequate calcium (64 ppm) molybdenum was beneficial at the low, but not at the normal, copper level. With a low calcium level, molybdenum was inhibitory at the normal level and beneficial at high and low levels, regardless of the copper supply.

Copper and phosphorus interacted significantly (Table XIII). Increased copper supply increased yields more with a low level of phosphorus (8 ppm) than with a higher level of 40 ppm. The 40 ppm phosphorus level was toxic at the normal copper level (0.064 ppm) but not at the low copper level (0.0064 ppm), where it was slightly beneficial. This effect was shown to be due to a direct effect of copper on phosphorus uptake.

Increased supply of phosphorus also increased copper uptake at low copper levels and at a low calcium level regardless of its effect on yields. Increased supply of copper increased nitrogen fixation greatly when calcium level was adequate and still showed some effect at a low calcium level under conditions of low (nontoxic) phosphorus supply, but copper had no effect on nitrogen fixation when phosphorus was present at a toxic level. In plants grown with nitrate the low copper level induced typical copper deficiency symptoms, but in the plants mainly dependent on nitrogen fixation, low copper supply caused an appearance of nitrogen deficiency. The copper requirement in nitrogen fixation was several orders greater than for the growth with fixed nitrogen supplied as nitrate. Second- and third-order interactions were found to be highly significant.

5. Zinc

a. Visible effects of zinc deficiency. Zinc deficiency produces changes in leaf morphology and in cell histology. Several well-known disorders include "little leaf" and "rosette" of apple, peach, pecan (*Carya pecan*); "mottle leaf" or "frenching" of citrus; "white bud" of maize; "sickle leaf" of cocoa; "bronzing" of tung (362), and walnut (*Juglans regia, J. hindsii*) "yellows." Trees are frequently affected plants. Maize, cotton, squash (*Cucurbita pepo* var.), tomato, and sunflower (489) are also especially sensitive. Early but detailed studies were carried out by Chandler, Hoagland and Hibbard (68–71, 229). Chandler (67) summarized observations on zinc deficiency in many trees, and the probable order of their decreasing sensitivity is given as sweet cherry, apple, Japanese plum, peach (possibly pear and pecan), walnut, apricot (*Prunus armeniaca*), avocado (*Persea americana* [*P. gratissima*]), citrus, grapes (*Vitis vinifera*). It is possible that citrus should be placed higher in this list. There is scarcely an area of the world where citrus trees do not show some signs of little leaf. Comparable studies were also described by Viets, Boawn, and Crawford (540a).

Symptoms usually appear first, or mainly, in older leaves of tobacco (337), tomato (221), peas, and French beans (218). In maize (28, 221, 541) young and old leaves both show distinctive symptoms. In trees such as apple, pecan, peach, and citrus, mature leaves may show the first symptoms of mottling, but the severe effects on morphology and rosetting often occur in young terminal leaflets or in the spurs. Flushing also affects the incidence of symptoms in citrus (62) and cocoa (165,

324), where leaves formed on a previous flush may not show symptoms whereas some or all leaves of a current flush may be affected. Young leaves and stem regions appear to be affected in tung (362) and broad bean (218). Necrosis may begin at the leaf attachment as in flax (355) or may occur generally.

With deficient zinc greatly decreased leaf size occurs in apple (92), peach (92), citrus (62, 73); the leaf may be less than one-twentieth

FIG. 29. Zinc deficiency in tomato (*Lycopersicon esculentum*) plants. Note telescoping of internodes, diminutive leaves with undercurling of leaflets, epinastic curvature of petioles, necrosis, and fading of chlorophyll.

the normal area (299). Leaf margins are often severely distorted into a wavy, twisted, or corrugated outline, as in peach (92), cocoa (165, 324), rubber (39), clovers (218, 357), beans (218), or curled to the undersides as in tomato (221) (Fig. 29). Characteristic "helmet" shaped or "beaked" leaves have been described for coffee (*Coffea robusta*). Asymmetric development of leaf lamina causing the leaf to assume a "sickle shape" occurs in cocoa (164, 165, 324) (Fig. 30) and also in beans and tomato (221). Leaf vein distortion is also produced in cocoa (324).

Dull yellow green, or bright yellow to ivory, interveinal mottling is often characteristic of zinc deficiency in apple and many deciduous stone-fruit trees (229). The contrast between dark green veins and bright yellow chlorosis is very striking in the diminutive spiky leaves of severely affected citrus (62, 67, 73, 229). Oat, tomato (221), and tobacco (337) are dull olive green when zinc deficient, and deep purple tints occur in maize on old leaves (221) with yellow or white chlorotic striping of young leaves in the "white bud" state (28). Zinc deficiency symptoms resemble the symptoms of phosphorus deficiency when the deficiency is severe.

Fig. 30. Zinc deficiency in cocoa (*Theobroma cacao*) showing "sickle leaf" shape and ivory-tinted translucent chlorotic areas between dark green veins and, especially, near midrib. From Greenwood and Hayfron (165).

Internode length is severely reduced by lack of zinc, producing the characteristic terminal rosette effect in many trees, e.g., in apple, stone fruits (67, 69–71), tung (362), cotton (50), pecan (140), clovers (357, flax, broad bean, tomato (Fig. 29), *Pinus radiata* (484), and rubber (39).

Irregular necrotic areas develop in interveinal or vascular tissues in leaves of tobacco (337), maize, oat, tomato, French beans (218, 221), tung (362), pecan (140), and cotton (50). Breakdown of the tissues results in the escape of cell contents as a brown fluid from leaves of maize and tomato (221); these plants, and also rubber, appear very liable to attack by fungi when zinc deficient, and the incidence of infection by *Oidium heveae* (39) is greatly intensified.

Seed production is severely depressed by lack of zinc in beans, pea, and other plants (430, 431, 441, 489). Fruit size is greatly reduced in citrus and the albedo is relatively very thick in proportion to the pulp. The shell of walnuts is tough and pliable instead of hard and brittle (67).

The importance of zinc in inflorescence development and seed production is clearly shown in the work of Riceman and Jones (441, especially their Figs. 2–5). Total yields of dry material of subterranean clover plants were increased but slightly by raising the zinc supply from 0.1 to 0.15 ppm in water culture, whereas the yield and numbers of inflorescences and seeds was increased over fourfold over this range. When the zinc supply was raised from 0.05 to 0.15 ppm, yields were approximately doubled but seed and flower production was increased about one hundred times. At 0.05 ppm zinc a few inflorescences were formed, but these mostly aborted and all but 2% of those that developed remained seedless. The individual weight of seed that developed was the same regardless of zinc supply. The effect of zinc was, therefore, on seed formation rather than on seed growth (Table XIV). Similar large increases occurred in the relative zinc

TABLE XIV

Effect of Zinc Supply on Seed Production in Subterranean Clover
(*Trifolium subterraneum*)[a]

Detail	Concentration of zinc in culture solution (mg/l)						
	0.05	0.1	0.125	0.15	0.175	0.2	0.4
Weight of seed per plant, oven dry (gm)	0.04	0.86	2.5	4.0	3.9	3.8	3.2
Number of seeds per plant	6.5	150	382	650	632	657	577
Number of mature burrs per plant	3	49	120	199	198	222	195
Number of seeds per mature burr	2.2	3.1	3.2	3.3	3.2	3.0	3.0
Weight of seed per mature burr (mg)	13	18	21	20	19	17	16
Mean weight per seed, oven dry (mg)	6.1	5.8	6.6	6.2	6.1	5.7	5.5
Percentage of inflorescences which produced mature burrs	1.8	23	37	33	37	39	37

[a] From Riceman and Jones (441).

content of inflorescence and seed as a proportion of the total zinc in the plants, especially over the period between 155 and 189 days when inflorescence growth reached maximum development (cf. Fig. 22 in ref. 441). There appeared to be a translocation of zinc from leaves to flowers at 189 days when luxury amounts were provided (0.2 ppm). On the other hand numbers of leaves and leaf primordia decreased sharply over the same range.

b. Anatomical and histological effects. Histological studies on zinc deficiency made by Reed (427–429), Reed and Dufrenoy (434–436), Eltinge and Reed (132), Carlton (64), and Millikan (357) showed several changes in the cells. The palisade and "spongy" mesophyll tissues in leaves of tomato, peach, apricot, and walnut were abnormally compact and the usual intercellular spaces were practically absent, a condition suggesting delayed differentiation. In tomato the numbers of leaf palisade cells were decreased; they were three to four times the

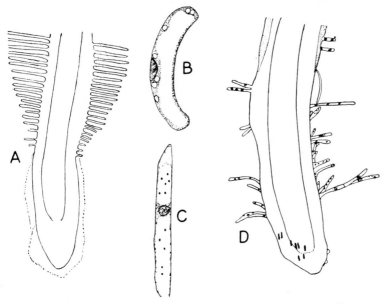

Fig. 31. Effects of zinc nutrition on the growth of roots of tomato (*Lycopersicon esculentum*) plants. Root tips grown in hanging drops. (A) Control root tip, 24 hours; ×37. (B) Exfoliated cell from (A) showing large starch grains; ×360. (C) Exfoliated cell from (D) showing deposits of tannin in vacuole; ×360. (D) Zinc-deficient root tip after 24 hours; ×37. From Eltinge and Reed (132).

normal length and about double the normal width, i.e., twelve to sixteen times greater in volume. Plastids were decreased in size and numbers. The mesophyll cells tended to be atrophied. In primordial leaves of orange, palisade cells remained undifferentiated and polygonal instead of becoming rhomboidal. Plastids remained primordial and undifferentiated. During the expansion of zinc-deficient leaves the palisade cells enlarged abnormally, but occasionally cells divided transversely or longitudinally and irregular cell sizes resulted.

The root tips of zinc-deficient tomato plants (Fig. 31) showed a series of three to six swellings at 1 or 2 mm intervals behind the apex (132),

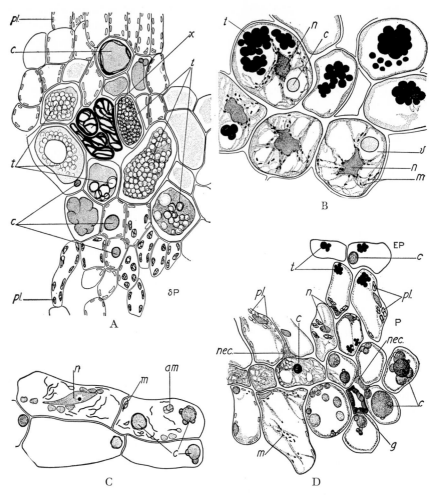

Fig. 32. Effects of zinc deficiency on growth of apricot (*Prunus armeniaca*), orange (*Citrus aurantium*), and walnut tissues.

(A) Portion of a transverse section of an apricot leaf affected with zinc deficiency in which the perivascular cells were replete with masses of catechol. In the immediate vicinity of the bundle (*x*) the catechol masses formed a continuous phase enmeshing a number of vacuoles (*t*). Other cells contained spherical masses of catechol (*c*) enveloped by precipitation membranes and may be considered autocomplex coacervates. The plastids (*pl*) showed abnormalities. (B) Cells from the apical region of a vegetative shoot of an affected apricot tree. The catechol material in some vacuoles (*v*) condensed into globular masses (*t*); in others it formed an aggregate (*c*) enveloped by a precipitation membrane. Nucleus (*n*); mitochondria (*m*). (C) Coacervated material demonstrated by the molybdenic reagent in hypoplastic cells from root of an orange seedling which had grown seven months in a nutrient solution without zinc, (*am*) amyloplast; (*c*) coacervates exhibiting vacuo-

and these were associated with the bulk of root hair production. Root hairs were often crooked. Tannins, calcium oxalate crystals, and oil globules appeared in root tip cells, but starch grains were rare. All cells, including those in the meristematic zone, were much enlarged prematurely. In tissues showing external symptoms, the meristematic cells were scarcely recognizable as such. Arrangement was irregular with numerous intercellular spaces. Mature cells were isodiametric instead of columnar, and differentiation was suppressed. Meristematic cells contained abnormally elongated and flattened vacuoles. Nucleoli were smaller than normal. Mitochondrial particles were extra elongated and spirally distorted instead of being rod shaped. The effects of cell enlargement and decreased differentiation in zinc-deficient tomato roots and stems are discussed by Carlton (cf. Figs. 7A and D and 8A and D of ref. 64).

The most pronounced changes however, were observed in contents of individual cells (Fig. 32, A–D). Plastids in green areas of mottled avocado leaves were often normal whereas in the chlorotic areas chloroplasts became agglutinated and segregated into groups at the inner ends of the cells. Plastids became vacuolated and tannin globules appeared. In apricot plastids (436), globules of lipid substances appeared in the stroma. This was also observed in tomato chloroplasts. Plastids became vacuolated and then shrank to a fusiform outline; they had increased capacity for staining with acid fuchsin and had a decreased starch content prior to disintegrating or dissolving by a process resembling lysis.

In maize (427) the plastids were much fewer, clumped together, and vacuolated; the nucleus migrated to one end of the cell. Plastids devoid of starch were more prone to this behavior. It was suggested that processes of disintegration were hastened by stronger illumination. This would be consistent with the known effects of season on the incidence of zinc deficiency symptoms described below. Nuclei were often more resistant to breakdown than plastids. In general, vacuolation and disintegration of plastids were the most consistent effects, but in many plants phenolic compounds and oil droplets also accumulated. Atrophy of the vascular system occurred in tomato. Tannins were present in

---

lated envelopes of phospholipid material; (*m*) mitochondria (frequently agglutinated); (*n*) elongated nucleus. (D) Portion of a transverse section of a walnut (*Juglans hindsii*) leaflet, dwarfed and chlorotic by "little leaf." The hypertrophied palisade cells had a definite polarization of contents, indicated by the position of vacuolar precipitates (*t*) at one, and nuclei (*n*) and plastids (*pl*) at the other, pole. The perivascular cells contained globulal masses (*c*) of catechol. Gum (*g*) and necrotic material (*nec*) occurred in intercellular spaces. From Reed and Dufrenoy (436).

apricot, peach, walnut, avocado, orange (434, 435), and buckwheat (436) and absent from sunflower, corn, and squash. This distinction was related to the relative extent to which zinc deficiency caused "little leaf" effects in the tannin-containing group. Calcium oxalate crystals appeared in tomato and orange leaves. Semipermeable properties of cell membranes to toluidine blue and neutral red were lost, and material staining with hematoxylin collected in intercellular spaces of walnut leaves (427). This is consistent with the observed exudations of cell contents from leaves of zinc-deficient plants.

In meristematic buds of zinc-deficient apricot the cells showed increased contents of tannin of two sorts, differentiated by staining capacity for methyl green. Vacuolation was premature and cell contents were often "polarized" to one end. Nuclei carried several small spherical bodies. Cell division appeared to be inhibited and cell expansion occurred prematurely. Plastid differentiation was delayed. Polarization of cell contents, with arrested development of plastids, was characteristic in the walnut (429). Reed and Dufrenoy (436) showed that where tannins accumulated on spherical droplets or complex coacervates they comprised catechol tannins surrounded by a phospholipid membrane. These appeared to have been produced very rapidly, as judged by the occasional inclusion in them of the cell fluids (Fig. 32).

Histological changes in flax, lucerne, and subterranean clover have been studied by Millikan (355–357). In flax two types of necrosis occur. Bronzing of the leaves was due to collapse of small groups of cells of the upper epidermis. Underlying cells sometimes became necrotic later. Necrosis of the leaf stalk and leaf base was associated with collapse and necrosis of parenchyma cells of the petiole and preceded any abnormality in the epidermis. The vascular tissues were the least affected. Bronzing of stem tips was related to necrosis of the cortex parenchyma followed by epidermal necrosis and, last of all, necrosis in the vascular tissues. Dieback of the stem apex was associated with necrosis of cells just behind the apical dome, and it occurred independently of the necrosis in leaves or petioles. Tannins were detected in cells of zinc-deficient tissues.

"Little leaf" effects in subterranean clover were associated with thickening of the leaves. This was due to proliferation of palisade cells. These either divided transversely to produce several layers of irregular, but still roughly columnar, cells, or, in regions where not thickened, the cells became rhomboidal and were not differentiated from the lower mesophyll cells. Cells of the upper epidermis produced irregular projections or collapsed completely into necrotic areas. Plastids became elongated and lysis caused their disappearance. This was associated with the irregular chlorosis and red-purple tinting of foliage. Cell necrosis in the "little leaf" tissues occurred first in the mesophyll. The first-formed leaves of zinc-deficient plants showed somewhat different behavior. Epidermal, palisade, and mesophyll cells remained normal in shape, but many cells were devoid of plastids. Cells of all tissues, especially those of the palisade, contained spherical coacervates with a phospho-lipid membrane. These preceded necrosis of the cells. The oldest leaflets of normal size on zinc-deficient plants showed necrosis in underlying tissues. Many of the effects described for subterranean clover were anal-ogous to those observed in citrus, tomato, and maize noted above. In lucerne the palisade cell contents disintegrated and the cells subdivided. Bronze necrotic spots developed in the upper epidermis.

The abnormalities in ovule development of peas were observed by Reed (430, 431) to occur at zinc levels above those adequate for normal vegetative growth. Absence of micropile or integument or of embryo sac nuclei were observed. Premature vacuolation was common, and lysis of cell contents also occurred. Ovules tended to be anatropous instead of campylotropous. The effects of zinc on the flower and seed production in subterranean clover have already been noted (441).

c. Relation to auxin activity and light. The zinc status of some plants probably affects the activity of auxins, in particular that of indoleacetic acid. The action may involve two independent effects. Skoog (481) found that zinc deficiency greatly decreased the amounts of indoleacetic acid obtained by diffusion, or ether extractions, from stem apices or leaves of tomato. The amounts obtained from deficient tissues were between one-tenth and one-fiftieth of the normal. The effects of zinc deficiency on auxin content preceded those on growth or the visual symptoms, in contrast to effects of copper or manganese deficiencies, where decreased auxin occurred only in advanced stages of deficiency. Auxin concentrations increased 2 days after restoration of the zinc supply, but renewed growth was not apparent until several days later.

Auxin was inactivated more rapidly in contact with zinc-deficient than with normal tissues. Blue light, which normally inhibits auxin responses, had a greater proportional effect on zinc-deficient than on normal tissues in this respect. Red light, which favors elongation, under auxin action permitted greater elongation of zinc-deficient tissues than occurred with normal light. Auxin inactivation by zinc-deficient tis-sues was decreased by red as compared with normal light, and in this respect red light decreased the effects of zinc deficiency. These relation-ships may have a bearing on the increased zinc requirements observed in long days and seasons of maximum light intensity. It was also found that peroxidase activity, as revealed by oxidation of benzidine in the presence of hydrogen peroxide, was greater in zinc-deficient than in normal tissues. Skoog reported work by Bean which had shown that blue light increased the peroxidase activity of tissues and also accelerated the breakdown of auxin. Increased peroxidase activity may occur in other plants when they are deficient in zinc (209, 371). It was concluded by Skoog (481) that zinc is responsible for maintaining auxin in an active state, but not for the synthesis of auxin. It seems possible, however, that auxin content decreased in zinc-deficient tissues because inactivation was more rapid, owing to increased auxin-oxidase or peroxidase activity as elucidated by Waygood and his collaborators (313, 570, 571) and by Kenten (264). The frequent observation that tannins accumulate in zinc-deficient tissues would also support the idea of increased oxidase activity.

The effects of light and season on zinc deficiency have been noted by several observers with some contradictory conclusions. Hoagland (228) reported that visible symptoms of zinc deficiency are restricted to the summer in California and are not observed in the winter. Ferres (139), however, found that zinc deficiency in subterranean clover in South Australia is most severe during the short-day period. Ozanne (397) concluded that both day length and light intensity are involved and that light intensity effects may be the more important. Median light intensities of 1400 foot-candles caused maximum immobilization of zinc in roots, and this intensity was similar to that to which zinc-deficient clover was exposed in the experiment by Ferres (139).

Zinc may, however, directly affect auxin production, according to Tsui (531), who concluded that zinc was required for synthesis, in tomato, of tryptophan, which is a precursor of auxin. It may be relevant that Nason (370) found that the production of an enzyme in *Escherichia coli,* which converted indole and serine to tryptophan, was dependent upon a supply of zinc. Zinc may therefore have two independent effects on auxin production. Carlton (64) observed effects resembling treatment with auxins in zinc-deficient tomato roots. Zinc also appears to increase the action of gibberellin on bean internodes, according to Dancer (90).

d. *Relation to nitrogen and phosphorus metabolism and enzyme activity.* Zinc deficiency caused great increases in amide and total amino nitrogen compounds in tomato (416). Glutamine was increased sevenfold and became the major soluble nitrogen compound. Asparagine was increased nearly fiftyfold and was second in importance to glutamine. There were also proportionally large increases in the levels of aspartic acid, lysine, histidine, arginine, serine, threonine, alanine, phenylalanine, valine, leucine, and proline. However, some decreases in the concentrations of substances were attributed to citrulline and ethanolamine (Table XVIII). Earlier observations by Steinberg (503, 505, 508) showed that zinc deficiency in common with most mineral deficiencies caused increases in the total soluble nitrogen of tobacco plants. Later data on amino acids, from analyses by Zacharias and Steward on samples supplied by Steinberg (507, 509), are given in Table XIX. Experiments in which various amino acids were fed to tobacco seedlings grown in sterile cultures (504) resulted in the production of leaf distortions and chlorotic mottling. L(+)-Isoleucine was especially active in this respect.

The resemblance between the effects of these amino acids upon mottled and diminutive strap-shaped leaves and some effects of zinc deficiency is striking; this suggests that some well-known effects of zinc deficiency may be the result of the accumulation of specific amino nitrogen compounds. The amides, glutamine, and asparagine were not however particularly active in causing leaf mottling or malformation, and leucines and proline did not accumulate in zinc-deficient tobacco plants (507) (Table XIX). High nitrogen supplies immobilized zinc in roots of subterranean clover, where Ozanne (396) found a correlation between protein nitrogen and zinc retention.

Reed (432) observed that zinc-deficient tomato had a higher concentration of inorganic phosphate than normal plants and also a high acid phosphatase activity, shown histochemically *in vivo*. This has also been confirmed in leaf extracts, the data being expressed on a protein basis, by Hewitt and Tatham (225) for tomato grown with different sources of nitrogen. The effect is not specific, however, as it occurred also with deficiencies of phosphorus, boron, and molybdenum and of copper when nitrogen was given as nitrite (Table XV). The association of zinc supply with aldolase activity in clover (419, 420) might account for effects of zinc on inorganic phosphorus status. Thus decreased aldolase would decrease the production of glyceraldehyde-3-phosphate, and this in turn could cause decreased phosphorylation of adenosine diphosphate during triosephosphate dehydrogenase action. Reed (432) reported decreased dehydrogenase activity in zinc-deficient tomato tissues. Zinc has also been identified as a probable constituent of several diphosphopyridine nucleotide-dependent dehydrogenases in yeast and animal tissues, and it may be similarly involved in plants. Loustalot *et al.* (305) found that zinc deficiency decreased photosynthetic carbon dioxide uptake by tung trees. This would be consistent with other effects described above.

Zinc-deficient tomato plants (371) may have greatly increased polyphenol oxidase and peroxidase activities, and these changes might

TABLE XV

EFFECTS OF MICRONUTRIENT DEFICIENCIES ON ACID PHOSPHATASE ACTIVITY IN
TOMATO (*Lycopersicon esculentum*) LEAF TISSUES[a]

Nitrogen source	Control	Minus B	Minus Fe	Minus Mn	Minus Cu	Minus Zn	Means
			A. On fresh weight basis				
NO_3	8.53	9.45	8.73	10.58	11.93	11.65	10.14
NO_2	9.10	10.70	14.20	17.00	62.78	52.63	27.73
NH_4	9.38	13.78	9.60	12.50	13.15	34.68	15.51
Means	9.00	11.31	10.84	13.36	29.28	32.98	—
LSD Separate treatments		5%, 10.74		Nitrogen sources (means)			5%, 4.38
LSD Separate treatments		1%, 14.33		Nitrogen sources (means)			1%, 5.85
LSD Separate treatments		0.1%, 18.72		Nitrogen sources (means)			0.1%, 7.64
			B. On protein basis				
NO_3	0.221	0.492	0.223	0.243	0.381	0.458	0.336
NO_2	0.226	0.551	0.347	0.478	1.626	1.662	0.815
NH_4	0.213	0.612	0.243	0.312	0.322	0.899	0.434
Means	0.220	0.551	0.271	0.345	0.776	1.006	—
LSD Separate treatments		5%, 0.337	Means of treatments	0.195	Nitrogen sources (means)		0.138
LSD Separate treatments		1%, 0.450	Means of treatments	0.260	Nitrogen sources (means)		0.184
LSD Separate treatments		0.1%, 0.588	Means of treatments	0.339	Nitrogen sources (means)		0.240

[a] From Hewitt and Tatham (225).

contribute to the accumulation of tannins that is observed in zinc-deficient tissues.

6. Boron

a. Visible symptoms of deficiency or excess. i. Deficiency. The literature on boron is extensive and can only be summarized here. A series of well-illustrated reviews by Dennis (106–110), papers by Löhnis (298a, 299), Brandenburg (44), Jamalainen (246), and Chandler (66) provide valuable summaries of the effects of boron deficiency on several plants.

Boron deficiency produces in different plants a wide variety of symptoms (553) to which are given descriptive names, such as "heart rot" of beet (553), "stem crack" of celery (553) "brown heart" or "rahn" of swede (110), "water-core" of turnip (*Brassica rapa*) (110), "yellows" of alfalfa (111), "top-sickness" of tobacco (534), "corky core," "internal cork," or "drought spot" of apple (23, 227, 246). In many respects, however, the symptoms can be grouped into effects on cambial and phloem tissues of storage roots, root or stem apical meristems, and leaf vascular cambia and on fruit or other organs which are capable of meristematic or high metabolic activity. Other factors that contribute to the diversity of the over-all effect are the extent to which boron is mobile in various plants as it tends to be retained by mature tissues (120), the age of the plant when the boron shortage develops, and the seasonal effects, which are to be discussed later.

Death of the stem apical meristem is a prominent feature of boron deficiency in many plants, including broad bean (560, 561), French beans, mustard, flax, potato (190, 192), tobacco (534), cocoa (324), tomato (433, 536), and many brassicas (66). Death or abnormality of the apical growing point often results in regeneration by numerous axillary buds, producing a bushy habit (256). In flax, axillary buds at the level of the cotyledons usually extend, but they soon die (Fig. 33). In dwarf and climbing French beans the buds may be killed before elongation begins. The bushy habit (256) produced in tomato contrasts markedly with the prolonged dormancy of axillary buds observed with calcium deficiency (190, 192). Death of the crown in mature sugar beet is followed by infection by *Phoma betae* in the upper part of the root and regeneration by numerous small shoots around the periphery of the crown (553). The shoot apex or leaf tip are often deflected sharply to the side in cocoa (324) and in tomato, cauliflower, mustard, and French beans (190, 192) before outward signs of breakdown occur.

Death of the apical growing point may be preceded by breakdown or other changes in young leaves (190, 192, 299, 333, 565). Interveinal tissues and minor veins may be crinkled (66). Basal regions of leaf margins of young leaves often become chlorotic and then necrotic as in tobacco (336), swede, broad bean, sunflower (489), beet (190), and subterranean clover (356). This effect contrasts with the chlorosis and suppression of growth that occur in the apical or median regions of leaf margins of young leaves in plants that are deprived of calcium (compare Fig. 2 and Fig. 38).

Very young leaves of brassicas may appear to be rudimentary, partly devoid of lamina, or irregularly expanded (66, 547); superficially they resemble some leaves borne on plants deficient in molybdenum, as described below. Leaflet shape is much distorted in tomato (256, 190). Young leaves often blacken or shrivel before they expand beyond a few millimeters in length, and laterals are lacking in carrot (565).

Young leaves of wheat remain white, rolled, and are frequently trapped at the apex within the rolled subtending leaf, as in copper deficiency. The leaf tip is corrugated by several transverse constrictions. Barley leaves develop marginal necrosis and splits, or they remain white, rolled, and limp and then fail to emerge, while the stem bases become swollen.

Fig. 33. Boron deficiency in flax (*Linum usitatissimum*): death of main growing point, followed by development of axillary shoots and subsequent dieback.

In semimature leaves red and purple tints often develop, e.g., in tomato, many brassicas (especially swede), carrot, both red and alsike clovers (192), lucerne (alfalfa yellows) (111), and subterranean clover (356). Leaves tend to be thicker than normal, turgid, brittle, and rolled. Petioles are often brittle as in tomato, in which breaking-off by lateral leaflets is an early symptom (192, 256). Splits and transverse corky ridges are often produced. Alternatively, raised or elongated necrotic areas that produce deep longitudinal splits in upper surfaces of petioles of swede and beet and transverse splits, followed by peeling back of the tissues above vascular bundles, occur on the lower surfaces of petioles of celery and of parsnip, which also become twisted and irregularly bent (44, 190, 192, 553). The leaflet stalks of subterranean clover leaves sometimes elongate abnormally (356).

External effects on stems include "bark measles" in apple (57) due to growth of smooth, rounded bark excrescences from lenticels; such

FIG. 34. Boron deficiency in dwarf bean (*Phaseolus vulgaris*): death of growing point after normal development of roots and prophylls; drastic enlargement of hypocotyl followed by longitudinal splits.

excrescences develop also in severely affected olive branches (46). Corky lesions in cauliflower stem (66), splitting of stems of kale and kohlrabi (*Brassica caulorapa*), and "stem browning" of potato tubers, with vascular necrosis, are other external effects in stem tissues. In dwarf French beans the epicotyl continues to increase in diameter after the death of the stem apex and may be double the normal size (Fig. 34). Longitudinal corky splits occur in the epidermis and cortex (192). Internally, necrosis of the stem pith parenchyma occurs in kale and cauliflower. Irregular areas turn brown and disintegrate leaving large stem cavities (66).

Severe necrosis also occurs in roots. These become blackened and enlarged at the tips in beans (561), peas (490), beet (44), and *Pinus radiata* (482a). Lateral roots may be more numerous and may develop in rosettes or from injured primary roots. Storage roots show the typical breakdown discussed below and give rise to names like "canker" in table beet, and "rahn" or "water core" in swede and turnip.

Flowering is often totally suppressed by boron deficiency. Flowers often fall without producing seed, possibly owing to the effects on pollen tube growth which are discussed below. Gauch and Dugger (149) especially noted the high levels of boron, particularly in flowers, ovary, and stigma. In cereals Löhnis (298a) observed that atrophy of the anthers was common, whereas the embryo sac and surrounding tissues were unaffected (299). This contrasts with effects of zinc (430). In alfalfa, deformed leaves sometimes replace petals (111), and flowers fall in the unopened bud stage (190). Browning occurs in cauliflower as a result of necrosis of the unexpanded flowers (66).

Fruit formation is often abnormal and may be one of the most obvious effects in less severe conditions (109). Parthenocarpic development causes "miller-anderage" in grapes (464), and to the numerous small fruits with an occasional normal one the name "hen and chickens" has been given in Australia. Apples are especially susceptible and show different types of symptoms. Boron-deficient apples become malformed, with numerous irregular concave areas on the surface (246). Surface cork and irregular splitting are known as "drought spot" (57, 138). Cork cells also occur in irregular groups either close to the center (corky core) or generally distributed, especially near the surface, often in malformed fruit (internal cork) (23, 138, 227). Citrus, especially grapefruit (*Citrus paradisi*) (360) shows "hard fruit" in which the fruit is badly shaped, thick skinned, and impregnated irregularly by gum in the albedo and around the central axis. Browning in apricot is also caused by boron deficiency (24). Tomato fruits develop a ring of short longitudinal corky splits around the calyx end of the fruits, which are small and malformed (Fig. 35), or, alternatively, on dead epidermal areas (257). Boron-deficient olive fruits are pitted, severely malformed, and necrotic from the apical end, which shrivels (466). Seed formation is especially susceptible to boron deficiency and may be totally suppressed (149).

ii. Symptoms of boron toxicity. Different species vary greatly in their tolerance to excess of boron. Early work by Neller and Morse (374) showed that beans and corn were more sensitive than potato.

Toxicity symptoms in corn included chlorosis and marginal scorch. Potato leaflets were blackened at the margins. Scofield and Wilcox (462) observed chlorosis in mature leaves of citrus species grown under irrigation with 0.6–5 ppm boron in the water supply. Walnut leaves developed dark brown scorching in a narrow marginal zone of mature

FIG. 35. Boron deficiency in tomato (*Lycopersicon esculentum*): small malformed fruit, corky lesions especially in a ring near the calyx.

leaves, and irregular necrotic areas in central interveinal regions. Narrow dark brown marginal scorch of older leaves occur in tomato (189, 256).

Eaton (122) showed that appearance of boron toxicity in older leaves of many plants was characteristic of accumulation of boron in these parts. In sunflower, which shows extreme sensitivity to boron deficiency (80, 306), a level of boron that produced an optimal growth in young leaves was perceptibly toxic to old leaves. The range between excess and deficiency is therefore very narrow in some plants; probably in most plants the range is less than for other micronutrients.

Leaf accumulation was increased by higher light intensity. Eaton (120) found that sugar beet was one of the most tolerant plants to high boron supply followed, in the order of decreasing tolerance, by radish, corn, and kidney bean. He also observed that toxic effects could appear in old leaves of plants which showed deficiency symptoms in young leaves. Accumulation of boron was not always related to tolerance to excess. Thus muskmelon (*Cucumis melo*) showed a high accumulation but also high tolerance to boron, and *Zinnia* showed both high accumulation and low tolerance (Figs. 36 and 37). Data for beet (120) showed that these plants generally had high tolerance to boron and a low level of accumulation.

b. *Anatomical and histological effects of deficiency.* In table beet (546, 258) the adventitious cambial rings that arise successively outside secondary xylem are usually the site of breakdown. This is most severe in tissues that are in their most active development at the time of the deficiency. Cell division is stimulated in the cambium. The cells so produced become much enlarged and thin walled; analogous effects occur in leaf and stem vascular cambia. Parenchyma develops at the expense of vascular tissues. Protoplasts in groups of cells turn brown. Cell walls become brown and cells collapse, probably under pressure from surrounding expanded tissues. The necrotic areas are surrounded by cells that temporarily undergo further divisions to produce localized "wound" cambia. Necrotic regions expand and coalesce.

Lorenz (304) also studied boron deficiency in beet. The first sign of breakdown in the storage roots was always seen in thin-walled parenchyma within the xylem ring. It began as a brown discoloration of the cell wall accompanied by the formation of intracellular deposits in the zone of the middle lamella; this region swelled and sometimes appeared lamellated and forced cells apart. The deposits were gumlike or cutinous and stained strongly with safranin, light green, and gentian violet in contrast to normal tissues, the middle lamella of which stained with ruthenium red, which reacts with pectins and hemicelluloses. Microchemical tests with ruthenium red, iodine-sulfuric acid, and cuprammonium suggested a progressive loss, first of pectic compounds and later of cellulose, from cells walls of abnormal tissues. Tannins accumulated and cells later collapsed. Vessels became plugged by brown gum.

"Rahn" or "brown heart" in swede and "water core" in turnip are described by Dennis and O'Brien (110), who report that Jamalainen found that necrosis is confined to xylem parenchyma within the cambium in the median region of the swollen root. Skok (476) observed that secondary phloem and cambium in radish disintegrate,

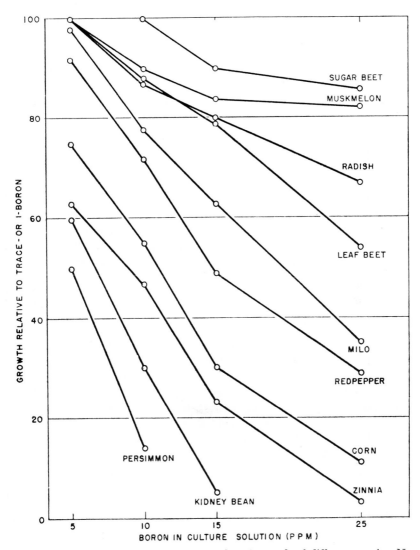

Fig. 36. Comparative effects of boron supply on growth of different species. Note tolerance of sugar beet and muskmelon as compared with sensitivity of kidney bean and persimmon. From Eaton (120).

xylem is thin walled, and vascular and ray parenchyma cells pro-liferate.

Van Schreven (534) described changes in roots of tobacco which exhibited necrosis in the procambium. This proliferated and produced enlarged phloem cells with brown walls. The cells were later com-

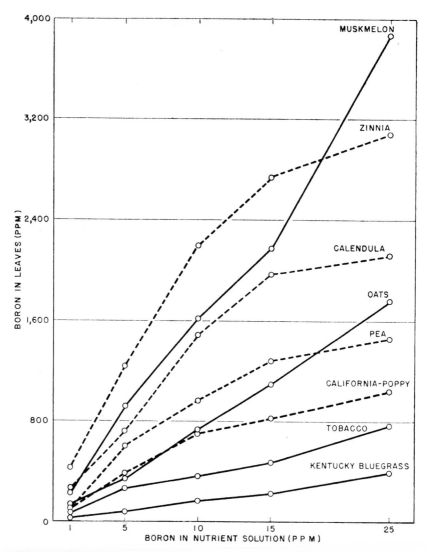

F<small>IG</small>. 37. Effects of boron supply on accumulation by different species. Note low accumulation by species such as Kentucky bluegrass (*Poa pratensis*) and tobacco (*Nicotiana tabacum*) compared with muskmelon (*Cucumis melo*) although muskmelon is one of the tolerant plants whereas *Zinnia* is sensitive to excess and also accumulates boron. Accumulation of boron in leaves of plants on solutions with 1–25 ppm of boron. Solid lines = plants with linear accumulation ratios; broken lines = plants with decreasing ratios. From Eaton (120).

pressed and distorted, and xylem was poorly differentiated and thin walled. Sommer and Sorokin (490) found that the apical region of the pea root became greatly enlarged owing, in part, to irregular and nearly twofold greater proliferation of cells in the plerome (prevascular tissues) with abnormal mitotic behavior and, in part, to enlargement of cells in the outer periblem tissues, while the nuclei were smaller. The resulting compression caused the collapse of the thin-walled cells in the plerome. Central plerome tissues were characteristically very irregular in contrast to the appearance of normal root tips. Differentiation of abortive lateral root primordia and of isolated xylem elements occurred prematurely. Resumption of organized meristematic activity could be detected 6 hours after the restoration of the boron supply. Root tips of Brussels sprouts also enlarged within 3 days of removal from a boron supply (66). This was caused by radial enlargement of cells that had ceased to divide. Numerous secondary root primordia occurred prematurely before root hair development. Premature differentiation of lateral roots was also observed for boron deficiency in excised tomato roots studied by Albert and Wilson (7b).

Whittington (581) found that cell division was suppressed by boron deficiency in stem apical meristems of broad bean. The interphase period was about doubled and the various phases of mitosis were about one-third as long as in normal plants. It was concluded that suppression of mitosis, not abnormal mitosis, was the cause of the lack of cell division. Whittington (581a) analyzed the changes in cell numbers and volumes produced in roots of field beans (*Vicia faba*) by boron deficiency. Cell division ceased within 48 hours of removing the boron supply, and cell volumes rapidly increased for a short time at approximately 2–3 mm behind the apex. Odhnoff (389) concluded that boron deficiency did not directly affect cell division in bean roots as there was increased production of lateral primordia, but their meristems soon died. Primordia developed abnormally close to the apex of enlarged root tips of boron-deficient maize (130). Neales (373) concluded that injury to root meristematic tissues is the initial result of boron deficiency in *Vicia faba*. The injury was apparently inevitable after 72 hours in the absence of boron but growth was resumed normally if the boron supply was restored within 48 hours, although the first effects of suppressing the boron supply could be observed in less than 24 hours. Some changes due to boron deficiency are therefore reversible, at least for a short time. Albert and Wilson (7b) observed visible external changes in tomato roots attached to plants 24 hours after and checked elongation 6 hours after they were transferred from normal to boron-deficient nutrients. The effects of boron supply are therefore more rapid than any others known, apart from toxicity effects.

In the broad bean, root nodule formation is impaired by lack of boron (45). The nodule remains vestigial and buried in the root cortex. The development of vascular tissues to the nodule is weak, or suppressed, and it may fail to penetrate the whole distance. Rhizobia become parasitic on the apical region of the nodule, which is normally meristematic. The changes were considered to reflect impaired translocation of carbohydrate to the nodule tissues.

In cabbage (*Brassica oleracea* var. *capitata*) lacking boron the stem cambium becomes abnormal (546). Cells enlarge, proliferate, and are often irregular in shape. Differentiation of xylem and phloem are both suppressed. The thin-walled pith cells develop isolated groups of dark, thick-walled cells. These are surrounded by abnormally large cells which undergo wall thickening. Beyond these the cells divide rapidly and have thin walls; cells with abnormal scalariform or reticulate pitting and thickening occur in this region. These whole regions collapse to produce the pith chambers already noted (66).

Chandler (66) and Löhnis (299) studied histological changes produced by lack of boron in brassicas, especially rutabaga or swede (*Brassica rapa* var. *napobrassica*). Storage roots showed great proliferation, enlargement, and loss of orderly arrangement of thin-walled cambial cells. Adjacent cells elongated excessively and collapsed under the pressure produced. Lack of differentiation into phloem cells was also observed. Swelling of the middle lamella region was observed with dark brown coloring, as reported for beet by Lorenz (304), and cells were filled with a foamy mass which gave reactions for fats and cellulose. Superficial cork cambia also proliferated and the cells enlarged radially or irregularly.

Alexander (8) decribed effects of boron deficiency in the squash (*Cucurbita maxima*) plant. Apical stem meristems showed increased staining, cell enlargement, and thickening of primary cell walls. Parenchyma of the cortex collapsed at the protoxylem level in the region corresponding to future collenchyma. In some plants cortex cell walls thickened and cells enlarged, causing collapse of vascular tissues. Vascular bundles of petioles showed thickening of parenchyma walls and marked radial extension especially in the abaxial cambium and in the parenchyma between xylem and phloem. Parenchyma cells surrounding vascular bundles became elongated into arc-shaped cells. Vascular bundles were radially elongated. Cambial cell division ceased prematurely. Roots showed a decreased meristematic region, premature differentiation, and increased lateral primordia. The stelar tissues were hypertrophied, cortical cells elongated, and there was a general tendency to cell enlargement and associated crushing of tissue. Neales (373) and Albert and Wilson (7b) also observed premature differentiation of lignified tissues in roots of *Vicia faba* and excised tomato roots, respectively. This response is considered later.

In subterranean clover (356) cell proliferation occurs because of lack of boron in the leaf palisade tissue which produces an increase of leaf thickness. The vascular bundles of both midrib and petiole also greatly increase in diameter as a result of apparently uncontrolled enlargement and proliferation of parenchymatous cells, which is followed by compression and necrosis of the surrounding cortical and pith cells. Palisade cells of tobacco leaf also increase by about twofold in each dimension (534) and contain up to three times as many chloroplasts. Cell enlargement in phloem and compression of thin-walled cells also occur in tomato (256, 536) and in the ventral cells of the bundle sheath in sugar cane (323) and in beet leaf palisade (304). Stomata develop abnormally in the epidermis of bean leaves apparently because of the production or survival of often only one guard cell and distortion of epidermal cells (25).

In cabbage leaves the production of wound cambia following a cut is suppressed in boron-deficient plants (66) and surrounding cells show excessive enlargement without cell division. Superficial necrotic swellings in leaves and petioles arise from disorganized proliferating cell masses. Reed (433) made detailed observations on the histology of boron deficiency in olive, celery, radish, tomato, and sunflower. Hypertrophy of vascular parenchyma cells and phloem necrosis followed by collapse due to crushing were general. In tomato leaves, chloroplasts tended to clump at one end of the cells; leucoplastids aggregated around the nucleus, and nuclei were lobed or enlarged, whereas in sunflower nuclei were flattened or ovoid. Particles described as mitochondria in tomato appeared more numerous, and in celery apices they appeared filamentous though this observation may not be valid in view of the limitations of the light microscope. Phloem and parenchyma cells were prematurely highly vacuolated and their contents appeared to be flocculated.

Staining by acid fuchsin and methyl green suggested the presence of oxidized phenolic compounds and melanins. Phenolic aggregates, or coacervates, in a separate phase from the aqueous medium of the vacuole were a pronounced feature of boron-deficient cells that showed enlarged and premature vacuolation. These phenolic coacervates appeared to have phospholipid boundaries as revealed by staining with Sudan III and a molybdenum-containing reagent. Collapsed cells, or those with abundant coacervates in disorganized protoplasts, appeared also to have excessive concentrations of inorganic phosphate adsorbed or occluded in the aggregated contents. Histochemical tests indicated high phosphatase activity. Hewitt and Tatham (225) observed some evidence for elevated acid phosphatase activity of boron-deficient tomato (Table XV). Peroxidase and oxidase activities appeared to be increased, as judged by oxidation of benzidine and indophenol blue formation with Nadi reagents (433).

It has been noted that the breakdown of the basal areas of young leaves may be an early symptom, and Lorenz (304) found the young leaves and petioles of beet to be collapsed before the apical meristem showed any signs of abnormality. The initial breakdown in the stem apex usually appeared in parenchyma adjacent to the procambium well below the apical dome. The apical meristem of brassicas also appears to remain normal after breakdown has occurred in vacuolated central tissue (66). In carrot (565) breakdown may occur behind or at the apex, and leaf and stem tissues appear to be affected before roots, unlike beet and turnip.

Scholz (458) (Fig. 38) showed that when rooted tobacco leaves were divided so that their two halves were supplied by separate root systems, one given boron, boron was translocated from the roots to the leaf lamina and especially to the leaf apex. There was very little translocation from the leaf apex to the leaf base and even less to the roots which were not supplied with boron. Growth of the basal part of the leaf where malformation is usually observed in boron-deficient plants was also suppressed in the half not supplied with boron from the roots. Albert and Wilson (7b) observed a similar effect with a split root experiment with tomato plants. On the other hand, Benson et al. (32a) concluded that rapidly expanding leaves of broccoli, nodes 7–22, yielded part of their boron to the younger leaves when the supply to the plant was stopped, whereas no boron was released by old expanded leaves, nodes 1–5. Leaves at nodes 24–26 at first gained and later lost boron.

The importance of boron at a stage just after that of cell division is shown in work by Skok (478). X-Ray injury to sunflower seedlings was decreased by boron deficiency, and Skok concluded that boron deficiency delayed a critical phase of development subsequent to cell division during early maturation. The prolonged interphase condition observed by Whittington (581) in anthers of boron-deficient *Trifolium* and *Vicia* may, however, be related to the effect described by Skok, since resting nuclei may be less susceptible to X-ray injury than nuclei during stages of mitosis. Moreover, boron deficiency hastens vacuolation.

In cereals, Löhnis (298a, 299) observed that the anthers appeared

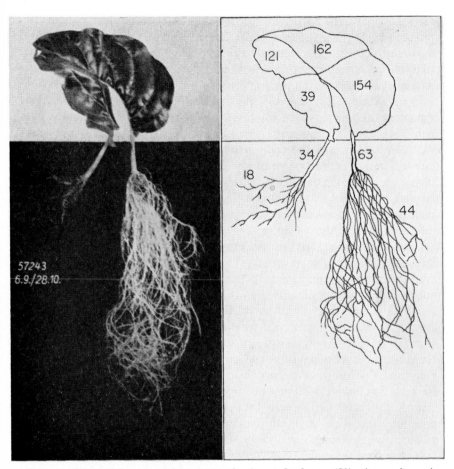

FIG. 38. Effect of boron supply on growth of rooted tobacco (*Nicotiana tabacum*) leaf in a split root arrangement where boron was given to one side only. Left: Note how, in the rooted leaf where no boron has been given, leaf expansion has been suppressed. In the sketch (right), the figures in each section indicate the concentrations (in parts per million) of boron found in those parts of the rooted leaf. From Scholz (458).

to be especially sensitive to boron deficiency. The breakdown occurred specifically in the sporogenous layer, which showed contracted abnormal nuclei due to inhibited division. Cell wall formation may be suppressed during early divisions and nuclei may fuse into giant nuclei. Cells were irregularly shaped and often enlarged, and they finally disintegrated. Where irregular pollen cells were produced, the walls appeared normal. The anther walls appeared capable of continued normal growth after this stage was reached, and the embryo sac remained normal. Whittington (581) also observed breakdown of the sporogenous layer in anthers of *Trifolium pratense* and *Vicia faba* and disintegration of spore tetrads. No abnormal meioses or changes in chiasma frequency were noted. Pollen germination and tube growth were not affected.

Spurr (496), (Figs. 39 and 40) made a careful study of the effects of boron nutrition on cell wall development in celery using a technique which avoided shrinkage of the cell walls during dehydration and embedding. Cell walls of collenchyma, in which the stem-crack symptoms of boron deficiency originated, were notably thinner, especially in respect to the characteristic thickenings. Measurements showed that the distance across the thickest walls in the mid-wall position decreased from 8–9 μ to 2–4 μ according to the variety of celery (Fig. 39). The decrease in wall thickness was evident at boron levels which were still sufficient to prevent the appearance of external visible symptoms of deficiency. Staining reactions with ruthenium red suggested that pectic substances (or possibly hemicelluloses) increased in amount in the interfacial regions between adjacent cells when boron deficient, although the thickness of this region possibly decreased. The effect might therefore have reflected a physical rather than a chemical change and was contrary to the observations of Lorenz (304). When the walls were swollen by reagents for cellulose it was found that the boron deficiency decreased the numbers of lamellae in thickened walls from 60 to about 20 and the lamellae themselves were similarly reduced in thickness from 0.3 to 0.2 μ in agreement with Lorenz (304). Cells toward the periphery of the collenchyma tended to have uniformly thickened walls when boron deficient, in place of the characteristic angular thickening.

It was concluded that boron affected the deposition of carbohydrates in cell walls, possibly in terms of the hypothesis that boron controls intracellular movement of carbohydrates, as suggested by Gauch and Dugger (148, 149).

By contrast with collenchyma cells, the cell walls of phloem and ground parenchyma increased in thickness with boron deficiency from about 1 μ usually to between 2 and 4 μ on the same range of boron supply (Fig. 40). Thickening was associated with an increased number of lamellae in the middle region of the wall thickness and showed increased affinity for staining by safranin A. These changes could have resulted from impaired transverse movement of carbohydrates. There was no evidence of phloem necrosis as a contributory cause.

Palser and McIlrath (400) made a detailed study of the anatomical effects of boron deficiency on tomato, turnips, and cotton. In general there was greatly increased cambial activity which led to poorly

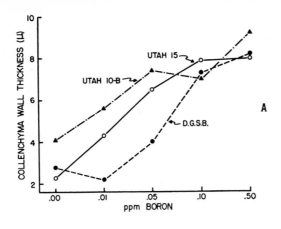

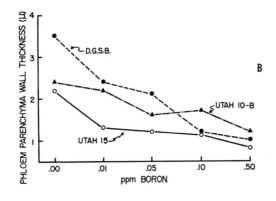

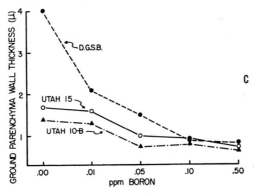

FIG. 39. The effect of boron supply in the nutrient solution on cell-wall thicknesses in three varieties of celery, Dwarf Golden Self Blanching, Utah 15, and Utah 10-B. The amount of boron supplied at 0.50 ppm is adequate for normal plant development. (A) Collenchyma cell walls become thinner as the supply of boron is decreased. (B) Phloem parenchyma cell walls increase in thickness as the supply of boron is decreased. (C) Ground parenchyma cell walls increase in thickness as the supply of boron is decreased. From Spurr (496).

differentiated secondary xylem or radially enlarged cells, which suffered
necrosis and abnormal division. In turnip roots cambia sometimes failed
to appear with the consequential absence of the xylem and phloem
normally derived from them. Enlargement of cambial tissues with

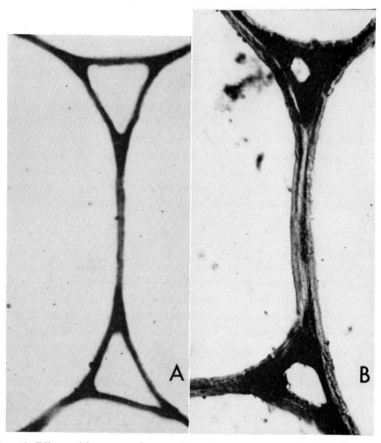

FIG. 40. Effects of boron supply on cell wall structures in celery (*Apium graveolens* var. *dulce*). Normal (A) and boron-deficient (B) cell wall of ground parenchyma after treatment with cellulose-swelling reagents. Note increase of wall
lamellae and intercellular thickening in these boron-deficient tissues. From Spurr
(496).

irregular cells, and irregular collapse, occurred in petioles. Vascular
necrosis occurred in leaves. Epidermal cells were smaller and stomata
were more frequent. Stem cambium and phloem tissues of cotton did
not show the expected hypertrophy. This, however, occurred in pith
cells adjoining the protoxylem and led to necrosis of pith cells. In-

creased cambial activity was observed in leaves and the resulting cells developed into xylem tissues. Palisade tissues were very compact, and epidermal cells were small. In tomato, stem cambial hypertrophy was irregular and led to irregular secondary xylem with groups of unlignified cells. Collenchyma was reduced, and xylem differentiation decreased. Radial enlargement of cambial cells led to necrotic collapse of crushed cells. Leaf thickness increased as a result of enlarged cells and larger intercellular spaces. Chloroplasts were smaller.

In summarizing, it appears that boron deficiency affects particularly cells in, or close to, meristematic regions. When death of an apical meristem is not involved, it appears that the cambial tissues are stimulated to prolific division, cells are much enlarged and have thin walls, and differentiation by phloem and xylem is inhibited. Compression is followed by cell collapse and necrosis. In apical meristems cell division is suppressed and premature differentiation occurs. Dennis and O'Brien (110) concluded from a comparative review that cell enlargement is the first response to occur in the sequence of events in storage tissues with secondary meristems. Most observers agree in recording the most severe or initial effects in tissues that have entered the phase of expansion or differentiation and are no longer undifferentiated meristematic cells.

c. *Physiological relationships of boron.* The possible roles of boron have been the subject of numerous investigations covering nearly fifty years, but in spite of this, no specific function has yet been identified as a critical role of the element. Gauch and Dugger (149) have discussed critically the evidence for the effects of boron in some fifteen possible ways and have also shown how, in many instances, apparently unconnected or contradictory reports may be reconciled in a uniform hypothesis that boron either facilitates the translocation of sugars or the production of dissociated ionic derivatives which might exhibit quite different properties at the surface of semipermeable membranes. Their informative and stimulating discussion comprises a major contribution to the understanding of the role of boron and is discussed in detail later. Skok (479) has more recently given another excellent review of the problem.

i. *Relationships with other elements.* One of the earliest ideas regarding the role of boron was that it controlled the action of calcium in the plant. Warington (563) concluded that boron increased calcium uptake relative to that of potassium and sodium. No effect of boron on total calcium uptake can be inferred from other experiments by Marsh (321), Shive (472), or Brennan and Shive (46), although the rate of absorption of calcium by carrot and turnip may be depressed by lack of boron (181). On the other hand, it appears that within plants such as soybean, and corn, calcium is more readily mobile or soluble in the presence of boron according to Smith (483), Marsh and Shive (322), Marsh (321), Hernandez-Medina and Shive (188). The ratio of soluble to total calcium is much higher in both monocotyledonous and dicotyledonous species when given boron than in its absence (321). This relationship holds for plants grown at low and normal calcium levels but may be observed in young leaves only of corn plants (188). The proportion of soluble to total calcium is greater in monocotyledons than in dicotyledons, and this was considered by Marsh (321) to explain the relatively lower boron requirements of monocotyledonous compared to dicotyledonous species (473). Increased soluble boron content was associated with increased soluble calcium, and the effect of boron was much greater in dicotyledons than in monocotyledons. Brennan and Shive (46) found that increasing calcium supply consistently decreased total sap-"soluble" boron in tomato expressed after freezing. Jones and Scarseth (259), Reeve and Shive (437), and Brennan and Shive (46) found that added calcium both accentuated boron deficiency and decreased boron toxicity. Increasing boron supply mainly decreased "soluble" calcium in young leaves but often increased "soluble" calcium in old leaves. Minarik and Shive (357a) observed a close relationship between boron supply in solution and the total calcium content of soybean leaves (Fig. 41). Reeve and Shive (437) observed that high levels of potassium increased the proportion of soluble boron in cell sap in high boron treatments and potassium accentuated both boron deficiency and boron toxicity effects.

    ii. Relation to cell growth and water content. The effects of boron seen in histological studies have been described, and it will be recalled that cell enlargement and proliferation of meristematic cells were usually the primary responses to deficiency conditions.

    Minarik and Shive (357a) (Fig. 42) observed a close negative correlation between tissue hydration of soybean leaves and boron supply. This is in agreement with the results reported by Scholz (457) for *Vicia faba.* Swelling and bursting of pollen cell tubes observed by Schmucker (455, 456) in the absence of boron may be a related effect. Pollen germination is often dependent on the supply of boron (149, 299, 362a, 455, 456, 464). There is at present no evidence that boron has a direct role in cell division though deficiency may suppress or delay this process (581, 581a). The cell enlargement and pollen tube swelling might be due either to excessive water imbibition or to the mechanical weakness of the cell wall. Excessively rapid water intake has been reported for boron-deficient pollen (456, 149). High water

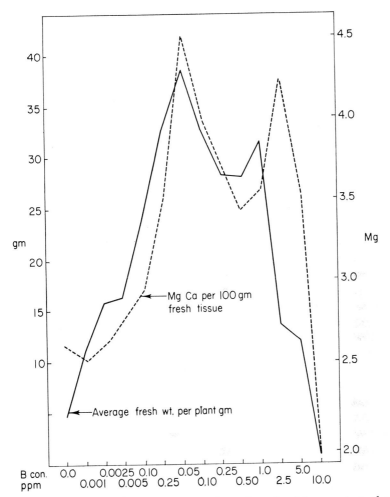

Fig. 41. Relationships between boron supply and total calcium content of soybean (*Glycine max*) leaves. Note close correspondence between calcium content and yield over a wide range of boron levels and the optimum value of boron at approximately 0.05–0.1 ppm. From Minarik and Shive (357a).

contents occur in boron-deficient tissues (359a), much evidence, however, is circumstantial and lower water contents also occur in instances reviewed by Gauch and Dugger (149).

A recent investigation on bean and tomato plants by Baker, Gauch, and Dugger (25) showed that leaves of boron-deficient plants contained more sugars, more furfural compounds indicative of hydrophilic pentosans and pectins, and a higher osmotic pressure in cell sap. The de-

260   E. J. Hewitt

ficient leaves resisted wilting for longer periods than normal leaves, when excised, and retained water longer than normal tissues under conditions of desiccation. The rates of water loss from excised leaves were initially greater from normal plants but decreased markedly after

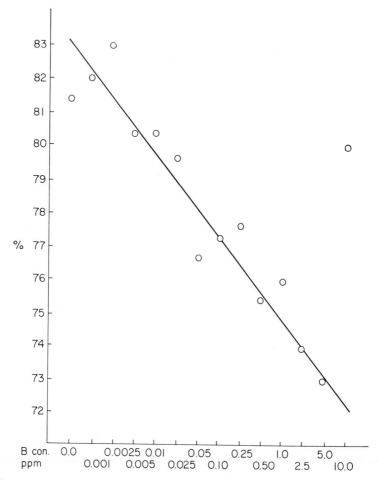

Fig. 42. Correlation between boron supply and soybean (*Glycine max*) leaf tissue hydration (%). From Minarik and Shive (357a).

about 1 hour whereas the rates of loss from deficient leaves were linear and after about an hour were two or three times those observed with normal leaves. Initial water contents were, however, similar. The initial differences in rates of wilting were attributed to the difference in sugar and hydrophilic polysaccharide content and to the presence of a high proportion of nonfunctional stomata in the thicker boron-deficient French bean leaves. Transpiration from leaves still attached to plants was, however, greater for those grown with boron. In root tips of tobacco, Scholz (457) found that boron deficiency increased water and decreased sugar. Respiration as oxygen uptake was also decreased. Whittington (581a) also found a marked decrease in respiration per cell in boron-deficient bean (*Vicia faba*) roots.

Swelling of cells, proliferation, bursting of pollen tube walls, and also apparent loss of geotropic response (8, 66) might all be related to some aspect of hormone control, including translocation of hormones. Translocation of growth hormones appears to be impeded by boron deficiency, though this effect may be indirect and related to the effect of boron on sugar translocation, as described by Mitchell, Dugger, and Gauch (359) below. The partial improvement observed by Eaton (118) when indoleacetic acid was applied to boron-deficient cotton could be explained on this basis. It is also possible that some aspect of pectin metabolism in cell walls is involved (110, 149, 304).

iii. Relation to nitrogen metabolism. Boron deficiency often results in accumulation, in mature parts of many plants, of ammonium nitrogen (48, 467, 544), soluble organic nitrogen (467), amino acids (503, 508), and amide (467). There are corresponding decreases in protein content (48, 467, 544). It appears that although carbon sources are present in sufficient quantities for amino acid production, these are not metabolized to form protein (149). This would be expected if the energy source provided by ATP for protein synthesis were to fail owing to lack of suitable carbohydrate supplies. In cells where carbohydrates have also accumulated owing to boron deficiency, as observed by Dearborn (95), this explanation does not appear satisfactory.

Lorenz (304) compared the composition of carefully selected pathological tissues of table beet with the composition of comparable regions from normal plants. In contrast with other observations there was a markedly increased concentration of protein in the pathological cells, but little or no increase in soluble nitrogen compounds. Shkolnik and Soloviyova (473a) reported that boron deficiency in sunflower was prevented by giving ribonucleic acid at 200 mg per liter in the nutrient solution. Whittington (581a) found no difference in deoxyribonucleic acid content in bean roots on a per cell basis. Ribonucleic acid was decreased by about 25% by boron deficiency, but nitrogen content was increased in cells of deficient roots.

iv. Relation to carbohydrate metabolism and permeability. Zittle (594) reviewed the possible functions of boron with particular reference to the formation of complexes between the borate ion and *cis*-poly-hydroxyl configurations such as occur in certain sugars and in mannitol. The complexes are of two types, (a) and (b) as shown below after Isbell *et al.* (241):

(a)

$$
\begin{array}{c}
=\!C\!-\!O \\
\hspace{1.2cm}\diagdown \\
\hspace{1.6cm}B\!-\!OH \\
\hspace{1.2cm}\diagup \\
=\!C\!-\!O
\end{array}
$$

(b)

$$
\left[
\begin{array}{c}
=\!C\!-\!O \quad\quad OH \\
\diagdown\;\;\diagup \\
B \\
\diagup\;\;\diagdown \\
=\!C\!-\!O \quad\quad OH
\end{array}
\right]^{-} H^{+}
\quad\quad
\left[
\begin{array}{c}
=\!C\!-\!O \quad\quad O\!-\!C\!= \\
\diagdown\;\;\diagup \\
B \\
\diagup\;\;\diagdown \\
=\!C\!-\!O \quad\quad O\!-\!C\!=
\end{array}
\right]^{-} H^{+}
$$

Phenyl borate derivatives described by Torssell (525) are also discussed later.

The complex ions so formed are more strongly dissociated than the free borate ion. They also confer properties of ionization on the complexing molecule or ligand and may thereby greatly change the degree to which membranes may exert semipermeable properties in respect of the ligand. Enzyme systems may exhibit changed activity also under such circumstances. Borate ions, through their complex functions, also change the normal equilibrium between the α- and β-isomers of D-glucopyranose. Winfield (589) was among the first to point out the complexing properties of boron and attempted without success to extract boron complexes from plants, but obtained an unidentified carbohydrate from boron-deficient squash plants.

Boron deficiency is associated almost without exception with increased concentrations of sugars and starch in expanded leaves of many plants (48, 95, 172, 172a, 256, 304, 389, 468, 534, 544, 580). The qualitative nature of the sugars may also be different (544, 589). Lorenz (304), however, found that pathological beetroot parenchyma contained markedly less total sugars. These comprised almost wholly sucrose, but the small amounts of reducing sugars were more abundant in the pathological cells. There was also a decrease in the ratio of acid-soluble to water-soluble pectins. Odhnoff (389) found that boron deficiency increased pectins, cellulose, and hemicellulose in bean roots but effects in leaves were not consistent. McIlrath and Palser (334) also observed increased levels of reducing sugars and decreased total sugars and nonreducing sugars in boron-deficient tomato leaves, but in stems and roots all sugars were decreased. All sugars were markedly decreased in turnip roots, and starch was increased in the leaves. An effect on translocation due to phloem necrosis may have been involved, but in tomato, starch was decreased in all parts. In cotton, starch was increased and reducing sugars were decreased by lack of boron in all parts, and nonreducing sugars were increased in stems and roots.

Gauch and Dugger (149) pointed out that although sugar accumulation in boron-deficient leaves could be explained by the effect of phloem necrosis in impeding translocation out of the leaves, there is evidence that sugar translocation is impeded before phloem necrosis is apparent in swede (110). This appears to be one of the first of many suggestions that boron deficiency causes interference in sugar translocation as such. Gauch and Dugger (149) record numerous experiments suggesting that carbohydrate translocation is upset (23, 181, 243, 468).

These observations and the known reactions between borate and polyhydroxyl compounds led Gauch and Dugger (148, 149) to postulate that a main role of boron is to facilitate the translocation of sugars in plants by formation of sugar-borate complexes that are then more readily able to pass through semipermeable cell membranes. The compounds would be weakly ionized with negative charge (594). The evidence obtained from measurements of the effect of 5 ppm boron on the rate of movement of C^{14}-labeled sucrose from a leaf to the stem tip of a tomato plant leaves little doubt of the marked effect of boron in accelerating the entry and movement of the sucrose. The same conclusions were obtained with respect to leaves regardless of the initial boron status of the plant though they were more striking in boron-deficient plants. Later experiments by Sisler et al. (475) showed that the natural products of photosynthesis in the presence of $C^{14}O_2$ were more readily translocated from the exposed leaf to the rest of the plant when it was grown with a normal boron supply than without boron. When plants were transferred to a boron-free medium the translocation rate was detectably decreased in 2–4 days. It may be noted, however, that Lowenhaupt (306) observed pathological changes in sunflower 24 hours after removing the external boron supply and Neales (373) detected changes in *Vicia* roots in a similar period. Albert and Wilson (7b) found that the elongation of attached tomato roots was checked in 6 hours after removal of the boron supply. Elongation of excised roots was much less affected and was still rapid 17 days after removal of the boron supply. Addition of sucrose to roots attached to plants did not reverse the effects of boron deficiency.

Odhnoff (389a) compared the effects of boric acid and phenylboric acid on root growth of *Phaseolus* in an attempt to elucidate the role of boron in cell wall growth. The results were interpreted in terms of the capacity of boric acid to form both mono- and bis-diol complexes with hydroxyl groups of carbohydrates whereas phenylboric acid can form only bis-diol complexes. It was found that elasticity of cell walls as determined by changes in length during repeated plasmolysis, and by an electromagnetic resonance technique, was decreased by boron deficiency and the phenylboric acid appeared to compete with boric acid in deficient tissues in this respect. Elasticity of cell walls decreased in the order of treatments: — boron + phenyl borate > + boron + phenyl borate > + boron — phenyl borate > — boron — phenyl borate. The high elasticity observed in the presence of phenyl borate without boron was interpreted as a result of the formation of mono-diol bonds almost exclusively due to the great excess of phenyl borate over borate. Borate was considered both to promote growth by allowing intussusception and microfibril deposition and to stabilize the walls so formed whereas phenyl borate could promote only the first function.

O'Kelley (391) observed that boron stimulated absorption of sucrose and glucose, but not that of fructose by pollen cells, and caused a corresponding increased rate of oxygen consumption. The two explanations suggested are (a) that boron combines with the sugar which passes the membrane and remains combined with boron until the sugar is metabolized in the cell, or (b) that boron is located in the membrane where it facilitates the passage of a sugar by a temporary reaction confined to the membrane site. The former appears less likely owing to the quantitative disparity between the total amount of boron and free (unmetabolized) sugar often present in a healthy plant. The possibility that boron is located at the membrane surface, and then reacts with the sugars, merits consideration and would also explain the continual immobilization of boron after absorption into plants.

Gauch and Dugger (149) point out that the immobilization of boron in aging tissues, inferred by Eaton (120), would be consistent with the need for a continual supply to keep pace with continued tissue production during growth and normal apical differentiation. Plants given boron in split root experiments, or in lanolin applied to the leaves, appeared to be able to make normal growth (66), but with split-rooted leaves tested by Scholz (458) this was not so. The often greater sensitivity of roots, as compared with stem apices, to boron deficiency is interpreted to mean that the roots depend on carbohydrate supply *from* leaves and that this outweighs the fact that roots come in contact with boron before aerial parts, owing to the greater distance of root than stem apices from the sugar sucrose. Neales (372), however, found adequate concentrations of several sugars in roots of boron-deficient flax seedlings. Whittington (581a) found that sugar levels were initially higher for 48 hours up to the time when cell division ceased, and then lower during a subsequent period of hypertrophy for 96 hours, compared with cells of normal bean roots. It is also clear from the work of Albert and Wilson (7b) that excised roots grown with a sugar are less dependent on boron than those attached to plants where sugars are translocated.

Gauch and Dugger (149) suggested that meristematic sensitivity, impairment of salt absorption, hormone translocation (359), and protein synthesis may all reflect direct or indirect effects of impaired carbohydrate translocation under conditions of boron deficiency.

Another effect which may be involved in the role of boron is its reaction as borate with sugar-phosphate esters. Borate forms complexes with glucose-6-phosphate, ribose-5-phosphate, and other esters where the 6- or 5-carbon positions are esterfied, but it does not appear to complex with 1-carbon esters. This reaction and the distinction between the esters concerned suggest that boron might be involved in phosphate ester metabolism as well as, or instead of, directly in sugar metabolism. Reed (433) showed that inorganic phosphate accumulated in boron-deficient plants. Dugger and Humphries (115) found that borate inhibited potato phosphorylase to the extent of 50% at 5×10^{-2} M. They suggested that sugar movement out of cells might be encouraged by this inhibition, but as plants may normally contain 20–40 ppm of boron in their dry matter, i.e., about 5×10^{-4} to 10^{-3} M concentration in cell sap, it seems unlikely that this effect is of physiological significance unless cell distribution factors (480) are also involved.

The observation by Dugger and Humphries (116) that boron or borate affects the synthesis of sucrose *in vitro* may provide an important clue to the problem. It was found that 10 μmoles per milliliter of boron (approximately 100 ppm) stimulated sucrose synthesis by a system containing uridine triphosphate (UTP), adenosine triphosphate (ATP), hexokinase, phosphoglucomutase, fructose, and pea seedling homogenate. It was concluded that boron either promoted the formation of, or stabilized, uridine diphosphoglucose (UDPG). Boron had no effect on hexokinase, phosphoglucomutase, or invertase but doubled the activity of uridine diphosphoglucose pyrophosphorylase.

$$\text{UTP} + \text{glucose-1-PO}_4 \overset{\text{boron}}{\rightleftharpoons} \text{UDPG} + \text{pyrophosphate}$$

Boron affected this equilibrium in favor of UDPG synthesis, but inhibited the reaction between UDPG and fructose.

$$\text{UDPG} + \text{fructose} \rightarrow \text{UDP} + \text{sucrose}$$

Further developments in this work will be eagerly awaited especially in view of the possible significance of the UDPG systems in pectin and other polysaccharide syntheses.

Borate might be expected to influence the equilibrium in phospho-glucomutase, in which glucose-1-phosphate and glucose-6-phosphate are interconvertible in a reversible reaction. The effect of boron might lie in its differential complexing capacity, already noted.

The difficulty with all such ideas is that the reactions are as important in animals and probably all microorganism as in higher plants and green algae, but boron requirements in the first two groups are nil, or extremely low, by comparison with the second two groups.

v. Relation to metabolism of phenolic compounds. Boron has not so far been shown to activate any enzyme system and there are no reports of consistently decreased activities specifically due to lack of boron. There are, however, consistent reports that tyrosinase, poly-phenol oxidase, or dihydroxyphenylalanine (DOPA) oxidase activity (279, 314, 371, 433) and melanin production are inversely related to boron status or to added concentrations of this nutrient. Borate may be a direct inhibitor of such enzymes. This may occur only at concentrations above 0.01 M (314), i.e., about twenty times those expected in normal cells, assuming boron to be uniformly distributed in the cell. Yasunobu and Norris (592), however, found at somewhat high pH values around pH 7.8 that 4.3 $\times$ 10^{-3} M borate caused 60% competitive inhibition of DOPA oxidation by tyrosinase, due to the formation, at high pH values, of borate-diphenol complexes. The increased oxidation of DOPA and catechol by boron-deficient tomato homo-genates recorded by Klein (279) was mainly eliminated in plants grown with 0.1 ppm boron. Experience suggests that such plants would not have contained more than about 5 $\times$ 10^{-4} M borate in the gross aqueous phase. At this level the directly inhibitory effects of borate would be negligible unless some tenfold greater concentration at least had occurred in certain cell fractions, e.g., mitochondria or chloroplasts with which phenolase enzymes may be associated. In this context Skok and McIlrath (480) found that mitochondria and microsomes contained the lowest, whereas nuclei, plastids, cell debris, and soluble cell phases contained the greatest, amounts of boron per cell. Hypotheses based on borate inhibition of phenolase activity require also that the effect of borate *in vivo*, owing to its combination with free polyphenols, causes the suppression of enzyme synthesis since the effects of adding *physiologically expected amounts* of borate are negligible *in vitro* in spite of the comparative suppression of enzyme activity in extracts of normal tissues.

The high polyphenolase, or tyrosinase, activities may be related to boron deficiency in another way. The fluorescence of tissues in boron-deficient celery petiole, observed by Spurr (495), which is associated with subsequent browning, may be explained by the observations of Perkins and Aronoff (403). The latter authors found that blue-fluorescent compounds including principally caffeic and chlorogenic acids, accumulate in tissues surrounding the necrotic areas in boron-deficient tomato, lettuce, radish, and sunflower. Shiroya and associates (471) found that browning in tobacco leaves is associated with the oxidation of caffeic or chlorogenic acids by polyphenolase, for which Nelson (375) has suggested that chlorogenic acid may be a natural substrate and a precursor of catechol tannins. These polyphenolase enzymes may be localized in cambial tissues in potato tubers (465) and possibly in other plants. Such a distribution could account for the browning in meristematic tissues caused by boron deficiency. The increased levels of the phenolic substrates might cause adaptive increases in phenolase enzymes of the order observed in boron-deficient tissues. Neales (373) suggested that premature differentiation of lignified tissues in boron-deficient roots of *Vicia faba* might be related to the accumulation of caffeic acid in the tissues. This compound is a potential precursor of lignin according to McCalla and Neish (328), and a substrate for peroxidase activity which is accentuated in boron-deficient tissues. Neales (373) also suggested that the well-known difference in quantitative requirements between dicotyledons and monocotyledons for boron might be due to the different pathways of lignin synthesis postulated by Brown *et al.* (53). As peroxidase, together with a monophenolic cofactor, is the basis of the indoleacetic acid "oxidase" (206, 264, 313, 425, 570, 571), it is possible that effects of boron status on peroxidase activity and on the nature and proportions of the mono- and polyphenolic constituents in cells (373, 403) may account for many of the effects of boron deficiency in terms of its apparent effect on responses controlled by auxins.

vi. Relationships with light. MacVicar and Struckmeyer (315) and Struckmeyer and MacVicar (519) studied the effect of photoperiod on boron requirements. Cocklebur (*Xanthium pennsylvanicum*) and "Biloxi" soybean, as examples of short-day plants, showed no effects of boron deficiency under short days which permitted flowering and also decreased or suppressed cambial activity, but showed severe boron deficiency symptoms under long days although growth decreased under both long and short days. Cocklebur plants grown for a week with boron and then transferred to a no-boron treatment on short days for 10 days, showed only slight effects of boron deficiency when they were subsequently grown under long-day conditions, under which cambial activity remained low. Tomato and sunflower, which were regarded as day-neutral species, showed acute boron deficiency under long or short days. Buckwheat (*Fagopyrum esculentum*), however, which is also day-neutral but produces flower primordia in 12 days from sowing, showed boron deficiency under long days when cambial activity was great, but not under short days with less cambial activity. MacVicar and Struckmeyer (315) concluded that the sensitivity, or otherwise, of plants to boron deficiency as affected by photoperiod was directly related to the extent to which cambial activity was induced or suppressed by the duration of light. When cambial activity was inhibited by a particular light treatment, boron deficiency was not induced by changing the photoperiod. Warington (562), Skok (476), Löhnis (298a), and Colwell (80) also found that short-day conditions decreased the severity of boron deficiency in several plants. Eaton (120) and Warington (562) tentatively concluded that the effects of boron toxicity were decreased by high light intensities whereas Eaton (122) and Colwell (80) observed decreased effects of deficiency in several plants under low light intensity conditions. There are, therefore, two independent effects of light on boron requirements, namely on cambial activity and on boron immobilization. It may be, in this connection, that the recent discovery of Humphries (233a) regarding effects of light quality on boron requirements is involved. Under short days of 8 hours light quality did not affect boron requirements of dwarf French bean roots produced from hypocotyls under long days of 16 hours; the introduction of additional incandescent, red-enriched, continuous spectrum type of light, however, decreased both growth and root initial production.

d. Interpretation of the role of boron. The chemical affinity of the borate ion for polyhydroxyl compounds with an ortho configuration (594) could thus account for possibly four distinct roles or regulatory mechanisms in many plants, namely (a) in translocation of sugars across membranes, possibly as weakly ionized, negatively charged compounds (148, 149); (b) previously suggested (198) regulatory effects on oxidation by polyphenolase activity; (c) by modification of equilibrium in phosphate ester metabolism; (d) in influencing the extent of the catalytic effects of o-diphenols in cell metabolism, including inhibition of indoleacetic acid oxidation and possibly promoting pyridine nucleotide-quinone reductase activity, which is especially high in roots.

Some extra light has been shed on the problem recently by Torssell (525) in an investigation of the chemistry and effects on wheat roots, of arylboric acid complexes. Several compounds having the general formula R-Ph-B(OH)$_2$ in which R comprised one or more groups on the phenyl radical (Ph) were synthesized. They formed dissociable complexes with polyhydroxy compounds, including sugars. This reaction was associated with the characteristic decrease in pH compared with the uncomplexed form, or free boric acid, and varied in relation to the degree of lipid solubility. Phenylboric acid formed the strongest complexes with maximum pH depression and had maximum lipid solubility. Phenylboric acid complexed more strongly than free boric acid. Many of the compounds tested at concentrations between 10^{-6} and 10^{-4} M stimulated cell expansion in wheat roots but had no effect on cell division. The greatest effects, namely a twofold increase in cell elongation, were observed with phenylboric acid and the least with compounds showing minimum lipid solubility and having the lowest affinity for the polyhydroxyl grouping. Phenylboric acid had no effect on amylase, phosphatase, or invertase activities or on yeast fermentation; effects on polyphenolase were not tested. Torssell suggested that cell walls normally increase in rigidity with age and tend to develop increasing crystallinity as the micelles become oriented by van der Waals' forces, which may increase with progressive dissociation of borate-hydroxyl complexes. The complexes would tend to inhibit this arrangement in the undissociated state. He suggested that organic borate complexes possessing high lipid solubility and high affinity for polyhydroxyl compounds promote cell wall elasticity by delaying the orientation that confers rigidity. In support of this concept it was found that phenyl borate and to a lesser extent borate itself delayed the retrogression of amylase associated with aggregation of oriented micelles. The property of lipid solubility was considered to be consistent with the inferred effects of boron on membrane permeability. Later experiments by Odhnoff (389a) based on Torssell's work have already been described in relation to cell wall growth.

The affinity of boric acid for o-hydroxyl configurations (525, 594), together with the obvious relationships between boron and metabolism of polyphenols and mobility of sugars, suggests that a number of functions of boron in plant nutrition may depend on the same basic chemical properties. Regulation of polyphenolase activity, possibly in regard to the oxidation of o-diphenols which form the borate complexes, might have important effects through controlling the levels and ratios of mono- and polyphenols in the cell. This action might have significance in the regulation of auxin activity if the peroxidative destruction of indoleacetic, elucidated by Waygood and his associates (313, 570, 571) and by Kenten (264) and discussed elsewhere (206, 425), actually occurs *in vivo*. The indoleacetic acid oxidation is competitively inhibited by o-diphenols (421) and such examples as chlorogenic and caffeic acids are known to accumulate in boron-deficient tissues (403). The naturally active diphenols might be inactivated in this respect if com-

plexed with borate. Under these conditions excessive levels of indoleacetic acid, or related auxins, might occur in certain tissues with various
effects such as excessive cell expansion and proliferation, dedifferentia-
tion, and excessive water uptake. Accumulation of auxin in meristematic cells and surrounding parenchyma, or in differentiating tissues, might cause adaptive production of excessive peroxidase activity
(145, 249) which, because of high diphenol levels (403), would not result in auxin destruction but would lead instead to browning reactions,
auxin hypertrophy, and cell death, and also to premature lignification
as suggested by Neales (373) and noted earlier. The suppression of cell
division might be a secondary effect of cell death in adjacent expanding
cells, which have been stated by Skok (478) to be those most sensitive
to injury by lack of boron.

Scott (463) has put forward a different general hypothesis regarding
the role of boron, namely that it has a "protective effect in preventing excessive polymerization of sugars at sites of sugar synthesis, having
regard to the concentrations of boron at sites of sugar synthesis." Scott
concluded that inhibition of polymerization reactions at critical sites
would be consistent with the observations reviewed here, by Dugger and
his associates; McIlrath and Palser; Torssell, Whittington; Odhnoff;
Spurr; and others. Any hypothesis should explain why boron requirements are high for plants and very low or nil for most microorganisms and animals.

7. Molybdenum

a. Visible effects of molybdenum deficiency or excess. i. Deficiency.
General symptoms: Following the initial work of Arnon and Stout (18)
and Piper (406) molybdenum deficiency is now known to be geo-
graphically widespread and has been recorded in a great many crop
plants (201, 204, 208, 215, 216, 218, 253, 516) despite the very small
amounts required in comparison with most other known micronutrient
elements. The effects of deficiency here described are considered from
two distinct aspects, namely: the source of nitrogen supply and the
plant species; the effects produced under the deficiency conditions may
be sharply distinguished with respect to these considerations. Detailed
descriptions and bibliographies of visible symptoms, growth responses,
and relative requirements of plants with respect to molybdenum have
been given in several papers in a recent issue of *Soil Science* edited by
Bear (29a). Informative papers by Anderson (8a, 9) present several
interesting viewpoints.

In plants grown with nitrate as the sole, or principal, source of nitrogen, the symptoms of acute deficiency of molybdenum are similar in

many plants. They commence usually in the oldest leaves and progress to the apex of the plant until it dies (Fig. 43). In many plants, e.g., tomato, brassicas, radish, mustard, beet, the cotyledons show no symptoms for several days or weeks after other parts are severely affected (Fig. 44). This point contrasts with the yellowing of (and presumably proteolysis in) cotyledons of nitrogen-deficient plants, or in molyb-

Fig. 43. Molybdenum deficiency in tomato (*Lycopersicon esculentum*) grown with nitrate: upcurling of leaf margins, interveinal yellow mottling followed by wilting and withering of apical leaflet and lateral leaflet in succession of older leaves and withering of all leaves in turn.

denum-deficient plants given ammonium sulfate, urea, etc., as sources of nitrogen. In tomato and more rarely in some brassicas, the first true leaf may be initially less affected; and in barley, mustard, potato (204) and tobacco (506) the younger or mid-stem leaves may be the first to show symptoms, which then progress to the youngest leaves. This distribution probably reflects the interaction between protein breakdown due to impaired nitrogen metabolism and the retention of molybdenum by protein, especially nitrate reductase.

In many plants, the symptoms of molybdenum deficiency commence as bright yellow-green or pale orange interveinal mottling distributed fairly generally over the leaf. These symptoms differ from those of nitrogen or magnesium deficiencies in many plants (553) by not leading to the bright red or purple tints, and they also differ from nitrogen

Fig. 44. Molybdenum deficiency in radish (*Raphanus sativus*) grown with nitrate, bright yellow-orange interveinal mottling of older leaves with inrolled marginal scorching; cotyledons remain green and turgid after appearance of severe symptoms.

deficiency in the markedly interveinal character of the mottle, which leads to severe necrosis rather than to a uniformly yellow leaf. In celery and sugar beet (216), however, moderate molybdenum deficiency may show a resemblance to nitrogen deficiency. The mottling is related to uneven distribution of molybdenum in tomato leaves (Fig. 43), in which Stout and Meagher (517), using Mo[99] as a radioactive tracer, showed that the mottled areas contained less molybdenum and also more nitrate than the greener regions that were adjacent to the veins. A similar distribution of nitrate or of oxidizing compounds, giving a reaction for nitrate, also occurs in melon, lettuce, and cauliflower (585, 587, 588).

Mottling is usually associated with, or followed by, marginal wilting in brassicas, and frequently by marginal cupping in broad-leaved plants with entire leaves, or by various types of marginal, or more general, inrolling of the lamina in such plants as tomato or potato. The presence, or absence, of marginal cupping may be determined by factors associated with leaf shape (215, 253). The marginal wilting is often preceded by the appearance of watersoaked areas, which occur in deficient leaves owing to the leakage of cell contents into the intercellular spaces and sometimes to their accumulation as brown fluid on the leaf surface. Watersoaked and wilted tissues rapidly develop papery necrosis, and leaves may pass from a mottled to a severely necrotic and withered condition in a day. Petioles may also wilt, though less frequently than leaves.

Flower formation is decreased or suppressed by molybdenum deficiency. In tomato the flowers may be almost sessile on the stem and may be reduced to a single abortive flower that falls before opening. In cauliflower the normal curd is separated into irregular groups by numerous bracts (559). Seed production in cauliflower may be abnormal and seeds may fail to develop after fertilization. The seed coats remain green or pale brown, and seeds may shrivel before they mature (220).

Symptoms have been described in citrus plants grown from cuttings in water culture (537) and in trees on acid soils (510, 511). In water culture, expanded leaves of a new flush are roughened in texture and have diffuse rounded mottled areas in the marginal and apical regions. These areas dry out to irregular pale brown necrosis and the leaf margins curl upward. In acid soils a disorder which has been known as "yellow spot" since it was described by Floyd (143, 143a) in 1908 was identified in 1952 as molybdenum deficiency (510, 511). Leaves develop, during flushing, oblong watersoaked areas that become enlarged and yellow. The watersoaked areas may occur irregularly or may develop in a regular row between major veins, generally within a green marginal zone. The outer yellow-green zones have a brown central necrosis. The spongy parenchyma was observed by Floyd (143) to swell, thereby filling up the intercellular spaces.

Legumes: Molybdenum is essential for nitrogen fixation by rhizobia so that in acid, molybdenum-deficient soils herbage legumes often show nitrogen deficiency as revealed in numerous trials by Anderson and his associates (8a–10, 12). It should be understood, however, that clovers, lucerne, peas, and beans have an absolute molybdenum requirement, in common with other plants, even when they are grown with nitrate as a source of nitrogen (136, 198, 208, 337b). The symptoms of deficiency include leaf paling, wilting, and marginal rolling and scorching. Their occurrence is often determined by the natural reserves of molybdenum in the seed (208, 218, 337b, 586) (Fig. 45). The seed effect is observed in the field, especially in relation to the "scald" disease of beans (586), which is now known to be caused by molybdenum deficiency. There are, however, several records of molybdenum deficiency in field legumes (208). In the absence of fixed nitrogen, molybdenum deficiency increases greatly the number of root nodules which are then very small compared with those in normal

Fig. 45. Effect of molybdenum status of seed on growth of peas (*Pisum sativum*) in sand culture. Left: without molybdenum, left-hand plants produced from seed saved from molybdenum-deficient plants; right-hand plants produced from normal seed. Right: plants grown from similar seed sources in presence of molybdenum.

roots of nodulated plants (10, 12); they are often green or brown instead of pink (208, 363, 366). Hewitt and Bond (219) have now shown that molybdenum is required for the growth of certain nonlegumes also when they are dependent on atmospheric nitrogen fixed by symbiotic organisms in root nodules. Species for which this requirement has been shown include *Casuarina cunninghamiana, Alnus glutinosa*, (in the field also, 30a) and *Myrica gale* (40a).

Brassica crops: One group of plants, namely brassicas, may show other symptoms of molybdenum deficiency in addition to those described already. These may be grouped under the name "whiptail" which was described as early as 1924 for field-grown plants by Clayton (76) and which occurs widely in Europe, America, Australia, and New Zealand (358, 366, 413a, 516, 559, 588) especially on acid soils (199). The experimental production of the symptoms in plants grown in sand cultures was first described by Hewitt and Jones (220). It has been shown since then that the symptoms appear under the following conditions: (a) In plants grown with nitrate at molybdenum levels that are intermediate between those causing the most severe symptoms and those adequate for normal growth (1, 211). These levels correspond probably with concentrations within the range 0.00001–0.001 ppm and especially 0.00005 ppm molybdenum. (b) In plants that have grown initially under severe deficiency conditions followed by a temporary period of limited recovery due to a slight increase in molybdenum supply that is still inadequate for continued normal growth (215, 220). (c) In plants grown with low (0.00005) or very low (0.000003–5 ppm) molybdenum levels in the presence of ammonium compounds, nitrite, urea, or glutamic acid as the main or sole source of nitrogen supply (4, 201, 204).

Plants grown with nitrate or ammonium nitrate in the presence of about 0.00005 ppm molybdenum may not show any mottling, or other symptoms, previously described in relation to the use of nitrate as nitrogen source. Plants grown with ammonium compounds (excepting ammonium nitrate) or with urea or glutamic acid also do not show the pronounced mottling and related symptoms, even at the lowest molybdenum concentrations. Cauliflower plants grown with nitrate at extremely low levels of molybdenum show the mottling and other symptoms as described but on obtaining temporarily a limited, but inadequate, supply of molybdenum these symptoms disappear or they do not recur.

In each of these groups however, plants develop new symptoms usually when 6–8 weeks old. Regardless of the treatment, the symptoms commence as one or several translucent oval areas situated in a row close to the midrib between major veins near the center, or base, of a young leaf usually when about 6–15 cm long. These areas rapidly become chlorotic (ivory tinted) and necrotic. The papery tissues perforate and the irregular "stellate" holes so produced enlarge as the leaf grows (1, 4, 215) (Fig. 46). This stage leads to the production of less regular chlorotic and necrotic areas which appear progressively nearer to, and finally along the leaf margins in the basal part of the young leaves. As they elongate the margins become torn and ragged. In still younger leaves a great part of the filamentous lamina becomes brown, necrotic and deliquescent when the leaves are only a few centimeters long. These may still elongate rapidly but they are practically devoid of lamina, or carry only a narrow irregular strip of much corrugated, thickened and distorted lamina, which is usually dark blue-green in color (Fig. 46).

Finally leaf primordia and the apical growing point are killed and exude a brown fluid before withering. Numerous variations in final form may occur (1, 4, 201, 204, 211, 215, 220, 366, 413a, 559, 588) according to the relative extents to which necrosis, leaf elongation, and suppression of lamina tissue occur prior to death of the growing point. A typical "whiptail" condition produced in a plant grown with

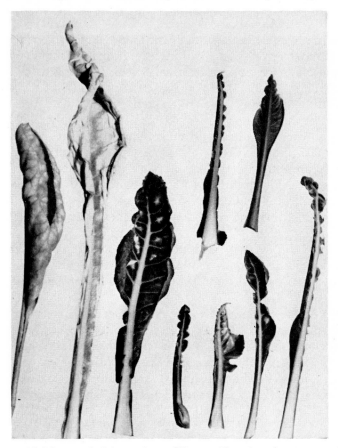

Fig. 46. Molybdenum deficiency in cauliflower (*Brassica oleracea* var. *botrytis*) grown with nitrate. The two left hand leaves show effects of severe deficiency, marginal cupping, interveinal mottling and withering of older leaves. Center: first symptoms of secondary condition preceding appearance of whiptail produced at about 0.00005 ppm molybdenum. Right: advanced effects of whiptail in young leaves.

ammonium sulfate is shown in Fig. 47. Growth is also markedly depressed under these circumstances (1, 4), but chlorophyll content remains normal in contrast to the decrease produced in the presence of nitrate (2, 4). Other brassica types show analogous symptoms which are fully described elsewhere (201, 204, 215).

Anatomical investigations (Hewitt and Hucklesby, unpublished work) on cauliflower leaves suggest that collapse of the epidermis is an early effect in the initial chlorotic lesions. Expansion of some cells and collapse of others in the palisade or spongy mesophyll may follow. Chloroplasts shrink and disintegrate, and these changes are the first

Fig. 47. Molybdenum deficiency in cauliflower (*Brassica oleracea* var. *botrytis*) grown with ammonium sulfate. Acute whiptail symptoms in young leaves, without development of chlorosis and withering in old leaves.

to be observed in areas producing the lesions, as described here in some detail.

In plants grown with nitrate nitrogen, chlorosis extended over the whole area of the leaf as already described. Before chlorosis was visible in the young leaf, and while the chloroplasts were still very small, abnormal accumulation of chloroplast starch occurred. During the development of the chlorosis, the chloroplasts became distended by their starch grains; at this stage they showed some resemblance to the condition produced by early stages of nitrogen or magnesium deficiencies, but lacked the typical production of lipid globules. Distension was sometimes so severe that breakdown of the chloroplast structure followed. This involved disintegration and spread of the lipoprotein part into the cytoplasm, leaving naked starch grains, which then dissolved away. More frequently, however, the process was arrested before breakdown by a second phase of events which was associated at first with the leaf margins and subsequently spread inward to involve the whole of the lamina. This consisted of a rapid lysis of the enlarged starch grains before chloroplast breakdown, leaving small rounded chloroplasts which contained abundant chlorophyll but little or no starch. These were unstable and gradually broke down into diffuse irregularly shaped masses with subsequent lysis of their material, as shown by loss of affinity for protein, lipid, and RNA stains.

The first cytological changes in the chlorotic regions of young leaves of cauliflower about to develop whiptail when grown with ammonium nitrogen was the amalgamation of the chloroplasts with each other and with the cytoplasm; so that the chloroplast material, especially protein and RNA (as shown by naphthol yellow and pyronine staining, respectively) became distributed throughout the cytoplasm. The chloroplast starch grains shrank and disappeared. The chloroplast grana rendered visible by their reaction with iodonitrotetrazolium and light tended to clump together, forming larger granules. This phase was followed by the loss of chlorophyll and the break-up of the fused chloroplast mass into irregular debris, which showed a much increased affinity for vital stains such as Janus green B. The ability of the fusing grana to reduce the tetrazolium reagent was gradually lost, and the chloroplast debris developed a strong reaction with a benzidine-hydrogen peroxide test. Subsequent lysis of the chloroplast debris occurred as shown by decreasing reactions for protein, lipid, and RNA. These changes were accompanied by copious formation of lipid droplets in the cytoplasm.

Effect of nitrogen supply: Tomato plants were grown by Hewitt and McCready (223) using the several sources of nitrogen already noted above in experiments with cauliflower. Although growth was usually significantly decreased by molybdenum deficiency under these conditions, the effects were markedly less severe than those produced with nitrate or ammonium nitrate (Table XVI). Symptoms similar to those observed in plants grown with nitrate were observed also in the presence of ammonium nitrate. In this treatment, however, chlorophyll production was greater than with nitrate, especially in areas adjacent to the veins. The plants given the different nitrogen

TABLE XVI

Effects of Molybdenum and Source of Nitrogen on Total Yield, Chlorophyll, Nitrate, and Total Ascorbic and Dehydroascorbic Acid Contents in Tomato (Lycopersicon esculentum)[a]

Nitrogen source	Yield (gm dry wt.)		Chlorophyll (mg/100 gm fresh wt.)		Nitrate (% dry matter)		Total ascorbic and dehydroascorbic acid (mg/100 gm fresh wt.)	
	Minus Mo	Plus Mo	Minus Mo	Plus Mo	Minus Mo	Plus Mo	Minus Mo	Plus Mo
Nitrate	12.8	23.8	11.1	18.1	5.18	1.06	99.1	194.5
Nitrate and CaCO₃	9.6	25.0	8.9	15.8	7.29	0.87	58.5	170.6
Nitrite and CaCO₃	9.5	18.7	17.9	19.9	1.11	0.65	141.9	169.8
Ammonium sulfate and CaCO₃	15.9	19.4	21.6	17.4	1.04	0.58	126.0	183.6
Ammonium nitrate and CaCO₃	13.7	23.6	12.9	17.0	4.75	1.09	95.8	179.6
Ammonium nitrite and CaCO₃	13.9	21.9	17.9	15.9	1.60	0.88	129.0	185.7
Urea and CaCO₃	12.3	27.6	16.9	18.7	0.85	0.92	142.4	170.6
Glutamic acid and CaCO₃	6.8	15.0	14.5	16.6	0.67	0.83	144.2	178.5
LSD, molybdenum effect								
$P < 0.05$	3.3		2.7		0.90		39.0	
$P < 0.01$	4.5		3.8		1.22		56.5	
$P < 0.001$	6.3		5.4		1.68		85.7	
LSD, nitrogen effect								
$P < 0.05$	3.0		2.4		0.86		27.9	
$P < 0.01$	4.0		3.2		1.14		37.1	
$P < 0.001$	5.1		4.2		1.48		48.2	

[a] From Hewitt and McCready (223).

sources did not show any symptoms analogous to whiptail in cauliflower, or to any effects which might be related to this condition. In later experiments (unpublished work with A. J. Abbott), distinct and characteristic symptoms have been observed in molybdenum-deficient tomato plants grown with ammonium sulfate or nitrogen source. These comprised a bright, pale yellow-green interveinal mottle of upper leaves without any associated necrosis. These symptoms have, however, always appeared for only a week or two and then disappeared. They were seen by W. R. Meagher (unpublished work) and are closely associated with molybdenum deficiency. In a later experiment (225) eight plants, including cauliflower and tomato, were grown with ammonium sulfate as nitrogen source; no symptoms of molybdenum deficiency were observed in tobacco, mustard, sunflower, lucerne, spinach-beet (*Beta vulgaris* var. *cicla*), or lettuce, whereas symptoms already noted were seen in tomato and cauliflower. Growth of lettuce was visibly decreased by omission of molybdenum with ammonium sulfate. Vanselow and Datta (537) observed symptoms of molybdenum which were similar in citrus plants given ammonium nitrate or nitrate. Hannay *et al.* (178) concluded that the growth of excised tomato roots in sterile culture was also stimulated by molybdenum when ammonium nitrogen or urea or casein amino acids were used as sources of nitrogen. The effect was more marked with lateral root growth than with the main axis.

ii. Molybdenum excess. A remarkable feature of molybdenum nutrition is the great range between levels of molybdenum which are associated with deficiency and excess. This is especially so by comparison with other elements. Molybdenum deficiency and excess may be observed, respectively, at levels of 0.00001 and 10 ppm or above— a range of 10^6-fold. Comparable effects on growth may occur with manganese or boron between 0.005 and 5 ppm, that is, over a range of 10^3-fold.

The symptoms of molybdenum excess were first described by Warington (564). Two main types of effect were observed. Golden yellow globules were produced in epidermal cells of potato tubers and in vascular tissues of tuber buds, where tannins were normally present. The tomato shoots were golden yellow, especially at the apex, and leaf laminae were reduced to narrow areas along midribs. However, leaf epidermal cells contained golden globules. Microchemical tests indicated the formation of molybdenum-tannin complexes where golden globules were produced.

In some plants, e.g., barley, and in certain regions of *Solanum nodiflorum*, i.e., leaf palisade cells and cortex and pith of peduncles, and also in subepidermal cells of leaf petioles of tomato, blue granules appeared. These were considered to be molybdenum-anthocyanin complexes and occurred in tissues which normally contain anthocyanin pigments. Members of the Solanaceae appeared to be more sensitive than broad bean to excess of molybdenum. Agarwala and Hewitt (1) observed blue granules in the cortex of petioles and in lower epidermal cells of leaves of cauliflower. Millikan (353) and Warington (566–568) observed golden yellow pigments in flax given excess molybdenum. The only records of leaf malformation under these circumstances appear to be those of Warington (564).

b. *Relation to nitrate accumulation and respiration.* As would be expected from the role of molybdenum in nitrate reductase, discussed by Nason and McElroy in Chapter 4, a deficiency of molybdenum leads to accumulation of high concentrations of nitrate as shown for many plants grown in culture (3, 220, 363, 517) or in the field (585, 587, 588), and these observations, following the forecast of Steinberg (502), provided the initial clue to the role of molybdenum in nitrate reduction in higher plants. This response has been discussed earlier in relation to the occurrence and distribution of leaf mottling symptoms. Nitrate concentrations may reach 10–17% of leaf dry weight in leaves (3, 223, 517) where accumulation is usually greatest. Injection of a few micrograms of molybdenum causes the rapid disappearance of accumulated nitrate in a few hours (114, 517).

Ducet and Hewitt (114) found that the abnormal concentrations of nitrate in molybdenum-deficient plants are associated with a high respiratory quotient (R.Q.) in leaf disk samples of cauliflower (114). The mean R.Q. values, for disks from leaves of normal and molybdenum-deficient plants grown with nitrate, were 1.04 and 1.15, respectively (significantly different at the 1% level); for Q_0 (fresh weight) the values were 0.417 and 0.260, respectively (significantly different at 0.1%). The introduction of molybdenum caused initially an increase in R.Q. This was detectable after 1 hour and reached values between 1.3 and 1.4 in 6 hours. The R.Q. then fell to that of the normal plants. During this period nitrate reduction occurred rapidly, especially during the first 6 hours (Fig. 48). The increase in R.Q. was caused by a simultaneous increase in carbon dioxide output and a decrease in oxygen uptake. Molybdenum-deficient plants grown with other sources of nitrogen, excluding nitrate, had normal R.Q. values around 0.95–1.0, and normal Q_{0_2} values, which were similar to those of plants grown with molybdenum. The conclusions drawn were: (a) that molybdenum is not directly involved in respiratory activity; (b) that high concentrations of nitrate in tissues inhibit or compete with

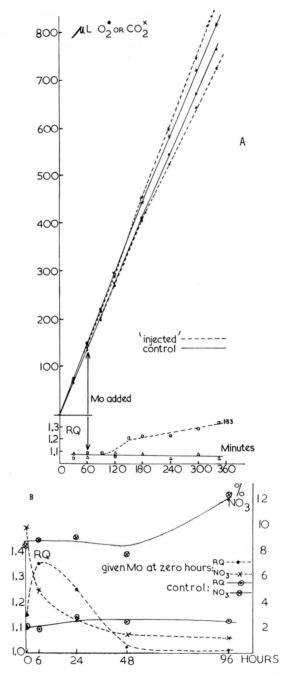

FIG. 48. Effect of addition of molybdenum on respiration of molybdenum-deficient

oxygen uptake; (c) that rapid reduction of high concentrations of nitrate already present causes both decreased oxygen uptake and increased carbon dioxide output. The association between nitrate reductase and cytochrome c reductase, observed by Kinsky and McElroy (277) for *Neurospora crassa*, could account for such relationships if the enzyme in higher plants possesses similar characteristics.

c. Relation to enzyme activity. Hewitt and Agarwala (212) observed that the enzymatic reduction of triphenyltetrazolium chloride by sections of intact tissues of cauliflower petiole is decreased in molybdenum-deficient tissues regardless of the nitrogen source used to grow the plants. The distribution of activity was similar to the distribution of molybdenum in the tissues revealed histochemically with thiocyanate and stannous chloride; it was highest in phloem and endodermis, and lowest in xylem and epidermis. The electron donor systems concerned have not been identified, but Mulder (366) reported that malate can serve the purpose in cauliflower, bean (*Phaseolus vulgaris*) and tomato. The conclusion that malic or succinic dehydrogenase may be decreased by molybdenum deficiency (366) does not necessarily follow. Anaerobic reduction of methylene blue by alfalfa (lucerne) leaf tissues is also decreased by molybdenum deficiency (136). Nitrate reductase in higher plants is adaptive to nitrate (63, 206, 210, 368, 450, 521) and enough may occur in nonsterile culture media to lead to an appreciable nitrate reductase activity. The diaphorase activity of nitrate reductase would be correspondingly determined and might account for the observed effects of molybdenum status on dye reduction. The failure to obtain dye reduction by *in vitro* preparations of nitrate reductase suggests that the activity is dependent also on some organizational feature which is destroyed when the cells are disrupted.

Certain enzyme systems show increased activities in molybdenum-deficient plants. Specific activities of polyphenol oxidase and peroxidase were double in molybdenum-deficient tomato leaf extracts (371), but ascorbic acid oxidase was not affected. Hewitt and Tatham (225), found that acid phosphatase activity was increased on a protein basis

---

cauliflower (*Brassica oleracea* var. *botrytis*) leaf disks. (A) Effect of molybdenum addition on respiratory quotients. Note increase in CO_2 production and decrease of O_2 uptake after approximately 100 minutes from addition of molybdenum from side arm of Warburg flask and steady increase in respiratory quotient after this time. (B) Changes in R.Q. as nitrate content of molybdenum-deficient cauliflower leaf disks declines following addition of molybdenum. Note increase in R.Q. after approximately 3–6 hours, followed by decrease and corresponding decrease in accumulated nitrate over the whole period of the experiment. These results are comparable with the changes shown in (A). From Ducet and Hewitt (114).

in eight species when deficient in molybdenum. Spencer (493) showed that molybdate at 10^{-4} to 10^{-6} M inhibited acid phosphatase *in vivo* and *in vitro* in tomato. Hewitt and Hucklesby (unpublished) showed histochemically a similar inhibition in cauliflower leaf cells. No inhibitory effect has been found for cauliflower extracts when compared 24 hours after infiltration with water or with molybdate at 10^{-4} M concentration (63), which would produce about 2×10^{-7} M concentration in the assay mixture.

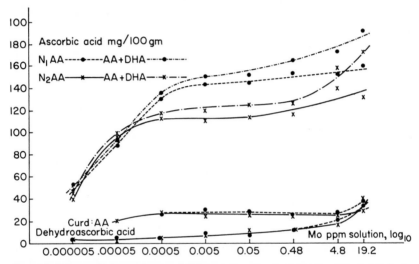

Fig. 49. Effects of increasing molybdenum levels on ascorbic acid and dehydro-ascorbic acid in leaf and curd of cauliflower grown with 24 meq (high) and 6 meq (low) nitrate levels. Note sharp increase from very low level of 0.000005 to 0.00005 ppm Mo at high nitrate level (crosses) and continued increase to 0.0005 ppm with low nitrate level (solid circles). From Agarwala and Hewitt (2).

d. Effects on ascorbic acid and sugar levels. Molybdenum deficiency consistently results in a marked decrease in ascorbic acid concentration in many plants (2, 213). The effects of molybdenum concentrations are shown in Fig. 49 for cauliflower. The level is restored to normal 3–5 days after injection of molybdenum and a response can be detected in 24 hours (Fig. 50). The effect of molybdenum deficiency is independent of the source of nitrogen used to grow cauliflower (4) Fig. 51; or tomato (223) (Table XVI).

The possibility that decreased ascorbic acid is due to lack of chlorophyll was considered to be excluded (2, 4, 223) and a similar limiting effect of sugar content was also regarded as unlikely (3, 4).

The content of ascorbic acid in plants varies widely, even during the day, and there are evidently many factors that affect the amounts observed in extracts; these factors require to be examined in relation to the effect of molybdenum. Increases in the activities of enzymes in-, cluding phenol oxidases and peroxidase (371), able to catalyze the oxidation of ascorbic acid may be involved in the effect of molybdenum on ascorbic acid concentration.

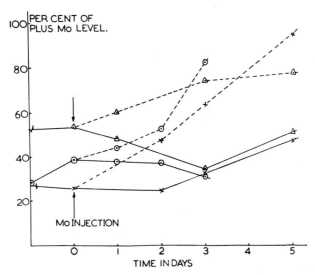

Fig. 50. Effect on ascorbic acid of injecting molybdenum through cut ends of petioles of molybdenum-deficient plants. Molybdenum was injected at time shown by arrows. Values for ascorbic acid as per cent of values in control plants grown with molybdenum. x, Tomato (*Lycopersicon esculentum*); ⊙, Brussels sprouts (*Brassica oleracea* var. *gemmifera*); △, Marrow stem kale (*B. oleracea* var. *acephala*). From Hewitt (201).

Comparisons between ascorbic acid concentrations in areas showing normal or early lesion development in deficient leaves have not shown any differences (unpublished work). It is nevertheless of interest to note that Arnon *et al.* (20, 21) and Ohmura (390) regard ascorbic acid as of possible importance in the preservation of chloroplasts in a functional state. The marked decrease in ascorbic acid content of tissues when they are molybdenum deficient might be significant in relation to the chloroplast disorganization that occurs at the onset of whiptail lesions observed by Hewitt and Hucklesby (unpublished). It is not clear, however, which effect is the cause or which the result.

Concentrations of total and reducing sugars in cauliflower are also

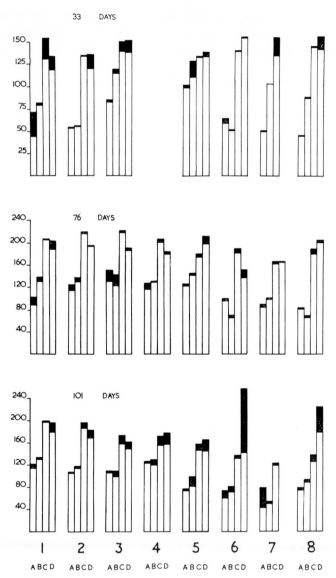

FIG. 51. Relationships of molybdenum supply and source of nitrogen to ascorbic (white bar) and dehydroascorbic (filled bar) acid contents (mg/100 gm fresh weight) of cauliflower foliage from plants at three different ages. A, B, C, and D refer to molybdenum levels of 0.000005, 0.00005, 0.5, and 50 ppm, respectively. The numbers 1–8, refer to nitrogen sources as follows: 1, nitrate; 2, nitrate with added calcium carbonate in the sand; 3, nitrite; 4, nitrate with citrate added to the nutrient solution; 5, ammonium sulfate with calcium carbonate added to the sand; 6, ammonium citrate; 7, urea; 8, ammonium nitrate. From Agarwala and Hewitt (4).

decreased by molybdenum deficiency (3). This effect is probably in-dependent of the source of nitrogen used to grow the plants (4). However, in plants grown with nitrate at the lowest molybdenum levels tested (about 0.000005 ppm) sugars may be present at higher con-centrations than in those given molybdenum at levels of 0.00005 ppm or more (3). Failure to reduce nitrate, and therefore to synthesize protein in the absence of molybdenum with consequent nonutilization of sugars, may outweigh the effect of molybdenum in increasing sugar production, which is evident at higher concentrations, possibly as a result of increasing chlorophyll content or of some other factor, e.g., inhibition of phosphatase activity.

 e. Effect on nitrogen fractions. Free nitrite rarely attains appreciable concentrations in plant tissue extracts obtained from normal plants. Addition of molybdenum to deficient tomato plants was observed by Spencer and Wood (494) to result in a significant increase in free nitrite concentration in leaf extracts which was maximal after 2 hours. Nitrite later disappeared and was followed by a relatively greater increase in ammonia concentrations after about 6 hours. Sequential changes in the activities of a series of related adaptive enzymes might be inferred. In independent experiments by Possing-ham (417) his data reveal decreases in some amino acids for 1 hour before the expected increases were observed following the addition of molybdenum (Fig. 52).

The role of molybdenum in nitrate reductase (380) accounts for the fact that molybdenum-deficient plants grown with nitrate contain markedly lower concentrations of protein, soluble organic nitrogen compounds, and ammonium nitrogen than normal plants (3, 214, 222, 416) and that the levels of these fractions increase rapidly after molybdenum has been supplied (363, 417, 494, 509).

The effects of molybdenum on free amino acid concentrations are complex and depend both on the nitrogen nutrition and on the par-ticular amino acids concerned. In tomato (416) and in cauliflower grown with nitrate (214, 222) large decreases occur when molyb-denum is deficient, particularly in glutamic acid, glutamine, aspartic acid, asparagine, glycine, β-alanine, and lysine (Tables XVII and XVIII). Increased concentrations may also occur, even in molybdenum-deficient plants grown with nitrate, and in tomato such changes have been reported by Possingham (416) for γ-aminobutyric acid, β-alanine, proline, and arginine (Table XVIII). Results for cauliflower (214) have shown inconsistent effects with a few amino acids including arginine, which has often shown higher concentrations in the deficient plants. Steinberg *et al.* (507, 509) reported an outstanding increase in lysine concentration in molybdenum-deficient tobacco grown with nitrate (Table XIX).

Molybdenum-deficient cauliflower grown with ammonium compounds, urea, nitrite, or glutamic acid have often contained higher

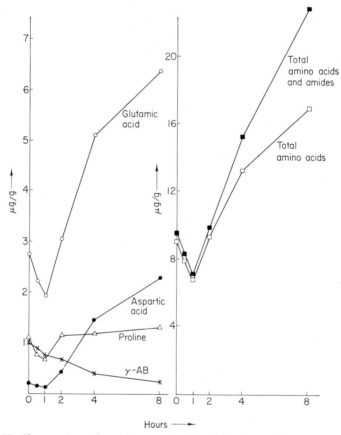

FIG. 52. Changes in amino acid concentrations following addition of molybdenum to molybdenum-deficient tomato plants. Drawn from data of Possingham (417). The concentrations of total amino acids and amides, glutamic acid, aspartic acid, and proline fall sharply for a period of about 1 hour after injection and then rise steadily. The concentration of γ-aminobutyric acid (γ-AB) falls steadily from the beginning of this period. Data obtained over longer periods of time which did not include estimations over the period of 0–8 hours do not show this effect.

concentrations of many amino acids than normal plants, and these differences are usually most marked for arginine and serine (Table XVII). It appears that molybdenum deficiency may affect amino acid concentrations in two ways. First, when the plants are grown with nitrate molybdenum causes, as expected, decreased concentrations of many amino acids. Another effect apparently tends to cause increased concentrations of certain particular amino acids. This second effect is fully revealed only when nitrogen metabolism is not limited by impaired nitrate reductase activity, but it may also be discerned for certain amino acids, including more particularly arginine and γ-aminobutyric acid, even under partially limiting conditions of nitrate reduction. This effect is also apparent in Possingham's (417) experiment although not emphasized by him. γ-Aminobutyric acid particularly, and to a lesser extent also phenylalanine, showed progressive decreases over a 24-hour period after molybdenum had been given to tomato plants that had been grown without this element.

f. Effects on phosphorus metabolism. Molybdate catalyzes the chemical hydrolysis of many ortho- and pyrophosphate esters (577). The effect of molybdate on certain phosphatase systems has been mentioned. Molybdenum also influences the proportions of inorganic and organic phosphorus in plants. The ratio of organic phosphorus is frequently increased (201, 205, 415) in molybdenum-deficient tomato and cauliflower plants. Possingham (415) found that addition of molybdenum to deficient tomato plants resulted in the conversion of inorganic phosphate, already absorbed, to an organic form. The significance of this effect is obscure. It may reflect the effects of cell growth on the capacity to produce organic phosphorus compounds, after a renewal of nitrogen assimilation, or it may result from decreased phosphatase activity. A reciprocal effect of phosphate on molybdenum uptake may be noted. Stout *et al.* (518) found that molybdenum uptake by whole tomato plants was almost linearly related to phosphate concentration in the nutrient solution. Increasing the phosphorus supply from 5 to 125 ppm increased the molybdenum concentration in leaves by tenfold.

g. Conclusions on molybdenum. It appears to be established beyond doubt that molybdenum is still required by plants which are grown under conditions such that they do not obviously depend to a major extent on the activity of nitrate reductase to provide available nitrogen. Such diverse effects as decreased concentrations of ascorbic acid and sugars, changed proportions of phosphorus fractions and of amino acids, and increased or decreased activities of certain enzymes often occur independently of the type of nitrogen nutrition of the plant. In cauliflower the lack of molybdenum is also associated with specific leaf symptoms regardless of the nitrogen source, whereas in tomato grown under similar conditions, molybdenum deficiency is revealed mainly by decreased growth. It is also likely from the work described above (3, 214) that the production of whiptail in cauliflower grown with nitrate at an intermediate level of molybdenum is associated with the capacity of the plant to synthesize an adequate level of soluble organic nitrogen compounds for growth. It is possible that the production of these symptoms at a critical molybdenum level, obviously still inadequate for normal growth, may provide the clue to understanding why molybdenum is required when the plant is not dependent essentially on nitrate reduction as a means of obtaining adequate soluble nitrogen compounds for protein synthesis. Re-examination of data given by Possingham (417), presented in Fig. 52 shows that, when molybdenum was given to deficient tomato plants grown with nitrate, there were marked decreases in the concentrations of aspartic and glutamic acids and proline to two-thirds their initial levels within 1 hour of giving molybdenum to the deficient plants. Total amides and total amino acids excluding aspartic and glutamic acids decreased by 25% over the same period, before the expected increases were observed. γ-Aminobutyric acid and phenylalanine showed a continued decrease during this period and for a further period of over twenty-four hours. These changes would be consistent with the demands on free amino acids during the induction of nitrate reductase protein synthesis, which has been shown to occur on adding molybdenum over a comparable time period of 1–5 hours (210) (Fig. 53). The experiments of Spencer and Wood (494), who studied the effects on nitrite formation of giving molybdenum to deficient tomato plants, and of Ducet and Hewitt (114), who observed changes in respiratory behavior of cauliflower leaves in relation to nitrate loss following addition of molybdenum, showed in separate ways that there were lag periods of about 1 hour before the changes following molybdenum addition were apparent.

It is therefore worth while to speculate whether the following observations: (a) amino acid decrease, which might be regarded as a lag in amino acid increase; (b) a lag in nitrite accumulation; (c) a lag in change in respiratory behavior; and (d) in some instances a lag in nitrate reductase induction (210, and unpublished work) following introduction of molybdenum, comprise a related series of events that reflect the changes preceding induction of the enzyme nitrate reductase as the primary response to the restoration of molybdenum.

It was suggested by Wilson and Waring (588) that whiptail symptoms might be attributable to some toxic effect due to nitrate accumulation in molybdenum-deficient plants. This idea, in its simplest form, was considered (4, 205) an unlikely explanation owing to the low concentration of nitrate which occurs when plants are grown with ammonium sulfate, urea, or glutamic acid, especially in comparison with similar levels produced in the presence of molybdenum, whether grown with nitrate, or nitrogen from other sources (4, 223). Recent work which has demonstrated the inducible nature of nitrate reductase may, however, call for a reconsideration (209) of the possible role of nitrate as a factor in the apparent molybdenum requirement for plants, especially cauliflower and tomato, grown substantially with other

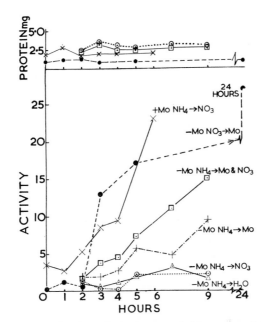

Fig. 53. Effects of introduction of nitrate or molybdenum on induction of nitrate reductase activity in excised cauliflower leaf tissues; note steady increase in enzyme activity over a period of several hours following an apparent lag period of 1 or 2 hours in a number of instances. Induction of enzyme is dependent upon the supply of nitrate and also upon the supply of molybdenum when plants were grown without this element. From Hewitt and Afridi (210).

sources of nitrogen. Thus, it is now conceivable that the steady uptake of nitrate from low concentrations produced by nitrification in non-sterile media, which has been shown to occur to a marked extent in conditions where nitrifying organisms have become abundant, or from impurities in the reagents or produced by autoclaving media containing nitrogen compounds, may all provide an inductive stimulus for formation of the enzyme apoprotein which, in the absence of molybdenum upon which the true holoenzyme synthesis is dependent, is converted into an alternative protein with unfavorable cell functions.

Alternatively it must be concluded that molybdenum has a multiple role not yet fully elucidated. If this is so, it is possible that in *Scenedesmus obliquus* (18a), vanadium may take over the part of molybdenum in those functions which are not related to nitrate reduction so that, when the organism is grown in the absence of nitrate but with vanadium, no molybdenum requirement can be detected or even suspected with the present limitations of technique (236a).

Thirdly it is possible that the one enzyme nitrate reductase has multiple functions and that its activity is still needed even in the absence of nitrate. Although no evidence is yet available from higher plants to support this idea, it is clear that the enzyme system from *Neurospora crassa*, as so far characterized, not only functions as a diaphorase but also has the properties of a cytochrome c reductase (277). In this system cytochrome c reduction and nitrate reduction are competitive and recall the observations of Ducet and Hewitt (114) regarding the apparent competition between nitrate reduction and oxygen uptake. The cytochrome c reductase activity of the *Neurospora* enzyme (277) is equally inducible by nitrate, but does not show the same dependence on phosphate or a metal, as nitrate reductase; therefore the idea of a dual-functioning enzyme which is evoked by a single stimulus is a definite possibility to be considered.

8. Chlorine

a. Visible and histological effects. In spite of early experiments by Nobbe and Siegert (388), Lipman (298), Eaton (119), and Raleigh (424), no conclusive evidence of the essentiality of chlorine was available until the work of Broyer *et al.* (56) on tomato.

In their experiments the plants developed first a pronounced wilt in the apical leaflets of the lower leaves. This was also associated with restricted growth of the tissues, and leaflets showed a marked reduction in width of the apex or became necrotic (Fig. 54). Injection of 2–20 μg chloride at this stage permitted complete recovery and renewal of growth in the unwilted basal areas of the leaf. Continued deficiency led to chlorosis, necrosis, and bronzing of the leaflets behind the wilted regions, and these leaflets were then unable to show any recovery. Fruiting was also suppressed and yields were increased in response to chloride application up to 100 μM per culture. Bromide could partially substitute for chloride at about 10 times the concentration. This work was extended by Johnson *et al.* (252) to several other species, and they also described in more detail the effects of chloride on the histology of tomato. The cells in the bronzed areas contained bronze-colored bodies which appeared to be coagulated cytoplasm,

A

B

FIG. 54. A. Effects of chloride supply on growth of tomato (*Lycopersicon esculentum*) plants in water culture. Left, without chloride; right, with chloride. B. Leaflets of tomato plants grown without added chloride (left); at a threshold level, 14 μmoles/liter chloride (center); and with 105 μmoles/liter chloride (right). Photographs courtesy of C. M. Johnson.

293

which also occupied intercellular spaces. The bronze pigment was insoluble in water, xylol, 5% sodium hydroxide or hydrochloric acid, butanol, ethanol, or methanol. Cell contents in these regions stained heavily with safranin. Cell collapse occurred randomly and was not related to anatomy. There were no notable anatomical differences due

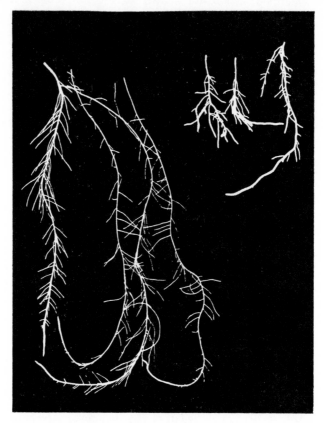

Fig. 55. Effect of chloride on root development of tomatoes. Comparative lateral root development of tomatoes in inorganic solution cultures, left with and right, without chloride additions. From Johnson *et al.* (252).

to chlorine deficiency. Roots became stunted and lateral branching was somewhat suppressed (Fig. 55). Lettuce appeared to be relatively susceptible to lack of chloride. Multiple branching of the lateral roots with clubbed tips was a particularly characteristic effect, as for tomato. Leaves wilted but did not show any characteristic injury. Cabbage also wilted readily, leaf margins "cupped," and younger leaves became chlorotic. There was a loss of the characteristic brassica odor, but roots were not greatly affected. Leaflets of lucerne (alfalfa) became cupped, necrotic at the apices, and reduced in area. Sugar beet showed marked wilting and clubbed root tips. Affected leaves of barley remained rolled and resembled some affected by copper deficiency. The relative effects upon yields are shown in Fig. 56. Ulrich and Ohki (533) also observed thickening and shortening of roots, chlorosis, and a raised appearance of the veins in the leaves of sugar beet.

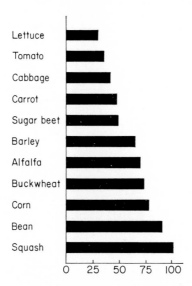

Yields as per cent of plus chloride control

Fig. 56. Effects of chloride on growth of different species. Plant yields from chloride-deficient cultures as per cent of those from adequately supplied chloride controls. From Johnson et al. (252).

Ozanne et al. (399) concluded that the beneficial effects of bromide when chloride was deficient were explained by increased translocation of limited chlorine from the roots to the tops. The quantitative relationships between yield, uptake, and supply are shown in Figs. 57–59. Their results show differential effects in roots and shoots with respect to the supply of chloride or bromide. In general, however, bromide is less effective and is required at higher concentrations than chloride. The relationships between uptake and yield also differ as shown in Fig. 58. The yields of subterranean clover tops and of tomato leaves were almost linearly related to the total chloride content of these regions (Fig. 59) computed as yield times concentration. This relationship means that over the concentration range in which supply of chloride severely limited growth there was no appreciable change in cell concentration as growth increased and all the available chloride was utilized in additional growth. In this respect chlorine differs in a quantitative way from most other nutrients. Woolley *et al.* (591)

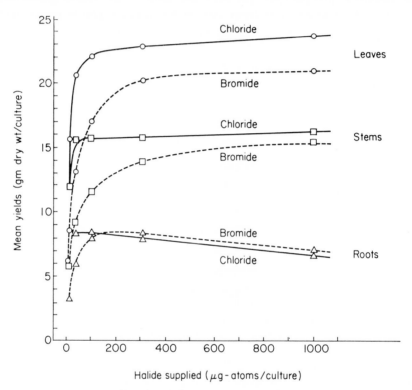

FIG. 57. Effects of chloride or bromide concentration on growth of tomato (*Lycopersicon esculentum*) plants grown in nutrient culture solutions with increase in concentrations of either element. Note extremely large response in growth at low levels of chloride and slightly more gradual response to similar increase in bromide. From Ozanne *et al.* (399).

found that chlorine normally accumulated in old leaves, but is translocated to younger leaves under deficiency conditions. Ozanne (398) has observed chlorine deficiency under field conditions in California and in Western Australia.

b. Effects on chloroplasts and photosynthesis. The role of chlorine is still obscure, but Warburg and Lüttgens (558) stated that chloride ions were essential for the production of oxygen by isolated chloroplasts

from beet or spinach leaves (cf. Volume IB, Chapter 4, p. 194 *et seq.*).
This observation was tested further by Arnon and Whatley (19), who
reached the following conclusions: Repeated washing of chloroplasts by
water destroyed their capacity to cause oxygen evolution, but this was
restored on adding back cytoplasmic fluid. The cytoplasmic fluid could
be replaced by chloride or bromide ions at a concentration of
3×10^{-3} M. Chloroplasts from apparently normal plants which had

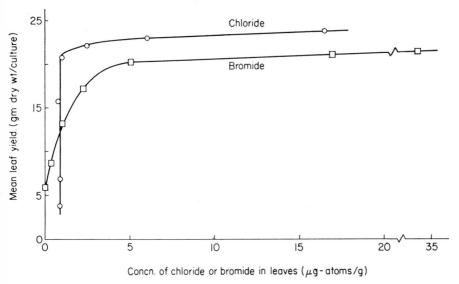

Fig. 58. Relationship in tomato (*Lycopersicon esculentum*) plants between concentration of chloride or bromide present in the leaves (dry basis) and the mean
leaf yield per culture. From Ozanne *et al.* (399).

been grown without chlorine had a greatly decreased capacity for
oxygen evolution, but this could be restored by adding chloride to the
preparation. It was also found that when normal chloroplasts were pre-
illuminated in the absence of a Hill reaction oxidant such as ferricyanide,
they lost irreversibly the capacity to evolve oxygen unless chloride
was present during the preillumination. Addition of chloride at the
same time as the ferricyanide was ineffective. It was concluded that
chloride ions protected isolated chloroplasts in a manner that was not
necessary in the intact cell. In view, however, of the discovery of the
essential nature of chlorine this view may require revision. The curves
that relate oxygen evolution of isolated chloroplasts to chloride concentration and yield to chloride concentration in nutrient solution (56)
are similar in their characteristics, for they show a very large response

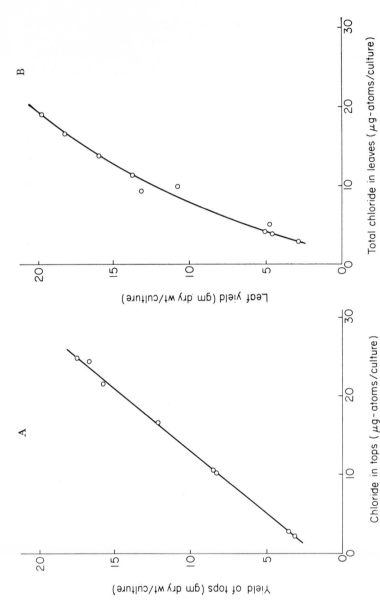

FIG. 59. (A) Effect of chloride content on yield of tops with subterranean clover (*Trifolium subterraneum*) cultured under very low chloride-supply conditions. (B) Effect of chloride content on yield of leaves of tomato (*Lycopersicon esculentum*) plants cultured under very low chloride-supply conditions. Note linear relationship for subterranean clover between total uptake by plants and mean yields of plants. In tomato, relationship is obviously curvilinear. From Ozanne *et al.* (399).

to small increments of chloride and a continued small response to much higher levels of supply. Half the maximal activity was obtained with only about one-twentieth of the optimum concentration (7×10^{-3} M). Bové (42) has also tested the effects of adding chloride at 3×10^{-4} M concentration on the photosynthetic activities of chloroplasts. Oxygen evolution, reduction of TPN, and noncyclic photophosphorylation were all stimulated by added chloride. Cyclic photophosphorylation catalyzed by riboflavin phosphate was also stimulated by chloride, but to a far lesser extent. Cyclic photophosphorylation catalyzed by vitamin K or phenazine methosulfate showed no response and was fully active without chloride addition. (For a prior discussion of photophosphorylation see Volume IB, Chapter 4, p. 212 *et seq.*). Bové concluded from this that chloride ions acted as electron transporting agents during their transfer between two cytochrome pigments, and that vitamin K was able to bypass this chloride-dependent step. There is, however, no direct evidence for these views and the cytochrome components have not yet been identified. Ulrich and Ohki (533) concluded that chlorine decreased the sucrose content of beet leaves with high potassium and increased sucrose at low potassium levels.

C. Effects of Nutrient Status on Free Amino Acids and Amides

Nutritional disorders produce marked changes in the concentrations of free amino acids and amides in plant tissues. Some features appear to be of general occurrence, but individual patterns may vary. It is, therefore, convenient to discuss this as a distinct aspect of nutritional disorders. Amino acids are the precursors of proteins and peptides and are also derived from them. They participate in several other reactions including amidation, transamination, decarboxylation, oxidative deamination, phosphorylation, and thiolation. Some amino acids may yield amines that modify physiological activity. The intermediary reactions of these compounds cannot be described here, but they are to be discussed in the chapters on nitrogen metabolism in Volume IV.

After frequent general associations between potassium as a nutrient and protein metabolism had been noted [for references see an early review by Steward (508a)], Gregory and Sen (169) and Richards and Templeman (449) specified the association between potassium deficiency and the accumulation of amide and amino nitrogen fractions. Later Steinberg (503, 505) suggested that mineral deficiencies in general frequently led to marked increases in the concentrations of free amino acids and amides. Steinberg *et al.* (508)

observed that deficiencies of calcium, magnesium, or potassium caused increases ranging from double to nearly sevenfold in the concentration of free α-amino nitrogen in leaves of tobacco. Deficiencies of phosphorus, nitrogen, or boron had smaller effects ranging from 48 to 26% increases. There were often notable increases in L(+)-isoleucine. On the basis of observations by Steinberg (503, 504) of toxic effects of certain naturally occurring amino acids on tobacco seedlings which developed chloroses and leaf malformations, it was suggested that several of the visual symptoms of mineral disorders reflected the accumulation of toxic concentrations of certain amino compounds of which L-hydroxyproline and L(+)-isoleucine were shown to be outstandingly toxic. L(+)-Isoleucine and hydroxyproline especially produced severe mottling, necrosis, strap-shaped leaves, and "rosetting." Methionine has been shown to induce the "yellow strap leaf" in chrysanthemums (589).

Bennett (31) and Iljin (238) drew attention to the high concentrations of soluble nitrogen compounds, especially amides and amino acids, in iron-deficient plants of several species. Hewitt et al. (222) first applied paper chromatography to observations of effects of mineral deficiencies on amino acid components in a study on the effects of manganese and molybdenum levels given to cauliflower leaves. Manganese deficiency increased, and molybdenum deficiency decreased the concentrations of arginine, α-alanine, aspartic acid, glutamic acid, proline, asparagine, and glutamine as revealed qualitatively by examination of paper chromatograms. Manganese deficiency decreased the concentration of γ-aminobutyric acid. Effects of molybdenum deficiency were accentuated by manganese excess. Since this earlier work, several investigations of effects of nutrition on amino acid pattern have been reported and are summarized below. Possingham (416) and Steward and his collaborators (143b, 509) and Steinberg (507) have made especially notable contributions for tomato, mint, banana (*Musa acuminata* 'Gros Michel'), and tobacco; important interactions between nutrition and environment have also been revealed for *Mentha piperita* (509). Hewitt et al. (214) pointed out that the effects of molybdenum deficiency on amino acid concentrations were possibly complex, as already mentioned. When nitrogen was given as ammonium compounds, urea, or glutamic acid, molybdenum deficiency increased the concentrations of most amino acids, especially those of arginine, serine, and glutamine. Table XVII shows data obtained by Hewitt and Williams using a semiquantitative method in which visual comparisons were made with standard concentrations chromatographed at the same time. When nitrate was given alone, molybdenum deficiency resulted in decreases of each of the five amino compounds shown. With ammonium nitrate, glutamic and aspartic acids and glutamine decreased, while serine and possibly arginine increased in concentration in deficient plants. When nitrite, ammonium nitrite, ammonium sulfate, urea, or glutamic acid were used to grow the plants, molybdenum deficiency resulted usually in large increases in each of the five amino compounds shown. Although very low concentrations of molybdenum caused over-all decreases in amino acids

TABLE XVII

CONCENTRATIONS OF SOME AMINO COMPOUNDS IN EXTRACTS OF LEAVES OF CAULIFLOWER GROWN WITH DIFFERENT NITROGEN AND MOLYBDENUM SUPPLIES[a]

	Amino compounds[b]									
	Aspartic acid		Glutamic acid		Serine		Glutamine		Arginine	
Nitrogen source	Plus Mo	Minus Mo	Plus Mo	Minus Mo	Plus Mo	Minus Mo	Plus Mo	Minus Mo	Plus Mo	Minus Mo
Nitrate	149	N.D.	353	116	101	67	701	116	83	28
Ammonium nitrate	43	N.D.	165	94	134	436	1285	630	1010	1220
Nitrite	171	234	356	681	151	404	504	1512	82	1250
Ammonium sulfate	22	66	141	217	436	1090	793	2100	694	1808
Ammonium nitrite	64	64	165	305	205	897	607	1403	167	1277
Urea	43	130	165	540	337	1260	489	1470	500	1475
Glutamic acid	106	213	356	750	205	470	607	1403	28	833

[a] Unpublished data (1952) of Hewitt and Williams.
[b] Mean values as micrograms per gram fresh weight for three sampling times taken in duplicate.

due to impaired nitrate assimilation in plants grown with nitrate, slightly greater concentrations of molybdenum sometimes produced increases in amino acid concentrations, presumably because nitrate assimilation was no longer limited although other aspects of metabolism were still abnormal.

Possingham (416) made a detailed comparative study of the effects of deficiencies of iron, manganese, copper, zinc, and molybdenum on the amino acid and amides of the tomato plants grown with nitrate (Table XVIII). The changes were complex in nature and each deficiency produced a different pattern of amino acid content.

Molybdenum deficiency generally caused marked decreases in amino acids and amides in accordance with its role in nitrate reduction, but the decreases occurred to different extents. There were also notable increases in the concentrations of β-alanine, γ-aminobutyric acid, arginine, proline, and an unidentified compound. By contrast with

TABLE XVIII

COMPARISON OF THE EFFECTS OF DIFFERENT DEFICIENCIES ON THE CONCENTRATION OF FREE AMINO ACIDS AND AMIDES AND ON DRY WEIGHT[a,b]

Amino acid	Control 2[c]	Minus Zn	Minus Cu	Minus Mn	Control 1[d]	Minus Fe	Minus Mo
Aspartic acid	1.526	4.408	5.553	4.996	0.985	2.303	0.152
Glutamic acid	5.107	7.624	7.116	6.683	5.848	6.911	2.500
Asparagine	0.343	16.58	0.738	0.545	0.415	6.307	0.161
Glutamine	3.850	26.27	2.277	1.400	2.180	10.27	0.306
Citrulline	0.447	Absent	0.399	0.407	0.199	0.582	0.245
Histidine	0.129	1.031	Absent	Absent	0.093	Absent	Absent
Lysine	0.068	0.749	Absent	Absent	0.063	0.340	Absent
Arginine	0.183	1.058	0.350	0.328	0.210	0.503	0.445
"Under arginine"	0.043	0.309	0.182	0.271	0.034	0.275	0.288
Serine	1.770	3.116	1.345	0.482	1.258	1.152	1.460
Glycine	1.810	2.474	0.755	0.202	0.797	0.548	0.191
Threonine	1.063	2.214	0.767	0.898	0.629	0.880	0.238
α-Alanine	1.730	1.823	1.359	1.166	1.299	0.895	0.885
β-Alanine	Absent	0.436	0.443	Absent	Absent	Absent	0.141
γ-Aminobutyric acid	0.439	0.527	0.328	0.532	0.184	0.495	0.924
Ethanolamine	0.288	Absent	0.241	0.330	0.220	1.125	0.226
Phenylalanine	0.194	1.355	Absent	0.192	0.239	0.329	0.178
Pipecolic acid	Absent	Absent	Absent	0.385	Absent	0.178	Absent
Valine	0.234	1.026	0.295	0.288	0.189	0.453	0.203
Leucine	0.266	1.892	0.298	0.358	0.226	0.604	0.267
Proline	0.681	1.505	2.022	0.766	0.545	1.133	0.843
Total amino acids	15.98	31.57	21.45	18.28	13.01	17.71	9.195
Total amides	4.193	42.85	3.015	1.945	2.595	16.58	0.467
Dry weight (mg per plant)	213.6	65.95	75.77	69.41	79.52	10.18	17.98

[a] From Possingham (416).

[b] Results are expressed as micrograms of amino acid or amide per milligram dry weight.

[c] Control 2 is comparable only with minus zinc, minus copper, minus manganese groups.

[d] Control 1 is comparable only with minus iron and minus molybdenum groups.

the effects of molybdenum, the other deficiencies caused notable increases in the concentrations of most amino acids and amides. In a joint study on tobacco, the symptoms of mineral deficiency were established by Steinberg, and samples of the severely deficient plants were analyzed chromatographically by Zacharias in the laboratory of

Steward. The data are given in Table XIX (507) and in the form of histograms in Fig. 60 (509). Steinberg *et al.* (507, 509) (Table XIX) observed an outstanding increase in lysine concentration in molybdenum-deficient tobacco, whereas γ-aminobutyric acid, α-alanine, glutamic acid, and proline were decreased. Tobacco and tomato therefore appear to present opposed effects with respect to the compounds

TABLE XIX

Effects of Micronutrient Deficiencies on Content of Free Amino Acids (as Per Cent of Total Free Amino N) in Fresh Leaves of Tobacco (Connecticut Broadleaf) Sampled at Flowering Time, and of Plants Given Full Nutrient[a]

				Treatment			
Amino compound	Complete	Minus Mo	Minus Fe	Minus B	Minus Cu	Minus Zn	Minus Mn
γ-Aminobutyric acid	18.6	8.1	3.5	7.6	5.5	3.4	9.0
α-Alanine	18.2	2.6	2.1	3.3	2.7	1.8	4.0
β-Alanine	—	—	—	Trace	—	—	—
Arginine	Trace	2.0	6.9	3.1	8.1	9.7	9.6
Asparagine	Trace	Nil	39.2	9.1	55.8	10.9	40.7
Aspartic acid	Trace	1.0	1.9	1.0	1.7	2.4	2.8
Glutamic acid	11.0	1.0	1.8	2.3	2.7	5.1	7.0
Glutamine	12.3	12.7	21.6	8.8	4.0	35.1	10.1
Glycine	8.2	4.1	—	—	—	5.8	1.5
Leucines	2.7	1.5	1.0	1.7	0.8	1.9	1.1
Lysine	Trace	56.4	3.3	4.0	4.0	2.0	0.9
Methionine sulfoxide	—	—	—	—	—	0.2	—
Phenylalanine	—	3.9	—	4.0	2.3	1.8	—
Proline	13.1	2.2	1.4	11.5	3.4	8.5	3.4
Serine	8.2	2.0	2.2	1.4	2.6	3.6	1.4
Threonine	5.4	1.0	0.9	1.4	1.4	4.0	1.6
Tyramine	—	—	10.6	38.7	3.1	1.3	6.9
Tyrosine	—	0.9	2.0	1.1	1.3	1.2	—
Valine	2.2	0.8	1.6	0.8	0.5	0.9	0.4
Total soluble N (µg/gm fresh wt.)	13.0	280.3	1695.2	879.7	1925.0	1072.5	366.6

[a] From Steinberg (507); see also (509).

γ-aminobutyric acid and proline. Tyramine was outstandingly increased in concentration in molybdenum-deficient tobacco (509) (Fig. 60).

Possingham (417) (Fig. 52) found that, although the restoration of molybdenum ultimately led to large increases in the concentrations of several free amino acids in tomato plants, there were initially decreases in some, including glutamic acid, glutamine, aspartic acid, and

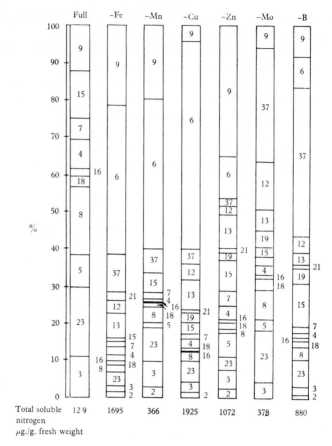

FIG. 60. Composition of the soluble nitrogen of *Nicotiana* leaves deficient in trace elements. (Nitrogen of each compound as a per cent of total soluble nitrogen.) From Steward *et al.* (509).

Key to numbers on histograms (Figs. 60–63): (1) cysteic acid (from cyst(e)ine); (2) aspartic acid; (3) glutamic acid; (4) serine; (5) glycine; (6) asparagine; (7) threonine; (8) alanine; (9) glutamine; (12) lysine; (13) arginine; (15) proline; (16) valine; (18) leucine(s); (19) phenylalanine; (23) γ-aminobutyric acid; (24) hydroxyproline; (26) pipecolic acid; (37) tyramine.

asparagine; the concentrations of γ-aminobutyric acid and phenyl-alanine, however, continued to decrease for several hours after molyb-denum was given, in accordance with the observations of Hewitt *et al.* (222). Steward *et al.* (509) also reported that γ-aminobutyric acid decreased after the addition of molybdenum to deficient tomato plants.*
The behavior of γ-aminobutyric acid in tobacco (507) (Table XIX)

* For a full account of this work, see *Contribs. Boyce Thompson Inst.* 21, 411–421 (1962).

when deprived of manganese was also contrary to that reported for tomato (416) in different experimental conditions.

Some of the most striking changes in amino acid patterns occur with zinc deficiency. Possingham (Table XVIII) observed a tenfold increase in total amides and double the total free amino acid level in zinc-deficient tomato leaves. Asparagine was increased nearly fiftyfold and glutamine was increased sevenfold to become the principal soluble nitrogen compound. There were five- to tenfold increases in the concentrations of lesser constituents such as β-alanine, histidine, lysine, arginine, phenylalanine, valine, and leucine. Other major constituents including aspartic acid, serine, glycine, and threonine were also substantially increased. On the other hand, there were notable relative decreases in citrulline and ethanolamine although these were initially present at much lower concentrations than the other substances mentioned.

Zinc deficiency in tobacco (507, 530) also caused large increases in asparagine, glutamine, and arginine, but decreases in γ-aminobutyric acid and α-alanine (Table XIX, Fig. 60).

Copper deficiency in tomato (416) contrasted sharply with that of zinc in that it did not cause the striking increases in the amides. There were, however, comparable increases in the concentrations of aspartic and glutamic acids, and in those of proline and β-alanine. Most other amino acids decreased in concentration, including glycine, phenylalanine, and histidine. In tobacco (507) (Fig. 60 and Table XIX) in contrast to tomato, the outstanding effect of copper deficiency was a large increase in asparagine and to a lesser extent in arginine, but many other amino compounds were also decreased.

Manganese deficiency in tomato (416) (Table XVIII), increased the concentration of aspartic acid, as occurred in cauliflower, but decreased that of glutamine, whereas levels of glutamic acid and asparagine were scarcely affected. There were moderate decreases in serine and glycine and an increase in an unknown compound, which was also increased by molybdenum deficiency. Pipecolic acid appeared, but it was undetected in control plants. The effects of manganese deficiency in tomato differed from those due to copper deficiency in the absence of β-alanine, the presence of phenylalanine, the appearance of pipecolic acid and the somewhat more marked decreases in glutamine and serine. Manganese deficiency also decreased serine in tomato plants grown by Steward et al. (509).* In tobacco (507) manganese deficiency

* The responses of the free amino acids and amides of tomato plants to the onset of, and recovery from, deficiency of Mn in presence of either NO_3 or NH_4 are described in more detail in Contribs. Boyce Thompson Inst. 21(6), 393–410, 1962.

resembled copper deficiency with respect to large increases in asparagine and arginine and decreases in many others (Fig. 60).

Iron deficiency increased the concentrations of asparagine and
glutamine in tomato (416) fifteen- and fivefold, respectively. These
changes were second only to those produced by lack of zinc (Table
XVIII). Aspartic acid was somewhat increased, but not glutamic acid.
There were also moderate increases in lysine, arginine, proline, valine,
and leucine. Pipecolic acid also appeared and there was a marked increase in ethanolamine, which was a unique effect of iron deficiency

TABLE XX

FREE AMINO ACIDS OF HEALTHY AND IRON-DEFICIENT LEAVES[a,b]

Amino acid	Bracken		Spinach-beet		Peas	
	N	D	N	D	N	D
Aspartic acid	0.7	10.8	6.0	13.2	9.0	7.0
Glutamic acid	1.0	80.4	17.3	26.5	14.1	26.9
Serine	1.3	59.0	3.9	15.3	2.5	4.5
Threonine	10.5	70.4	1.6	5.5	16.0	45.7
Tyrosine	2.8	23.8	1.0	4.1	0.6	0.6
Alanine	5.7	118.1	4.9	6.6	3.0	4.5
γ-Aminobutyric acid	22.9	54.0	2.1	8.6	1.9	3.7
Valine	38.0	208.3	2.3	3.1	1.3	3.9
Leucine-isoleucine	70.0	258.0	4.1	6.2	1.4	2.5
Phenylalanine	178.0	418.2	0.7	1.4	3.1	6.6
Histidine	6.5	P	2.8	3.9	—	—
Lysine	0.8	3.3	1.4	1.0	1.2	4.2
Arginine	2.1	5.6	3.8	3.3	18.7	24.9
Asparagine	0.4	66.5	6.5	19.6	4.4	12.5
Glutamine	7.8	7.4	0.7	2.3	2.2	0.4
Proline	6.0	40.3	44.1	48.1	4.4	11.1
Tryptophan	38.5	30.5	1.3	1.9	0.7	1.1
Total	393.0	1454.6	104.5	170.6	84.5	160.1

[a] From De Kock and Morrison (100).
[b] Symbols: —, not detected; P, present in fair quantity but not determined. Results are expressed as milligrams per 100 gm of fresh leaf for both normal (N) and
iron-deficient (D) leaves.

and is to be contrasted with that of zinc. Demetriades (103) observed
a similar increase in asparagine due to iron deficiency in *Hibiscus
esculentus*. Holley and Cain (231) reported that iron deficiency in
apple and blueberry (*Vaccinium myrtillus*) resulted in very great increases in their arginine content, but other amino acids did not show
notable effects. Chlorosis induced by excess of cobalt or nickel was also
associated with similar increases in arginine content in blueberry.
De Kock and Morrison (100) (cf. Table XX) made a comparative

study of the effects of iron deficiency on the amino acid patterns in bracken (*Pteridium aquilinum*), spinach-beet (*Beta vulgaris* var. *cicla*), pea, and mustard. In all four plants, there were great increases in many amino compounds and the differences were outstanding in bracken and relatively small in spinach-beet. Asparagine was increased in iron-deficient bracken leaves by one hundred and fifty times.

TABLE XXI

Free Amino Acid of Mustard Leaves Grown in Nutrient Solutions A, B, C, and D Containing 0.1, 0.5, 2.5, and 1.25 ppm of Iron, Respectively[a]

	Concentration[b] (mg/100 gm of fresh leaf)			
	A	B	C	D
Aspartic acid	43.6	31.1	36.2	32.7
Glutamic acid	136.3	79.8	54.1	51.1
Serine	24.7	24.1	12.3	15.3
Threonine	10.5	8.6	8.0	7.4
Alanine	20.9	8.9	6.5	8.4
Tyrosine	3.0	2.7	2.2	1.0
γ-Aminobutyric acid	9.1	4.7	3.6	4.5
Valine	12.1	6.0	6.7	5.4
Leucine-isoleucine	9.4	5.2	2.6	4.4
Phenylalanine	2.0	T	T	T
Lysine	2.5	0.7	T	—
Arginine	70.1	18.2	5.2	T
Asparagine	15.8	5.1	4.5	1.7
Glutamine	8.0	8.8	3.8	3.0
Histidine	5.0	—	—	—
Proline	39.5	37.7	31.8	28.2
Total	412.5	241.6	177.5	163.0

[a] From De Kock and Morrison (100).

[b] Symbols: —, not detected; T, detected but too weak for determination.

Glutamic acid was increased eightyfold, serine forty-fivefold, and aspartic acid fifteenfold. Asparagine was increased in all the species; threefold in beet and pea and ninefold in mustard. There was a great increase in arginine concentration in mustard, but only small increases occurred for arginine in the other species. By contrast with bracken, aspartic acid was decreased in pea by iron deficiency.

Decreasing iron levels given to mustard (100) appeared to produce differential effects on the amino acids present (Table XXI). Decreased iron from 12.5 (high) to 2.5 ppm (normal) increased only arginine and asparagine. A decrease of iron from 2.5 to 0.5 ppm (a suboptimal level) increased glutamic acid, serine, and arginine; and a decrease from 0.5 to 0.1 ppm (marked deficiency) increased also aspartic acid, alanine, γ-aminobutyric acid, valine, and asparagine as well as arginine and glutamic acid.

Iron deficiency in tobacco (507, 509, 530) similarly caused large increases in arginine, asparagine, and glutamine and in the appearance of the amine tyramine. There were also comparable decreases in alanine, γ-aminobutyric acid, glutamic acid, and proline. In *Mentha* (509) on the other hand, iron deficiency did not produce such striking effects, but there was a moderate increase in asparagine concentration (Fig. 62).*

Effects of boron deficiency on the accumulation of soluble nitrogen compounds in plants have been discussed already. Changes in specific compounds have been reported for tobacco (507, 509), in which especially large increases in concentrations of tyramine and asparagine, and notable decreases in γ-aminobutyric acid, α-alanine, serine, glutamic acid, and glycine were observed. Tso and McMurtrey (530) did not, however, observe the great increase in tyramine in boron-deficient tobacco, but there was a similarly great increase in asparagine, and in one series a decrease also in serine as reported by Steinberg *et al.* (507, 509).

The effects of potassium deficiency and its interrelationships with rubidium, sodium, and calcium on the soluble nitrogen fractions of barley and some other plants have been studied in detail by Richards and Berner (445), Coleman and Richards (79), Coleman and Hegarty (78), and Richards and Coleman (446). The gray lesions in potassium-deficient barley leaves were identically reproduced by feeding normal plants with the diamino compound putrescine, which had been identified chromatographically as the major product, comprising 0.2% of the dry weight, in potassium-deficient barley leaves (79, 446).

Richards and Berner (445) have made a survey, by semiquantitative paper chromatographic means, of the effects of various nutrient levels on the nonprotein nitrogen compounds of barley at different stages of its development. Two-directional paper chromatograms were made of the alcohol-soluble nitrogenous compounds and the various substances revealed on the paper by the ninhydrin reagent. The authors recorded their findings in the form of charts which represented in a numerical manner the intensity of the color of each spot as judged by visual means, prior to the more quantitative methods now available. Several interesting trends were observed in this general and pioneer survey of the problem.

---

* For a fuller account of the growth, metabolism, and nutrition of *Mentha*, see Memoir 379, New York State Agricultural Experiment Station, Cornell University, Ithaca, New York, 1962.

Potassium was supplied at three nutrient levels (K_1, K_3 and K_5 at relative concentrations of 1.0, $\frac{1}{9}$, $\frac{1}{81}$) in three types of nutrient solutions, namely one solution in which sodium accompanied nitrate and phosphate, one in which calcium was the cation, and another in which ammonium was the accompanying cation. Moreover, in the potassium-deficient solutions, this element was partially replaced by either sodium or rubidium. The following example explains the symbols which were used to designate these solutions. Ca:K_3Na designates the calcium type of solution at the potassium level K_3 and with Na to replace the monovalent cation up to the value of K_1. If the nutrient was based on Na or NH_4, these replaced Ca in the symbol. Moreover, if Rb supplemented K at the level of K_3 or K_5, this was indicated by Rb or rb depending on the high or low level of rubidium which was furnished. With these conventions in mind, the findings of Richards and Berner can be summarized as follows.

Potassium deficiency caused marked increases in concentrations of lysine in barley, when grown with ammonia or nitrate. In potassium-deficient treatments, sodium partially suppressed lysine production by plants grown with ammonia whereas rubidium at a low level suppressed lysine accumulation in the presence of nitrate and high calcium supply. Sodium did not produce this effect. The amides glutamine and asparagine increased markedly with lack of potassium at the expense of the corresponding glutamic and aspartic acids, probably owing to amidation following deamination of other amino acids and ammonia production or uptake. This effect was greater with CaK_3 and NH_4K_3 and less where sodium or rubidium was given (NaK_3, K_3rb). Arginine also accumulated, especially with nitrate nutrition and, to a lesser extent, when ammonium sulfate was given to potassium-deficient plants. Glycine, serine, leucine, tyrosine, and phenylalanine also increased in concentration in the deficient plants. The addition of rubidium or sodium, which are well known as partial substitutes for inadequate potassium (443, 444), mainly restored the abnormal amino pattern, but the effect of rubidium on aspartic and glutamic acids was less than that of sodium. Glutamic, aspartic, and γ-aminobutyric acids were increased, and glutamine, asparagine, arginine, valine, leucine, and threonine were decreased in concentration by these treatments. Both rubidium and sodium also suppressed the accumulation of an unknown substance, which was later identified as putrescine, under conditions of potassium deficiency, and this was related to their beneficial effect in preventing the appearance of the leaf lesions. When potassium deficiency was severe, rubidium had little beneficial effect and excess rubidium produced effects resembling those of low potassium in causing high levels of the amides (79, 445).

Study of the comparative physiology of barley, wheat, clover, and flax by Coleman and Richards (79) showed that potassium deficiency led to putrescine production, in barley especially. In clover, the putrescine which was produced was further metabolized to an unknown compound which was also accumulated. Barley appears to be devoid of amine oxidase whereas clovers at certain stages of growth contain a highly active system which oxidizes putrescine (267). Slight putrescine accumulation also occurred in wheat. In flax, however, neither putrescine nor the unidentified compound was detected in plants deficient in potassium. Freiburg and Steward (143b) observed an accumulation of putrescine in leaves of banana plants that were severely deficient in potassium. Putrescine may be produced from ornithine by decarboxylation (78). Proline appeared in potassium-deficient flax only with nitrate (CaK_3). Tyrosine appeared in wheat and barley with both nitrate and ammonia treatments. Flax appeared to show the least, and the cereals the greatest, changes with potassium supply. The different types of response produced by giving either lithium, sodium, potassium, or rubidium to potassium-deficient barley have also been reported (79). Each metal produced different effects in the over-all picture. The changes usually occurred more rapidly with potassium than with sodium or rubidium, especially with respect to the disappearance of putrescine, where lithium was the least effective. Lithium also appeared to cause an accumulation of asparagine whereas sodium caused a temporary increase followed by a decrease in asparagine.

Coleman and Hegarty (78) fed C^{14}-labeled ornithine to potassium-deficient barley and observed the production of labeled putrescine. In normal barley and white clover, ornithine was apparently converted to citrulline, arginine, and proline. These reactions may depend on phosphorylation reactions utilizing ATP. If so, the potassium requirement in pyruvic kinase, partially replaceable by rubidium, sodium, or ammonium ions, would be consistent with the observed effects of the deficiency. On the other hand, for a similar reason, amide accumulation should be impaired rather than increased. The incorporation of amino acids into protein, which depends on several nucleoside triphosphates and potassium (573) might have an overriding effect on all changes described, and a net amidation of ammonia might result.

Mulder (364) found that potassium deficiency increased the free tyrosine content of potato tubers by about threefold. Magnesium deficiency caused somewhat smaller increases, and deficiencies of phosphorus or of copper had little effect. There were no differences in amounts of protein-combined tyrosine. In general agreement with

Mulder's findings, Tso and McMurtrey (530) observed little difference in the proportions of several amino acids present in the 4 N HCl hydrolyzate of alcohol-insoluble nitrogen residues from tobacco leaves. In banana (143b), where tyrosine is a minor soluble nitrogen constituent,

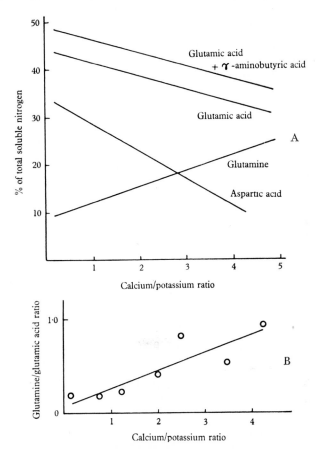

FIG. 61. Composition of the soluble nitrogen (A) and the ratio of glutamine to glutamic acid (B) in leaves of *Mentha piperita* L. grown under glass on long days and at high night temperature (70°F), as affected by the Ca:K ratio in the nutrient solution. Nitrogen as percentage of total soluble nitrogen. From Steward *et al.* (509).

deficiencies of potassium, magnesium, calcium, and phosphorus consistently decreased the small amounts normally present.

Steward *et al.* (509) (Fig. 61) showed that an increase in the calcium:potassium ratio in *Mentha piperita* caused an increase both in the ratio of glutamine to glutamic acid and of glutamine as a proportion of total soluble nitrogen under both long-day and short-day conditions. Glutamic and aspartic acids decreased with increasing calcium: potassium ratios. Calcium deficiency was associated with an increased concentration of proline under both long and short days, of asparagine under long days, and of glutamine under short days. Potassium deficiency produced a glutamine:asparagine ratio of about 0.15:1 with short days and of about 3:1 with long days; total soluble nitrogen was increased about eightfold under short days. Tso and McMurtrey (530) found that accumulation of asparagine and loss of proline were the outstanding changes associated with potassium deficiency in tobacco. Glutamine did not show a consistent effect. Calcium deficiency produced effects similar to those of potassium deficiency.

The effects of macronutrient deficiencies of phosphorus, potassium, magnesium, and calcium on the concentrations of soluble nitrogen compounds in banana (*Musa acuminata* 'Gros Michel') leaves was studied in great detail by Freiberg and Steward (143b). Potassium deficiency effects were outstanding in leading to pronounced glutamine accumulation before visible symptoms were produced, and when severe, glutamine accounted for 24% of the total soluble nitrogen compounds that reacted with ninhydrin as compared with about 1.3% in normal leaves. Deficient leaves contained between 40 and 70 times as much glutamine as the normal leaves on a fresh-weight basis. Glutamic acid, asparagine, serine, and pipecolic acid increased notably in the later stages of potassium deficiency whereas, alanine, γ-aminobutyric acid, and proline, and to a lesser extent valine, decreased in terms of proportions of total soluble nitrogen but not as concentrations in fresh weight, except for proline where the decrease was striking at this stage but was not observed in early stages. Potassium deficiency also produced previously unreported changes in ureido compounds in banana leaves (143b). Allantoin appeared exclusively in older leaves of potassium-deficient plants, in which deficiency was more advanced, and was not seen in any other treatments; the appearance of allantoin was associated with a decrease in the concentrations of allantoic acid. Calcium deficiency in banana produced few changes of any magnitude, the main one being an increase in glutamic acid in young and old leaves, in glycine in old leaves, and an increase in young leaves but a decrease in older leaves in amounts of glutamine. Proline also decreased especially in young leaves. As in *Mentha* (509), therefore, a decreased calcium:potassium ratio increased glutamic acid content, but the effects of calcium deficiency on proline content were reversed in the two different plants.

Changes in the amino acid pattern due to magnesium deficiency were described by Mulder and Bakema (367) and Sheldon et al. (469). In

potato tubers, magnesium deficiency led to an accumulation of asparagine and, to lesser extents, of arginine, threonine, leucine, and phenylalanine, whereas glutamic acid, alanine, and γ-aminobutyric acid were
decreased. In lucerne, magnesium deficiency caused a decrease in
tryptophan concentration, and in the sulfur-containing amino acid,
methionine. Magnesium deficiency did not produce striking effects in
Mentha (509), except for an increase under short days in the gluta-
mine:asparagine ratio from about 1.5:1 to about 15:1, whereas their
sum increased only about 20% (Fig. 62). In tobacco, Tso and McMurtrey (530) observed an increase in proline and asparagine and a decrease in serine in one series with severe deficiency, but not in another,
with moderate deficiency. Magnesium deficiency in banana (143b) produced an outstanding increase in the usually negligible concentrations
of pipecolic acid which then accounted for 13–17% of the total soluble amino acid nitrogen of the leaf. Aspartic acid also increased, especially in older leaves, whereas glutamine increased in young leaves.
Glutamic acid decreased in young leaves but greatly increased in older
leaves. γ-Aminobutyric acid and alanine decreased in young leaves.
Freiberg and Steward (143b) pointed out that lysine disappeared as
pipecolic acid increased, and they drew attention to the possible conversion of lysine to pipecolic acid by ring closure. The normal amounts
of lysine were, however, much less than the abnormal amounts of
pipecolic acid.

The effects of phosphorus deficiency on free amino acids in alfalfa
(lucerne) were studied by Gleites and Parker (158). There were increases in concentrations of asparagine, glutamine, and arginine and
decreases in those of glutamic acid and proline. In *Mentha* (509)
changes were not marked, but lysine and valine increased somewhat
under short days, and asparagine increased under long days (Fig. 62).
Tso and McMurtrey (530) found that phosphorus deficiency increased
the concentration of glutamine and asparagine in one series, and decreased that of glutamine in the other series, but produced no other
notable changes. In banana (143b) phosphorus deficiency produced
large increases in aspartic and glutamic acids and glutamine in young
and older leaves, the change in glutamine being tenfold. Alanine
and γ-aminobutyric acid decreased in young and older leaves, whereas
asparagine and valine concentrations decreased in older leaves only.
Citrulline increased in both young and older leaves, but arginine and
threonine increased only in older leaves, where deficiency effects were
more acute.

The comparative effects of sulfur deficiency on soluble nitrogen
fractions of several plants were recorded by Coleman (77) by methods

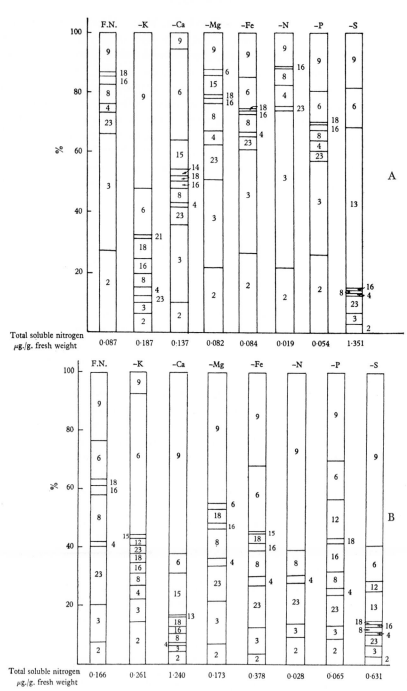

Fig. 62. Composition of the soluble nitrogen leaves of *Mentha piperita* L. grown

similar to those of Richards and Berner (445). There were marked increases in the concentrations of glycine and serine in white clover (*Trifolium repens*), flax, tomato, barley, and *Desmodium uncinatum*. Arginine also increased in all species except barley. Glutamine and asparagine increased in all species, and glutamic acid decreased in flax. In the legumes the main effect of sulfur deficiency was to produce an increase in asparagine, and in tomato there was an increase mainly in glutamine; both increased markedly in barley. Citrulline was observed to accumulate in sulfur-deficient flax. Merz and Matsumoto (341) and Merz *et al.* (342) described effects of sulfur deficiency on the amino acid content of alfalfa. Aspartic acid increased from 1.2 to 12.9% of dry matter, and arginine content was doubled; concentrations of glutamic acid, histidine, isoleucine, and tryptophan were halved; and that of methionine was reduced to one-third of the level in normal plants. Changes were much greater in stems than in leaves for aspartic and glutamic acids and methionine, but were greater in leaves for arginine. Giving sulfur to deficient plants decreased arginine and aspartic acid and increased especially methionine, threonine, and tryptophan. The electrophoretic patterns of the leaf proteins were also significantly altered in proportions by the level of sulfur nutrition. Sheldon *et al.* (470) observed large increases in methionine content on giving sulfate to alfalfa (lucerne), soybean, and Sudan grass (*Sorghum sudanense*). Sulfur deficiency in *Mentha* (509) produced a striking increase in arginine level under long days, whereas under short days glutamine showed the principal increase. The increase in the total of glutamine, asparagine, and arginine was, however, the outstanding effect of sulfur deficiency (Fig. 62) but there were also decreases in glutamic and γ-aminobutyric acids. Sulfur deficiency decreased proline and increased asparagine in tobacco, according to Tso and McMurtrey (530). Tisdale *et al.* (524) found that the relative ability to synthesize methionine and cystine by two clonal strains of alfalfa differed when compared over a range of increasing sulfur supply. The decrease in arginine associated with recovery from sulfur deficiency was dependent on light, while in darkness asparagine was produced (Fig. 63).

Freney *et al.* (144) found that chlorine deficiency also caused characteristic accumulation of several amino acids in cauliflower and cab-

---

under glass, on long or short days and at high night temperature (70°F), with full nutrient and various mineral deficiencies. Key to numbers on histograms as in Fig. 60. Nitrogen of each amino acid expressed as percentage of total soluble nitrogen. (A) long days; (B) short days. From Steward *et al.* (509).

bage (Table XXII). Arginine increased outstandingly in both species and proline, methioninesulfoxide, glutamine, and asparagine and several others also increased to lesser relative, or absolute, extents. Aspartic acid showed no appreciable change or decrease. γ-Aminobutyric acid,

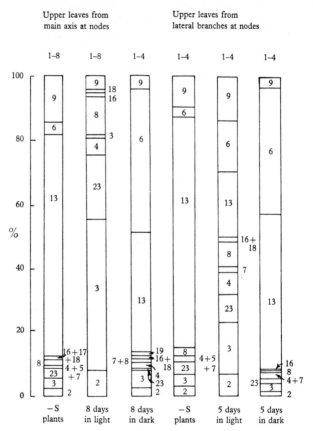

Fig. 63. Composition of the soluble nitrogen of leaves on the main axis and lateral branches of *Mentha piperita* L. subject to sulfur deficiency and subsequent recovery in light and dark following addition of sulfur. Nodes numbered in basipetal succession. Nitrogen as percentage of total soluble nitrogen. Key to numbers in Fig. 60. From Steward *et al.* (509).

which increased with manganese deficiency (222, 582) also showed little change.

The observations described above show that mineral deficiencies result in large changes in the composition of the soluble nitrogen fractions and often lead to large increases in the concentrations of many amino compounds. It is evident that the effects differ where studied in different plants, and, subject to the very important factors inherent in different experimental conditions, emphasized by Steward et al. (509) (e.g., Figs. 62, 63), appear to differ also for different deficiency conditions. It would be premature in the present state of knowledge to attempt to explain the reasons for all these complex changes and their differences. Marked accumulation of free amino compounds could result from impaired protein synthesis. Increased proteolysis might account for many of the changes observed. The different patterns associated

TABLE XXII

EFFECTS OF CHLORINE SUPPLY ON CONTENT OF FREE AMINO ACIDS OF CABBAGE AND CAULIFLOWER SHOOTS[a,b]

Amino compounds	Cabbage			Cauliflower		
	Cl	Minus Cl	Ratio	Plus Cl	Minus Cl	Ratio
Arginine	<1**	113	>113	29***	115	40
Proline	3***	150	50	32***	227	7.1
Methionine sulfoxide	<1**	29	>29	<3**	27	>9
Glutamine	99***	359	3.6	146**	494	3.4
Asparagine	36**	124	3.4	111**	230	2.1
Pipecolic acid	9	29	3.2	9**	40	4.4
Glycine	15*	36	2.4	24	35	1.5
Valine	21*	49	2.3	39***	92	2.4
Leucine	18	41	2.3	20**	66	3.3
Serine	63***	138	2.2	86**	189	2.2
α-Alanine	71*	154	2.2	109	210	1.9
Ethanolamine	19	41	2.2	33***	85	2.6
Threonine	32	67	2.1	50**	86	1.7
γ-Aminobutyric acid	43	62	1.4	59	69	1.2
Glutamic acid	116	163	1.4	149	162	1.1
Aspartic acid	50	44	0.9	60	64	1.1

[a] From Freney et al. (144).
[b] Results as micrograms of amino acid per gram (fresh weight) of shoots. *, **, *** = Significantly different at 10, 5, or 1%, respectively.

with species or nutritional condition might reflect secondary effects of differences in other metabolic systems interacting with amino acid and amide nitrogen radicles, e.g., transamination, decarboxylation, oxidation, etc. It is possible that accumulation or depletion of certain essential amino acids might exert effects on the qualitative composition of proteins as observed by Schütte and Schendel (459) in spite of other predominantly negative reports in this respect (364, 530), and possibly of certain enzymes. Naturally occurring amino acid analogs such as isoleucine may interfere in formation of adaptive malic enzyme synthesis by bacteria (26), and relationships between amino acid patterns and enzyme complement produced under conditions of a nutritional disorder merit consideration. Amino acids have also, as stated above, led to reproducible changes in leaf development, and such effects may be important in determining the symptoms of mineral deficiencies (503, 504, 589a).

D. Beneficial and Other Elements

Numerous observations suggest that certain elements produce beneficial effects on growth although attempts to demonstrate direct effects of their absence are rarely successful. Some examples of beneficial effects are described here. The mode of action may be viewed in several ways (206, 207, 209). In some instances the element, e.g., sodium or rubidium, may substitute in part for the functions of another element, potassium, and thereby produce beneficial effects at deficiency levels of the essential element. The success of the partially substituting element will depend on the extent to which the residual limiting amounts of the deficient element can fulfil functions which the alternative element cannot satisfy. A beneficial effect may occur when one element modifies the translocation or distribution of another which is in limited supply (250, 399).

Beneficial effects may also occur where there is no evidence of a partial deficiency of an essential element. In such cases four possibilities may be considered (209): (a) The beneficial element may be more efficient in a particular function than some other element which may be essential for other reasons. (b) The beneficial element may stimulate the production of a substance which has beneficial effects, either ecologically in relation to competition or symbiosis, or in a metabolic sense without evidence that it is strictly essential to the existence of the organism, e.g., cobalt requirement for symbiotic nitrogen fixation. (c) The beneficial element may antagonize the toxic effect of some other element, e.g., the effect of aluminum on copper toxicity. (d) The beneficial element may replace another whose action has been specifically inhibited, e.g., reversal by manganese (385a) of fluoride inhibition of the manganese-activated systems in which manganese can replace magnesium.

1. Alkali Metals

a. Sodium. The effects of sodium as a beneficial element were noted by Hellriegel and Willfarth about 1898 (187). Early culture experiments on the value of sodium in place of potassium were made by Hartwell, Wheeler, and Pember (184, 185). The effects of sodium as a nutrient for higher plants with special reference to potassium supply have been reviewed by Dorph-Petersen and Steenbjerg (113) and by

Lehr (284). Response to sodium depends on both the species and on the composition of the nutrient supply, especially the potassium level. Harmer *et al.* (180) classified several crop species into four groups. These were: (a) crops that benefit from sodium when potassium is deficient, e.g., alfalfa, barley, oat, tomato, Brussels sprouts, carrot; (b) crops that show little benefit under these conditions, e.g., corn, red clover, lettuce, onion (*Allium cepa*), potato; (c) crops that apparently benefit slightly when potassium is adequate, e.g., some brassicas, wheat, pea; (d) those that benefit greatly when potassium is adequate, e.g., celery, beet, turnip. Beet, as is well known, benefits greatly when potassium is deficient. Hartt (182) concluded that sodium had no beneficial effect at all for potassium-deficient sugar cane. Holt and Volk (232), Mullison and Mullison (369), Eaton (117a) concluded that sodium is beneficial for many plants including barley when adequate potassium is also provided. Lehr (285, 286) concluded that sodium nitrate was superior to calcium nitrate for beet at all levels of potassium fertilization. In summarizing the results of seven years of field trials, Lehr (288) reported that oats responded to sodium only at the nil potassium level, whereas potato, beet, turnip, ryegrass (*Lolium perenne*), lupine, and flax (290) responded to sodium at added levels of potassium, but in decreasing degrees with increasing amounts of potassium. Subsequently Lehr (289) concluded that oats were also benefited by sodium in the presence of potassium. Lehr concluded that sodium could substitute in part for potassium in spinach (287) and up to seven-eighths of the potassium needs of barley (291). Sugar beets grown without sodium have dark, dull green foliage. The laminae are limp and plants often wilt during hot weather. Leaf margins develop dark brown necrosis and scorch. Petioles wilt and collapse as in potassium deficiency, but do not show dark brown lesions. Plants grown without either sodium or potassium are very severely stunted. Leaves are small and thin. The color is dark green and lusterless. Older leaves show marginal paling and bronze or purple tints, followed by dark brown marginal scorching and withering.

Brownell and Wood (55) have produced convincing evidence that, for certain plants, e.g., *Atriplex vesicaria*, sodium behaves as an essential micronutrient. When great care was taken to eliminate sodium from the reagents and the water supply, there was a great decrease in growth to less than one-tenth of that of the plants given sodium. Symptoms of a physiological disorder were also observed. These were prevented by the addition of 0.1 meq sodium per liter (2.3 ppm sodium). There seems to be little doubt that a specific sodium requirement exists for this species.

The sparing action of sodium observed with potassium deficiency may also occur under conditions of calcium deficiency in certain circumstances which may be related to potassium nutrition. Joham (250) found that calcium deficiency in cotton plants grown in sand or water cultures led to acute wilting and leaf shedding, but that these symptoms were eliminated by including in the nutrient solution 10 meq of sodium per liter. The addition of sodium under low potassium conditions restored fruiting to normal levels, and under low calcium conditions extra sodium increased fruiting from 4 to 40% of the complete nutrient values. Analysis of the plants revealed that with calcium deficiency the fruit bolls had 0.8 meq of potassium and 0.16 meq of calcium, whereas with extra sodium these values increased to 3.9 and 0.78, respectively, i.e., by about fivefold. On the other hand, the total potassium and calcium content of the plants was not changed by sodium, which had apparently exerted its effects by encouraging the translocation of calcium and potassium from leaves and stems into the fruit bolls.

Williams (584) reported that sodium greatly increased the growth of the halophyte *Halogeton glomeratus*, a poisonous plant which accumulates oxalic acid. The oxalic acid content was directly related to sodium supply which also prevented incipient wilting. Sodium chloride was also superior to the sulfate or nitrate, and yields were increased fivefold over basal values by giving 0.1 M sodium chloride.

b. Rubidium. Richards (443, 444) reviewed early work on the effects of rubidium and studied the effects of rubidium on the growth pattern of barley under different conditions of potassium, phosphorus, and nitrogen supplies. Three effects were distinguished: (a) Rubidium had a direct toxic effect at high concentrations, which led initially to the production of dark green, abnormally wide leaves. These were brittle, excessively twisted and had prominent midribs. Leaf shape and color changed abruptly after some weeks, and later leaves were graygreen and very short and narrow. Tillering was excessive, and up to 100 tillers were produced by a single plant. (b) Rubidium was particularly beneficial when potassium levels were low, and a partial replacement of potassium by rubidium was inferred. This beneficial effect was particularly evident at the high phosphorus level. (c) It was concluded that an antagonism with phosphorus, which counteracted phosphorus excess, was the third effect of rubidium. Richards also suggested that rubidium could function similarly to potassium with respect to the conversion of ammonia nitrogen to nontoxic products. This point is considered again.

Rubidium increased the net assimilation rate at low potassium levels.

Rubidium increased the number of ears, but had a complex effect on grain formation. At low potassium or low phosphorus levels, rubidium increased sterility; but at medium or high potassium levels with high phosphorus or with ammonia nitrogen, rubidium increased the production of fertile grain. Rubidium decreased water content. Rubidium often initially decreased tillering, but effects were reversed with age: tillering was always finally increased, unless depression of phosphorus uptake to deficiency levels had occurred, when tillering was decreased.

c. *Biochemical functions.* The beneficial effects of sodium and rubidium under conditions of potassium deficiency are partly explained by recent biochemical studies. Thus Miller and Evans (349) and McCollum *et. al.* (329), have shown that rubidium or sodium can replace potassium, which is required in addition to magnesium or manganese in the widespread pyruvic kinase enzyme of higher plants. Latzko (282) showed that rubidium can replace potassium, but with decreased efficiency, in photosynthetic phosphorylation. Injurious effects of rubidium (444), on the other hand, may be related to the toxic effect of rubidium on protein synthesis in cell-free microsomal preparations from peas as studied by Webster (573), who has also found a potassium requirement for protein synthesis. Richards and Berner (445) showed that the beneficial effects of rubidium or sodium under conditions of potassium deficiency in barley were at least partly due to the ability of these elements to prevent the production or accumulation of putrescine. The abnormal pattern of amino acid concentrations caused by potassium deficiency was also largely corrected by rubidium or sodium, whereas excess rubidium reproduced some of the effects of potassium deficiency. The effects of rubidium or potassium in promoting the conversion of ammonia nitrogen to harmless products, as earlier concluded by Richards (442a, 444), can now be understood in terms of amino acid metabolism. The generation of adenosine triphosphate, which is essential for amino acid activation, protein synthesis, and amide synthesis from ammonia, would be impaired by depression of the pyruvic kinase system. The extent to which this enzyme system contributes to total ATP production is not known, but it may be considerable.

Further insight into the interrelationships between potassium, rubidium, and sodium is provided by recent work of Hiatt and Evans (226) on the acetic thiokinase system of higher plants. This enzyme which catalyzes the reversible pyrophosphorylation: acetate $+$ ATP $+$ CoA $\rightleftharpoons$ acetyl CoA $+$ AMP $+$ pyrophosphate, resembles pyruvic kinase in requiring a divalent ion (magnesium or manganese) in addition to a monovalent cation (potassium or rubidium or ammonium). These are of equal effectiveness at comparable concentrations of 4×10^{-2} M.

The interesting point here is the failure of sodium to replace potassium, and this may explain the fact that sodium may partly replace potassium (i.e., in pyruvic kinase), but not wholly (i.e., not at all in acetic thiokinase). Failure of rubidium wholly to replace potassium may lie in the rubidium inhibition of protein synthesis already noted or in its failure to produce integrated optimal rates when several different enzymes are affected.

2. Strontium

Walsh (557) reviewed earlier work regarding the value of strontium for higher plants and concluded that beneficial effects had been observed under conditions of low calcium supply. Oats growing in a neutral soil which did not respond to calcium carbonate were slightly benefited by strontium carbonate. In an acid soil of pH 4.5, with a lime requirement of 2 tons per acre, three successive crops of mustard were obtained by using 3 tons per acre of strontium carbonate, and growth was nearly equal to that obtained with lime. In the absence of either, the crops failed and with barium carbonate or sodium carbonate they also failed. Strontium carbonate replaced calcium carbonate for straw production, but not for grain formation, in oats grown in a sand-peat mixture, and here, strontium increased the calcium content of the straw. A similar effect was observed with wheat straw and grain. The increased calcium level produced, however, was still below that present in low calcium treatments, and the stimulation of calcium uptake would not appear wholly to explain the beneficial effect of strontium. It is possible, nevertheless, that differences in calcium distribution which were not revealed by the analyses, were also involved, as appeared for effects of bromine on chlorine distribution (399) or of sodium on calcium (250). Growth of barley was markedly improved by strontium in the absence of calcium with respect to straw but not to grain: there was no increase in calcium content in barley given strontium. Toxic effects of strontium were also observed in the form of dark green foliage, free tillering, and delayed maturation. Whereas calcium carbonate provides both calcium and a neutralizing function, strontium carbonate may function only in the latter respect in acid soils. Mevius (343, 344) found that strontium was able partially to replace calcium in plants such as *Onobrychis sativa*, which has a high calcium requirement.

3. Cobalt

Evidence that cobalt is essential for higher plants is still lacking, but symptoms observed by Maskell *et al.* (324) in cocoa (*Theobroma cacao*) grown in water culture from which cobalt was omitted, merit description. Young leaves were pale and mid-shoot leaves showed a diffuse chlorosis distinct in character from any produced by effects of other mineral deficiencies. Old leaves produced a severe but localized marginal scorch. This appeared suddenly and leaves turned yellow and dropped almost immediately. Inclusion of cobalt in the nutrient or injection of cobalt chloride resulted in normal plants or marked recovery in young leaves. It is not clear whether the possible effects of chloride deficiency can be excluded owing to the use of cobalt chloride, but the maritime environment would make this explanation seem unlikely.

A beneficial effect of cobalt given at 0.005 ppm to *Hevea* grown in purified sand cultures has also been reported by Bolle-Jones and Mallikarjuneswara in terms of increased stem height (40). Reinert and White (438) concluded that cobalt as B_{12} was required for the growth of excised tumor tissues from *Picea glauca* when cultured *in vitro*.

Cobalt apparently affects cell expansion as judged by the expansion of leaf disks from etiolated pea and bean and elongation of etiolated plumular hooks on *Avena* coleoptiles (345, 346, 522) (Fig. 64). The effect of cobalt in *Avena* was optimal at approximately $3 \times 10^{-5} M$, i.e., 2 ppm, and at $3 \times 10^{-3} M$ in pea; the effects of light and cobalt were additive. Cobalt chloride markedly increased the elongation of etiolated pea stem sections when given with indoleacetic acid and sucrose, but was inhibitory with acetate. Manganese had a similar effect at a higher level in pea. As cobalt and manganese are alternative activators for some dissociable enzyme systems (207, 209), it is possible that the observed effects and similarity between the elements were due to stimulation by either in some enzyme system from which manganese had been leached during immersion of the cut tissues. Elimination of peroxide accumulation might also result. A biochemical basis for a function of cobalt is provided in some aspects of amide metabolism. Dénes (105) and Varner (538) have found that cobalt modifies the optical specificity *in vitro* of the glutamotransferase and synthetase systems of pigeon liver and pea seed. Thus, whereas magnesium activation permits the synthesis of comparable amounts of both D- and L-hydroxamate, cobalt favors almost entirely the synthesis of the L isomer. Varner (539) has further found that the synthesis of glutamine itself is similarly directed in favor of the natural L isomer of cobalt. The optimal concentration for cobalt is much less than that of magnesium, and cobalt is the more efficient metal (104). It may, therefore, have a beneficial function in this important aspect of metabolism.

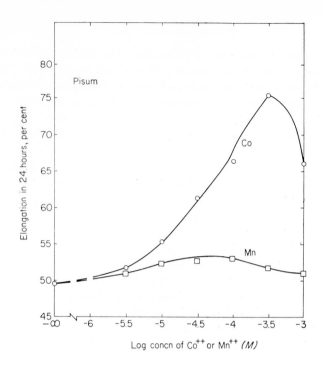

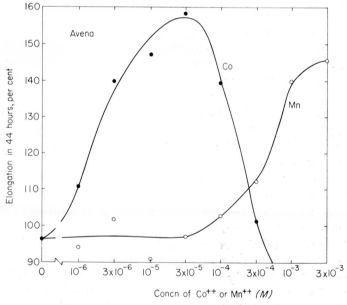

Fig. 64. Effects of cobalt or manganese on elongation of pea stem or *Avena* coleoptile sections in the presence of sucrose and indoleacetic acid. From Thimann (522).

Ahmed and Evans (6, 7) observed a profound effect of cobalt in inorganic form or as B_{12} on the growth of soybean that is dependent on symbiotic nitrogen fixation. Yields were increased 50% by 0.005 ppm cobalt, and symptoms of apparent nitrogen deficiency appeared when cobalt was omitted. A function of cobalt in *Rhizobium* metabolism may be involved, but some aspect of amide metabolism

O.I PPB CO   O CO

Fig. 65. Effects of cobalt supply on growth of soybean (*Glycine max*) plants in nutrient culture when dependent on atmospheric nitrogen. Photograph by courtesy of Dr. H. Evans.

might also be concerned. The nodules of the plants given 0.05 ppm cobalt contained 519 mμg per gram fresh weight of a B_{12} type of compound, whereas those deprived of cobalt contained 0.13 mμg per gram. Plants given 0.001 ppm cobalt in inorganic form or as B_{12} contained 0.65 and 7.8 mμg per gram of B_{12}-type compounds, respectively (7). In later experiments with soybean grown with atmospheric nitrogen, Ahmed and Evans (7a) were able to decrease yields to less than 10% of the values produced in the presence of 0.0001 ppm of cobalt (Fig. 65).

There was little difference between yields at this level and at 0.001 ppm cobalt. B_{12} levels were increased from 0.3 to 0.7 mμg per gram of nodule when cobalt was given at 0.0001 ppm and further increased to 2.8 mμg per gram at the 0.001 ppm level. Hemoglobin was increased from 115 to 162 μg per gram and to 178 μg per gram, respectively, over the same range. When fixed nitrogen as nitrate was given, no response whatsoever to cobalt could be detected; Ahmed and Evans concluded that the requirement, if any, under these conditions is extremely low and may be less than 0.000001 ppm. Reisenauer (439) similarly observed an outstanding effect of cobalt on nitrogen fixation and growth by lucerne dependent on rhizobial action. Delwiche et al. (102) concluded that the effect of cobalt, which could be detected in 2 hours in terms of $N_2{}^{15}$ fixation by excised Medicago root nodules, was on the fixation process, not on increasing the growth of the rhizobia. Hallsworth et al. (176) found that cobalt stimulated nitrogen fixation by subterranean clover. Bond and Hewitt (40b) have described comparable results showing a pronounced effect of cobalt on nitrogen fixation in Alnus and Casuarina.

4. Selenium

Trelease and Trelease (526) and Levine (295) concluded that a few parts per million of selenium were beneficial for the growth of Astragalus racemosus (Table XXIII), A. pattersonii, white lupine (Lupinus albus), and timothy grass (Phleum pratense). Many species of Astragalus flourish on seleniferous soils. Miller and Byers (350) showed that some species, e.g., A. racemosus and A. bisulcatus, accumulate over 1000 ppm selenium (see Table XXIII) whereas others, e.g., A. missouriensis, contain only about 1–5 ppm when grown under similar soil conditions. Selenium can replace sulfur in analogs of certain amino acids, e.g., selenomethionine or selenocystine found in tenmarq wheat by Schwarz and Folz (461), but no essential role for selenium has yet been identified in higher plants. The data of Table XXIII also illustrate the antagonism between selenium as selenite and sulfate. Selenium nutrition in higher plants and animals has been reviewed by Shrift (473b).

5. Aluminum

Aluminum is notable for its toxic effects, many of which may account for the injury shown by certain plants when grown in acid soils (194, 195, 199, 335). There have, however, been reports that aluminum is directly beneficial, or necessary, for higher plants, especially for cereals as in the experiments by Mazé (325, 326), Stoklasa (514),

TABLE XXIII

Influence of Selenium on Dry Yields of *Astragalus racemosus* Grown in
Solutions at pH 5.2 with Different Selenium and Sulfur Concentrations.
Culture Period: October 21, 1937, to January 9, 1938[a]

Solution[b]		Dry weight per culture of 5 plants (gm)	Ratio to yield of Se-free control[c]	Se content of plants (ppm)
Se (ppm)	S (ppm)			
0	0	2.17	—	T[d]
0	0	2.28	—	T[d]
0	27	1.91	—	T[d]
0	81	2.16	—	T[d]
0	243	1.83	—	T[d]
0	729	1.65	—	T[d]
0	2187	0.73	—	T[d]
1	0	2.37	1.09	360
1	3	3.38	1.48	258
1	9	3.83	1.68	166
1	27	2.89	1.51	177
3	0	1.79	0.82	609
3	9	3.06	1.34	466
3	27	3.56	1.86	319
3	81	3.53	1.63	419
9	0	1.84	0.85	1413
9	27	2.96	1.55	1221
9	81	4.02	1.86	953
9	243	2.20	1.20	939
27	0	1.36	0.63	3345
27	81	1.67	0.77	1386
27	243	2.78	1.52	1361
27	729	1.99	1.21	1265
81	0	0.36	0.17	3624
81	243	0.44	0.24	3023
81	729	0.40	0.24	2429
81	2187	0.14	0.19	2098

[a] From Trelease and Trelease (526).
[b] All solutions contained: 0.001 M KH$_2$PO$_4$, 0.005 M KNO$_3$, 0.002 M Ca(NO$_3$)$_2$, 0.003 M NH$_4$NO$_3$, 0.001 M MgCl$_2$, 0.00005 M Fe(NO$_3$)$_3$, K-citrate, 15 ml per liter of S-free microtrophic stock (Trelease and Trelease, 1935). Selenium was added as sodium selenite (Na$_2$SeO$_3$) and sulfur as sodium sulfate (Na$_2$SO$_4$ 10 H$_2$O). With each selenium concentration the sulfur:selenium ratios were 0, 3, 9, and 27.
[c] The ratios are between yields of selenium cultures and selenium-free controls receiving the same concentration of sulfur in parts per million.
[d] T = very low—considered as little more than zero.

Sommer (488), Lipman (298) and others reviewed by McLean and Gilbert (335). In Sommer's work (488) there was a remarkable effect on germination and growth of millet seed saved from plants grown with different amounts of aluminum but no other trace elements.

Indirect effects of aluminum, as a counteracting influence against the toxic effects of copper, have also been observed (296), and these may be analogous to the interactions of cobalt and manganese (5). It is not possible from the early experiments to decide whether such an antagonism may account for this apparently beneficial effect of aluminum. Chenery (75) reviewed reports on the apparent essential or beneficial effects of aluminum and concluded that tea, which accumulates high concentrations of aluminum, definitely requires this element. He observed that severe chlorosis induced in tea that was growing in alkaline soil was corrected by injections of aluminum, but there was scarcely any response to iron. Aluminum accumulators which may contain over 40,000 ppm of aluminum in dry matter (74) are not injured by the uptake or supply of the element. The effect of aluminum on flower color in *Hydrangea macrophylla* (74) is a special case where great accumulation of aluminum occurs in plants on acid, aluminum-containing soils, but not in neutral or alkaline soils.

6. Silicon

Many plants contain silica in their ash and possibly in special organs such as the stinging hairs of nettle (*Urtica dioica*). Isolated reports by Mazé (325), Lipman (298), Sommer (488), Raleigh (422, 423), and Wagner (545) record apparently the effects of omission of silicon from nutrient solutions used to grow several species. There was, however, the possibility that other elements, including molybdenum, were also lacking, as they were not purposely included in the nutrient, or that colloidal phenomena in the presence of silica gel were involved. The account by Wagner (545) was particularly extensive, and rice (*Oryza sativa*) and gherkin (*Cucumis sativus*) appeared to be the most sensitive of several species tested and were the only ones to show symptoms. Yields, however, were also decreased notably for all the others. Williams and Vlamis (583) concluded that soluble silicates decreased manganese toxicity by preventing necrosis due to its localized accumulation in leaves of barley grown in water culture, without altering the total manganese uptake. The effect of silicates on copper excess has not been tested, but it is noteworthy that Wagner gave 0.5 ppm copper in water cultures—a high level by present standards. Most of the earlier experiments on silicon were, however, quite inconclusive by satisfactory criteria of micronutrient investigation and cannot now be regarded as reliable evidence of a silicon requirement.

The deposition of silica takes various forms in different plant species. Lanning et. al. (281) found silica present as opal in *Sorghum vulgare* (*S. subglabrescens*), wheat, sunflower, maize, and a species of bamboo, and as α-quartz also in *Lantana camara*. In maize and sorghum, regular dumbell-shaped silica residues remained after ashing leaves, as well as rectangular and irregular silica deposits, and these occurred on all epidermal cell walls. There was by contrast no deposition of silica on cell walls or the formation of regular residues in dicotyledons. Silica in the skeleton structure of diatoms is of course familiar.

7. Other Elements

a. Germanium. Skok (477) concluded that germanium was beneficial to sunflower when grown deficient in boron. Symptoms of boron deficiency were delayed 5–6 days by germanium, but total replacement was not possible. The effect of germanium was considered to be related to the similar properties of the two elements in relation to complex formation.

b. Fluorine. Organic compounds of fluorine are known to occur in some African species. Marais (320) discovered fluoroacetic acid as a natural constituent of *Dichapetalum cymosum* ("Gifblaar") and Peters *et al.* (405) identified fluoro-oleic acid in *D. toxicarium* (ratsbane). Presumably fluoroacetate can be metabolized into fatty acids in these species in a manner analogous to the normal metabolism of acetate. Peters (404) reports that *D. cymosum* may contain 60–235 μg of fluorine per gram, and Marais found 150 μg per gram dry weight. Mazé (326) once concluded that fluorine and iodine were beneficial to maize in water cultures, and iodine is considered desirable in nutrient media used to grow excised roots (White, 579a, b).

REFERENCES

1. Agarwala, S. C., and Hewitt, E. J. Molybdenum as a plant nutrient III. The interrelationships of molybdenum and nitrate supply in the growth and molybdenum content of cauliflower plants grown in sand culture. *J. Hort. Sci.* 29, 278–290 (1954).
2. Agarwala, S. C., and Hewitt, E. J. Molybdenum as a plant nutrient IV. The interrelationships of molybdenum and nitrate supply in chlorophyll and ascorbic acid fractions in cauliflower plants grown in sand culture. *J. Hort. Sci.* 29, 291–300 (1954).
3. Agarwala, S. C., and Hewitt, E. J. Molybdenum as a plant nutrient V. The interrelationships of molybdenum and nitrate supply in the concentrations

of sugars, nitrate and organic nitrogen in cauliflower plants grown in sand culture. *J. Hort. Sci.* **30**, 151–162 (1955).

4. Agarwala, S. C., and Hewitt, E. J. Molybdenum as a plant nutrient VI. The effect of molybdenum supply on the growth and composition of cauliflower plants given different sources of nitrogen supply in sand culture. *J. Hort. Sci.* **30**, 163–180 (1955).

5. Ahmed, M. B., and Twyman, E. S. Relative toxicity of manganese and cobalt to and tomato plant. *J. Exptl. Botany* **4**, 164–172 (1953).

6. Ahmed, S., and Evans, H. J. The effect of cobalt on the growth of soybeans in the absence of supplied nitrogen. *Biochem. Biophys. Research Comm.* **1**, 271–275 (1959).

7. Ahmed, S., and Evans, H. J. Cobalt: a micronutrient element for the growth of soybean plants under symbiotic conditions. *Soil Sci.* **90**, 205–210 (1960).

7a. Ahmed, S., and Evans, H. J. The essentiality of cobalt for soybean plants grown under symbiotic conditions. *Proc. Natl. Acad. Sci. U.S.* **47**, 24–36 (1961).

7b. Albert, L. S., and Wilson, C. M. Effect of boron on elongation of tomato root tips. *Plant Physiol.* **36**, 244–251 (1961).

8. Alexander, T. R. Anatomical and physiological responses of squash to various levels of boron supply. *Botan. Gaz.* **103**, 475–491 (1942).

8a. Anderson, A. J. Molybdenum as a fertilizer. *Advances in Agron.* **8**, 163–202 (1956).

9. Anderson, A. J. The role of molybdenum in plant nutrition. *In* "Inorganic Nitrogen Metabolism" (W. D. McElroy and B. Glass, eds.), pp. 3–58. Johns Hopkins Univ. Press, Baltimore, Maryland, 1956.

10. Anderson, A. J., and Spencer, D. Molybdenum in nitrogen metabolism of legumes and non-legumes. *Australian J. Sci. Research* **133**, 414–430 (1950).

11. Anderson, A. J., and Spencer, D. Sulphur in nitrogen metabolism of legumes and non-legumes. *Australian J. Sci. Research* **133**, 431–449 (1950).

12. Anderson, A. J., and Thomas, M. P. Plant responses to molybdenum as a fertilizer I. Molybdenum and symbiotic nitrogen fixation. *Australian Council Sci. and Ind. Research, Bull.* **198**, 7–24 (1946).

13. Anderson, I., and Evans, H. J. Effect of manganese and certain other metal cations in isocitric dehydrogenase and malic enzyme activities in *Phaseolus vulgaris. Plant Physiol.* **31**, 22–28 (1956).

14. Anderssen, F. G. Chlorosis of deciduous fruit trees due to a copper deficiency. *J. Pomol. Hort. Sci.* **10**, 130–146 (1932).

15. Andreae, W. A. The photoinduced oxidation of manganous ions. *Arch. Biochem. Biophys.* **55**, 584–586 (1955).

16. Arnon, D. I. Ammonium and nitrate nitrogen nutrition of barley at different seasons in relation to hydrogen ion concentration, manganese, copper and oxygen supply. *Soil Sci.* **44**, 91–114 (1937).

16a. Arnon, D. I. Copper enzymes in isolated chloroplasts; polyphenolase in *Beta vulgaris. Plant Physiol.* **24**, 1–15 (1949).

17. Arnon, D. I. Chloroplasts and photosynthesis. *Brookhaven Symposia in Biol. No.* **11**, 181–235 (1958).

18. Arnon, D. I., and Stout, P. R. Molybdenum as an essential element for higher plants. *Plant Physiol.* **14**, 599–602 (1939).

18a. Arnon, D. I., and Wessel, G. Vanadium as an essential element for green plants. *Nature* **172**, 1039–1041 (1955).

19. Arnon, D. I., and Whatley, F. R. Is chloride a co-enzyme of photosynthesis? *Science* 110, 554–556 (1949).

20. Arnon, D. I., Whatley, F. R., and Allen, M. B. Assimulatory power in photosynthesis. Photosynthetic phosphorylation by isolated chloroplasts is coupled with TPN reduction. *Science* 127, 1026–1034 (1958).

21. Arnon, D. I., Whatley, F. R., and Allen, M. B. Triphosphopyridinenucleotide as a catalyst of photosynthetic phosphorylation. *Nature* 180, 182–185 (1957).

22. Ashby, E. Studies in the morphogenesis of leaves. I. An essay on leaf shape. *New Phytologist* 47, 153–176 (1948).

23. Askew, H. O. The boron status of fruit and leaves in relation to "Internal Cork" of apples in the Nelson district. *New Zealand J. Sci. Technol.* A 17, 388–391 (1935).

24. Askew, H. O., and Williams, W. R. L. Brown spotting of apricots, a boron deficiency disease. *New Zealand J. Sci. and Technol.* A21, 103–106 (1939).

25. Baker, J. E., Gauch, H. G., and Dugger, W. M., Jr. Effect of boron on the water relations of higher plants. *Plant Physiol.* 31, 89–94 (1956).

26. Ball, E., Humphries, J., and Shive, W. Some antagonisms between naturally occurring amino acids, peptides and keto acids in adaptive enzyme synthesis and growth. *Arch. Biochem. Biophys.* 73, 410–419 (1957).

27. Bamford, R. Changes in root tips of wheat and corn grown in nutrient solutions deficient in calcium. *Bull. Torrey Botan. Club* 58, 149–178 (1931).

28. Barnette, R. M., and Warner, J. D. A response of chlorotic corn plants to the application of zinc sulphate to the soil. *Soil Sci.* 39, 145–156 (1935).

28a. Baumeister, W. Hauptnährstoffe. *In* "Encyclopaedia of Plant Physiology" (W. Ruhland, ed.), Vol. IV, pp. 482–557. Springer, Berlin, 1958.

29. Bayer, E. Biologische und Chemische Wege zur Anreicherung von Spurenelementen. *Experientia* 12, 365–368 (1956).

29a. Bear, F. E., (Ed.). Symposium on molybdenum. *Soil Sci.* 81, 159–258 (1956).

30. Bear, F. E., (Ed.). Symposium on bicarbonates. *Soil Sci.* 89, 241–302 (1960).

30a. Becking, J. H. A requirement of molybdenum for the symbiotic nitrogen fixation in alder (*Alnus glutinosa* Gaertn.). *Plant and Soil* 15, 217–227 (1961).

31. Bennett, J. P. Iron in leaves. *Soil Sci.* 60, 91–105 (1945).

32. Bennet-Clark, T. A. Salt accumulation and mode of action of auxin; a preliminary hypothesis. *In* "Chemistry and Mode of Action of Plant Growth Substances" (R. L. Wain and F. Wightman, eds.), pp. 284–291. Butterworth, London, 1956.

32a. Benson, N. R., Degman, E. S., and Chmelir, I. C. Translocation and re-use of boron in broccoli. *Plant Physiol.* 36, 296–304 (1961).

33. Benzian, B., and Warren, R. G. Copper deficiency in Sitka spruce seedlings. *Nature* 178, 864–865 (1956).

34. Biddulph, O. The absorption and translocation of sulfur in red kidney beans. *Plant Physiol.* 31, 28–33 (1956).

35. Bledsoe, R. W., Comar, C. L., and Harris, H. S. Absorption of radio-active calcium by the peanut fruit. *Science* 109, 329–330 (1949).

36. Bolle-Jones, E. W. Production in potato of leaf symptoms observed in plants on acid soils together with associated tuber necrosis. *Nature* 167, 568–569 (1951).

37. Bolle-Jones, E. W. The interrelationships of iron and potassium in the potato plant. *Plant and Soil* 6, 129–173 (1955).

38. Bolle-Jones, E. W. Copper: its effects on the growth and composition of the rubber plant, *Hevea braziliensis*. *Plant and Soil* 9, 160–178 (1957).

39. Bolle-Jones, E. W., and Hilton, R. N. Zinc deficiency of *Hevea braziliensis* as a predisposing factor to *Oidium* infection. *Nature* 177, 619 (1956).

40. Bolle-Jones, E. W., and Mallikarjuneswara, V. R. A beneficial effect of cobalt on the growth of *Hevea braziliensis. Nature* 179, 738–739 (1957).

40a. Bond, G., and Hewitt, E. J. Molybdenum and the fixation of nitrogen in *Myrica* root nodules. *Nature* 190, 1033–1034 (1961).

40b. Bond, G., and Hewitt, E. J. Cobalt and the fixation of nitrogen by root nodules of *Alnus* and *Casuarina. Nature* 195, 94–95 (1962).

41. Bosemark, N. O. The influence of nitrogen on root development. *Physiol. Plantarum* 7, 497–502 (1954).

41a. Bould, C. Iron chelates in plant nutrition. *J. Sci. Food Agr.* 8, Suppl., S1–S5 (1957).

42. Bové J. Le rôle des ions chlorures en photosynthèse. *Bull. soc. franç. phys. veg.* 5, 193–199 (1959).

42a. Bowen, H. J. M. (U. K. Atomic Energy Authority). Private communication (1961).

43. Brady, N. C. The effect of period of calcium supply and mobility of calcium in the plant on peanut fruit filling. *Soil Sci. Soc. Am. Proc.* 12, 336–341 (1947).

44 Brandenburg, E. Über die Grundlagen der Boranwendung in der Landwirtschaft. *Phytopathol. Z.* 12, 1–112 (1939).

45. Brenchley, W. E., and Thornton, H. G. The relation between the development, structure and functioning of the nodules of *Vicia faba* as influenced by the presence or absence of boron in the nutrient medium. *Proc. Roy. Soc.* B98, 373–399 (1925).

46. Brennan, E. G., and Shive, J. W. Effect of calcium and boron nutrition of the tomato on the relation between these elements in the tissue. *Soil Sci.* 66, 65–75 (1948).

47. Briggs, G. E. Experimental researches on vegetable assimilation and respiration. XVI. The characteristics of subnormal photosynthetic activity resulting from a deficiency of nutrient salts. *Proc. Roy. Soc.* B94, 20–35 (1922).

48. Briggs, G. O. Effects of boron in the substrate on the rate of nitrate absorption and on nitrogen distribution in *Nasturtium. Plant Physiol.* 18, 415–432 (1943).

49. Brown, J. C. An evaluation of bicarbonate-induced iron chlorosis. *Soil Sci.* 89, 246–247 (1960).

49a. Brown, J. C., Holmes, R. S., and Tiffin, L. O. Iron chlorosis in soybeans as related to the genotype of rootstock. 3. Chlorosis susceptibility and reductive capacity at the root. *Soil Sci.* 91, 127–132 (1961).

50. Brown, L., and Wilson, C. C. Some effects of zinc on several species of *Gossypium* L. *Plant Physiol.* 27, 812–817 (1952).

51. Brown, R., and Possingham, J. V. Intracellular incorporation of iron[59] into the root cells of *Pisum. Nature* 180, 653–654 (1957).

52. Brown, R., and Possingham, J. V. Iron deficiency and the growth of pea roots. *Proc. Roy. Soc.* B147, 145–166 (1957).

53. Brown, S. A., Wright, D., and Neish, A. C. Studies of lignin biosynthesis using isotopic carbon. VII. The role of p-hydroxyphenylpyruvic acid. *Can. J. Biochem. and Physiol.* 37, 25–34 (1959).

54. Brown, T. E., Eyster, H. C., and Tanner, H. A. Physiological effects of manganese deficiency. *In* "Trace Elements" (C. A. Lamb, O. G. Bentley, and J. M. Beattie, eds.), pp. 135–155. Academic Press, New York, 1958.

55. Brownell, P. F., and Wood, J. G. Sodium as an essential element for *Atriplex vesicaria* (Heward). *Nature* 179, 635–636 (1957).

56. Broyer, T. C., Carlton, A. B., Johnson, C. M., and Stout, P. R. Chlorine—a micronutrient element for higher plants. *Plant Physiol.* **29**, 526–532 (1954).
57. Burrell, A. B. The boron deficiency disease of apple. *N.Y. Agr. Expt. Sta. Bull.* **428** (1940).
58. Burström, H. Über die Schwermetallkatalyse der Nitratassimilation. *Planta* **29**, 292–305 (1939).
59. Burström, H. Studies on growth and metabolism of roots. VIII. Calcium as a growth factor. *Physiol. Plantarum* **5**, 391–402 (1952).
60. Burström, H. Studies on growth and metbolism of roots. X. Investigations of the calcium effect. *Physiol. Plantarum* **7**, 332–343 (1954).
61. Burström, H., and Tullin, V. Observations on chelates and root growth. *Physiol. Plantarum* **10**, 406–417 (1957).
62. Camp, A. F., Chapman, H. D., Bahrt, G. M., and Parker, E. R. Symptoms of citrus malnutrition. *In* "Hunger Signs in Crops" (G. Hambidge, ed.), pp. 267–311. American Society of Agronomy and National Fertilizer Society, Washington, D.C., 1941.
63. Candela, M. I., Fisher, E. G., and Hewitt, E. J. Molybdenum as a plant nutrient. X. Some factors affecting the activity of nitrate reductase in cauliflower plants grown with different nitrogen sources and molybdenum levels in sand culture. *Plant Physiol.* **32**, 280–288 (1957).
64. Carlton, W. M. Some effects of zinc deficiency on the anatomy of the tomato. *Botan. Gaz.* **116**, 52–64 (1954).
65. Carr, D. J., and Ng, E. K. The sequestration of calcium from preparations of wheat coleoptile cell walls. *Physiol. Plantarum* **12**, 264–274 (1959).
66. Chandler, F. B. Mineral nutrition of the genus *Brassica* with special reference to boron. *Maine Agr. Expt. Sta. Bull.* **404**, 307–400 (1941).
67. Chandler, W. H. Zinc as a nutrient for plants. *Botan. Gaz.* **98**, 625–646 (1937).
68. Chandler, W. H., Hoagland, D. R., and Hibbard, P. L. "Little leaf" or rosette of fruit trees. *Proc. Am. Soc. Hort. Sci.* **28**, 556–560 (1931).
69. Chandler, W. H., Hoagland, D. R., and Hibbard, P. L. "Little leaf" or rosette of fruit trees. II. The effect of zinc and other treatments. *Proc. Am. Soc. Hort. Sci.* **29**, 255–263 (1932).
70. Chandler, W. H., Hoagland, D. R., and Hibbard, P. L. "Little leaf" or rosette of fruit trees. III. *Proc. Am. Soc. Hort. Sci.* **30**, 70–86 (1933).
71. Chandler, W. H., Hoagland, D. R., and Hibbard, P. L. "Little leaf" or rosette of fruit trees. IV. *Proc. Am. Soc. Hort. Sci.* **32**, 11–19 (1934).
72. Chapman, H. D., and Brown, S. M. The effects of sulfur deficiency on citrus. *Hilgardia* **14**, 185–201 (1941).
73. Chapman, H. D., Vanselow, A. P., and Liebig, G. F., Jr. The production of citrus mottle leaf in controlled nutrient cultures. *J. Agr. Research* **58**, 365–379 (1937).
74. Chenery, E. M. Are hydrangea flowers unique? *Nature* **158**, 240–241 (1946).
75. Chenery, E. M. A preliminary study of aluminum and the tea bush. *Plant and Soil* **6**, 174–200 (1955).
76. Clayton, E. E. Investigation of cauliflower diseases on Long Island. *N.Y. Agr. Expt. Sta. Bull.* **506** (1924).
77. Coleman, R. G. The effect of sulphur deficiency on the free amino acids of some plants. *Australian J. Biol. Sci.* **10**, 50–56 (1957).
78. Coleman, R. G., and Hegarty, N. P. Metabolism of DL ornithine 2^{14}C in normal and potassium deficient barley. *Nature* **179**, 376–377 (1957).

79. Coleman, R. G., and Richards, F. J. Physiological studies in plant nutrition. XVIII. Some aspects of nitrogen metabolism in barley and other plants in relation to potassium deficiency. *Ann. Botany (London)* [N.S.] **20**, 393–409 (1956).
80. Colwell, W. E. A biological method for determining the relative boron contents of soils. *Soil Sci.* **56**, 71–94 (1943).
81. Cooil, B. J. Potassium deficiency and excess in Guayule. II. Cation-anion balance in the leaves. *Plant Physiol.* **23**, 403–424 (1948).
82. Cooil, B. J., and Slattery, M. C. Effect of potassium deficiency and excess upon certain carbohydrate and nitrogenous constituents in Guayule. *Plant Physiol.* **23**, 425–442 (1948).
83. Cooper, H. P. Nutrient deficiency symptoms in cotton. *In* "Hunger Signs in Crops" (G. Hambidge, ed.), pp. 125–145. American Society of Agronomy and National Fertilizer Society, Washington, D.C., 1941.
84. Cormack, R. G. H. The development of root hairs in angiosperms. *Botan. Rev.* **15**, 583–612 (1949).
85. Cormack, R. G. H. Action of pectin enzymes on surface cells of living brassica roots. *Science* **122**, 1019–20 (1955).
86. Crooke, W. M. Further aspects of the relationship between nickel toxicity and iron supply. *Ann. Appl. Biol.* **43**, 465–476 (1956).
87. Crooke, W. M., Hunter, J. G., and Vergnano, O. The relationships between nickel toxicity and iron supply. *Ann. Appl. Biol.* **41**, 311–324 (1954).
88. Crooke, W. M., and Inkson, R. H. E. The relationship between nickel toxicity and major nutrient supply. *Plant and Soil* **6**, 1–15 (1955).
89. Crooke, W. M., and Knight, A. M. The relationship between nickel toxicity symptoms and the absorption of iron and nickel. *Ann. Appl. Biol.* **43**, 454–464 (1955).
90. Dancer, J. Synergistic effect of zinc and giberellin. *Nature* **183**, 901–902 (1959).
91. Davidson, F. M., and Long, C. M. The structure of the naturally occurring phosphoglycerides. 4. Action of cabbage leaf phospholipase. *Biochem. J.* **69**, 458–466 (1958).
92. Davidson, O. W. Nutrient deficiency symptoms in deciduous fruits. *In* "Hunger Signs in Crops" (G. Hambidge, ed.), pp. 191–239. American Society of Agronomy and National Fertilizer Society, Washington, D.C., 1941.
93. Davis, D. E. Some effects of calcium deficiency on the anatomy of *Pinus taeda*. *Am. J. Botany* **36**, 276–282 (1949).
94. Day, D. Some chemical aspects of calcium deficiency effects on *Pisum sativum*. *Plant Physiol.* **10**, 811–816 (1935).
95. Dearborn, C. H. Boron nutrition of cauliflower in relation to browning. *N.Y. Agr. Expt. Sta. Bull.* **778** (1942).
96. De Kock, P. C. Iron nutrition of plants at high pH. *Soil Sci.* **79**, 167–175 (1955).
97. De Kock, P. C. Heavy metal toxicity and iron chlorosis. *Ann. Botany (London)* [N.S.] **20**, 133–142 (1956).
97a. De Kock, P. C. Commissong, K., Farmer, V. C., and Inkson, R. H. E. Interrelationships of catalase, peroxidase, hematin and chlorophyll. *Plant Physiol.* **35**, 599–604 (1960).
98. De Kock, P. C., and Hall, A. The phosphorus-iron relationship in genetical chlorosis. *Plant Physiol.* **30**, 293–295 (1955).

99. De Kock, P. C., Hall, A., and McDonald, M. A relation between the ratios of phosphorus to iron and potassium to calcium in mustard leaves. *Plant and Soil* **12**, 128–142 (1960).

100. De Kock, P. C., and Morrison, R. I. The metabolism of chlorotic leaves. 1. Amino acids. *Biochem. J.* **70**, 266–272 (1958).

101. De Kock, P. C., and Morrison, R. I. The metabolism of chlorotic leaves. 2. Organic acids. *Biochem. J.* **70**, 272–277 (1958).

102. Delwiche, C. C., Johnson, C. M., and Reisenauer, H. M. Influence of cobalt on nitrogen fixation by *Medicago. Plant Physiol.* **36**, 73–78 (1961).

103. Demetriades, O. D. Sur l'accumulation d'asparagine chez L'*Hibiscus esculentus*. *Ann. Inst. Phytopathol. Benaki*, **10**, 13–21 (1956).

104. Dénes, G. Die enzymatische Synthese des Glutamins in *Lupinus albus. Experientia* **9**, 24–25 (1953).

105. Dénes, G. Glutamic synthetase, its stereospecificity and changes induced by activating ions. *Biochim. et Biophys. Acta* **15**, 296–297 (1955).

106. Dennis, A. C., and Dennis, R. W. G. Boron and plant life. III. *Fertilizer, Feeding Stuffs and Farm Supplies J.* **24**, 55–59, 85–88, 118–121, 159–161, 187–190, 222–224 (1939).

107. Dennis, A. C., and Dennis, R. W. G. Boron and plant life. IV. *Fertilizer, Feeding Stuffs and Farm Supplies J.* **25**, 391–394, 407–410, 423–427, 439–440. (1940): **26**, 4–5, 15–17, 33–35, 47–50 (1941).

108. Dennis, A. C., and Dennis, R. W. G. Boron and plant life. V. *Fertilizer, Feeding Stuffs and Farm Supplies J.* **29**, 119–126, 151–157, 175–185, 199–205, 223–230, 245–252 (1943).

109. Dennis, R. W. G. A review of development in the application of boron in agriculture and horticulture. 1935–1937. *Fertilizer, Feeding Stuffs and Farm Supplies J.* **22**, 479–483, 507–511, 535–538, 573–576 (1937).

110. Dennis, R. W. G., and O'Brien, O. G. Boron in agriculture. *West Scotland Agr. Coll. Research Bull.* **5** (1937).

111. De Turk, E. E. Plant mineral deficiency symptoms in legumes. *In* "Hunger Signs in Crops" (G. Hambidge, ed.), pp. 241–266. American Society of Agronomy and National Fertilizer Society, Washington, D.C., 1941.

112. Dickey, R. D., Drosdoff, M., and Hamilton, J. Copper deficiency of Tung in Florida. *Florida Univ. Agr. Expt. Sta. (Gainesville), Bull.* **447** (1948).

113. Dorph-Petersen, K., and Steenbjerg, F. Investigation of the effect of fertilizer containing sodium. *Plant and Soil* **2**, 283–300 (1950).

114. Ducet, G., and Hewitt, E. J. Relation of molybdenum status and nitrogen supply to respiration in cauliflower. *Nature* **173**, 1141–1142 (1954).

115. Dugger, W. M., Jr., and Humphries, T. E. The influence of boron on starch phosphorylase and its significance in translocation of sugars in plants. *Plant Physiol.* **32**, 364–370 (1957).

116. Dugger, W. M., Jr., and Humphries, T. E. Influence of boron on enzymatic reactions associated with biosynthesis of sucrose. *Plant Physiol.* **35**, 523–530 (1960).

117. Dunne, T. C. "Withertip" or "Summer Dieback," a copper deficiency disease of apple trees. *J. Dept. Agr. W. Australia* **15**, 120–126 (1938).

117a. Eaton, F. M. Automatically operated sand culture equipment. *J. Agr. Research* **53**, 433–444 (1936).

118. Eaton, F. M. Interrelation with the effect of boron and indoleacetic acid on plant growth. *Botan. Gaz.* **101**, 701–705 (1940).

119. Eaton, F. M. Toxicity and accumulation of chloride and sulphate in plants. *J. Agr. Research* **64**, 357–399 (1942).
120. Eaton, F. M. Deficiency, toxicity and accumulation of boron in plants. *J. Agr. Research* **69**, 237–279 (1944).
121. Eaton, S. V. Influence of sulphur deficiency on the metabolism of the soybean. *Botan. Gaz.* **97**, 68–100 (1935).
122. Eaton, S. V. Effects of boron deficiency and excess on plants. *Plant Physiol.* **15**, 95–107 (1940).
123. Eaton, S. V. Influence of sulphur deficiency on metabolism of the sunflower. *Botan. Gaz.* **102**, 533–556 (1941).
124. Eaton, S. V. Influence of sulphur deficiency on metabolism of black mustard. *Botan. Gaz.* **104**, 306–315 (1942).
125. Eaton, S. V. Effect of phosphorus deficiency on growth and metabolism of sunflowers. *Botan. Gaz.* **110**, 449–464 (1949).
126. Eaton, S. V. Effects of phosphorus deficiency on growth and metabolism of soybean. *Botan. Gaz.* **111**, 426–436 (1950).
127. Eaton, S. V. Effects of sulphur deficiency on the growth and metabolism of the tomato. *Botan. Gaz.* **112**, 300–307 (1951).
128. Eaton, S. V. Effect of phosphorus deficiency on growth and metabolism of black mustard. *Botan. Gaz.* **113**, 301–309 (1952).
129. Eaton, S. V. Effects of potassium deficiency on growth and metabolism of sunflower plants. *Botan. Gaz.* **114**, 165–180 (1952).
130. Eltinge, E. T. Effect of boron deficiency upon structure of *Zea mays*. *Plant Physiol.* **11**, 765–778 (1936).
131. Eltinge, E. T. Effects of manganese deficiency upon the histology of *Lycopersicon esculentum*. *Plant Physiol.* **16**, 189–195 (1941).
132. Eltinge, E. T., and Reed, H. S. Effect of zinc deficiency upon the roots of *Lycopersicon esculentum*. *Am. J. Botany* **27**, 331–335 (1940).
133. Ergle, D. R. Effects of low nitrogen and sulphur supply on their accumulation in the plant. *Botan. Gaz.* **14**, 417–426 (1953).
134. Ergle, D. R. Utilization of storage sulphur by cotton and the effect on growth and chloroplast pigment. *Botan. Gaz.* **115**, 225–234 (1953).
135. Ergle, D. R., and Eaton, F. M. Aspects of phosphorus metabolism in the cotton plant. *Plant Physiol.* **32**, 106–113 (1957).
136. Evans, H. J., Purvis, E. R., and Bear, F. E. Molybdenum nutrition of alfalfa. *Plant Physiol.* **25**, 555–556 (1950).
137. Eversole, R. A., and Tatum, E. L. Chemical alteration of crossing-over frequency in *Chlamydomonas*. *Proc. Natl. Acad. Sci. U.S.* **42**, 68–73 (1956).
138. Ferguson, W., and Wright, L. E. Microelement studies with special reference to the element boron. *Sci. Agr.* **20**, 470–487 (1940).
139. Ferres, H. M. Influence of light and temperature on nutrient uptake and use with special reference to zinc. *In* "British Commonwealth Scientific Official Conference," Specialist Conference in Agriculture, Australia, 1949, pp. 240–243. H. M. Stationery Office, London, 1951.
140. Finch, A. H. Pecan rosette, a physiological disease apparently susceptible to treatment by zinc. *Proc. Am. Soc. Hort. Sci.* **29**, 264–266 (1932).
141. Florell, C. The influence of calcium on root mitochondria. *Physiol. Plantarum* **9**, 236–242 (1956).
142. Florell, C. Calcium, mitochondria and anion uptake. *Physiol. Plantarum* **10**, 781–790 (1957).

143. Floyd, B. F. Leaf spotting of citrus. *Florida Univ. Agr. Expt. Stas. (Gainesville) Ann. Rept.* **1908**, 91 (1908).

143a. Floyd, B. F. Yellow spotting of citrus leaves. *Florida Univ. Agr. Expt. Stas. (Gainesville) Ann. Rept.* **1909**, 86 (1909).

143b. Freiberg, S. R., and Steward, F. C. Physiological investigations on the banana plant. III. Factors which affect the nitrogen compounds of the leaves. *Ann. Botany (London)* [N.S.] **24**, 247–157 (1960).

144. Freney, J. R., Delwiche, C. C., and Johnson, C. M. The effect of chloride on the free amino acids of cabbage and cauliflower plants. *Australian J. Biol. Sci.* **12**, 160–167 (1959).

145. Galston, A. W., and Dalberg, L. V. The adaptive function and physiological significance of indoleacetic acid oxidase. *Am. J. Botany* **41**, 373–380 (1954).

146. Garner, W. W., McMurtrey, J. E., Jr., Bacon, L. W., and Moss, E. G. Sanddrown, a chlorosis of tobacco due to magnesium deficiency and the relation of sulphates and chlorides of potassium to the disease. *J. Agr. Research* **23**, 27–40 (1923).

147. Garner, W. W., McMurtrey, J. E., Jr., Bowling, J. D., and Moss, E. G. Magnesium and calcium requirements of the tobacco crop. *J. Agr. Research* **40**, 145–168 (1930).

148. Gauch, H. G., and Dugger, W. M., Jr. The role of boron in the translocation of sucrose. *Plant Physiol.* **28**, 457–466 (1953).

149. Gauch, H. G., and Dugger, W. M., Jr. The physiological role of boron in higher plants: a review and interpretation. *Univ. Maryland Agr. Expt. Sta. Tech. Bull.* **A80** (1954).

150. George, P. Chemical nature of the secondary hydrogen peroxide compound formed by cytochrome-c peroxidase and horseradish peroxidase. *Nature* **169**, 612–613 (1952).

151. Gerretsen, F. C. Manganese in relation to photosynthesis. I. Carbon dioxide assimilation and the typical symptoms of deficiency in oat. *Plant and Soil* **1**, 346–358 (1949).

152. Gerretsen, F. C. Manganese in relation to photosynthesis. II. Redox potentials of illuminated crude chloroplast suspensions. *Plant and Soil* **2**, 159–193 (1950).

153. Gerretsen, F. C. Manganese in relation to photosynthesis. III. Uptake of oxygen by illuminated crude chloroplast suspensions. *Plant and Soil* **2**, 323–343 (1950).

154. Gilbert, S. G. The place of sulphur in plant nutrition. *Botan. Rev.* **17**, 671–691 (1951).

155. Gilbert, S. G. A biochemical basis for copper/nitrogen balance in tung. *Plant Physiol.* **26**, 398–405 (1951).

156. Gilbert, S. G., Sell, H. M., and Drosdoff, M. The effect of copper deficiency on the metabolism and oil synthesis of the tung tree. *Plant Physiol.* **21**, 290–303 (1946).

157. Ginzburg, B. Z. A protein component of the middle lamella: a possible site for indoleacetic acid action. *Nature* **181**, 398–400 (1958).

157a. Ginzburg, B. Z. Evidence for a protein-gel structure cross-linked by metal cations in the intercellular cement of plant tissue. *J. Exptl. Botany* **12**, 85–107 (1961).

158. Gleites, M. E., and Parker, H. E. The effect of phosphorus deficiency on the free amino acids of alfalfa. *Arch. Biochem. Biophys.* **71**, 430–436 (1957).

159. Glenister, P. R. Effects of iron deficiency on respiration of sunflower plants. *Botan. Gaz.* **106**, 33–40 (1944).

160. Goodall, D. W., Slater, W. G., and Grant-Lipp, A. E. Nutrient interactions and deficiency diagnosis in the lettuce. *Australian J. Biol. Sci.* **10**, 57–65 (1957).

161. Goss, J. A. Ammonium bicarbonate in plant nutrition. *Soil Sci.* **89**, 296–302 (1960).

162. Granick, S. Iron metabolism in animals and plants. *In* "Trace Elements" (C. A. Lamb, O. G. Bentley, and J. M. Beattie, eds.), pp. 365–382. Academic Press, New York, 1958.

162a. Granick, S. Magnesium protoporphyrin monoester and protoporphyrin monomethyl ester in chlorophyll biosynthesis. *J. Biol. Chem.* **236**, 1168–1172 (1961).

163. Greenwood, E. A. N., and Hallsworth, E. G. Studies on the nutrition of forage legumes. II. Some interactions of calcium, phosphorus, copper and molybdenum on the growth and chemical composition of *Trifolium subterraneum* L. *Plant and Soil* **12**, 97–127 (1960).

164. Greenwood, M., and Djokoto, R. K. Symptoms of mineral deficiency in cacao. *J. Hort. Sci.* **27**, 223–236 (1952).

165. Greenwood, M., and Hayfron, R. J. Iron and zinc deficiency in cacao in the Gold Coast. *Empire J. Exptl. Agr.* **19**, 73–86 (1951).

166. Greenwood, M., and Posnette, A. F. A morphological change induced in leaves of *Theobroma cacao*. *Nature* **159**, 542–543 (1947).

167. Gregory, F. G., and Baptiste, E. C. D. Physiological studies in plant nutrition. V. Carbohydrate metabolism in relation to nutrient deficiency and to age in barley leaves. *Ann. Botany (London)* **50**, 579–619 (1936).

168. Gregory, F. G., and Richards, F. J. Physiological studies in plant nutrition. I. The effect of manurial deficiency on the respiration and assimilation rate in barley. *Ann. Botany (London)* **43**, 119–161 (1929).

169. Gregory, F. G., and Sen, P. K. Physiological studies in plant nutrition. VI. The relation of respiration rate to carbohydrate and nitrogen metabolism of the barley leaf as determined by nitrogen and potassium deficiency. *Ann. Botany (London)* [N.S.] **1**, 521–561 (1937).

170. Guest, P. Root contact phenomena in relation to iron nutrition and growth of citrus. *Proc. Am. Soc. Hort. Sci.* **44**, 43–48 (1944).

171. Haas, A. R. C. Phosphorus deficiency in citrus. *Soil Sci.* **42**, 93–118 (1936).

172. Haas, A. R. C., and Klotz, L. J. Some anatomical and physiological changes in citrus produced by boron deficiency. *Hilgardia* **5**, 175–186 (1931).

172a. Haas, A. R. C., and Klotz, L. J. Further evidence for the necessity of boron for health in citrus. *Botan. Gaz.* **92**, 94–100 (1931).

173. Haas, A. R. C., and Quale, H. J. Copper content of citrus leaves and fruit in relation to exanthema and fumigation. *Hilgardia* **9**, 143–177 (1935).

174. Habermann, H. M. Light dependant oxygen metabolism of chloroplast preparations. *Plant Physiol.* **35**, 307–312 (1960).

175. Hale, V. Q., and Wallace, A. Bicarbonate and phosphorous effects on uptake and distribution in soybeans of iron chelated with ethylenediamine di-o-hydroxyphenyl acetate. *Soil Sci.* **89**, 285–287 (1960).

176. Hallsworth, E. G., Wilson, S. B., and Greenwood, E. A. N. Copper and cobalt in nitrogen fixation. *Nature* **187**, 79–80 (1960).

177. Hambidge, G. (Ed.). "Hunger Signs in Crops." American Society of Agronomy and National Fertilizer Society, Washington, D.C., 1941.

178. Hannay, J. W., Fletcher, B. L., and Street, H. E. Studies on the growth of excised roots. IX. The effects of other nutrient ions upon the growth of excised tomato roots supplied with various nitrogen sources. *New Phytologist* **58**, 142–154 (1959).

179. Hansteen, B. Über das Verhalten des Kulturpflanzen zu den Bodensalzen. *Jahrb. wiss. Botan.* **47**, 289–376 (1910).

180. Harmer, P. M., Benne, E. J., Laughlin, W. M., and Key, C. Factors affecting crop response to sodium applied as common salt on Michigan muck soil. *Soil Sci.* **76**, 1–17 (1953).

181. Harris, G. H. Some effects of microelements on growth and storage of carrots and turnips. *Proc. Am. Soc. Hort. Sci.* **43**, 219–224 (1943).

182. Hartt, C. E. Some effects of potassium on the growth of sugar cane and upon the absorption and migration of ash constituents. *Plant Physiol.* **9**, 399–452 (1934).

183. Hartt, C. E. Some effects of potassium upon the amounts of protein and amino forms of nitrogen, sugars and enzyme activity of sugar cane. *Plant Physiol.* **9**, 453–490 (1934).

184. Hartwell, B. L., and Pember, F. R. Sodium as a partial substitute for potassium. *Univ. Rhode Island Agr. Expt. Sta. Ann. Rept.* **21**, 243 (1908).

185. Hartwell, B. L., Wheeler, H. J., and Pember, F. R. The effects of the addition of sodium to deficient amounts of potassium upon the growth of plants in both water and sand cultures. *Univ. Rhode Island Agr. Expt. Sta. Ann. Rept.* **20**, 299 (1907).

186. Heilbrunn, L. V. "The Dynamics of Living Cytoplasm." Academic Press, New York, 1956.

187. Hellriegel, H., and Willfarth, H. Vegetationsversuche über den Kalibedarf einiger Pfanzen. *Arb. deut. Gesl. Heft* **34** (1898). Cited by Dorph-Petersen and Steenbjerg (113).

188. Hernandez-Medina, E., and Shive, J. W. Calcium-boron relationships in the nutrition of corn and the distribution of these elements in the plants. *J. Agr. Univ. Puerto-Rico* **30**, 251–291 (1946).

189. Hewitt, E. J. Experiments in mineral nutrition. Progress Report 1. *Long Ashton Research Sta. Ann. Rept.* **1943**, 33–47 (1944).

190. Hewitt, E. J. Experiments in mineral nutrition. Progress Report 2. *Long Ashton Research Sta. Ann. Rept.* **1944**, 50–60 (1945).

191. Hewitt, E. J. Marsh spot in beans. *Nature* **155**, 22–23 (1945).

192. Hewitt, E. J. Experiments in mineral nutrition. Progress Report 3. *Long Ashton Research Sta. Ann. Rept.* **1945**, 44–50 (1946).

193. Hewitt, E. J. The resolution of the factors in soil acidity: some effects of manganese toxicity. *Long Ashton Research Sta. Ann. Rept.* **1946**, 50–61 (1947).

194. Hewitt, E. J. The resolution of the factors in soil acidity; the relative effects of aluminum and manganese toxicities on farm and market garden crops. *Long Ashton Research Sta. Ann. Rept.* **1947**, 82–96 (1948).

195. Hewitt, E. J. The resolution of the factors in soil acidity; the relative effects of aluminium and manganese toxicities on some farm and market garden crops (continued). *Long Ashton Research Sta. Ann. Rept.* **1948**, 58–65 (1949).

196. Hewitt, E. J. Experiments on iron metabolism in plants. I. Some effects of metal induced iron deficiency. *Long Ashton Research Sta. Ann. Rept.* 1948. 66–80 (1949).

197. Hewitt, E. J. Relation of manganese and some other metals to the iron status of plants. *Nature* **161**, 489–491 (1948).

197a. Hewitt, E. J. Experiments on iron metabolism in plants. III. The relation of molybdenum and nitrogen supply to metal induced iron deficiency in sugar beet. *Long Ashton Research Sta. Ann. Rept.* **1950**, 64–70 (1951).

198. Hewitt, E. J. The role of the mineral elements in plant nutrition. *Ann. Rev. Plant Physiol.* **2**, 25–52 (1951).

199. Hewitt, E. J. A biological approach to the problems of soil acidity. *Trans. Intern. Soc. Soil Sci., Dublin, 1952* **I**, 107–118 (1953).

200. Hewitt, E. J. "Sand and Water Culture Methods Used in the Study of Plant Nutrition." *Commonwealth Bur. of Hort. Tech.-Commun.* **22**, East Malling (1952).

201. Hewitt, E. J. The importance of molybdenum in the nutrition of horticultural plants. *Proc. 13th Intern. Hort. Congr. London 1952* **I**, 375–385 (1953).

202. Hewitt, E. J. Metal interrelationships in plant nutrition. I. Effects of some metal toxicities on sugar beet, tomato, oat, potato and marrowstem kale in sand culture. *J. Exptl. Botany* **4**, 59–64 (1954).

203. Hewitt, E. J. Metal interrelationships in plant nutrition. II. The relation of metal toxicity, molybdenum and nitrogen source to chlorophyll and magnesium content of sugar beet in sand culture. *J. Exptl. Botany* **5**, 110–118 (1955).

204. Hewitt, E. J. Symptoms of molybdenum deficiency in plants. *Soil Sci.* **81**, 159–172 (1956).

205. Hewitt, E. J. Aspects of molybdenum as an essential nutrient for higher plants. *J. Sci. Food Agr.* **8**, Suppl., 56–514 (1957).

206. Hewitt, E. J. Some aspects of micronutrient element metabolism in plants. *Nature* **180**, 1020–1022 (1957).

207. Hewitt, E. J. The role of mineral elements in the activity of plant enzyme systems. *In* "Encyclopaedia of Plant Physiology" (W. Ruhland, ed.), pp. 427–481. Springer, Berlin, 1958.

208. Hewitt, E. J. Some aspects of mineral nutrition in the legumes. *In* "Nutrition of the Legumes" (E. G. Hallsworth, ed.), pp. 15–41. Butterworth, London, 1958.

209. Hewitt, E. J. The metabolism of micronutrient elements in plants. *Biol. Revs. Cambridge Phil. Soc.* **34**, 333–377 (1959).

210. Hewitt, E. J., and Afridi, M. M. R. K. Adaptive synthesis of nitrate reductase in higher plants. *Nature* **183**, 57–58 (1959).

211. Hewitt, E. J., and Agarwala, S. C. Production of "Whiptail" in cauliflower grown in sand culture. *Nature* **167**, 733 (1951).

212. Hewitt, E. J., and Agarwala, S. C. Reduction of triphenyltetrazolium chloride by plant tissues and its relation to molybdenum. *Nature* **169**, 545–546 (1954).

213. Hewitt, E. J., Agarwala, S. C., and Jones, E. W. Effect of molybdenum status on the ascorbic acid content of plants in sand culture. *Nature* **166**, 1119–1120 (1950).

214. Hewitt, E. J., Agarwala, S. C., and Williams, A. H. Molybdenum as a plant nutrient. VIII. The effect of different molybdenum levels and nitrogen supplies on the nitrogen fractions in cauliflower plants grown in sand culture. *J. Hort. Sci.* **32**, 34–48 (1957).

215. Hewitt, E. J., and Bolle-Jones, E. W. Molybdenum as a plant nutrient. I. The influence of molybdenum on the growth of some brassica crops in sand culture. *J. Hort. Sci.* **27**, 257–265 (1952).

216. Hewitt, E. J., and Bolle-Jones, E. W. Molybdenum as a plant nutrient. II. The effects of molybdenum deficiency on some horticultural and agricultural crops grown in sand culture. *J. Hort. Sci.* **27**, 257–265 (1952).

217. Hewitt, E. J., and Bolle-Jones, E. W. Studies in iron deficiency of crops. II. The interrelationships of iron and potassium in the potato plant. *J. Hort. Sci.* **28**, 185–195 (1953).

218. Hewitt, E. J., Bolle-Jones, E. W., and Miles, P. The production of copper, zinc and molybdenum deficiency in crop plants grown in sand culture with special reference to some effects of water supply and seed reserves. *Plant and Soil* **5**, 205–222 (1954).

219. Hewitt, E. J., and Bond, G. Molybdenum and the fixation of nitrogen in *Casuarina* and *Alnus* root nodules. *Plant and Soil* **14**, 159–175 (1961).

220. Hewitt, E. J., and Jones, E. W. The production of molybdenum deficiency in plants grown in sand culture, with special reference to tomato and brassica crops. *J. Pomol. Hort. Sci.* **23**, 254–262 (1947).

221. Hewitt, E. J., and Jones, E. W. The effect of zinc and copper deficiencies on crop plants grown in sand culture. *Long Ashton Research Sta. Ann. Rept.* **1950**, 56–63 (1951).

222. Hewitt, E. J., Jones, E. W., and Williams, A. H. Relation of molybdenum and manganese to the free amino acid content of the cauliflower. *Nature* **163**, 681–682 (1949).

223. Hewitt, E. J., and McCready, C. C. Molybdenum as a plant nutrient. VII. The effects of different molybdenum and nitrogen supplies on yields and composition of tomato plants grown in sand culture. *J. Hort. Sci.* **31**, 284–290 (1956).

224. Hewitt, E. J., and Miles, P. The effects of deficiencies and excesses of some mineral nutrients on the growth of tulip and daffodil bulbs in sand culture. *J. Hort. Sci.* **29**, 237–244 (1954).

225. Hewitt, E. J., and Tatham, P. Interaction of mineral deficiency and nitrogen supply on acid phosphatase activity in leaf extracts. *J. Exptl. Botany* **11**, 367–376 (1960).

226. Hiatt, A. J., and Evans, H. J. Influence of certain cations on activity of acetic thiokinase from spinach leaves. *Plant Physiol.* **35**, 673–677 (1960).

227. Hill, H., and Davis, M. B. Physiological disorders of apples. *Sci. Agr.* **17**, 199–208 (1936).

228. Hoagland, D. R. "Inorganic Plant Nutrition." Prather Lectures. Chronica Botanica, Waltham, Massachusetts, 1944.

229. Hoagland, D. R., Chandler, W. H., and Hibbard, P. L. Little leaf or rosette of fruit trees. V. Effect of zinc on the growth plants of various types in controlled soil and water culture experiments. *Proc. Am. Soc. Hort. Sci.* **33**, 131–141 (1935).

230. Hoffer, G. N. Testing corn stalks chemically to aid in determining their plant food needs. *Purdue Univ. Agr. Expt. Sta., Ext. Bull.* **298** (1930).

231. Holley, R. W., and Cain, J. C. Accumulation of arginine in plants affected with iron deficiency-type chlorosis. *Science* **121**, 172–173 (1955).

232. Holt, M. E., and Volk, N. J. Sodium as a plant nutrient and substitute for potassium. *J. Am. Soc. Agron.* **37**, 821–827 (1945).

233. Hopkins, E. F., Pagan, V., and Ramirez-Silva, F. J. Iron and manganese in relation to plant growth and its importance in Puerto-Rico. *J. Agr. Univ. Puerto-Rico* **28**, 43–99 (1944).

233a. Humphries, E. C. Effects of quality of light on development of roots of dwarf bean hypocotyls in presence and absence of boron. *Nature* **190**, 701–703 (1961).

234. Hunter, J. G., and Vergnano, O. Nickel toxicity in plants. *Ann. Appl. Biol.* **39**, 279–284 (1952).

235. Hunter, J. G., and Vergnano, O. Trace element toxicities in oat plants. *Ann. Appl. Biol.* **40**, 761–777 (1955).

236. Hyde, B. B., and Paliwal, R. L. Studies on the role of cations in the structure and behaviour of plant chromosomes. *Am. J. Botany* **45**, 433–438 (1958).

236a. Ichioka, P. S., and Arnon, D. I. Molybdenum in relation to nitrogen metabolism. II. Assimilation of ammonium and urea without molybdenum by *Scenedesmus*. *Physiol. Plantarum* **8**, 552–560 (1955).

237. Iljin, W. S. Die Kalkchlorose der Pflanzen und ihre Biochemie. *Jahrb. Wiss. Botan.* **90**, 464–498 (1942).

238. Iljin, W. S. Metabolism of plants affected with lime-induced chlorosis. I. Nitrogen metabolism. *Plant and Soil* **3**, 239–256 (1951).

239. Iljin, W. S. Metabolism of plants affected by lime-induced chlorosis. II. Organic acids and carbohydrates. *Plant and Soil* **3**, 339–351 (1951).

240. Irving, H. M., and Williams, R. J. P. Some factors controlling the selectivity of organic reagents. *Analyst* **77**, 813–829 (1952).

241. Isbell, H. S., Brewster, J. F., Holt, N. B., and Frush, H. L. *J. Research Natl. Bur. Standards* **40**, 129–149 (1948). Cited by Zittle (594).

242. Jacob, A. "Magnesium, the Fifth Major Plant Nutrient" (Transln. N. Walker). Staples, London, 1958.

243. Jacob, W. C., and White-Stevens, R. H. Studies in the minor element nutrition of vegetable crops. II. The interrelation of potash, boron and magnesium upon the flavour and sugar content of melons. *Proc. Am. Soc. Hort. Sci.* **39**, 369–373 (1941).

244. Jacobson, L. Iron in the leaves and chloroplasts of some plants in relation to chlorophyll content. *Plant Physiol.* **20**, 233–245 (1945).

245. Jacobson, L., and Oertli, J. J. The relation between iron and chlorophyll contents in chlorotic sunflower leaves. *Plant Physiol.* **31**, 199–204 (1957).

246. Jamelainen, E. A. The effect of boron on the occurrence of cork disease in apple. *Agr. Exptl. Activities of the State. Helsinki Publ.* m89 (1936).

247. Janssen, G., and Bartholemew, R. P. The translocation of potassium in tomato plants and in relation to their carbohydrate and nitrogen distribution. *J. Agr. Research* **38**, 447–465 (1929).

248. Janssen, G., and Bartholemew, R. P. The influence of the potash concentration in the culture medium on the production of carbohydrate in plants. *J. Agr. Research* **40**, 243–261 (1930).

249. Jensen, W. A. The histochemical localisation of peroxidase in roots and its induction by indoleacetic acid. *Plant Physiol.* **30**, 426–432 (1955).

250. Joham, H. E. The calcium and potassium nutrition of cotton as influenced by sodium. *Plant Physiol.* **30**, 4–10 (1955).

251. Joham, H. E. Carbohydrate distribution as affected by calcium deficiency in cotton. *Plant Physiol.* **32**, 113–117 (1957).

252. Johnson, C. M., Stout, P. R., Broyer, T. C., and Carlton, A. B. Comparative chlorine requirements of different plant species. *Plant and Soil* **8**, 337–353 (1957).

253. Johnson, C. M., Pearson, G. A., and Stout, P. R. Molybdenum nutrition of

crop plants. II. Plant and soil factors concerned with molybdenum deficiencies of crop plants. *Plant and Soil* **4**, 178–196 (1952).

254. Johnson, M. O. Manganese chlorosis of pineapples; its cause and control. *Hawaii Agr. Expt. Sta. Bull.* **52** (1924).

255. Johnson, M. O. Control of chlorosis of the pineapple and other plants. *Ind. Eng. Chem.* **20**, 724–725 (1928).

256. Johnston, E. S., and Dore, W. H. The influence of boron on the chemical composition and growth of the tomato plant. *Plant Physiol.* **4**, 31–62 (1929).

257. Johnston, E. S., and Fischer, P. L. The essential nature of boron to the growth and fruiting of the tomato, *Plant Physiol.* **5**, 387–392 (1930).

258. Jolivette, J. P., and Walker, J. C. Effect of boron deficiency on histology of garden beet and cabbage. *J. Agr. Research* **66**, 167–182 (1943).

259. Jones, H. E., and Scarseth, G. D. The calcium boron balance in plants as related to boron needs. *Soil Sci.* **57**, 15–24 (1944).

260. Kalra, G. S. Responses of the tomato plant to calcium deficiency. *Botan. Gaz.* **118**, 18–37 (1956).

261. Katoh, S. A new copper-protein from *Chlorella ellipsoidea. Nature* **186**, 533–534 (1960).

262. Katoh, S., and Takamiya, A. A new leaf copper protein, "Plastocyanin," a natural Hill oxidant. *Nature* **189**, 665–666 (1961).

263. Kelley, W. P. The function and distribution of manganese in plants and soil. *Hawaii Agr. Expt. Sta. Bull.* **26** (1912).

264. Kenten, R. H. The oxidation of indolyl-3-acetic acid by waxpod bean root sap and peroxidase systems. *Biochem. J.* **59**, 110–121 (1955).

265. Kenten, R. H., and Mann, P. J. G. The oxidation of manganese by plant extracts in the presence of hydrogen peroxide. *Biochem. J.* **45**, 255–263 (1949).

266. Kenten, R. H., and Mann, P. J. G. The oxidation of manganese by peroxidase systems. *Biochem. J.* **46**, 67–73 (1950).

267. Kenten, R. H., and Mann, P. J. G. The oxidation of amines by extracts of pea seedlings. *Biochem. J.* **50**, 360–369 (1951).

268. Kenten, R. H., and Mann, P. J. G. The action of peroxidase systems on ferrocyanide, molybdate, tungstate, and vanadate. *Biochem. J.* **50**, 29–34 (1952).

269. Kenten, R. H., and Mann, P. J. G. The oxidation of manganese by enzyme systems. *Biochem. J.* **52**, 125–130 (1952).

270. Kenten, R. H., and Mann, P. J. G. The oxidation of certain dicarboxylic acids by peroxidase systems in the presence of manganese. *Biochem. J.* **53**, 498–505 (1953).

271. Kenten, R. H., and Mann, P. J. G. The oxidation of manganese by illuminated chloroplast suspensions. *Biochem. J.* **61**, 279–286 (1955).

272. Kenten, R. H., and Mann, P. J. G. Manganese oxidation in the pea plant (*Pisum sativum* L.) grown under conditions of manganese toxicity. *Biochem. J.* **65**, 179–185 (1956).

273. Kessler, E. On the role of manganese in the oxygen-evolving system of photosynthesis. *Arch. Biochem. Biophys.* **59**, 527–529 (1955).

274. Kessler, E. Manganese as a cofactor in photosynthetic oxygen evolution. *In* "Research in Photosynthesis" (H. Gaffron, ed.), pp. 243–249. Interscience, New York, 1957.

275. Kessler, E. Stoffwechselphysiologische Untersuchungen an Hydrogenase Enthaltenden Grünalgen. I. Über die Rolle des Mangans bei Photoreduktion und Photosynthese. *Planta* **49**, 435–454 (1957).

275a. Kessler, E. Reduction of nitrate by green algae. *In* "Utilization of Nitrogen and Its Compounds by Plants," *Symposia Soc. Exptl. Biol. No.* **13**, 87–105 (1959).

276. Kidson, E. B. An ash skeleton method for the diagnosis of magnesium and potassium deficiencies in apple leaves and for the determination of their distribution in the leaf. *New Zealand J. Sci. Technol.* **B24**, 140–145 (1942).

277. Kinsky, S. C., and McElroy, W. D. *Neurospora* nitrate reductase: the role of phosphate, flavin and cytochrome-c reductase. *Arch. Biochem. Biophys.* **73**, 466–483 (1958).

278. Kirby, K. S. A new method for the isolation of deoxyribonucleic acids. Evidence on the nature of bonds between deoxyribonucleic acid and protein. *Biochem. J.* **66**, 495–504 (1957).

279. Klein, R. M. The relation of gas exchange and tryosinase activity of tomato tissues to the level of boron nutrition by the plants. *Arch. Biochem. Biophys.* **80**, 207–214 (1951).

280. Labbe, R. F., and Hubbard, N. Preparation and properties of the iron-protoporphyrin chelating enzyme. *Biochim. et Biophys. Acta* **41**, 185–191 (1960).

281. Lanning, F. C., Ponnaiya, B. W. X., and Crumpton, C. F. The chemical nature of silica in plants. *Plant Physiol.* **33**, 339–343 (1958).

282. Latzko, E. Die Funktion des Kaliums im Stoffwechsel der energiereichen Phosphate pflanzlicher und kierischer Organismen. *Agrochimica* **3**, 148–164 (1959).

283. Leeper, G. W. Manganese deficiency and accumulation of nitrates in plants. *J. Australian Inst. Agr. Sci.* **7**, 161–162 (1941).

284. Lehr, J. J. The importance of sodium for plant nutrition. I. *Soil Sci.* **52**, 237–244 (1941).

285. Lehr, J. J. The importance of sodium for plant nutrition. II. Effect on beets of the secondary ions in nitrate fertilizers. *Soil Sci.* **52**, 373–379 (1941).

286. Lehr, J. J. The importance of sodium for plant nutrition. III. The equilibrium of cations in the beet. *Soil Sci.* **53**, 399–411 (1942).

287. Lehr, J. J. Exploratory experiments on sensitiveness of different crops to sodium, A. Spinach. *Plant and Soil* **2**, 37–48 (1949).

288. Lehr, J. J. Importance of sodium for plant nutrition. V. Response of crops other than beets. *Soil Sci.* **72**, 157–166 (1951).

289. Lehr, J. J. Exploratory experiments on sensitiveness of different crops to sodium, B. Oats. *Plant and Soil* **4**, 289–297 (1953).

290. Lehr, J. J., and Wybenga, J. M. Exploratory pot experiments on sensitiveness of crops to sodium, C. Flax. *Plant and Soil* **6**, 251–261 (1955).

291. Lehr, J. J., and Wybenga, J. M. Exploratory pot experiments on sensitiveness of different crops to sodium, D. Barley. *Plant and Soil* **9**, 237–253 (1958).

292. Lenhoff, H. M., Nicholas, D. J. D., and Kaplan, N. O. Effects of oxygen, iron and molybdenum on alternative routes of electron transfer in *Pseudomonas fluorescens. J. Biol. Chem.* **220**, 983–995 (1956).

293. Letham, D. S. Maceration of plant tissues with ethylenediaminetetraacetic acid. *Nature* **181**, 135–136 (1958).

294. Levine, R. P. Chromosome structure and the mechanism of crossing over. *Proc. Natl. Acad. Sci. U.S.* **41**, 727–730 (1955).

295. Levine, V. E. The effect of selenium compounds upon growth and germination in plants. *Am. J. Botany* **12**, 82–91 (1925).

296. Liebig, G. F., Jr., Vanselow, A. P., and Chapman, H. D. Effects of aluminum on

copper toxicity as revealed by solution cultures and spectrographic studies of citrus. *Soil Sci.* **53**, 341–351 (1942).

297. Lindner, R. C., and Harley, C. P. Nutrient interrelations in lime-induced chlorosis. *Plant Physiol.* **19**, 420–439 (1944).

298. Lipman, C. B. Importance of silicon, aluminum and chlorine for higher plants. *Soil Sci.* **45**, 189–198 (1938).

298a. Löhnis, M. P. Plant development in the absence of boron. *Mededel. Landbouwhogeschool Wageningen* **41**, Part 3 (1937).

299. Löhnis, M. P. Histology of symptoms of boron deficiency in plants. *Mededel. Landbouwhogeschool Wageningen* **44**, 3–36 (1940).

300. Löhnis, M. P. Manganese toxicity in field and market garden crops. *Plant and Soil* **3**, 193–222 (1951).

301. Löhnis, M. P. Effect of magnesium and calcium supply on the uptake of manganese by various crop plants. *Plant and Soil* **12**, 339–376 (1960).

302. Loneragan, J. F. Calcium in the nitrogen metabolism of subterranean clover. *Australian J. Biol. Sci.* **12**, 26–39 (1959).

303. Loneragan, J. F., and Dowling, E. J. The interaction of calcium and hydrogen ions in the nodulation of subterranean clover. *Australian J. Agr. Research* **9**, 464–472 (1958).

304. Lorenz, O. A. Internal breakdown of table beets. *Cornell Univ. Agr. Expt. Sta. Mem.* **246** (1942).

305. Loustalot, A. J., Burrows, F. W., Gilbert, S. G., and Nason, A. Effect of copper and zinc deficiencies on the photosynthesis activity of the foliage of young tung trees. *Plant Physiol.* **20**, 283–288 (1945).

306. Lowenhaupt, B. Nutritional effects of boron on growth and development of the sunflower. *Botan. Gaz.* **104**, 316–322 (1942).

307. Lucas, R. E. Effect of copper fertilization on carotene, ascorbic acid, protein and copper contents of plants grown on organic soils. *Soil Sci.* **65**, 461–469 (1948).

308. Lundegårdh, H. Mangan als Katalysator der Pflanzenatmung. *Planta* **29**, 419–426 (1939).

309. Lutman, B. F. Cell size and structure in plants as affected by inorganic elements. *Univ. Vermont Agr. Expt. Sta. Bull.* **383** (1934).

310. Lyon, C., and Garcia, C. R. Anatomical responses of tomato stems to variations in the macronutrient anion supply. *Botan. Gaz.* **105**, 394–405 (1944).

311. Lyon, C., and Garcia, C. R. Anatomical responses in the anatomy of tomato stems to variations in the macronutrient cation supply. *Botan. Gaz.* **105**, 441–456 (1944).

312. Lyttleton, J. W. Stabilization by manganous ions of ribosomes from embryonic plant tissue. *Nature* **187**, 1026–1027 (1960).

313. MacLachlan, G. A., and Waygood, E. R. Kinetics of the enzymically catalysed oxidation of indole acetic acid. *Can. J. Biochem. Physiol.* **34**, 1233–1250 (1956).

314. MacVicar, R., and Burris, R. H. Relation of boron to certain plant oxidases. *Arch. Biochem.* **17**, 31–39 (1948).

315. MacVicar, R., and Struckmeyer, B. E. The relation of photoperiod to the boron requirements of plants. *Botan. Gaz.* **107**, 454–461 (1946).

316. Maizel, J. V., and Benson, A. A. Identification of phosphorylcholine as an important constituent in plant saps. *Plant Physiol.* **31**, 407–408 (1956).

317. Maley, L., and Mellor, D. P. Stability of some metal complexes of histidine. *Nature* **165**, 453 (1956).

318. Mallette, M. F. The nature of the copper enzymes involved in tyrosinase oxidation. *In* "Copper Metabolism" (W. D. McElroy and B. Glass, eds.), pp. 48–75. Johns Hopkins Univ. Press, Baltimore, Maryland, 1950.

319. Mangin, L. Étude historique et critique sur la presence des composés pectiques dans les tissus végétaux. *J. botan.* **6,** 12–19 (1892).

320. Marais, J. S. C. Monofluoroacetic acid, the toxic principle of "Gifblaar" *Dichapetalum cymosum* (Hook.) Engl. *Onderstepoort J. Vet. Sci. Animal Ind.* **20,** 67–73 (1944).

321. Marsh, R. P. Comparative study of the calcium-boron metabolism of dicots and monocots. *Soil Sci.* **53,** 75–78 (1942).

322. Marsh, R. P., and Shive, J. W. Boron as a factor in the calcium metabolism of the corn plant. *Soil Sci.* **51,** 141–151 (1941).

323. Martin, J. P. Boron deficiency symptoms in sugar cane. *Hawaiian Planters' Record* **28,** 95–107 (1934).

324. Maskell, E. J., Evans, H., and Murray, D. B. The symptoms of nutritional deficiencies in cacao produced in sand and water cultures. *In* "Report on Research on Cocoa (1945–1951)," pp. 54–64. Imperial College Tropical Agriculture, Trinidad, 1953.

325. Mazé, P. Détermination des elements minéraux rares nécessaires au développement du maïs. *Compt. rend. acad. sci.* **160,** 211–214 (1915).

326. Mazé, P. Recherche d'une solution purement minérale capable d'assurer l'évolution complète du maïs culturé à l'abri des microbes. *Ann. inst. Pasteur* **33,** 139–173 (1919).

327. Mazia, D. The particulate organization of the chromosome. *Proc. Natl. Acad. Sci. U.S.* **40,** 521–527 (1954).

328. McCalla, D. R., and Neish, A. C. Metabolism of phenylpropionoid compounds in *Salvia.* II. Biosynthesis of phenolic cinnamic acids. *Can. J. Biochem. Physiol.* **37,** 537–547 (1959).

329. McCollum, R. E., Hageman, R. H., and Tyner, E. H. Influence of potassium upon pyruvic kinase from plant tissue. *Soil Sci.* **86,** 324–331 (1958).

329a. McCool, M. M. Effect of light intensity on the manganese content of plants. *Contribs. Boyce Thompson Inst.* **7,** 427–437 (1935).

330. McElroy, W. D., and Nason, A. Mechanism of action of micronutrient elements in enzyme systems. *Ann. Rev. Plant Physiol.* **5,** 1–30 (1954).

331. McGeorge, W. T. The chlorosis of pineapple plants grown in manganiferous soils. *Soil Sci.* **16,** 269–274 (1923).

332. McGeorge, W. T. Lime induced chlorosis: relation between active iron and citric and oxalic acids. *Soil Sci.* **68,** 381–390 (1949).

333. McHargue, J. S., and Calfee, R. K. Effect of boron on the growth of lettuce. *Plant Physiol.* **7,** 161–164 (1932).

334. McIlrath, W. J., and Palser, B. F. Responses of tomato, turnip and cotton to variations in boron nutrition. I. Physiological responses. *Botan. Gaz.* **118,** 43–52 (1956).

335. McLean, F. T., and Gilbert, B. E. Aluminium toxicity. *Plant Physiol.* **3,** 293–302 (1928).

336. McMurtry, J. E., Jr. The effect of boron deficiency on the growth of tobacco in aerated and unaerated solutions. *J. Agr. Research* **38,** 371–380 (1929).

337. McMurtry, J. E., Jr. Plant nutrient deficiency in tobacco. *In* "Hunger Signs in Crops" (G. Hambidge, ed.), pp. 15–24. American Society of Agronomy and National Fertilizer Society, Washington, D.C., 1941.

337a. McMurtry, J. E., Jr. Visual symptoms of malnutrition in plants. *In* "Diagnostic Techniques for Soils and Crops" (H. B. Kitchen, ed.), Chapter 8, pp. 231–289. American Potash Institute, Washington, D.C., 1948.

337b. Meagher, W. R., Johnson, C. M., and Stout, P. R. Molybdenum requirements of leguminous plants supplied with fixed nitrogen. *Plant Physiol.* **27**, 223–230 (1952).

338. Mehler, A. H. Studies on reactions of illuminated chloroplasts. I. Mechanisms of the reduction of oxygen and other Hill reagents. *Arch. Biochem.* **33**, 66–77 (1951).

339. Mehler, A. H. Studies on reactions of illuminated chloroplasts. II. Stimulation and inhibition of the reaction with molecular oxygen. *Arch. Biochem.* **34**, 339–351 (1951).

340. Mellor, D. P., and Maley, L. Stability constants of internal complexes. *Nature* **159**, 370 (1947).

340a. Mellor, D. P., and Maley, L. Order of stability of metal complexes. *Nature* **161**, 436–437 (1948).

341. Mertz, E. T., and Matsumoto, H. Further studies on the amino acids and proteins of sulphur deficient alfalfa. *Arch. Biochem. Biophys.* **63**, 50–63 (1956).

342. Mertz, E. T., Singleton, V. L., and Garey, C. L. The effect of sulphur deficiency on the amino acids of alfalfa. *Arch. Biochem.* **38**, 139–145 (1952).

343. Mevius, W. Kalzium ion und Wurzelwachstum. *Jahrb. Wiss. Botan.* **66**, 183–253 (1927).

344. Mevius, W. Weitere Beiträge zum Problem des Wurzelwachstum. *Jahrb. Wiss. Botan.* **69**, 119–190 (1928).

345. Miller, C. O. Relationship of the cobalt and light effects on expansion of etiolated bean discs. *Plant Physiol.* **27**, 408–412 (1952).

346. Miller, C. O. The influence of cobalt and sugars upon the elongation of etiolated pea stem segments. *Plant Physiol.* **29**, 79–82 (1954).

347. Miller, G. W., and Evans, H. J. Inhibition of plant cytochrome oxidase by bicarbonate. *Nature* **178**, 974–976 (1956).

348. Miller, G. W., and Evans, H. J. The influence of salts on the activity of particulate cytochrome oxidase from roots of higher plants. *Plant Physiol.* **31**, 357–364 (1956).

349. Miller, G. W., and Evans, H. J. The influence of salts on pyruvic kinase from tissues of higher plants. *Plant Physiol.* **32**, 346–354 (1957).

350. Miller, J. T., and Byers, H. G. Selenium in plants in relation to its occurrence in soils. *J. Agr. Research* **55**, 59–68 (1937).

351. Millikan, C. R. "Withertop" (calcium deficiency) disease in plants. *J. Dept. Agr. Victoria* **42**, 79 (1944).

352. Millikan, C. R. Effect of molybdenum on the severity of toxicity in flax induced by an excess of either Mn, Zn, Cu, Ni, or Co in the nutrient solution. *J. Australian Inst. Agr. Sci.* **13**, 180–186 (1947).

353. Millikan, C. R. Effects on flax of a toxic concentration of boron, iron, molybdenum, aluminium, copper, zinc, manganese, cobalt or nickel in the nutrient solution. *Proc. Roy. Soc. Victoria* **61**, 25–42 (1949).

354. Millikan, C. R. Relation between nitrogen source and the effect on flax of an excess of manganese or molybdenum in the nutrient solution. *Australian J. Sci. Research* **B3**, 450–473 (1950).

355. Millikan, C. R. Diseases of flax and linseed. *Dept. Agr. Victoria Tech. Bull.* **9** (1953).

356. Millikan, C. R. Nutritional disorders in subterranean clover. *Dept. Agr. Victoria Tech. Bull.* 11 (1953).

357. Millikan, C. R. Relative effects of zinc and copper deficiencies on lucerne and subterranean clover. *Australian J. Biol. Sci.* 6, 164–177 (1953).

357a. Minarik, C. E., and Shive, J. W. The effect of boron in the substrate on calcium accumulation by soybean plants. *Am. J. Botany* 26, 827–831 (1939).

358. Mitchell, K. J. Preliminary note on the use of ammonium molybdate to control whiptail in cauliflower and broccoli crops. *New Zealand J. Sci. Technol.* A27, 287–293 (1945).

359. Mitchell, J. W., Dugger, W. M., Jr., and Gauch, H. G. Increased translocation of plant growth-modifying substances due to application of boron. *Science* 118, 354–355 (1953).

359a. Molisch, H. "Mikrochemie der Pflanzen," 3rd ed. Gustav Fischer, Jena, 1923.

360. Morris, A. A. Some observations on the effects of boron treatment in the control of "hard fruit" in citrus. *J. Pomol. Hort. Sci.* 16, 167–181 (1938).

361. Morton, A. G., and Watson, D. J. A physiological study of leaf growth. *Ann. Botany (London)* [N.S.] 12, 281–310 (1948).

362. Mowry, H., and Camp, A. F. A preliminary report on zinc sulphate as a corrective for bronzing of tung trees. *Univ. Florida Agr. Expt. Sta. Bull.* 273 (1934).

362a. Muhr, G. R. Plant symptoms of boron deficiency and the effects of borax on the yield and chemical composition of several crops. *Soil Sci.* 54, 55–65 (1942).

363. Mulder, E. G. Importance of molybdenum in the nitrogen metabolism of microorganisms and higher plants. *Plant and Soil* 1, 94–119 (1948).

364. Mulder, E. G. Mineral nutrition in relation to the biochemistry and physiology of potatoes. *Plant and Soil* 2, 59–121 (1949).

365. Mulder, E. G. Mineral nutrition of plants. *Ann. Rev. Plant Physiol.* 1, 1–24 (1950).

366. Mulder, E. G. Molybdenum in relation to growth of higher plants and microorganisms. *Plant and Soil* 5, 368–415 (1954).

367. Mulder, E. G., and Bakema, K. The effect of the nitrogen phosphorus, potassium and magnesium nutrition of potato plants on the content of free amino acids and on the amino acid composition of the protein of the tubers. *Plant and Soil* 7, 135–166 (1956).

368. Mulder, E. G., Boxma, R., and Van Veen, W. L. The effect of molybdenum and nitrogen deficiencies on nitrate reduction in plant tissues. *Plant and Soil* 10, 335–355 (1959).

369. Mullison, W. R., and Mullison, E. Growth responses of barley seedlings in relation to potassium and sodium nutrition. *Plant Physiol.* 17, 632–644 (1942).

370. Nason, A. Effect of zinc deficiency on the synthesis of tryptophane by *Neurospora* extracts. *Science* 112, 111–112 (1950).

371. Nason, A., Oldewurtel, H. A., and Propst, L. M. Role of micronutrient elements in the metabolism of higher plants. I. Change in oxidative enzyme constitution of tomato leaves deficient in micronutrient elements. *Arch. Biochem. Biophys.* 38, 1–13 (1952).

372. Neales, T. F. Effect of boron supply on the sugars soluble in 80 per cent ethanol in flax seedlings. *Nature* 183, 483 (1959).

373. Neales, T. F. Some effects of boron on root growth. *Australian J. Biol. Sci.* 13, 232–248 (1960).

374. Neller, T. R., and Morse, W. J. Effect upon the growth of potatoes, corn and beans resulting from the addition of borax to the fertilizer used. *Soil Sci.* **12**, 79–131 (1921).

375. Nelson, J. M. Phenol oxidase and plant respiration. *In* "Copper Metabolism" (W. D. McElroy and B. Glass, eds.), pp. 76–88. Johns Hopkins Univ. Press, Baltimore, Maryland, 1950.

376. Ng, E. K., and Carr, D. J. Effects of pH on the activity of chelating agents and auxins in cell extension. *Physiol. Plantarum* **12**, 275–287 (1959).

377. Nicholas, D. J. D. Manganese and iron content of crop plants as determined by chemical methods. *J. Hort. Sci.* **25**, 60–77 (1949).

378. Nicholas, D. J. D. Some effects of metals in excess on crop plants grown in soil culture. III. Effects of cobalt, nickel and zinc on growth, metal and chlorophyll contents of tomato. *Long Ashton Research Sta. Ann. Rept.* **1951**, 87–102 (1952).

379. Nicholas, D. J. D. Some effects of metals in excess on crop plants grown in soil culture. I. Effects of copper, zinc, lead, cobalt, nickel and manganese on tomato grown in an acid soil. *Long Ashton Research Sta. Ann. Rept.* **1950**, 96–108 (1951).

380. Nicholas, D. J. D., and Nason, A. Mechanisms of action of nitrate reductase from *Neurospora. J. Biol. Chem.* **211**, 183–197 (1954).

381. Nicholas, D. J. D., and Thomas, W. D. E. Some effects of heavy metals on plants grown in soil culture. I. The effect of cobalt on fertilizer and soil phosphate uptakes and the iron and cobalt status of tomato. *Plant and Soil* **5**, 67–80 (1953).

382. Nicholas, D. J. D., and Thomas, W. D. E. Some effects of heavy metals on plants grown in soil culture. II. The effect of nickel on fertilizer and soil phosphate uptakes and the iron and nickel status of tomato. *Plant and Soil* **5**, 182–183 (1954).

383. Nightingale, G. T., Addoms, R. M., Robbins, W. R., and Schermerhorn, L. G. Effect of calcium deficiency on nitrate absorption and on metabolism in tomato. *Plant Physiol.* **6**, 605–630 (1931).

384. Nightingale, G. T., Schermerhorn, L. G., and Robbins, W. R. Some effects of potassium deficiency on the histological structure and nitrogenous and carbohydrate constituents of plants. *New Jersey Agr. Expt. Sta. Bull.* **499** (1930).

385. Nightingale, G. T., Schermerhorn, L. G., and Robbins, W. R. Effect of sulphur deficiency on metabolism in plants. *Plant Physiol.* **7**, 565–595 (1932).

385a. Nilsson, R., Alm, F., and Burström, D. Manganese as a substitute for magnesium in the metabolism and anabolism of the cell. *Arch. Mikrobiol.* **12**, 353–376 (1942).

386. Njoku, E. The effect of mineral nutrition and temperature on leaf shape in *Ipomoea caerulea. New Phytologist* **56**, 154–171 (1957).

387. Noack, K., and Liebich, H. Die Eisengarnitur der Chloroplasten von Spinat. *Naturwissenschaften* **29**, 302 (1941).

388. Nobbe, F., and Siegert, T. Über das Chlor als Spezifischer Nährstoff des Buchweizenpflanze. *Landwirtsch. Ver. Sta.* **4**, 318–340 (1862).

389. Odhnoff, C. Boron deficiency and growth. *Physiol. Plantarum* **10**, 984–1000 (1957).

389a. Odhnoff, C. The influence of boric acid and phenylboric acid on the root growth of bean (*Phaseolus vulgaris*). *Physiol. Plantarum* **14**, 187–220 (1961).

390. Ohmura, T. Photophosphorylation by chloroplasts. *Biochem. J. (Japan)* **45**, 319–331 (1958).

350 E. J. HEWITT

391. O'Kelley, J. C. Boron effects on growth, oxygen uptake and sugar absorption by germinating pollen. *Am. J. Botany* **44**, 239–245 (1957).
391a. Olsen, C. Iron absorption and chlorosis in green plants. *Compt. rend. trav. lab. Carlsberg. Sér. chim.* **21**, 15–32 (1935).
392. Olsen, C. Absorption of calcium and formation of oxalic acid in green plants. *Compt. rend. trav. lab. Carlsberg. Sér. chim.* **23**, 101–124 (1939).
393. Olsen, S. R., Watanabe, F. S., and Cole, C. V. Effect of sodium bicarbonate on the solubility of phosphorus in calcareous soils. *Soil Sci.* **89**, 288–291 (1960).
394. Oserkowsky, J. Quantitative relation between iron in green plants and chlorotic pear leaves. *Plant Physiol.* **8**, 449–468 (1933).
395. Oserkowsky, J., and Thomas, Harold E. Exanthema in pear and copper deficiency. *Plant Physiol.* **13**, 451–467 (1938).
396. Ozanne, P. G. The effect of nitrogen on zinc deficiency in subterranean clover. *Australian J. Biol. Sci.* **8**, 47–55 (1955).
397. Ozanne, P. G. The effect of light on zinc deficiency in subterranean clover (*Trifolium subterraneum* L.). *Australian J. Biol. Sci.* **8**, 344–353 (1955).
398. Ozanne, P. G. Chlorine deficiency in soils. *Nature* **182**, 1172–1173 (1958).
399. Ozanne, P. G., Woolley, J. T., and Broyer, T. C. Chlorine and bromine in the nutrition of higher plants. *Australian J. Biol. Sci.* **10**, 66–79 (1957).
400. Palser, B. F., and McIlrath, W. J. Responses of tomato, turnip and cotton to variations in boron nutrition. II. Anatomical responses. *Botan. Gaz.* **118**, 53–71 (1956).
401. Pearsall, W. H., and Hanby, A. M. The variation in leaf form in *Potamogeton perfoliatus*. *New Phytologist* **24**, 112–120 (1925).
402. Penston, N. L. Studies of the physiological importance of the mineral elements in plants. III. A study by microchemical methods of the distribution of potassium in the potato plant. *Ann. Botany (London)* **45**, 673–692 (1931).
403. Perkins, H. J., and Aronoff, S. Identification of the blue-fluorescent compounds in boron deficient plants. *Arch. Biochem. Biophys.* **64**, 506–507 (1956).
404. Peters, R. A. Fluorine compounds in African plants. *Biochem. J.* **76**, 32P (1960).
405. Peters, R. A., Hall, R. J., Ward, P. F. V., and Sheppard, N. The chemical nature of toxic compounds containing fluorine in the seeds of *Dichapetalum toxicarium*. *Biochem. J.* **77**, 17–23 (1960).
406. Piper, C. S. Molybdenum as an essential element for plant growth. *J. Australian Inst. Agr. Sci.* **6**, 162–164 (1940).
407. Piper, C. S. The symptoms and diagnosis of minor-element deficiencies in agricultural and horticultural crops. Part I. Diagnostic methods. Boron. Manganese. *Empire J. Exptl. Agr.* **8**, 85–96 (1940).
408. Piper C. S. The symptoms and diagnosis of microelement deficiencies in agricultural and horticultural crops. Part II. Copper. Zinc. Molybdenum. *Empire J. Exptl. Agr.* **8**, 199–206 (1940).
409. Piper, C. S. Marsh spot of peas: a manganese deficiency disease. *J. Agr. Sci.* **31**, 448–453 (1941).
410. Piper, C. S. Investigations on copper deficiency in plants. *J. Agr. Sci.* **32**, 143–178 (1942).
411. Pirson, A. Functional aspects of mineral nutrition of green plants. *Ann. Rev. Plant Physiol.* **6**, 71–114 (1955).
412. Pirson, A. Mineralstoffe und Photosynthese. *In* "Encyclopaedia of Plant Physiology" (W. Ruhland, ed.), pp. 355–381. Springer, Berlin, 1958.

413. Pirson, A. Manganese and its role in photosynthesis. *In* "Trace Elements" (C. A. Lamb, O. B. Bentley, and J. M. Beattie, eds.), pp. 81–98. Academic Press, New York, 1958.

413a. Plant, W. The control of "whiptail" in broccoli and cauliflower. *J. Hort. Sci.* **26**, 109–117 (1951).

414. Portsmouth, G. B. The effects of manganese on carbon assimilation in the potato plant as determined by a modified half-leaf method. *Ann. Botany (London)* [N.S.] **13**, 113–133 (1949).

415. Possingham, J. V. The effect of molybdenum on the organic and inorganic phosphorus of plants. *Australian J. Biol. Sci.* **7**, 221–224 (1954).

416. Possingham, J. V. The effect of mineral nutrition on the content of free amino acids and amides in tomato plants. I. A comparison of effects of deficiencies of copper, zinc, manganese, iron and molybdenum. *Australian J. Biol. Sci.* **9**, 539–551 (1956).

417. Possingham, J. V. The effect of mineral nutrition on the content of free amino acids and amides in tomato plants. II. A study of the effect of molybdenum. *Australian J. Biol. Sci.* **10**, 40–49 (1957).

418. Possingham, J. V., and Brown R. The nuclear incorporation of iron and its significance in growth. *J. Exptl. Botany* **9**, 277–284 (1958).

419. Quinlan-Watson, T. A. F. Aldolase activity in zinc deficient plants. *Nature* **167**, 1033–1034 (1951).

420. Quinlan-Watson, T. A. F. The effect of zinc deficiency on the aldolase activity in the leaves of oats and clover. *Biochem. J.* **53**, 457–460 (1953).

421. Rabin, R. S., and Klein, R. M. Chlorogenic acid as a competitive inhibitor of indole-acetic acid oxidase. *Arch. Biochem. Biophys.* **70**, 11–15 (1957).

422. Raleigh, G. J. Evidence for the essentiality of silicon for growth of the beet plant. *Plant Physiol.* **14**, 823–828 (1939).

423. Raleigh, G. J. Silicon in plant growth. *Soil Sci.* **60**, 133–135 (1945).

424. Raleigh, G. J. Effects of the sodium and chloride ions in the nutrition of table beet in culture solutions. *Proc. Am. Soc. Hort. Sci.* **51**, 433–436 (1948).

425. Ray, P. M. Destruction of auxin. *Ann. Rev. Plant Physiol.* **9**, 81–118 (1958).

426. Reed, H. S. The value of certain nutritive elements to the plant cell. *Ann. Botany (London)* **21**, 501–543 (1907).

427. Reed, H. S. Cytology of leaves affected with "little-leaf." *Am. J. Botany* **25**, 174–186 (1938).

428. Reed, H. S. The relation of copper and zinc salts to leaf structure. *Am. J. Botany* **26**, 29–33 (1929).

429. Reed, H. S. Effect of zinc deficiency on cells of vegetative buds. *Am. J. Botany* **28**, 10–17 (1941).

430. Reed, H. S. The relation of zinc to seed production. *J. Agr. Research* **64**, 635–644 (1942).

431. Reed, H. S. The growth of ovules of *Pisum* in relation to zinc. *Am. J. Botany* **31**, 193–199 (1944).

432. Reed, H. S. Effect of zinc deficiency on phosphate metabolism of the tomato plant. *Am. J. Botany* **33**, 778–784 (1946).

433. Reed, H. S. A physiological study of boron deficiency in plants. *Hilgardia* **17**, 377–411 (1947).

434. Reed, H. S., and Dufrenoy, J. The effect of zinc and iron salts on the cell structure of mottled orange leaves. *Hilgardia* **9**, 113–137 (1935).

435. Reed, H. S., and Dufrenoy, J. Modification in cell structure accompanying "little-leaf" of the orange. *Am. J. Botany* **22**, 311–328 (1935).

436. Reed, H. S., and Dufrenoy, J. Catechol aggregates in the vacuoles of zinc deficient plants. *Am. J. Bot.* **29**, 544–551 (1942).

436a. Reed, H. S., and Haas, A. R. C. The pseudo-antagonism of sodium and calcium in dilute solutions. *J. Agr. Research* **24**, 753–758 (1923).

437. Reeve, E., and Shive, J. W. Potassium-boron and calcium-boron relationships in plant nutrition. *Soil Sci.* **57**, 1–15 (1944).

438. Reinert, J., and White, P. R. The cultivation *in vitro* of tumour and normal tissues of *Picea glauca*. *Physiol. Plantarum* **9**, 177–189 (1956).

439. Reisenauer, H. M. Cobalt in nitrogen fixation by a legume. *Nature* **186**, 375–376 (1960).

440. Reuther, W., and Burrows, F. W. The effect of manganese sulphate on the photosynthetic activity of tung foliage. *Proc. Am. Soc. Hort. Sci.* **40**, 73–76 (1942).

440a. Rhoads, W. A., and Wallace, A. Possible involvement of dark fixation of CO_2 in lime-induced chlorosis. *Soil Sci.* **89**, 248–256 (1959).

441. Riceman, D. S., and Jones, G. B. Distribution of zinc and copper in subterranean clover (*Trifolium subterraneum* L.) grown in culture solutions supplied with graduated amounts of zinc. *Australian J. Agr. Research* **9**, 73–122 (1958).

442. Richards, F. J. Physiological studies in plant nutrition. III. Further studies of the effect of potash deficiency on the rate of respiration in leaves of barley. *Ann. Botany (London)* **46**, 367–388 (1932).

442a. Richards, F. J. Physiological studies in plant nutrition. VIII. The relation of respiration rate to the carbohydrate and nitrogen metabolism of the barley leaf as determined by phosphorus and potassium supply. *Ann. Botany (London)* [N.S.] **2**, 491–534 (1938).

443. Richards, F. J. Physiological studies in plant nutrition. XI. The effects on growth of rubidium with low potassium supply and modification of this effect by other nutrients. Part I. The effect on total dry weight. *Ann. Botany (London)* [N.S.] **5**, 263–296 (1941).

444. Richards, F. J. Physiological studies in plant nutrition. XI. The effects on growth of rubidium with low potassium supply and modification of this effect by other nutrients. Part 2. The effect on dry weight distribution net assimilation rate, tillering, fertility, etc. *Ann. Botany (London)* [N.S.] **8**, 323–356 (1944).

445. Richards, F. J., and Berner, E. Physiological studies in plant nutrition. XVII. A general survey of the free amino acids of barley as effected by mineral nutrition with special reference to potassium supply. *Ann. Botany (London)* [N.S.] **18**, 15–33 (1954).

446. Richards, F. J., and Coleman, R. G. Occurrence of putrescine in potassium deficient barley. *Nature* **170**, 460 (1952).

447. Richards, F. J., and Shih, Sheng-Han. Physiological studies in plant nutrition. X. Water content of barley leaves as determined by the interaction of potassium with certain other nutrients. Part I. The relationship between water content and nutrient composition. *Ann. Botany (London)* [N.S.] **4**, 165–176 (1940).

448. Richards, F. J., and Shih, Sheng-Han. Physiological studies in plant nutrition. X. Water content of barley leaves as determined by the interaction of potassium and other nutrients. Part 2. The relation between water content and the composition of the leaves. *Ann. Botany (London)* [N.S.] **4**, 403–426 (1940).

449. Richards, F. J., and Templeman, W. G. Physiological studies in plant nutrition. IV. Nitrogen metabolism in relation to nutrient deficiency and age in leaves of barley. *Ann. Botany (London)* 50, 367–402 (1936).

450. Rijven, A. H. G. C. Effects of some inorganic nitrogenous substances on growth and nitrogen assimilation of young plant embryos *in vitro. Australian J. Biol. Sci.* 11, 142–154 (1958).

451. Ruck, H. C., and Bolas, B. D. The effect of manganese on the assimilation and respiration rate of isolated rooted leaves. *Ann. Botany (London)* [N.S.] 18, 267–297 (1954).

452. Samuel, G., and Piper, C. S. "Greyspeck" (manganese deficiency) disease of oats. *J. Dept. Agr. S. Australia* 31, 696–705, 789–799 (1928).

453. Samuel, G., and Piper, C. S. Manganese as an essential element for plant growth. *Ann. Appl. Biol.* 16, 493–524 (1929).

454. Sarata, U. Studies in the biochemistry of copper. XVII. Copper and the pigmentation of flowers and leaves. *Japanese J. Med. Sci. II. Biochem.* 3, 197–205 (1937). Cited by Steinberg (504a).

454a. Sayre, J. D. Accumulated iron in the nodes of corn plants. *Plant Physiol.* 5, 393–398 (1930).

454b. Schmid, W. E., and Gerloff, G. C. A naturally occurring chelate of iron in xylem exudation. *Plant Physiol.* 36, 226–231 (1961).

455. Schmucker, T. Über den Einfluss von Borsaure auf Pflanzen ins besondere Keimende Pollenkörner. *Planta* 18, 641–650 (1933).

456. Schmucker, T. Über den Einfluss von Borsaure auf Pflanzen ins besondere Keimende Pollenkörner. *Planta* 23, 264–283 (1934).

457. Scholz, G. Über die physiologische Wirkung des Bors auf Keimwurzeln von *Vicia faba. Flora (Jena)* 148, 295–305 (1959).

458. Scholz, G. Über die Translokation des Bors in Tabak-Blattstecklingen mit geteilten Wurzelsystem. *Flora (Jena)* 148, 484–488 (1960).

459. Schütte, K. H., and Schendel, H. E. The influence of trace elements upon plant protein composition. *Nature* 182, 958 (1958).

460. Schwabe, W. W. Physiological studies in plant nutrition. XVI. The mineral nutrition of bracken. Part I. Prothallial culture and the effects of phosphorus and potassium supply on leaf production in the sporophyte. *Ann. Botany (London)* [N.S.] 15, 417–446 (1951).

461. Schwarz, K., and Foltz, C. M. Factor 3 activity of selenium compounds. Reference to Thesis by A. L. Smith 1949 S. Dakota State Coll. Arg. & Mechanic Arts. *J. Biol. Chem.* 233, 245–251 (1958).

462. Scofield, C. S., and Wilcox, L. V. Boron in irrigation waters. *U.S. Dept. Agr. Tech. Bull.* 264 (1931).

463. Scott, E. G. Effect of supra-optimal boron levels on respiration and carbohydrate metabolism of *Helianthus annuus. Plant Physiol.* 35, 653–661 (1960).

464. Scott, L. E. Boron nutrition of the grape. *Soil Sci.* 57, 55–65 (1944).

465. Scott, L. E., Appleman, L. O., and Wilson, H. The discoloration of sweet potatoes during preparation for processing and the oxidase in the roots. *Univ. Maryland Agr. Expt. Sta. Tech. Bull.* A33 (1944).

466. Scott, L. E., Thomas, Harold E., and Thomas, H. E. Boron deficiency in the olive. *Phytopathology* 33, 933–942 (1943).

467. Scripture, P. N., and McHargue, J. S. Effect of boron deficiency on the soluble nitrogen and carbohydrate content of alfalfa. *J. Am. Soc. Agron.* 35, 988–992 (1943).

468. Scripture, P. N., and McHargue, J. P. Boron supply in relation to carbohydrate metabolism and distribution in radish. *J. Am. Soc. Agron.* **37**, 360–364 (1945).
469. Sheldon, V. L., Blue, W. G., and Albrecht, W. A. Biosynthesis of amino acids according to soil fertility. I. Trytophane in forage crops. *Plant and Soil* **3**, 33–40 (1951).
470. Sheldon, V. L., Blue, W. G., and Albrecht, W. A. Biosynthesis of amino acids according to soil fertility. II. Methionine content of plants and the sulphur applied. *Plant and Soil* **3**, 361–365 (1951).
471. Shiroya, M., Shiroya, T., and Hattori, S. Studies on the browning and blackening of plant tissues. IV. Chlorogenic acid in the leaves of *Nicotiana tabacum*. *Physiol. Plantarum* **8**, 594–605 (1955).
472. Shive, T. W. The effect of boron in the substrate on calcium accumulation by soybean plants. *Am. J. Bot.* **26**, 827–831 (1939).
473. Shive, J. W. Significant roles of trace elements in the nutrition of plants. *Plant Physiol.* **16**, 435–445 (1941).
473a. Shkolnik, M. J., and Soloviyova, E. A. Studies in the physiological role of boron. I. Elimination of the deleterious effect of boron deficiency by supplying nucleic acid. *Botan. zhur.* **46**, 161–173 (1961).
473b. Shrift, A. Biological activities of selenium compounds. *Botan. Rev.* **24**, 550–583 (1958).
474. Sideris, C. P., and Young, H. Y. Growth and chemical composition of *Ananas comosus* (L.) Merr., in solution cultures with different iron-manganese ratios. *Plant Physiol.* **24**, 416–440 (1949).
475. Sisler, E. C., Duggar, W. M., Jr., and Gauch, H. G. The role of boron in the translocation of organic compounds in plants. *Plant Physiol.* **31**, 11–17 (1956).
476. Skok, J. Effect of boron on the growth and development of the radish. *Botan. Gaz.* **103**, 280–294 (1941).
477. Skok, J. The substitution of complexing substances for boron in plant growth. *Plant Physiol.* **32**, 308–312 (1957).
478. Skok, J. Relationships of boron nutrition to radiosensitivity of sunflower plants. *Plant Physiol.* **32**, 648–658 (1957).
479. Skok, J. The role of boron in the plant cell. *In* "Trace Elements" (C. A. Lamb, O. G. Bentley, and J. M. Beattie, eds.), pp. 227–243. Academic Press, New York, 1958.
480. Skok, J., and McIlrath, W. J. Distribution of boron in cells of dicotyledons in relation to growth. *Plant Physiol.* **33**, 428–431 (1958).
481. Skoog, F. Relationships between zinc and auxin in the growth of higher plants. *Am. J. Botany* **27**, 939–951 (1940).
482. Smith, J. H. C. Organic compounds of magnesium and phosphorus in relation to chlorophyll formation. *J. Am. Chem. Soc.* **69**, 1492–1496 (1947).
482a. Smith, M. E. Micronutrients essential for the growth of *Pinus radiata*. *Australian Forestry* **7**, 22–27 (1943).
483. Smith, M. E. The role of boron in plant metabolism. I. Boron in relation to the absorption and solubility of calcium. *Australian J. Exptl. Biol. Med. Sci.* **22**, 257–263 (1944).
484. Smith, M. E., and Bayliss, N. S. The necessity of zinc for *Pinus radiata*. *Plant Physiol.* **17**, 303–310 (1942).
485. Smith, R. E., and Thomas, Harold E. Copper sulphate as a remedy for exanthema in prunes, apples, pears and olives. *Phytopathology* **18**, 449–454 (1928).
486. Somers, I. I., Gilbert, S. G., and Shive, J. W. The iron-manganese ratio in

relation to the respiratory CO_2 and deficiency-toxicity symptoms in soybeans. *Plant Physiol.* **17**, 317–320 (1942).

487. Somers, I. I., and Shive, J. W. The iron-manganese relation in plant metabolism. *Plant Physiol.* **17**, 582–602 (1942).

488. Sommer, A. L. Studies concerning the essential nature of aluminum and silicon. *Univ. California Publ. Agr. Sci.* **5**, 57–81 (1926).

489. Sommer, A. L., and Lipman, C. B. Evidence of the indispensable nature of zinc and boron for higher plants. *Plant Physiol.* **1**, 231–249 (1926).

490. Sommer, A. L., and Sorokin, H. Effects of the absence of boron and some other essential elements on the cell and tissue structure of the root tips of *Pisum sativum. Plant Physiol.* **3**, 237–254 (1928).

491. Sorokin, H., and Sommer, A. L. Changes in the cells and tissues of root tips induced by the absence of calcium. *Am. J. Botany* **16**, 23–39 (1929).

492. Sorokin, H., and Sommer, A. L. Effects of calcium deficiency upon the roots of *Pisum sativum. Am. J. Botany* **27**, 308–318 (1940).

493. Spencer, D. The effect of molybdate on the activity of tomato acid phosphatases. *Australian J. Biol. Sci.* **7**, 151–160 (1954).

494. Spencer, D., and Wood, J. G. The role of molybdenum in nitrate reduction in higher plants. *Australian J. Biol. Sci.* **7**, 425–434 (1954).

495. Spurr, A. R. Fluorescence in ultraviolet light, in the study of boron deficiency in celery. *Science* **116**, 421–423 (1952).

496. Spurr, A. R. The effect of boron on cell wall structure in celery. *Am. J. Botany* **44**, 637–650 (1957).

497. Spurr, A. R. Anatomical aspects of blossom-end rot in the tomato with special reference to calcium nutrition. *Hilgardia* **28**, 269–295 (1959).

498. Steffensen, D. Induction of chromosome breakage at meiosis by a magnesium deficiency in *Tradescantia. Proc. Natl. Acad. Sci., U.S.* **39**, 613–620 (1953).

499. Steffensen, D. Irregularities of chromosome division in *Tradescantia* grown on low sulphate. *Exptl. Cell. Research* **6**, 554–556 (1954).

500. Steffensen, D. Breakage of chromosomes in *Tradescantia* with a calcium deficiency. *Proc. Natl. Acad. Sci. U.S.* **41**, 155–160 (1955).

501. Steffensen, D. Chromosome aberration in calcium deficient *Tradescantia* produced by irradiation. *Nature* **182**, 1750–1751 (1958).

502. Steinberg, R. A. Role of molybdenum in the utilisation of ammonium and nitrate nitrogen by *Aspergillus niger. J. Agr. Research* **55**, 891–902 (1937).

503. Steinberg, R. A. A possible explanation of symptom formation in tobacco, with frenching and mineral deficiencies. *Science* **110**, 714–715 (1949).

504. Steinberg, R. A. Symptoms of amino acid action on tobacco seedlings in aseptic culture. *J. Agr. Research* **78**, 733–741 (1949).

504a. Steinberg, R. A. The copper nutrition of green plants and fungi. *In* "Copper Metabolism" (W. D. McElroy and B. Glass, eds.), pp. 115–140. Johns Hopkins Univ. Press, Baltimore, Maryland, 1950.

505. Steinberg, R. A. Correlation between protein-carbohydrate metabolism and mineral deficiencies in plants. *In* "Mineral Nutrition of Plants" (E. Truog, ed.), pp. 359–386. Univ. Wisconsin Press, Madison, Wisconsin, 1951.

506. Steinberg, R. A. Symptoms of molybdenum deficiency in tobacco. *Plant Physiol.* **28**, 319–322 (1953).

507. Steinberg, R. A. Metabolism of inorganic nitrogen by plants. *In* "Inorganic Nitrogen Metabolism" (W. D. McElroy and B. Glass, eds.), pp. 153–158. Johns Hopkins Univ. Press, Baltimore, Maryland, 1956.

508. Steinberg, R. A., Bowling, J. D., and McMurtrey, J. E., Jr. Accumulation of amino acids as a chemical basis for physiological symptoms in tobacco manifesting frenching and mineral deficiency symptoms. *Plant Physiol.* **25**, 279–288 (1956).

508a. Steward, F. C. Mineral nutrition of plants. *Ann. Rev. Biochem.* **4**, 519–544 (1935).

509. Steward, F. C., Crane, F., Millar, K., Zacharias, R. M., Rabson, R., and Margolis, D. Nutritional and environmental effects on the nitrogen metabolism of plants. *In* "Utilization of Nitrogen and its Compounds by Plants," *Symposia Soc. Exptl. Biol. No.* **13**, 148–176 (1959).

510. Stewart, I., and Leonard, C. D. Molybdenum deficiency in Florida citrus. *Nature* **170**, 714–715 (1952).

511. Stewart, I., and Leonard, C. D. Correction of molybdenum deficiency in Florida citrus. *Proc. Am. Soc. Hort. Sci.* **62**, 111–115 (1953).

512. Stiles, W. "Trace Elements in Plants." Univ. Press, Cambridge, 3rd ed., 1961.

513. Stiles, W. Essential micro- (trace) elements. *In* "Encyclopaedia of Plant Physiology" (W. Ruhland, ed.), Vol. IV, pp. 558–598. Springer, Berlin, 1958.

513a. Stiles, W. Other elements. *In* "Encyclopaedia of Plant Physiology" (W. Ruhland, ed.), Vol. IV, pp. 599–614. Springer, Berlin, 1958.

514. Stoklasa, J. (1922) cited by G. E. Hutchinson. Aluminium in soils, plants and animals. *Soil Sci.* **60**, 29–40 (1945).

515. Storey, H. H. and Leach R. A sulphur deficiency disease of the tea bush. *Ann. Appl. Biol.* **20**, 23–56 (1933).

516. Stout, P. R., and Johnson, C. M. Molybdenum deficiency in horticultural and field crops. *Soil Sci.* **81**, 183–197 (1956).

517. Stout, P. R., and Meagher, W. R. Studies of the molybdenum nutrition of plants with radioactive molybdenum. *Science* **108**, 471–473 (1948).

518. Stout, P. R., Meagher, W. R., Pearson, G. A., and Johnson, C. M. Molybdenum nutrition of crop plants. I. The influence of phosphate and sulphate on the absorption of molybdenum from soils and from solution cultures. *Plant and Soil* **3**, 51–87 (1951).

519. Struckmeyer, B. E., and MacVicar, R. Further investigations on the relation of photoperiod to the boron requirements of plants. *Botan. Gaz.* **109**, 237–249 (1948).

520. Sutton, C. D., and Hallsworth, E. G. Studies on the nutrition of forage legumes. I. The toxicity of low pH and high manganese supply to lucerne as affected by climatic factors and calcium supply. *Plant and Soil* **9**, 305–317 (1958).

521. Tang, Pei-Sung, and Wu, Hsiang-Yu. Adaptive formation of nitrate reductase in rice seedlings. *Nature* **179**, 1355–1356 (1957).

522. Thimann, K. V. Studies on the growth and inhibition of isolated plant parts. V. The effects of cobalt and other metals. *Am. J. Botany* **43**, 241–250 (1956).

523. Thorne, D. W., and Wallace, A. Some factors affecting chlorosis of high lime soils. I. Ferrous and ferric iron. *Soil Sci.* **57**, 299–312 (1944).

524. Tisdale, S. L., Davis, R. L., Kingsley, A. F., and Mertz, E. T. Methionine and cystine content of two strains of alfalfa as influenced by different concentrations of the sulphate ion. *Agronomy* **42**, 221–225 (1950).

524a. Tören, J. Effets des carences minérales sur l'anatomie des tissus végétaux culturés *in vitro*. *Rev. gen. botan.* **62**, 392–421 (1955).

525. Torssell, K. Chemistry of aryl boric acids. VI. Effects of aryl boric acids on wheat roots and the role of boron in plants. *Physiol. Plantarum* 9, 652–664 (1956).

526. Trelease, S. F., and Trelease, H. M. Selenium as a stimulating and possibly essential element for indicator plants. *Am. J. Botany* 25, 372–380 (1938).

527. True, R. H. The significance of calcium for higher green plants. *Science* 55, 1–6 (1922).

528. Truog, E., Goates, R. J., Gerloff, G. L., and Berger, K. C. Magnesium-phosphorus relationships in plant nutrition. *Soil. Sci.* 63, 19–25 (1947).

529. T'so, P. O. P. Structure of microsomal nucleoprotein particles from pea seedlings. *In* "Microsomal Particles and Protein Synthesis" (R. B. Roberts, ed.), pp. 156–168. Pergamon, Cambridge, Massachusetts, 1958.

529a. T'so, P. O. P., Bonner, J., and Vinograd, J. Physical and chemical properties of microsomal particles from pea seedlings. *Plant Physiol. Suppl.* 32, xii (1957).

530. Tso, T. C., and McMurtrey, J. E., Jr. Mineral deficiency and organic constituents in tobacco plants. II. Amino acids. *Plant Physiol.* 35, 865–870 (1960).

531. Tsui, Chen. The role of zinc in auxin synthesis in the tomato plant. *Am. J. Botany* 35, 172–178 (1948).

531a. Twyman, E. S. The iron-manganese balance and its effect on the growth and development of plants. *New Phytologist* 45, 18–24 (1946).

532. Twyman, E. S. The iron and manganese requirements of plants. *New Phytologist* 50, 210–226 (1951).

533. Ulrich, A., and Ohki, K. Chlorine, bromine and sodium as nutrients for sugar beet plants. *Plant Physiol.* 31, 171–181 (1956).

534. Van Schreven, D. A. Uitwendige en inwendige symptonen van boriumgebrek bij tabak. *Tijdschr. Plantenziekten* 40, 98–129 (1934).

535. Van Schreven, D. A. Calcium deficiency as a cause of medullary necrosis of potato tubers. (English summary.) *Tijdschr. Plantenziekten* 40, 226 (1934).

536. Van Schreven, D. A. Uitwendige en inwendige symptomen van borium gebrek bij tomato. (English summary.) *Tijdschr. Plantenziekten* 41, 1–26 (1935).

537. Vanselow, A. P., and Datta, N. P. Molybdenum deficiency of the citrus plant. *Soil Sci.* 67, 363–375 (1949).

538. Varner, J. E. Unpublished work cited by G. C. Webster. The biosynthesis of amide peptide bonds. *In* "Utilisation of Nitrogen and its Compounds by Plants" *Symposia Soc. Exptl. No.* 13, 330–344 (1959).

539. Varner, J. E. The influence of the metal ion activation on the optical specificity of glutamine synthetase. *Federation Proc.* 18, Part 2 (No. 1357) (1959).

540. Vergnano, O., and Hunter, J. G. Nickel and cobalt toxicities in oat plants. *Ann. Botany (London)* [N.S.] 17, 317–328 (1952).

540a. Viets, F. G., Boawn, L. C., and Crawford, C. L. Zinc contents and deficiency symptoms of 26 crops grown in a zinc-deficient soil. *Soil Sci.* 78, 305–316 (1954).

541. Viets, F. G., Jr., Boawn, L. C., Crawford, C. L., and Nelson, C. E. Zinc deficiency in corn in central Washington. *Agronomy* 45, 559–560 (1953).

542. Wade, G. C. Production of copper deficiency symptoms in citrus in solution cultures. *Australian J. Agr. Sci.* 10, 176–177 (1944).

543. Wadleigh, C. H., and Brown, J. W. The chemical status of bean plants affected with bicarbonate-induced chlorosis. *Botan. Gaz.* 113, 373–392 (1952).

544. Wadleigh, C. H., and Shive, J. W. A microchemical study of the effect of boron deficiency in cotton seedlings. *Soil Sci.* **47**, 33–36 (1939).

545. Wagner, F. Die Bedeutung des Kieselsäure für das Wachstum einiger Kulturpflanzen ihren Nährstoff-haushalt und ihre Auffälligkeit gegen echte Mehlaupilze. *Phytopathol. Z.* **12**, 427–479 (1940).

546. Walker, J. C. Histologic-pathologic effects of boron deficiency. *Soil Sci.* **57**, 51–54 (1944).

547. Walker, J. C., McLean, H. G., and Jolivette, J. P. The boron deficiency disease in cabbage. *J. Agr. Research* **62**, 573–587 (1941).

548. Wallace, T. Leaf scorch on fruit trees. *J. Pomol. Hort. Sci.* **6**, 243–281 (1928).

549. Wallace, T. Leaf scorch on fruit trees. *J. Pomol. Hort. Sci.* **7**, 1–31 (1928).

550. Wallace, T. Investigations of chlorosis of fruit trees. II. The composition of leaves, wood and bark of current seasons shoots in cases of lime-induced chlorosis. *J. Pomol. Hort. Sci.* **7**, 172–198 (1928).

550a. Wallace, T. Some effects of deficiencies of essential elements on fruit trees. *Ann. Appl. Biol.* **17**, 649–657 (1930).

551. Wallace, T. Experiments on the manuring of fruit trees. III. The effects of deficiencies of potassium, calcium and magnesium respectively on the content of these elements and of phosphorus in the shoot and trunk regions of apple trees. *J. Pomol. Hort. Sci.* **8**, 23–43 (1930).

552. Wallace, T. Magnesium deficiency of fruit trees. *J. Pomol. Hort. Sci.* **17**, 150–166 (1940).

553. Wallace, T. "The Diagnosis of Mineral Deficiencies in Plants (A Colour Atlas and Guide)," 3rd ed. H. M. Stationery Office, London, 1961.

554. Wallace, T., and Hewitt, E. J. Studies on iron deficiency of crops. I. Problems of iron deficiency and the interrelationships of mineral elements in iron nutrition. *J. Pomol. Hort. Sci.* **22**, 133–161 (1946).

555. Wallace, T., and Hewitt, E. J. Effects of calcium deficiency on potato sets in acid soils. *Nature* **161**, 28 (1948).

556. Wallace, T., Hewitt, E. J., and Nicholas, D. J. D. Determination of factors injurious to plants in acid soils. *Nature* **156**, 778–779 (1945).

557. Walsh, T. The effect on plant growth of substituting strontium for calcium in acid soils. *Proc. Roy. Irish Acad.* **B50**, 287–294 (1945).

558. Warburg, O., and Lüttgens, W. *Biokhimiya* **11**, 303 (1946). Cited by Arnon and Whatley (19).

559. Waring, E. J., Shirlow, N. S., and Wilson, R. D. Whiptail of cauliflower; control by use of ammonium molybdate and sodium molybdate. *Agr. Gaz. New S. Wales* **59**, 625–630 (1948).

560. Warington, K. The effect of boric acid and borax on the broad bean and certain other plants. *Ann. Botany (London)* **37**, 629–672 (1923).

561. Warington, K. The changes induced in the anatomical structure of *Vicia faba* by the absence of boron from the nutrient solution. *Ann. Botany (London)* **40**, 27–42 (1926).

562. Warington, K. The influence of length of day on the response of plants to boron. *Ann. Botany (London)* **47**, 429–457 (1933).

563. Warington, K. Studies in the absorption of calcium from nutrient solutions with special reference to the presence or absence of boron. *Ann. Botany (London)* **48**, 743–776 (1934).

564. Warington, K. Observations on the effect of molybdenum on plants with reference to the Solanaceae. *Ann. Appl. Biol.* **24**, 475–493 (1937).

565. Warington, K. The growth and anatomical structure of the carrot (*Daucus carota*) as affected by boron deficiency. *Ann. Appl. Biol.* **27**, 176–183 (1940).

566. Warington, K. Some interrelationships between manganese, molybdenum and vanadium in the nutrition of soybeans, flax and oats. *Ann. Appl. Biol.* **38**, 624–641 (1951).

567. Warington, K. The influence of iron supply on the toxic effects of manganese, molybdenum and vanadium on soybean, peas and flax. *Ann. Appl. Biol.* **41**, 1–22 (1954).

568. Warington, K. The influence of high concentrations of ammonium and sodium molybdate on flax, soybean and peas grown in nutrient solutions containing deficient or excess iron. *Ann. Appl. Biol.* **43**, 709–719 (1955).

569. Warington, K. The influence of the pH of the nutrient solution and the form of iron supply on the counteraction of iron deficiency in pea, soybean and flax by high concentrations of molybdenum. *Ann. Appl. Biol.* **45**, 428–447 (1957).

570. Waygood, E. R., and MacLachlan, G. A. The effect of catalase, riboflavin and light on the oxidation of indoleacetic acid. *Physiol. Plantarum* **9**, 608–617 (1956).

571. Waygood, E. R., Oaks, A., and MacLachlan, G. A. The enzymatically catalyzed oxidation of indoleacetic acid. *Can. J. Botany* **34**, 905–926 (1956).

572. Webster, G. C. The occurrence of a cytochrome oxidase in the tissues of higher plants. *Am. J. Botany* **39**, 739–745 (1952).

573. Webster, G. C. Effects of monovalent cations on the incorporation of amino acids into protein. *Biochim. et Biophys. Acta* **20**, 565–566 (1956).

574. Webster, G. C., and Varner, J. E. Peptide bond synthesis in higher plants. II. Studies on the mechanism of synthesis of γ-glutamylcysteine. *Arch. Biochem. Biophys.* **52**, 21–32 (1954).

575. Webster, G. C., and Varner, J. E. Peptide bond synthesis in higher plants. III. The formation of glutathione from γ-glutamylcysteine. *Arch. Biochem. Biophys.* **55**, 95–103 (1955).

576. Wedin, W. F., and Struckmeyer, B. E. Effects of chloride and sulphate ions on the growth, leaf burn and anatomical structure of tobacco (*Nicotiana tabacum* L.). *Plant Physiol.* **33**, 133–139 (1958).

577. Weil-Malherbe, H., and Green, R. H. The catalytic effect of molybdate on the hydrolysis of organic phosphates. *Biochem. J.* **49**, 286–292 (1951).

578. Weinstein, L. H., and Robbins, W. R. The effect of different iron and manganese nutrient levels on the catalase and cytochrome oxidase activities on green and albino sunflower leaf tissue. *Plant Physiol.* **30**, 27–32 (1955).

579. Welkie, G. W., and Miller, G. W. Iron nutrition of *Nicotiana tabacum* L. in relation to riboflavin, riboflavin-5-phosphate and flavin adenine dinucleotide. *Plant Physiol.* **35**, 516–520 (1960).

579a. White, P. R. Accessory salts in the nutrition of excised tomato roots. *Plant Physiol.* **13**, 391–398 (1938).

579b. White, P. R. Nutrient deficiency studies and an improved inorganic nutrient for cultivation of excised tomato roots. *Growth* **7**, 53–65 (1943).

580. White-Stevens, R. H. Carbohydrate metabolism in relation to boron nutrition. *Proc. Am. Soc. Hort. Sci.* **36**, 537–543 (1938).

581. Whittington, W. J. The role of boron in plant growth behaviour. I. The effect on general growth, seed production and cytological behaviour. *J. Exptl. Botany* **8**, 353–367 (1957).

581a. Whittington, W. J. The role of boron in plant growth. II. The effect on growth of the radicle. *J. Exptl. Botany* **10**, 93–103 (1959).

582. Williams, A. H. The application of chromatography to nutritional problems in plants. *J. Sci. Food Agr.* **8**, Suppl., S 533–537 (1957).

583. Williams, D. E., and Vlamis, J. The effect of silicon on yield and manganese-54 uptake and distribution in the leaves of barley plants grown in culture solutions. *Plant Physiol.* **32**, 404–409 (1957).

584. Williams, M. C. Effect of sodium and potassium salts on growth and oxalate content of *Halogeton*. *Plant Physiol.* **35**, 500–505 (1960).

585. Wilson, R. D. Some responses of lettuce to the application of molybdenum. *J. Australian Inst. Agr. Sci.* **14**, 180–187 (1948).

586. Wilson, R. D. Molybdenum in relation to the scald disease of beans. *J. Australian Inst. Agr. Sci.* **11**, 209–211 (1948).

587. Wilson, R. D. A field response of rock melons to molybdenum. *J. Australian Inst. Agr. Sci.* **15**, 118–121 (1949).

588. Wilson, R. D., and Waring, E. J. Some observations and experiments concerning the role of molybdenum in nutrition of the cauliflower plant. *J. Australian Inst. Agr. Sci.* **14**, 141–145 (1948).

589. Winfield, M. E. The role of boron in plant metabolism. II. An account of some attempts to isolate boron complexes from plant tissues. *Australian J. Exptl. Biol. Med. Sci.* **23**, 111–117 (1945).

589a. Woltz, S. S., and Jackson, C. R. Production of "yellow strapleaf" of chrysanthemum and similar diorders by amino acid treatment. *Plant Physiol.* **36**, 197–201 (1961).

590. Wood. J. G., and Womersley, H. B. S. Development and metabolism of copper deficient oat plants. *Australian J. Exptl. Biol. Med. Sci.* **24**, 79–94 (1946).

591. Woolley, J. T., Broyer, T. C., and Johnson, G. V. Movement of chlorine within plants. *Plant Physiol.* **33**, 1–8 (1958).

592. Yasunobu, K. T., and Norris, E. R. Mechanism of borate inhibition of diphenol oxidation by tyrosinase. *J. Biol. Chem.* **227**, 473–482 (1957).

593. Zillig, W., Krone, W., and Albers, M. Untersuchungen zur Biosynthese des Proteins. III. Beitrag zur Kenntnis des Zusammensetzung und Struktur des Ribosomen. *Physiol. Chem. Hoppe-Seyler's Z.* **317**, 131–143 (1959).

594. Zittle, C. A. Reaction of borate with substances of biological interest. *Advances in Enzymol.* **12**, 493–527 (1951).

PREAMBLE TO CHAPTER 3

Knowledge of mineral nutrition of plants owes much to the study of microorganisms. Bacteria, fungi, and some algae can be grown in pure cultures of genetically pure lines, and they may produce rapidly a relative large crop from the minute inoculum which is added to an otherwise purified medium. Thus it is understandably easier to demonstrate limitingly low concentrations of one or another of the essential nutrients in the medium than it is by the growth of seed plants.

Although the microorganisms are thus well adapted to the demonstration and proof of essentiality of a given element, the various criteria by which the symptoms may be described must rely heavily upon total growth or upon chemical and metabolic characteristics, for the morphogenetic responses of the Thallophyta are apt to be so inconspicuous that they do not result in very visible symptoms. This is especially true of bacteria, or if the test organism is a member of the Fungi Imperfecti, or even if it is only the imperfect stage of a fungus for which the sexual stage is known. Thus, for the role of essential elements in differentiation and in morphogenesis, one should still turn to studies on higher plants (Chapter 2).

One of the earliest beneficial and conscious additions of zinc to a plant culture medium was that made to the medium prescribed by Raulin (1869) for the growth of fungi, and this antedated by nearly 70 years the recognition of the essentiality of zinc for angiosperms (cf. Chapter 2). Similarly, the molybdenum requirement for fungi was known (Steinberg, 1937) before the critical demonstration of its role in flowering plants by Arnon and Stout (1939). Early work of Hopkins and Wann on iron (1927) and by Hopkins on manganese requirement (1930) used *Chlorella* as the test organism, and this paved the way for the role of pure cultures of this plant in the investigation of inorganic nutrition which ranks with its adoption as an experimental object in the study of photosynthesis. Furthermore, the nutrition of certain microorganisms which fix elementary nitrogen is so important that it warrants a separate chapter which deals with biological nitrogen fixation (Chapter 5).

It is appropriate, therefore, to devote a special chapter of this treatise to the inorganic nutrition of microorganisms, even though in most cases the demonstrated metabolic role of the essential nutrient may prove to be the same as in higher plants.

CHAPTER THREE

Inorganic Nutrient Nutrition of Microorganisms

D. J. D. Nicholas

I. Introduction

The study of mineral requirements of microorganisms has received only incidental treatment until comparatively recently and almost all the observations have been confined to a few genera only. Pasteur showed that the addition of ash constituents of yeast to viable cultures of other yeast markedly stimulated growth, and this was probably the first unequivocal demonstration of the importance of inorganic substances for growth of a microorganism. Since that time, mainly as the result of pure culture work, the precise inorganic requirements of some microorganisms have been determined as well as their possible role in metabolism.

II. Mineral Element Requirements

A. ESSENTIAL AND NONESSENTIAL ELEMENTS

At the present time the mineral nutrients found in microorganisms are divided into two arbitrary groups: (a) *essential elements* (N, P, K, Mg, Ca, S, Fe, Cu, Zn, Mn, Mo, B, Cl, Na, Co, V) known to be indispensable for the growth of at least some organisms. (b) *other elements* (Ni, Ti, Se, Pb, Ag, Au, Br, I, etc.) often present in the ash of microorganisms but not yet shown to be essential for growth.

Not all the elements listed under (a) are universally required, but all of them have been found to be necessary for some type of organism. The essential elements are sometimes subdivided into two main groups: the *major* or *macro-, nutrients* and the *micronutrients, trace elements* or *oligoelements;* as the names suggest, they reflect a large or a small requirement for the elements.

Calcium and sulfur, which are usually required in much smaller amounts by microorganisms than by higher plants should therefore be classed as micronutrients for the former plant group. Boron, which is universally required by higher plants is also essential for some algae (Pirson 230) but not thus far for the growth of fungi or bacteria. Another interesting difference is that cobalt, a constituent of vitamin B_{12}, is required by some bacteria, e.g., *Lactobacillus leichmannii, Rhizobium japonicum, Azotobacter vinelandii*, and by algae, e.g., *Euglena gracilis* (116–118, 156, 220b, 220c). Recently cobalt was shown to be essential for legumes that are fixing nitrogen in association with the root nodule bacteria but not for legumes being grown on combined nitrogen (1, 2, 103, 244). This may be due solely to a cobalt requirement by nodule bacteria when they are fixing nitrogen, and thus far there is no unequivocal evidence that cobalt is essential for the growth of higher plants. Recently *Rhizobium japonicum* grown on nitrate outside the host plant was shown to have a requirement for cobalt (156, 220b, 220c). Another contrast concerns vanadium, not yet shown to be required by higher plants, although it is essential for the growth of the green alga *Scenedesmus obliquus* (10). There are no further reports, however, that vanadium is required by other algae. Bortels (34), Horner *et al.* (113), Bové *et al.* (35), and Nicholas *et al.* (218) have all shown that vanadium can partially replace molybdenum in the fixation of nitrogen in some species of *Azotobacter*. The evidence that gallium is essential for growth of *Aspergillus* (281) has not been substantiated in other laboratories, and the original claim has now been withdrawn.

Even in the micronutrient category there is a very wide range of requirement, e.g., the need for iron may be a thousand times that for molybdenum and a hundred times that for cobalt or vanadium. There is some justification, therefore, for an "ultramicronutrient group" of biologically important metals to include molybdenum, vanadium, and possibly cobalt. Other nutrients may be added to this list in due course when pure culture methods are developed further, and requirements for other micronutrients are established, or when these metals are found to play an indispensable role in cell metabolism.

Microorganisms have a regulatory mechanism for controlling the uptake of essential mineral nutrients from the medium as have roots of higher plants, but this breaks down when they grow under adverse conditions, e.g., high or low pH, high ionic strength, or toxic concentrations of nutrients. It is also clear that microorganisms contain in addition trace metals that are not known to perform any useful function in metabolism, e.g., iodine, in marine algae.

B. Criteria for Essentiality of Nutrients for Growth

Three criteria of essentiality for a nutrient were proposed by Arnon (9) for higher plants, and these may also be applied to microorganisms. These criteria are (a) the organism cannot complete its life cycle without the particular element, (b) its action must be specific and cannot be replaced by another, (c) its effect on the plant must be direct. As pointed out previously (208, 209, 220) concept (b) is perhaps too rigid in the light of recent work. Two examples illustrate this point. Molybdenum is required for nitrogen fixation by *Azotobacter*, but in some species vanadium has a sparing action. Both trace metals which function in nitrogen fixation occur in some habitats in roughly equivalent amounts so that either could be utilized. In higher plants, chloride is necessary for growth but bromide at higher concentrations can substitute for it (cf. Chapter 2). According to Arnon's definition neither vanadium nor chloride can be accepted as an essential element. To overcome this difficulty it has been proposed that the concept of a "functional nutrient" in contrast to an "essential nutrient" be used to include any mineral nutrient that may function in some precise way in plant metabolism irrespective of whether or not its action is completely specific or indispensable. This would also avoid problems that arise when an element is required only when certain substrates are present; thus in *Scenedesmus obliquus*, the molybdenum requirement is abolished when ammonia or urea is substituted for nitrate but the micronutrient is essential when the alga is utilizing nitrate (11, 119).

C. PURE CULTURE METHODS

As early as 1869 Raulin showed that small amounts of iron and zinc were required for growth of the mold *Aspergillus niger* (242). This was a remarkable achievement since the results were obtained before the advent of pure culture methods which involve the rigorous removal of trace metals from the culture solutions. At that time Raulin's results were disputed by others who assumed wrongly that the effects of trace metals on the mold were akin to those of toxic substances. Thus the old Arndt-Schultze hypothesis of chemical stimulation, first used to explain the effects of heavy metals on abnormal growth of animal tissues, was subsequently applied by Pfeffer (229) to account for the effects of trace metals on plant cells. This controversy was finally resolved in favor of Raulin by the careful work of subsequent workers. Thus Bertrand and Javillier (29) and later Bertrand (26) showed that manganese and zinc were indispensable for normal growth in *Aspergillus*. Steinberg, a pioneer in pure culture methods, demonstrated a 5000% increase in yields of the same fungus by returning iron and zinc to media which had previously been treated with calcium carbonate to adsorb the two metals (282–285). Other workers have amply confirmed and extended Raulin's findings (193, 202, 203, 213).

Since the preparation of culture solutions free from trace metals is an important feature of a study of requirements of microorganisms, a brief account will now be given of some of the methods used. Hewitt (108) (cf. Chapter 2) has discussed the methods used for growing higher plants in cultures freed from trace metals, but the methods to be discussed in the following section apply particularly to work with microorganisms.

1. Water Supply

Distilled water prepared from a tinned-copper still is further distilled twice from a Quickfit Pyrex glass electric distillation apparatus which is fitted with double-splash heads that are heated with a tape coil to avoid creep of the water condensate into the receiver flask (117). Data relating to the removal of metal at each stage of the distillation are given in Table I.

Water from a tinned copper still is unsuitable for the demonstration of trace metal deficiencies. The metal contents of the water are markedly reduced by distillation either once or twice from Pyrex glass stills, but there is no further reduction after a third distillation. The efficiency of the glass still can be checked by putting carrier-free radioactive cobalt-58 in the flask and checking the radioactivity in the receiver flask. Good grade deionized water checked with a conductivity cell may be used instead of glass-distilled water, but water thus treated may contain amines and other materials, especially when the resin material has aged. These substances chelate with trace metals and could interfere with critical studies of the mineral micronutrient requirements of some microorganisms. Pyrogens are also present in deionized water, and

TABLE I

TRACE-METAL CONTENT[a] OF WATER DISTILLED BY VARIOUS METHODS[b]

Method of distillation	Copper	Zinc	Manganese	Iron	Molybdenum
Tinned-copper still	0.5	0.10	0.05	0.1	0.1
Water from copper still distilled once from Pyrex glass	0.05	0.006	0.01	0.005	0.0001
Water from copper still distilled twice from Pyrex glass	0.025	0.002	0.005	0.001	0.00005
Water from copper still distilled thrice from Pyrex glass	0.020	0.002	0.005	0.001	0.00005

[a] Values in micrograms per 50 ml.
[b] Reproduced from Nicholas (203).

these can adversely affect some of the slime molds, actinomycetes, and protozoa.

2. Culture Containers

Culture vessels made of hard glass are usually used, but with the advent of toughened polythene (after neutron irradiation) and polyvinyl chloride tubing and more recently polypropylene, an inert plastic material that can be steam sterilized and readily cleaned, there is a tendency to use these materials. A word of warning should be interposed here since, during the process of toughening polythene, certain trace metals including copper, chromium, and molybdenum are used as catalysts. Glassware should be thoroughly cleaned by washing with warm 6 N nitric acid to remove surface contamination and then several times with distilled water and finally with glass-distilled or deionized water. Glassware can be checked for the presence or absence of metals by rinsing with 0.001% solution of diphenylthiocarbazone (dithizone) in carbon tetrachloride at pH 6.5. The presence of metal dithizonates is shown by a color change from the green of dithizone to red.

3. Preparation of Culture Solutions Free from Trace Metals

Since macrosalts of the culture solutions contain sufficient of the micronutrients as contaminants to support optimum growth of most microorganisms, it is necessary to remove them from the basal culture solution in order to show that they are required for growth. The methods used should have little or no effect on other constituents of the medium. The techniques so far developed are in the main applicable to culture solutions which contain inorganic salts with either a sugar or an organic acid as a carbon source (193, 202, 203, 213). The removal of trace metals from complex media is more difficult since constituents such as peptone tend to hold the metals even against the stripping action of chelating agents. Organic solvents which may be used to remove the metal chelates also take out essential growth factors. A variety of methods used to remove trace metals from culture solutions have been reviewed elsewhere (193, 202, 203, 213, 234). Some of the methods now in use are discussed under the headings a–e below.

a. *Biological depletion.* Raulin was able to reduce the iron and zinc contents of a culture solution by growing in it several generations of *Aspergillus niger* (242). Molisch (190), Molliard (189, and Bertrand and Javillier (29) using similar techniques confirmed Raulin's findings and, in addition, they showed manganese to be an additional requirement for the mold. MacLeod and Snell (163) used this method to remove manganese from cultures of lactic acid bacteria. This method is, however, unsatisfactory since several other constituents of the media are also depleted during growth and these may become rate limiting for the subsequent growth of the test organism.

b. *Inorganic reagents.* Recrystallization of macrosalts is not satisfactory since trace metals are seldom removed completely by this process (202, 203, 273). Boron is an exception since it is effectively removed from macrosalts by recrystallizing them several times from methyl alcohol since methyl borate is readily soluble.

Coprecipitation methods are often used to remove trace metals from a solution of the macrosalts and sugar. Thus Bertrand and Javillier used magnesium ammonium phosphate to adsorb manganese (29), Bortels used active carbon (33), Steinberg introduced the calcium carbonate adsorption method (280, 282), and a combination of the last two methods was used by Roberg (247). A number of investigators have employed the copper sulfide coprecipitation method to remove molybdenum and copper from macrosalts (202, 203, 213, 289).

c. *Organic reagents.* Numerous organic reagents have been used to form metal complexes which are extracted into nonpolar solvents such as carbon tetrachloride, chloroform, and ethyl acetate. The reagents include dithizone, 8-hydroxyquinoline, o-phenanthroline, α,α-dipyridil and hydroxyorganic acids, and ethylenediaminetetraacetic acid or versene. Copper, iron, zinc, and molybdenum can be removed by shaking a solution of macronutrients including a simple sugar (pH 5.5) with 5% w/v 8-hydroxyquinoline, in redistilled chloroform (202, 203, 205, 318). This method is also effective for preparing culture solutions free from zinc, iron, cobalt, and gallium. A summary of these methods is given in Table II.

d. Ion-exchange resins. Numerous resins have been used to remove metals from nonionic constituents of culture solutions, e.g., sugars. Most cation exchange resins contain microgram amounts of iron, copper, and zinc, and these are removed by percolating a 5% w/v solution of sodium chloride or magnesium sulfate (freed of metals before use by the quinoline procedure) through the columns until no more trace metals are detected by the dithizone test. The efficacy of ion-exchange methods in removing trace metals is shown in Table III.

Chemical methods of purification are usually preferable since they are more effective and specific than the ion-exchange procedures. Macrosalts are also exchanged on resin columns so that culture solutions treated in this way may become deficient in a macronutrient. Ion-exchange methods are satisfactory only for treating the nonionic components of the media, e.g., sugars.

e. Micronutrients. Only microgram amounts of trace metals are added to culture solutions so that Analar, or C.P. grade materials are usually satisfactory. Spectrographically checked trace metals are now readily available (Johnson & Matthey, London, England) for culture work. Dilute standards of the trace metals are prepared each week in graduated flasks (hard glass) so that risk of adsorption of metals onto glass from dilute solutions is minimized. Ferric chloride dissolved in 6 N hydrochloric acid is purified by extracting it into isopropyl ether, a procedure that leaves other metals in the aqueous phase (202, 203, 205).

4. Preparation of Inocula

Several serial transfers of bacteria are necessary before deficiency effects of trace metals are produced. Thus in *Escherichia coli, Pseudomonas aeruginosa, Clostridium pasteurianum* and in *Azotobacter* species deficiencies of copper, molybdenum, and manganese can be obtained only by subculturing the organisms several times in culture solutions from which the appropriate trace metal has been removed. To produce a copper or a manganese deficiency in these bacteria it is necessary to

TABLE II

REMOVAL OF TRACE METALS FROM A SOLUTION OF INORGANIC
MACRONUTRIENTS[a] AND DEXTROSE[b]

Trace metal removed	Method used for its removal	Residual metal after purification (μg/50 ml culture solution)
Copper and molybdenum	The solution was adjusted with 6 N HCl to pH 2.0, and 5 ml 20% w/v copper sulfate solution was added. H_2S from Kipp's apparatus was passed through for 15 min (H_2S is passed through a saturated barium hydroxide solution before entry into media to remove polysulfides). The solution was allowed to stand for 15 min then filtered through a No. 50 Whatman filter paper into a clean 2-liter Erlenmeyer flask. H_2S was eliminated by boiling and aerating the solution. A sintered glass funnel (No. 4) and Quickfit Büchner flask are convenient for filtering.	Cu 0.05 Mo 0.00005
Zinc, iron cobalt	The solution was adjusted to pH 5.5 with 5 N NaOH in a 2-liter Pyrex separating funnel. 30 ml 5% w/v 8-hydroxyquinoline in chloroform was added and shaken for 1 min. The chloroform phase was discarded. This was repeated twice more with similar amounts of quinoline. Three lots of 30 ml redistilled chloroform were added to remove excess quinoline; each time it was shaken for 1 min. Three lots of 30 ml redistilled diethyl ether were then added to remove excess chloroform. The ether was removed by heating the solution in a 2-liter flask on an electric hotplate at 80°C, it was aerated continuously and the flask periodically shaken.	Fe 0.01 Zn 0.01 Co 0.001
Manganese	Ten grams of $CaCO_3$, 10 ml 20% w/v K_2HPO_4, 10 ml 10% w/v calcium chloride were added and then autoclaved for ¾ hr at 15 pounds per square inch. This was cooled and filtered through a No. 42 Whatman filter paper. The pH was adjusted to 7.5.	Mn 0.005

[a] Macronutrients and dextrose, sufficient for 5 liter of media, dissolved in 400 ml of deionized water.

[b] Reproduced from Nicholas (213).

grow the organisms through a series of about 10 cultures deficient in the metal. In this way the inoculum is depleted of the particular trace metal. The cells are washed several times with the metal-deficient media before being used as an inoculum. It may also be necessary to collect spores from fungi which have been grown in culture solutions deficient in trace metals, but in *Aspergillus niger* and in *Neurospora crassa* there is little evidence of a substantial carry-over of trace metals in the spores. Some investigators have leached spores with dilute alkali to remove metals. In the author's experience this seldom leads to an

TABLE III

TRACE METAL CONTENT OF SOLUTION OF INORGANIC MACRONUTRIENTS AND DEXTROSE AFTER PASSAGE THROUGH ION-EXCHANGE RESINS COMPARED WITH THAT AFTER CHEMICAL TREATMENT[a,b]

Resin	Copper	Zinc	Iron	Manganese	Molybdenum
Amberlite IR-100	0.6	1	2	0.05	0.05
IR-100 + anion exchange IR-4B	0.05	0.5	0.05	5	0.0005
Zeocarb 215	0.05	1	2	0.01	0.05
Zeocarb 215 + anion exchange IR-4B	0.05	0.5	0.05	5	0.005
Amberlite IRC-50	0.8	5	3	1	0.002
IRC-50 + anion exchange IR-4B	1	4	2	10	0.005
Chemical method	0.05	0.1	0.01	0.01	0.00005

[a] Values in micrograms per 50 ml.
[b] From Nicholas (203).

improvement and, in fact, the drastic procedure endangers the viability of the spores.

5. Use of Microorganisms for Bioassay of Mineral Nutrients

The basis of the method is that the element to be determined is required specifically by a microorganism for growth. In its absence the yield or production of a measurable metabolite is markedly depressed. An increase in an essential nutrient from a deficiency to a sufficiency amount, when all others are present in adequate supply, results in a specific, and a quantitative increase in growth. In this way a standard growth series can be prepared for any of the essential nutrients. For bioassay a known amount of the test material is added to a culture solution that contains all the essential nutrients other than the one to be tested. Under these conditions the growth depends on the amount of the test element that the organism derives from the material which is added. The growth or some related property which is readily measured and which is dependent upon it, is referred to a standard series for the element.

Many bacteria have been used to bioassay nutrients; these include *Streptococcus faecalis, Leuconostoc mesenteroides* for potassium (range 5–30 ppm), and magnesium (range 0.1–0.5 ppm), and *Lactobacillus plantarum arabinosus* (*L. arabinosus*) for manganese (range 0.1–0.4 ppm) (273).

Several fungi have been investigated in the determination of mineral nutrients which are available in soils to crop plants. Thus the genus *Aspergillus* was used by Butkewitsch (43, 44) and Koscelecki͏̈ (138) to determine phosphate in Russian soils and since then *Aspergillus niger* has been found suitable for determining available potassium, phosphorus, magnesium, copper, zinc, manganese, and molybdenum in soils, in plant extracts, and in enzymes (69, 106, 193, 202, 203, 213). The sensitivity of the method for determining molybdenum is illustrated in Fig. 1.

As little as 1×10^{-4} μg molybdenum may be determined by this assay procedure. Other fungi which are used for the bioassay of nutrients include *Cunninghamella* species (179), *Rhizopus* species (260), *Neurospora crassa* (273), and *Penicillium glaucum* (203).

III. Requirement for Nitrogen and Its Compounds

The utilization of nitrogen and its compounds ranges from that by microorganisms that fix atmospheric nitrogen to utilization by those that require amino acids or even peptides for their growth.

A. BIOLOGICAL FIXATION OF NITROGEN

Free-living soil bacteria of the genus *Azotobacter* and some of the clostridia and pseudomonads are able to utilize atmospheric nitrogen for growth (323, 324). Root nodule bacteria associated with legumes and nonlegumes also fix atmospheric nitrogen.* The fixation process is also widespread in blue-green algae; according to Fogg and Wolfe (86) and Watanake (319) this occurs in 21 species belonging to 8 genera, as shown in Table IV. They are primarily confined to the Myxophyceae. Members of the Chroococcales and Oscillatoriaceae have not yet been shown to utilize atmospheric nitrogen.

Blue-green algae were first shown to fix nitrogen in 1889 when Frank (88) found that gains in combined nitrogen in soil cultures incubated in

---

* The problem of biological fixation of nitrogen, especially in relation to the symbiotic nodule fixation in legumes and nonlegumes is the subject of Chapter 5 in this volume.

FIG. 1. The growth *of Aspergillus niger* as a measure of the content of molybdenum (Mo) in a series of standard solutions. Growth of *Aspergillus niger* after 6 days at 25° in culture solutions containing the following amounts of Mo in micrograms $\times 10^{-4}$ per 50 ml of culture solution: a, 0; b, 5; c, 10; d, 50; e, 100; f, 500.

TABLE IV

Distribution of the Capacity to Assimilate Elementary
Nitrogen in the Myxophyceae[a]

Order and family	Species able to fix nitrogen	Species not able to fix nitrogen

Chroococcales	—	*Chroococcus turgidus*
		Chroococcus spp.
		Coccochloris peniocystis
		  (*Gloeothece linearis*)
		Diplocystis (*Microcystis*)
		  aeruginosa
		Gloeocapsa membranina
		G. dimidiata
		Synechococcus cedrorum

Chamaesiphonales	—	—
Pleurocapsales	—	—
Nostocales Oscillatoriaceae	—	*Lyngbya aestuarii* *Lyngbya* spp. *Oscillatoria* spp. *Phormidium foveolarum* *P. tenue* *P. lividum* *Phormidium* spp.
Nostocaceae	*Anabaena ambigua* *A. cylindrica* *A. fertilissima* *A. gelatinosa* *A. humicola* *A. naviculoides* *A. variabilis* *Anabaena* spp. *Anabaenopsis* sp. *Aulosira fertilissima* *Cylindrospermum gorakhpurense* *C. licheniforme* *C. maius* *Nostoc paludosum* *N. punctiforme* *N. muscorum* *Nostoc* spp.	*Anabaena variabilis* *Anabaena* spp. *Aphanizomenon flos-aquae*
Rivulariaceae	*Calothrix brevissima* *C. parietina*	
Scytonemataceae	*Tolypothrix tenuis*	*Plectonema notatum* *P. nostocorum*
Stigonematales	*Mastigocladus laminosus*	—

[a] Reproduced from Fogg and Wolfe (86).

the light were associated with the development of these organisms. Subsequently Beijerinck (19) found that *Anabaena catenula* fixed nitrogen in soil cultures when incubated in the light. Drewes (71) provided the first unequivocal evidence that bacteria-free cultures of *Nostoc punctiforme* and *Anabaena variabilis* fixed nitrogen, and this has been amply confirmed by others (9, 85, 86, 88). More recent techniques include the use of nitrogen-15 to demonstrate fixation in *Nostoc muscorum* (38) and *Calothrix parietina* (38).

There are not sufficient critical data to show whether other algal groups and flagellates fix nitrogen since relatively few species have been examined in detail. It is claimed that some blue-green algae have symbiotic relations with higher plants. Thus *Nostoc* isolated from the root parenchyma of *Gunnera* (327) and from the lichen *Collema* (105) fix nitrogen and release soluble compounds into the culture medium. The extracellular secretions of *Anabaena cylindrica* contain mostly polypeptides and only small amounts of free amino acids (85). The peptides do not appear to be utilized by either *Anabaena* or *Chlorella*. The extracellular substances produced by *Nostoc* in lichens are readily assimilated by the fungus with which it is in association. Bond and Scott (32) using nitrogen-15 found that two lichens and a liverwort containing *Nostoc* incorporated the stable isotope. Numerous authors have found that blue-green algae in rice paddies fix appreciable amounts of nitrogen during the growing season (66, 271, 319).

Claims have been put forward that fungi fix nitrogen, but the evidence thus far is not convincing. Even in *Phoma* species, often found in the mycorhizal flora, there is no incorporation of the stable isotope of nitrogen (323). In *Alnus glutinosa*, although there is an incorporation of atmospheric nitrogen, the causal organism has been variously described as a bacterium, an actinomycete or a filamentous fungus (240) and more recently as a member of the Plasmodiophorales (104).

The most recent development in nitrogen fixation, which is dealt with in more detail in Chapter 5, has been the preparation of cell-free extracts from *Clostridium pasteurianum* (48, 49, 255), *Azotobacter vinelandii* (216, 217, 219), blue-green algae and *Rhodospirillum rubrum* (255), and from *Chromatium* (12) that can fix atmospheric nitrogen. Carnahan et al. (48, 49) have shown that the addition of sodium pyruvate enhances fixation in extracts of *C. pasteurianum*. Nicholas and Fisher (216, 217) showed that cell-free extracts of *Azotobacter vinelandii* fixed nitrogen provided they were disrupted in the medium in which they were grown. These results have been confirmed by the use of radioactive nitrogen-13 since cell-free extracts of *Azotobacter* incorporated the tracer after exposure for a period of 10 minutes (219).

B. Ammonia

Ammonia is utilized by a wide range of microorganisms, much more readily in fact than by higher plants. Studies with bacteria have shown that ammonia is readily assimilated provided the pH of the culture medium does not become too acid during growth. Studies with the fungus *Scopulariopsis brevicaulis* have shown that both oxygen and a carbon source are required before ammonia is assimilated (58). Its

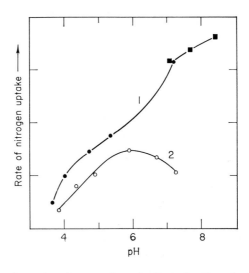

Fig. 2. The rate of uptake of ammonia and nitrate by *Scopulariopsis brevicaulis* as a function of pH. Curve *1*, ammonia (two buffers); curve *2*, nitrate. From Morton and MacMillan (191) by permission of the Oxford University Press.

utilization increased with pH, and unlike nitrate absorption it has no definite pH optimum (cf. Fig. 2) (191).

It is claimed that ammonia freely enters and leaves the cell by passive diffusion of the undissociated ammonia or ammonium molecule; thus respiration has little influence on the process. The primary product of ammonia utilization in most microorganisms is glutamic acid from α-ketoglutaric acid and then other amino acids are formed by transamination processes. Via other keto acids ammonia may also be incorporated into alanine and aspartic acid and into the amides asparagine and glutamine. The breakdown of glucose provides the carbon skeleton for these compounds. Claims in the literature that fungi will not grow in media containing ammonium salts must be treated with reserve unless the pH effect has been excluded experimentally. There is good evidence, however, that some of the lower phycomycetes, e.g., *Blastocladiella emersonii* (17), *Sapromyces elongatus* (95), and *Leptomitus lacteus* (256) are unable to utilize ammonium salts as the sole nitrogen source. Apart from these few exceptions and those bacteria and fungi that require amino acids or even peptides for their growth, ammonia is usually a suitable source of nitrogen for microorganisms provided the pH of the medium is near neutrality. Ammonia, at high concentrations, is toxic. Resulting spore aberrations are alleviated in some fungi by phosphate.

Recent reviews by Syrett (293) and Fogg and Wolfe (86) give an excellent account of the utilization of ammonia and of nitrate by green

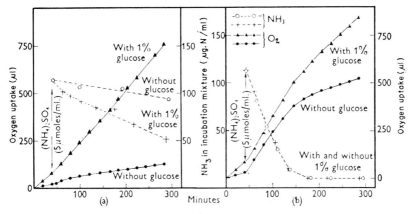

Fig. 3. The effect of glucose on the oxygen uptake and ammonia assimilation by *Chlorella vulgaris* at 25° and pH 6.1. a. Normal cells (4.75 mg dry weight per milliliter). b. Nitrogen-starved cells (7.65 mg dry weight per milliliter). From Syrett (293).

and blue-green algae. In an adequately buffered medium autotrophic growth of *Chlorella* is the same whether nitrate or ammonia is the nitrogen source (293), but in these experiments growth may have been limited by the rate of carbon assimilation. Most workers agree that, when both ammonium and nitrate ions are supplied together, *Chlorella* assimilates much more ammonia than nitrate (293).

Ammonia assimilation in nitrogen-starved cells has been studied. Syrett (293) showed that cells of *Chlorella vulgaris* which were grown in a nitrogen-free medium in the light for 16 hours assimilated added ammonia more readily in darkness than did normal cells. The rate of assimilation of ammonia by the normal cells was increased by adding glucose; that of nitrogen-starved cells was not (Fig. 3).

Presumably the nitrogen-starved cells contained sufficient carbon reserve to satisfy the enzyme systems involved in assimilation. When large amounts of ammonia are added, assimilation continues until the carbon supply is exhausted and addition of more glucose results in further utilization of ammonia.

The interrelation between carbon and nitrogen in the nutrition of algae may be summarized as follows: (a) When the external supply

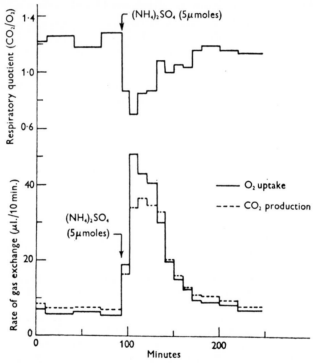

FIG. 4. The effect of ammonia on the respiration of nitrogen-starved cells of *Chlorella vulgaris* at 25° and pH 6.2. Each manometer contained 14.7 mg, dry weight, of cells. From Syrett (293).

of nitrogen or carbon is not rate limiting the absorption of either or both should be conditioned by other factors that determine growth and it is here that the effect of light or dark conditions might apply. (b) When growth is limited by either nitrogen or carbon supply, the response to either can be interpreted as interactions between them.

The effect of adding ammonium sulfate to cells of *Chlorella pyrenoidosa* respiring glucose in the dark was followed by a decrease in the rate of carbon dioxide production; the rate of oxygen consumption remained constant, and the respiratory quotient (R.Q.) decreased from 1.4 to 1.18 (293). The change in R.Q. was very sharp when nitrogen-deficient cells were used. The high R.Q. before the ammonia was added showed that glucose was being assimilated to more reduced cellular materials, possibly fat. Syrett claims that the decrease in R.Q. after adding ammonia indicates that less reduced products, e.g., proteins, were being formed. The effect of ammonia on respiration of nitrogen-starved cells of *Chlorella vulgaris* is shown in Fig. 4.

The addition of ammonia to nitrogen-starved cells resulted in a respiration rate as high as that of normal cells respiring glucose. The addition of ammonia to these cells allowed a rapid metabolism of carbon reserves. Syrett (293) showed that 2,4-dinitrophenol reduced the assimilation of ammonia by nitrogen-starved cells of the alga *Chlorella vulgaris* (Table V). This effect was interpreted as an uncoupling of phosphorylation from respiration since the latter was stimulated.

TABLE V

THE EFFECT OF 2,4-DINITROPHENOL (DNP) ON THE RESPIRATION AND AMMONIA ASSIMILATION OF NITROGEN-STARVED CELLS OF
Chlorella vulgaris AT 25° AND pH 6.1[a,b]

	Before ammonia addition				After ammonia addition				
2,4-DNP (M)	Q_{O_2}	% Control	Q_{CO_2}	% Control	Q_{O_2}	% Control	Q_{CO_2}	% Control	Q_{NH_3}	% Control
0	2.9	100	3.3	100	16.5	100	13.8	100	21.8	100
1.8×10^{-4}	7.2	246	7.5	228	14.7	89	13.4	97	15.2	70
2.2×10^{-4}	8.3	285	8.7	264	14.5	88	13.3	96	11.9	54

[a] Cells were suspended in 0.0025 M $MgSO_4$ and 0.1 M phosphate. In this experiment and those following, respiration was measured by Warburg's "direct" method and a correction for carbon dioxide retention was applied. Each manometer contained 16.5 mg dry weight of cells. Initially, 1.5 μmoles $(NH_4)_2SO_4$ was added and the Q_{NH_3} was calculated from ammonia determinations at 15 and 30 minutes.
[b] Reproduced from Syrett (293).

Effects similar to those reported for the green algae have also been found to occur in the blue-green types (86). Concentrations of ammonium as low as 5×10^{-5} M suppress the formation of heterocysts by *Anabaena cylindrica*.

C. ASSIMILATION AND DISSIMILATION OF NITRATES

Nitrates may be utilized as the sole source of nitrogen by a range of bacteria and fungi, although in some instances there may be a lag period in growth pending the induction of the nitrate-reducing enzymes. Some bacteria require complex nitrogenous sources and will not grow on nitrate, e.g., Actinomycetes and some fungi, notably members of the Basidiomycetes (58), Saprolegniaceae (243), and Blastocladiales (47), are also unable to grow on nitrate. It is also found that even within a genus individual species vary markedly in their use of nitrate. The capacity to utilize nitrate as a nitrogen source can be lost by mutation and thus may have ecological significance since those that carry the mutation may survive only if there are other suitable nitrogenous compounds

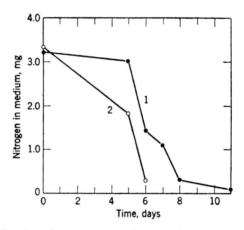

Fig. 5. The utilization of ammonium and nitrate by *Scopulariopsis brevicaulis* in a medium containing glucose, succinate, and ammonium nitrate. Curve *1*, nitrate concentration in the medium; curve *2*, ammonium concentration in the medium. From Morton and Macmillan (191).

in the habitat. It is of interest that nitrate cannot be utilized by spores of *Streptomyces griseus* but a pregrown mycelium uses nitrate readily (56).

When ammonium nitrate is supplied it is usual for the ammonium radical to be used first since there is an initial drop in pH. In *Scopulariopsis brevicaulis* and other fungi, nitrate utilization is not prominent until the ammonium has been absorbed from the medium (Fig. 5) (191).

This effect has also been observed in *Neurospora crassa*. In some cases ammonium salts inhibit the utilization of nitrate, but nitrite is not so affected. The effect of ammonia is to depress the nitrate reductase enzyme which reduces nitrate to nitrite. One interesting phenomenon is that nitrate reductase is induced in *Neurospora* grown in media containing ammonium nitrate but when ammonium salts are added aseptically to the fungus grown in a medium containing sodium nitrate there is an immediate reduction of the enzyme even when the amount of ammonia added is as small as 10^{-8} M (Table VI).

Many microorganisms reduce nitrate nitrogen to ammonia with subsequent formation of amino acids and cell nitrogen. This process is usually termed *nitrate assimilation*. Under certain conditions some microorganisms use nitrate or some of its reduction products as a terminal hydrogen acceptor instead of oxygen; this process is known

TABLE VI

The Effect of Adding Ammonium Chloride *in Vivo* to Fungal Felts of *Neurospora crassa*[a] Grown with Nitrate as Sole Source of Nitrogen on the Nitrate Reductase Activity in the Felts[b]

Felts harvested at times indicated after adding 10^{-8} M (NH₄Cl) to the medium (hours)	Nitrate reductase (mμmoles NO₂/10 min/mg protein)
0	38.1
0.5	26.2
1	21.4
2	10.9
4	4.7

[a] Ammonium chloride (10^{-8} M) was added to *N. crassa* grown for 40 hours in the nitrate medium; the enzyme was determined in cell-free extracts of the felts after the further incubation times stated.

[b] Walker and Nicholas (unpublished results).

as *"nitrate respiration"* or *"dissimilatory nitrate reduction."* Many classifications have been proposed for the various types of nitrate reduction in microorganisms. Thus Jensen (124) suggested five categories according to the products of the reaction whereas Verhoeven (303, 304) differentiated three types as follows: (a) nitrate assimilation in which nitrate is reduced for subsequent formation of cell protein; (b) incidental dissimilation in which nitrate acts as a nonessential hydrogen acceptor; (c) true dissimilatory nitrate reduction in which nitrate acts usually when oxygen is limiting as the essential hydrogen acceptor, which enables the organism to grow.

The Japanese school (72, 73, 253, 298), however, do not think it necessary to differentiate between Verhoeven's last two categories and have proposed a classification of nitrate-reducing organisms based on the behavior of their cytochromes toward nitrate: (a) those in which cytochrome participates in nitrate reduction, e.g., *Escherichia coli* and

Micrococcus denitrificans; (b) those in which cytochromes do not participate in nitrate reduction, e.g., *Neurospora crassa;* (c) those organisms which reduce nitrate but have no cytochrome components, e.g., *Clostridium perfringens.*

It is the author's view that subdivision into assimilation and dissimilation of nitrates is adequate to cover nitrate utilization in microorganisms. Denitrification can be regarded as a special instance of nitrate dissimilation in which the oxides of nitrogen or nitrogen gas are usually produced (82, 84).

TABLE VII

The Oxidation-Reduction States of Some Nitrogen Compounds

Oxidation-reduction state of N atom	Formula	Name
+7	N_2O_7 HNO_4	Nitrogen peroxide Pernitric acid
+6	NO_3 H_2NO_4	Nitrogen peroxide Pernitrous acid
+5	N_2O_5 HNO_3	Nitrogen peroxide Nitric acid
+4	N_2O_4 NO_2	Nitrogen tetroxide Nitrogen dioxide
+3	N_2O_3 HNO_2	Nitrogen sesquioxide Nitrous acid
+2	NO H_2NO_2	Nitric oxide Hydronitrous acid
+1	NOH N_2O $H_2N_2O_2$ $NO_2:NH_2$ $NH(OH)_2$	Nitroxyl Nitrous oxide Hyponitrous acid Nitramide; imido nitric acid Dihydroxyammonia
0	N_2 $OH \cdot NH \cdot NH \cdot OH$	Nitrogen Dihydroxylhydrazine
−1	NH_2OH	Hydroxylamine
−2	$H_2N \cdot NH_2$	Hydrazine
−3	NH_4OH	Ammonium hydroxide

1. Nitrate Reduction

Since early intermediates are common to the dissimilation and assimilation of nitrates they will be considered together. The oxidation states of nitrogen compounds are given in Table VII.

Gayon and Dupetit presented equations for the over-all process of denitrification but recognized nitrite as an intermediate (92). Beijerinck and Minkman suggested that nitrous oxide might be formed directly from either nitrate or nitrite and that nitrogen was formed exclusively from nitrous oxide (21). Others have suggested that nitrite, dihydroxyammonia, hydroxylamine, ammonia, and nitrous oxide might be intermediates (22, 89). Kluyver and Donker presented a scheme of reduction (Eqs. 1, 2) of nitrate to nitrous oxide (134).

$$N\underset{O}{\overset{OK}{=}}O \quad + \quad 2\,H \quad \longrightarrow \quad N\underset{O}{\overset{OK}{<}} \quad +\quad H_2O \quad (1)$$

potassium nitrate   potassium nitrite

$$2\,N\underset{O}{\overset{OK}{<}} \quad \begin{matrix} + & 2\,H \\ + & 2\,H \end{matrix} \Bigg\} \quad \longrightarrow \quad \overset{N-OK}{\underset{N-OK}{\|}} \quad + \quad 2\,H_2O \quad (2)$$

potassium hyponitrite

The hyponitrite was thought to decompose spontaneously to give nitrous oxide and nitrogen (Eq. 3).

$$\overset{N}{\underset{N}{\|}}O \quad + \quad 2\,H \quad \longrightarrow \quad \overset{N}{\underset{N}{\|}} \quad + \quad H_2O \quad (3)$$

anhydride of
hyponitrous acid

Since that time many pathways have been suggested on the assumption that reduction proceeds via a number of two-electron steps. The Delft school (135, 136, 303, 304) has been very active in this field and

$$
\begin{array}{l}
NO_3^- \\
\downarrow \\
NO_2^- \\
\downarrow \\
\text{nitroxyl (NOH)} \longrightarrow \overset{NOH}{\underset{NOH}{\|}} \longrightarrow N\underset{N}{\overset{OH}{<}}O \longrightarrow \overset{OH}{\underset{NH}{N=O}} \longrightarrow N_2O \quad (4) \\
\downarrow \\
NH_2OH \\
\downarrow \\
NH_4^+
\end{array}
$$

have suggested the scheme shown in sequence 4. They suggest that nitrate is reduced to a compound of the nitroxyl type (NOH) which in the assimilatory process is reduced further via hydroxylamine to ammonia. They suggest that during denitrification nitroxyl (NOH) is converted by complex molecular reorientation to nitrous oxide and then to nitrogen gas as shown in their scheme. They consider that nitrite can also be reduced to nitric oxide and that this in turn is converted to N_2 gas via nitrous oxide.

Quastel *et al.* (238) found that *Escherichia coli* (*Bacillus coli*) produced nitrite when grown anaerobically; subsequently nitrite was identified as a product of nitrate reduction in bacteria, fungi, and higher plants. Nitrate reductase, the enzyme responsible for the reduction of nitrate to nitrite, has been studied in detail in a number of microorganisms. Nitrate or nitrite is required for its induction in *Neurospora crassa*, *Escherichia coli*, and other microorganisms (204, 206, 231). Farkas-Himsley and Artman (78a) reported a constitutive nitrate reductase in *E. coli*, but this is unlikely since the peptone used in the medium contained nitrate which induced the enzyme.

The assimilatory nitrate reductase from *Neurospora* and *E. coli* was shown to be flavoprotein containing molybdenum; and mechanism of enzyme action, which is discussed more fully in Chapter 4, is shown in sequence 5.

$$\text{DPNH} \underset{\text{DPN}}{\overset{\text{FADH}_2}{\searrow\nearrow}} \underset{\text{FAD}}{\overset{\text{Mo}^{5+(2e)}}{\searrow\nearrow}} \underset{\text{Mo}^{6+}}{\overset{\text{NO}_2^-}{\searrow\nearrow}} \text{NO}_3^- \tag{5}$$

It is of interest that the enzyme is present in the fungus felts at the 4-day stage when they are growing in an aerobic environment. Walker and Nicholas (314) have shown that when the felts were submerged, nitrate was dissimilated and there was an additional iron requirement (Fig. 6). When the felts were growing in an aerobic environment, after 5 days' growth, only the assimilatory nitrate reductase was present so that there was no longer a requirement for iron. The dissimilatory enzyme is similar to the nitrate reductase from *Pseudomonas aeruginosa* (79, 82, 84); the nitrate reductase functions during denitrification as shown in sequence 6.

$$\text{DPNH} \rightarrow \text{FAD} \rightarrow \text{cytochrome c} \overset{\nearrow \overset{\text{cytochrome} \rightarrow O_2}{\text{oxidase}}}{\searrow \underset{(\text{Mo}) \rightarrow NO_3^-}{\text{nitrate reductase}}} \tag{6}$$

A cytochrome component is not required by the assimilatory nitrate reductase system since this has a slower turnover than the more active dissimilatory enzyme. Cytochrome c ($E_0' + 260$ millivolts pH 7) is effective in the dissimilatory system in bridging the electrode potential gap between flavin (E_0' approximately -100 millivolts, pH 7) and nitrate ($E_0' + 350$ millivolts pH 7) thus ensuring a rapid flow of electrons from the substrate to nitrate, the terminal acceptor. It also facilitates a switch of the electrons to the alternative acceptor, oxygen, when the bacteria are grown in an aerobic environment.

A large number of bacteria and algae use hydrogen gas for nitrate reduction: *Aerobacter aerogenes, Azotobacter* species, *Bacterium formi-*

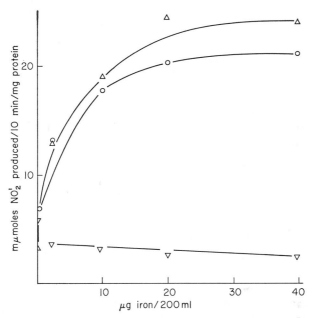

Fig. 6. Effect of the iron content of the culture medium on nitrate reductase activity in homogenates of *Neurospora crassa* harvested after 2, 3, and 5 days. Neurospora was grown at 25°C in still culture depleted of iron to which 2, 10, 20, or 40 μg of iron per 200 ml was returned. ▽, Felts harvested after 5 days' growth (314). From Walker and Nicholas (314).

cum, Clostridium welchii ($=$ *C. perfringens*), *Micrococcus denitrificans, Proteus vulgaris* (15, 141, 328), and the algae *Scenedesmus obliquus* and *Ankistrodesmus braunii* (129–131).

A porphyrin requirement for nitrate reduction has been shown in *Haemophilus influenzae* (97) and *Staphylococcus aureus* (141). Cytochrome c is required for nitrate reduction in *Pseudomonas aeruginosa* and *Micrococcus denitrificans* when they are actively denitrifying (79, 80, 82–84). The addition of nitrate to whole cells resulted in oxidation of the cytochromes.

In all studies so far made on nitrate reductases it is clear that the enzyme is a flavoprotein containing molybdenum of the type described in *Neurospora* (204, 205, 207–209, 211, 212). The possible exception is that of *Photobacterium fischeri* (250). Recent work in this laboratory, however, has shown that molybdenum is required when nitrate is reduced by this organism (220a). Although cytochromes play an important part in the over-all reduction sequence in the dissimilatory reduction of nitrate, they are unlikely to be involved in the terminal step of electron transfer to nitrate (79, 82–84). They probably act as carriers in the electron chain before the terminal molybdenum-containing nitrate reductase.

TABLE VIII

THE FORMATION OF AMMONIA AND NITRITE FROM NITRATE (INITIAL CONCENTRATION 0.02 M) BY *Chlorella vulgaris* SUSPENDED IN 0.067 M PHOSPHATE AT pH 6.0[a]

	μg N/40 × 10^6 cells			
	In dark		In light	
Time (hr)	Nitrite N	Ammonia N	Nitrite N	Ammonia N
24	4.6	—	46	—
96	3.8	1.4	70	12.6
144	5.2	12.9	73	29.2

[a] From Syrett (293) after Mayer (175).

Some algae assimilate nitrate in the dark, but others do so only in the light (86, 293), and this is in accord with Burström's observations in higher plants (40, 41). Warburg and Negelein found that *Chlorella pyrenoidosa* reduced nitrate to ammonia under aerobic conditions but when oxygen supply was decreased nitrite accumulated (316). Mayer (175) found that *C. vulgaris* produced both ammonia and nitrite from sodium nitrate in the light but in darkness less ammonia and nitrite were formed (Table VIII).

Kessler (130, 131) on the other hand showed that nitrite accumulated in *Ankistrodesmus braunii* cultures when grown in the dark with nitrate. Nitrite did not accumulate in the light. The discrepancy between the two investigations can be explained by the difference in experimental conditions. Kessler used thin suspensions so that photosynthesis was rapid whereas Mayer used thick algal suspensions and photosynthesis did not compensate for respiration. Nitrate is utilized by nearly all the blue-green algae which have been examined in pure culture (86). In many, however, there may be a lag period pending the induction of the reductive enzymes, e.g., in *Anabaena cylindrica*. This organism was found to continue fixing nitrogen after being maintained without combined nitrogen and then subcultured into a medium containing nitrate (86). Nitrate is assimilated rapidly by *Anabaena* in the dark in an atmosphere of hydrogen (to depress nitrogen fixation). After about 3–5 hours, assimilation of nitrate ceases but its absorption into the cells continues. During assimilation the respiratory quotient rises from 0.9 to 1.0 to above 2. Whereas in *Chlorella* a similar rise in R.Q. during nitrate assimilation is caused by an increased output of carbon dioxide (86), the rise in *Anabaena* has frequently been found to be due to a decrease in oxygen consumption, the carbon dioxide output remaining the same as in the absence of nitrate. Thus it appears that algae can also use nitrate as an alternative hydrogen acceptor to oxygen.

2. Nitrite

The immediate product of nitrate reduction in microorganisms has been identified as nitrite. A nitrite reductase enzyme has been characterized in a range of bacteria, fungi, and algae. In the assimilatory sequence nitrite is reduced to ammonia (200), and when dissimilating nitrate, nitric oxide, and nitrogen are products. Recently it was shown that the immediate product of nitrite reduction in both dissimilation and assimilation is nitric oxide (80, 81, 198, 315). The enzyme from *Pseudomonas aeruginosa* (79) and *Neurospora crassa* (214) is a flavoprotein which requires copper and iron for its activity. Cells of *Desulfovibrio desulfuricans* reduce nitrite to ammonia when either hydrogen gas or pyruvate is the hydrogen donor, and ferrocytochrome c reduced nitrite nonenzymatically (261–263).

Nitrite serves as a nitrogen source for a number of fungi, *Fusarium niveum* (329), *Coprinus* species (90), *Phymatotrichum omnivorum* (295), *Scopulariopsis brevicaulis* (191), and *Rhizophyctis rosea* (237). Species of *Aspergillus* differ markedly in their ability to use nitrite, (251, 282–284). Most bacteria and fungi fail to use nitrite and it is often secreted into the medium, especially when nitrate is used as an alternative hydrogen acceptor to oxygen. Growth in the presence of nitrite is best in an alkaline medium, a result which indicates that the nonionized acid is probably the toxic factor. Nitrite toxicity in *Fusarium lini* results in accumulation of pyruvic acid (222), and it produces morphological variants in *Aspergillus* species (286, 287). In *Neurospora crassa*, nitrite secreted into media during active dissimilation of nitrate in submerged felts is reabsorbed later and is reduced to ammonia when the felts break the surface of the culture fluid; oxygen is then the alternative hydrogen acceptor (314, 315).

Kessler (130, 131) showed that nitrite is formed from nitrate in the alga *Ankistrodesmus* in darkness. The accumulation of nitrite is greater the lower the pH, partly because the rate of nitrite assimilation decreases with increasing acidity. Nitrite is assimilated by the algae provided the concentration is not too high or the pH too low so that it is likely to be an intermediate in the assimilation of nitrate. Nitrite is a suitable source of nitrogen for a number of blue-green algae (86). Maertens found it to be suitable for growth of *Oscillatoria* species, but not for *Nostoc*, *Cylindrospermum*, or *Calothrix* species (161). At concentrations up to 13.6 mg nitrogen per liter, nitrite is as effective as nitrate for *Microcystis aeruginosa*. The effect of high concentrations of nitrite on this alga was not recorded, but 27 mg nitrate nitrogen per liter inhibits growth of *Anabaena cylindrica* (86).

3. Nitric Oxide

Gayon and Dupetit described the conversion of nitrate to nitrite, nitric oxide, nitrous oxide, nitrogen and to ammonia in a soil bacterium (92). Since then nitric oxide has been identified as a product of nitrite reduction in denitrifying bacteria, e.g., *Pseudomonas aeruginosa* and *P. stutzeri* (62, 63, 80, 81, 123), *Bacillus subtilis* (62, 63), *Thiobacillus denitrificans* (14), and in *Micrococcus* species (83). Nitric oxide was also shown to be utilized by *Escherichia coli* (Bn) as the sole nitrogen source (165, 166). Fewson and Nicholas (80) have shown recently that nitric oxide is readily utilized by a range of bacteria, fungi, and algae when they were grown on nitrate but not when grown on ammonium salts (Table IX). They also showed that nitric oxide was utilized by nitrogen-fixing organisms, e.g., *Azotobacter vinelandii*, *Clostridium pasteurianum*, by the blue-green algae *Nostoc muscorum* and *Anabaena cylindrica*, and also by root nodule bacteria when they were actively fixing atmospheric nitrogen (Table X).

This may mean that nitric oxide or a compound with which it equilibrates is formed during nitrogen fixation as well as in nitrate dissimilation and assimilation. Nitric oxide reductase from *Pseudomonas aeruginosa* was shown to be a flavoprotein dependent on iron only (81), but contrary to earlier reports (63) copper is not essential for its activity.

4. Nitrous Oxide

Dehérain and Marquenne (67) first reported the production of nitrous oxide by soil microorganisms. Kluyver and Verhoeven (135) have concluded that nitrous oxide production and utilization is common to all denitrifying bacteria. There is convincing evidence, however, that nitrous oxide is a nonobligatory intermediate in denitrification. Sacks and Barker (249) observed a lag in the reduction of nitrous oxide by cells of *Pseudomonas denitrificans* adapted to nitrate. Thus adaptation

TABLE IX

UTILIZATION OF NITRIC OXIDE BY BACTERIA, FUNGI, AND GREEN PLANTS[a,b]

Group	Organism	Nitrogen source during growth	
		NH_4^+	NO_3^-
Bacterium	*Escherichia coli* (B)[c]	2	16
Fungi	*Aspergillus niger* (M)	6	24
	Neurospora crassa (wild type *Em*, 5297a)	10	29
	Candida utilis	23	31
	Cryptococcus diffluens	2	14
	Hansenula anomala	1	11
	Torulopsis versatilis	0	3
Alga	*Chlorella pyrenoidosa* (211-8c)	7	17
Higher plants	*Cucurbita pepo* (marrow)[d]		
	Leaf laminae	24	22
	Root tissue	8	6
	Fragaria chiloensis var. *ananassa* (strawberry)[d]		
	Leaf laminae	—	12
	Brassica oleracea var. *botrytis* (cauliflower)[d]		
	Leaf laminae	12	14
	Triticum vulgare (wheat)[e]		
	Root tissue	7	34

[a] The nitric oxide uptake was measured in homogenates of various organisms with the following Warburg reaction mixture: Main vessel, 1.0 ml homogenate, 1.2 ml 0.1 M phosphate buffer (pH 7.5); side arm, 0.1 mg crystalline alcohol dehydrogenase, 0.1 ml 2% v/v ethyl alcohol, 0.1 ml (300 mμmole) reduced diphosphopyridine nucleotide; center well, 0.2 ml 20% w/v potassium hydroxide. Gas phase, 25% NO; 75% N_2. Temperature, 30°C. Boiled enzyme controls were always included. Values are given as microliters nitric oxide per milligram nitrogen per hour.

[b] Reproduced from Fewson and Nicholas (80).

[c] Adapted to grow on nitrate as sole nitrogen source.

[d] Grown under nonsterile conditions.

[e] Grown under strictly aseptic conditions.

to nitrate did not include the induction of an enzyme that could utilize nitrous oxide. On the other hand, Allen and van Niel (7) found a simultaneous adaptation to nitrate and nitrous oxide in *Pseudomonas stutzeri* but levels of cyanide that inhibited the reduction of nitrate to nitrite or the reduction of nitrous oxide did not inhibit the production of nitrogen from nitrite. Kluyver and Verhoeven (135) concluded that nitrous oxide is the actual intermediate and that an alternative pathway exists whereby nitrogen can be produced by direct hydrogenation of an intermediate such as nitramide of imidonitric acid ($NO_2 \cdot NH_2$). Delwiche (68) used N^{15}-labeled nitrate and showed that high levels of nitrate resulted in large production of nitrous oxide but the gas was not utilized further. Under these conditions there was a lag period before the cells adapted to nitrous oxide. With low levels of nitrate, however, nitrous oxide was readily utilized after a short lag period. These results

TABLE X

UTILIZATION OF NITRIC OXIDE BY ORGANISMS WHICH FIX ATMOSPHERIC NITROGEN[a,b]

Group	Organism	Nitrogen source during growth[c]		
		NH_4^+	NO_3^-	N_2
Bacteria	*Azotobacter vinelandii* (0)	3	29	23
	Clostridium pasteurianum (W-S)	10	23	44
Blue-green algae	*Anabaena cylindrica* (1403-2)	3	18	12
	Nostoc muscorum (1453-12)	0	10	8
Higher plants (symbiotic nitrogen fixers)	*Vicia faba* (broad bean)			
	Root tissue	—	—	6
	Nodular tissue	—	—	20
	Casuarina equisetifolia			
	Root tissue	—	—	2
	Nodular tissue	—	—	7

[a] The reaction mixture is described in Table IX.
[b] Reproduced from Fewson and Nicholas (80).
[c] Values are nitric oxide uptake in microliters nitric oxide per milligram nitrogen per hour.

suggest that nitrous oxide is a nonobligatory metabolite which arises only when high concentrations of nitrite are employed. Under these conditions nitrous oxide may be formed by dehydration of a compound at the hyponitrite level of oxidation.

5. *Hyponitrite, Nitramide, and Imidonitric Acid* ($H_2N_2O_2$)

Corbet (59) reported that hyponitrite was present in growing cultures of nitrifying organisms, but the specificity of the assay was questioned by Rao, *et al.* (241). Other workers found a compound in cyanide-inhibited cultures of *Micrococcus denitrificans* which evolved nitrous oxide when heated *in vacuo* at 70°C. There is no evidence, however, that hyponitrite is utilized by the following bacteria: *Pseudomonas denitrificans, P. stutzeri, P. aeruginosa,* and *Micrococcus denitrificans* (62). In contrast, cells of *Escherichia coli* (Bn) when adapted to grow on nitrate can grow after a short lag period with hyponitrite as the sole nitrogen source. McNall and Atkinson suggested that hyponitrite or an intermediate to which it is readily converted is an intermediate in the reduction of nitrate to ammonium (176, 177). A hyponitrite reductase enzyme found in *Neurospora* (176, 177) was shown to be a flavoprotein dependent on iron and copper for its functioning. Allen and van Niel (7) claimed that *Pseudomonas stutzeri* converted nitramide to nitrogen gas, but this work has not been verified. Nitramide is very unstable at physiological pH, i.e., between 5 and 9, and decomposes to give nitrous oxide and water. Although Kluyver and Verhoeven (135) consider that nitramide (or imidonitric acid) is an intermediate in denitrification, this is unlikely.

6. Nitrogen

The production of nitrogen gas during decomposition of plant residues was first reported by Davy in 1814 (65) and subsequently confirmed by others. Goppelsröder (96) showed that nitrogen was produced from nitrate by microorganisms. Since that time denitrification has been shown to be a widespread phenomenon in microorganisms. The first types to be isolated were all non-spore formers of the genera *Pseudomonas, Micrococcus*, and *Spirillum*. Beijerinck (19, 20) reported denitrification in the chemautotrophic bacteria *Thiobacillus denitrificans* and *Thiobacillus thioparus*. In a study of about 400 bacterial types from sea water and marine products, 55% were found to reduce nitrate and 9% to reduce nitrite to nitrogen gas. The most common genera that do this are *Pseudomonas, Micrococcus*, and *Achromobacter*.

7. Hydroxylamine

This compound has been suggested as an intermediate in nitrate reduction (211, 212). Organohydroxylamino compounds, particularly oximes, have been demonstrated in *Torulopsis utilis* (308, 309). Hydroxylamine was found in the medium in which *Azotobacter chroococcum* was grown when it was fixing nitrogen and also when grown with nitrate as sole nitrogen source. Woods (328) showed that hydroxylamine was reduced to ammonia in *Clostridium welchii* (= *C. perfringens*) when hydrogen gas was the donor. A similar reduction of hydroxylamine was reported in extracts of *Escherichia coli* when reduced viologen dye, malate, or formate—but not succinate—was the hydrogen donor (296, 297). McNall and Atkinson found that a strain of *E. coli* (Bn) grew when hydroxylamine was the sole nitrogen source (165, 166).

Resting cells of *Azotobacter vinelandii* reduced hydroxylamine to ammonia and the enzyme was subsequently purified two- to fourfold and shown to require DPNH* or TPNH and FAD or FMN and manganese for its activity (275). The enzyme purified from a halo-tolerant bacterium was shown to reduce hydroxylamine when either methylene blue or reduced FAD was the donor. The enzyme was in-hibited by chelating agents and more recently it has been suggested that it requires cytochrome c and manganese for its activity. Walker and Nicholas (315) showed that a reductase enzyme from *Pseudomonas aeruginosa* reduced hydroxylamine to ammonia when leuco forms of either pyocyanine, methylene blue, riboflavin, FMN, or FAD was the donor. Manganese was required for enzyme activity; cobalt was only one-tenth as effective. The enzyme has also been found in fungi. Four mutants of *Neurospora* possessed nitrite and hydroxylamine reductases yet were unable to grow with nitrite as sole nitrogen source (269). Silver and McElroy consider that these results can be explained should oximes be utilized as in sequence 7.

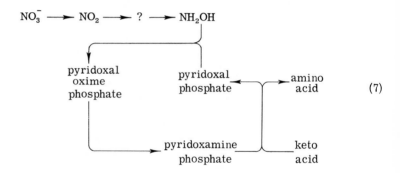

$$\text{(7)}$$

This sequence remains to be established since oximes labeled with C^{14} are not utilized by *Neurospora* (208, 209, 211, 212, 214). The work with the mutants can be interpreted in other ways: (a) nitrite is known to be exceptionally toxic, hence its nonutilization; (b) a key enzyme between nitrite and hydroxylamine could be affected.

Neither hydroxylamine nor oximes have been detected in the medium or in cells of *Anabaena* grown with nitrate although ammonia is present. Hydroxylamine does not support growth of *Chlorella* (157). When small amounts of ammonia, nitrite, or hydroxylamine are added to nitrogen-starved cells of *Chlorella vulgaris* the rate of respiration in-creases and the compounds are utilized as shown in Fig. 7.

The gas exchanges following the addition of ammonia, nitrite, or nitrate are consistent with assimilation of all of them to the same nitro-

---

* Abbreviations: DPNH and TPNH, reduced di- and triphosphopyridine nucleotides, respectively; FAD, flavin adenine dinucleotide; FMN, flavin mononucleotide.

gen compounds. Should hydroxylamine be assimilated in the same way, the gas exchange following its addition should be intermediate between those following the addition of nitrite and ammonia. Since it is different, Syrett (293) considers that this indicates an alternative way for assimilating hydroxylamine and that free hydroxyalmine is unlikely to be an intermediate in nitrate reduction. It seems to the author that there is insufficient definitive evidence at the present time either

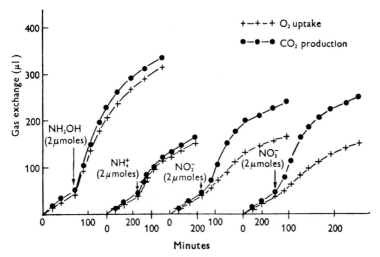

FIG. 7. The effect of ammonia, hydroxylamine, nitrite, and nitrate on the respiration of nitrogen-starved cells of *Chlorella vulgaris* at 25° and pH 6.2. Each manometer contained 13.5 mg, dry weight, of cells suspended in 0.067 M phosphate, 0.0017 M KCl, and 0.0017 M MgSO. Reproduced from Syrett (293).

to establish or to exclude hydroxylamine as an intermediate in nitrate reduction in algae.

8. Ammonia

There is general agreement that ammonium is probably the final inorganic product of nitrate assimilation which combines with α-keto acids to form amino acids. Work with nitrate or nitrogen gas labeled with nitrogen-15 shows heavy labeling of ammonia in microorganisms that utilize nitrate or fix nitrogen. Ammonia may also be produced during *"nitrate respiration"* under anaerobic conditions as in *Bacillus licheniformis* (303, 304) and in *Bacillus pumilus* (296, 297).

The assimilatory and dissimilatory routes may be represented diagrammatically as in sequence 8.

Oxidation-reduction
state of N atom

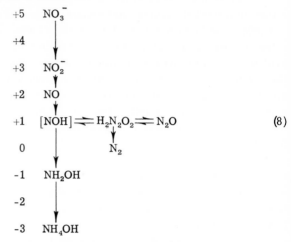

+5   NO₃⁻

+4

+3   NO₂⁻

+2   NO

+1   [NOH] ⇌ H₂N₂O₂ ⇌ N₂O   (8)

0   N₂

-1   NH₂OH

-2

-3   NH₄OH

9. Organonitro Compounds

It has been suggested that during N_2 fixation hydroxylamine is incorporated into amino acids via oximes, and this is discussed in Chapter 5 by Virtanen and Miettinen. The condensation of hydroxylamine with oxalacetic acid and reduction of the oxime to aspartic acid which is then transaminated to form other amino acids has been suggested as a possible mechanism (307, 308–311). This scheme, however, is not now generally accepted.

The incorporation of hydroxylamine into amino acids via oximes in *Neurospora* proposed by Silver and McElroy (269) has been mentioned previously. Silver and McElroy found that pyridoxine-requiring mutants of *Neurospora* accumulated nitrite when the vitamin was deficient, a result suggesting that pyridoxine is required for nitrite reduction. They suggest that pyridoxine may act by condensing with hydroxylamine to form pyridoxal oxime, which could then be reduced to an amine with subsequent formation of amino acids by transamination reactions. Extracts of wild-type *Neurospora* however did not utilize pyridoxal phosphate oxime (211, 212, 214), and in another pyridoxine-requiring mutant there was no increased requirement for pyridoxine when it was grown in media containing nitrate (214). It has been suggested by Nicholas (212) that one of the functions of oximes in plants is to detoxicate hydroxylamine. It is still an open question whether oximes are utilized by microorganisms since care must be taken in interpreting data obtained when large amounts of exogenous substrates are added to an extract of a microorganism. It is clear that oximes (should they be utilized) would occur in very small amounts in association with the enzymes that might convert them to amino acids. The endogenous substrates or intermediates are also made reactive in association with the appropriate enzymes in cell metabolism.

Little (152) claimed that *Neurospora crassa* might utilize nitrate via nitroaliphatic compounds such as nitroethane since the nitroethane oxidizing system, which produced nitrite, was induced by nitrate in the medium. There was no definite correlation, however, between the ability to utilize nitrate and the presence of nitroethane reductase in extracts of the fungal felts. The oxidation of organonitro compounds has been shown to occur in *Pseudomonas* and in *Nocardia* species (46, 50, 51, 270).

It has been suggested that, when nitrates are utilized, the nitrate so formed combines with an organic compound which is then reduced to an amine. Thus *Neurospora* mutants were unable to grow in a minimal medium containing ammonia but utilized nitrate and nitrite (269). Silver and McElroy claim that nitrate or nitrite reduction involve a coupling to organic compounds which are then reduced to amino acids. Another interpretation is that ammonium ions are toxic to these mutants and that the mutants are also adversely affected by the low pH of the ammonium cultures.

Nitroaromatic compounds are utilized by many microorganisms and are reduced to the corresponding arylamine. *Neurospora* reduced *m*-dinitrobenzene (I) to *m*-dinitroaniline (IV) with DPNH or TPNH as the hydrogen donor (334). The intermediates were identified as *m*-nitrosonitrobenzene (II) and *m*-nitrophenylhydroxylamine (III).

m-dinitrobenzene

(I)

m-nitroso-
nitrobenzene

(II)

m-dinitroaniline

(IV)

m-nitrophenyl-
hydroxylamine

(III)

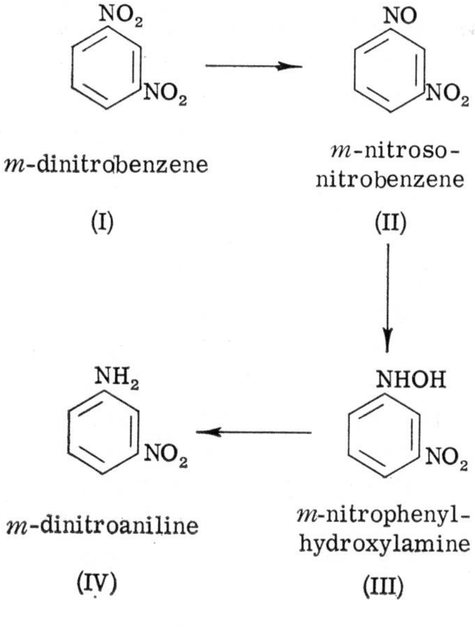

Escherichia coli reduced the nitro group in chloramphenicol. The enzyme is a flavoprotein which requires manganese for its activity. It is of interest that the differential response of nitroreductase to Aureomycin in a resistant and nonresistant strain was related to the degree of binding of flavin and manganese to the enzyme. The flavin and metal are less firmly bound to the enzyme in the nonresistant strain and the enzyme is therefore more susceptible to the chelating action of Aureomycin (254). A nitroreductase of a *Nocardia* species was purified 200-fold (305, 306). The enzyme catalyzed the reduction of *m*- and *p*-dinitrobenzene with DPNH as the hydrogen donor. The purified enzyme was not fully characterized, but evidence was presented that flavin and an unidentified metal might be involved in electron transfer between DPNH and the nitro compound.

The physiological role of these enzymes is less clear. The enzyme is induced in *Neurospora* by adding either *m*- or *p*-dinitrobenzene only to the cultures whereas enzymes in the nitrate-reducing sequence to ammonia are induced by nitrate. There is no evidence that a wide range of aromatic nitro compounds are assimilated by extracts of *Neurospora*. The enzymes, therefore, may only provide a detoxication mechanism in the fungus and act as suitable redox acceptors only, since there is no evidence that they are incorporated into cell nitrogen (211, 212).

D. Nitrification

The oxidation of ammonia to nitrite and nitrate in soils is brought about primarily by microorganisms and the process is usually termed nitrification. The biochemical aspects of nitrification are discussed in detail in Chapter 6. Schloesing and Muntz (257) and Warington (317) showed that chloroform vapor inhibited nitrite formation in soil and demonstrated that bacteria were involved. Winogradsky (326), who had worked previously with iron and sulfur bacteria, showed that the bacteria were autotrophs and concluded that they grew without organic matter. He isolated *Nitrobacter* and *Nitrosomonas* and grew them on silica gel plates. Since that time various forms of nitrifiers have been isolated from various habitats including soils and seas (144–151).

Cultures of *Nitrosomonas* and *Nitrobacter* can be maintained in simple inorganic liquid medium containing ammonia or nitrite, respectively, and trace metals, especially iron. Solid calcium carbonate was for many years assumed to be essential for growth since it was thought that the bacteria would grow only when attached to particles (150, 180, 181). Engel and Alexander (75, 76) and Skinner and Walker (271a), however, obtained good growth of *Nitrosomonas* in particle-free medium by substituting potassium carbonate for calcium carbonate. Under these conditions 72.4 mg dry weight yield was obtained with 0.083 M nitrous acid produced. The energy derived from the oxidation of ammonia to nitrate is utilized for anabolic processes in the organism. Kingman-Boltjes (132) showed that no growth occurred in the absence of CO_2, and recently C^{14}-labeled carbonate was shown to be the sole source of cell carbon (150). These results confirm that *Nitrosomonas* is an autotrophic organism, but there have been suggestions that certain growth factors may be required (101a). A number of workers, however, did not find any effect of adding a range of vitamins and amino acids to the cultures but reported that corn-steep liquor or a dialyzed extract of its ash reduced the lag phase of nitrite production (150). Meiklejohn (180) found that iron was required at a relatively high concentration, 6 mg per liter, but this is probably due to residual quinoline chelating the added iron in the medium.

Lees and Quastel (143, 144), using their ingenious soil percolation techniques (see Chapter 6), studied in detail nitrification in soil; they concluded that ammonia is first adsorbed onto the surface of soil colloids before it is oxidized. This may only be a reflection of the site where the bacteria proliferate, where there is maximum aeration, and does not necessarily imply a requirement per se for particles. Meyerhof (182) showed that the pH optimum was between 8.5 and 8.8 for ammonia concentration of 0.01 N. These values for ammonia are probably low since Engel and Alexander have shown that 3 gm per liter is not toxic to *Nitrosomonas* (75, 76). Lees (150) using washed suspensions of cells found that a wide variety of nitrogenous constituents were not oxidized to nitrate and that chelating agents inhibit the oxidation of ammonia. Hofman and Lees (111, 112) showed that ammonia was quantitatively oxidized to nitrite and detected hydroxylamine as an intermediate. Alkyl thiourea inhibited the oxidation of ammonia non-competitively, but not that of hydroxylamine. Hydrazine inhibited the oxidation of hydroxylamine to nitrite. This effect, also obtained in cell-free extracts by Nicholas and Jones (215), was shown by them to be due to a competition for cytochrome c in the organism. These workers showed that methylene blue, phenazine methosulfate, and benzyl viologen were suitable acceptors whereas ferricyanide, 2,3,6-trichloro-indophenol dye, DPN, TPN, or glutathione had little effect.

In *Nitrobacter*, Lees and Simpson (151) reported absorption maxima at λ 589, 557, 520, and 525 mμ when nitrite or dithionite was added to bacterial suspensions. Aleem and Nason (4) suggested that the oxidation of nitrite involved the transfer of electrons from nitrite to molecular oxygen via cytochrome c and a_1 (Eq. 9).

$$NO_2^- \rightarrow \text{cytochrome c} \rightarrow \text{cytochrome } a_1 \rightarrow O_2 \qquad (9)$$

They subsequently demonstrated that there is a phosphorylation coupled to the oxidation of nitrite although the P:O ratios were never more than 0.2, a relatively inefficient system (5). Malavolta *et al.* (168) have also studied phosphorylation and the fixation of carbon dioxide in extracts of *Nitrobacter*.

Heterotrophic fungi also oxidize ammonia to nitrite and nitrate. Thus *Aspergillus aureus*, *A. batatae* produce nitrate from nitrite (251). *Aspergillus flavus* was shown to oxidize ammonia to nitrite and nitrate after it had completed its growth (258). *Nocardia corallina* oxidizes pyruvic oxime and hydroxylamine to nitrite (126). *Streptomyces nitrificans* was shown by Isenberg and co-workers to form nitrite from urea or ammonium carbonate, but nitrate was not formed (121, 143). An unusual finding is that preformed mycelia of *Aspergillus niger* will utilize the nitrogen from cyanide (122) and that the latter compound stimulated growth in *Fusarium lini* (221). These results are not unequivocal since the effect of cyanide might be due to a metabolic disturbance diverting more carbon into dry matter (61). A soil organism, an aerobic actinomycete, has been reported to use cyanide as the sole nitrogen and carbon source (58).

IV. Requirements for Other Nutrient Elements

A. PHOSPHORUS

Phosphorus is indispensable for all microorganisms since it is required for the utilization of glucose (see Chapter 3, Volume IA, by Goddard and Bonner) and is an important constituent of essential cell metabolites including nucleotides of adenine, pyridine, flavin, and uridine, and other coenzymes, including pyridoxal phosphate and thiamine pyrophosphate. It is a basic constituent of all nucleic acids.

In culture solutions monobasic or dibasic phosphates are usually supplied and the optimum concentrations vary widely depending on the composition of the medium. Thus when only ammonium salts are used then the dibasic phosphate is preferred to offset the drop in pH associated with the uptake of ammonium ions. The molarity of culture solutions varies between 0.001 and 0.005 M phosphate.

Orthophosphate can be replaced for some fungi by other forms of inorganic phosphate (70) and either phytic acid (266), adenosine phosphates (272), or casein (30) can also be used. Phosphites and hypophosphites are not readily metabolized by the microorganisms.

Phosphate is absorbed readily by fungi during the early stages of growth since it is required for glycolysis and energy systems of the cell. Its absorption in aerobes is dependent on oxygen, and inhibitors of respiration also depress phosphate intake. The phosphate uptake in relation to growth in *Aspergillus niger* is illustrated in Fig. 8. Combined forms of phosphate are usually hydrolyzed by phosphatases in the fungal mats. Both alkaline and acid phosphatases have been reported in fungi, but their specificity is in doubt (169).

Bacteria and fungi, often associated with the rhizosphere (cf. Chapter 6) of plants, are able to dissolve calcium hydrogen phosphate. Phosphorus was more readily released from tricalcium phosphate and pyrophosphate by bacteria than by fungi (170). It has been suggested that

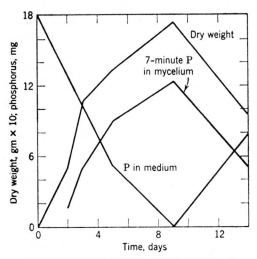

Fig. 8. Growth and phosphorus changes in *Aspergillus niger*. Seven-minute phosphorus is organic phosphorus mineralized by acid hydrolysis of 7 minutes' duration. From data of Mann (169).

the liberation of phosphorus from organic compounds is due to the action of enzymes of the esterase type and that liberation from insoluble mineral phosphates is due to effect of carbon dioxide or organic acids originating in microbial metabolism (196). *Streptomyces* species, *Aspergillus*, and *Penicillium* have all been shown to solubilize soil phosphates (292). Harley (103a), using labeled phosphate, has studied the uptake of phosphate by excised mycorhizal roots of beech, and Swaby and Sherber (292) showed that species of the genera *Arthrobacter*, *Pseudomonas*, *Xanthomonas*, *Achromobacter*, *Flavobacterium*, *Streptomyces*, *Aspergillus*, and *Penicillium* released phosphate from hydroxyapatite by producing organic acids. Numerous bacterial types including *Bacillus subtilis*, *B. cereus* var. *mycoides* (*B. mycoides*), *B. megaterium*, and "*B. mesentericus*" release soluble phosphorus from calcium and iron phosphates, calcium glycerophosphate, and lecithin (103a). In *Pinus radiata*, phosphorus uptake from plants inoculated with mycorhiza was greater than in those not containing the microorganisms (103a).

B. Potassium and Sodium

Potassium is universally required by microorganisms, but there is evidence that it can be replaced by rubidium in *Streptococcus faecalis* (Fig. 9). In other bacteria potassium is only partially replaced by

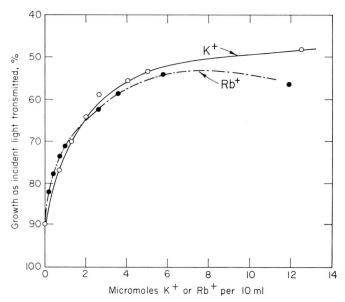

Fig. 9. Comparative effects of K⁺ and Rb⁺ on growth of *Streptococcus faecalis* as measured by density of a suspension. Redrawn by permission of the *Journal of Biological Chemistry* (162).

rubidium, and this is often referred to as the sparing effect of one ion for another. An example of this is in *Leuconostoc mesenteroides;* as shown in Fig. 10, presumably rubidium substitutes for potassium in some but not in all its metabolic functions.

The counteraction of the stimulatory or inhibitory effect of one ion by another is usually known as *ion interaction.* This phenomenon has been widely studied since antagonisms vary greatly between organisms (195). MacLeod and Snell (163) showed that many instances of ion interaction could be explained by assuming that ions which suppress growth do so because they interfere with other ions involved in metabolism. In Fig. 11 is shown the effect of sodium on the potassium requirement of *Lactobacillus casei* (162). Here sodium is antagonistic since it

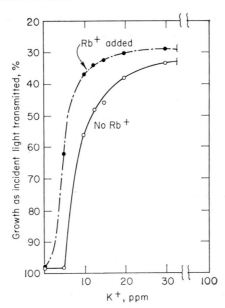

Fig. 10. The effect of Rb⁺ on the K⁺ requirement *Leuconostoc mesenteroides* 8042 as measured by density of a suspension. Redrawn by permission of the *Journal of Bacteriology* (163).

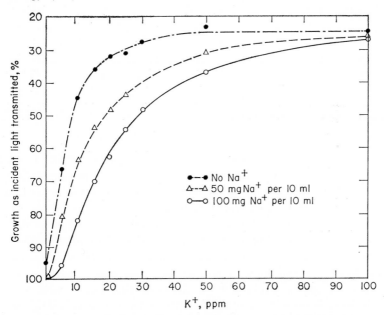

FIG. 11. The effect of Na⁺ on the K⁺ requirement of *Lactobacillus casei* as measured by density of a suspension. Redrawn by permission of the *Journal of Biological Chemistry* (162).

increased the requirement for the essential ion potassium. These effects are frequently complex since a single ion may replace another for some function but antagonize it in others and the two effects may or may not be observed independently at different concentrations. Thus at low concentrations rubidium decreased the requirement of *Leuconostoc mesenteroides* for potassium, but at higher concentrations it inhibited growth by competing with potassium for sites that specifically require the latter ion (164). Similar phenomena also occur between essential cations and related nonessential ions. A rubidium-potassium effect has also been observed by Lavollay in *Aspergillus niger* (142). Barton-Wright (18) showed that a regular dose-response curve to potassium could be obtained with *Streptococcus faecalis*, and he used this organism for determining potassium. In this bacterium rubidium also has a sparing action on potassium. *Leuconostoc mesenteroides* P-60 has also been used to assay potassium, but sufficient rubidium is put into the medium to eliminate the sparing effect of this ion on the potassium requirement.

Levels of potassium used for fungal cultures vary between 0.001 and 0.004 M, which is regarded as adequate. A shortage of the element in some fungi results in oxalic acid formation (189) and also poor utilization of the carbon source, especially carbohydrates (58, 245). Sodium only partially replaces potassium in *Aspergillus niger*, and under certain conditions rubidium and cesium and other alkali metals have slight effects only (288). Burris and Harris (39) showed that *Azotobacter chroococcum* was able to grow in media deficient in potassium and sodium.

Allen and Arnon (8) have shown that sodium is essential for the blue-green alga *Anabaena cylindrica* and that 5 ppm was sufficient for optimum growth. Neither potassium, lithium, rubidium, nor cesium replaced sodium for growth, and there is no evidence that larger amounts are harmful. It is likely that sodium is generally required by blue-green algae, and Allen (6) has found that 25 cultures of various Cyanophyceae grow well in a sodium-containing medium in the absence of added potassium, but no attempts were made to remove potassium from the constituents of the culture solutions. Gerloff, *et al.* (93) report a beneficial effect of sodium on *Microcystis aeruginosa*, and Kratz and Myers (139) found that logarithmic growth of *Anabaena variabilis*, *Anacystis nidulans*, and *Nostoc muscorum* cannot be maintained without sodium.

C. Magnesium and Calcium

Although calcium is required in small amounts by microorganisms, it will be considered here together with magnesium since in the literature interactions between the two nutrients are often reported.

Magnesium is usually required by microorganisms in larger amounts than calcium. A calcium requirement is difficult to demonstrate in some bacteria and fungi since it amounts to only a few parts per million. Thus, calcium is a micronutrient for microorganisms. This is understandable when one considers the function of the two elements. Magnesium is required in phosphorylation systems, especially in the glycolytic pathways, often acting as a link between substrate, enzyme, and coenzyme, e.g., adenosine and uridine triphosphates. No precise function however has been assigned to calcium in microorganisms.

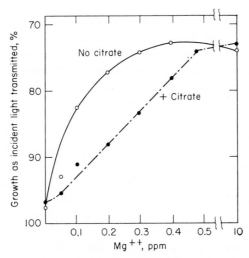

Fig. 12. The comparative response of *Streptococcus faecalis* to Mg^{++} in the presence and absence of citrate (20 mg citrate ion per milliliter) as measured by density of suspension. Redrawn by permission of the author and *Journal of Bacteriology* (164).

Webb demonstrated that for many bacteria magnesium is needed for cell division (320, 321). Henry and Stacey (107) have shown it to be required for the formation of the gram-staining complex. The comparative response of *Streptococcus faecalis* to magnesium in the presence and absence of citrate, shown in Fig. 12, demonstrates that a chelating agent reduces the availability of the metal to the fungus.

Shooter and Wyatt (267) showed that *Staphylococcus pyogenes* ($= S.$ *aureus*) required magnesium and calcium after the medium had been passed through an ion exchange resin. They suggest that calcium is required for the formation of proteases. The effect of magnesium only and the interaction between magnesium and calcium on growth are shown in Figs. 13 and 14.

Maximal yield was obtained after 18 hours' growth with 0.2 mg ions of magnesium per liter. When calcium only was added growth was less than that obtained with magnesium only. This effect was noted when 0.005 mg ions of calcium per liter was added and increased slowly up to 2.5 mg ions calcium per liter. While both magnesium and calcium stimulated growth singly, the two elements together were more effective and optimal growth was obtained with 0.02 mg per liter of magnesium and 0.05 mg ions per liter of calcium.

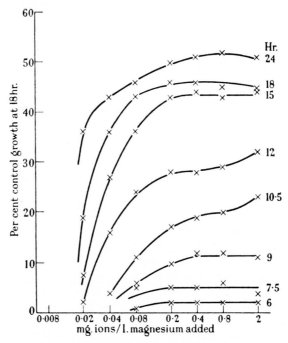

Fig. 13. Effect of the addition of Mg^{++} on the growth of *Staphylococcus pyogenes* between 6 and 24 hours. From Shooter and Wyatt (267).

Norris and Jensen (223) showed that calcium was essential for nitrogen fixation in *Azotobacter vinelandii, A. chroococcum, A. beijerinckii,* and *A. insignis* in media with or without combined nitrogen in the form of ammonium acetate. They showed that strontium could replace calcium. *A. agilis* did not appear to require calcium, but this may be required at a lower level.

Strains of *Rhizobium* require trace amounts of calcium only and larger amounts of magnesium for growth (224, 225). Bush and Wilson (42) showed that *Azotobacter vinelandii,* grown in a nitrogen-free medium, required calcium for nitrogen fixation. *Azotobacter agilis* grew well in a calcium-deficient medium and its growth was only slightly stimulated by adding the mineral nutrient. Several strains including *A. chroococcum, A. beijerinckii,* and *A. macrocytogenes* require calcium for nitrogen fixation but not for the assimilation of ammonia. *Azotobacter indicus* grew better in the absence of calcium.

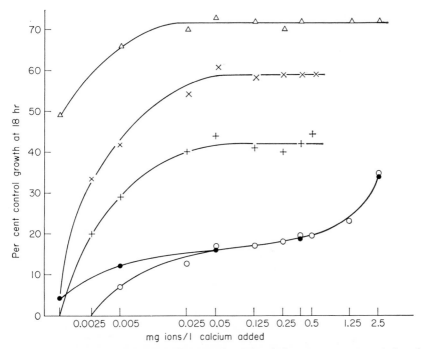

Fig. 14. Effect at 18 hours on the growth of *Staphylococcus pyogenes* of the addition of Ca^{++}, Ca^{++} and arginine, and Ca^{++} and Mg^{++} (broth batch L.2). ◯, Ca^{++}; ●, Ca^{++} and 0.0005 M arginine; +, Ca^{++} and 0.004 mg ions per liter of Mg^{++}; X, Ca^{++} and 0.008 mg ions per liter Mg^{++}; △, Ca^{++} and 0.08 mg ions per liter Mg^{++}. From Shooter and Wyatt (267).

The first report on the calcium requirements of fungi is by Young and Bennett in 1922 (330). Since that time there has been much confusion in regard to claims for essentiality of this nutrient since the effects of adding calcium have not been disentangled from those of pH. It is clear, however, that about 19 genera of fungi respond to additions of calcium, but often at very low levels between 0.2 and 20 ppm. Some fungi, e.g., *Aspergillus* species, *Neurospora* species, do not appear to have a calcium requirement (282). The growth response of *Coprinus ephemerus* to calcium is shown in Fig. 15.

In several fungi strontium replaces the calcium requirement, e.g., *Allomyces arbuscula* (120). Calcium is known to protect many organisms from the injurious effects of hydrogen ion or potassium, and there is some evidence that in bacteria it offsets zinc toxicity (58). Thus caution is required in interpreting data indicating an absolute and specific requirement for the nutrient. A calcium requirement should be evident, irrespective of pH or of constitution of media, and this can be achieved in most cases only by prior removal of calcium from the basal media. This has only been done in very few instances. Calcium,

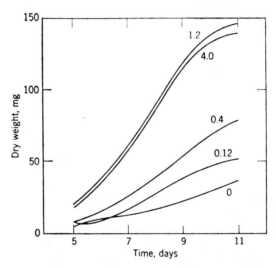

Fig. 15. The growth of *Coprinus ephemerus* at different levels of calcium (milligrams per liter). Redrawn from Fries (91) by permission of the *Svensk Botanisk Tidskrift*.

like magnesium, may be made less available to the organism by chelating agents in the medium, e.g., citrate or tartrate.

The magnesium content of the media for fungi is usually about 0.001 *M*, but this varies with the type of carbon source and the rate at which it is utilized (282, 283). *Aspergillus niger* requires about 10 mg magnesium per liter of culture solution for optimum growth (202, 203, 282). *Aspergillus terreus* seems to require more magnesium when grown in still culture than it does in shake culture. Enzymes activated by magnesium *in vitro* are often stimulated to a lesser extent by manganese, but under usual growth conditions magnesium is the physiologically active element. The absorption of magnesium is usually slower in neutral than in acid solution since it is readily precipitated under alkaline conditions. Because of this it is often necessary to sterilize phosphates separately from the rest of the culture media and the two portions of the media are mixed when cold since this avoids precipitation of magnesium and calcium phosphates. There are reports of magnesium offsetting toxicity effects of aluminum, copper, and mercury in fungi and also in bacteria (58, 153, 154). MacLeod and Snell (162, 163) have proposed that this antagonism is due to the metals competing

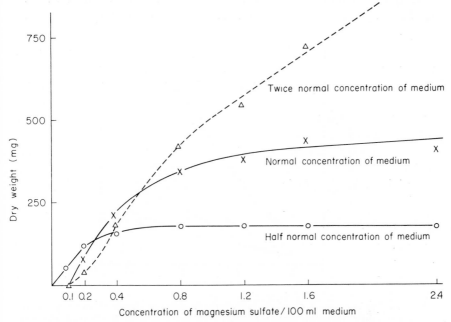

FIG. 16. Concentration of magnesium sulfate per 100 ml media. Yield curves for *Aspergillus niger*, in relation to the magnesium content of the medium, of three levels of other constituents of the medium. From Lavollay (142).

with magnesium for active enzyme sites and the resulting metal enzyme complexes are inactive. Magnesium prevents the absorption of copper by conidia of *Sclerotinia fructicola* (58). Beryllium has been claimed to replace magnesium in some fungi, but this needs confirmation (282, 288).

Lavollay studied in detail the antagonistic effects of media on magnesium uptake by *Aspergillus niger* (142). His results are illustrated in Fig. 16.

It is clear that the response to magnesium depends on the concentration of other constituents in the media.

Pearsall (227) considers that a monovalent:divalent ratio (M:D) below 1.5 is favorable for growth of diatoms of oligotrophic waters. Chu (60) and Vollenweider (313) found that the diatoms *Fragilaria*, *Asterionella*, and *Tabellaria* are all stimulated by high calcium and that potassium interacts with calcium and magnesium. This interaction is considered by Vollenweider (313) as antagonistic whereas Chu interprets this to mean that high potassium values render these organisms tolerant to higher concentrations of divalent ions.

Vollenweider (313) showed that calcium stimulated cell division in *Oscillatoria rubescens* and in *Ankistrodesmus falcatus* during early growth, but later growth depends on the magnesium content. When magnesium was at suboptimal level, calcium partially substituted for it and vice versa. The same interchange between calcium and magnesium was noted by Vishniac using marine *Labyrinthula* species (312). Provasoli *et al.* (235) and Provasoli (236) studied the effects of calcium magnesium ratios from 24:1 to 1:24 in a wide range of microorganisms. The organisms studied seem to have a wide flexibility toward different calcium:magnesium ratios which seem to narrow with unfavorable M:D ratios. At high M:D ratios, calcium may become essential, as in *Fragilaria capucina*. The same phenomenon holds for marine organisms, but at higher concentrations of sodium chloride. Provasoli *et al.* (235) and Provasoli (236) have formulated chemically defined marine media by having less calcium than magnesium and replacing phosphate with glycerophosphates and by adding metal chelators. These media are suitable for a wide range of marine littoral algae and flagellates. Provasoli and associates concluded that calcium and magnesium are widely interchangeable in marine algae. This wide versatility gives them an ecological advantage since rock pools are subjected to wide changes in salinity and M:D ratios.

The calcium or strontium requirement of *Chlorella* has been discussed by Walker (313a).

D. SULFUR

Sulfur is a well-known constituent of amino acids, such as methionine, cysteine, and cystine; of the tripeptide glutathione; of the vitamins, thiamine, biotin; and of antibiotics, penicillin, gliotoxin. It is therefore indispensable for the metabolism of most microorganisms. Thus sulfur is incorporated into a variety of cell materials. There is also evidence for adenosine 3'-phosphate, 5'-sulfatophosphate (276), from which sulfate can be transferred to various acceptors by specific sulfokinases to form sulfate esters or sulfamino compounds (72).

Reviews by Starkey (279), Updegraff and Wren (300), Butlin and Postgate (45), Postgate (233), ZoBell (333); and Kluyvel and van Niel (136) have considered aspects of the nutrition and physiology of the bacteria reducing sulfate. The culture media recommended for growing these bacteria, usually *Desulfovibrio* species, contain a considerable amount of iron, presumably to act as an indicator since black iron sulfide is formed during growth. The mesophilic sulfate-reducing bacteria are more exacting in their requirements for anaerobic condi-

TABLE XI

The Sulfur Nutrition of Some Fungi[a,b]

Source of sulfur	Saprolegnia delica	Brevilegnia gracilis	Pythium sp.	Pestalotia malorum	Aspergillus niger	Penicillium chrysogenum
Sulfate	0	+	+	+	+	+
Persulfate	0	+	+	+	+	
Sulfite	0	+	+			+
Bisulfite	0	+	+	0	+	
Dithionate	0	0	0	+	0	
Hyposulfite	+	+	+	0	+	+
Thiosulfate	+	+	+	+	+	+
Sulfide	+	+	+	+	+	+
Disulfide				+	+	+
Cysteine	+	+	+	+	+	+
Cystine					+	+
Methionine					+	
Thiourea	+	+	+	+	0	+
Thiocyanate						+

[a] + = growth, 0 = no growth.
[b] Reproduced from Cochrane (58).

tions of growth than are most anaerobes since they require an E*h* of approximately 0.2 millivolts for growth. Cysteine or Na₂S accelerates growth, presumably by lowering the E*h* sufficiently; reducing agents of more oxidizing E_0' values such as ascorbate or ferrous ions are less effective. *Desulfovibrio desulfuricans* will utilize SO_4^{--}, SO_3^{--}, $S_2O_3^{--}$, $S_4O_6^{--}$, $S_2O_4^{--}$, $S_2O_5^{--}$, and even colloidal sulfur. Postgate (232, 233) showed that the kinetics of substrate reduction in hydrogen by whole cells were consistent with sulfite being an intermediate. This was confirmed by Millet (187) with labeled sulfur-32. Aubert suggested that sulfur entered organic combination at the sulfite level of oxidation (13). Sulfate does not appear to penetrate the bacterial cell easily, and

it has been suggested that the anion might require a preliminary endergonic activation and that the activated sulfate would then enter the
cell. Proof for this theory is lacking and aryl sulfatases which activate
sulfate have not been found in *D. desulfuricans. Thiobacillus* species
oxidize sulfide to sulfuric acid and sulfate-reducing bacteria reduce
sulfate to sulfur (233).

Fungi that utilize sulfate are usually grown in media that contain
between 0.0001 and 0.0006 *M* sulfur. Most fungi reduce sulfate and
incorporate it into the sulfur-containing amino acids and glutathione.

Aquatic Phycomycetes, Saprolegniales, and Blastocladiales (47) do
not use sulfate, but other Phycomycetes, including Chytridiales, Lep-
tomitales, Peronosporales, and Zygomycetes utilize sulfate (58).
Mutants requiring reduced sulfur compounds have been obtained from
Neurospora crassa (114), *Aspergillus nidulans* (231a, 265), *Penicillium
chrysogenum* (110), *Ophiostoma multiannulatum* (58), and *Ustilago
zeae* (228). A summary of sulfur sources for fungi is given in Table
XI. Most fungi utilize sulfide, thiosulfate, and the more oxidized forms
of inorganic sulfur (except dithionite), but because of the instability
of these compounds in culture solutions, the data on the reduced forms
are questionable. Steinberg found that *Aspergillus niger* grew better on
aged than on fresh samples of sodium sulfide or disulfide, presumably
since it utilizes the more oxidized forms of these compounds (285). The
pathway suggested for sulfate reduction is: sulfate (SO_4^{--}) $\rightarrow$ sulfite
(SO_3^{--}) $\rightarrow$ sulfide (S^{--}) or thiosulfate ($S_2O_3^{--}$) $\rightarrow$ cysteine $\rightarrow$ methionine.

Spencer and Harada (276) have recently put forward a tentative
scheme for sulfate utilization in fungi (Scheme I).

SCHEME I

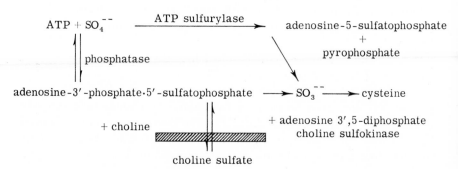

They suggest that all fungi which utilize inorganic sulfate as sole
source of sulfur for growth can produce adenosine-3'-phosphate 5'-

sulfatophosphate. Work with mutant strains of *Aspergillus nidulans* has shown that the reduction of sulfate to sulfite is an obligatory step in the formation of cysteine from inorganic sulfate (265). The reaction (Eq. 10).

$$SO_4^{--} + 2H \rightarrow SO_3^{--} + H_2O \tag{10}$$

is endergonic and has a standard free energy change of $+14$ kcal.

Choline sulfate, an ester widely distributed in fungi, is also utilized by them as sole source of sulfur (64a, 128). Since mutant strains of *Aspergillus nidulans* and *Penicillium notatum* do not utilize inorganic sulfate or choline sulfate as sulfur sources, and the parent strains grow readily on either compound, it is assumed that the two have common metabolic pathways (265). Egami and Itahashi (72) showed that *Aspergillus oryzae* utilize choline sulfate more readily than inorganic sulfate; competitive metabolism experiments with two sulfur compounds were interpreted to mean that choline sulfate is an intermediate in the utilization of sulfur of inorganic sulfate.

Blastocladiella emersonii grows with either cysteine or methionine and is presumably blocked prior to cysteine synthesis (17). *Allomyces arbuscula*, however, can utilize methionine only (99). Reduction of sulfate to sulfide is not effected by fungi as it is in some bacteria. *Candida* species reduce elemental sulfur to hydrogen sulfide (184, 259) and *Neurospora crassa* reduces selenite to selenium (331). Sulfur and its compounds are oxidized by fungi, e.g., *Penicillium luteum* and *Aspergillus niger* (192) and sulfur-containing amino acids by *Microsporum gypseum* (277). Cysteine sulfinic acid has been suggested as an intermediate in cysteine oxidation (277).

E. IRON

It is well known that iron is a constituent of respiratory enzymes and is found chiefly in association with porphyrins in the form of heme compounds. A number of enzymes also require inorganic iron for their activity.

Waring and Werkman (318) studied the effect of iron deficiency on a number of heterotrophic bacteria. The growth of *Aerobacter indologenes, Escherichia coli, Pseudomonas aeruginosa,* and *Klebsiella pneumoniae* was enhanced when iron was added to a medium previously treated with 8-hydroxyquinoline. *Pseudomonas aeruginosa* required three to four times more iron than the others, probably because of its complete four-band cytochrome and cytochrome oxidase system and its catalase and peroxidase activity. In *Aerobacter indologenes* ($= A.$ *cloacae* var.), hydrogenase, formic dehydrogenase, formic hydrogenylase, and cytochrome were dependent on the amount of iron in the medium. The oxidation of ammonia to nitrite in enrichment cultures of *Nitrosomonas* species was accelerated by 6 mg iron per liter, after use of quinoline purification methods (180). It is now known that this extraordinarily high requirement is due to residual quinoline in the culture solution since a large part of the added iron complexes with the chelate. The metal is also essential for the growth of *Nitrobacter* (3, 175).

Bacteria not containing heme compounds also require iron for their metabolism, e.g., in *Clostridium pasteurianum*, the metal is essential for nitrogen fixation and also for hydrogenase action (218).

An obligate requirement for iron has been shown when bacteria and fungi dissimilate nitrate, as discussed under nitrogen. In some cases heme compounds are required for nitrate reduction, as in *Haemophilus influenzae* (97) and in a strain of *Staphylococcus aureus* (141). In *H. influenzae*, only porphyrin compounds with a vinyl side chain functioned whereas *S. aureus* could utilize hematin but not protoporphyrin.

Fungi usually require between 0.1 and 0.3 ppm iron for growth and are able to utilize either ferrous or ferric iron. Iron-containing constituents of fungi include the heme compounds, as in bacteria. The pigment pulcherrimin in *Torulopsis pulcherrima* contains iron (58, 136, 248) as does aspergillin, the black pigment in spores of *Aspergillus niger*, which contains 0.25% of the metal (239). Some fungi, especially species of *Aspergillus*, release large amounts of organic acids, including citric and gluconic acids, which bind ferric iron; the ecological value of this is obvious. Metabolic events requiring iron in fungi include organic acid formation (87), penicillin production (137, 299), sporulation, (202, 203, 282), but it is more than likely that these are non-specific and indirect effects. It is claimed that the production of penicillin and streptomycin require more iron than is needed for maximum growth (58).

Most of the critical work on iron requirements in algae has been done with *Chlorella* (112a,b), *Scenedesmus*, and *Anabaena*, but it is likely that all algae require iron for their metabolism since the types so far examined contain functional heme compounds (86, 197, 293).

F. COPPER

Copper is a well-known constituent of a number of enzymes, polyphenol oxidase, monophenol oxidase, laccase, ascorbic acid oxidase, nitrite reductase, discussed fully in Chapter 3 of Volume IA.

Copper is a well-known inhibitor of growth in microorganisms and has been used extensively as a fungicide. It is required for growth in very minute amounts, however, and this can be demonstrated only in media rigorously treated to remove copper. In one of the early studies on yeast, Elvehjem showed that copper was required in addition to iron for maximum growth (74). Hutner investigated the growth requirements of *Rhodospirillum rubrum* and *Rhodopseudomonas* and showed that copper was one of the essential trace metals (116). In *Pseudomonas aeruginosa*, copper is required for denitrification, espe-

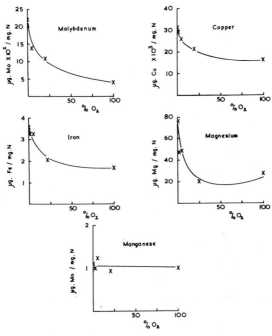

FIG. 17. Trace metal contents of *Pseudomonas aeruginosa* grown under various oxygen tensions. Various gas mixtures (N_2; 1% O_2 in N_2; 5% O_2 in N_2; air; and O_2) were dispersed through Pyrex glass sinters under a pressure of 3 pounds per square inch and the flasks were shaken at 100 oscillations per minute through a horizontal displacement of about 2 inches.

cially when the organism is utilizing nitrite (79, 84). As with iron, the copper requirement decreased with increased aeration, as shown in Fig. 17. To produce a copper deficiency in *Pseudomonas aeruginosa* it was necessary to subculture the bacterium through a series (5 to 7) of copper-deficient culture media. The deficient cells were very mucilaginous and when they were transferred into the complete media, growth was initially retarded, presumably because copper in the usual media was toxic. This effect was not observed, however, in copper-deficient media. It is the author's experience that the amounts of copper used in several of the recommended media for microorganisms are often unnecessarily high, and in some at toxic concentrations.

There is evidence that copper is required for nitrogen fixation. Thus Gribanov (101) showed that optimum rates of nitrogen fixation by *Azotobacter chroococcum* were achieved at the extraordinarily high level of 5 mg. copper per liter. Higher concentrations reduced the fixation process. Loginova (155) observed that the addition of 10 kg of copper sulfate per hectare had no effect on the number of nodules in vetch but markedly increased their weight since copper increased the nitrogen-fixing capacity of young nodules. With aged nodules the effect of copper decreased. Greenwood (100) showed that when clover was supplied with sufficient combined nitrogen to suppress the symbiotic fixation of the gas, withholding copper produced copper-deficiency symptoms but when the plants were dependent on atmospheric nitrogen, a deficiency of the metal resulted in symptoms of nitrogen deficiency. It is claimed that copper affects nitrogen fixation by depressing hemoglobin synthesis.

Lees (145) showed that removal of the metal by sodium diethyldithiocarbamate inhibited microbial nitrification in a soil percolated with ammonium sulfate and this could be completely restored by adding copper sulfate or manganese sulfate. This effect is, therefore, nonspecific. On the basis of a thiourea inhibition of ammonia oxidation by *Nitrosomonas*, Lees (150) suggested a possible copper requirement for the reaction, but this is not unequivocal evidence. Lees and Meiklejohn (146) showed that the addition of 14 or 28 μg copper to cultures of *Nitrosomonas* increased yield by about 17%. This effect, however, is not very significant.

Copper is required by fungi for normal growth at about 0.01–0.1 ppm. Higher concentrations are toxic although some fungi grow in saturated copper sulfate solution (58, 87, 278). The uptake of the metal is somewhat greater at moderate pH than at low values. In *Aspergillus niger*, copper affects the pigmentation of the spores: at low levels they are pale yellow and with increasing amounts of the micronutrient they appear brown and eventually black. The effective range is 0.05–2 μg copper per 50 ml basal culture solution (193, 202). A similar effect on spore color by copper is found in *Trichoderma viride* (37). A deficiency of copper in *Aspergillus niger* does not greatly depress the yield; in this respect it differs markedly from a deficiency of either iron, zinc, or molybdenum. Copper requirement has also been shown for dermatophytic fungi, e.g., *Trichophyton* species (58, 87, 246).

Algae so far examined require copper for growth, but the requirement is small and varies in amount in the different algal groups. In some blue-green algae the concentration of copper which inhibited *Phormidium tenue* stimulated *Spirulina* species (230). As in bacteria, the limiting range between deficiency and toxicity for copper is very narrow. Thus 10^{-7} M copper inhibited photosynthesis in *Chlorella* as did a series of copper inhibitors; yet at a lower concentration, copper is an essential element for *Chlorella* (98, 197, 230, 293).

G. ZINC

A deficiency of zinc in microorganisms results in an upset metabolism. Thus in *Neurospora crassa*, alcohol dehydrogenase and tryptophan synthetase are reduced but other enzymes have increased activity, e.g., diphosphopyridine nucleotidase (DPNase) (199). Hexokinase is also reduced in felts deficient in zinc (178), and this is in accord with the reported accumulation of inorganic phosphate in tomato leaves which suggested a possible role for the element in the hexokinase enzyme (230). Pyruvic carboxylase was limiting in *Rhizopus nigricans* deficient in zinc. Vallee has shown that alcohol, lactic and glutamic dehydrogenases contain zinc (301).

Very little is known about the zinc requirements of bacteria since there have been few studies on the subject. The requirement is usually quite low and can be demonstrated only by using rigorous purification methods.

Raulin showed that zinc is required by *Aspergillus* (242), and this was confirmed by Bertrand and Javillier (29). Steinberg (282, 284) showed that 0.18 mg zinc per liter was required for maximum growth, and Nicholas and Fielding (202) gave 0.2 mg zinc per liter as the optimal value. The addition of 1×10^{-3} μg zinc to 1 liter of a purified culture solution increased the dry weight twofold. In yeast, zinc stimulates growth at concentrations from 0.2 to 200 ppm, and McHargue and Calfee (160, 161) claim 10 ppm stimulated production of carbon dioxide. Texera reported that the zinc content of cultures determines the nature of antibiotics produced by *Fusarium hyperoxysporum* (299). In the absence of the metal the culture filtrates inhibited both gram-positive and gram-negative bacteria, but with zinc present only gram-positive ones were inhibited.

The respiratory coefficient (grams CO_2 evolved) : (grams dry weight of felt) is usually increased by traces of zinc in species of *Aspergillus*, *Penicillium*, *Trichothecium*, *Rhizopus nigricans* and in others. It is claimed that zinc is required for a more complete oxidation of carbohydrates and that when the metal is deficient (54, 55) organic acids accumulate. It is unlikely, however, that this is a specific effect since deficiencies of other trace metals have similar effects. Thus oxalic, gluconic, citric, lactic, and fumaric acids accumulate in *Aspergillus* and *Penicillium* species owing to a variety of causes other than a zinc deficiency (58). In *Ustilago sphaerogena*, zinc is required for the synthesis of cytochromes (201).

H. Manganese

Manganese can substitute for magnesium in a number of reactions involving adenosine triphosphate since it combines with the pyrophosphate

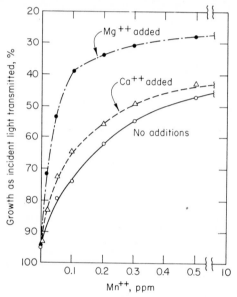

Fig. 18. The effect of Ca^{++} and Mg^{++} requirements of *Lactobacillus plantarum* (*L. arabinosus*). Density of a suspension measured. Redrawn by permission of the *Journal of Bacteriology*.

component of the nucleotide as does magnesium. It can thus operate in the glycolysis of sugars and in the decarboxylation reactions in the citric acid cycle. Hydroxylamine reductase requires manganese for its activity, and it is also essential for photosynthesis in algae (see Chapter 4). The manganese requirements for optimum growth in *Lactobacillus plantarum, L. casei,* and *Streptococcus faecalis* are 0.1, 0.03, and <0.03 ppm, respectively (164). In the former the manganese requirement is greatly decreased in the presence of magnesium while calcium or strontium have a definite but sparing effect as shown in Fig. 18. The effect of manganese on acid production is shown in Fig. 19.

Bertrand and Javillier, in 1911, showed that manganese is required for sporulation in *Aspergillus niger* (29), and since then their work has been amply confirmed. The requirement in fungi is between 0.005 and 0.01 ppm, and it is clear that the nutrient is essential for all genera thus far studied (58). A deficiency of the metal can be demonstrated in *Neurospora* without removing it from the medium, but in *Aspergillus*, since the requirement is less, manganese must be removed from constituents of the media before it can be shown to be essential for growth (203). A deficiency of the metal reduced the yields by only one-half since the mycelia usually coalesce into rough colonies in the absence

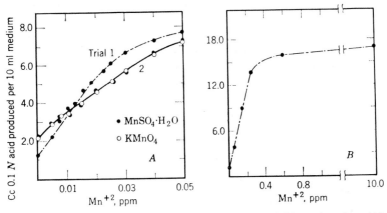

Fig. 19. The response of *Lactobacillus plantarum* (*L. arabinosus*) to low (A) and high (B) concentrations of Mn^{++} in manganese-deficient medium. From MacLeod and Snell, (162); reproduced by permission of the *Journal of Biological Chemistry*.

of manganese. In yeast the nutrient concentrated in cells even from media containing very minute amounts of it. About 10 ppm manganese stimulates growth in yeast and toxic effects are noted only at concentrations as high as 500 ppm (58).

Chlorella pyrenoidosa requires 10^{-7} M manganese for heterotrophic growth and 10^{-4} M for autotrophic growth. Autotrophic growth, Hill reaction, and photosynthesis responded equally when increments of the metal were added to manganese-deficient cultures (130, 131). Similar results were obtained with *Scenedesmus quadricauda, Nostoc muscorum,* and *Porphyridium cruentum.* Chlorophyll content of 1-day-old autotrophic cultures of *Chlorella* and *Scenedesmus* was not affected by manganese deficiency, but after being illuminated for 3 days, deficient cultures of *Chlorella* had much less chlorophyll than similarly treated nondeficient cultures. *Chlorella* in a medium containing manganese just sufficient for maximum photosynthesis and Hill reaction had a manganese:chlorophyll molar ratio of 1:600 (131).

I. MOLYBDENUM

It is well established that molybdenum is required for nitrate reduction in bacteria, fungi, and algae since it is a constituent of the assimilatory and dissimilatory nitrate reductases (79–84, 204–208, 209, 211, 212). In fact, whenever nitrate is utilized there is an obligatory requirement for the micronutrient (82). The trace metal requirement although much reduced when ammonia is the sole source of nitrogen is not completely eliminated in *Neurospora* (204), as it is in the alga *Scenedesmus obliquus* (11). In *Neurospora crassa* a deficiency of molybdenum resulted in decreased amounts of catalase and peroxidase. The enzymes were restored to normal amounts by returning the element *in vivo* to the deficient felts. This effect on the iron enzymes is probably indirect, resulting from a decrease in the activity of molybdenum-dependent flavoproteins which produce hydrogen peroxide, the common subtrate for catalase and peroxidase (210).

Since the classic work of Bortels (34), it has been known that molybdenum is required for nitrogen fixation in *Azotobacter* species and that vanadium can partially replace it in this process. Horner *et al.* (113), Jensen (125), Nicholas *et al.* (218), Bové *et al.* (35), all confirmed that molybdenum is essential when *Azotobacter* is utilizing atmospheric nitrogen although its partial replacement by vanadium varies with the species. The molybdenum requirement for nitrogen fixation in *A. chroococcum* is illustrated in Fig. 20a, and its replacement to the extent of about 7% by vanadium is illustrated in Fig. 20b. In other strains of *Azotobacter* the sparing action of vanadium was not observed. Takahashi and Nason (294) and Keeler and Varner (129) showed that tungstate is a competitive inhibiter of molybdate in nitrogen fixation, and the latter demonstrated the incorporation of tungstate into the same protein fractions as molybdenum. Bershova showed that active cells of *Azotobacter* absorb more Mo^{99} from the medium than do resting cells and that some of the absorbed molybdenum is secreted later into the medium, but this could result from autolysis (25). A similar requirement for molybdenum was found in *Clostridium* species (218) when fixing nitrogen gas.

Molybdenum is also required for the fixation of nitrogen by bacteria in the root nodules of legumes and nonlegumes, but its mode of action is not known (109, 323). It is of interest that much more of the micronutrient is required for nitrogen fixation than for nitrate reduction.

Blue-green algae also require 0.2 mg molybdenum per liter when

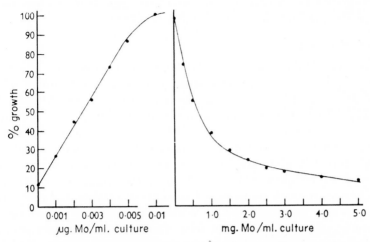

Fig. 20a. Effect of molybdenum content of culture medium on the growth of *Azotobacter chroococcum* 8003. Ordinate: % growth based on turbidity measurements; abscissa; micrograms or milligrams of molybdenum per milliliter of medium. From Nicholas *et al.* (218).

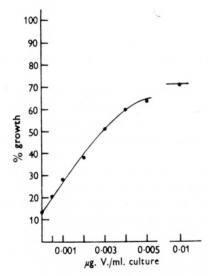

Fig. 20b. Effect of sodium vanadate in replacing sodium molybdate for the growth of *Azotobacter chroococcum* 8003. From Nicholas *et al.* (218).

they utilize either gaseous nitrogen or nitrate nitrogen: 0.2 mg molybdenum per liter (86, 197, 230). In Fig. 21 are shown the results of an experiment with *Anabaena cylindrica* in which the basal medium was freed from traces of molybdenum by coprecipitation with Fe and 8-hydroxyquinoline in the presence of acetic acid as described by Nicholas and Fielding (202). Molybdenum is required for the utilization of nitrogen gas or nitrate by the alga, but not when grown on ammonium only. Both figures show that the rate of assimilation are greater at

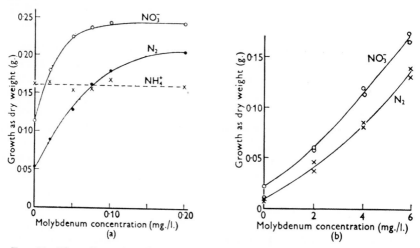

Fig. 21. The effect of molybdenum concentration on the growth of *Anabaena cylindrica*. a. With gaseous nitrogen, potassium nitrate or ammonium chloride as nitrogen source; cultures grown for 18 days (N_2, NO_3^-) or 14 days (NH_4^+). b. With gaseous nitrogen or potassium nitrate as nitrogen source in the presence of ethylenediaminetetraacetic acid (0.05 gram per liter; cultures grown for 14 days). From Fogg and Wolfe (86).

lower concentrations of molybdenum when the nitrogen source was nitrate than when molecular nitrogen was utilized. It is the growth of the organism only which is reduced in the absence of the trace metal; the rate of nitrate uptake from the medium is unaffected by molybdenum concentration. Similar results were obtained with the yeast *Hansenula anomala* (269a). The addition of the element to molybdenum-deficient cultures resulted immediately in nitrate reduction. This suggests a role for molybdenum in nitrate reduction.

Root nodules of Leguminosae and nonlegumes contain several times the molybdenum content of their roots. Nodule bacteria contains a particularly active nitrate reductase (52, 53).

The essentiality of the micronutrient for *Aspergillus niger* was established by the careful work of Steinberg (282, 284)). The requirements are small, as illustrated in Fig. 1. The *A. niger* assay method detects as little as 1×10^{-4} μg molybdenum and is more sensitive than the Mo^{99} radioassay method. All fungi appear to require the element when they are utilizing nitrate (82).

A report by Zavarzin that molybdenum is required for oxidation of nitrites in nitrifying bacteria has not been confirmed in other laboratories (332).

J. Vanadium and Gallium

Vanadium can partly replace molybdenum in nitrogen fixation in *Azotobacter chroococcum* as shown in Fig. 20b. This is not a general phenomenon in *Azotobacter* since in *A. indicus* and *A. vinelandii*, vanadium has no sparing action on molybdenum. Arnon and Wessel (10) showed that vanadium was an essential micronutrient for growth of *Scendesmus obliquus*. The amount required, up to 100 μg per liter, is much higher than its need for molybdenum at 0.1 μg per liter. A deficiency of vanadium does not reduce the chlorophyll content as markedly as does a shortage of molybdenum. In strong light, photosynthetic oxygen production in cells deficient in vanadium was inhibited, but it could be reactivated slowly by returning vanadium. A deficiency of vanadium appears to affect the dark reaction in photosynthesis. According to Bertrand the element is widely distributed in microorganisms, especially those in marine habitats (28). Bertrand claims that vanadium stimulated growth in *Aspergillus niger*, but the effect is small and needs confirmation (27).

Steinberg suggested that gallium was required for optimum growth by *Aspergillus niger* at 0.01 μg per liter, and none of 27 other elements tested replaced it (281). He was unable to substantiate this finding because his supply of purified sugar was used up. This work has not thus far been confirmed in other laboratories. Steinberg also claimed that scandium was beneficial when glycerol was the carbon source, but again no further reports are available to substantiate this observation (282).

At this stage it should be pointed out that although trace metals may not be essential for normal growth processes they may exert an influence on metabolic processes by stimulating or inhibiting them. Thus in *Penicillium japonicum*, colombium, molybdenum, tungsten, and chromium increase fat production. This may be due to a nonspecific activation of enzymes by a variety of metals of equivalent valency, or they may block certain reactions resulting in a "shunt" metabolism to fat synthesis (58).

K. COBALT

Vitamin B_{12} (cyanocobalamin) and hydroxocobalamin (vitamins B_{12a} and B_{12b}) are present in a number of microorganisms including bacteria and algae. Vitamin B_{12} is believed to be required in methylation processes and for synthesis of nucleic acids.

Strains of lactic acid bacteria are known to require vitamin B_{12}, as do algal flagellates, and these have been used to bioassay the vitamin and its analogs. It was estimated that 0.01 mμg B_{12} is required to form 880,-000 *Euglena* cells or 1.13×10^{-17} gm B_{12} per cell, which is equivalent to approximately 5000 molecules of vitamin B_{12} per *Euglena* cell. From this Hutner suggested a requirement of 6×10^{-13} gm cobalt per milliliter of culture medium (117, 118, 235, 236). The task of removing the trace metal to these low amounts is beyond the capacity of purification techniques in current use. The element has been shown to be required for the growth of numerous blue-green algae (93).

Recently a cobalt requirement has been found for *Bacillus circulans* when grown in nitrate medium (220a).

The synthesis of cobalamins occurs in certain bacteria and especially in species of *Streptomyces* and *Nocardia* of the Actinomycetales. The addition of cobalt to the culture medium increases the yield of cyanobalamin from *Streptomyces griseus*. In addition to cyanocobalamin, species of *Streptomyces* form hydroxocobalamin (vitamin B_{12a}, B_{12b}) in which the cyanide of cyanocobalamin is replaced by hydroxyl and vitamin B_{12c} containing a nitrite radical in place of cyanide; all three forms have been isolated from *Streptomyces griseus* (58).

Synthesis of vitamin B_{12} in filamentous fungi has not been shown conclusively, but substances active for *Lactobacillus leichmannii* are formed by *Ashbya gossypii* (58) and *Aspergillus niger* (203). It appears that 1,2-dimethyl-4,5-diaminobenzene is a precursor of cobalamins as well as flavins (58). Thus *Streptomyces olivaceus* incorporates the labeled 5,6-dimethylbenzimidazole into the cobalamin molecule.

Cobalt accumulated in *Neurospora crassa*; the degree of concentration was 23 times that in the external medium. More than 40% of the cobalt was bound to cell protein. The iron content of the medium influenced the uptake of cobalt by the fungus (16).

Nicholas (203) showed that vitamin B_{12} in *Aspergillus niger* was reduced by a deficiency of cobalt although the dry weight yield of the felts was not depressed as shown in Table XII. This result suggests either that vitamin B_{12} is not required by the fungus for its metabolism or that purification methods used were not sufficiently rigorous to reduce cobalt to a deficiency level. The latter interpretation is more likely to be correct.

Ahmed and Evans (1, 2) showed that the addition of cobalt to cultures of soybean plants grown under symbiotic conditions resulted in marked increase in the dry weight of shoots and prevented the development of nitrogen deficiency symptoms that were present in plants not given the micronutrient. The experiments of Reisenauer (244) showed that growth of alfalfa without combined nitrogen was stimulated by cobalt. Hallsworth et al. (103) showed a requirement for both

TABLE XII

Assay of Vitamin B$_{12}$ in Cultures of *Aspergillus niger* by *Lactobacillus leichmannii*[a]

Cobalt in 50 ml of culture solution of A. niger (µg)	Vitamin B$_{12}$ in	
	Undried felt (µg/gm)	Broth (µg per 50 ml of culture solution)
0	0 to 0.00018	Not detected
1	0.001	0.001

[a] Reproduced from Nicholas (203).

cobalt and copper by legumes when fixing nitrogen. The vitamin B$_{12}$ content of root nodules was dependent on the cobalt supplied, thus a value of 0.13 mµg B$_{12}$ per gram fresh nodule tissue in the cobalt-free cultures increased to 519 mµg B$_{12}$ when 50 mµg cobalt was given (2). Further investigations by Low et al. (156) have shown that *Rhizobium japonicum* grown in pure culture with nitrate as nitrogen source requires cobalt for maximum growth, as shown in Table XIII.

Cobalt is required for the growth of *Rhizobium japonicum* outside the host plant. In this respect it resembles *Bacillus circulans*, which also requires the micronutrient when grown on nitrate. Nicholas (220a) has shown recently that when *Azotobacter* is fixing atmospheric nitrogen or utilizing nitrate its vitamin B$_{12}$ content is more than when it is supplied with ammonia nitrogen as shown in Table XIV. Thus these results are in agreement with those for *Rhizobium* and for *Bacillus circulans*. The B$_{12}$ contents which are much higher in *Clostridium* than in *Azotobacter*, are not significantly affected by the nitrogen source.

Nicholas, *et al.* (220b) found that the nitrate reductase enzyme was markedly reduced in cells of *Rhizobium japonicum* deficient in cobalt. The requirement for growth on nitrate is less than 2 μg/liter. Since the micronutrient (labeled with Co^{58}) did not concentrate in purified

TABLE XIII

Effects of Cobalt on the Growth of *Rhizobium japonicum*[a]
on Nitrate Nitrogen

| | Turbidity | | Nitrogen |
Treatment	5 Days (O.D.)	7 Days (O.D.)	content[b] (mg/flask)
Experiment I			
0 cobalt[c]	0.02	0.35	0.53
0.5 ppb cobalt	0.19	1.27	4.75
5.0 ppb cobalt	0.21	1.40	5.00
Experiment II			
0 cobalt[c]	—	0.39	0.62
0.5 ppb cobalt	—	1.33	5.50
5.0 ppb cobalt	—	1.38	5.12

[a] Reproduced from Lowe *et al.* (156).
[b] Nitrogen contents of cells were determined after a growth period of 7 days.
[c] Values for the 0-cobalt treatment in both experiments are means of determinations on duplicate cultures. Other measurements were made on single cultures.

TABLE XIV

Vitamin B_{12} Contents of *Azotobacter vinelandii* (0) and *Clostridium pasteurianum* (W-2)[a,b]

Bacteria	N source in medium	*Ochromonas* assay	*Escherichia coli* assay
Azotobacter	N_2 gas	1.15	1.28
	NO_3^-	1.32	1.60
	NH_4^+	0.33	0.41
Clostridium	N_2 gas	6.3	7.09
	NO_3^-	5.3	6.6
	NH_4^+	4.0	5.0

[a] Vitamin B_{12} μg $\times$ 10^{-3}/gm wet weight of cells.
[b] Nicholas (unpublished).

factions of the enzyme and could be dialyzed from the enzyme preparations without loss of activity they suggested that the metal is required for enzyme formation rather than for its action. Nicholas *et al.* (220c) showed that cobalt or vitamin B_{12} is essential for a range of microorganisms utilizing nitrate including other species of *Rhizobium*, *Azotobacter vinelandii* (OP), *Escherischia coli* and a diploid yeast *Saccharomyces fragilis* × *Saccharomyces dobzhanskii*. The growth response in *Rhizobium* (μg cobalt/liter) is between 0.1 and 2 but for the other microorganisms it is about one-tenth, 0.01 to 0.2. Vitamin B_{12} was more effective than cobalt at equivalent concentrations. They confirmed that nitrate reductase activity was drastically reduced in all these microorganisms when grown in nitrate medium, deficient in cobalt. They also established a requirement for the micronutrient or vitamin B_{12} in *Azotobacter vinelandii* when it is fixing atmospheric nitrogen.

L. BORON

Since boron deficiency in higher plants is usually associated with a breakdown in the meristematic cells, it is unlikely that it will be required for this purpose in bacteria and fungi. In fact, it was long thought that bacteria and fungi do not require boron. Even now, very little is known about the function of boron in either higher plants or microorganisms.

Gerretsen and Hoop (94) showed that 2 ppm boron was required by *Azotobacter chroococcum* for nitrogen fixation in liquid culture, and 5 ppm in sand culture. Jordan and Anderson (127) showed that soils treated with 5–160 pounds of sodium borate per acre increased the amount of nitrogen fixed at pH 6.0–9.5 by 100–150%. Increases of nitrogen fixed in 7 days after treatment with boron were significant on agar plates and on broth cultures inoculated with the bacteria. Matuoshvili (174), on the other hand, claimed that the micronutrient is not essential for fixation in *Azotobacter vinelandii*.

Gerretsen and Hoop (94) have claimed that boron is necessary for the growth of *Aspergillus niger*, but this has not been confirmed in other laboratories. Eyster (78) showed that boron deficiency in *Nostoc muscorum* inhibited growth and chlorophyll production.

Winfield was unable to find a boron requirement for a range of fungi (325).

V. Toxicity Effects of Metals

It is beyond the scope of this review to consider in detail the effects of toxic amounts of metals on the growth of microorganisms, and only a few salient points will be considered. Reviews by Horsfall (115), Martin (172), and McCallan (159) should be consulted.

Copper, mercury, and silver are well-known inhibitors of growth of bacteria, fungi, and algae. Horsfall (115) has suggested the following order of toxicity for cations against fungi: Ag > Hg > Cu > Cd > Cr > Ni > Pb > Co > Zn > Fe > Ca, but the order differs with various organisms. Tests are usually done with germinating fungal spores because of the chelation of metals by constituents of the medium, e.g., amino acids.

Silver, mercury, and copper at equivalent concentrations are probably the most toxic metals. Inorganic salts of the same metal may vary in their toxicity effects on microorganisms. Thus copper as cupric ammonium sulfate is more firmly bound by spores than is copper sulfate (31, 173), and silver iodide is less toxic than are the other silver halides (184–185). In work reviewed by Martin (172) and McCallan (159) it is clear that substances secreted by fungal spores, e.g., amino acids and hydroxy acids, form soluble chelate complexes with copper which then readily penetrate the spore. Monomethylamine is liberated by spores of *Tilletia caries*, and this complexes with copper (58). Not all copper complexes, however, are toxic to spores, and it is clear that other factors including concentration, ratio of complexing agent to metal, are also important. When the ratio of the complexing agent to copper is between five and ten, toxicity is often decreased. The cell competes successfully for copper when the chelate:copper ratio is low and when the metal complex is unstable, but when a stable one is formed as with copper ethylenediaminetetraacetic acid, the toxicity is abolished at a 1:1 molar ratio of metal to chelate (31, 194).

It has been observed that organic mercurials are more toxic than inorganic ones in bacteria and fungi (115). This may be due to a more effective uptake of the organic mercury compounds (226) although phenyl mercuric acetate is more toxic in the ionic form (58). The mercurials are well-known inhibitors of sulfhydryl enzymes. Stannous or stannic ions are usually nontoxic, but tri-n-butyltin acetate inhibits the growth of fungi between 0.1 and 0.5 ppm (302).

In early studies with fungal spores it was found that copper uptake followed the Freundlich adsorption isotherm, i.e., there was a nonlinear uptake in relation to external copper concentration (58). Divalent cations were shown to reduce both uptake and toxicity of heavy metals (31). Thus the uptake of silver by spores was reduced by copper and more completely by mercury (185). Competition by hydrogen ion was equally important, as shown in Fig. 22.

Somers claims that a plot of the toxicity of metal cations to spores of *Botrytis fabae* against the electronegativities of the metals is reasonably linear (cf. Fig. 23) (274). This he presents as evidence supporting Horsfall's hypothesis that fungicidal action of metal ions is primarily due to interaction at the fungal cell surface (115). Somers suggests that

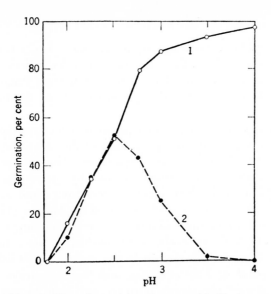

FIG. 22. The effect of pH on the toxicity of copper chloride to spores of *Alternaria tenuis*. Curve *1* (solid line), control; curve *2* (dashed line), 0.0001 *M* CuCl₂. Drawn from Biedermann and Müller (31).

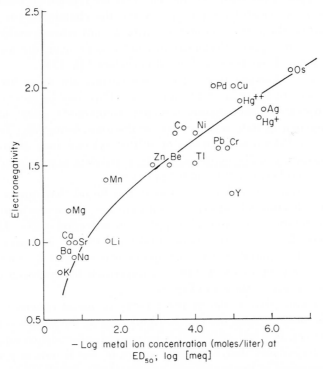

FIG. 23. Graph of toxicity of metal cations to *Botrytis fabae* against electronegativity of the metal. From Somers (274).

427

the primary toxic action of metal cations is the formation of nonionized complexes with surface ionogenic groups, e.g., phosphate, carboxyl, and sulfhydryl, and that the different toxicities of the metals can be correlated with the varying strengths of surface binding. Miller however contests this viewpoint.

Two hypotheses have been put forward to account for the accumulation of metals in spores. The first assumes that the entire spore protoplasm accumulates the metal so that it moves freely across the semipermeable barriers. In support of this, the rapid exchange of extracellular zinc with the metal in the protoplasm of *Aspergillus niger* (184, 185) and the rapid loss of potassium from bacteria (140) are often cited. The second interpretation is that there is a differential adsorption of the metal on to interfaces usually associated with permeability barriers. The idea of an ion-exchange process has the advantage of explaining ion competition effects and the fact that the uptake of copper is accompanied by equivalent loss of other ions. The adsorption concept does not invoke an actively metabolizing system since uptake of metals continues long after spore germination has been completely inhibited (183).

In experiments with dye uptake in bacteria (158) and in ascospores of *Neurospora* (290), it was shown that uptake was independent of temperature so that it is unlikely to be a metabolically controlled reaction. Indeed, dead cells adsorb the dyes as readily as do living ones. In yeast various cations compete for a number of negative binding sites on the cell surface. There is some evidence that metals depress the permeability to other constituents; thus copper retards the entry of glycerol into erythrocytes (64) and mercury reduces phosphate uptake in bacteria (188) and silver increases loss of phosphate from fungal spores (185). The suggested mechanism of action for these reactions is, however, based on vague theories lacking experimental proof.

Divalent metals are known to inhibit sulfhydryl enzymes by forming mercaptides. Thus mercury is a well-known inhibitor and reacts as shown in Eq. 11.

$$\text{Enzyme} \begin{array}{c} \diagup \text{SH} \\ \diagdown \text{SH} \end{array} + HgCl_2 \rightarrow \text{Enzyme} \begin{array}{c} \diagup \text{S} \\ \diagdown \text{S} \end{array} Hg + 2HCl \qquad (11)$$

This reaction can usually be reversed by adding another sulfhydryl compound, e.g., cysteine or glutathione, which then removes the mercury from the complex. A monovalent metal or an organic mercurial like p-chloromercuribenzoate reacts with a single sulfhydryl group. Shaw (264) has proposed that toxicity is correlated with the insolubility of the metal sulfides as in Eq. 12.

$$\text{metal}^{++} + S^{--} \rightleftarrows \text{metal sulfide} \qquad (12)$$

He showed that the order of insolubility of the metal sulfides is in the order of their toxicities: mercury $\cong$ silver > copper > lead > cadmium > zinc, which is also the affinity for the sulfhydryl group in a number of enzymes (133). The sulfhydryl inhibition will not account for all

TABLE XV

The Relative Toxicities of Sulfur and Hydrogen Sulfide[a,b]

Species	Wettable sulfur	Colloidal sulfur	Hydrogen sulfide
Monilinia fructicola	54	0.5	2.8[c]
Cephalosporium acremonium	>1000	0.3	12[c]
Aspergillus niger	>1000	0.3	15[c]
Glomerella cingulata	>1000	0.4	20[c]
Neurospora sitophila	>1000	1.0	38[c]
Rhizopus nigricans	>1000	2.7	5.9
Alternaria oleracea	>1000	18	15
Stemphylium sarcinaeforme	>1000	31	8.8

[a] From Miller, et al. (183).
[b] Toxicity is expressed as the dose, in parts per million, required to kill 50% of spores in an exposure of 24 hours; concentrations are of the external solution or suspension.
[c] Highly significant difference between colloidal sulfur and hydrogen sulfide.

metal toxicity effects since a number of enzymes are not dependent on sulfhydryl groups.

Inorganic sulfur was one of the earliest fungicides used and now organic sulfur compounds are extensively employed. McCallan (159) and Horsfall (115) in their reviews have considered evidence for production of hydrogen sulfide (from elementary sulfur), which is fungistatic and somewhat fungicidal. It is clear that sulfur on a weight basis is more fungicidal than an equivalent amount of hydrogen sulfide. Fungi differ markedly in their sensitivity to sulfur (Table XV).

It has been suggested recently that sulfur acts as a toxicant since it depletes the hydrogen donor system in the spores and is itself reduced to the sulfide, thus resulting in oxidation of cell constituents and up-setting energy utilization mechanisms (159). In support of this hypo-thesis it was shown that methylene blue prevents the reduction of sulfur by spores of *Neurospora sitophila* (184).

Selenium and tellurium are much less toxic than sulfur and their reduction by yeast cells is less rapid. Selenate inhibits competitively the uptake of sulfur by *Aspergillus niger* and by *Chlorella vulgaris* (58, 268, 322).

VI. Conclusions

Although it is beyond the scope of this chapter to anticipate future developments in the study of inorganic nutrient requirements of micro-organisms, mention can be made of present trends and of areas where further work is required.

Thus it is likely that pure culture methods will be developed further, thereby establishing other trace metal requirements for growth. In this connection certain advances in allied fields might help. Two examples will suffice to illustrate this: (a) the newer plastic materials, e.g., polypropylene containers, which can be readily cleaned and sterilized may eventually replace glassware for this type of work; (b) use of radio-activation analysis to determine millimicrogram quantities of trace metals, thus far of limited application because of the high cost, may become more widely used to check the efficacy of purification methods in removing metals. At the present time, bioassay methods are em-ployed to determine residual metals in purified media.

A review of the literature has shown that mineral nutrient require-ments of but a few genera and species of microorganisms have been determined. A study of a wider variety of microorganisms is required; the nutrition of marine microorganisms should be rewarding since they may show unusual mineral requirements and osmotic features as-sociated with their saline environment.

A fashionable, yet equally difficult approach is to establish a specific function for a mineral nutrient in metabolism. This method often re-quires the preliminary use of a nutrition-type experiment to establish whether an enzyme is dependent on a particular metal for its activity. Further data must then be obtained to decide whether the metal is di-rectly concerned with the formation of the enzyme or whether it is a functional constituent of it, or both. This leads to experiments on the mode of action of metals during enzyme action. Thus the transition metals are known to act as electron carriers during biological oxidation undergoing valency changes (36, 205, 211, 212). The techniques used to establish these facts include separation of the valency states of metals by paper and column chromatography for subsequent use in purified enzyme systems (205) and the recent use of electron paramagnetic resonance techniques to establish that valency changes occur during enzyme action (36, 79, 82, 84). Although some of the functions of trace metals, e.g., iron, copper, molybdenum, zinc, and manganese, have been established in microorganisms, it is surprising that very little is known about the role in metabolism of some of the major nutrients, e.g., potassium and calcium.

There is a tendency in this era of metabolic studies to forget that microorganisms are organized living units with definite ultra-fine structures. The results obtained with isolated enzymes in the test tube must always be related to their functions in the intact cells. There is therefore a need to study enzymatic changes in living cells. The methodology of double-beam spectrophotometry developed by Chance is an excellent beginning for studies with whole cells (51a).

It must also be emphasized that nutrients are associated with other important physiological functions in microorganisms. These include integrity of cell membranes, maintenance of osmotic barriers and gradients within cells. Indeed, critical studies of this type with microorganisms have barely begun.

REFERENCES

1. Ahmed, S., and Evans, H. J. Effect of cobalt on the growth of soybeans in the absence of supplied nitrogen. Biochem. Biophys. Research Communs., 1, 271–275 (1959).
2. Ahmed, S., and Evans, H. J. Cobalt: A micronutrient element for the growth of soybean plants under symbiotic conditions. Soil Sci. 90, 205–210 (1960).
3. Aleem, M. I. H., and Alexander, M. Cell-free nitrification by Nitrobacter. J. Bacteriol. 76, 510–514 (1958).
4. Aleem, M. I. H., and Nason, A. Nitrite oxidase, a particulate cytochrome electron transport system from Nitrobacter. Biochem. Biophys. Research Communs. 1, 323–327 (1959).
5. Aleem, M. I. H., and Nason, A. Phosphorylation coupled to nitrate oxidation by particles from the chemoautotroph Nitrobacter agilis. Proc. Natl. Acad. Sci. U.S. 46, 763–769 (1960).
6. Allen, M. B. The cultivation of Myxophyceae. Arch. Mikrobiol. 17, 34–42 (1952).
7. Allen, M. B., and van Niel, C. B. Experiments on bacterial denitrification. J. Bacteriol. 64, 397–412 (1952).
8. Allen, M. B., and Arnon, D. I. Studies on nitrogen-fixing blue-green algae. II. Sodium requirement of Anabaena cylindrica. Physiol. Plantarum 8, 653–660 (1955).
9. Arnon, D. I. Criteria of essentiality of inorganic micronutrients for plants. In "Trace Elements in Plant Physiology" (T. Wallace, ed.) pp. 31–39. Chronica Botanica, Waltham, Massachusetts, 1954.

10. Arnon, D. I., and Wessel, G. Vanadium as an essential element for green plants. *Nature* **172**, 1039–1041 (1953).

11. Arnon, D. I., Ichioka, P. S., Wessel, G., Fujiwara, A., and Woolley, J. T. Molybdenum in relation to nitrogen metabolism. I. Assimilation of nitrate nitrogen by *Scenedesmus*. *Plant Physiol.* **8**, 538–555 (1955).

12. Arnon, D. I., Losada, M., Nozaki, M., and Tagawa, K. Photofixation of nitrogen and photoproduction of hydrogen by thiosulphate during bacterial photosynthesis. *Biochem. J.* **77**, 23–24 (1960).

13. Aubert, J. P. "Colloque sur la biochimie du soufre" p. 81. Centre National de la Recherche Scientifique, Paris, France (1956).

14. Baalsrud, K., and Baalsrud, K. S. Studies on *Thiobacillus denitrificans*. *Arch. Mikrobiol.* **20**, 34–62 (1954).

15. Back, K. J. C., Lascelles, J., and Still, J. L. Hydrogenase. *Australian J. Sci.* **9**, 25–31 (1946).

16. Ballantine, R. The biosynthesis of stable cobalto-proteins by plants. *J. Cellular. Comp. Physiol.* **37**, 369–388 (1951).

17. Barmer, H. D., and Cantino, E. C. Nutritional relationships in a new species of *Blastocladiella*. *Am. J. Botany* **39**, 746–751 (1952).

18. Barton-Wright, E. C. The theory and practice of the microbiological assay of vitamin-B complex, together with the assay of selected amino acids and potassium. *Analyst* **70**, 283–295 (1945).

19. Beijerinck, M. W. Über oligonitrophile Microben. *Zentr. Bakteriol. Parasitenk. Abt. II*, **7**, 561–570 (1901).

20. Beijerinck, M. M. *Arch. neérl. sci. exactes et naturelles, Harlem Ser. II* **9**, 131–141 (1904).

21. Beijerinck, M. W., and Minkman, D. C. J. Bildung und Verbrauch von Stickoxydeel durch Bakterien. *Zentr. Bakteriol. Parasitenk. Abt. II*, **25**, 30–63 (1910).

22. Beijerinck, M. W. Über das Nitratferment und über physiologische Artbildung. *Folia Microbiol., Delft* **3**, 91–102 (1914).

23. Beinert, H. Flavin coenzymes. *In* "The Enzymes" (P. D. Boyer, A. Lardy, and Karl Myrbäck, eds.), 2nd ed., Vol. 2, pp. 340–416. Academic Press, New York, 1960.

24. Bentley, O. G., Snell, E. E., and Phillips, P. H. A microbiological method for the determination of manganese. *J. Biol. Chem.* **170**, 343–350 (1947).

25. Bershova, O. I. The effect of trace elements on soil bacteria. Part I. Utilization of molybdenum by a culture of *Azotobacter*. *Mikrobiol. Zhur. Akad. Nauk Ukr. R.S.R.* **18**, 5–12 (1956).

26. Bertrand, D. Sur l'extraordinaire sensibilité de l'*Aspergillus niger* visà vis du manganèse. *Bull. soc. chim. France* **4**, 11–18, 400 (1942).

27. Bertrand, D. Le vanadium comme élément oligosynergique pour l'*Aspergillus niger*. *Ann. inst. Pasteur* **68**, 58–68 (1942).

28. Bertrand, D. Survey of contemporary knowledge of biogeochemistry. 2. The biogeochemistry of vanadium. *Bull. Am. Museum Nat. His.* **94**, 407–455 (1950).

29. Bertrand, G., and Javillier, M. Influence du manganèse sur le développement de l'*Aspergillus niger*. *Compt. rend. acad. sci.* **152**, 225–228 (1911).

30. Bhargava, K. S. Physiological studies on some members of the family *Saprolegniaceae*. Part II. Sulphur and phosphorus requirements. *Proc. Indian Acad. Sci.* **B21**, 344–349 (1943).

31. Biedermann, W., and Müller, E. Die Inaktivierung des gelösten Kupfers (11) in Fungiziden. *Phytopathol. Z.* **18**, 307–338 (1952).

32. Bond, G., and Scott, G. D. An examination of some symbiotic systems for fixation of nitrogen. *Ann. Botany (London)* **19**, 67–77 (1955).

33. Bortels, H. Über die Bedeutung von Eisen, Zenk und Kupfer für Mikroorganismen. *Biochem. Z.* **182**, 301–358 (1927).

34. Bortels, H. Molybdäns als Katalysator bei der Biologischen Stickstoffbindung. *Arch. Mikrobiol.* **1**, 333–342 (1930).

35. Bové J., Bové, C., and Arnon, D. I. Molybdenum and vanadium requirements of *Azotobacter* for growth and nitrogen fixation. *Plant Physiol.* **32**, *Suppl. 23* (1957).

36. Bray, R. C., Malmström, B. G., and Vänngård, T. The chemistry of xanthine oxidase. 5. Electron-spin resonance of xanthine oxidase solutions. *Biochem. J.* **73**, 193–197 (1959).

37. Brian, P. W., and Hemming, H. G. Some nutritional conditions affecting spore production by *Trichoderma viride*. *Brit. Mycol. Soc. Trans.* **33**, 132–141 (1950).

38. Burris, R. H., and Wilson, P. W. Characteristics of the nitrogen fixing enzyme system in *Nostoc muscorum*. *Botan. Gaz.* **108**, 254–262 (1946).

39. Burris, C. M., and Harris, J. O. The influence of sodium, potassium and ammonium ions on the respiration of *Azotobacter chroococcum* as related to the composition of the growth medium. *Soil Sci. Soc. Am. Proc.* **17**, 245–246 (1953).

40. Burström, H. Über die schwermetalkatalyse der nitratassimilation. *Planta* **29**, 292–305 (1939).

41. Burström, H. The nitrate nutrition of plants. A general survey of the occurrence and assimilation of nitrate. *Lantbruks-Högskol. Ann.* **13**, 1–86 (1945).

42. Bush, J. A., and Wilson, P. W. The calcium requirements of the *Azotobacter* for nitrogen fixation. *Bacteriol. Proc. (Soc. Am. Bacteriologists)* **58**, 9–10 (1958).

43. Butkewitsch, W. The culture of the fungus *Aspergillus niger* as a method of soil investigation. *Zhur. Opyt. Agron.* **10**, 136–141 (1909).

44. Butkewitsch, W. Über die Bildung der oxalsäure und des Ammoniaks in den Kulturen von *Aspergillus niger* auf Pepton. *Biochem. Z.* **129**, 445–454 (1922).

45. Butlin, K. R., and Postgate, J. R. The economic importance of autotrophic microorganisms. *Symposium Soc. Gen. Microbiol.* **4**, 271–305 (1954).

46. Cain, R. B. The microbial metabolism of nitro-aromatic compounds. *J. Gen. Microbiol.* **19**, 1–14 (1958).

47. Cantino, E. C. Physiology and phylogeny in water moulds—a revaluation. *Quart. Rev. Biol.* **30**, 138–149 (1955).

48. Carnahan, J. E., Mortensen, L. E., Mower, H. F., and Castle, J. E. Nitrogen fixation in cell-free extracts of *Clostridium pasteurianum*. *Biochim. et Biophys. Acta* **38**, 188–189 (1960).

49. Carnahan, J. E., Mortenson, L. E., Mower, H. F., and Castle, J. E. Nitrogen fixation in cell-free extracts of *Clostridium pasteurianum*. *Biochim. et Biophys. Acta* **44**, 520–535 (1960).

50. Cartwright, N. J., and Cain, R. B. Bacterial degradation of the nitrobenzoic acids. 2. Reduction of the nitro-group. *Biochem. J.* **73**, 305–314 (1959).

51. Cartwright, N. J., and Cain, R. B. Bacterial degradation of nitrobenzoic acid. *Biochem. J.* **71**, 248–261 (1959).

51a. Chance, B., and Williams, G. R. Respiratory chain and oxidative phosphorylation. *Advances in Enzymol.* **17**, 65–135 (1956).

52. Cheniae, G. M., and Evans, H. J. On the relation between nitrogen fixation and nodule nitrate reductase of soybean root nodules. *Biochim. et Biophys. Acta* **26**, 654–655 (1957).

53. Cheniae, G. M., and Evans, H. J. Physiological studies of nodule-nitrate reductase. *Plant Physiol.* **35**, 454–462 (1960).

54. Chesters, C. G. C., and Rolinson, G. N. Trace elements and streptomycin production. *J. Gen. Microbiol.* **5**, 559–565 (1951).

55. Chesters, C. G. C., and Rolinson, G. N. Zinc in the metabolism of *Aspergillus niger*. *J. Gen. Microbiol.* **5**, 553–558 (1951).

56. Cochrane, V. W. The metabolism of species of *Streptomyces*. III. The nitrate metabolism of *Streptomyces griseus*. *Bull. Torrey Botan. Club* **77**, 176–180 (1950).

57. Cochrane, V. W., and Conn, J. E. The metabolism of species of *Streptomyces*. II. The nitrate metabolism of *S. coelicolor*. *Bull. Torrey Botan. Club* **77**, 10–18 (1950).

58. Cochrane, V. W. "Physiology of Fungi" 524 pp. Wiley, New York, 1958.

59. Corbet, A. S. The formation of hyponitrous acid as an intermediate compound in the biological or photochemical oxidation of ammonia to nitrous acid. *Biochem. J.* **28**, 1575–1582 (1934).

60. Chu, S. P. The influence of the mineral composition of the medium on the growth of Planktonic algae. *J. Ecol.* **30**, 284–325 (1942).

61. Chughtai, I. D., and Walker, T. K. The influence of cyanide on *Aspergillus niger*. *Biochem. J.* **56**, 484–487 (1954).

62. Chung, C. W., and Najjar, V. A. Cofactor requirements for enzymatic denitrification. 1. Nitrite reductase. *J. Biol. Chem.* **218**, 617–626 (1956).

63. Chung, C. W., and Najjar, V. A. Cofactor requirements for enzymatic denitrification. II. Nitric oxide reductase. *J. Biol. Chem.* **218**, 627–632 (1956).

64. Davson, H., and Danielli, J. F. "The Permeability of Natural Membranes" 361 pp. Macmillan, New York, 1943.

64a. Davis, B. D. Intermediates in amino acid biosynthesis. *Advances in Enzymol.* **16**, 247–312 (1955).

65. Davy, H. "Elements of Agricultural Chemistry" Griffin, Glasgow, 1814.

66. De, P. K. The role of blue-green algae in nitrogen fixation in rice fields. *Proc. Roy. Soc.* **B127**, 121–130 (1939).

67. Dehérain, P. P., and Marquenne, L. Sur la réduction des nitrates dans la terre arable. *Compt. rend. acad. sci.* **95**, 691–693 (1882).

68. Delwiche, C. C. Production and utilization of nitrous oxide by *Pseudomonas aeruginosa*. *J. Bacteriol.* **77**, 55–59 (1959).

69. Donald, C., Passey, B. I., and Swaby, R. J. Bioassay of available trace metals from Australian soils. *Australian J. Agr. Research* **3**, 305–325 (1952).

70. Dox, A. W. The phosphorus assimilation of *Aspergillus niger*. *J. Biol. Chem.* **10**, 77–80 (1911).

71. Drewes, K. Über die Assimilation des Luftstickstaffs durch Blaualgen. *Zentr. Bakteriol. Parasitenk. Abt. II*, **76**, 88 (1935).

72. Egami, F., and Itahashi, M. Biochemical studies on the choline sulfate ester. 1. *Aspergillus oryzae* grows in a medium with choline-sulfate ester as sulfur source. *Igaku to Seibutsugakii* **19**, 292–294 (1951).

73. Egami, F., Yamada, T., and Taniguchi, S. Respiration and the oxidation and reduction enzymes of a halotolerant bacterium. *Congr. intern. biochim. 2nd Congr. Paris*, 78 (1952).

74. Elvehjem, C. A. The role of iron and copper in the growth and metabolism of yeast. *J. Biol. Chem.* **90**, 111–113 (1931).
75. Engel, M. S., and Alexander, M. Growth and autotrophic metabolism of *Nitrosomonas europaea*. *J. Bacteriol.* **217**, 76–82 (1958).
76. Engel, M. S., and Alexander, M. Culture of *Nitrosomonas europaea* in media free of insoluble constituents. *Nature* **181**, 136–137 (1958).
76a. English, M. P., and Barnard, N. H. The effect of tract metal deficiency on some *Trichophyton* strains. *Brit. Mycol. Soc. Trans.* **38**, 78–82 (1955).
77. Esposito, R. G., and Wilson, P. W. Trace metals in the nutrition of *Azotobacter vinelandii* (O). *Biochim. et Biophys. Acta* **22**, 186–187 (1956).
78. Eyster, C. Necessity of boron for *Nostoc muscorum*. *Nature* **170**, 755–756 (1952).
78a. Farkas-Himsley, H., and Artman, M. Studies on nitrate reduction by *Escherichia coli*. *J. Bacteriol.* **74**, 690–692 (1957).
79. Fewson, C. A., and Nicholas, D. J. D. Nitrate reduction in *Pseudomonas aeruginosa*. *Biochem. J.* **77**, 3–4 P (1960).
80. Fewson, C. A., and Nicholas, D. J. D. Utilization of nitric oxide by microorganisms and higher plants. *Nature* **188**, 794–796 (1960).
81. Fewson, C. A., and Nicholas, D. J. D. Nitric oxide reductase from *Pseudomonas aeruginosa*. *Biochem. J.* **78**, 9 (1961).
82. Fewson, C. A., and Nicholas, D. J. D. The utilization of nitrate by microorganisms. *Nature* **190**, 2–7 (1961).
83. Fewson, C. A., and Nicholas, D. J. D. Respiratory enzymes in *Micrococcus dentrificans*. *Biochim. et Biophys. Acta* **48**, 208–210 (1961).
84. Fewson, C. A., and Nicholas, D. J. D. Nitrate reductase from *Pseudomonas aeruginosa*. *Biochim. et Biophys. Acta* **49**, 335–349 (1960).
85. Fogg, G. E. The production of extracellular nitrogenous substances by a blue-green alga. *Proc. Roy. Soc.* **B139**, 372–380 (1952).
86. Fogg, G. E., and Wolfe, M. Nitrogen metabolism of blue-green algae. *Symposium Soc. Gen. Microbiol.* **4th**, 99–125 (1954).
87. Foster, J. W. "Chemical Activities of Fungi" 648 pp. Academic Press, New York, 1949.
88. Frank, B. Über den experimentellen Nachweis der Assimilation freien stickstoffs durch erdbodenbewohninde Algen. *Ber. deut. botan. Ges.* **7**, 34–42 (1889).
89. Frazen, H., and Löhmann, E. Beiträge zur Biochemie der Mikroorganismen. *Z. physiol. Chem. Hoppe-Seyler's* **63**, 52–102 (1909).
90. Fries, L. Studies in the physiology of *Coprinus*. I. Growth substance, nitrogen and carbon requirements. *Svensk. Botan. Tidskr.* **49**, 475–535 (1955).
91. Fries, L. Studies in the physiology of *Coprinus*. II. Influence of pH, metal factors and temperature. *Svensk. Botan. Tidskr.* **50**, 47–96 (1956).
92. Gayon, U., and Dupetit, G. Recherches sur la réduction des nitrates par les infiniment petits. *Mém. soc. sci. phys. nat. (Bordeaux)*, 3ᵉ *Sér.* **11**, 201–307 (1886).
93. Gerloff, C. G., Fitzgerald, G. P., and Skoog, F. The mineral nutrition of *Microcystis aeruginosa*. *Am. J. Botany* **39**, 26–32 (1952).
94. Gerretsen, F. C., and Hoop, H. de. Boron, an essential micro-element for *Azotobacter chroococcum*. *Plant and Soil* **5**, 349–367 (1954).
95. Golueke, C. G. Comparative studies of the physiology of *Sapromyces* and related genera. *J. Bacteriol.* **74**, 337–343 (1957).

96. Goppelsröder, F. Beiträge zum studium der saltpeterbildungen. *Ann. Physik* 115, 127–137 (1862).

97. Granick, S., and Gilder, H. The porphyrin requirements of *Haemophilus influenzae* and some functions of the vinyl and propionic acid side chains of haem. *J. Gen. Physiol.* 30, 1–13 (1946).

98. Green, L. F., McCarthy, J. F., and King, C. G. Inhibition of respiration and photosynthesis in *Chlorella pyrenoidosa* by organic compounds that inhibit copper catalysis. *J. Biol. Chem.* 128, 447–453 (1939).

99. Greenfield, S. S. Inhibitory effects of inorganic compounds on photosynthesis in *Chlorella. Am. J. Botany* 29, 121–131 (1942).

100. Greenwood, E. A. N. The interaction of copper and phosphorus in legume nutrition. *In* "Nutrition of the Legumes" (E. G. Hallsworth, ed.) pp. 69–72. Butterworths, London (1958).

101. Gribanov, V. M. The effect of different doses of copper and manganese on the fixation of nitrogen by *Azotobacter chroococcum. Mikrobiol. Zhur. Akad. Nauk Ukr. R.S.R.* 16, 18–21 (1954).

101a. Gundersen, K. Effects of B vitamins and amino acids on nitrification. *Physiol. Plantarum* 8, 136–142 (1955).

102. Hacskaylo, J., Lilly, V. G., and Barnett, H. L. Growth of fungi on three sources of nitrogen. *Mycologia* 46, 691–701 (1954).

103. Hallsworth, E. G., Wilson, S. B., and Greenwood, E. A. N. Copper and cobalt in nitrogen fixation. *Nature* 187, 79–80 (1960).

103a. Harley, J. L. Associations between micro-organisms and higher plants (Mycorrhiza). *Ann. Rev. Microbiol.* 6, 367–386 (1952).

104. Hawker, L. E., and Fraymouth, J. A re-investigation of the root-nodules of species of *Elaeagnus, Hippophae, Alnus and Myrica,* with special reference to the morphology and life histories of the causative organisms. *J. Gen. Microbiol.* 5, 369–386 (1951).

105. Henricksson, E. Nitrogen fixation by a bacteria-free, symbiotic *Nostoc* strain isolated from *Collema. Physiol. Plantarum* 4, 542–552 (1951).

106. Henriksen, A., and Jensen, H. L. Chemical and microbiological determinations of copper in soil. *Acta Agr. Scand.* 8, 432–469 (1958).

107. Henry, H., and Stacey, M. Histochemistry of the Gram-staining reaction for micro-organisms. *Proc. Roy. Soc.* B133, 391–406 (1946).

108. Hewitt, E. J. The use of sand and water culture methods in the study of plant nutrition. *Commonwealth Bur. Hort. Plantation Crops (Gt. Brit.) Tech. Commun. No.* 22 (1952).

109. Hewitt, E. J., and Bond, G. Molybdenum and the fixation of nitrogen in *Casuarina* and *Alnus* root nodules. *Plant and Soil* 14, 159–175 (1961).

110. Hockenhull, D. J. D. Studies in penicillin production by *Pencillium notatum* in surface culture. 2. Further studies in the metabolism of sulphur. *Biochem. J.* 43, 498–504 (1948).

111. Hofman, T., and Lees, H. The biochemistry of the nitrifying organisms. 2. The free energy efficiency of *Nitrosomonas. Biochem. J.* 52, 140–142 (1952).

112. Hofman, T., and Lees, H. The biochemistry of the nitrifying organisms. 4. The respiration and intermediary metabolism of *Nitrosomonas. Biochem. J.* 54, 579–583 (1953).

112a. Hopkins, E. F., and Wann, F. B. The effect of the H ion concentration on the availability of iron for *Chlorella* sp. *J. Gen. Physiol.* 9, 205–210 (1925).

112b. Hopkins, E. F., and Wann, F. B. Iron requirement for *Chlorella*. *Botan. Gaz.* **84**, 407–427 (1927).

113. Horner, C. K., Burk, D., Allison, F. E., and Sherman, M. S. Nitrogen fixation by *Azotobacter* as influenced by molybdenum and vanadium. *J. Agr. Research* **65**, 173–183 (1942).

114. Horowitz, N. H. Biochemical genetics in Neurospora. *Advances in Genet.* **3**, 33–71 (1950).

115. Horsfall, J. G. "Principles of Fungicidal Action" 279 pp. Chronica Botanica, Waltham, Massachusetts, 1956.

116. Hutner, S. H. Growth requirements of the photosynthetic bacterium *Rhodospirillum rubrum*. *Arch. Biochem.* **3**, 439–444 (1944).

117. Hutner, S. H., Provasoli, L., Schatz, A., and Haskins, C. P. Some approaches to the study of the role of metals in the matabolism of microorganisms. *Proc. Am. Phil. Soc.* **94**, 152–170 (1950).

118. Hutner, S. H., Provasoli, L., Schatz, A., and Haskins, C. P. Inorganic requirements of plant flagellates (Protozoa). *Proc. Am. Phil. Soc.* **94**, 152–163 (1950).

119. Ichioka, P. S., and Arnon, D. I. Molybdenum in relation to nitrogen metabolism. II. Assimilation of ammonia and urea without molybdenum by *Scenedesmus*. *Physiol. Plantarum* **8**, 552–560 (1955).

120. Ingraham, J. L., and Emerson, R. Studies of the nutrition and metabolism of the aquatic phycomycete, *Allomyces*. *Am. J. Botany* **41**, 146–152 (1954).

121. Isenberg, H. D., Schatz, A., Angrist, A. A., Schatz, V., and Trelawny, G. S. Microbial metabolism of carbamates. II. Nitrification of urethane by *Streptomyces nitrificans*. *J. Bacteriol.* **68**, 5 (1954).

122. Iwanoff, N. N., and Osnizkaja, L. K. Die Blausäure als N-Quelle für *Aspergillus niger*. I. *Biochem. Z.* **271**, 22–31 (1934).

123. Iwasaki, H., Matsubayashi, R., and Mori, T., Denitrification. II. Production of nitric oxide and its utilization in the N-N linkage formation by denitrifying bacteria. *J. Biochem. (Tokyo)* **43**, 295–305 (1956).

124. Jensen, H. Denitrifikation und Stickstoffentbindung. *In* "Handbuch der Technischen Mykologie" Vol. III, p. 182. H. Lafar (ed.), 1904.

125. Jensen, H. L. The influence of molybdenum, calcium and agar on nitrogen fixation by *Azotobacter indicum*. *Proc. Linnean Soc. N. S. Wales* **72**, 299–310 (1947).

126. Jensen, H. L. Nitrification of oxime compounds by heterotrophic bacteria. *J. Gen. Microbiol.* **5**, 360–367 (1951).

127. Jordan, J. V., and Anderson, G. R. Effect of boron on nitrogen fixation by *Azotobacter*. *Soil Sci.* **69**, 311–319 (1950).

128. Kaji, A., and McElroy, W. D. Enzymic formation of choline sulphate. *Biochim. et Biophys. Acta* **30**, 190–191 (1958).

129. Keeler, R. F., and Varner, J. E. Tungstate as an antagonist of molybdate in *Azotobacter vinelandii*. *Arch. Biochem. Biophys.* **70**, 585–590 (1957).

130. Kessler, E. Über den Mechanismus der Nitratreduktion von Grünalgen. *Flora (Jena)* **140**, 1–11 (1953).

131. Kessler, E., Arthur, W., and Brugger, J. E. The influence of manganese and phosphate on delayed light emission, fluorescence, photoreduction and photosynthesis in algae. *Arch. Biochem. Biophys.* **71**, 326–335 (1957).

132. Kingma-Boltjes, T. Y. Untersuchungen über die nitrifizierenden Bakterien. *Arch. Mickrobiol.* **6**, 79–86 (1935).

438 D. J. D. NICHOLAS

133. Klotz, I. M. Thermodynamic and molecular properties of some metal-protein complexes. *In* "Mechanism of Enzyme Action" (W. D. McElroy and B. Glass, eds.) pp. 257–284. Johns Hopkins Press, Baltimore, Maryland, 1954.
134. Kluyver, A. J., and Donker, R. J. L. Die Einheit in der Biochemie. *Chem. Zelle u. Gewebe* **13**, 134–190 (1926).
135. Kluyver, A. J., and Verhoeven, W. Studies on true dissimilatory nitrate reduction. II. The mechanism of denitrification. *Antonie van Leeuwenhoek. J. Microbiol. Serol.* **20**, 241–262 (1954).
136. Kluyver, A. J., and van Niel, C. B. "The Microbe's Contribution to Biology" Harvard Univ. Press, Cambridge, Massachusetts, 1956.
137. Koffler, H., Knight, S. G., and Frazier, W. C. The effect of certain mineral elements on the production of penicillin in shake flasks. *J. Bacteriol.* **53**, 115–123 (1947).
138. Kosceleckii, A. Soil fertility in relation to phosphoric acid. *Zhur. Opyt. Agron.* **10**, 321–331 (1909).
139. Kratz, W., and Myers, J. Nutrition and growth of several blue-green algae. *Am. J. Botany* **42**, 282–287 (1955).
140. Krebs, H. A., Wittam, R., and Hems, R. Potassium uptake by *Alcaligenes faecalis*. *Biochem. J.* **66**, 53–60 (1957).
141. Lascelles, J. An assay for protoporphyrin based on the reduction of nitrate by a variant strain of *Staphylococcus aureus:* synthesis of iron protoporphyrin by suspensions of *Rhodopseudomonas spheroides*. *J. Gen. Microbiol.* **15**, 404–416 (1956).
142. Lavollay, J. Les oligo éléments dans la nutrition et la croissance des microorganisms. *VIe Congr. Intern. Microbiol. Symposium, Roma, 1953* **LXII**, No. 3–4, pp. 1–25 (1953).
143. Lees, H., Simpson, J. R., Jensen, H. L., and Sørensen. Formation of nitrite from oximes and hydroxylamine by micro-organisms. *Nature* **173**, 358–359 (1954).
144. Lees, H., and Quastel, J. H. Bacteriostatic effects of potassium chlorate on soil nitrification. *Nature* **155**, 276–278 (1945).
145. Lees, H. The effect of zinc and copper on soil nitrification. *Biochem. J.* **42**, 534–538 (1948).
146. Lees, H., and Meiklejohn, J. Trace elements and nitrification. *Nature* **161**, 398–399 (1948).
147. Lees, H. Soil percolation technique. *Plant and Soil* **1**, 221–239 (1949).
148. Lees, H. Isolation of the nitrifying organisms from soil. *Nature* **167**, 355–356 (1951).
149. Lees, H. The biochemistry of the nitrifying organisms. I. The ammonia-oxidising systems of *Nitrosomonas*. *Biochem. J.* **52**, 134–141 (1952).
150. Lees, H. "Biochemistry of Autotrophic Bacteria" Butterworths, London, 1955.
151. Lees, H., and Simpson, J. R. Biochemistry of the nitrifying organisms. 5. Nitrite oxidation by *Nitrobacter*. *Biochem. J.* **65**, 297–305 (1959).
152. Little, H. N. Oxidation of nitroethane by extracts from *Neurospora*. *J. Biol. Chem.* **193**, 347–358 (1951).
153. Lockwood, L. B., and Reeves, M. D. Some factors affecting the production of itaconic acid by *Aspergillus terreus*. *Arch. Biochem.* **6**, 455–469 (1945).
154. Lockwood, L. B., and Nelson, G. E. N. Some factors affecting the production of itaconic acid by *Aspergillus terreus* in agitated cultures. *Arch. Biochem.* **10**, 365–374 (1946).
155. Loginova, E. B. The effect of copper on the activity of vetch nodule bacteria. *Sbornik. Nauch. Trudov Ivanovsk. Energet. Inst.* **7**, 53–60 (1955).

156. Lowe, R. H., Evans, H. J., and Ahmed, S. The effect of cobalt on the growth of *Rhizobium japonicum. Biochem. Biophys. Research Communs.* 3, 675–678 (1960).
157. Ludwig, C. A. The availability of different forms of nitrogen to a green alga. *Am. J. Botany* 25, 448 (1938).
158. McCalla, T. M. The adsorption of H⁺ by bacteria as measured by the glass electrode. *J. Bacteriol.* 41, 775–784 (1941).
159. McCallan, S. E. A. The nature of the fungicidal action of copper and sulfur. *Botan. Rev.* 15, 629–643 (1949).
160. McHargue, J. S., and Calfee, R. K. Effect of manganese, copper and zinc on growth and metabolism of *Aspergillus flavus* and *Rhizopus nigricans. Botan. Gaz.* 91, 183–193 (1931).
161. McHargue, J. S., and Calfee, R. K. Effect of manganese, copper and zinc on the growth of yeast. *Plant Physiol.* 6, 559–566 (1931).
162. MacLeod, R. A., and Snell, E. E. The effect of related ions on the potassium requirement of lactic acid bacteria. *J. Biol. Chem.* 176, 39–52 (1948).
163. MacLeod, R. A., and Snell, E. E. The relation of ion antagonism to the inorganic nutrition of lactic acid bacteria. *J. Bacteriol.* 59, 783–792 (1950).
164. MacLeod, R. A. Further mineral requirements of *Streptococcus faecalis. J. Bacteriol.* 62, 337–345 (1951).
165. McNall, E. G., and Atkinson, D. E. Nitrate reduction. I. Growth of *E. coli* with nitrate as sole source of nitrogen. *J. Bacteriol.* 72, 226–229 (1956).
166. McNall, E. G., and Atkinson, D. E. Nitrate reduction. II. Utilization of possible intermediates as nitrogen sources and electron acceptors. *J. Bacteriol.* 74, 60–66 (1957).
167. Maertens, H. Das Wachstum von Blaualgen in mineralischen Nährlösungen. *Beitr. Biol. Pflanz.* 12, 439–444 (1914).
168. Malavolta, E., Delwiche, C. C., and Burge, W. D. Carbon dioxide fixation and phosphorylation by *Nitrobacter agilis. Biochem. Biophys. Research Communs.* 2, 445–449 (1960).
169. Mann, T. Studies on the metabolism of mould fungi. *Biochem. J.* 38, 345–351 (1944).
170. Manson, V. D., and Tomashevska, O. G. The influence of micro-organisms on the solubility of fertilizer phosphorus and on its uptake by plants. *Dopovidi Akad. Nauk Ukr. R.S.R.* No. 6, 600–605 (1955).
171. Marshall, B. H. Some effects of inorganic nutrients on the growth and pathogenicity of five fungal pathogens of gladiolus. *Phytopathology* 45, 676–680 (1955).
172. Martin, H. "The Scientific Principles of Plant Protection" 4th ed., 385 pp. Edward Arnold, London, 1959.
173. Martin, H., Wain, R. L., and Wilkinson, E. H. Studies upon the copper fungicides. V. A critical examination of the fungicidal value of copper compounds. *Ann. Appl. Biol.* 29, 412–438 (1942).
174. Matuoshvili, S. I. The effect of boron and molybdenum on the morphology and physiology of *Azotobacter chroococcum. Mikrobiologiya* 16, 19–31 (1947).
175. Mayer, A. M. Problems of the assimilation of nitrogen by *Chlorella vulgaris.* Ph.D. thesis, University of London, England, 1950.
176. Medina, A., and Nicholas, D. J. D. Metallo-enzymes in the reduction of nitrate to ammonia in *Neurospora. Biochem. et Biophys. Acta* 25, 138–41 (1957).
177. Medina, A., and Nicholas, D. J. D. Hyponitrite reductase in *Neurospora. Nature* 179, 533–534 (1957).

178. Medina, A., and Nicholas, D. J. D. Some properties of a zinc-dependent hexokinase from *Neurospora crassa. Biochem. J.* **66**, 573–578 (1957).
179. Mehlich, A., Fred, E. B., and Truog, E. The *Cunninghamella* plaque method of measuring available phosphorus in soil. *Soil Sci.* **38**, 445–452 (1934).
180. Meiklejohn, J. Iron and the nitrifying bacteria. *J. Gen. Microbiol.* **8**, 58–65 (1953).
181. Meiklejohn, J. Some aspects of the physiology of the nitrifying bacteria. *Symposium Soc. Gen. Microbiol.* **4th**, 68–83 (1954).
182. Meyerhof, O. Untersuchungen über den Atmungsvorgang nitrifizierender Bakterien. *Arch. ges. Physiol. Pflüger's* **166**, 240–280 (1917).
183. Miller, L. P., McCallan, S. E. A., and Weed, R. M. Quantitative studies on the role of hydrogen sulfide formation in the toxic action of sulfur to fungus spores. *Contribs. Boyce Thompson Inst.* **17**, 151–171 (1953).
184. Miller, L. P., McCallan, S. E. A., and Weed, R. M. Rate of uptake and toxic dose on a spore weight basis of various fungicides. *Contribs. Boyce Thompson Inst.* **17**, 173–195 (1953).
185. Miller, L. P., and McCallan, S. E. A. Toxic action of metal ions to fungus spores. *J. Agr. Food Chem.* **5**, 116–122 (1957).
187. Millet, J. *In* "Colloque sur la biochimie du soufre" Vol. 77, p. 79. Centre National de la Recherche Scientifique, Paris, 1956.
188. Mitchell, P. Transport of phosphate through an osmotic barrier. *Symposia Soc. Exptl. Biol. No.* **8**, 254–261 (1954).
189. Molliard, M. Caractères physiologiques présentés pour le *Sterigmatocystis nigra* en inanition de zinc et de fer. *Compt. rend. acad. sci.* **189**, 417–420 (1929).
190. Molisch, H. "Die Eisenbakterien." Fischer, Jena, Germany, 1910.
191. Morton, A. G., and MacMillan, A. The assimilation of nitrogen from ammonium salts and nitrate by fungi. *J. Exptl. Botany* **5**, 232–252 (1954).
192. Mothes, K. Über den schwefelst offwechsel der pflanzen. II. *Planta* **29**, 67–109 (1939).
193. Mulder, E. G. Sur l'influence du cuivre sur la croissance des microorganismes. *Ann. Ferment.* **4**, 513–533 (1938).
194. Müller, E., and Biedermann, W. Der einflus von Cu^{+2}-Ionen auf den Keimungsablauf. *Phytopathol. Z.* **19**, 343–350 (1952).
195. Muntz, J. A. The role of potassium and ammonium ions in alcoholic fermentation. *J. Biol. Chem.* **171**, 653–665 (1947).
196. Murometsev, G. S. The utilization of water-insoluble phosphate by soil microorganisms. *Doklady Akad. Saukh Nauk* **5**, 35 (1955).
197. Myers, J. Physiology of the Algae. *Ann. Rev. Microbiol.* **5**, 157–180 (1951).
198. Najjar, V. A., and Allen, M. B. Formation of nitrogen, nitrous oxide and nitric oxide by extracts of denitrifying bacteria. *J. Biol. Chem.* **206**, 209–214 (1954).
199. Nason, A., Kaplan, N. O., and Colowick, S. P. Changes in enzymatic constitution in zinc-deficient *Neurospora. J. Biol. Chem.* **188**, 397–406 (1951).
200. Nason, A., Abraham, R. G., and Averbach, B. C. Enzymatic reduction of nitrite to ammonia by reduced pyridine nucleotides. *Biochem. et Biophys. Acta* **15**, 159–161 (1954).
201. Neilands, J. B. Some aspects of microbial iron metabolism. *Bacteriol. Revs.* **21**, 101–111 (1957).
202. Nicholas, D. J. D., and Fielding, A. H. The use of *Aspergillus niger* (M) for the determination of magnesium, zinc, copper and molybdenum available in soils to crop plants. *J. Hort. Sci.* **26**, 125–147 (1951).

203. Nicholas, D. J. D. The use of fungi for determining trace metals in biological materials. *Analyst* **77**, 629–642 (1952).

204. Nicholas, D. J. D., Nason, A., and McElroy, W. D. Molybdenum and nitrate reductase. I. Effect of molybdenum deficiency on the *Neurospora* enzyme. *J. Biol. Chem.* **207**, 341–351 (1954).

204a. Nicholas, D. J. D., and Nason, A. Molybdenum and nitrate reductase. II. *J. Biol. Chem.* **207**, 352–360 (1954).

205. Nicholas, D. J. D., and Stevens, H. M. Valency changes of molybdenum during the enzymatic reduction of nitrate in *Neurospora*. *Nature* **176**, 1066–1067 (1955).

206. Nicholas, D. J. D., and Nason, A. Diphosphopyridine nucleotide-nitrate reductase from *Escherichia coli*. *J. Bacteriol*. **69**, 580–583 (1955).

207. Nicholas, D. J. D. Role of metals in enzymes with special reference to flavoproteins. *Nature* **179**, 800–804 (1957).

208. Nicholas, D. J. D. The function of trace metals in the nitrogen metabolism of plants. *Ann. Botany (London)* **21**, 587–598 (1957).

209. Nicholas, D. J. D. Role of trace metals in the nitrogen metabolism of plants with special reference to micro-organisms. *J. Sci. Food Agr.* **8**, S15–S25 (1957).

210. Nicholas, D. J. D. The effect of molybdenum deficiency on the catalase and peroxidase content of *Neurospora crassa*. *J. Gen. Microbiol.* **17**, 689–698 (1957).

211. Nicholas, D. J. D. Metallo-enzymes in nitrate assimilation of plants with special reference to micro-organisms. *Symposia Soc. Exptl. Biol. No.* **13**, 1–26 (1959).

212. Nicholas, D. J. D. Metabolism of inorganic nitrogen and its compounds in plants. *4th Intern. Congr. Biochem. Vienna* **XIII** (Colloquia), 307–331 (1959). Pergamon Press, London.

213. Nicholas, D. J. D. The use of fungi for determining trace metals in biological materials. *In* "Proceedings of International Symposium on Microchemistry" R. Belcher (ed.) pp. 205–211. Pergamon Press, London, 1959.

214. Nicholas, D. J. D., Medina, A., and Jones, O. T. G. A nitrite reductase from *Neurospora crassa*. *Biochem. et Biophys. Acta* **37**, 468–476 (1960).

215. Nicholas, D. J. D., and Jones, O. T. G. Oxidation of hydroxylamine in cell-free extracts of *Nitrosomonas europaea*. *Nature* **185**, 512–514 (1960).

216. Nicholas, D. J. D., and Fisher, D. J. Nitrogen fixation in extracts of *Azotobacter vinelandii*. *Nature* **186**, 735–736 (1960).

217. Nicholas, D. J. D., and Fisher, D. J. Nitrogen fixation in extracts of *Azotobacter vinelandii*. *J. Sci. Food Agr.* **10**, 603–608 (1960).

218. Nicholas, D. J. D., Fisher, D. J., Redmond, W. J., and Wright, M. A. Some aspects of hydrogenase activity and nitrogen fixation in *Azotobacter* spp. and in *Clostridium pasteurianum*. *J. Gen. Microbiol.* **22**, 191–205 (1960).

219. Nicholas, D. J. D., Silvester, D. J., and Fowler, J. F. The use of radioactive nitrogen in studying nitrogen fixation in bacteria and their extracts. *Nature* **189**, 634–636 (1961).

220. Nicholas, D. J. D. Minor mineral elements. *Ann. Rev. Plant Phys.* **13**, 63–90 (1961).

220a. Nicholas, D. J. D. unpublished results (1961).

220b. Nicholas, D. J. D., Maruyama, Y., and Fisher, D. J. The effect of cobalt deficiency on the utilization of nitrate nitrogen in *Rhizobium*. *Biochem. et Biophys. Acta* **56**, 623–626 (1962).

220c. Nicholas, D. J. D., Kobayashi, M., and Wilson, P. W. Cobalt requirement for nitrogen metabolism in microorganisms. *Microbiol. Proc.* p. 101 (1962) and *Proc. Nat. Acad. Sci. U.S.* **49** (1962).

221. Nord, F. F. Enzymatische Umsetzungen durch Fusarien. *In* "Beitrag zum Mechanimns der alkoholischen Gärung in Ergebnisse der Enzymforsuch" (F. F. Nord, and R. Weidenhagen, eds.) 7th ed. Akademische, Verlagsgese. Leipzig, 1939.

222. Nord, F. F., and Mull, R. P. Recent progress in the biochemistry of *Fusaria*. *Enzymologia* **5**, 165–205 (1945).

223. Norris, J. R., and Jensen, H. L. The calcium requirements of *Azotobacter*. *Nature* **180**, 1493–1494 (1957).

224. Norris, D. O., Rhizobium needs magnesium and calcium for growth. *Nature* **182**, 734–735 (1958).

225. Norris, D. O. The role of calcium and magnesium in the nutrition of *Rhizobium*. *Australian J. Agr. Research* **10**, 651–698 (1959).

226. Parker-Rhodes, A. F. Studies on the mechanism of fungicidal action. IV. Mercury. *Ann. Appl. Biol.* **29**, 404–411 (1942).

227. Pearsall, W. H. Phytoplankton in the English Lakes. II. The composition of the phytoplankton in relation to dissolved substances. *J. Ecol.* **20**, 241–262 (1932).

228. Perkins, D. D. Biochemical mutants in the smut fungus *Ustilago maydis*. *Genetics* **34**, 607–626 (1949).

229. Pfeffer, W. Ueber Election organischer Nährstoffe. *Jahrb. wiss. Botan.* **28**, 205–268 (1895).

230. Pirson, A. Functional aspects in mineral nutrition of green plants. *Ann. Rev. Plant Physiol.* **6**, 71–114 (1955).

231. Pollock, M. R. Adaptation of "nitratase" in washed suspensions of bacteria. *Brit. J. Exptl. Pathol.* **27**, 419–432 (1946).

231a. Pontecorvo, G. The genetics of *Aspergillus nidulans*. *Advances in Genetics* **5**, 141–238 (1953).

232. Postgate, J. R. On the nutrition of *Desulphovibrio desulphuricans*—a correction. *J. Gen. Microbiol.* **9**, 440–444 (1953).

233. Postgate, J. R., Sulphate reduction by bacteria. *Ann. Rev. Microbiol.* **13**, 505–520 (1959).

234. Provasoli, L., McLaughlin, J. J. A., and Pinter, I. J. Relative and limiting concentrations of major mineral constituents for the growth of algal flagellates. *Trans. N.Y. Acad. Sci. Ser. II* **16**, 412–417 (1954).

235. Provasoli, L., McLaughlin, J. J. A., and Droop, M. R. The development of artificial media for marine algae. *Arch. Mikrobiol.* **25**, 392–428 (1957).

236. Provasoli, L. Nutrition and ecology of Protozoa and algae. *Ann. Rev. Microbiol.* **12**, 279–308 (1958).

237. Quartz, L. Untersuchungen über die Ernährungsphysiologie einiger neiderer Phycomyceten. *Jahrb. wiss. Botan.* **91**, 120–160 (1943).

238. Quastel, J. H., Stephenson, M., and Whetham, M. D. Some reactions of resting bacteria in relation to anaerobic growth. *Biochem. J.* **19**, 304–317 (1925).

239. Quilco, A., and Di Capua, R. Sopra l'aspergillina, il pigmento delle spore del *Aspergillus nigra*. *Atti accad. naz. Lincei Ser. 6*, **17**, 177–182 (1933).

240. Quispel, A. Symbiotic nitrogen-fixation in non-leguminous plants. 1. Preliminary experiments on the root-nodule symbiosis of *Alnus glutinosa*. *Acta. Botan. Neerl.* **3**, 495–511 (1954).

241. Rao, W. V. S., Krishmamurti, P. V. and Rao, G. G. Mechanism of the microbiological oxidation of ammonia. Part I. Formation of intermediate products *J. Ind. Chem. Soc.* **15**, 599–603 (1938).

242. Raulin, J. Études chimiques sur la végétation. *Ann. sci. nat. V. Botan.* **11,** 92–299 (1869).

243. Reischer, H. S. Growth of *Saprolegniaceae* in synthetic media. II. Nitrogen requirements and the role of Krebs cycle acids. *Mycologia* **43,** 319–328 (1951).

244. Reisenauer, H. M. Cobalt in nitrogen fixation by a legume. *Nature* **186,** 375–376 (1960).

245. Rippel, A., and Georg, B. Über die Bedeutung des Kaliums im Stoffwechsel von *Aspergillus niger*. *Arch. Mikrobiol.* **5,** 561–577 (1934).

246. Robbins, W. J. Growth requirements of Dermatophytes. *Ann. N.Y. Acad. Sci.* **50,** No. (10), 1357–1361 (1950).

247. Roberg, M. Über die Wirking von Eisen-Zink, und Kupfersalzen auf Aspergillen. *Zentr. Bakteriol. Parasitenk. Abt. II* **74,** 333–370 (1928).

248. Roberts, C. The effect of iron and other factors on the production of pigment by the yeast *Torulopsis pulcherrima*. *Am. J. Botany* **33,** 237–244 (1946).

249. Sacks, L. E., and Barker, H. A. The influence of oxygen on nitrate and nitrite reduction. *J. Bacteriol.* **58,** 11–22 (1949).

250. Sadana, J. C., and McElroy, W. D. Nitrate reductase from *Achromobacter fischeri*. Purification and properties: function of flavins and cytochrome. *Arch. Biochem.* **67,** 16–34 (1957).

251. Sakaguchi, K., and Wang, Y. Biochemistry of filamentous fungi. IV. *Bull. Agr. Chem. Soc. Japan* **12,** 63–74 (1936).

252. Sandell, E. B. "Colorimetric Determination of Traces of Metals" Interscience, New York, 1944.

253. Sato, R. The cytochrome system and microbial reduction of nitrate. *In* "Inorganic Nitrogen Metabolism" (W. D. McElroy and B. Glass, eds.) pp. 163–175. Johns Hopkins Press, Baltimore, Maryland, 1956.

254. Saz, A. K., and Martinez, L. M. Enzymatic basis of resistance to chloramphenicol. I. Difference between flavoprotein nitro-reductase of sensitive and resistant strains of *Escherichia coli*. *J. Biol. Chem.* **223,** 285–292 (1956).

255. Schneider, K. C., Bradbeer, C., Singh, R. N., Wang Li Chuan, Wilson, P. W., and Burris, R. H. Nitrogen fixation by cell-free preparations from microorganisms. *Proc. Natl. Acad. Sci. U.S.* **46,** 726–730 (1960).

256. Schade, A. L., and Thimann, K. V. The metabolism of the water-mould *Leptomitus lacteus*. *Am. J. Botany* **27,** 659–670 (1940).

257. Schloesing, T., and Müntz, A. Sur la nitrification par les ferments organisés. *Compt. rend. acad. sci.* **84,** 301–309 (1877).

258. Schmidt, E. L. Nitrate formation by a soil fungus. *Science* **119,** 187–189 (1954).

259. Sciarini, L. J., and Nord, F. F. On the mechanism of enzyme action. Part 22. Elementary sulphur as hydrogen acceptor in dehydrogenations by living Fusaria. *Arch. Biochem.* **3,** 261–267 (1943).

260. Seidel, K. Eine neue mikrobiologische Methode zur Beurteilung der Nährstoffverhältnisse eines Bodens. *Arch. Planzenbau* **6,** 536–541 (1931).

261. Senez, J. C., Pichinoty, F., and Konovalchikoff-Mazoyer, M. Reduction of nitrite and hydroxylamine by suspensions and extracts of *Desulfovibrio desulfuricans*. *Compt. rend. acad. sci.* **242,** 570–573 (1956).

262. Senez, J. C., and Pichinoty, F. Production of hydroxylamine bound to the hydrogenase activity of *Desulfovibrio desulfuricans*. I. Activity of cells and extracts. *Biochim. et Biophys. Acta* **27,** 569–580 (1958).

263. Senez, J. C., and Pichinoty, F. Reduction of hydroxylamine bound to the

hydrogenase complex of *Desulfovibrio desulfuricans*. II. Nature of the enzyme system and of the electron transport system of reaction. *Biochim. et Biophys. Acta* **28**, 355–369 (1958).

264. Shaw, W. H. R. Toxicity of cations towards living systems. *Science* **120**, 361–363 (1955).

265. Sheperd, C. J. Pathways of cysteine synthesis in *Aspergillus nidulans*. *J. Gen. Microbiol.* **15**, 29–38 (1956).

266. Shibata, C. On the occurrence of phytase in some yeasts and *Aspergillus oryzae*. *Zentr. Bakteriol. Parasitenk. Abt. II*, **71**, 232–247 (1927).

267. Shooter, R. A., and Wyatt, H. V. Mineral requirements for growth of *Staphylococcus pyogenes*. Effect of magnesium and calcium ions. *Brit. J. Exptl. Pathol.* **36**, 341–350 (1955).

268. Shrift, A. (1) Sulfur-selenium antagonism. I. Antimetabolite action of selenate on the growth of *Chlorella vulgaris*. (2) Sulfur-selenium antagonism. II. Antimetabolite action of seleno-methionine on the growth of *Chlorella vulgaris*. *Am. J. Botany* **41**, 223–230 and 345–352 (1954).

269. Silver, W. S., and McElroy, W. D. Enzyme studies on nitrate and nitrite mutants. *Arch. Biochem. Biophys.* **51**, 379–394 (1954).

269a. Silver, W. S. Pyridine nucleotide-nitrate reductase from *Hansenula anomala*, a nitrate reducing yeast. *J. Bacteriol.* **73**, 241–246 (1957).

270. Simpson, J. R., and Evans, W. C. The metabolism of nitrophenols by certain bacteria. *Biochem. J.* **55**, xxiv (1953).

271. Singh, R. N. The fixation of elementary nitrogen by some of the commonest blue-green algae from the paddy field soils of the United Provinces and Bihar. *Indian J. Agr. Sci.* **12**, 743–750 (1942).

271a. Skinner, F. A., and Walker, N. Growth of *Nitrosomonas europaea* in batch and continuous culture. *Arch. Mikrobiol.* **38**, 339–349 (1961).

272. Smith, V. M. On the mechanism of enzyme action. XXXIX. A comparative study of the metabolism of carbohydrates in the presence of inorganic and organic phosphates by *Merulius lacrymans* and *Marasmius chordalis*. *Arch. Biochem.* **23**, 446–472 (1949).

273. Snell, E. E. Microbiological techniques (inorganic ions). In "Trace Analysis" (J. H. Yoe and H. J. Koch, eds.) p. 547. Wiley, New York, 1957.

274. Somers, E. Fungitoxicity of metal ions. *Nature* **187**, 427–428 (1960).

275. Spencer, D., Takahashi, H., and Nason, A. Relationship of nitrite and hydroxylamine reductases in nitrate assimilation and nitrogen fixation in *Azotobacter agile*. *J. Bacteriol.* **73**, 553–562 (1957).

276. Spencer, B., and Harada, T. Role of choline sulphate in the sulphur metabolism of fungi. *Biochem. J.* **77**, 305–315 (1960).

277. Stahl, W. H., McQue, B., Mandels, G. R., and Sin, R. G. H. Studies on the microbiological degradation of wool. I. Sulphur metabolism. *Arch. Biochem.* **20**, 422–432 (1949).

278. Starkey, R. L., and Waksman, S. A. Fungi tolerant to extreme acidity and high concentrations of copper sulphate. *J. Bacteriol.* **45**, 509–519 (1943).

279. Starkey, R. L. Relations of micro organisms to transformation of sulphur in soil. *Soil Sci.* **70**, 55–65 (1950).

280. Steinberg, R. A. A study of some factors in the chemical stimulation of the growth of *Aspergillus niger*. *Am. J. Botany* **6**, 330–372 (1919).

281. Steinberg, R. A. Essentiality of gallium to growth and reproduction of *Aspergillus niger*. *J. Agr. Research* **57**, 569–574 (1938).

282. Steinberg, R. A. Growth of fungi in synthetic nutrient solutions. *Botan. Rev.* 5, 327–350 (1939).

283. Steinberg, R. A., and Bowling, J. D. Optimum solutions as physiological reference standards in estimating nitrogen utilization by *Aspergillus niger. J. Agr. Research* 58, 717–732 (1939).

284. Steinberg, R. A. Effects of nitrogen compounds and trace elements on growth of *Aspergillus niger. J. Agr. Research* 59, 731–742 (1939).

285. Steinberg, R. A. Sulfur and trace element nutrition of *A. niger. J. Agr. Research* 63, 109–127 (1941).

286. Steinberg, R. A., and Thorn, C. Reversions in morphology of nitrite-induced "mutants" of *Aspergilli* grown on acids. *J. Agr. Research* 64, 645–652 (1942).

287. Steinberg, R. A. Variants in fungi: formation, reversion and prevention. *Science* 100, 10–11 (1944).

288. Steinberg, R. A. Specificity of potassium and magnesium for growth of *Aspergillus niger. Am. J. Botany* 33, 210–214 (1946).

289. Stout, P. R., and Meagher, W. R. Studies of the molybdenum nutrition of plants with radioactive molybdenum. *Science* 108, 471–472 (1948).

290. Sussman, A. S., and Lowry, R. J. Physiology of the cell surface of *Neurospora* ascospores. *J. Bacteriol.* 70, 675–685 (1955).

291. Susuki, N., and Susuki, S. Hydroxylamine reduction and hydrazine oxidation by *Azotobacter vinelandii. Sci. Repts. Tôhoku Univ. 4th Ser.* 20, 195–201 (1954).

292. Swaby, R. J., and Sherber, J. Phosphate-dissolving micro-organisms in the rhizosphere of legumes. *In* "Nutrition of the Legumes" (E. G. Hallsworth, ed.) p. 289. Academic Press, New York, 1958.

293. Syrett, P. J. Nitrogen assimilation by green algae. *Symposium Soc. Gen. Microbiol.* 4th, 126–151 (1954).

294. Takahashi, H., and Nason, A. Tungstate as a competitive inhibitor of molybdate in nitrate assimilation and in N_2 fixation by *Azotobacter. Biochem. et Biophys. Acta* 23, 433–435 (1957).

295. Talley, P. J., and Blank, L. M. Some factors influencing the utilization of inorganic nitrogen by the root rot fungus. *Plant Physiol.* 17, 52–67 (1942).

296. Taniguchi, S., Mitsui, H., Toyoda, J., Yamada, T., and Egami, F. Successive reduction from nitrate to ammonia by cell-free enzyme systems. *J. Biochem. (Tokyo)* 40, 175–186 (1953).

297. Taniguchi, S., Sato, R., and Egami, F. The enzymic mechanisms of nitrate and nitrite metabolism in bacteria. *In* "Inorganic Nitrogen Metabolism" (W. D. McElroy and B. Glass, eds.) pp. 87–108. Johns Hopkins Press, Baltimore, Maryland, 1956.

298. Taniguchi, S., Asano, A., Iida, K., Kono, M., Ohmachi, K., and Egami, F. The enzymatic electron transfer to nitrate, nitrite and hydroxylamine. *In* "Proceedings of the International Symposium on Enzyme Chemistry, Tokyo-Kyoto, 1957" (K. Ichihara, ed.) pp. 238–245. Academic Press, 1958.

299. Texera, D. A. Production of antibiotic substances by *Fusaria. Phytopathology* 38, 70–81 (1948).

300. Updegraff, D. M., and Wren, J. B. The release of oil from petroleum bearing materials by sulphate-reducing bacteria. *Appl. Microbiol.* 2, 309 (1954).

301. Vallee, B. Metal and enzyme interactions: Correlation of composition, function and structure. *In* "The Enzymes" (P. D. Boyer, H. Lardy, and K. Myrbäck, eds.) 2nd ed., Vol. 3, pp. 225–276. Academic Press, New York, 1960.

302. Van der Kerk, G. J. M., and Luitjen, J. G. A. Investigations on organo-tin compounds. III. The biocidal properties of organo-tin compounds. *J. Appl. Chem.* **4**, 314–319 (1954).

303. Verhoeven, W. Aerobic spore forming nitrate reducing bacteria. Ph.D. Thesis, University of Delft, Netherlands, 1952.

304. Verhoeven, W. Nitrate and nitrite metabolism in micro-organisms. In "Inorganic Nitrogen Metabolism" (W. D. McElroy and B. Glass, eds.), pp. 61–86. Johns Hopkins Press, Baltimore, Maryland, 1956.

305. Villanueva, J. R. Purification of nitro-reductase enzyme of a *Nocardia* species. *Biochem. J.* **72**, 36 (1959).

306. Villanueva, J. R. Nitro-reductase of a *Nocardia* species. *J. Gen. Microbiol.* **20**, 6 (1959).

307. Virtanen, A. I., and Laine, T. Investigations on the root nodule bacteria of leguminous plants. *Biochem. J.* **33**, 412–420 (1939).

308. Virtanen, A. I., and Csàky, T. Z. Formation of oxime nitrogen in *Torula* yeast fed with potassium nitrate. *Nature* **161**, 814–815 (1948).

309. Virtanen, A. I., and Rautanen, N. Nitrogen assimilation. In "The Enzymes" (J. B. Sumner and K. Myrbäck, eds.) 1st ed., Vol. II, Part 2, pp. 1089–1130. Academic Press, New York, 1952.

310. Virtanen, A. I., and Saris, N. E. Organic hydroxylamine compounds formed from nitrite in *Torulopsis utilis. Acta Chem. Scand.* **9**, 337–339 (1955).

311. Virtanen, A. I., and Saris, N. E. Organic hydroxylamine compounds formed from nitrite in *Torulopsis utilis*. II. Acetylhydroxamic acid. *Acta. Chem. Scand.* **10**, 483–485 (1956).

312. Vishniac, H. S. The nutritional requirements of isolates of *Labyrinthula* spp. *J. Gen. Microbiol.* **12**, 455–63 (1955).

313. Vollenweider, R. A. Ökologische Untersuchungen von planktischen Algen auf experimenteller Grundlage. *Schweiz. Z. Hydrol.* **12**, 194–262 (1950).

313a. Walker, J. B. Inorganic micronutrient requirements of *Chlorella*. 1. Requirement for calcium (or strontium), copper and molybdenum. *Arch. Biochem. Biophys.* **46**, 1–10 (1953).

314. Walker, G. C., and Nicholas, D. J. D. An iron requirement for a dissimilatory nitrate reductase in *Neurospora crassa. Nature* **189**, 141–142 (1961).

315. Walker, G. C., and Nicholas, D. J. D. Nitrite reductase from *Pseudomonas aeruginosa. Biochem. J.* **77**, 4–5P (1960); *Biochim. et Biophys. Acta* **49**, 350–360 (1961).

316. Warburg, O., and Negelein, E. Über die Reduktion der Salzpetersäure in grunen Zellen. *Biochem. Z.* **110**, 66 (1920).

317. Warington, R. On nitrification. *J. Chem. Soc.* **33**, 44–50 (1878).

318. Waring, W. S., and Werkman, C. H. Iron requirements of heterotrophic bacteria. *Arch. Biochem.* **1**, 425–433 (1943); **4**, 75–87 (1944).

319. Watanabe, A. Production in cultural solution of some amino acids by the atmospheric nitrogen-fixing blue-green algae. *Arch. Biochem. Biophys.* **34**, 50 (1951).

320. Webb. M. The effect of magnesium on the growth and cell division of various bacterial species in complex media. *J. Gen. Microbiol.* **3**, 410–417 (1949).

321. Webb, M. The influence of magnesium on cell division. The effect of mg on the growth of bacteria in chemically-defined media of varying complexity. *J. Gen. Microbiol.* **5**, 485–495 (1951).

322. Weillman, R. H., and McCallan, S. E. A. An analysis of factors causing varia-

tion in spore germination tests of fungicides. IV. Time and temperature. *Contribs. Boyce Thompson Inst.* **12**, 431–450 (1942).

323. Wilson, P. W. Biological nitrogen fixation. *In* "Bacterial Physiology" (C. H. Werkman and P. W. Wilson, eds.) pp. 467–494. Academic Press, New York, 1951.

324. Wilson, P. W. Asymbiotic nitrogen fixation. *In* "Handbuch der Pflanzenphysiologie" (K. Mothes, ed.) Vol. 8, pp. 9–42. Springer Verlag, Berlin, 1958.

325. Winfield, M. E. The role of boron in plant metabolism. 3. The influence of boron on certain enzyme systems. *Australian J. Exptl. Biol.* **23**, 267–272 (1945).

326. Winogradsky, S. Recherches sur les organismes de la nitrification. *Ann. inst. Pasteur* **4**, 213, 257, 760 (1890).

327. Winter, G. Über die Assimilation des Luftstickstoffs durch endophytische Blaualgen. *Beitr. Biol. Pflanz.* **23**, 295 (1935).

328. Woods, D. The reduction of nitrate to ammonia by *Clostridium welchii*. *Biochem. J.* **32**, 2000–2016 (1938).

329. Yoshii, H. Pathological studies of water melon wilt. V. Metabolism of *Fusarium niveum* with special reference to its gas evolution. *Bul. Sci. Fak. Terkult. Kjusu Imp. Univ. Fukuoka Japan* **6**, 321–28 (1935).

330. Young, H. C., and Bennett, C. W. Growth of some parasitic fungi in synthetic culture media. *Am. J. Botany* **9**, 459–469 (1922).

331. Zalokar, M. Reduction of selenite by *Neurospora*. *Arch. Biochem. Biophys.* **44**, 330–337 (1953).

332. Zavarzin, G. A. The participation of molybdenum in the oxidation of nitrites by nitrifying bacteria. *Doklady Akad. Nauk S.S.S.R.* **113**, 1301–1352 (1957).

333. ZoBell, C. E., "Marine Microbiology" Chronica Botanica, Waltham, Massachusetts, 1946.

334. Zucker, M., and Nason, A. Nitroaryl reductase from *Neurospora crassa*. *In* "Methods in Enzymology" (S. P. Colowick and N. O. Kaplan, eds.) Vol. II, pp. 406–411. Academic Press, New York, 1956.

PREAMBLE TO CHAPTER 4

The reasons for the essentiality of the mineral elements which are required by plants are now based on knowledge that must be mobilized from many branches of science, i.e., from physical chemistry, from enzymology, and from the study of metabolism and a knowledge of its intermediary reactions. These topics, therefore, receive special attention in Chapter 4 with reference both to the elements required in larger quantity and to those other elements which are needed only in trace amounts. Although metabolism is the main topic of Volume IV, those aspects which are essential to the discussion of the role of the mineral elements are summarized here. The purification of enzyme proteins and the recognition of the role of certain metals in metalloproteins gave a new impetus and direction to research on inorganic plant nutrition. Moreover, the newer knowledge of intermediary metabolism, particularly of the ways in which energy changes are mediated in cells, and of the role of coenzymes and of phosphorylated compounds, has pointed to many previously unexpected ways in which the inorganic elements may specifically intervene to determine steps which are essential for metabolism and for growth. It will be seen, therefore, that knowledge of a specific role for some of the essential elements (e.g. molybdenum) is now quite precise, whereas the role of others (e.g. potassium), which are equally or even more important, can only be recognized even now by their more diffuse effects upon the growth and behavior of plants.

Since the chapter deals prominently with the effects of essential elements on metabolism, the authors have found it convenient to use the following abbreviations throughout: ATP and ADP, adenosine tri- and diphosphate respectively; DPN and DPNH, oxidized and reduced diphosphopyridine nucleotide, respectively; TPN and TPNH, oxidized and reduced triphosphopyridine, nucleotide, respectively; FAD and $FADH_2$, oxidized and reduced flavin adenine dinucleotide, respectively; FMN, flavin mononucleotide.

CHAPTER FOUR

Modes of Action of the Essential Mineral Elements

ALVIN NASON AND WILLIAM D. McELROY

I. Introduction

Nutrients are necessary for maintenance of the physical organization and activities of living cells by virtue of their function in the generation or release of energy, the building and repair of protoplasm, and the regulation of metabolic processes. They are usually classified into those groups which can be used as (a) an energy source, (b) a carbon source,

* For the authors' reasons for treating chlorine in this section rather than as a micronutrient see page 517. (Ed.)

(c) a nitrogen source, (d) organic growth factors, and (e) mineral salts or inorganic nutrients. The latter group is the subject of the present chapter.

All cells and organisms require the presence of certain inorganic ions for growth and reproduction. Salts contribute to the regulation of osmotic pressure (see Chapters 2 and 4 in Volume II), the maintenance of cellular membranes and to the functioning of the metabolic machine. Some of the elements are required in large amounts (macronutrient or major elements) while others are required in relatively small amounts (micronutrient or trace elements). Our most complete knowledge of the mineral requirements of living forms has been attained with higher plants in contrast to the relatively limited information in this respect with animals and microorganisms. This is probably explained by the fact that higher plants lent themselves best to controlled nutritional experimentation in the late nineteenth and early twentieth centuries, and there was an obvious incentive in the economic importance of plant crops. It has been established that for higher plants the macronutrient elements include nitrogen, phosphorus, sulfur, potassium, magnesium, and calcium. Recent evidence (cf. Chapters 1 and 2) has also implicated sodium and chlorine as essential nutrient elements. The micronutrient elements required by plants are iron, zinc, manganese, copper, molybdenum, boron, and vanadium. The last three have not been shown to be essential for animals. Iodine and cobalt are essential for animals, but apparently not for plants. Although most of the elements of the periodic table have been found in living cells, this does not necessarily mean that all are essential to life (218). About 95% of the dry weight of most plants is composed of four elements—carbon, hydrogen, oxygen, and nitrogen. Another 4% is made up of potassium, phosphorus, calcium, magnesium, silicon, aluminum, sulfur, chlorine, and sodium. The remaining 1% or less of the weight of the plant is accounted for by the micronutrient and by certain dispensable elements.

The function of the essential nutrient elements, especially the micronutrients, has received considerable attention in recent years. Particular emphasis has been placed upon their role in catalytic processes. In several reviews (40, 128, 136) there is discussion, in some detail, of the general problems of metal chelation and metalloprotein complexes, chiefly from the standpoint of the physical properties of the ions and the structural linkages between metal ions and organic molecules. Reviews have also appeared on the function of metals in peptidases (242), on the problems of phosphorylation and the influence of metal ions on these processes (134), on the general problem of multiple metal effects on enzyme systems and on the alteration of the enzyme patterns during growth (145). During the last few years there have also been reviews on the mechanism of action of metal ions in enzyme systems (146, 174) including a detailed account of the role of metals in yeast fermentation (173) as well as a comprehensive treatment of the metabolic role of the trace elements in plants and animals (98, 257). The broad area of mineral nutrition of both plants and animals, covering many papers in this field and including the history and geographical distribution of individual elemental deficiencies, has been the subject of a recently published volume (83). No attempt has been made, therefore, to refer to all the literature which is concerned with the function of the essential elements. The reader is referred to the reviews mentioned for additional references and details.

II. General Functions of the Essential Nutrient Elements

A number of attempts have been made to uncover underlying generalizations which relate the essential elements and their chemical properties to function and mechanism of action. Of some interest is the proposal by Thatcher (262) in 1934 suggesting a classification of the essential elements based on their role in plant nutrition. He indicated that nearly all the elements known or proposed to have a function in plants occur in the first four periods of the periodic table. He classified (a) hydrogen and oxygen as energy-exchange elements; (b) carbon, nitrogen, sulfur, and phosphorus as energy storers; (c) sodium, potassium, calcium, and magnesium as translocation regulators; and (d) manganese, iron, copper, and zinc (as well as cobalt and nickel) as oxidation-reduction regulators. The remaining elements of the scheme were placed into four other groups, but their functions were listed as unknown. Similar relationships between biological essentiality of the elements and their atomic structures have been suggested by other workers (73, 253).

Our present knowledge of mineral nutrition indicates that one of the most important functions of the essential elements is to act as cofactors or activators in enzyme systems. There are obvious exceptions. Nitrogen and sulfur appear to serve primarily in a structural capacity, the former as a component atom of proteins and nucleic acids and the latter of certain amino acids and vitamins. Phosphorus, in addition to its structural role in nucleic acids, nucleotides, phosphagens, and phospholipids has an important function in intermediary metabolism (e.g., glycolysis and the oxidative pathway as well as in the utilization, transfer, and release of the energy of metabolism). All the other elements, except boron, have been shown to have a direct catalytic role in some enzyme system. It is highly likely that an enzymatic role for boron will be demonstrated in due time. Aside from the catalytic role assigned to most of the mineral elements, a number of them have additional functions. The structural organization of protoplasm depends to a great extent upon the binding of metals to proteins and other organic molecules. Much remains to be done before we can clearly state how these metals function in the maintenance of such structures as the chromosomes, mitochondria, microsomes, and the various cell membranes.

It is at present widely accepted that the primary role of the micronutrient elements and many of the macronutrient elements in cell physiology can be explained in terms of their function as active groups of various important enzymes. The fact that the micronutrients are needed in only small quantities is taken as an indication that they act in some catalytic role, usually as part of an enzyme system. In this respect the function of these elements is similar to that of the organic micronutrients—the vitamins.

In terms of the metal requirements of enzymes two broad groups can be designated: (a) those enzymes in which a specific metal has been shown to be an integral component, and (b) those enzymes for which one or more metals serve as an activator. While the physiological significance of the specific metal components of enzymes seems well defined, that of metal activators at times is open to question. An activating effect by a metal in a cell-free system does not necessarily establish a physiological function for the metal in question. For example, arginase can be activated by Ni^{++}, Co^{++}, Fe^{++}, and Mn^{++}. Although Mn^{++} is regarded as the normally active ion, the physiological effects of the other ions are not known. This also raises a question of the possible role of metals which are regarded as not being essential although they do exercise an activating effect *in vitro* (e.g., Ni^{++} and Co^{++} in the above example), and, therefore, possibly *in vivo*. It must also be considered that physiological control of enzyme action by metal ions might also be governed by metal ion availability and metal ion antagonisms. The classical antagonism between K^+ and Ca^{++} or the competition between tungstate and molybdate in a process such as nitrogen fixation reflects the need for evaluating these phenomena in terms of their role in the intact organism. For example, the growth of certain microorganisms has been shown to be dependent on alkali metal ions, a number of antagonistic effects having been demonstrated among the metals of this series (150). There also appears to be a complete functional replacement of K^+ by Rb^+ in the nutrition of some varieties of *Chlorella* (203) and certain bacteria (150). Similarly a requirement for Ca^{++} for growth has been reported to be met equally well by Sr^{++} for the phycomycete *Allomyces* (111). It is difficult to decide which is the essential ion in these cases.

It would seem that whichever one is available could be used efficiently, thus reflecting the fact that organisms have a wider use for metal ions in their environment than is indicated by their minimum nutritional requirements. In addition to the complete substitution of one metallic ion for another there is the more common partial replacement or sparing action that one ion may show for another. As an example, the manganese requirement of *Lactobacillus arabinosus* (= *L. plantarum*) is markedly lowered by magnesium and to a lesser extent by calcium or strontium. In evaluating effects of metal ions as well as requirements, for metal ions, consideration must also be given to the substrates used and the metabolic pathways involved. Molybdenum is required in much higher amounts by fungi and higher plants when nitrate rather than ammonia serves as the nitrogen source (cf. Section V, D, 2). This has been demonstrated to be due to the fact that molybdenum is the metal component of the nitrate-reducing enzyme, nitrate reductase. It is quite likely that many more of these phenomena will be explained eventually within the scope of metal-enzyme-substrate interactions. Hewitt (98) has recently reviewed various aspects of this important problem of metal interaction.

III. Catalytic Properties of Metalloproteins

The basic question, therefore, with regard to the mode of action of almost all the mineral elements centers about the role of their ions in enzyme systems.

A. Model Systems for Catalytic Activity of Metal Ions

In a number of cases the catalytic activity of metalloenzymes is already present in a primitive form in the free metal ions. Model systems have provided some basis for insight into the mechanism of action of a limited number of metals at the enzyme level, notably in oxidases and other oxidation-reduction reactions involving copper and iron. This has also been true to a more limited extent in decarboxylation and hydrolysis reactions. On the other hand, there are no model catalyses known for many other metalloenzymes or metal-activated enzymes.

1. Copper-Catalyzed Oxidations

The nonenzymatic catalyses of the autoxidation of ascorbic acid and catechol by heavy metals including copper are well known. Their copper-enzyme counterparts are ascorbic acid oxidase and polyphenol oxidase, respectively (cf. Volume IA, Chapter 3, pp. 287–293). The catalysis of ascorbic acid oxidation by Cu^{++} is increased approximately

1000-fold by the copper enzyme, ascorbic acid oxidase. Another important difference between the inorganic model and enzyme systems concerned with ascorbic acid oxidation is that hydrogen peroxide is not produced by the enzymatic reaction, a fact indicating a possible difference in mechanisms in the two cases. Copper catalyses probably involve a reversible $Cu^{++} \leftrightarrow Cu^+$ reaction in both the models and the oxidases. This has been clearly demonstrated for polyphenol oxidase (132, 133) and experimentally suggested for ascorbic acid oxidase (114, 115). A study of the mechanism of copper ion catalyses of autoxidation of ascorbic acid implies (143, 286, 287) that Cu^{++} is reduced to Cu^+ by an intramolecular electron shift within the coordination complex of the monovalent ascorbate ion and Cu^{++} to give a semiquinone free radical of ascorbate. The resultant Cu^+ which does not readily coordinate with hydroxyl compounds is released and oxidized by oxygen while the ascorbate free radical is then pictured as reducing O_2 to either H_2O_2 or H_2O. A similar proposal for the mechanism of metal-catalyzed catechol oxidation has been indicated by Szent-Györgyi and his colleagues (19). A number of the copper enzymes such as the polyphenol oxidase of potatoes (*Solanum tuberosum*) and of mushrooms, but not laccase, are inhibited by carbon monoxide, and these inhibitions are not reversed by light, in agreement with the known properties of copper carbonyls (197). In view of the existence of a very active copper ion catalysis of ascorbic acid autoxidation as well as an enhancement of catalytic activity when copper is complexed with nonspecific proteins, the existence of a true ascorbic acid oxidase has been questioned. This is discussed under Section V, B, 1 on copper enzymes.

2. Iron-Catalyzed Oxidations

Iron provides another example of the enhancement of the catalytic properties of metal ions when combined with a specific protein. The various catalytic properties of heme proteins are already present in simple iron compounds. Iron salts are known to catalyze the oxidation, by molecular oxygen, of different organic compounds such as phenols, thiols, ascorbic acid, etc. This is analogous to cytochrome oxidase activity, while the ability of ferricyanide ions to accept electrons to form ferrocyanide is suggestive of electron transfer activity (87, 255). The oxidation of ferrous hydroxide by O_2 to the ferric state in the presence of a reducing substance, such as thioglycolic acid, is an example of primitive oxidase activity. Thus the ferric ion as a thioglycolic acid complex may be reduced to the ferrous state again with the formation of dithioglycolic acid followed by the subsequent oxidation of Fe^{++} to Fe^{+++} by molecular oxygen. This results in the over-all catalytic oxidation of thioglycolic acid. The ferricyanide system cited above represents a model electron transport substance, being reversibly oxidized and reduced with the exchange of single electrons.

Iron salts also exhibit catalase and peroxidase properties of a low degree. When iron is incorporated into the porphyrin ring, the catalase and peroxidase activities originally associated with the inorganic iron are increased although the porphyrins by themselves show no catalytic action. When the iron porphyrins in turn become attached to specific proteins, the resulting protein complex shows a tremendous increase in catalytic activity and specificity in addition to being stabilized and protected. The catalase activities of the enzyme and the iron porphyrin is 10^9 and 10^3 times greater, respectively, than that of iron salts. The function and specificity of action of the heme is dependent on the protein to which it is attached (197). Heme when combined with certain proteins can serve as a transporter of molecular oxygen (hemoglobin), a transporter of electrons (cytochrome b or c), an activator of oxygen (cytochrome oxidase), an activator of hydrogen peroxide (peroxidase), and a decomposer of hydrogen peroxide (catalase). Inorganic iron salts are regarded as evolutionary precursors of the iron porphyrins, the properties of the heme proteins being already present in a primitive form in ferrous and ferric iron itself (87). Iron in its ionic state tends to form octahedral complexes with six coordinate bonds, coordinating generally with oxygen or nitrogen groups containing unshared electron pairs as in the heme compounds.

3. Metal-Catalyzed Decarboxylations

Other model systems concerned with metal ion catalysis and its relation to enzyme catalyses have been investigated in decarboxylation reactions. Although numerous studies have been carried out on nonenzymatic, metal-catalyzed, and enzyme-catalyzed decarboxylations of certain metabolically significant organic acids, there is no general agreement as to the mechanisms involved. Here model systems have only partially elucidated the mode of action of a metal component or activator of a catalytic protein. This aspect has been treated in a number of reviews (40, 136, 145, 146, 193, 290).

Catalytic amounts of some polyvalent cations markedly accelerate the decarboxylation of oxalacetic and oxalosuccinic acid. This was first observed by Krebs (131), who found that the most active polyvalent cations for the nonenzymatic decarboxylation of oxalacetic acid were Co^{++}, Zn^{++}, Cu^{++}, Fe^{++}, Fe^{+++}, and Al^{++}. At similar concentrations Ca^{++}, Ba^{++}, Mg^{++}, and Mn^{++} were much less effective. The decarboxylation of oxalosuccinic acid, like that of oxalacetic acid, is accelerated by aniline and by polyvalent cations (192). This catalysis seems to be due to the capacity of the active cations to form labile metal complexes with the keto acids or their enol forms (129), the metal complexes undergoing rapid decarboxylation. Acetoacetic acid is exceptional in that it appears to form stable metal complexes. The complex with Fe^{+++} forms an intense red color whereas the complex formed with Al^{+++} absorbs light only in the ultraviolet region. The absorption bands of the metal complexes of both oxalacetic and oxalosuccinic acid disappear very rapidly as a result of decarboxylation. Mg^{++} or Mn^{++} as relatively ineffective catalysts of the nonenzymatic decarboxylation gave only slight changes

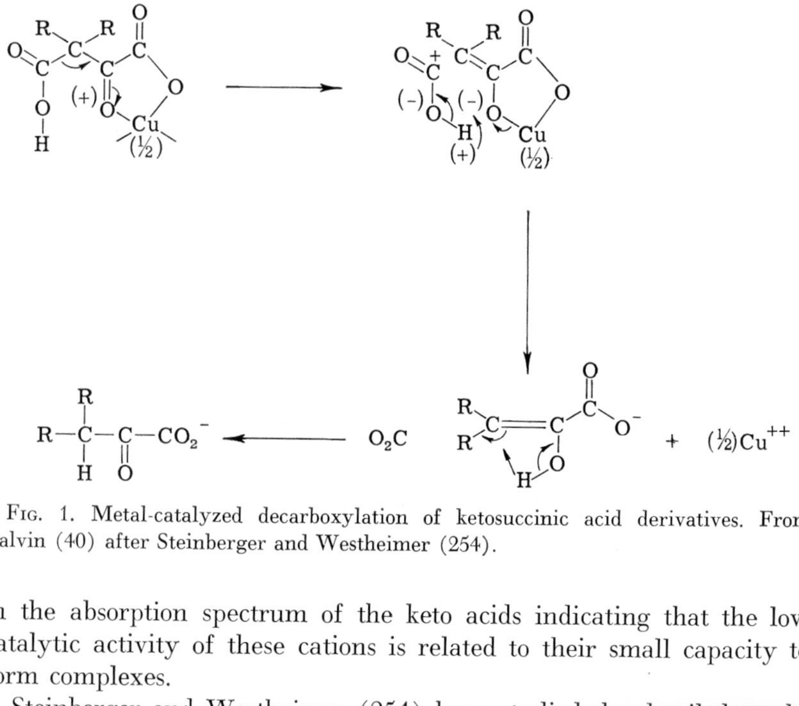

Fig. 1. Metal-catalyzed decarboxylation of ketosuccinic acid derivatives. From Calvin (40) after Steinberger and Westheimer (254).

in the absorption spectrum of the keto acids indicating that the low catalytic activity of these cations is related to their small capacity to form complexes.

Steinberger and Westheimer (254) have studied the detailed mechanism of nonenzymatic β-decarboxylation of the dimethyl-substituted acids. They proposed, as the active intermediate, the formation of a chelate structure between the metal and the carbonyl and the α-carboxyl group of the substrate. It was suggested that the formation of the chelate structure results in an electron shift toward the metal ion and away from the β-carboxyl, leading to decarboxylation as shown in Fig. 1. Other evidence has been reviewed (146), however, which emphasizes the possibility of formation of several different complexes, dependent in part on the pH of the medium. Some of these complexes may be inactive. A more serious objection arises, however, when these proposals are applied to enzymatic reactions. While zinc, copper, iron, and other metals are effective in catalyzing the nonenzymatic decarboxylation of keto acids, these are not the active metals in the enzymatic reactions. Manganese, the most effective metal in enzymatic decarboxylation of oxalacetate and oxalosuccinate, is virtually ineffective in the nonenzymatic reaction. It was found that Mn^{++} catalyzed the oxidative nonenzymatic decarboxylation of oxaloacetic acid, but the product was malonic acid in contrast to pyruvic acid which is formed enzymatically. A somewhat similar effect of Mn^{++} on α-ketoglutaric acid oxidation yielded unknown products. Apparently Mn^{++} does not catalyze an oxidative decarboxylation similar to that obtained when the enzyme is present.

There is no question that the various metals will form bridges between the substrate and the protein, but whether these will lead to the formation of an inhibitory complex or an active intermediate apparently depends on a number of factors. Additional studies on the nature of the metal-substrate-protein complex are necessary before the formation of a chelate structure can be completely accepted as the active intermediate in enzyme-catalyzed decarboxylations. Evidence in favor of the formation of a complex between the protein, keto acid, and Mn^{++} in the enzymatic decarboxylation of oxalacetic and oxalosuccinic acid has been provided by the experiments of Kornberg, Ochoa, and Mehler (129). On mixing Mn^{++}, oxalosuccinate, and oxalosuccinic carboxylase, there is a very rapid and pronounced increase in light absorption at 240 mμ, suggesting complex formation, followed by a decrease due to decarboxylation. It was assumed that despite the low affinity of Mn^{++} for the keto acids, the specific binding of both Mn^{++} and keto acid by the carboxylation protein would enable the formation of the unstable complex at low Mn^{++} concentrations. It is an open question whether the carboxylase accelerates the formation of a keto acid-manganese complex which would then decarboxylate spontaneously or whether decarboxylation occurs in a ternary complex of protein, Mn^{++}, and keto acid.

4. Other Metal-Catalyzed Models

There are also cases of metal-catalyzed nonenzymatic reactions which resemble certain enzymatic reactions although the latter have no metal requirement. For example, Metzler and Snell (160) showed that the transamination between glutamic acid and pyridoxal is catalyzed by metal ions in the ascending order of effectivity: Mn^{++}, Co^{++}, Ni^{++}, Cu^{++}, and Zn++. Transaminase, however, has no known metal requirement. Actually transaminations were discovered as spontaneous reactions before the enzymatic reactions were known. It has been suggested that a Schiff's base between the aldehyde of pyridoxal condensed with the amino group of the acid is an intermediate in transamination. The model systems implicate the formation of a Schiff's base by pyridoxal with an amino acid in the presence of a metal ion (Fig. 2), although a

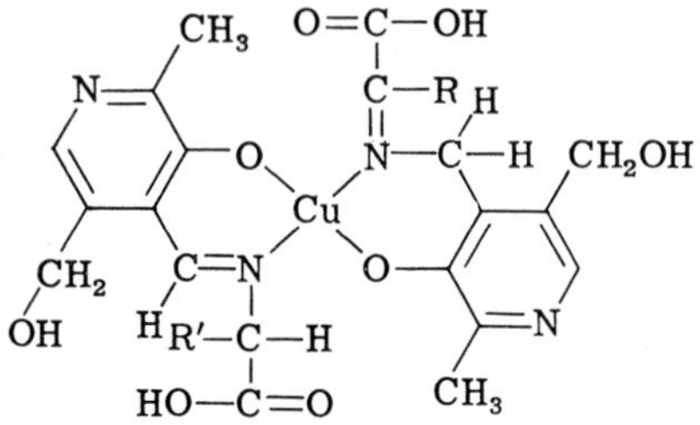

Pyridoxal   Pyridoxamine

+   +

Amino acid   Ketoacid

Transamination; oxidative deamination and reductive amination.

$$Cu^{++} > Al^{3+} \simeq Fe^{++} \simeq Fe^{3+} > Ni^{++} \simeq Co^{++}$$

(relative activities in nonenzymatic reaction)

FIG. 2. Model system for the formation of a Schiff's base by pyridoxal with an amino acid in the presence of a metal ion (40).

metal requirement for the enzymatic system has not yet been demonstrated.

B. METALLOPROTEINS

The increased catalysis, which arises from the combination of a metal ion with a specific protein resides at least in part in the nature of the physicochemical bonding between the metal ion and the protein. Two types of bonds are involved in metal ion reactions with organic molecules. First, there is the ionic bond which arises from electrostatic attraction between two oppositely charged ions. An important class of electrostatic bonding is the ion-dipole bond resulting from electrostatic attraction between a positively-charged metal ion and a dipolar molecule. Examples of such complexes range from the simple $Cu(H_2O)_4^{++}$

to the intricate forms such as the ionic iron complex hemoglobin. The second kind of bond, the covalent linkage, is one in which a pair of electrons is shared between the metal ion and an atom of the group bound. The transition metals are quite active in participating in coordination complexes, forming essentially covalent linkages between the metal and the coordinated molecule. The transition metals may also form ionic complexes. Actually ionic complexes and covalent linkages represent two extremes. Many coordination complexes have properties which are intermediate between these two types of bonds.

The metal ion may coordinate with a number of molecules of a substance as indicated by the coordination number. Generally there are definite spatial arrangements such as planar and tetrahedral for the metals with coordination number 4, and often octahedral for the metals with number 6. Frequently coordination may take place with two groups of the same molecule. In the formation of chelate complexes the most stable are those leading to relatively strain-free rings such as 5- or 6-membered rings. Many amino acids form metal chelate complexes by coordination through the carboxyl and amino groups (Fig. 3). Despite the preparation and study of various coordination complexes of metals with organic molecules, our knowledge of the nature and stability of complexes of physiologically important ions with physiologically important substances (e.g., proteins, phosphorylated compounds, etc.) under physiological conditions is meager. The best examples of chelates of high stability under biological conditions are the hemes and chlorophylls.

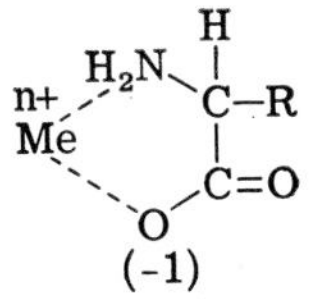

Fig. 3. Metalloamino acid chelate structure. R is the carbon chain and Me^{+n} is the metal ion.

The reactions of metal ions with protein molecules are of great interest. Only certain specific polar side chains of proteins act as ligands for the formation of metal protein complexes. A ligand is usually described as an atom, or a group of atoms, which is capable of donating electrons to a separate metal atom. This tendency to donate electrons will lead to the formation of "complex" compounds between two or more such ligands. Such compounds are chelates (Claw). Klotz (128) reviewed the various properties of polar side chains of proteins and concluded that the following are known to be involved in complex formation with at least some metals: phosphoric acid, carboxyl, imidazolium, α- and ε-ammonium, phenolic, and sulfhydryl groups. Most proteins have at least a number of these side chains. Therefore, it is expected that they form stable complexes with many metals. Metal ions may also function by acting as a bridge, thus linking proteins to low molecular weight compounds. It has been possible to show the binding of uncharged organic molecules to serum albumin provided certain metals are present—the metal, protein, and organic molecule apparently acting together to form a ternary complex. For example, in the binding of azopyridine dyes with pepsin those metals which promoted the combination of dye with protein were effective in forming chelates with the dye in the absence of protein. Calcium and magnesium did not combine with the dye and were also inactive in bringing about complex formation. Studies of the complex formation of metals with proteins and chelate formation of metals with low molecular weight compounds provide useful information in interpreting the mechanism of action of metal ions in certain enzyme-catalyzed reactions.

Klotz (128) stressed three general categories in which metals in combination with proteins or prosthetic groups may act as catalysts.

1. Primary Effects of Protein on the Properties of the Metal

Examples of this group include the copper and heme enzymes already indicated above. This frequently involves oxidation-reduction reactions in which the primitive catalytic properties of the metallic ions are considerably enhanced by combination with specific proteins.

2. Primary Effect of Metal on the Properties of the Enzyme Protein

The combination of metals with proteins may alter a number of properties of the protein. This could possibly occur by changing the net charge of the proteins and thus from purely electrostatic effects alter the combination of substrate with enzyme. By changing the ratio of zinc and magnesium, Sadasivan (222) observed a shift in the pH optimum of phosphatase activity to either the acid or alkaline range. Massey (158) demonstrated that a number of anions, such as sulfate, selenate, and borate, were effective in activating salt-free crystalline fumarase as well as shifting the optimal pH to the alkaline side. Studies by others have shown an activating effect of such cations as Ca^{++}, Co^{++}, Cd^{++}, and Mn^{++} on the esterase and amidase activities of trypsin although there is no absolute requirement for a metal. The electrostatic effect of metals on proteins may be responsible for the profound influence of nonessential metals on the metabolism of both plants and animals. In addition to this direct electrostatic effect, however, metals may also activate by the removal of inhibitory substances. The enzyme leucine aminopeptidase provides another example of an indirect effect of a metal. The purest enzyme preparations are strongly activated by Mn^{++}, but the action of Mg^{++} is quite poor. However, the stability of the crude or purified enzyme is greatly increased by Mg^{++}. A protecting effect on

yeast arginine desiminase (arginine→citrulline + NH₃) has been exhibited by cobalt and nickel in crude extracts, but not in partially purified fractions.

3. Cooperative Effects of Metal and Protein

Metals and protein may act cooperatively to increase catalytic
activity. Hellerman and Stock (95) were among the first to suggest

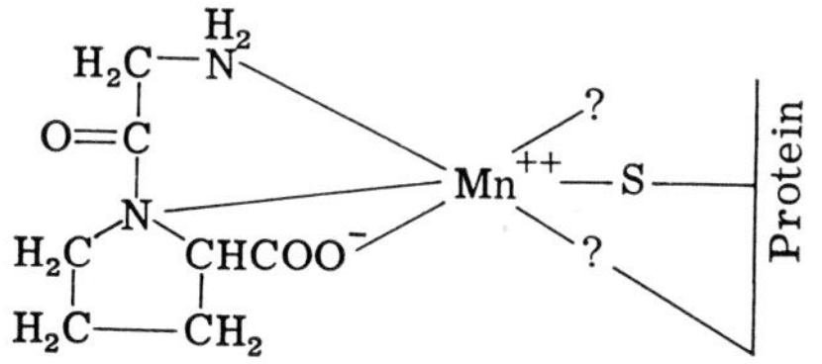

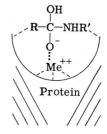

Fig. 4. Postulated coordination of glycyl-L-proline with Mn^{++} and prolidase (242).

that metals may serve as a bridge between substrate and protein. In the
case of peptidase activity Smith and his colleagues (242) stressed the
importance of a chelate structure between the metal ion and the substrate as a prerequisite for enzymatic activity. In the case of the man-
ganese-requiring enzyme prolidase, a dipeptidase which catalyzes the
hydrolysis of glycyl-L-proline, a 5-membered ring
structure is proposed whereby manganese acts as a
ligand in the formation of an active intermediate
(Fig. 4). The metal is pictured as attaching itself to
the uncharged amino group and the ionized carboxyl
group. An alternate mechanism has been proposed
(128) whereby the primary function of the metal
is to stabilize the formation of an active intermediate
(Fig. 5). In addition to favoring the formation of an
active intermediate, the positively charged metal
would increase the local concentration of OH^-, and
these two factors would tend to speed up the hydrolysis. The role of metal ions in enzymatic decarboxylation reactions discussed previously would
fit into this category.

Fig. 5. Stabiliza-
tion of an inter-
mediate for a re-
action by a metal-
protein complex
(128).

Under appropriate conditions or with suitable substrates such as
pyrophosphate-containing compounds, Mg^{++} or Mn^{++} may be expected
to form chelate structures more readily. Bauer (23) suggested that the
action of inorganic pyrophosphatase depended upon the formation of an
enzyme-metal-substrate chelate structure. Calvin emphasized the importance of the pyrophosphate structure for the linkage of coenzymes

or substrates to the enzyme via a chelate structure with Mg^{++} or Mn^{++} (Fig. 6). Other groups on the protein must be effective in bringing about complex formation with pyrophosphate since metals are not required in all cases. In those cases where metals are required, the chelate structure may be an intermediate. This mechanism would have a bearing on those Mg^{++}- or Mn^{++}-activated enzymes where a pyrophosphate-containing compound such as ADP or ATP is involved.

It is important to stress that the combination of a metal ion with substrate and enzyme is not sufficient to produce biological activity. The effect of metal ions in activating enzymes must have some specificity beyond mere combination with substrate and protein. Enolase, the enzyme which catalyzes the conversion of 2-phosphoglycerate to phospho-enol pyruvate, was shown by Malmström (149) to be inhibited by

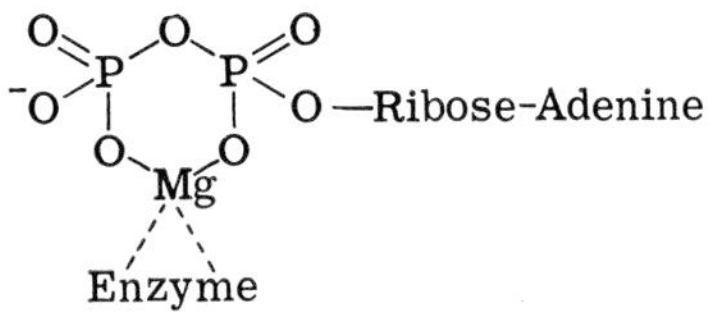

FIG. 6. Chelate structure of the pyrophosphate group of ADP (or ATP) with Mg^{++} and its chelate binding to the enzyme.

beryllium, calcium, and nickel although these ions formed complexes with the enzyme. Mg^{++}, which happens to form the weakest complex with enolase and substrate, gives the best enzymatic activity, whereas Zn^{++}, which binds strongly with the enzyme, shows high activity also. It is apparent that the effect of metal ions in activating enzymes must have some specificity beyond mere combination with the substrate and protein.

IV. Metal Requirements of Enzymes

In terms of the metal requirements of enzymes, two broad groups can be designated: (a) those enzymes in which a specific metal has been shown to be an integral component, and (b) those enzymes for which one or more metals serve as an activator. At times the lines dividing these two groups are difficult to distinguish. The emerging pattern shows that such trace elements as zinc, iron, copper, and molybdenum have been clearly established as specific and integral components for a number of enzyme systems. Magnesium and manganese, on the other hand, are most frequently involved as activators. In certain enzymes, however, they are regarded as specific components.

All these examples will be discussed under the individual metals in the sections which follow.

V. Mechanism of Action of the Micronutrient Elements

No attempt will be made to review historical development, effects of deficiencies, excesses or interrelationships of the nutrient elements in plant metabolism since these aspects have been covered in Chapters 1 and 2 of this volume. Special phases of these topics will be included, however, in those cases where they may have a particular bearing on the mode of action of the mineral element in question.

A. ZINC

Although zinc was shown by earlier workers to stimulate the growth of various organisms, probably the first definite evidence for zinc as an essential element was presented in 1914 by Mazé (159), who demonstrated that without added zinc, normal growth of maize (*Zea mays*) was not possible. He considered zinc to be an essential element for growth, not merely a stimulant. In 1919 Steinberg (250) provided proof that zinc is also indispensable for the normal growth of fungi. Since that time a host of reports have presented irrefutable data in support of zinc as a micronutrient element [see reviews by Chesters and Rolinson (42), Gilbert (83), and Hoch and Vallee (105)]. More recently the work of Vallee and his associates (105) has provided new evidence for the role of zinc as a component of pyridine nucleotide dehydrogenases.

1. Relationship with Auxin

Thus far the most prominent role for zinc in plants appears to be in its interrelationship with auxin. Zinc deficiency in higher plants is characterized by a failure of stem elongation as first described by Skoog (241). Tomato (*Lycopersicon esculentum*) plants deficient in zinc were shown to be deficient in auxin, incipient deficiencies resulting in a reduction of 50% or more in auxin content before the appearance of diminished growth. This effect was not produced by deficiencies of copper or manganese, which gave marked growth depressions before affecting auxin content. The addition of zinc to deficient plants resulted in an increase in auxin within 24 hours.

Skoog considered the relation of zinc to auxin to be an indirect one. He suggested that the low level of auxin in zinc-deficient plants was due to destruction of the hormone by oxidation rather than to a lack of synthesis resulting from an altered oxidation-reduction balance in deficient plants. The disappearance of auxin was accompanied by an increase in the oxidizing capacity of zinc-deficient plants, arising in part from an increased peroxidase activity. Sections from zinc-deficient stems inactivated indole-3-acetic acid more rapidly than sections from healthy plants. In contrast, Tsui (267) furnished evidence in tomato plants implicating zinc in the synthesis of auxin by way of tryptophan. Zinc-deficient plants, which were also low in auxin, similarly showed a decrease in tryptophan content. The enzyme system allegedly responsible for the formation of indole-3-acetic acid by oxidative deamination of tryptophan was found to be the same in deficient as in healthy plants. From these results it would appear that zinc is required for the synthesis of tryptophan and therefore indirectly for the synthesis of auxin. In keeping with this suggestion is the earlier indication by Hoagland (104) of a direct correlation between the distribution of auxin and tryptophan in different parts of the leaf as well as the fact that the apical part of the leaf which contains more auxin and tryptophan also accumulates zinc. Further support for this hypothesis was provided by the finding that in *Neurospora* tryptophan synthetase, the enzyme which catalyzes the formation of tryptophan from indole and serine, is markedly and specifically decreased by a zinc deficiency (178). The results imply that zinc is either a component of the enzyme system or that a deficiency indirectly leads to a decrease in the enzyme protein. The first possibility has not been eliminated.

2. Zinc Deficiency and Enzyme Systems

The necessity of a metal ion for the activity or synthesis of specific enzymes may at times be indicated by growing the organism under conditions of metal deficiency and comparing its enzyme systems with those of normal tissues. This approach has been taken in attempting to uncover the mode of action of zinc. Reed (209) reported that in zinc-deficient tomato plants dehydrogenase activity was lowered, while the quinones arising by action of phenol oxidases were not decreased. The accumulation of inorganic phosphate suggested a possible role of zinc in the activation of a phosphate-transferring enzyme, perhaps hexokinase. It was also found that pyruvic carboxylase is absent in zinc-deficient *Rhizopus nigricans* (72). Zinc is not regarded as a constituent of the carboxylase since no correlation was obtained between zinc content and enzymatic activity of mycelial extracts. The metal is probably necessary for the synthesis of the enzyme itself.

Zinc deficiency in *Neurospora* does not lead simply to the production of less mycelium, but it specifically results in the production of fungus having drastically altered metabolic characteristics as indicated by the marked changes in enzymatic constitution (178). The alterations involved not only the virtual disappearance of certain enzyme activities such as that of alcohol dehydrogenase and the tryptophan synthetase, but also remarkable increases in the activities of other enzymes. The concentration of diphosphopyridine nucleotidase (DPNase), an enzyme which splits DPN at the nicotinamide riboside linkage, increased ten- to twentyfold. Other enzymes including fumarase, hexokinase, aldolase, and triosephosphate dehydrogenase were unaffected. The basic defect in zinc deficiency seemed to be not in the synthesis of vitamins, amino acids, purines, or pyrimidines, but presumably in their subsequent metabolism.

A working hypothesis to explain the above phenomena is that those enzymes which increase in nutritionally deficient cells are proteins of relatively simple structure. Their synthesis can proceed even in the absence of certain key reactions which are necessary for the building of more complex protein molecules. A metal deficiency such as zinc may eliminate one of several competing reactions for available amino nitrogen, resulting in a relative increase in certain enzymes and decreases in others. The competition may be for the polypeptide made at the enzyme-forming center. For example, in the case of tryptophan synthetase, zinc appears to be essential not only for its function, but also for the synthesis of the protein part of the enzyme. Thus in many ways zinc behaves as a specific inducer for the formation of certain enzymes. Under limited zinc deficiency, however, protein synthesis apparently proceeds normally. With the loss of specific enzymes, the polypeptide pool can be used for the increased synthesis of other enzymes. It is possible, therefore, that a single template can function as a site for the formation of a single polypeptide chain, which in turn is the primary structure for a number of enzymes. The secondary and tertiary structure, which in part is under nutritional control, determines the specificity of catalytic activity.

Protein synthesized in the zinc-deficient mycelia is not available for new enzyme synthesis since nitrogen as well as zinc is essential for the restoration of the diphosphopyridine nucleotidase and alcohol dehydrogenase levels of zinc-deficient mats (179). Also a zinc deficiency as well as a number of other metal deficiencies in tomato plants elevated the concentration of polyphenol oxidase, peroxidase, ascorbic acid oxidase, and glycolic acid oxidase (180). Although it has been shown (180) that such metalloenzymes as polyphenol oxidase, ascorbic acid oxidase, and peroxidase are decreased in concentration in plants deficient in the specific metal concerned, it does not necessarily follow that other nutritive conditions would fail to decrease these enzymes. It would be fallacious to conclude that a particular enzyme contains a specific metal component simply because a deficiency of the latter results in a decreased concentration of the enzyme. At most such evidence is suggestive. As pointed out below, the decrease in alcohol dehydrogenase in zinc-deficient *Neurospora* can now be ascribed to its properties as a zinc protein. Quinlan-Watson (208) reported a decrease in aldolase of higher plants under conditions of zinc deficiency, whereas a copper deficiency had no effect. Far more evidence is necessary to establish this enzyme as a zinc protein. This is exemplified by the case of alcohol dehydrogenase given below.

3. Alcohol Dehydrogenase and Other Pyridine Nucleotide Dehydrogenases

The above-mentioned decreases in the content of alcohol dehydrogenase as a result of a zinc deficiency can be attributed to the fact that the enzyme is a zinc protein. The recent work of Vallee and his associates (105) has implied that pyridine nucleotide dehydrogenases contain zinc, which probably serves to bind the pyridine nucleotide to the protein moiety. They first showed that yeast alcohol dehydrogenase (ADH) contains uniformly large amounts of zinc firmly bound to the protein and suggested that the metal is a functional component of the molecule in its enzymatic activity. Their data demonstrated that four molecules of zinc are bound to one molecule of the enzyme protein, constituting an integral part of the protein molecule in the natural state. This complex which has a zinc content of approximately 0.2% has been assigned the empirical formula $(ADH)Zn_4$. One molecule of crystalline yeast ADH has also been shown to bind four molecules of DPN (or DPNH). In a more recent report, Kägi and Vallee (116) observed that the irreversible, time-dependent inhibition of the enzyme by 1,10-phenanthroline and 8-hydroxyquinoline-5-sulfonic acid is accompanied by the dissociation of its apoenzyme of molecular weight 151,000 into four subunits with a molecular weight of 36,000 each. They envisage the empirical structural formula of yeast alcohol dehydrogenase as $[(YADH)_4Zn_4]$ $(DPN)_4$ where YADH represents a single apoenzyme unit of molecular weight 36,000. They have reported that the rates of inactivation and of the loss of zinc from the enzyme as well as the degree of dissociation of the apoenzyme are directly correlated. The zinc atoms are thought to stabilize the quaternary structure of the enzyme through the formation of bridges between the monomers to form the enzymatically active tetramer. A three-point attachment of DPN to two adjacent monomeric units of the apoenzyme and to the binding zinc atom is postulated to account for the interrelationship between the functional and structural features of the enzyme and its zinc content.

Zinc has also been reported by Vallee and his colleagues to be a component of liver alcohol dehydrogenase and other pyridine nucleotide dehydrogenases such as liver glutamic dehydrogenase (1) and muscle lactic dehydrogenase (105). The presence of two to four atoms of zinc in crystalline beef liver glutamic dehydrogenase, the inhibition of the system by a number of metal-binding agents, and the demonstration by Frieden (75) that the enzyme can be dispersed into protein subunits by one of these chelating agents as well as by the addition of DPNH have led to the suggestion that four enzyme fragments are bound by zinc atoms to form the larger kinetic molecular unit (1). The recent work of Yielding and Tomkins (296), however, in which various steroid hormones also promoted disaggregation of the glutamic dehydrogenase macromolecule into subunits, has cast some doubts on the above interpretation. It may also well be that these enzymes from the tissues of higher plants will also prove to have a zinc component.

Hoch and Vallee (105) feel that the hypothesis of a metal as a component of many, if not all, of the pyridine nucleotide-dependent dehydrogenases is a natural extension of their studies on the above enzymes. They report zinc, copper, and iron to be the only metals consistently present in significant concentrations in glyceraldehyde 3-phosphate dehydrogenase of yeast and rabbit muscle, the α-glycerophosphate dehydrogenase of rabbit muscle, the malic dehydrogenase of pig heart, and the TPN-glucose 6-phosphate dehydrogenase of yeast. These enzymes are all inhibited by a number of chelating agents known to form strong complexes with these metals.

4. Carbonic Anhydrase

This is the first enzyme for which zinc was established as a metal component. Carbonic anhydrase was highly purified from bovine red blood cells and shown to contain approximately 0.3% zinc in a tightly bound form (119). Based on a molecular weight of 30,000, the reported zinc content varies from 0.9 to 1.5 gram atoms per mole. The enzyme which catalyzes the reaction, $H_2O + CO_3 \rightleftarrows H_2CO_3$, is inhibited by such metal-binding agents as cyanide, azide, and sulfide and is the only zinc-containing substance with carbonic anhydrase properties. Keilin and Mann reported that inorganic zinc salts, simple organozinc compounds, zinc porphyrin, insulin, and Zn^{++} complexes of various proteins lacked this activity. In contrast to earlier reports (228, 268) of the inability to dissociate the zinc of carbonic anhydrase from the protein, Lindskog and Malmström (140) have recently been able to remove the metal reversibly from the enzyme at pH 5 in the presence of certain chelating agents. The dissociation of zinc causes a loss of enzymatic activity which can be fully restored by the addition of zinc. Other types of substances have catalytic activity in the hydration of carbon dioxide or the dehydration of carbonic acid, although all but one are not metals. These include hydrogen peroxide, hypochlorite, various organic bases such as histidine, sulfate, selenite, and arsenite. Their mechanism of action is different from that of the enzyme.

Carbonic anhydrase activity has been observed by a number of workers to be present in the leaves of several plants [see review by Hoch and Vallee (105)]. As yet zinc has not been clearly demonstrated to be a component of the plant enzyme. Day and Franklin (52) were among the first to establish the presence of carbonic anhydrase in plants. They found that zinc was associated in a nondialyzable form with the enzyme protein but did not prove a functional relationship. Bradfield (34) reported a wide distribution of the enzyme in several plants and indicated the susceptibility of the system to zinc deficiency. Wood and Sibly (295) obtained a decrease in carbonic anhydrase in zinc-deficient oats. They questioned whether such data were indicative of the zinc nature of the enzyme and decided that the observed decrease could best be ascribed to an indirect effect on protein formation. Whether or not zinc is a component of carbonic anhydrase from plants must await further study. The basic mechanism of the role of zinc in carbonic anhydrase from animals has not been investigated, although the suggestion has been made that zinc may function by uniting enzyme and substrate in a coordination complex.

5. Other Zinc Enzymes

Zinc has been reported to be a metal component of the animal peptidases, dehydropeptidase (299), glycylglycine dipeptidase (139), and carboxypeptidase (269). Crystalline preparations of the latter contain 0.98 gram atoms of zinc per mole of enzyme. The metal can be removed by dialysis, the loss of enzyme activity being proportional to the loss of metal (270). Enzymatic activity can be restored to the metal-free enzyme by the addition of Zn^{++} or by certain ions of the first transition period, such as Cr^{+++}, Ni^{++}, Co^{++}, Fe^{++}, and Mn^{++}. Evidence has also been presented which suggests that the phosphatases of *Penicillium chrysogenum* (221) and certain animal tissues may be zinc-containing enzymes. Zinc has been implicated by Warburg and Christian (276) as a possible metal component of yeast zymohexase. The enzyme was characterized as a dissociable metal-protein which could be inhibited by the formation of complexes with pyrophosphate, cysteine, and

glutathione. Although an earlier investigation found that highly purified preparations of uricase, the enzyme that catalyzes the oxidation
of uric acid to allantoin, contained 0.13% zinc (106), a more recent
report has implicated the enzyme from kidney as a copper protein
containing 0.05% copper (152). A number of isolated enzyme systems
such as lecithinase, histidine deaminase, and oxaloacetic decarboxylase
have been shown to be activated by zinc, among other metal ions. The
effect is not specific for zinc and raises the question of its significance
in the intact cell.

6. Other Effects of Zinc

In addition to the apparent relationship between zinc and auxin
content in plants as previously discussed, other biological phenomena
have been associated with the metal. The above-described auxin effect
possibly accounts for impaired flower setting and seed production, which
is a conspicuous symptom of zinc deficiency in high plants. There are
reports that in fungi zinc increases the uptake of calcium, phosphorus,
and magnesium as well as the efficiency of sugar utilization. Some
workers have indicated zinc to be unfavorable for citrate production in
fungi, but others have reported the opposite effect [see Chesters and
Rolinson (42)].

B. Copper

Sommer (244) is credited with the first demonstration that copper is
an essential element for higher plants. The metal has been established
as a component of a number of different plant enzymes—polyphenol
oxidase, monophenol oxidase, laccase, and ascorbic acid oxidase.

1. Enzymatic Role

One of the general properties ascribed to the copper enzymes is the
catalysis of the direct oxidation of their substrates by atmospheric
oxygen according the equation

$$BH_2 + \tfrac{1}{2}O_2 \xrightarrow{\text{Copper enzyme}} B + H_2O$$

and their failure to function anaerobically [see review by Dawson and
Tarpley (50)]. The inherent property of inorganic copper salts in
catalyzing the oxidation of various organic substrates by molecular
oxygen was discussed previously. Polyphenol oxidase, also called
catecholase or tyrosinase, catalyzes the oxidation of o-diphenols by
molecular oxygen to form the corresponding quinones and water (Fig.
7), as shown by the early work of Raper. m- or p-Diphenols are not

acted upon by this enzyme. Monophenolase, as exemplified by the enzyme from mushroom, catalyzes the conversion of a monophenol to the o-diphenol by molecular oxygen. This enzyme has also been called cresolase or tyrosinase; it is always accompanied by polyphenolase activity, although polyphenolase does not always have monophenolase activity. Laccase, which is obtained from the latex of certain species of lacquer trees can oxidize p-diphenols and o-diphenols to the corresponding quinones and water. Ascorbic acid oxidase catalyzes the oxidation of ascorbic acid to form dehydroascorbic acid and water (see Fig. 7).

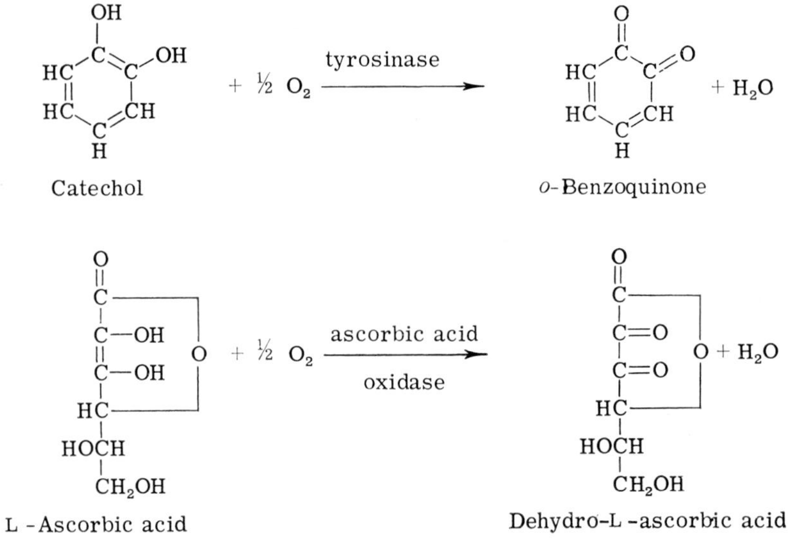

FIG. 7. Over-all reactions of tryosinase and ascorbic acid oxidase.

The activities of these oxidases are dependent on the copper content, which in purified preparations ranges between 0.1 and 0.35%. The copper is tightly bound and cannot be removed by dialysis against water. However, treatment with acids or cyanide and subsequent dialysis result in the removal of copper from the protein. Reconstitution of these enzymes has been accomplished by adding back copper. The copper oxidases are inhibited by a number of metal binding agents, carbon monoxide inhibiting the phenol oxidases of potato and mushroom but not laccase. Inhibition by carbon monoxide is not reversed by light in agreement with the properties of copper-carbon monoxide models.

The best evidence thus far for the mechanism of action of copper was presented by Kubowitz (132, 133). Using potato polyphenol oxidase, he obtained data indicating that copper is concerned in electron transport apparently by undergoing cyclic oxidation-reduction between Cu^{++} and Cu^+ during the enzymatic transfer of electrons from substrate to oxygen. He showed that 1 mole of o-diphenol reduced the Cu^{++} enzyme to the cuprous form, yielding 1 mole of o-quinone. In the reaction of a molecule of o-diphenol, 2 cupric atoms are reduced to the cuprous (Cu^+) form as the carbon monoxide complex, the uptake of carbon monoxide being determined manometrically. In the presence of one molecule of o-diphenol, 2 cupric atoms are reduced to the cuprous form, since one molecule of carbon monoxide is bound to two atoms of phenolase copper. This constitutes the best evidence thus far for an oxidation-reduction role of copper at the enzymatic level. The copper of laccase, by analogy to polyphenolase, presumably acts in the same manner.

The monophenolase activity which often accompanies polyphenolase activity has been a controversial and much-discussed subject. The facts that the ratio of the two activities is easily altered and that added copper readily exchanges with the enzyme's copper during polyphenolase action, and to a lesser extent during monophenolase action, suggest that the two activities are independent of one another. This does not exclude the possibility that these two activities are due to two different sites on the same protein molecule and that each may require copper as a prosthetic group. In support of this idea are the observations that the two activities are associated with the same electrophoretic and ultracentrifugal component and that they are similarly inhibited by the same metal-binding reagents and competitive substrates [see reviews by Dawson and Tarpley (50) and Mason (156)].

The recent experiments of Dressler and Dawson (57, 58) have shed further light on this question. By studying the exchange between radioactive Cu^{64} cupric ions and resting (nonfunctioning) tyrosinase (purified from the mushroom *Psalliota campestris*) as well as the catalytically functioning enzyme they obtained data which support the hypothesis of two distinct activity centers, i.e., monophenolase (cresolase) and polyphenolase (catecholase) sites. Their results suggested that copper is firmly bound to the tyrosinase protein and that the *resting enzyme* essentially does not undergo exchange with radioactive cupric ions except when the enzyme contains copper bonded at inactive sites, i.e., only when the enzyme is impure or partially inactivated. However, when the enzyme was actively catalyzing the oxidation of polyphenols an exchange between the copper of the enzyme with ionic Cu^{64} occurred depending on the amount of substrate employed (on the number of o-dihydric phenol molecules oxidized) and on the type of tyrosinase preparation used. Of the two general types of tryosinase preparations, the one having a low molecular weight and a catecholase to cresolase activity ratio of about twenty or higher (called "high catecholase" enzyme) incorporated much more radioactive copper during catalysis of the oxidation of o-dihydric phenols than the "high cresolase" enzyme type (high molecular weight and a catecholase to cresolase activity ratio of about ten or lower). Dressler and Dawson (58) have concluded, on the basis of the above experiments, that the copper at the functioning catecholase activity sites is exchangeable whereas that at the cresolase sites is nonexchangeable. They feel that the catecholase sites are little, or not at all, involved in the oxidation of monophenols and that the oxidation of a monophenol by tyrosinase may not proceed via an o-dihydric phenol.

An opposing viewpoint has attributed monophenolase activity to a nonenzymatic, copper-catalyzed reaction. Kertesz (123), studying the mechanism of phenolase oxidate of monohydric phenols with a purified potato enzyme, reported that additions of Cu^{++} determined further increases in monophenolase activity; and that cobalt, vanadium, and nickel could replace copper, though less effectively. He interpreted these data to mean that the monophenolase activity of tyrosinase was due to free metallic ions which accelerated the nonenzymatic reaction between o-quinones and monohydric phenols as follows:

$$o\text{-dihydric phenol } (polyphenolase)\ o\text{-quinone} \qquad (1)$$

$$o\text{-quinone} + \text{monohydric phenol} + H_2O \xrightarrow[\text{metal}]{\text{free}} 2o\text{-dihydric phenol} \qquad (2)$$

Thus he contended polyphenolase or tyrosinase to be a complex system composed of an o-dihydric phenol (or o-quinone), an enzyme specific for o-dihydric phenols, and free metallic ions, the latter catalyzing the spontaneous reaction between o-quinone and monophenols (e.g., tyrosine). As shown by Eqs. 1 and 2, the second phenolic group of dihydric phenol arising from the monophenol should come from water. This viewpoint, however, has been very effectively refuted by the recent experiments of Mason, Fowlks, and Peterson (157). They used O_2^{18} and H_2O^{18} in separate experiments and found that all the oxygen introduced as the hydroxyl group in the benzene ring of monophenol derivatives by the action of phenolase (tyrosinase) came from molecular oxygen. In other words, monophenolase is an enzyme belonging to the broad group of oxygen transferases [see review by Mason (156)].

The question concerning the existence of a true ascorbic acid oxidase enzyme has been raised from time to time. Although it has been suggested that the catalytic activity of ascorbic acid oxidase may be attributed to traces of ionic copper resulting from an ionization of copper bound to nonspecific protein matter or other colloidal material, the present evidence is heavily against this view (49, 50). The work of Dawson and his colleagues (49, 50) with ascorbic acid oxidase also suggests a mechanism of a Cu^{++}-Cu^+ cycle for this enzyme. Using Cu^{64}, they were able to show an exchange between the copper of ascorbic acid oxidase with ionic copper only when the enzyme was actively catalyzing the oxidation of ascorbic acid. No exchange took place in the resting enzyme, in the enzyme inactivated during the course of the reaction, or in the absence of oxygen even with substrate present. The copper of ascorbic acid oxidase, which is initially in the divalent state, presumably shuttles reversibly between the divalent and monovalent forms during enzyme catalysis. The fact that both ascorbic acid and oxygen are necessary for the Cu^{++}-Cu^+ reaction of the enzyme, suggests the formation of an intermediary ternary complex of oxygen, ascorbic acid, and enzyme. In model systems the usual type of covalent complex formed by Cu^{++} is one with a coordination number of 4 having a square coplanar configuration for the directed valences of the copper atom (289). Cu^+ with a coordination number of 4 exists in a tetrahedral configuration. Since square coplanar bonds are considered to be much stronger than tetrahedral bonds (199), copper exchange would be more likely to occur when the copper bond is in the tetrahedral configuration. The report (112) that covalent nickel compounds of the square planar type do not exchange with radioactive nickelous ions in solution, whereas the tetrahedral nickel complexes which are of a weaker bond strength do, tends to support the above hypothesis. The copper enzymes may have a significant role in terminal respiration of some plants although additional evidence is necessary in support of this function.

Benhamow et al. (26) observed that the reaction inactivation of functioning ascorbic acid oxidase was greatly increased in the presence of free cupric ions whereas the nonfunctioning enzyme was unaffected. This has led them to suggest that Cu^{++} inactivation involves chemical groupings (possibly —SH) which are present (or not exposed) in the resting or nonfunctioning enzyme and which become exposed when the enzyme functions.

The light blue color of purified ascorbic acid oxidase is probably due to its copper content. This is very likely also the case for hemocuprein, a copper-bearing protein insolated from the red blood cells of mammals. On the other hand the phenolase studied by Kubowitz (132, 133) had a faint yellow color and showed no outstanding absorption other than that of the characteristic tyrosine-trytophan spectrum in the ultraviolet region. Hemocyanin, a copper-protein complex found in the blood of certain invertebrates, exists naturally in the cuprous condition and is blue when oxygenated and only faintly colored when deoxygenated. It was thus presumed at one time that the blue color of highly purified laccase was a property of the copper by analogy with the blue color of the oxygenated hemocyanins and hemocuprein. It was later shown, however, that the blue color was due to a carbohydrate-containing component free of protein and copper. It can be seen from these examples that the relationship between color and valence state of the copper in the various copper proteins is not entirely clear. The possible role of these copper-containing oxidases in the respiration of plants is discussed in another chapter of this series.

More recently a new addition has been proposed to the list of copper enzymes. Mahler and co-workers (152) reported that purified samples of kidney uricase contain 0.05% copper. An earlier report had implicated uricase as a zinc enzyme (221).

The original suggestion of Keilin and Hartree (117) that cytochrome oxidase of animal tissues contains significant quantities of copper (and iron) has now been confirmed by numerous workers (60, 148, 196). Moreover, a number of investigators have observed that animals subjected to a copper-deficient diet showed a conspicuous decrease in cytochrome oxidase activity (44, 76, 109, 298). Purified cytochrome oxidase preparations contain one atom of copper per atom of iron per mole of cytochrome a, a proportion which is maintained at all stages of purification (90, 224, 258). However, there is no common agreement among workers in this area as to the state and function of copper in this enzyme system. Sands and Beinert (223) using paramagnetic resonance spectrometry obtained data which are consistent with the idea that the copper of cytochrome oxidase is reduced by electron-donating substrates of the purified enzyme, a reduction which is specific and possibly connected with the function of the system. A similar view is held by Griffiths and Wharton (90) and Takemori (258). The latter has indicated that the copper in cytochrome a exists in cupric form in contrast to the results of Vandra and Wainio (272), who reported that the copper of cytochrome oxidase is mostly in the cuprous state and firmly bound to the enzyme. The inhibition of cytochrome oxidase by alleged copper-chelating agents such as ferrocyanide, salicytaldoxime, ethylxanthate (258) and bathocuproine sulfonate sodium salt (or 2,9-dimethyl-4,7-diphenyl-1,10-phenanthroline sodium disulfonate) (297) has been contradicted by the experiments of Griffiths and Wharton (90), who were unable to observe an effect by the latter compound. Yonetani (297) has concluded that although the copper in oxidized cytochrome oxidase is in the cupric state and is enzymatically reducible (corresponding to 60–70% of the total copper), it does not participate in the electron transfer system of cytochrome oxidase. Griffiths and Wharton (90) attribute Yonetani's results to a contamination by ionic copper and contend that copper is involved in cytochrome oxidase activity by being firmly bound in a specific configuration so that it is not vulnerable to copper-chelating agents.

Asano (15, 16) has reported the separation of an enzymatic nitrite-reducing system from a *Micrococcus* strain into a soluble component which is activated by Cu^+ and Cu^{++} ions, and a particulate component which is enhanced by Fe^{++} and Fe^{+++}.

2. Effects of Copper Deficiency

Plants deficient in copper have been shown to contain decreased activities of the copper enzymes measured, namely polyphenol oxidase and ascorbic acid oxidase (180). A striking observation was made in the specific association of a ten- to thirtyfold increase in the concentration of isocitric dehydrogenase in copper-deficient tomato leaves (171). As already indicated above for other enzymes which increase under various metal deficiency conditions, the effect of copper in this system can probably be ascribed to an alteration of protein metabolism. It is of interest that oxalosuccinate carboxylase activity in extracts of copper-deficient leaves paralleled the observed rise in isocitric dehydrogenase activity, thus providing further support for the idea that these two activities are catalyzed by the same enzyme as claimed for animal tissues (85).

3. Other Functions of Copper

The most important function of copper in plants appears thus far to be as a component of the phenolases, laccase, ascorbic acid oxidase, and perhaps of cytochrome oxidase by analogy to the results obtained with the enzyme from animal tissues as indicated above. On the basis of indirect evidence, there would seem to be a function for copper in photosynthesis. Neish (182) found that 75% of the total copper in the clover (*Trifolium* sp.) leaf was localized in the chloroplasts, most of it in organic combination. Arnon (10) speculated that if a quinone-like substance should prove to be the natural primary acceptor of hydrogen in photosynthesis, a copper enzyme such as polyphenol oxidase may be responsible for its regeneration, by oxidation of a corresponding phenolic compound. Arnon and his co-workers observed that the Hill reaction is inhibited by metal-binding agents such as o-phenanthroline and potassium ethylxanthate indicative of a metal requirement for the light reaction of photosynthesis. The latter chelating agent is regarded by some (89) as fairly specific for copper enzymes, although this is a controversial point. Arnon's group found that either dialysis or the addition of copper reversed this inhibition and hinted therefore that copper might be the metal involved.

Indoleacetic acid oxidase from bean (*Phaseolus vulgaris*) roots and pea (*Pisum sativum*) seedlings has been suggested to be a copper protein by Wagenknecht and Burris (275) in contrast to earlier evidence of Tang and Bonner (259), who were inclined to regard the system as an iron protein, probably a heme-containing enzyme. More recent evidence now implicates manganese as the metal involved in indoleacetic acid oxidation. Evidently free trivalent manganese ions catalyze the oxidative decarboxylation of indoleacetic acid. The resulting free divalent manganese ions are in turn enzymatically reoxidized by a system including peroxidase, hydrogen peroxide, and a monophenol [see review by Mason (156)].

The possibility that copper has a function in chlorophyll formation has been put forth by a number of workers. In large part this contention is based on (a) the observations that spraying with copper increased the chlorophyll content of various plants, and (b) the report that chlorophyll is extracted with more difficulty from copper-sprayed plants than from unsprayed ones [literature citations in Gilbert (83)]. It has also been suggested that copper treatment may have a protective effect against chlorophyll destruction. A further postulate is that copper is needed for the synthesis of the iron porphyrin precursor of chlorophyll. Elvehjem (62) found that 0.1 ppm copper was essential for the formation of cytochrome a in yeast, although cytochromes b and c were hardly affected. This would be in keeping with its role as a component of cytochrome oxidase already indicated above.

C. IRON

Symptoms of iron deficiency in plants have been specifically recognized since the mid-nineteenth century. In the large majority of such cases the cause has been due not to an actual lack of iron in the soil, but rather to such factors as too high a pH or a mineral imbalance resulting in an unavailability of iron. As the fourth most abundant element on the earth's surface (4.2%) there appears to be a sufficient supply of iron in nearly all soils.

1. Role of Iron in Porphyrins

Iron in living cells is found chiefly in the form of porphyrins. As previously pointed out, the various catalytic properties of the heme proteins are already present in simple compounds of iron. Although

other heavy metals are also known to catalyze a number of these reactions and to form complexes with porphyrins, only iron porphyrins
(hemes) and magnesium porphyrins (chlorophylls) have been found
in nature in any abundance [see reviews by Granick and Gilder (87),
Lemberg and Legge (137), and Granick (86)].

The heme structure consists fundamentally of four pyrrole rings
and the iron atom, which are probably coplanar, as indicated for the
most part by X-ray analysis. The fifth and sixth coordination bonds
are at right angles to the plane, above and below it. One of these two
coordination positions may be open for combination with molecular
oxygen, hydrogen peroxide, carbon monoxide, cyanide, or other compounds while the other may be occupied by certain groups of the
protein. For example in cytochrome c, both the fifth and sixth positions
are taken by linkages to protein, a fact that probably accounts for its
stability toward such poisons as cyanide and carbon monoxide. Theorell
(263) envisaged the heme of cytochrome c as being built into a crevice
of the protein, the fifth and sixth coordination places probably being
taken by covalent linkages to the imidazole groups of the protein.
The state of the iron atom and the nature of its linkages with the different components of purified heme proteins varies with the individual
proteins and contributes in determining its properties and therefore
its role in physiological function. The fact that cytochrome c differs
from hemoglobin in not being autoxidizable, in not forming compounds
with carbon monoxide, fluoride, and cyanide in the physiological pH
range, and in undergoing valence change during physiological function
can be ascribed in part to those linkages. Unfortunately the other cytochromes including b, b_5, a, and a_3 have not yet been obtained sufficiently pure to permit studies of its various properties. The peroxidases and catalases, which are widely distributed in plants, are iron
porphyrin-containing enzymes that catalyze reactions in which hydrogen peroxide is an electron acceptor.

The terminal respiratory chain in animals, and to an undetermined
extent in plants, which involves the transfer of electrons from substrates (for example DPNH, succinate) to oxygen are mediated almost
exclusively by the iron porphyrin-containing series of cytochromes including b, b_5, c_1, c, a, and a_3. The iron of the cytochromes apparently
undergoes alternate oxidation-reduction between Fe^{+++} and Fe^{++} during
electron transport, although this has not been conclusively demonstrated for all systems. Increasing evidence is being provided for the
general existence of cytochrome-containing systems in plants and for
their role in terminal respiration [see reviews (66, 84, 86, 99) and
Chapter 2 in Volume IA]. Claims have been made that the respiratory

energy required for salt uptake and accumulation in plants is mediated by the heme-containing systems (cf. Chapter 4 of Volume II). The uniqueness of the leguminous nodules in containing abundant hemoglobin and the close correlation between the symbiotic nitrogen-fixing capacity of legumes and the hemoglobin concentration in its nodules point to a role of this iron-porphyrin-protein complex in nitrogen fixation. In some microorganisms which are capable of nitrate respiration, namely the ability to use nitrate as the terminal electron acceptor in place of molecular oxygen, cytochrome-containing enzymes are involved (261). A relatively new compound related to the cytochrome group with a characteristic absorption spectrum at 555 mμ (α-band) has been found in all leaves examined and has been designated as cytochrome f (100). There is no evidence for its presence in the plant other than in the chloroplasts, thus suggesting a possible role in photosynthesis. Cytochrome f thus far has not been detected in yeast or in animal tissue. Plant cells in addition to the customary cytochromes of animal cells contain a cytochrome b_3. In leaves a cytochrome b_6 has been reported and for the *Arum* spadix a cytochrome b_7 [see Granick (86)].

The peroxidases catalyze the reaction between hydrogen peroxide and a number of oxidizable substrates and apparently act in the ferric state without undergoing a reversible valence change. Horseradish peroxidase is the most extensively studied enzyme of this group and is not inhibited by carbon monoxide. However, peroxidase may act as an oxidase when dihydroxymaleic acid serves as the substrate. In this reaction a reversible valence change of the iron occurs, as indicated by carbon monoxide inhibition.

The significance of peroxidases in the metabolism of the cell is not clear. The fact that some peroxidases activate ferrocytochrome c suggests a possible role in biological electron transport. The configuration of the peroxidase molecule has some resemblance to ferrihemoglobin in that the iron (ferric) is ionically bound to porphyrin and to the protein moiety. At least one position is open for coordination with substrate or competing substance in view of its ready reaction with cyanide, azide, hydrogen peroxide, sulfide, and certain other substances. The enzyme forms at least three different spectrophotometrically observable complexes with hydrogen peroxide [see review by Theorell (263)]. Two of these complexes are intermediates, complex I representing an essentially ionic complex which proceeds to an intermediate level of reduction to form complex II, which then reacts to yield the products. Complex III is regarded as being the result of a side reaction not related to the main chain of events.

Catalase can be considered as a peroxidase in which a dismutation essentially occurs, one mole of hydrogen peroxidase serving to reduce another to give molecular oxygen and water. The iron is probably bound to porphyrin and protein by essentially ionic linkages. Although Keilin and Hartree (118) have proposed a mechanism of action involving a cyclic ferric-ferrous exchange, present evidence reflects that iron remains in the ferric form during catalase action. The ability of catalase to catalyze the oxidation of alcohol and other substrates by hydrogen peroxide may be regarded as a peroxidative function of catalase, especially since the complexes of peroxidase and catalase with hydrogen peroxide show many similarities.

The lactic dehydrogenase of yeast, unlike that of muscle, does not involve any dissociable coenzyme. Instead it was shown to be a flavoprotein (FMN) with a cytochrome component, designated as cytochrome b_2 (9, 17). Both the flavin and heme groups are instantly reduced on the addition of lactate.

The bacterial enzyme hydrogenase, which is responsible for the activation and formation of molecular hydrogen, has been implicated as an iron and possibly a molybdenum enzyme. It is uncertain, if iron is involved, whether the metal is part of an iron porphyrin or present as another chelate form (81).

2. Nonporphyrin Iron as an Enzyme Component

Iron has also been reported to be a component of DPN-cytochrome c reductase from pigheart (147). When iron is removed from the system, cytochrome c reduction is greatly decreased. The activity of diaphorase, the flavoprotein involved in catalyzing dye reduction but not the reduction of cytochrome c, functions normally, however. Mahler and Elowe (151) suggested that the iron is essential for coupling electron transfer from the flavin component to cytochrome c, and that diaphorase is a transformed cytochrome c reductase without its iron. The experiments of Sands and Beinert (223), employing paramagnetic resonance spectrometry, indicate that approximately 25% of the total iron found by chemical analysis in purified mammalian DPNH-cytochrome c reductase undergoes a reversible oxidative change

$$(\mathrm{Fe}^{++} \underset{-e}{\overset{e}{\rightleftharpoons}} \mathrm{Fe}^{+++})$$

during the course of electron transport. Their results also suggest a sequence of electron flow from substrate to flavin to iron. It is not unlikely that this relationship may be extended to the similar plant enzymes.

Other iron-enzyme systems have been identified in animal tissues and they are mentioned here since they may ultimately be shown to be somewhat the same in plant cells. These include succinic dehydrogenase, which has been recently isolated from animal tissues as a soluble, essentially homogenous protein and shown to be a ferro-flavoprotein with a tightly bound flavin component (237). The enzyme contains 4 atoms of ferrous (nonhemin) iron and a mole of flavin per mole of protein. Evidence has been presented for the reversibility of the reaction (239) and for the identity of the system with "fumaric dehydrogenase," also originally designated as an iron protein (93). In view of the reversibility of succinic dehydrogenase, Singer and co-workers (239) feel that there is no reason to assume the existence of a separate "fumaric dehydrogenase," at least in animal tissues.

Xanthine oxidase, which has been characterized as a molybdenum enzyme, has also been shown to contain iron. The enzyme from milk and from chicken liver contains iron in the ratio of 8:1 with molybdenum, establishing xanthine oxidase as an iron system (212, 213) by the same criteria which established it as a molybdenum enzyme. Evidence has been offered to suggest that the oxidation of sulfite by xanthine oxidase using a purine substrate results in the generation of ferrous iron. The latter is probably oxidized by O_2 resulting in the formation of an oxygen-free radical which is then postulated to initiate a free radical chain of sulfite oxidations (74).

The aldolase of *Clostridium perfringens* has been indicated to be an iron enzyme (20). Certain chelating agents (dipyridyl and o-phenanthroline) resulted in an enzyme inhibition which could be reversed by ferrous, and less completely by cobaltous ions. A partially purified 5'-nucleotidase from *Clostridium sticklandii* which catalyzes the cleavage of 5'-nucleotides but not of 2'- or 3'-nucleotides has been reported to be completely dependent upon ferrous ions (63). The Fe^{++} is postulated to be serving in a dual role, both as a heavy metal activator as well as "reductant" presumably maintaining certain sites of the enzyme in a reduced state.

3. Effects of Iron Deficiency

A number of reports describe decreases in known heme-containing enzymes as a result of subjecting the organism to iron-deficient conditions [see review by McElroy and Nason (146)].

The most outstanding symptom of iron deficiency in higher plants is a severe chlorosis of the leaves, due to resultant chlorophyll deficiency. The general tendency has been to attribute the chlorophyll deficiency appearing upon excessive treatment with other metal salts to a disturbance in iron metabolism and availability. Whether or not heme-induced chlorosis can be explained by an iron deficiency is still a controversial question [see review by Pirson (243)]. The role of iron in the synthesis or degradation of chlorophyll is uncertain. A number of workers feel that iron is involved primarily in the formation of chloroplastic protein in leaves, either directly or indirectly (78). A commonly held view is that ferrous iron is the active form in chlorophyll production although there is no strong evidence to support this idea. Granick (86) suggested that protoporphyrin 9, which he identified as a precursor of chlorophyll, could go on to chlorophyll or hematin depending upon whether magnesium or iron was inserted into the structure. The possible ways in which iron and other metals, especially manganese may be interrelated in plant nutrition are discussed in another chapter of this volume (see Hewitt). This includes the suggested possibility that manganese-induced iron deficiency may arise from competition between manganese and iron in a porphyrin chlorophyll precursor with the production of an inactive manganese-containing intermediate (236).

D. Molybdenum

Molybdenum was first indicated to be of biological importance about thirty years ago by Bortels (33) in the fixation of gaseous nitrogen. The metal has since been firmly established as indispensable for nitrogen fixation as well as an essential trace element for fungi and higher plants in the process of nitrate assimilation. Its electron carrier role as the metal component of nitrate reductase has been elucidated, and its function has been indicated as a metal component of a number of enzymes of animal origin, suggesting that it may possibly be an essential micronutrient element for animals. The fact that molybdenum is a metal component of the xanthine oxidase and aldehyde oxidase of animals does not necessarily make molybdenum an essential element. It is important to show that molybdenum-containing enzymes are necessary for the well-being or normal physiology of the animal, and this has not been conclusively established.

1. Molybdenum in Nitrogen Fixation

Bortel's original work (33) demonstrated the essentiality of the metal for the assimilation of gaseous nitrogen by the aerobic bacterium *Azotobacter chroococcum* and has since been confirmed by numerous other workers. Molybdenum has also been shown to be necessary for other *Azotobacter* species, the anaerobic soil bacterium *Clostridium pas-*

teurianum and other *Clostridium* species. Experiments by various workers since 1945, including observations of the wide occurrence of molybdenum deficiency symptoms in legumes grown in certain soils of Australia have definitely established the metal as an essential trace element in symbiotic nitrogen fixation by leguminous plants [see reviews by Anderson (7), Nason (175), and Evans (67)]. There is also good evidence that molybdenum is necessary for the fixation of nitrogen by the algae *Nostoc* and *Anabaena* (cf. Chapter 5). Although the mechanism of action of molybdenum in nitrate reduction has been considerably clarified (see section below), the function of molybdenum in nitrogen fixation is still obscure. This has been due in large part to our limited knowledge of the biochemistry of nitrogen fixation. With the recent breakthrough in nitrogen fixation at the cell-free level (cf. Chapter 5) characterization of the mechanism of action of molybdenum in this process should be considerably enhanced.

It has been established that there is a requirement for considerably more molybdenum by *Azotobacter* which are fixing nitrogen gas, as compared to those which are utilizing nitrate as a nitrogen source (168). Studies on the distribution of molybdenum in cell-free preparations of *Azotobacter vinelandii* resulted in a 150-fold purification of a molybdenum-protein fraction, the addition of which to cell-free extracts did not stimulate nitrogen fixation. Apparently a large portion of the molybdenum taken up by *Azotobacter* cells is associated with this or a similar particulate fraction [see review by Nason and Takahashi (181)]. It has also been reported that Mo^{99} uptake by growing *Azotobacter* cells was influenced by aeration and the iron level of the medium and was unaffected by the nitrogen source, except for molecular nitrogen. In comparing several species of *Azotobacter* it was observed that some failed to fix nitrogen in the absence of added molybdenum to purified medium, whereas other species made considerable growth and fixed nitrogen at about 50% of optimal without the inclusion of molybdenum. Vanadium was reported to be capable of partially replacing molybdenum. Various studies have tended to indicate that vanadium can replace molybdenum as a catalyst in nitrogen fixation by a number of soil bacteria, although there is no evidence that vanadium is required in the presence of molybdenum. The reports on this point, however, are contradictory (175). For example, it has been shown that although tungstate is a competitive inhibitor of molybdate in nitrogen fixation and nitrate assimilation by *Azotobacter*, vanadate did not compete with tungstate, thus suggesting that vanadium cannot replace the molybdenum requirement. It has also been reported by

Allen (6) that vanadium cannot substitute for the molybdenum requirement of blue-green algae of the genus *Anabaena*.

The general hypothesis which is presently emerging with regard
to the mechanism of nitrogen fixation implicates hydrogen gas at lower
tensions as an electron donor in the fixation process. Molecular hydrogen, at relatively high tensions, acts as a competitive inhibitor of both
aerobic and anaerobic nitrogen fixation. A number of workers have
suggested that hydrogen competes with molecular nitrogen for the
active sites of nitrogenase, the presumed nitrogen-fixing enzyme
system(s). A possible mechanism for the interaction of hydrogenase
and nitrogenase has originated from several sources, and postulates
chemisorption of molecular nitrogen to a metalloenzyme containing
two metal atoms, presumably molybdenum or iron which form single
or double covalent bonds to nitrogen [see review by Nason and
Takahashi (181)]. Another enzyme, a flavoprotein such as hydrogenase
would transfer hydrogen atoms to the chemisorbed nitrogen with the
ultimate release of the nitrogen as ammonia. This proposed mechanism
(Eq. 3) is at best hypothetical and awaits experimental confirmation
or rejection.

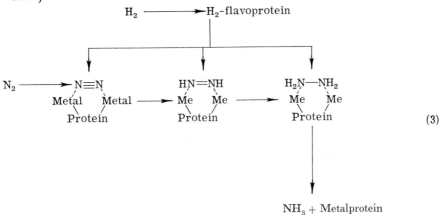

$$\text{(3)}$$

Hydrogenase was partially purified from *Clostridium pasteurianum*
and characterized as a flavoprotein whose capacity to reduce cytochrome c or nitrate was specifically restored by the addition of MoO_3
[Shug *et al.* (235)]. Other elements including vanadium could not
substitute for molybdenum in this respect. Whether or not hydrogenase
is a molybdoprotein is not entirely clear. It may well be that in the
above system the restoration effect of added MoO_3 in the enzymatic
transfer of electrons from molecular hydrogen to cytochrome c is an

artificial model electron transport system and that hydrogenase is really an iron protein.

2. Molybdenum in Nitrate Assimilation

The work of Steinberg (251, 252) demonstrated that *Aspergillus niger* required small quantities of molybdenum when grown on a nitrate medium, whereas the response to the metal with ammonium nitrogen was considerably less. These findings provided evidence that molybdenum was needed for growth and other processes apart from nitrogen fixation. The first clear-cut proof of the essentiality of traces of molybdenum for higher plants was demonstrated by Arnon and Stout (13) in water culture experiments with tomato plants. The deficiency was characterized by mottling of leaves and involution of the laminae which was prevented specifically by molybdenum, the 19 other elements tested, including vanadium, having no effect. The results were confirmed by numerous workers for other higher plants including oats (*Avena sativa*), lettuce (*Lactuca sativa*), white mustard (*Brassica hirta* [*Sinapis alba*]), and plum (*Prunus* sp.) seedlings, thus demonstrating the essentiality of molybdenum for plant growth in general [see reviews by Nason (175) and Evans (67)].

The work of Mulder (168) confirmed and demonstrated a number of fundamental relationships between molybdenum and nitrogen metabolism in various organisms. It showed that *Azotobacter* and *Aspergillus* respond more to molybdenum when provided with nitrate nitrogen than with ammonium nitrogen. Mulder used the growth-rate curve and the increasing sporulation of *Aspergillus niger* with increasing amounts of molybdenum to estimate minute quantities of molybdenum in various materials. He also showed that molybdenum-deficient tomato plants contained a high concentration of nitrate and that denitrifying bacteria grown on a molybdenum-deficient medium failed to reduce nitrate.

Molybdenum has been shown more recently to be essential for the growth and cell division of the green alga *Scenedesmus obliquus*, the molybdenum-deficient cells failing to assimilate nitrate nitrogen. The accumulation of nitrate in plants is not specific for a molybdenum deficiency since plants deficient in manganese or sulfur also give rise to the same effect [see review by Nason (175)].

3. Role of Molybdenum as a Component of Nitrate Reductase

The first step in nitrate assimilation in higher plants and in certain microorganisms is catalyzed by nitrate reductase. Definite proof of the specific involvement of molybdenum in nitrate assimilation by fungi, higher plants, and certain bacteria was obtained as a result of the isolation and characterization of nitrate reductase. The enzyme was characterized from *Neurospora crassa* and soybean (*Glycine max*) leaves by Nason and Evans (177) and Evans and Nason (69) as a sulfhydryl metallo-FAD-protein which catalyzes the transfer of electrons from reduced pyridine nucleotide (TPNH for the *Neurospora* enzyme, TPNH or DPNH for the soybean enzyme) to nitrate to form nitrite:

$$\text{TPNH (or DPNH)} + \text{H}^+ + \text{NO}_3^- \rightarrow \text{TPN}^+ \text{ (or DPN}^+) + \text{NO}_2^- + \text{H}_2\text{O}$$

In the early stages of these studies the significant sensitivity of the enzyme to a number of metal-binding agents such as cyanide, azide (but not carbon monoxide), potassium ethyl xanthate, o-phenanthroline and 8-hydroxyquinoline indicated a metal component. That molybdenum is the metal component of the *Neurospora* and soybean enzymes was established by the following findings (183, 184, 186, 187): (a) only a molybdenum deficiency resulted in a significant decrease of nitrate reductase in cell-free extracts of *Neurospora* (Table I). Enzyme activity of molybdenum-deficient *Neurospora* was restored to normal within 12 hours after the addition of molybdenum; (b) an increased specific activity of nitrate reductase in various enzyme fractions is accompanied by a proportional increase in molybdenum concentration (Fig. 8); (c) during dialysis of the enzyme against a buffered cyanide solution there is a decrease in molybdenum content (to one-thirtieth of the control) concomitant with a decrease in enzyme activity. Subsequent redialysis against molybdenum-free phosphate and glutathione to remove the cyanide from the enzyme gave no restoration of nitrate reductase nor any increase in the negligible molybdenum content of the enzyme; and (d) there is a specific reactivation of the cyanide-dialyzed enzyme by molybdenum. The addition of molybdenum trioxide or sodium molybdate reactivated the enzyme of 85% of the original value. Preincubation with other metals including iron, zinc, manganese, nickel, cobalt, mercury, tungsten, uranium, vanadium, or boron were ineffective in place of molybdenum.

It is of interest that the removal of molybdenum from the nutrient medium results in a decrease in nitrate reductase which is quite different from the loss of activity brought about by removal of molybdenum from the purified enzyme, for example, by cyanide dialysis. In the latter case the inactivated enzyme can be restored almost completely by adding the metal back to the protein whereas, in the case of molybdenum deficiency the addition of the metal to the cell-free

TABLE I
Effect of Nutrient Deficiencies on Nitrate Reductase in Cell-Free Extracts of *Neurospora crassa*[a] (187)

Treatment	+Ca	−Ca	+N	−N[b]	+Mg	−Mg[b]	+Fe	−Fe
Per cent growth	100	16	100	8	100	20	100	0.7
Nitrate reductase	26	38	43	5	49	41	29	55

	+Cu	−Cu	+Zn	−Zn	+Mn	−Mn	+Mo	−Mo	+Biotin	−Biotin
Per cent growth	100	40	100	28	100	30	100	29	100	15
Nitrate reductase	27	79	25	39	30	34	53	10	27	21

[a] Wild type 146. Values are units of enzyme activity per milligram protein.
[b] N and Mg were supplied at one-thirtieth and one-hundredth, respectively, of the level in the controls.

extract is ineffective. Molybdenum, therefore, also appears to be necessary for the adaptive formation of nitrate reductase in the presence of nitrate or nitrite by *Neurospora* during growth, presumably for the synthesis of the protein moiety of the enzyme.

It has also been demonstrated that flavin and molybdenum function as electron carriers in *Neurospora* nitrate reductase in the following sequence:

$$\text{TPNH} \rightarrow \text{FAD (or FMN)} \rightarrow \text{Mo} \rightarrow \text{NO}_3^-$$

That flavin precedes molybdenum in the above sequence was indicated by the observation that molybdenum-free enzyme cannot catalyze the

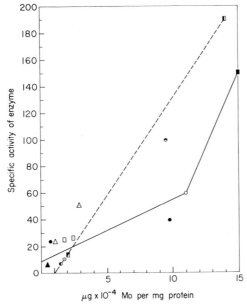

FIG. 8. Relation between molybdenum contents and specific activity of nitrate reductase of various protein fractions from *Neurospora* (183).

reduction of nitrate to nitrite by TPNH or reduced flavin. The metal-free enzyme, however, will catalyze the reduction of FAD or FMN by TPNH. Addition of molybdenum specifically restored the ability of the enzyme to catalyze the formation of nitrite from nitrate by reduced flavin or TPNH or TPNH plus flavin. The enzymatic oxidation of FMNH₂ by molybdate under anaerobic conditions in the absence of nitrate suggested that the metal was acting as an electron carrier [Nicholas and Nason (184)]. Direct evidence for the role of molybdenum as an electron carrier was demonstrated by experiment in which reduced molybdate prepared with $Na_2S_2O_4$, enzymatically reduces nitrate to nitrite in the absence of added FAD. The molybdenum appears to be undergoing an oxidation-reduction reaction from an oxidation state $+6$ to a more reduced level, probably $+5$ [Nicholas and Stevens (189)]. Molybdenum forms compounds corresponding to oxidation states of $+2$, $+3$, $+4$, $+5$, and $+6$.

Similar studies which identify molybdenum as the metal component, as well as demonstrating the sequence and mechanism of electron transport by molybdenum to be the same as for the *Neurospora* enzyme, have also been made with nitrate reductase from soybean leaves [Nicholas and Nason (186)]. That molybdenum is a component of soybean leaf nitrate reductase has also been indicated by Evans and Hall (68). The properties of a somewhat similar pyridine nucleotide-nitrate reductase in *Escherichia coli* and its identification as a metalloflavoprotein with molybdenum as the probable metal component, have also recently been shown (185). Recent evidence by Kinsky and McElroy (125) as well as by Nicholas and Scawin (188) indicates that phosphate is required for the function of the molybdenum containing nitrate reductase. These authors suggest that a phosphomolybdenum complex is the probable electron acceptor from reduced flavin.

Highly purified nitrate reductase from *Neurospora* is also capable of catalyzing the reduction of cytochrome c by TPNH. In an effort to determine whether this cytochrome c reductase was the same as nitrate reductase, Kinsky and McElroy (125) studied these two enzymatic activities with varying amounts of nitrate in the growth medium. Both activities were induced by the nitrate, a result suggesting that the enzymatic activities were associated with the same protein or that there was a dual induction by a single inducer (see Fig. 9). Their results point to two kinds of TPN cytochrome c reductases: (a) a constitutive enzyme with no associated nitrate reductase as indicated by the adaptive experiments with ammonia-grown mycelia; and (b) an enzyme associated with nitrate reductase activity. The number of enzymes concerned in nitrate reductase and cytochrome c reductase activities in *Neurospora* and higher plants has not been answered conclusively.

The results by Egami, Sato, Taniguchi, and associates (see 261) as well as Sadana and McElroy (220) indicate that there are different pathways for electron transfer for nitrate reduction. These essentially fall into two general classes called (a) *nitrate assimilation,* which represents the biological conversion of nitrate to ammonia or to the amino acid or amide level for the ultimate synthesis of nitrogen-containing cell constituents such as proteins and (b) *nitrate respiration* in which nitrate is used by several microorganisms (for example, *Escherichia coli*) under anaerobic or partially anaerobic conditions as a terminal electron acceptor in place of oxygen. The first step in nitrate assimilation has been characteristically associated with the pyridine nucleotide-molybdoflavoprotein, nitrate reductase, while the corresponding step in nitrate respiration has been indicated to be intimately involved with a cytochrome system possessing non-heme iron [see review

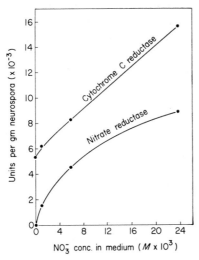

Fig. 9. Effect of nitrate concentration on the adaptive formation of nitrate and cytochrome c reductase activity (125).

by Nason and Takahashi (181)]. The respiratory type of nitrate reductase from *Escherichia coli*, however, has very recently been reported to contain one atom of molybdenum and forty atoms of non-heme iron per molecule of enzyme (110, 260). While there is no evidence as to the role of molybdenum (or iron) in this system, the finding of molybdenum in nitrate respiratory enzyme lends further support to the general pattern that has emerged, namely that molybdenum may be a necessary component of all enzymes capable of catalyzing the reduction of nitrate to nitrite (for example, the nitrate reductase of the assimilatory type, that of the respiratory type, and xanthine oxidase and aldehyde oxidase, as indicated in the section below on molybdenum in animals).

Evidence that a specific cytochrome as well as iron are essential

components of the nitrate-reducing system in *Photobacterium fischeri*
(*Achromobacter fischeri*) has come from nutritional, inhibitory, and
enzyme purification studies. In these studies it was possible to separate
nitrate reductase activity from the TPNH(DPNH)-flavin reductase activity. Reduced benzylviologen was used as the electron donor for
nitrate reduction. The purified nitrate reductase, however contains an
iron porphyrin which is capable of transferring electrons to nitrate.
The reduction of this cytochrome component by TPNH requires the
addition of a second protein fraction as well as flavin and inorganic
iron. From these and other studies it is suggested that the inorganic
iron and molybdenum determine the direction of electron flow as far
as nitrate reduction is concerned. It is likely that the iron-containing
system is important for the "nitrate respiration" system of microorganisms. It is also possible that future studies will show that *Neurospora* nitrate reductase activity is associated with two proteins, one
catalyzing the reduction of flavin (and subsequently cytochrome c)
and the second a phosphomolybdoprotein which is capable of reducing
nitrate by accepting electrons from reduced flavin. The accompanying
scheme (Eq. sequence 4) indicates the possible relationships:

$$\text{TPNH} \to \text{flavin} \to \text{Fe}^{+++} \to \text{cytochrome} \to \text{O}_2 \tag{4}$$

$$\begin{array}{cc} \downarrow & \downarrow \\ \text{nitrate reductase} & \text{nitrate reductase} \\ \text{(Mo-protein)} & \text{(Mo-protein)} \\ \downarrow & \downarrow \\ \text{NO}_3^- & \text{NO}_3^- \end{array}$$

4. Molybdenum in Other Biological Processes

Molybdenum is also essential in the metabolism of plants for
processes other than nitrate reduction and nitrogen fixation. There are
definite indications that the metal is required for fungi using ammonia
nitrogen as the sole nitrogen source. Cauliflower (*Brassica oleracea*
var. *botrytis*) plants grown on urea and ammonium as nitrogen sources
still developed characteristic molybdenum deficiency symptoms known
as "whiptail" [Agarwala (2)]. Molybdenum deficiency in higher plants
is accompanied by a decreased concentration of ascorbic acid in the
tissues and a lowered capacity to reduce a number of artificial dyes. It
has also been reported (205) that molybdenum-deficient tomato (*Lycopersicon esculentum*) plants convert less inorganic phosphorus to the
organic form as compared to the controls. This may be related to the
observation that molybdate is an inhibitor of acid phosphatases from
the tomato plant (246).

The marked inhibition in growth of *Neurospora* by high concentrations of molybdate in the culture medium and its reversal by various

sulfur compounds have led to the suggestion that the main effect of molybdenum toxicity is an interference with methionine synthesis (225).

5. Molybdenum in Animals

Molybdenum has been shown to be a metal constituent of two enzymes from animals, xanthine oxidase and liver aldehyde oxidase. It was first indicated by the need for adequate dietary molybdenum in order to establish normal levels of xanthine oxidase in rat tissues, especially in the intestine. The enzyme was subsequently demonstrated to contain molybdenum as one of its components in the ratio of 1 atom of molybdenum per 2 moles of flavin [De Renzo et al. (54)]. Molybdenum in xanthine oxidase is present as an anion and is apparently associated with an unidentified chromogen, which acts as a dehydrogenase group for purine and aldehyde substrates. There seems to be a lack of agreement concerning the restoration of enzyme activity by added MoO_3 following dialysis, or aging. Some have reported that the loss in activity resulting from the parallel removal of molybdenum by aging and dialysis is not restored by molybdenum, whereas others have claimed a partial restoration by relatively high concentrations of the metal. There is also some evidence that molybdenum restores enzyme activity as complex molybdates, such as silicomolybdates, which are the effective agents. As yet the role of molybdenum in xanthine oxidase has not been elucidated. Of great interest is the observation that the enzyme from milk and chicken liver contains eight times as much iron as molybdenum, thus establishing xanthine oxidase as an iron system by essentially the same criteria which designated it as a molybdenum enzyme. Liver aldehyde oxidase is a molybdoprotein (152a) which has iron-porphyrin groups as well and can be reactivated by silicomolybdates as already indicated for xanthine oxidase. Both enzymes, interestingly enough, are capable of utilizing nitrate as an electron acceptor to a limited extent, resulting in its reduction to nitrite.

There is no conclusive evidence that the molybdoproteins—xanthine oxidase and aldehyde oxidase—are essential for the well-being or growth of the animal. The alternate basis for establishing molybdenum as a necessary trace element, namely the demonstration of an absolute requirement for the element in animal nutrition, has not been conclusively shown. The use of sodium tungstate as a competitive inhibitor of molybdate has been applied to produce an apparent molybdenum deficiency in chicks. Such evidence, however, cannot be regarded as final proof of the essentiality of molybdenum. There also exists in animal tissues a complex interrelationship among molybdenum, copper, sulfur, and manganese which has an important bearing on molybdenum toxicity (55).

E. Manganese

The above four metals (copper, zinc, iron, and molybdenum) constitute a group in which each member has been established to be a

TABLE II
Specific Metalloenzymes (146)

Enzyme	Reaction	Metal
Carbonic anhydrase	$CO_2 + H_2O \rightleftarrows H_2CO_3$	Zn
Dehydropeptidase	Glycyldehydrophenylanine $\rightarrow NH_3 +$ phenylpyruvic acid	Zn
Glycylglycine dipeptidase	Glycylglycine $\rightarrow$ glycine	Zn
Carboxypeptidase	Carbobenzoxyglycyl-L-phenylalanine $\rightarrow$ phenylalanine	Zn
Alcohol dehydrogenase	Ethanol + DPN $\rightleftarrows$ acetaldehyde + DPNH	Zn
Glutamic dehydrogenase	Glutamate + DPN $\rightleftarrows$ ketoglutarate + DPNH + NH_3	Zn
Lactic dehydrogenase	Lactate + DPN $\rightleftarrows$ pyruvate + DPNH	Zn
Inorganic pyrophosphatase	Pyrophosphate + $H_2O \rightarrow PO_4^{--}$	Mg
Succinic dehydrogenase	Succinic acid $- 2H \rightarrow$ fumaric acid + 2H	Fe
Catalase	$2H_2O_2 \rightarrow 2H_2O + O_2$	Fe
Peroxidase	H_2O_2 oxidation of aromatic amines and other compounds	Fe
Cytochromes	Electron transport	Fe
DPNH-cytochrome c reductase	DPNH + cytochrome c $(Fe^{+++}) \rightarrow$ DPN + cytochrome c (Fe^{++})	Fe
Uricase	Uric acid + $O_2 \rightleftarrows$ allantoin + $H_2O_2 + CO_2$	Cu
Tyrosinase	Tyrosine + $\frac{1}{2}O_2 \rightarrow$ dihydroxyphenylalanine	Cu
Laccase	Phenols $\rightarrow$ o-, and p-quinones	Cu
Ascorbic acid oxidase	Ascorbic acid $\rightarrow$ dehydroascorbic acid	Cu
Prolidase	Glycylproline $\rightarrow$ proline	Mn
Nitrate reductase	$NO_3^- + TPNH + H^+ \rightarrow NO_2^- + TPN^+ + H_2O$	Mo
Xanthine oxidase	Xanthine + $O_2 \rightarrow H_2O_2 +$ uric acid	Mo
Aldehyde oxidase	Acetaldehyde + cytochrome $C(Fe^{+++}) \rightarrow$ acetate + cytochrome C (Fe^{++})	Mo
Hydrogenase	H_2 + cytochrome C $(Fe^{+++}) \rightarrow$ cytochrome C (Fe^{++})	Mo

specific and integral metal component of one or more enzymes (Table II). As shown in the case of one enzyme, magnesium is also regarded as a specific enzyme component. The remaining trace metals, including manganese, generally serve as activators of enzyme systems often replaceable by one or more other metal ions.

Manganese was demonstrated to be an essential element for plants by McHargue (147) in 1922, who showed that plants deficient in manganese were characteristically chlorotic and produced no seed. The element tends to accumulate in the leaves, exceeding that of the seeds and stalk tissue.

1. Manganese in Enzyme Systems

The metal can serve as an activator for a wide variety of enzymes including those which catalyze oxidation-reduction reactions, decarboxylations, hydrolysis, and group transfers. Table III indicates most of the different enzymes that are activated by manganese. In many cases one or more other metal ions (frequently magnesium) can substitute in place of manganese. Activation by manganese has also been demonstrated for a number of enzymes (citric acid cycle decarboxylations) in higher plants, including soybean leaf nitrite reductase and hydroxylamine reductase which catalyze the transfer of electrons from reduced pyridine nucleotides to nitrite and hydroxylamine, respectively, to form ammonia (176). Mn^{++} is essential for the enzyme system which catalyzes the conversion of isocitric acid to α-ketoglutaric acid. As already indicated in an earlier section, the metal ion has been implicated in the enzymatic decarboxylation of oxalosuccinate to ketoglutarate rather than in the preceding dehydrogenation of isocitrate to oxalosuccinate. This is in keeping with the requirement of Mn^{++} for the analogous enzymatic decarboxylation of oxaloacetate to pyruvate. Manganese seems to be the predominant metal ion in the citric acid cycle. This role of manganese is related to the important oxidative and nonoxidative decarboxylation steps which occur during the metabolism of di- and tricarboxylic acids.

2. Role of Manganese in Photosynthesis

That manganese appears to play a direct and primary role in photosynthesis has been indicated by a number of workers in this area (cf. Chapter 4, Volume IB). A good deal of study has been devoted to green algae subjected to manganese-deficient media, and according to Pirson (203) the following characteristic metabolic pattern emerges. In contrast to all other hitherto examined cases of mineral deficiency, there is a lowering of photosynthesis, whereas respiration, nitrate reduction, and the oxidative assimilation of glucose in the dark are unaffected. The decrease in photosynthesis can be shown to be independent of any influence on chlorophyll level since the decrease was demonstrated in an early stage of manganese deficiency prior to any real

TABLE III
Enzymes Activated by Manganous Ions

Enzyme	Reaction	Metal[a]
Glucokinase	Glucose + ATP → glucose-6-PO$_4$ + ADP	Mg^{++}, Mn^{++}
Hexokinase	Fructose, Glucose, Mannose } + ATP → hexose-6-PO$_4$ + ADP	Mg^{++}, Mn^{++}
Phosphoglucokinase	Glucose-1-PO$_4$ + ATP → glucose-1,6-di-PO$_4$ + ADP	Mg^{++}, Mn^{++}
Phosphoglucomutase	Glucose-1-PO$_4$ ⇌ glucose-6-PO$_4$	Mg^{++}, Mn^{++}, Co^{++}, Cr^{++}
Phosphoglyceric acid kinase	3-PO$_4$-glyceric acid ⇌ 1,3-enol-PO$_4$-pyruvic acid + H$_2$O	Mg^{++}, Mn^{++}, Zn^{++}
Adenosine kinase	Adenosine + ATP → ADP + AMP	Mg^{++}, Mn^{++}
Arginine kinase	Arginine + ATP → Arg-PO$_4$ + ADP	Ca^{++}, Mn^{++}, Mg^{++}
DPN kinase	DPN + ATP → TPN + ADP	Mg$^{+?}$, Mn$^{+?}$
Yeast apyrase	ATP + H$_2$O → AMP + PO$_4$	Mn^{++}
Glutamyl transferase	Glutamine + NH$_2$OH + ATP → glutamohydroxamic acid + NH$_3$	Mn^{++}
Glutamine synthesizing enzyme	Glutamic + NH$_3$ + ATP → glutamine + ADP	Mg^{++}, Mn^{++}
Dephospho-CoA kinase	Dephospho-CoA + ATP → CoA + ADP	Mg^{++}, Mn^{++}
Pyruvic carboxylase	Pyruvate → acetaldehyde + CO$_2$	Mg^{++}, Mn^{++}
Pyruvic oxidase	Pyruvate + PO$_4$ → acetyl-PO$_4$ + CO$_2$	Mg^{++}, Mn^{++}
Oxalacetic decarboxylase	Oxalacetic acid → pyruvic acid + CO$_2$	Mg^{++}, Co^{++}, Zn^{++}, Mn^{++}
Isocitric dehydrogenase	Isocitric acid + TPN ⇌ oxalosuccinic + TPNH	Mg^{++}, Mn^{++}
Oxalosuccinic decarboxylase	Oxalosuccinic → ketoglutaric acid + CO$_2$ + O$_2$	Mn^{++}
α-Ketoglutarate oxidase	Ketoglutaric acid → succinic + CO$_2$	Mg^{++}, Mn^{++}
Malic enzyme	Malate + TPN → pyruvate + CO$_2$ + TPNH	Mn^{++}, Co^{++}
Condensing enzyme	Oxalacetic acid + acetyl CoA → citric acid	Mg^{++}, Mn^{++}
Yeast phosphatase	Glycerophosphate → glycerol + PO$_4$	Mg^{++}, Mn^{++}, Co^{++}, Fe^{++}, Ni^{++}
Acid and alkaline phosphatases	Numerous phosphorylated substrates	Mg^{++}, Mn^{++}, & others
Arginase	Arginine + H$_2$O → ornithine + urea	Mn^{++}, Co^{++}, Ni^{++}, Fe
Lecithinase	Lecithin → PO$_4$-choline + diglyceride	Ca^{++}, Mg^{++}, Co^{++}, Zn^{++}, Mn^{++}
Cysteine desulfhydrase	Cysteine → H$_2$S + NH$_3$ + pyruvate	Zn^{++}, Mg^{++}, Mn^{++}
DNase	Depolymerization of DNA	Mg$^{+?}$, Mn$^{+?}$, Co^{++}, Fe^{++}
Nitrite reductase	NO$_2^-$ + DPNH → NH$_3$ + DPN	Mn^{++}
Hydroxylamine reductase	NH$_2$OH + DPNH → NH$_3$ + DPN	Mn^{++}

[a] The indication of a single metal activator does not necessarily mean that this is a specific metal requirement.

chlorosis. After manganese addition, complete restoration of normal photosynthetic activity occurs within 1 or 2 hours (203).

The involvement of manganese in photosynthesis has also been indicated by experiments with *Chlorella* in which no inhibition of heterotrophic growth occurred with glucose in the absence of manganese. These cells showed a striking and reversible inhibition of photosynthesis when exposed to light. However, evidence has been presented showing that growth and glucose uptake cease in manganese-deficient heterotrophic dark cells upon exposure to moderate or strong light (203, 204). The lack of an effect on the metabolism of cells in manganese-deficient media in the dark may be due to the 100- to 1000-fold requirement difference in light and dark. Whereas Pirson and his colleagues (203) reported an essentially unaltered respiration during manganese deficiency, Kessler (124) found a generally reduced oxygen consumption, and Brown *et al.* (36) observed a doubling of respiration within 3 days of autotrophic growth by manganese-deficient *Chlorella*. The Hill reaction as well as photosynthesis is strongly inhibited in manganese-deficient algae, complete recovery occurring upon addition of manganese. The site of action of manganese in the photosynthesis process has been implicated in the oxygen-evolving step. Experiments along similar lines with higher plants have not yielded such clear-cut results.

Although isolated chloroplasts do not accumulate manganese, but rather iron and copper, some of the properties of manganese itself as well as its effects have led to considerations of its possible function in photosynthesis. Thus Kenten and Mann (122) observed an oxidation of bivalent manganese to the trivalent form by isolated chloroplasts in the light suggesting that the metal might be involved in the oxidative aspect of photosynthesis. Peroxidase promoted manganese oxidation. Manganese may also be involved at other sites in the photosynthetic process, particularly in CO_2 fixation (36, 204). Finally, manganese functions directly or indirectly in chloroplast formation, probably in their multiplication (36). The metal may also be involved in chlorophyll synthesis or breakdown in view of the occurrence of chlorosis as a common symptom of manganese deficiency.

3. Interrelationship of Manganese and Iron

As suggested above, manganese may function directly in oxidation-reduction phenomena. According to an early proposal of Somers and Shive (243), the metal serves as an oxidizing agent especially in relation to iron compounds, an excess of manganese inducing symptoms of iron deficiency by converting the available iron into the inactive ferric condition. Hewitt (97) seriously questioned this proposal in view of the ability of seven other metals to induce symptoms of iron deficiency, manganese being the least active. The order of effectiveness bore no relation to the oxidation-reduction potentials of these ions. The hypothesis that photosynthesis involved a photochemical reduction of ferric iron by divalent manganese indicates valency changes which are the reverse of those originally suggested by Somers and Shive. Iron and manganese definitely have independent roles in plant nutrition. Simultaneous deficiency symptoms of both metals have been recorded, and a clear distinction between manganese toxicity and iron deficiency symptoms has been described in a variety of plants. Pirson (204) states that iron and manganese act in photosynthesis in different ways and that there is no indication of an oxidation-reduction system between these two elements.

The data relating to the antagonisms and interactions among the essential elements manganese, iron, and molybdenum and their effects on plant growth are still highly contradictory. For example, Millikan (163, 164) concluded that manganese-induced iron-deficiency symptoms in higher plants could be alleviated by the addition of molybdenum. Other investigators (96, 169, 277) obtained directly contrasting results, namely, that the iron chlorosis induced by high concentrations of metals was accentuated, rather than alleviated, by added molybdenum leading to a further decrease in growth. More recently Gerloff et al. (80) found that the manganese-induced iron chlorosis in tomato plants was also accentuated by molybdenum. As little as 0.67 ppm molybdenum added to the culture medium induced iron chlorosis and reduced growth. They proposed that the interaction is due to the formation in roots of an iron-molybdenum precipitate of very low solubility, which makes iron unavailable for shoot growth.

4. Other Functions of Manganese

Burström's proposal (39) for a role of manganese in nitrate assimilation by green plants has recently received support from the findings that manganese serves as an activator for hydroxylamine and nitrite reductases of soybean leaves (172, 220). Ammonia has also been reported to be preferentially used instead of nitrate by manganese-deficient cells; and nitrite reduction by hydrogen-adapted green algae is dependent on manganese.

Recent evidence implicates manganese in the destruction of indoleacetic acid. Evidently free trivalent manganese ions catalyze the oxidative decarboxylation of indoleacetic acid, the resulting free divalent manganese ions being in turn enzymatically reoxidized by a system including peroxidase, hydrogen peroxide, and a monophenol [see review by Mason (156)]. Presumably peroxidase is responsible for the oxidation of Mn^{++} to Mn^{+++}, the latter in turn oxidizing the auxin (120, 149). A similar suggestion has been made for peroxidase-catalyzed oxidations of dicarboxylic acids, namely that the reactions are dependent upon the formation of manganic ions (121). In general the requirement for manganese in different peroxidase-catalyzed reactions has been observed to be quite specific, such metals as zinc, magnesium, copper, cobalt, iron, nickel, cadmium, calcium, aluminum, tin, and molybdenum having proved to be inactive, or inhibitory (4, 256, 275). Mudd and Burris (166), however, demonstrated that horseradish (*Armoracia lapathifolia*) peroxidase catalyzed the oxidation of cerous ions by hydrogen peroxide in the presence of low concentrations of resorcinol. In addition manganous ions could be replaced by cerous ions in the peroxidase-catalyzed oxidations of indoleacetic acid, 2-nitropropane, and DPNH.

The observation that manganous ion protected against the loss in activity caused by dilution of β-galactosidase in crude extracts of *Escherichia coli* has led to the suggestion that this cation stabilizes the protein, in some way, by maintaining the intactness of the secondary or tertiary structure of the enzyme molecule (214).

F. Boron

The first evidence pointing to the essential nature of boron for higher plants was published in 1910 by Agulhon (3). Since that time numerous workers have demonstrated the essentiality of boron and correlated its action in the prevention of certain physiological diseases ("heart rot" in beets and "cracked stem" in celery). The role of boron in the living plant cell has as yet not been clarified. Two extensive and excellent reviews of the possible functions of this element have appeared within the past few years [Gauch and Duggar (79), Skok (240)].

1. Possible Role of Boron in Enzyme Systems

Thus far there is no evidence that boron is a specific activator or metal component of any enzyme. Reed (210) reported that cells of boron-deficient plants were characterized by an accumulation of phenolic substances and an increase in catechol oxidase. While other workers have also reported that polyphenol oxidase was increased in boron-deficient plant tissues, these effects were shown to be nonspecific since they also occurred with other metal deficiencies (180). The effects of boron deficiency and excess on a number of enzymes including aldehyde oxidase, catalase, peroxidase, and invertase have been examined without producing any consistent relationship. The suggestion has been made that boron may be directly involved in the synthesis of inositol since the metal and meso-inositol reversed the inhibitory effect of malonate on fermentation by *Clostridium saccharobutyricum* (= *C. butyricum*) (219). The possibility has been presented by Skok (240) that boron may not be acting as part of an enzyme but rather as part of the substrate.

2. Possible Role of Boron in Sugar Translocation

The borate ion has the outstanding property of complexing with various polyhydroxy and related compounds including several of the common sugars. Gauch and Duggar (79) were the first to propose that a relationship might exist between the complexing property of borate and sugar translocation. They suggested that a major function of boron is in the translocation of sugar as (a) a sugar-borate complex which passes more readily through cell membranes, or (b) a constituent of the membranes forming a temporary union with sugar at these sites to effect its passage. They considered that boron deficiency symptoms typified by necrosis of terminal buds and root tips was in reality a manifestation of sugar deficiency since presumably a boron deficiency prevents the movement of sugar to the active growing regions where an energy source is required. There is a difference of opinion, in view of the experimental results of various workers, as to whether or not boron functions primarily in the translocation of sugars (240). While it seems quite likely that some relationship between boron and sugar translocation does exist, Skok feels that it is indirect and related to cellular activity and growth rather than directly to the formation of a boron-sugar complex. Germanium, an element that forms complexes similar to boron complexes, partially and only temporarily alleviates boron-deficiency symptoms, thus providing support that some physiological functions of boron may be related to the complexing property of the borate ion (240).

3. Possible Role of Boron in Cellular Differentiation and Development

A deficiency of boron often results in a collapse of the meristematic cells and a retarded development of normal vascular tissue characterized by poor differentiation as well as disintegration and necrosis of both phloem and xylem. Some workers have reported that boron is required for normal cell division, whereas others indicate that it exercises its effect on cellular activity subsequent to division, primarily in maturation and differentiation of the plant cell. Boron has been implicated in the regulation of cell-wall formation possibly as complexes between boric acid and carbohydrates. There also seems to be a direct relationship between lignification of the cell wall and boron nutrition, boron-deficient plants exhibiting poor lignification of xylem elements. Skok (240) proposed, following an examination of the literature, that the reportedly high catalase activity in boron-deficient plants may account for the lowered level of hydrogen peroxide, the peroxide apparently contributing to the conversion of phenolic compounds to lignin. While a number of investigators have considered boron to be related to the formation of pectic substances, the matter is still in a contradictory state. Reports of a lowered level of pectic substances in boron-deficient plants are not consistent. An interesting correlation has been pointed out by Winfield (294) that *Aspergillus niger* and *Penicillium glaucum*, which have been indicated to require neither boron nor calcium, cannot synthesize true pectic compounds.

4. Other Possible Roles of Boron

At various times there have been reports involving boron in virtually every phase of the physiology of plants (79). These have included numerous reports of a pronounced accumulation of boron in floral structures, particularly the pistil, which has led to the postulation that boron plays a special role in fertilization. This has been supported by reports of sterility and malformations of the reproductive tissue in boron-deficient plants, as well as indications that boron is essential for the proper germination of pollen grains and the growth of pollen tubes. The element has also been implicated in nitrogen metabolism, carbohydrate metabolism (presumably by virtue of its proposed action in translocation), active salt absorption, hormone metabolism, water relations, fat metabolism, phosphorus metabolism, and photosynthesis. A definite relationship between boron and calcium has also been observed in a number of laboratories whereby the external calcium level affects the boron level in plants. External boron, on the other hand, has little or no effect on the internal total calcium. Thus as external calcium is increased, the degree of boron-deficiency symptoms increases or boron toxicity symptoms decreases. The level of boron within the plant is reduced by an increase of external calcium. Within the plant, however, boron seems to affect the level of the soluble calcium fraction, the available boron in the plant tending to maintain the calcium in an available condition. It is quite possible that indirect relationships of boron with other elements may occur by way of calcium. Thus an element such as potassium which has been reported to reduce the uptake of calcium may indirectly affect the plants boron level or the calcium:boron ratio.

Although approximately a dozen different functions have been postulated for boron in the plant cell, the mechanism by which this trace element exercises its effect has not been elucidated. In certain respects boron presents a challenge to the plant physiologist in terms of clarifying and describing its exact mechanism of action in the living plant.

G. Vanadium

The elements vanadium and molybdenum have somewhat similar properties. In the periodic system both are classified as transition metals, vanadium belonging to group 5a and the first long period, and molybdenum belonging to the adjacent group 6a and the second long period. Vanadium possesses oxidation states ranging from +2 to +5; its salts, like those of molybdenum, have very marked catalytic properties. The average concentration of vanadium in the lithosphere is 100 ppm, as compared to 10 ppm for molybdenum; vanadium is the twentieth most prevalent element in the earth's crust. In view of its presence in the lithosphere, one would expect vanadium to be widely distributed in both plants and animals.

Bertrand, who has reviewed the literature on the ubiquity of the metal in plants, reported vanadium present in every sample of 62 pieces of plants analyzed (29). He found that plants growing in soils that were richest in vanadium had greater amounts than those growing in poorer soils, the root nodules of leguminous plants having 3 to 4 ppm, which is three to four times higher than in most plants.

1. Essentiality and Function of Vanadium in Plants

Earlier work, starting in the late nineteenth century, on the effect of vanadium salts on the growth of higher plants and microorganisms reported that vanadium concentrations of 10–20 ppm or greater were generally toxic to higher plants, whereas in a number of cases lower concentrations proved to be stimulatory, especially for microorganisms. In 1941, Bertrand concluded that vanadium was an essential micronutrient since it acted as a growth factor for *Aspergillus niger* in concentrations of about 10^{-9} M. Earlier there had been mixed reports with regard to the effects of the element on the growth of higher plants; some investigators contended that it was favorable for asparagus (*Asparagus officinalis* var. *altilis*), lettuce, rice (*Oryza sativa*), and corn (*Zea mays*) and others indicated that it was unimportant for clover and wheat (*Triticum* sp.).

The most convincing evidence thus far in support of vanadium as an essential trace element is that of Arnon and Wessel (14). They obtained an eightfold increase in growth rates of the green alga *Scenedesmus obliquus* upon the addition of vanadium to the purified nutrient solution. The earlier observations of increased growth rates with added iron were ascribed to a vanadium impurity in the iron. Only vanadium, of 19 different elements tested, stimulated growth. The requirement for vanadium could not be replaced by molybdenum and there was no evidence for the replacement of molybdenum by vanadium. While the report of Arnon and Wessel demonstrates the essentiality of the metal for a green alga, there is still no proof that vanadium is an essential micronutrient element for higher plants. On a purely speculative basis, one might guess that vanadium is functioning in biological oxidation-reduction reactions in view of its different oxidation states as well as its similarity to molybdenum.

2. Can Vanadium Replace Molybdenum in Nitrogen Fixation?

Numerous reports [see review by Nason (175)] have implicated vanadium in nitrogen fixation. These studies indicated that the addition of vanadium (or molybdenum) to soils or to the growth medium stimulated nitrogen fixation and growth where nitrogen was not added in combined form. For example, Horner *et al.* (108) reported that molybdenum or vanadium was essential for nitrogen fixation by a number of *Azotobacter* species with similar concentration ranges for both metals. The maximum effect by vanadium was 50–80% of that produced by molybdenum. The responses to tungsten were due to a molybdenum impurity. Although the above tends to indicate that vanadium can replace molybdenum as a catalyst in nitrogen fixation by a number of soil bacteria, there is no evidence that vanadium is required in the presence of molybdenum. On the other hand, it has been shown by two groups of investigators that although tungstate is a competitive inhibitor of molybdate in nitrogen fixation and nitrate assimilation by *Azotobacter*, vanadate did not compete with tungstate. This would suggest that vanadium cannot replace the molybdenum requirement.

Additional arguments against a role of vanadium in nitrogen fixation are the report by Esposito and Wilson (65) that vanadium cannot replace molybdenum in *Azotobacter vinelandii* O, and the review by Allen (6) declaring that the molybdenum requirement of the blue-green alga *Anabaena cylindrica* for nitrogen fixation and nitrate reduction cannot be replaced by vanadium. In view of the controversial evidence it would appear that a role for vanadium in nitrogen fixation has as yet not been established.

3. Possible Role of Vanadium in Animals

Thus far vanadium has not been established as an essential element for animals. The vanadium in the blood of tunicates is in the form of vanadium-protein complex in special blood cells called vanadocytes. There is some question whether vanadium is indeed a part of an organic compound within the vanadocyte or bound as the inorganic ion to the cell membrane or some protein. The function of the vanadium chromogen of the blood of tunicates is unknown. There is no clear evidence that the metal chromogen serves as a respiratory pigment, the combination of oxygen with the pigment not being comparable with that of oxygen with hemoglobin. The possibility has not been eliminated that the pigment serves in reduction processes, perhaps in the reduction of carbon dioxide for the production of the celluloselike substance of the tunic. There are a number of reports in the literature concerning the effects of vanadium salts on the development of cells, on hemoglobin formation and other processes, and as an inhibitor of certain enzymes [see review by Nason (175)]. There seems to be a relationship between vanadium and lipid metabolism. Small concentrations of sodium metavanadate or vanadium acetate markedly increased oxidation of phospholipid by washed rat or guinea pig liver suspensions (28). The fact that manganese nullified both the stimulatory effect of vanadium on phospholipid oxidation as well as the depressant action on cholesterol synthesis suggests a possible link between the metabolism of cholesterol and liver phospholipids. There is also some evidence that vanadium inhibits cholesterol synthesis and accelerates cholesterol breakdown. There also are indications that vanadium may be functioning in teeth by increasing the hardness of the apatite structure as well as serving as a binding substance between the organic and inorganic matter in enamel and dentine.

H. Cobalt, Selenium, and Iodine

Although these three elements have been established or implicated as necessary nutrients for higher animals, there is little or no evidence for their essentiality in plant nutrition.

Cobalt appears to be required by ruminant animals and certain microorganisms solely because it is a constituent of vitamin B_{12} (48, 113, 151). In ruminants the mechanism of action of cobalt is concerned with the formation of vitamin B_{12} and of related vitamin B_{12}-like substances by microorganisms in the digestive tract. Vitamin B_{12} is required by most animal species. It is apparently synthesized only by microorganisms and is concerned with (a) protein metabolism, (b) the synthesis of methyl groups in animals, and (c) very probably the utilization of other single carbon compounds [see review by Dinning (56)]. Barker and co-workers (21, 22, 284, 285) have isolated a vitamin B_{12} coenzyme from *Clostridium tetanomorphum* which serves as an essential cofactor for the enzymatic conversion of glutamate to β-methylaspartate. The enzyme has been shown to be present in several bacteria and in rabbit liver (248, 285). Barker's vitamin B_{12} coenzyme is also essential for the isomerization of succinyl coenzyme A to methylmalonyl coenzyme A (59, 247). The suggestion has been made that the coenzyme may play a general role in one-carbon metabolism of a large number of bacteria (248).

Higher plants normally have no vitamin B_{12} in their tissues. What little vitamin B_{12}-like activity has been found in plant extracts was shown to be due to deoxyribosides or possibly related to the occurrence of associated organisms containing vitamin B_{12}. The deoxyribosides of adenine, of hypoxanthine and of cytosine, deoxyribonucleic acid, and thymidine can substitute for vitamin B_{12} in the nutrition of certain bacteria, presumably because these compounds are able to provide an essential metabolic substance which the cells cannot produce in the absence of vitamin B_{12} (151). Vitamin B_{12} is required, however, for the nutrition of the chlorophyll-containing flagellate *Euglena gracilis* and cannot be replaced by thymidine. There are also a number of reports on the response to, or the occurrence of, vitamin B_{12} factors in certain algae (78, 203). Although there is no experimental evidence that cobalt is an essential nutrient for green plants, a number of interesting effects of cobalt have been reported. Miller (161) and Thimann (264) observed an enhanced elongation of etiolated pea stems in auxin and sugar solutions. The expansion of slices of etiolated bean leaves was also favored by Co^{++} (161). The possibility has been suggested that cobalt acts specifically on the properties of the cell membrane or in some manner makes more energy available for growth. Evidence has also been presented which indicates that cobalt may also be concerned in the depression of peroxide formation or in facilitation of peroxide decomposition in plant tissues. Although added cobalt resulted in significant increases in dry weight, plant height, and stem girth in tomato and rubber plants supplied with purified nutrient solutions, the lack of cobalt failed to produce visual symptoms of deficiency (32). Cobalt was therefore not claimed to be an essential element for higher plants. Relatively high concentrations of cobalt (greater than 0.1 mg Co per milliliter) in water cultures are toxic to plants which may be offset by further addition of molybdenum (155).

Most recently, however, there have been a number of independent findings which implicate cobalt as an essential nutrient in the symbiotic fixation of nitrogen by leguminous plants. The first of these, by Shaukat-Ahmed and Evans (229), shows that added cobalt produced a marked increase in the dry weight of soybean shoots of the *Rhizobium*-soybean system as well as prevented nitrogen-deficiency symptoms; this was followed, almost simultaneously, by similar or related reports by Reisenauer (53, 211) and Hallsworth *et al.* (91) using different leguminous plants. The cobalt-containing vitamin B_{12} had already been shown to be present in the roots of nonleguminous species (46) and in the nodules of leguminous plants with its concentration in pink nodules being four times as great as in white ones (138). In the former case the vitamin was attributed to soil microorganisms and in the latter case to the nitrogen-fixing bacteria in the nodules. Of special interest is the early report by Holm-Hansen *et al.* (107) which demonstrated that certain blue-green algae are dependent upon either cobalt or vitamin B_{12} for normal growth and that those species that fix nitrogen display a greater response than those which require a source of fixed nitrogen.

Further experiments have indicated that cobalt is an essential element for the growth of soybean plants under symbiotic conditions, but no response could be demonstrated in experiments where adequate fixed nitrogen was supplied (230). A more recent report indicates that cobalt is also an important growth factor for the bacterium *Rhizobium japonicum* in pure culture, a symbiotic partner in leguminous nitrogen fixation (142). It therefore appears that cobalt has an essential role in the bacteria regardless of whether it is grown with or without the leguminous plant. It seems quite possible that the requirement of symbiotically grown legumes for cobalt can be accounted for simply in terms of the requirement of the bacteria for the metal. It may be that cobalt functions as part of the vitamin B_{12} molecule which in turn may also be more directly involved in nitrogen fixation.

At the enzymatic level it has been found that the inhibition of incorporation of acetate into fatty acids in homogenates of *Saccharomyces cerevisiae* by ethylenediaminetetracetic acid was completely and specifically removed by Co^{++} (127). The glycylglycine dipeptidase from bakers' yeast has been reported to be specifically activated by Co^{++} (191), while carboxypeptidase A experiences a 100% increase in peptidase activity with no apparent increase in esterase activity by specific incubation with cobaltous ions (71).

Selenium has recently been implicated as an essential element in animal nutrition. There have been a number of independent reports that selenium in very low concentrations is effective in the prevention of liver necrosis in rats and of exudative diathesis in chicks when they are maintained on a special diet containing *Torula* yeast (274). The term "factor 3" or "active selenium" has been used to designate the biologically active selenium-containing component(s) in nutrients and other biological material (227). It was originally observed as an unidentified substance that prevented necrotic liver degeneration of rats fed a diet containing protein supplied by *Torula* yeast (226). The unclassified complexity of the biological relationship between factor 3 and vitamin E in preventing or alleviating exudative diathesis in the chick, muscular dystrophy in laboratory animals, dialuric acid-induced hemolysis, resorption gestation in rats, and depigmentation of rat incisor teeth has recently been summarized by Vasington *et al.* (273).

In higher plants it has been demonstrated that the growth of certain species is stimulated by selenium (cf. Chapter 2). These particular plants, which are classified in the genera *Stanleya, Oonopsis* (= *Haplopappus*), *Xylorrhiza* (= *Machaeranthera*), and *Astragalus,* apparently grow on soils which contain selenium. These plants have served as valuable indicators of seleniferous soils and seleniferous soil areas (165, 266), and selenium has been referred to as an essential element for these "indicator" plants. The element occurs in plants in concentrations as high as 3500 ppm in organic and inorganic forms, the latter being present for the most part as selenate. A number of species have been reported to have the selenium present only in the organic form. Amino acids of seleniferous wheat protein hydrolyzates showed much of its selenium by paper chromatographic analysis to be in the same areas as methionine and cystine. The toxicity of selenium in the selenium analog of cystine is comparable to the toxicity of selenium in naturally seleniferous grains and in sodium selenite. According to a recent report (135) selenate interferes competitively with the absorption of sulfate by plants. Shrift (234) has recently reviewed the chemical properties of selenium and the biological activities of selenium compounds with particular emphasis on its effects and possible roles in plants. He has indicated that sulfate is the one substance which has been consistently found to counteract selenate toxicity in microorganisms and higher plants. The antagonism is competitive and seems to be best explained on the basis of the structural similarity of the two ions. The ratio dependence of metabolite to antimetabolite has been reported in a number of growth studies with *Chlorella vulgaris* (232), *Saccharomyces cerevisiae* (70), *Aspergillus niger* (288), and *Desulfovibrio desulfuricans* (206). The assumption is often made that unlike most antimetabolites selenate can be converted by plants into organic forms by the same enzymes that convert sulfate. These organic selenium compounds in turn are believed to be competitive. The recent work with the sulfate "activating" system (ATP + sulfate → AMP — sulfate + pyrophosphate) indicates that the enzyme designated as ATP-sulfurylase prepared from animal and *Neurospora* tissues is inhibited by selenate and not reversed by sulfate (102). A similar system from yeast yielded only trace amounts of the corresponding AMP-selenate implying a hydrolysis of the adenosine phosphoselenate, but no experiments were reported to demonstrate an actual competition between sulfate and selenate (293).

At the organic selenium level, experiments with animal enzymes have shown that the selenium analog of methionine is converted to "active selenomethionine" (Se-adenosylselenomethionine) at a rate which is similar to that at which "active methionine" is formed under identical conditions (167). The Se-adenosylselenomethionine can in turn serve as a methyl donor for the biosynthesis of creatine (167) and choline (35) in enzymatic transmethylation reactions using cell-free liver preparations. The manner in which selenium is built into protein molecules and to what extent sulfur can be replaced by selenium without impairment of protein function are very much in need of clarification.

The work of Pinsent (202) represents the only report of a specific enzyme requirement for selenite. She observed a specific need for selenite (and molybdate) in the formation of formic dehydrogenase by members of the *coli-aerogenes* group of bacteria. In the absence of these ions from the nutrient medium no enzyme activity could be detected even though growth was normal.

Iodine, which is an essential element for animals and functions as a component of the thyroxine molecule, has thus far not been shown to be a necessary nutrient for plants.

VI. Mechanism of Action of the Macronutrient Elements

A. Nitrogen

Nitrogen as a macronutrient element obviously functions as a necessary component of such biologically important molecules as proteins, amino acids, purines, pyrimidines, coenzymes. The various forms in which the nitrogen atom enters the plant cell and the means by which it is converted to the organic state are to be treated in another chapter of this treatise (see Volume IV).

B. Phosphorus

Phosphorus as an essential macronutrient element is found in plants as part of the phosphate group, in both the inorganic and organic forms.

Unlike nitrate and sulfate, the phosphorus atom of phosphate is not reduced to a different oxidation state in the cell. Phosphorus is absorbed by plants chiefly as the orthophosphate ion. Plants characteristically accumulate and maintain a high concentration of inorganic phosphate within their tissues, despite the low concentration of this ion in the soil solution. Phosphate is a mobile nutrient within the plant being transported from one site to another, and is present in highest concentration in cells possessing high metabolic activity. Under deficient conditions, a redistribution of phosphorus within the plant occurs whereby phosphate is withdrawn from the older, metabolically less active cells to the younger more active cells. The role of phosphorus in plant physiology and biochemistry has been surveyed by Arnon (11). Phosphate plays a key role in energy transfer, in respiration and in photosynthesis. These aspects are considered in great detail in other chapters.

Phosphate is found in the organic form in a great variety of naturally occurring substances. Of special interest with regard to plants is phytic acid, the hexaphosphoric acid ester of inositol or hexahydroxycelo-

$$\begin{array}{c} OPO_3H_2 \\ H_2O_3PO \underset{\displaystyle OPO_3H_2}{\overset{\displaystyle OPO_3H_2}{\bigcirc}} OPO_3H_2 \\ H_2O_3PO \qquad OPO_3H_2 \end{array}$$

Phytic acid

hexane. It is usually present in the plant as calcium or magnesium salts known as phytin. Phytin apparently serves as the storage form of phosphate in seeds which have very little inorganic phosphate, the phosphate of phytin becoming available during germination for the phosphorylation reactions in the metabolism of the seedlings (5).

Other organic compounds of phosphate concerned in the metabolism of cells include the phospholipids, phosphorylated sugars and their intermediary metabolic breakdown products as found in the glycolytic and the alternate oxidative pathways, nucleoproteins and nucleic acids, purine and pyridine nucleotides, flavin nucleotides, and other coenzymes such as pyridoxal phosphate and thiamine pyrophosphate.

C. CALCIUM

Calcium in contrast to phosphate is relatively immobile and is not readily redistributed in plant tissues. Older leaves may have large calcium reserves, whereas younger leaves on the same plant may exhibit a deficiency. The fact that symptoms of calcium deficiency manifest themselves primarily in the growing points (buds and young leaves) has been taken as additional evidence of the relative immobility of this element in the plant. Other relatively immobile elements such as iron and boron also show deficiency symptoms in meristematic tissues in contrast to the more noticeable deficiency symptoms in mature leaves for freely translocated elements (e.g., nitrogen and potassium).

The role of calcium in the plant is not entirely clear. It appears to be a commonly accepted view that calcium is one of the few essential elements entering into the structure of the plant, namely as calcium pectate, a constituent of the middle lamella. There is some opposition to this viewpoint, however, as indicated by experiments with calcium-starved plants where no evidence of cell wall separation due to the breakdown of middle lamella or its failure to form was obtained (51, 245). The proposal (27, 41) that auxin induces elongation of stems and of coleoptiles by removing calcium ions [possibly by chelation (27, 94) or by methylation of the carboxyl groups attached to calcium (198)] which are presumed to cross-link the pectin chains of the cell wall, has been recently challenged. Cleland (43) has reported that the loss of calcium from *Avena* coleoptile and from maize mesocotyl cell walls is not enhanced by auxin and that auxin does not cause a redistribution of the element between pectin and propectin. Calcium however does stimulate indoleacetic acid uptake by pea roots (8) although its mode of action in this respect is not clear.

Kozloff and Lute (130) have reported that in bacteriophage T2 calcium ions appear to be bound to the ATP binding sites of the tail protein of intact phage and they are released when the tail protein contracts after interaction with the host cell walls. They have concluded that the calcium stimulates the hydrolysis of the ATP during the contraction of the phage tail protein during viral invasion.

An earlier consideration that calcium functioned in plants by preventing the accumulation of toxic quantities of oxalic acid by forming insoluble calcium oxalate has been discarded. Oxalic acid is not formed by some plants which still require calcium, and it is not a very strong poison to a number of other plants. Hewitt (97) is of the opinion that calcium to some extent acts in a complementary fashion to potassium in maintaining cell organization, hydration, and permeability, thus indirectly influencing many enzyme systems.

The physiological effects of the calcium ion on the state of protoplasm are probably best reflected by its action in decreasing cell permeability and antagonizing the action of K^+ in this respect. The inability of some plant species to absorb or assimilate nitrate in the absence of calcium

(190) may well be due to an indirect effect rather than to a direct role of calcium in nitrate assimilation. At the enzymatic level Ca^{++} has been shown to act as an activator for such isolated enzymes as arginine kinase, adenosine triphosphatase, adenyl kinase, and potato apyrase (146). A number of investigators have reported that calcium is an integral component of amylase from various animal tissues and microorganisms including *Bacillus subtilis* and *Aspergillus oryzae* (194, 195, 249, 271, 291). In general there seems to be agreement among these workers that the calcium ions (which can be replaced by magnesium or strontium) serve in a stabilizing role by maintaining the proper configuration of the amylase molecule, possibly in its secondary and tertiary structure, for catalytic activity (194, 271). This may be responsible for conferring on the amylase molecule a resistance to proteolytic degradation (249, 271). Several phospholipases from a number of different organisms including higher plants are known to be activated by calcium ions. This has been reported, for example, for the lecithinase c (or phospholipase c), which splits choline from phosphatidyl choline, from cabbage (*Brassica oleracea* var. *capitata*) (47, 283), and from carrots (*Daucus carota* var. *sativa*) (61).

Calcium has also been implicated in an interrelationship with phosphate during nitrogen fixation in the aerobic nitrogen-fixing organism *Azotobacter vinelandii* as an essential nutrient for the synthesis of polymetaphosphate (64). On the basis of their results Bullock *et al.* (38) suggested that *Azotobacter* species may be associated into three groups according to their requirement for Ca^{++}: (a) those in which there is a definite requirement for growth on free nitrogen as compared to combined nitrogen (*A. vinelandii*, *A. chroococcum*, and *A. beijerinckii*), (b) those having no demonstrable requirement for the metal (*A. agilis*), and (c) those in which Ca^{++} is definitely inhibitory independent of the nitrogen source (*A. indicus*).

D. Magnesium

Magnesium as a constituent of the chlorophyll molecule is obviously concerned in photosynthesis. Whether or not the magnesium of chlorophyll serves as an active site in the photosynthetic process is still undetermined. It is the only metal contained in chlorophyll and comprises 2.7% of the molecule. This, however, represents approximately 10% of the total leaf magnesium. A deficiency of magnesium not only results in chlorosis, but also causes a loss in the yellow pigments xanthophyll and carotene (103). Gilbert (83) states that magnesium is present in the plant in at least two other forms in addition to its specific linkage in the chlorophyll molecule, namely "in combined form in the protoplasm" and in a free or inorganic salt in the cell sap. A high concentration of magnesium in a plant tissue has been associated with physiologically young cells, rapid growth, active mitosis, and high protein concentration (24). With increasing plant maturity magnesium is withdrawn from the vegetative parts and is used in seed formation.

Studies of isolated enzyme systems from plant and animal tissues have indicated that magnesium plays a predominant role in the activity of the various enzymes concerned with carbohydrate metabolism. Table IV shows a compilation of some of the enzymes involved in carbohydrate metabolism and their metal activators. In most cases, Mn^{++} will substitute for magnesium, but the activity is somewhat lower. Magnesium also serves as an activator for those enzymes which catalyze reactions involving nucleotide substrates. The pattern that emerges from these studies is that magnesium and to a certain extent manganese are required primarily for those reactions involving group transfer, namely those in which phosphate participates. In recent years, it has become increasingly clear that magnesium participates intimately in group transfer by serving as the intermediate carrier. Magnesium plays a predominant role in promoting the formation of the enzyme substrate complex and the resulting intermediate of the reaction. The presence of a pyrophosphate structure in many of the cofactors and substrates involved in group transfer suggest that a chelate structure with magnesium is probable (Fig. 5). The fact that magnesium like phosphorus accumulates in the seed suggested to Loew (141) almost sixty years ago that one of the functions of magnesium was to serve as a carrier for phosphoric acid. The recent results of Shibko and Pinchot (231) demonstrate that Mg^{++} ions are essential in order that cell-free particles from the bacterium *Alcaligenes faecalis* may carry out oxidative phosphorylation with DPNH as the substrate. Their evidence indicates a unique system in which Mg^{++} is necessary for the binding action by a polynucleotide of a soluble, heat-labile factor necessary for phosphorylation to the enzyme particles. The latter alone catalyze the oxidation of DPNH without concomitant phosphate esterification. Of four different divalent cations tested, Mg^{++} was by far the most effective while Ca^{++}, Co^{++}, and Mn^{++} were considerably less active in that order.

E. Potassium

The specific role of potassium in plants is as yet unknown. It is absolutely essential to plants and cannot be completely replaced by other elements such as the chemically similar sodium or lithium. Potassium occurs in higher plants principally as soluble inorganic salts and to a lesser extent as salts of organic acids. The meristematic tissues are

TABLE IV
Metal Activation of Enzymes Concerned with Carbohydrate Metabolism (146)

Enzyme	Reaction[b]	Metal[a]
Galactokinase	Galactose + ATP → galactose-1-P + ADP	Mg^{++}
Fructokinase	Fructose + ATP → fructose-1-P (or fructose-6-P) + ADP	Mg^{++}, K^+
Glucokinase	Glucose + ATP → glucose-6-P	Mg^{++}, Mn^{++}
Hexokinase	Fructose, Glucose, Mannose } + ATP → hexose-6-P + ADP	Mg^{++}, Mn^{++}
Trikinase	Glyceraldehyde + ATP → 3-phosphoglyceraldehyde	Mg^{++}
Ribokinase	Ribose + ATP → ribose-5-P + ADP	Mg^{++}
Gluconokinase	Gluconic acid + ATP → 6-phosphogluconic acid + ADP	Mg^{++}
Phosphoglucokinase	Glucose-1-P + ATP → glucose-1,6-diphosphate + ADP	Mg^{++}, Mn^{++}
Phosphoglucomutase	Glucose-1-P ⇄ glucose-6-P	Mg^{++}, Mn^{++}, Co^{++}, Cr^{++}
Phosphofructokinase	Fructose-6-P + ATP → fructose-1,6-diphosphate + ADP	Mg^{++}
Yeast and *Clostridium* aldolase	Fructose-1,6-P ⇄ phosphoglyceraldehyde + dihydroxyacetone phosphate	Fe^{++}, Co^{++}, or Zn^{++}
Phosphoglyceric acid kinase	3-Phosphoglyceric acid + ATP ⇄ 1,3-diphosphoglyceric acid	Mg^{++}, Mn^{++}
Enolase	2-Phosphoglyceric acid ⇄ 1,3-enolphosphopyruvic acid + H_2O	Mg^{++}, Mn^{++}, or Zn^{++}
Pyruvic acid kinase	Pyruvic acid + ATP ⇄ phosphopyruvate + ADP	Mg^{++}, K^+, NH_4^+ or Rb^+

[a] The indication of a single metal activator does not mean to imply that this is a specific metal requirement.
[b] P = phosphate.

particularly rich in this element, the metabolically active regions of the plant (i.e., buds, young leaves, root tips) containing high concentrations of potassium at the expense of older and mature tissues. The element is highly mobile and is readily redistributed within the plant during the life cycle.

A large volume of data has been collected over the years with regard to the effects of potassium starvation on higher plants. As one would expect there are experiments to indicate involvement of potassium in virtually everyone of the metabolic processes examined. A deficiency of potassium has been reported to result in leaf damage, high water or low water content of leaves, decrease in photosynthetic activity, disturbed carbohydrate metabolism, increased respiration, insufficient chlorophyll development in some species, accumulation of certain other elements, a lower protein content and a higher percentage of soluble organic nitrogen compounds. The initially increased carbohydrate content of potassium-deficient tissues is undoubtedly due in part to the decrease in protein synthesis. There is little question that the element is necessary to maintain cell organization, permeability, and hydration.

At the enzymatic level K^+ can act as an activator for a number of enzyme systems such as fructokinase, pyruvic acid kinase, and transacetylase. Pyruvic kinase in extracts of seeds and leaves of various plants has been shown to have essentially the same monovalent cation requirements for enzymatic activity as the enzyme extracted from rabbit muscle. In general K^+ was the most effective while the other monovalent cations Rb^+, NH_4^+, and Na^+ in that order also activated the enzyme (144, 162). The association of K^+ with protein metabolism has been verified, and a more specific catalytic role has been assigned to K^+ according to the experiments of Webster (278–281). Using extracts of higher plants, he has reported an absolute requirement for potassium in the activation of enzymes that synthesize certain peptide bonds. He has also indicated that K^+ enhances the incorporation of amino acids into protein (278). Experiments with Ehrlich ascites tumor cells also point to a potentiation of amino acid uptake or transport by an adequate cellular level of K^+ (215). Recent studies in the enzymology of virus-infected bacteria have demonstrated that the deoxyguanalate kinase of normal bacterial cells is stimulated five- to tenfold by K^+ (and to a considerably lesser extent by Rb^+ and NH_4^+ ions) whereas the corresponding enzyme in the extracts of cells infected by T2, T4, T5, or T6 bacteriophages shows no requirement for K^+ (25).

Sodium may substitute in part, but not completely, for the potassium requirement in a number of plants. It is known that symptoms of potassium deficiency may manifest themselves sooner and more severely in barley in the absence of sodium ions in culture solution (170). Beneficial effects have been observed for sodium applications in the field on soils low in potassium, but to a lesser extent on soils high in potassium. Harmer et al. (92) characterized the reactions of numerous plants to sodium according to a classification which ranged from those plants which showed little or no response even with a potassium insufficiency, to those which responded despite an adequate potassium supply. In some cases, two-thirds of the normal potassium requirement has been reported to be replaced with sodium without causing growth disturbances (77). The effect of sodium is at least partially due to an intracellular synergism of potassium and sodium and probably to a specific enhancement by sodium. The mechanism of action, however, of potassium (or of sodium in those cases where it has an enhancement effect) is still obscure. Despite the fact that potassium and rubidium are so closely similar in chemical properties as to make their analytical separation difficult, the latter cannot substitute for potassium in the growth of higher plants. As late as 1944, Hoagland (104) felt that there was no conclusive proof that rubidium could take the place of potassium. He discounted previous reports on the basis of a potassium contamination of the rubidium salt preparations. A partial substitution of potassium by rubidium in some plants was observed in the range of low potassium supply as well as an effect of rubidium in preventing the accumulation of amino acids and amides in potassium deficiency (203). The latter effect was also obtained with sodium and even with lithium. Cesium can in no way replace potassium in growth.

F. Sulfur

In his review on the place of sulfur in plant nutrition Gilbert (82) pointed out that the amount of the element varies considerably in different genera and families of plants, usually ranging between 0.1 and 1% on a dry weight basis. Some groups of plants for example, the brassicaceous plants (cabbage tribe of the mustard family), have a high concentration of the element and are considered to be sulfur carriers. It is usually absorbed by roots as the sulfate ion, or enters by way of the leaves as SO_2 when that gas is present in the atmosphere (265).

The sulfate obviously undergoes reduction within the plant since it is a constituent of the amino acids cystine, cysteine, and methionine. A number of recent studies have indicated that sulfate reduction and incorporation into cysteine, methionine, and eventually proteins includes first an activation step which involves ATP. The active sulfate which is known to act as a sulfate donor in the sulfurylation of phenols and other compounds was identified by Robbins and Lipmann (216) as

3'-phosphoadenosine-5'-phosphosulfate (PAPS). Subsequent studies by a number of workers indicate that PAPS is formed in two independent enzymatic steps (18, 217). The first step involves the activation of sulfate by ATP and the enzyme sulfurylase to form adenosine-5'-phosphosulfate (APS) and inorganic pyrophosphate.

$$\text{ATP} + \text{SO}_4^{--} \rightleftarrows \text{APS} + \text{PP}$$

APS is converted into PAPS by a second reaction which is catalyzed by a specific kinase:

$$\text{APS} + \text{ATP} \rightarrow \text{PAPS} + \text{ADP}$$

The present evidence indicates that either APS or PAPS is the active substrate for sulfate reduction (126, 292) to sulfite, which in turn is reduced to hydrogen sulfide (200). Hilz and Kettler (101) have presented evidence, using a yeast preparation, that sulfate reduction is brought about by a thiolytic split of PAPS by dihydrolipoic acid (Eqs. 5, 6). The earlier observations that reduced pyridine nucleotide was

$$\text{(5)}$$

$$\text{(6)}$$

required for sulfate reduction could be accounted for on the basis of a reduction of lipoic acid to its active form. Because of the oxidation-reduction potential of the lipoic acid and pyridine nucleotide systems it is not surprising that the reduction of sulfate has been difficult to demonstrate if the above pathway is correct.

Nothing is known about the site of sulfate reduction in plants although involvement of a "c" type cytochrome in this process in certain bacteria has been indicated by Postgate (207). According to Gilbert (82), however, a high concentration of sulfur is present in plants in the inorganic form, principally as sulfates. Apparently some of the sulfur of organic molecules may be oxidized to the sulfate form and possibly utilized again in other parts of the plant. However, sulfur, like calcium, is regarded as being relatively immobile in plants. The element is fairly evenly distributed throughout the plant with deficiency symptoms appearing for the most part in the new growth, thus reflecting little or no apparent translocation from the older to the younger tissues. Biddulph *et al.* (30, 31), however, reported that a portion of the total sulfur within the plant remains mobile and moves freely from one organ to another and concluded that it moved principally in the phloem at a downward rate similar to that for phosphorus and sucrose.

Certainly one function of sulfur is to serve as a component of proteins since it is a constituent of the amino acids cystine, cysteine, and methionine. It is also directly involved in metabolism by way of the sulfur-bearing vitamins such as thiamine, biotin, and coenzyme A. Sulfhydryl groups have been also shown to be necessary for the activity of an appreciable number of enzymes. That sulfur is also directly involved in electron transport has been demonstrated by the characteristics of glutathione reductase (45, 154). Sulfur also occurs in certain plants in the volatile form in mustard oils (as glucosides), allyl and vinyl sulfides, and the mercaptans (201). Little is known of the significance of these compounds to the plants. Selenate inhibition of plant cells has been shown to be competitively overcome by sulfate apparently at the levels of absorption and growth (135, 233, 288). The sulfur amino acids are also effective in this respect, and there is a competitive relationship of methionine with the homologous selenium compound (233).

Sulfur-deficient plants are chlorotic and have an impaired photosynthesis. This has been attributed to an indirect effect on the protein level and the chlorophyll content of the chloroplasts (203). Root development and nodule development on the roots of legumes are also promoted by sulfur fertilization practices (82).

G. CHLORINE

Chlorine, as chloride, has recently been shown to be an essential element for higher plants (37) by the demonstration that deficiency symptoms can be produced in tomato plants. It is regarded by some as a micronutrient, although the minimal amount of chloride required in plant tissue is several thousand times greater than for molybdenum. The latter is presently recognized as the micronutrient required in the least amount. The mode of action of chlorine in the plant is unknown. Bromine appears to substitute in part for chlorine in a way reminiscent of the sparing effect of sodium for potassium.

VII. Mineral Nutrients in Metabolic Pathways and Processes

A. Glycolysis

As shown in Fig. 10, all but three of the twelve enzymatic steps in fermentation are known to have a metal requirement. All six of the steps which are activated by magnesium involve phosphate transfer.

B. Hexose Monophosphate Shunt (Pentose Phosphate Pathway)

At least two enzymes of the seven demonstrated thus far to make up this pathway show a metal requirement. These include 6-phosphogluconic dehydrogenase which needs Mg^{++} or Mn^{++} and transketolase which requires $Mg.^{++}$

C. Krebs Citric Acid Cycle

With the exception of fumarase, all other enzymes of the citric acid cycle have been shown to have a metal constituent or requirement (Table V).

D. Terminal Respiration

At the enzymatic level iron, other than in the cytochromes, has been implicated as a constituent of DPN-cytochrome c reductase and succinic-cytochrome c reductase in mammalian tissues (238). Copper is present in the cytochrome oxidase portion of the terminal respiratory system (88). Its role is not known. Copper is the metal constituent, as discussed in detail in a previous section, of phenolases and ascorbic acid oxidase, although it is not certain that these enzymes function as terminal oxidases in plant respiration, though they may well have other metabolic roles.

E. Photosynthesis

The role of metals, particularly molybdenum, vanadium, and manganese, in photosynthesis has been recently reviewed by Arnon (12). A deficiency of molybdenum or vanadium results in a decrease of photosynthesis by algal cells on a unit-chlorophyll basis. The vanadium deficiency also gives a substantially lowered chlorophyll content, but in

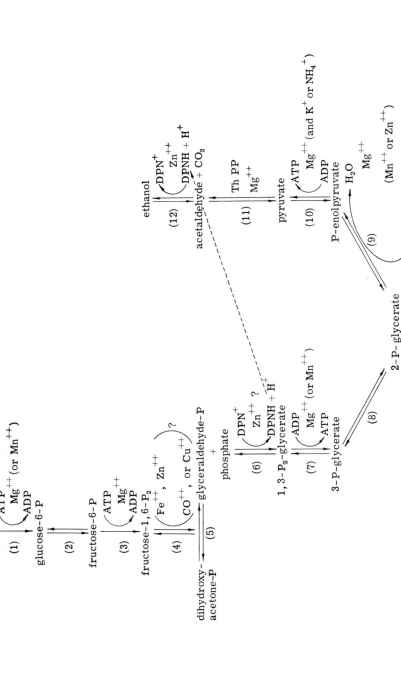

Fig. 10. Sites of action of metal ions in the fermentation pathway (173). Enzymes involved are: (1) hexokinase, (2) phosphogluco-isomerase, (3) phosphofructokinase, (4) aldolase, (5) triosephosphate isomerase, (6) 3-phosphoglyceraldehyde dehydrogenase, (7) ATP-phosphoglyceric transphosphorylase, (8) phosphoglyceromutase, (9) enolase, (10) ATP-phosphopyruvate transphosphorylase (pyruvic acid kinase), (11) pyruvate carboxylase, and (12) alcohol dehydrogenase.

TABLE V

The Role of Metals in the Activation of Enzymes of the Citric Acid Cycle

Enzyme	Reaction	Metal[a]
Pyruvic carboxylase	Pyruvic acid → acetaldehyde + CO_2	Mg^{++}, Mn^{++}
Pyruvic oxidase	Pyruvic acid + H_3PO_4 → acetyl-P + CO_2	Mg^{++}, Mn^{++}
Pyruvic oxidase	Pyruvic acid + CoA → acetyl CoA + CO_2	Mg^{++}
Oxalacetic decarboxylase	Oxalacetic acid → pyruvic acid + CO_2	Mg^{++}, Co^{++}, Zn^{++}, Mn^{++}
Transacetylase	Acetyl phosphate + CoA $\rightleftarrows PO_4$ + acetyl CoA	Mg^{++}, K^+
Isocitric dehydrogenase	Isocitric acid + $TPN^+ \rightleftarrows$ oxalosuccinic + TPNH	Mg^{++}, Mn^{++}
Oxalosuccinic decarboxylase	Oxalosuccinic → ketoglutaric acid + CO_2 + O_2	Mn^{++}
α-Ketoglutarate oxidase (plant)	α-Ketoglutaric acid → succinic acid + CO_2	Mg^{++}, Mn^{++}
Succinic dehydrogenase	Succinic acid → fumaric acid + 2H	Ca^{++}, Al^{+++}, Cr^{++}, Fe^{++}
"Malic enzyme"	Malate + $TPN^+ \rightarrow$ pyruvate + CO_2 + TPNH	Mn^{++}, Co^{++}
Condensing enzyme	Oxalacetic acid + acetyl CoA $\rightleftarrows$ citric acid	Mg^{++}, Mn^{++}
Aconitase	Citric acid $\rightleftarrows$ aconitic acid $\rightleftarrows$ isocitric acid	Fe^{++}

[a] The indication of a single metal activator does not mean to imply that this is a specific metal requirement.

weaker light there is no significant difference between the control and deficient cultures in the rate of photosynthesis. While a manganese deficiency, unlike a vanadium deficiency, did not reduce the chlorophyll content, it did decrease the rate of photosynthesis in both weak and strong light. Arnon and co-workers found a prompt restoration of a normal rate of photosynthesis in the minus-manganese cells by the addition of manganese. In addition, manganese stimulated photosynthesis of isolated chloroplasts as measured by carbon dioxide fixation. The nature of this manganese effect is still not clear. Other aspects of the relationship between manganese and photosynthesis have already been discussed in Section V, E, 2 dealing with the function of this metal.

VIII. Concluding Remarks

Nutritional and physicochemical studies on the function of mineral nutrients in plant metabolism reveal several general patterns. With some exceptions, it appears that those metals most closely associated with electron transferring systems are iron, copper, and molybdenum. These metals already have the inherent capacity to function as electron mediators in nonenzymatic oxidation-reduction reactions. The unanswered biochemical questions have to do with (a) the remarkably enhanced capacity of these metals for catalyzing oxidation-reduction reactions when combined with specific proteins, and (b) the nature of the linkages which permit specific coupling of these metal systems to others allowing the transfer of electrons along specific pathways.

Magnesium, and to a limited extent manganese are apparently involved in phosphate transfer. The magnesium ion apparently plays a role in the formation of the enzyme substrate complex and perhaps in the resulting intermediate of the reaction. It is quite likely that the ion forms a chelate with the pyrophosphate structure since the latter is found in many of the cofactors and substrates involved in group transfer.

The predominant metal involved in general enzymatic decarboxylation and hydrolysis reactions is manganese (and to some extent zinc and magnesium). There is no general agreement, however, as to the primary mechanism of action of these metals. Perhaps they form an essential structure with the substrate bringing the latter into combination with the protein. Another alternative is that the metal combines with the enzyme and functions primarily to accelerate and, therefore, increase the concentrations of an essential intermediate in the reaction.

The recent work on zinc indicated that many pyridine nucleotide dehydrogenases are zinc enzymes in which the metal probably serves in the capacity of binding the pyridine nucleotide to the protein moiety. The effect of zinc and other metals on the synthesis of specific enzymes also suggests that the micronutrient elements are important for the function of the protein-forming centers.

The importance of the mineral nutrients as integral parts of all biological processes is well established. Undoubtedly future studies will open up new and interesting relationships.

Acknowledgments

Contribution No. 362 of the McCollum-Pratt Institute. Some of the experimental data provided represent portions of studies by the authors supported in part by research grants from the National Institutes of Health (No. 2332), of the U.S. Public Health Service, The National Science Foundation, U.S. Atomic Energy Commission, and The Office of Naval Research.

References

1. Adelstein, S. J., and Vallee, B. L. Zinc in beef liver glutamic dehydrogenase. *J. Biol. Chem.* **233**, 589–593 (1958).
2. Agarwala, S. C. Relation of nitrogen supply to the molybdenum requirement of cauliflower grown in sand culture. *Nature* **169**, 1099 (1952).
3. Agulhon, H. Emploi du bore comme engrais catalytique. *Compt. rend. acad. sci.* **150**, 288–291 (1910).
4. Akazawa, T., and Conn, E. E. The oxidation of reduced pyridine nucleotides by peroxidase. *J. Biol. Chem.* **232**, 403–415 (1958).
5. Albaum, H. G., and Umbreit, W. W. Phosphorus transformations during the development of the oat embryo. *Am. J. Botany* **30**, 553–558 (1943).
6. Allen, M. B. Photosynthetic nitrogen fixation by blue-green algae. *Sci. Monthly* **83**, 100–106 (1956).
7. Anderson, A. J. Role of molybdenum in plant nutrition. *In* "Inorganic Nitrogen Metabolism" (W. D. McElroy and H. B. Glass, eds.), 3–49. Johns Hopkins Press, Baltimore, Maryland, 1956.
8. Andrea, W. A., and van Ysselstein, M. W. N. Studies on 3-indoleacetic acid metabolism. V. Effect of calcium ions on 3-indoleacetic acid uptake and metabolism by pea roots. *Plant Physiol.* **35**, 220–232 (1960).
9. Appelby, C. A., and Morton, R. K. Crystalline cytochrome b₂ and lactic dehydrogenase of yeast. *Nature* **173**, 749–752 (1954).
10. Arnon, D. I. Functional aspects of copper in plants. *In* "Copper Metabolism" (W. D. McElroy and H. B. Glass, eds.), pp. 89–110. Johns Hopkins Press, Baltimore, Maryland, 1950.
11. Arnon, D. I. The physiology and biochemistry of phosphorus in green plants. *Agronomy* **4**, 1–42 (1953).
12. Arnon, D. I. The role of micronutrients in plant nutrition with special reference to photosynthesis and nitrogen assimilation. *In* "Trace Elements" (C. A. Lamb, O. G. Bentley, and J. M. Beattie, eds.), pp. 1–32. Academic Press, New York, 1958.

13. Arnon, D. I., and Stout, P. R. Molybdenum as an essential element for higher plants. *Plant Physiol.* **14**, 599–602 (1939).
14. Arnon, D. I., and Wessel, G. Vanadium as an essential element for green plants. *Nature* **172**, 1039–1040 (1953).
15. Asano, A. Studies on enzymic nitrite reduction. II. Separation of nitrite reductase to particulate and soluble components. *J. Biochem.* (*Tokyo*) **46**, 1235–1242 (1959).
16. Asano, A. Studies on enzymic nitrite reduction. III. Effects of metal ions on soluble and particulate components of nitrite reductase. *J. Biochem.* (*Tokyo*) **47**, 678–684 (1960).
17. Bach, S. J., Dixon, M., and Zerfas, L. G. Yeast lactic dehydrogenase and cytochrome b₂. *Biochem. J.* **40**, 229–239 (1946).
18. Bandurski, R. S., Wilson, L. G., and Squires, C. L. The mechanism of "active sulfate" formation. *J. Am. Chem. Soc.* **78**, 6408–6409 (1956).
19. Banga, I., Gerendas, M., Laki, K., Papp, G., Porges, E., Straub, F., and Szent-Györgyi, A. Über die dehydrierende autoxydaton und die biologischen oxydationen. *Z. physiol. Chem. Hoppe-Seyler's* **254**, 147–206 (1938).
20. Bard, R. C., and Gunsalus, I. C. Glucose metabolism of *Clostridium perfringens:* existence of a metallo-aldolase. *J. Bacteriol.* **59**, 387–400 (1950).
21. Barker, H. A., Weissbach, H., and Smyth, R. D. A coenzyme containing pseudovitamin B₁₂. *Proc. Natl. Acad. Sci. U. S.* **44**, 1093–1097 (1958).
22. Barker, H. A., Smyth, R. D., Weissbach, H., Munch-Peterson, A., Toohey, J. I., Ladd, J. N., Volcani, B. E., and Wilson, R. M. Assay, purification, and properties of the adenylcobamide coenzyme. *J. Biol. Chem.* **235**, 181–190 (1960).
23. Bauer, E. The activation mechanism of phosphatases (pyrophosphatases II). *Z. physiol. Chem. Hoppe-Seyler's* **248**, 213–226 (1937).
24. Bear, F. E., Prince, A. L., Toth, S. J., and Purvis, E. R. Magnesium in plants and soils. New Jersey *Agr. Expt. Sta. Bull. No.* **760**, 3–24 (1951).
25. Bello, L. J., Van Bibber, M. J., and Bessman, M. J. The enzymology of virus-infected bacteria. I. Demonstration of two forms of deoxyguanalate kinase in infected *Escherichia coli. J. Biol. Chem.* **236**, 1467–1470 (1961).
26. Benhamow, N., Magee, R. J., and Dawson, C. R. The effect of cupric ion on the reaction inactivation of ascorbic acid oxidase. *Arch. Biochem. Biophys.* **81**, 135–145 (1959).
27. Bennet-Clark, T. A. A hypothesis on salt accumulation and the mode of action of auxin. *In* "The Chemistry and Mode of Action of Plant Growth Substances" (R. L. Wain and F. Wightman, eds.), pp. 284–294. Academic Press, New York, 1956.
28. Bernheim, F., and Bernheim, M. L. C. The action of vanadium on the oxidation of phospholipides in certain tumors. *J. Biol. Chem.* **127**, 353–360 (1939).
29. Bertrand, D. Survey of contemporary knowledge of biogeochemistry. 2. The biogeochemistry of vanadium. *Bull. Am. Museum Nat. Hist.* **94**, 403–456 (1950).
30. Biddulph, O., Cory, R., and Biddulph, S. F., The absorption and translocation of sulfur in red kidney bean. *Plant Physiol.* **31**, 28–33 (1956).
31. Biddulph, S. F. Visual indications of S³⁵ and P³² translocation in the phloem. *Am. J. Botany* **43**, 143–148 (1956).
32. Bolle-Jones, E. W., and Mallikarjuneswara, V. R. A beneficial effect of cobalt on the growth of the rubber plant (*Hevea brasiliensis*). *Nature* **179**, 738–739 (1957).

33. Bortels, H. Molybdän als Katalysator bei der biologischen Stickstoffbindung. *Arch. Mikrobiol.* **1**, 333 (1930).
34. Bradfield, J. R. G. Plant carbonic anhydrase. *Nature* **159**, 467–468 (1947).
35. Bremer, J., and Natori, Y. Behavior of some selenium compounds in transmethylation. *Biochim. et Biophys. Acta* **44**, 367–370 (1960).
36. Brown, T. E., Eyster, H. C., and Tanner, H. A. Physiological effects of manganese deficiency. *In* "Trace Elements" (C. A. Lamb, O. G. Bentley, and J. M. Beattie, eds.), pp. 135–155. Academic Press, New York, 1958.
37. Broyer, T. C., Carlton, A. B., Johnson, C. M., and Stout, P. R. Chlorine—a micronutrient element for higher plants. *Plant Physiol.* **29**, 526–532 (1954).
38. Bullock, G. L., Bush, J. A., and Wilson, P. W. Calcium requirements of various species of Azotobacter. *Proc. Soc. Exptl. Biol. Med.* **105**, 26–30 (1960).
39. Burström, H. Über die Schwermetallkatalyse der Nitratassimilation. *Planta* **29**, 292–305 (1939).
40. Calvin, M. Chelation and catalysis. *In* "Mechanism of Enzyme Action" (W. D. McElroy and H. B. Glass, eds.), pp. 221–256. Johns Hopkins Press, Baltimore, Maryland, 1954.
41. Carlier, A., and Buffel, K. Polysaccharide changes in the cell walls of water-absorbing potato tuber tissue in relation to auxin action. *Acta Botan. Neerl.* **4**, 551–564 (1955).
42. Chesters, G. G. C., and Rolinson, G. N. The role of zinc in plant metabolism. *Biol. Revs. Cambridge Phil. Soc.* **26**, 239–252 (1951).
43. Cleland, R. Effect of auxin upon loss of calcium from cell walls. *Plant Physiol.* **35**, 581–584 (1960).
44. Cohen, E., and Elvehjem, C. A. The relation of iron and copper to the cytochrome and oxidase content of animal tissues. *J. Biol. Chem.* **107**, 97–105 (1934).
45. Conn, E. E., and Vennesland, B. Glutathione reductase of wheat germ. *J. Biol. Chem.* **192**, 17–28 (1951).
46. Darken, M. A. Production of vitamin B_{12} by micro-organisms and its occurrence in plant tissues. *Botan. Rev.* **19**, 99–130 (1953).
47. Davidson, F. M., and Long, C. The structure of the naturally occurring phosphoglycerides. 4. Action of cabbage-leaf phospholipase D on ovolecithin and related substances. *Biochem. J.* **69**, 458–466 (1958).
48. Davis, G. K. Metabolic function and practical use of cobalt in nutrition. *In* "Trace Elements" (C. A. Lamb, O. G. Bentley, and J. M. Beattie, eds.), pp. 193–211. Academic Press, New York, 1958.
49. Dawson, C. R. The copper protein, ascorbic acid oxidase. *In* "Copper Metabolism" (W. D. McElroy and H. B. Glass, eds.), pp. 18–47. Johns Hopkins Press, Baltimore, Maryland, 1950.
50. Dawson, C. R., and Tarpley, W. B. Copper oxidases. *In* "The Enzymes" (J. B. Summer and K. Myrbäck, eds.), 1st ed., Vol. II, Part I, pp. 454–498. Academic Press, New York, 1951.
51. Day, D. Some effects on *Pisum sativum* of a lack of calcium in the nutrient solution. *Science* **68**, 426–427 (1928).
52. Day, R., and Franklin, J. Plant carbonic anhydrase. *Science* **104**, 363–365 (1946).
53. Delwiche, C. C., Johnson, C. M., and Reisenauer, H. M. Influence of cobalt on nitrogen fixation by Medicago. *Plant Physiol.* **36**, 73–78 (1961).
54. DeRenzo, E. C., Heytler, P. G., and Stolzenberg, S. *In* "Inorganic Nitrogen Metabolism" (W. D. McElroy and H. B. Glass, eds.), pp. 507–512. Johns Hopkins Press, Baltimore, Maryland, 1956.

4. MODES OF ACTION OF ESSENTIAL MINERAL ELEMENTS 525

55. Dick, A. T. Molybdenum in animal nutrition. *Soil Sci.* **81**, 229–258 (1956).
56. Dinning, J. S. Water-soluble vitamins. II. *Ann. Rev. Biochem.* **29**, 437–452 (1960).
57. Dressler, H., and Dawson, C. R. On the nature and mode of action of the copper protein, tyrosinase. I. Exchange experiments with radioactive copper and the resting enzyme. *Biochim. et Biophys. Acta* **45**, 508–514 (1960).
58. Dressler, H., and Dawson, C. R. On the nature and mode of action of the copper protein, tyrosinase. II. Exchange experiments with radioactive copper and the functioning enzyme. *Biochim. et Biophys. Acta* **45**, 515–524 (1960).
59. Eggerer, H., Overath, P., Lynen, F., and Stadtman, E. R. On the mechanism of the cobamide coenzyme dependent isomerization of methylmalonyl CoA to succinyl CoA. *J. Am. Chem. Soc.* **82**, 2643–2644 (1960).
60. Eichel, B., Wainio, W. W., Person, P., and Cooperstein, S. J. A partial separation and characterization of cytochrome oxidase and cytochrome b. *J. Biol. Chem.* **183**, 89–103 (1950).
61. Einset, E., and Clark, W. L. The enzymatically catalyzed release of choline from lecithin. *J. Biol. Chem.* **231**, 703–715 (1958).
62. Elvehjem, C. A. The role of iron and copper in the growth and metabolism of yeast. *J. Biol. Chem.* **90**, 111–132 (1931).
63. Elvehjem, C. A., Hart, E. B., and Sherman, W. C. The availability of iron from different sources for hemoglobin formation. *J. Biol. Chem.* **103**, 61–70 (1933).
64. Esposito, R. G., and Wilson, P. W. Calcium and polymetaphosphate synthesis in *Azotobacter vinelandii* O. *Biochim. et Biophys. Acta* **22**, 186–187 (1956).
65. Esposito, R. G., and Wilson, P. W. Trace metal requirements of azotobacter. *Proc. Soc. Exptl. Biol. Med.* **93**, 564–567 (1956).
66. Evans, H. J. The biochemical role of iron in plant metabolism. *In* "Symposium on Mineral Nutrition of Trees." Duke Univ. School of Forestry, Bull. **15** (1959).
67. Evans, H. J. Role of molybdenum in plant nutrition. *Soil Sci.* **81**, 199–208 (1956).
68. Evans, H. J., and Hall, N. S. Association of molybdenum with nitrate reductase from soybean leaves. *Science* **22**, 922–923 (1955).
69. Evans, H. J., and Nason, A. Pyridine nucleotide-nitrate reductase from extracts of higher plants. *Plant Physiol.* **28**, 233–254 (1953).
70. Fels, I. G., and Cheldelin, V. H. Selenate inhibition studies. III. The role of sulfate in selenate toxicity in yeast. *Arch. Biochem.* **22**, 402–405 (1949).
71. Folk, J. E., and Gladner, J. A. Cobalt activation of carboxypeptidase A. *J. Biol. Chem.* **235**, 60–63 (1960).
72. Foster, J. W., and Denison, F. W., Jr. Role of zinc in metabolism. *Nature* **166**, 833–834 (1940).
73. Frey-Wyssling, A. Die unentbehrlichen Elemente der Pfanzennahrung. *Naturwissenschaften* **23**, 767–769 (1935).
74. Fridovich, I., and Handler, P. Xanthine oxidase. IV. Participation of iron in internal electron transport. *J. Biol. Chem.* **233**, 1581–1585 (1958).
75. Frieden, C. The dissociation of glutamic dehydrogenase by reduced diphyosphopyridine nucleotide (DPNH). *Biochim. et Biophys. Acta* **27**, 431–432 (1958).
76. Gallagher, C. H., Judath, J. H., and Ress, K. R. The biochemistry of copper deficiency. I. Enzymological disturbances, blood chemistry and excretion of amino acids. *Proc. Roy. Soc.* **B145**, 134 (1956).

77. Gammon, N. Sodium and potassium requirements of Pangola and other pasture grasses. *Soil Sci.* **76**, 81–90 (1953).
78. Gauch, H. G. Mineral nutrition of plants. *Ann. Rev. Plant Physiol.* **8**, 31–64 (1957).
79. Gauch, H. G., and Duggar, W. M., Jr. The physiological action of boron in higher plants: a review and interpretation. *Univ. Maryland, Agr. Expt. Sta. College Park Bull. No.* **A-80** (1954).
80. Gerloff, G. C., Stout, P. R., and Jones, L. H. P. Molybdenum-manganese-iron antagonisms in the nutrition of tomato plants. *Plant Physiol.* **34**, 608–613 (1959).
81. Gest, H., Judis, J., and Peck, H. D., Jr. Reduction of molecular nitrogen and relationships with photosynthesis and hydrogen metabolism. *In* "Inorganic Nitrogen Metabolism" (W. D. McElroy and H. B. Glass, eds.), pp. 298–315. Johns Hopkins Press, Baltimore, Maryland, 1956.
82. Gilbert, F. A. The place of sulfur in plant nutrition. *Botan. Rev.* **17**, 671–691 (1951).
83. Gilbert, F. A. "Mineral Nutrition and the Balance of Life." Univ. of Oklahoma Press, Norman, Oklahoma, 1957.
84. Goddard, D. R., and Stafford, H. A. Localization of enzymes in the cells of higher plants. *Ann. Rev. Plant Physiol.* **5**, 115–132 (1954).
85. Grafflin, A. L., and Ochoa, S. Partial purification of isocitric dehydrogenase oxalosuccinic carboxylase. *Biochim. et Biophys. Acta* **4**, 205–210 (1950).
86. Granick, S. Iron metabolism in animals and plants. *Harvey Lectures Ser.* **44**, 220–245 (1950).
87. Granick, S., and Gilder, H. Distribution, structure, and properties of the tetrapyrroles. *Advances in Enzymol.* **7**, 305–368 (1947).
88. Green, D. E., Basford, R. E., Mackler, B. The role of iron and copper in terminal electron transport. *In* "Inorganic Nitrogen Metabolism" (W. D. McElroy and H. B. Glass, eds.), pp. 628–649. Johns Hopkins Press, Baltimore, Maryland, 1956.
89. Green, L. F., McCarthy, J. F., and King, C. G. Inhibition of respiration and photosynthesis in *Chlorella pyrenoidosa* by organic compounds that inhibit copper catalysis. *J. Biol. Chem.* **128**, 447–453 (1939).
90. Griffiths, D. E., and Wharton, D. C. Copper in cytochrome oxidase. *Biochem. Biophys. Research Communs.* **4**, 199–204 (1961).
91. Hallsworth, E. G., Wilson, S. B., and Greenwood, E. A. N. Copper and cobalt in nitrogen fixation. *Nature* **187**, 79–80 (1960).
92. Harmer, P. M., Benne, E. J., Laughlin, W. M., and Key, C. Factors affecting crops response to sodium applied as common salt on Michigan muck soil. *Soil Sci.* **76**, 1–17 (1953).
93. Harrison, K. Activation of fumaric dehydrogenase by ferrous ions. *Nature* **172**, 509 (1953).
94. Heath, O. V. S., and Clark, J. E. Chelating agents as plant growth substances. *Nature* **177**, 1118–1121 (1956).
95. Hellerman, L., and Stock, C. C. Activation of enzymes. V. *J. Biol. Chem.* **125**, 771–792 (1938).
95a. Herman, E. C. Jr., and Wright, B. E. A 5'-nucleotidase activated by ferrous iron. *J. Biol. Chem.* **234**, 122–125 (1959).
96. Hewitt, E. J. Metal interrelationships in plant nutrition. 2. The relation of metal toxicity, molybdenum, and nitrogen source to chlorophyll and magnesium content of beet in sand culture. *J. Exptl. Botany* **5**, 110–118 (1954).

97. Hewitt, E. J. The role of the mineral elements in plant nutrition. *Ann. Rev. Plant Physiol.* **2**, 25–52 (1951).

98. Hewitt, E. J. The role of mineral elements in the activity of plant enzymes systems. *In* "Handbuch der Pflanzenphysiologie—Encyclopedia of Plant Physiology," Vol. 4, pp. 427–481. Springer, Berlin, 1958.

99. Hill, R., and Hartree, E. F. Hematin compounds in plants. *Ann. Rev. Plant Physiol.* **4**, 115–150 (1953).

100. Hill, R., and Scarisbrick, R. The haematin compounds of leaves. *New Phytologist* **50**, 98–111 (1951).

101. Hilz, H., and Kittler, M. Reduction of active sulfate (PAPS) by dihydrolipoic acid as substrate. *Biochem. Biophys. Research Communs.* **3**, 140–142 (1960).

102. Hilz, H., and Lipmann, F. The enzymatic inactivation of sulfate. *Proc. Natl. Acad. Sci. U.S.* **41**, 880–890 (1955).

103. Hinkle, D. A., and Eisenmenger, W. S. Chloroplast pigments in relation to magnesium deficiency. *Soil Sci.* **70**, 213–220 (1950).

104. Hoagland, D. R. "Lectures on the Inorganic Nutrition of Plants." Chronica Botanica, Waltham, Massachusetts, 1944.

105. Hoch, F. L., and Vallee, B. L. The metabolic role of zinc. *In* "Trace Elements" (C. A. Lamb, O. G. Bentley, and J. M. Beattie, eds.), pp. 337–363. Academic Press, New York, 1958.

106. Holmberg, C. G. Uricase purification and properties. *Biochem. J.* **33**, 1901–1906 (1939).

107. Holm-Hansen, O., Gerloff, G. C., and Skoog, F. Cobalt as an essential element for blue-green algae. *Physiol. Plantarum* **7**, 665–675 (1954).

108. Horner, C. K., Burk, D., Allison, F. E., and Sherman, M. S. Nitrogen fixation by *Azotobacter* as influenced by molybdenum and vanadium. *J. Agr. Research* **65**, 173–193 (1942).

109. Howell, J. M., and Davison, A. N. The copper content and cytochrome oxidase activity of tissues from normal and swayback lambs. *Biochem. J.* **72**, 365–368 (1959).

110. Iida, C., and Yamasaki, K. Spectrographic determination of molybdenum in the nitrate reductase from *Escherichia coli*. *Biochim. et Biophys. Acta* **44**, 352–353 (1960).

111. Ingraham, J. L., and Emerson, R. Studies of the nutrition and metabolism of the aquatic phycomycete, Allomyces. *Am. J. Botany* **41**, 146–152 (1954).

112. Johnson, J. E., and Hall, N. F. A study of the exchange of nickel in certain complex compounds using radioactive nickel. *J. Am. Chem. Soc.* **70**, 2344–2348 (1948).

113. Johnson, R. R., and Bentley, O. G. Cobalt and the synthesis of vitamin B_{12}-like substances by rumen micro-organisms. *In* "Trace Elements" (C. A. Lamb, O. G. Bentley, and J. M. Beattie, eds.), pp. 213–225. Academic Press, New York, 1958.

114. Joselow, M., and Dawson, C. R. The copper of ascorbic acid oxidase; experiments with an ion exchange resin. *J. Biol. Chem.* **191**, 1–10 (1951).

115. Joselow, M., and Dawson, C. R. The copper of ascorbic acid oxidase; exchange studies with radioactive copper. *J. Biol. Chem.* **191**, 11–20 (1951).

116. Kägi, J. H. R., and Vallee, B. L. The role of zinc in alcohol dehydrogenase. V. The effect of metal-binding agests on the structure of the yeast alcohol dehydrogenase molecule. *J. Biol. Chem.* **235**, 3188–3192 (1960).

117. Keilin, D., and Hartree, E. F. Cytochrome a and cytochrome oxidase. *Nature* **141**, 870–871 (1938).
118. Keilin, D., and Hartree, E. F. On the mechanism of the decomposition of hydrogen peroxide by catalase. *Proc. Roy. Soc.* **B124**, 397–405 (1938).
119. Keilin, D., and Mann, T. Carbonic anhydrase. *Biochem. J.* **34**, 1163–1176 (1940).
120. Kenten, R. H., and Mann, P. J. G. The oxidation of manganese by plant extracts in the presence of hydrogen peroxide. *Biochem. J.* **45**, 255–263 (1949).
121. Kenten, R. H., and Mann, P. J. G. The oxidation of certain dicarboxylic acids by peroxidase systems in presence of manganese. *Biochem. J.* **53**, 498–505 (1953).
122. Kenten, R. H., and Mann, P. J. G. The oxidation of manganese by illuminated chloroplasts preparations. *Biochem. J.* **61**, 279–286 (1955).
123. Kertesz, D. Tyrosinase and polyphenoloxidase; the role of metallic ions in melanogenesis. *Biochim. et Biophys. Acta* **9**, 170–179 (1952).
124. Kessler, E. Stoffwechselphysiologische Untersuchungen an Hydrogenase Enthaltenden Grünalgen. *Planta* **49**, 435–454 (1957).
125. Kinsky, S. C., and McElroy, W. D. Neurospora nitrate reductase: the role of phosphate, flavine, and cytochrome c reductase. *Arch. Biochem. Biophys.* **73**, 466–483 (1958).
126. Kittler, M., and Knape, G. Die Reduktion fon sulfat inder hefe. *Biochem. Z.* **332**, 151–166 (1959).
127. Klein, H. P. Cobalt activation of fatty-acid synthesis in yeast homogenates. *Science* **128**, 1135–1136 (1958).
128. Klotz, I. M. Thermodynamic and molecular properties of some metal-protein complexes. *In* "Mechanism of Enzyme Action" (W. D. McElroy and H. B. Glass eds.), pp. 257–285. Johns Hopkins Press, Baltimore, Maryland, 1954.
129. Kornberg, A., Ochoa, S., and Mehler, A. H. Spectrophometric studies on the decarboxylation of β-keto acids. *J. Biol. Chem.* **174**, 159–172 (1948).
130. Kozloff, I. M., and Lute, M. Calcium content of bacteriophage T2. *Biochim. et Biophys. Acta* **37**, 420–424 (1960).
131. Krebs, H. A. The effect of inorganic salts on the ketone decomposition of oxaloacetic acid. *Biochem. J.* **36**, 303–305 (1942).
132. Kubowitz, F. Über die chemische Zusammensetzung der Kartoffeloxydase. *Biochem. Z.* **292**, 221–229 (1937).
133. Kubowitz, F. Staltung und Rb Synthese der Polyphenoloxydase und des Hämocyanins. *Biochem. Z.* **299**, 32–57 (1938).
134. Lardy, H. A. The influence of inorganic ions on phosphorylation reactions. *In* "Phosphorus Metabolism" (W. D. McElroy and H. B. Glass, eds.), Vol. I, pp. 477–479. Johns Hopkins Press, Baltimore, Maryland, 1951.
135. Leggett, J. E., and Epstein, E. Kinetics of sulfate absorption by barley roots. *Plant Physiol.* **31**, 222–226 (1956).
136. Lehninger, A. L. Role of metal ions in enzyme systems. *Physiol. Revs.* **30**, 393–429 (1950).
137. Lemberg, R., and Legge, J. W. "Hematin Compounds and Bile Pigments." Interscience, New York, 1947.
138. Levin, A. P., Funk, H. B., and Tendler, M. D. Vitamin B$_{12}$, rhizobia, and leguminous plants. *Science* **120**, 784. (1954).
139. Linderstrøm-Lang, K. Über den Antagonismus von Zink und Blausäure bei deren Eienwirkung auf die Teptidasenaktivitat. *Z. physiol. Chem. Hoope-Seyler's* **224**, 121–126 (1934).

140. Lindskog, S., and Malmström, B. G. A reversible dissociation of zinc in bovine carbonic anhydrase. *Biochem. Biophys. Research Communs.* **2**, 213–217 (1960).

141. Loew, O. The physiological role of mineral nutrients in plants. *U.S. Dept. Agr. Bureau Plant Ind. Bull.* **45**, 9–70 (1903).

142. Lowe, R. H., Evans, H. J., and Shaukat-Ahmed. The effect of cobalt on the growth of *Rhizobium japonicum. Biochem. Biophys. Research Communs.* **3**, 675–678 (1960).

143. LuValle, J. E., and Goddard, D. R. The mechanism of enzymatic oxidations and reductions. *Quart. Rev. Biol.* **23**, 197–228 (1948).

144. McCollum, R. E., Hageman, R. H., and Tyner, E. H. Influence of potassium on pyruvic kinase from plant tissue. *Soil Sci.* **86**, 324–331 (1958).

145. McElroy, W. D. The role of trace elements in enzyme systems. *In* "Symposium on Nutrition" (R. M. Herriott, ed.), pp. 262–286. Johns Hopkins Press, Baltimore, Maryland, 1953.

146. McElroy, W. D., and Nason, A. Mechanism of action of micronutrient elements in enzyme systems. *Ann. Rev. Plant Physiol.* **5**, 1–30 (1954).

147. McHargue, J. S. The role of manganese in plants. *J. Am. Chem. Soc.* **44**, 1592–1598 (1922).

148. Mackler, B., and Penn, N. Studies on the electron transport system. IX. Fragmentation of DPNH oxidase. *Biochem. et Biophys. Acta* **24**, 294–300 (1957).

149. MacLachlan, G. A., and Waygood, E. R. Kinetics of the enzymically catalyzed oxidation of indoleacetic acid. *Can. J. Biochem. and Physiol.* **34**, 1233–1250 (1956).

150. MacLeod, R. A., and Snell, E. E. The effect of related ions on the potassium requirement of lactic acid bacteria. *J. Biol. Chem.* **176**, 39–52 (1948).

151. Mahler, H. R., and Elowe, D. G. Studies on metalloflavoproteins. II. *J. Biol. Chem.* **210**, 165–179 (1954).

152. Mahler, H. R., Hubscher, G., and Baum, H. Studies on uricase. I. *J. Biol. Chem.* **216**, 625–641 (1955).

152a. Mahler, H. R., Mackler, B., Green, D. E. and Bock, R. M. Studies on metalloflavoproteins. III. Aldehyde oxidase: a molybdoflavoprotein. *J. Biol. Chem.* **210**, 465–480 (1954).

153. Malmström, B. G. Interaction of manganous ions with enolase. *Nature* **171**, 392–393 (1953).

154. Mapson, L. W., and Goddard, D. R. The reduction of glutathione by plant tissues. *Biochem. J.* **49**, 592–601 (1951).

155. Marston, H. R. Cobalt, copper, and molybdenum in the nutrition of animals and plants. *Physiol. Revs.* **32**, 66–121 (1952).

156. Mason, H. S. Mechanisms of oxygen metabolism. *Advances in Enzymol.* **19**, 79–233 (1957).

157. Mason, H. S., Fowlks, W. L., and Peterson, E. Oxygen transfer and electron transport by the phenolase complex. *J. Am. Chem. Soc.* **77**, 2914–2915 (1955).

158. Massey, V. Studies on fumarase. *Biochem. J.* **53**, 67–71 (1953).

159. Mazé, P. Influence respective des éléments de la solution minérale sur le développement du maïs. *Ann. inst. Pasteur* **28**, 1–5 (1914).

160. Metzler, D. E., and Snell, E. E. Some transamination reactions involving vitamin B₆. *J. Am. Chem. Soc.* **74**, 979–983 (1952).

161. Miller, C. O. Relationship of the cobalt and light effects on expansion of etiolated bean leaf disks. *Plant Physiol.* **27**, 408–412 (1952).

162. Miller, G., and Evans, H. J. The influence of salts on pyruvate kinase from tissues of higher plants. *Plant Physiol.* **32,** 346–354 (1957).
163. Millikan, C. R. Effects of molybdenum on the severity of toxicity symptoms in flax induced by an excess of either manganese, zinc, copper, nickel, or cobalt in the nutrient solution. *J. Australian Inst. Agr. Sci.* **13,** 180–186 (1947).
164. Millikan, C. R. Antagonism between molybdenum and certain heavy metals in plant nutrition. *Nature* **161,** 528 (1948).
165. Moxon, A. L. Selenium: its occurrence in rocks and soils, absorption by plants, toxic action in animals, and possible essential role in animal nutrition. *In* "Trace Elements" (C. A. Lamb, O. G. Bentley, and J. M. Beattie, eds.), pp. 175–191. Academic Press, New York, 1958.
166. Mudd, J. B., and Burris, R. H. Participation of metals in peroxidase-catalyzed oxidations. *J. Biol. Chem.* **234,** 2774–2777 (1959).
167. Mudd, S. H., and Cantoni, G. L. Selenomethionine in enzymatic transmethylations. *Nature* **180,** 1052 (1957).
168. Mulder, E. C. Importance of molybdenum in the nitrogen metabolism of microorganisms and higher plants. *Plant and Soil* **1,** 94–119 (1948).
169. Mulder, E. C. Molybdenum in relation to growth of higher plants and microorganisms. *Plant and Soil* **5,** 368–415 (1954).
170. Mullison, W. R., and Mullison, E. Growth responses of barley seedlings in relation to potassium and sodium nutrition. *Plant Physiol.* **17,** 632–644 (1942).
171. Nason, A. Metabolism of micronutrient elements in higher plants. II. Effect of copper deficiency on the isocitric enzyme in tomato leaves. *J. Biol. Chem.* **198,** 643–653 (1952).
172. Nason, A. Enzymatic steps in the assimilation of nitrate and nitrite in fungi and green plants. *In* "Inorganic Nitrogen Metabolism" (W. D. McElroy and H. B. Glass, eds.), pp. 109–136. Johns Hopkins Press, Baltimore, Maryland, 1956.
173. Nason, A. The role of metal ions in yeast fermentation. *Am. Brewer* (February, 1957). pp. 49–55.
174. Nason, A. The function of metals in enzyme systems. *Soil Sci.* **85,** 63–77 (1958).
175. Nason, A. The metabolic role of vanadium and molybdenum in plants and animals. *In* "Trace Elements" (C. A. Lamb, O. G. Bentley, and J. M. Beattie, eds.), pp. 269–296. Academic Press, New York, 1958.
176. Nason, A., Abraham, R. G., and Averbach, B. C. The enzymic reduction of nitrite to ammonia by reduced pyridine nucleotides. *Biochim. et Biophys. Acta* **15,** 159–161 (1954).
177. Nason, A., and Evans, H. J. Triphosphopyridine nucleotide-nitrate reducttase in *Neurospora. J. Biol. Chem.* **202,** 655–673 (1953).
178. Nason, A., Kaplan, N. O., and Colowick, S. P. Changes in enzymatic constitution in zinc-deficient *Neurospora. J. Biol. Chem.* **188,** 397–406 (1951).
179. Nason, A., Kaplan, N. O., and Oldewurtel, H. A. Further studies of nutritional conditions affecting enzymatic constitution in *Neurospora. J. Biol. Chem.* **201,** 435–444 (1953).
180. Nason, A., Oldewurtel, H. A., and Propst, L. M. Role of micronutrient elements in the metabolism of higher plants. I. *Arch. Biochem. Biophys.* **38,** 1–13 (1952).
181. Nason, A., and Takahashi, H. Inorganic nitrogen metabolism. *Ann. Rev. Microbiol.* **13,** 203–246 (1958).
182. Neish, A. C. Studies on chloroplasts. II. Their chemical composition and the distribution of certain metabolites between the chloroplasts and the remainder of the leaf. *Biochem. J.* **33,** 300–308 (1939).

183. Nicholas, D. J. D., and Nason, A. Molybdenum and nitrate reductase. II. *J. Biol. Chem.* **207**, 353–360 (1954).
184. Nicholas, D. J. D., and Nason, A. Mechanism of action of nitrate reductase from *Neurospora. J. Biol. Chem.* **211**, 183–197 (1954).
185. Nicholas, D. J. D., and Nason, A. Diphosphopyridine nucleotide-nitrate reductase from *Escherichia coli. J. Bacteriol.* **69**, 580–583 (1955).
186. Nicholas, D. J. D., and Nason, A. Role of molybdenum as a constituent of nitrate reductase from soybean leaves. *Plant Physiol.* **30**, 135–143 (1955).
187. Nicholas, D. J. D., Nason, A., and McElroy, W. D. Molybdenum and nitrate reductase. I. *J. Biol. Chem.* **207**, 341–351 (1954).
188. Nicholas, D. J. D., and Scawin, J. H. A phosphate requirement for nitrate reductase from *Neurospora crassa. Nature* **178**, 1474–1475 (1956).
189. Nicholas, D. J. D., and Stevens, H. M. Valence changes of molybdenum during the enzymatic reduction of nitrate in *Neurospora. Nature* **176**, 1066–1067 (1955).
190. Nightingale, G. T. Potassium and calcium in relation to nitrogen metabolism. *Botan. Gaz.* **98**, 725–734 (1937).
191. Nishi, A. Activation and inhibition by bivalent metal ions of yeast glycylglycine dipeptidase. *J. Biochem. (Tokyo)* **45**, 991–1004 (1958).
192. Ochoa, S. Biosynthesis of tricarboxylic acids by carbon dioxide fixation. 1. The preparation and properties of oxalosuccinic acid. *J. Biol. Chem.* **174**, 115–122 (1948).
193. Ochoa, S. Biological mechanism of carboxylation and decarboxylation. *Physiol. Revs.* **31**, 56–106 (1951).
194. Oikawa, A. The role of calcium in taka-amylase A. II. The exchange reaction of calcium. *J. Biochem. (Tokyo)* **46**, 463–473 (1959).
195. Oikawa, A., and Maeda, A. The role of calcium in taka-amylase A. *J. Biochem. (Tokyo)* **44**, 745–752 (1957).
196. Okunuki, K., Sekuzu, I., Yonetani, T., and Takemori, S. Studies on cytochrome a. I. Extraction, purification, and some properties of cytochrome a. *J. Biochem. (Tokyo)* **45**, 847–854 (1958).
197. Oppenheimer, C., and Stern, K. G. "Biological Oxidation." Junk, The Hague, 1939.
198. Ordin, L., Cleland, R., and Bonner, J. Methyl esterification of cell wall constituents under the influence of auxin. *Plant Physiol.* **32**, 216–220 (1957).
199. Pauling, L, "The Nature of the Chemical Bond and the Structure of Molecules and Crystals," 2nd ed. Cornell Univ. Press, Ithaca, New York, 1948.
200. Peck, H. D., Jr. The ATP-dependent reduction of sulfate with hydrogen in extracts of *Desulfovibrio desulfuricans. Proc. Natl. Acad. Sci. U.S.* **45**, 701–708 (1959).
201. Peterson, W. H. Forms of sulfur in plant materials and their variation with the soil supply. *J. Am. Chem. Soc.* **36**, 1290–1300 (1914).
202. Pinsent, J. The need for selenite and molybdate in the formation of formic dehydrogenase by members of the *coli-aerogenes* group of bacteria. *Biochem. J.* **57**, 10–16 (1954).
203. Pirson, A. Functional aspects in mineral nutrition of green plants. *Ann. Rev. Plant Physiol.* **6**, 71–114 (1955).
204. Pirson, A. Manganese and its role in photosynthesis. *In* "Trace Elements" (C. A. Lamb, O. G. Bentley, and J. M. Beattie, eds.), pp. 81–98. Academic Press, New York, 1958.

205. Possingham, J. V. The effect of molybdenum in the organic and inorganic phosphorus metabolism of plants. *Australian J. Biol. Sci.* **7**, 221–224 (1954).

206. Postgate, J. R. Competitive and non-competitive inhibitors of bacterial sulfate reduction. *J. Gen. Microbiol.* **6**, 128–142 (1952).

207. Postgate, J. R., Presence of cytochrome in an obligate anaerobe. *Biochem. J.* **56**, xi–xii (1954).

208. Quinlan-Watson, T. A. F. The effect of zinc deficiency on the aldolase activity in the leaves of oats and clover. *Biochem. J.* **53**, 457–460 (1953).

209. Reed, H. S. Effects of zinc deficiency on phosphate metabolism of the tomato plant. *Am. J. Botany* **33**, 778–784 (1946).

210. Reed, H. S. A physiological study of boron deficiency in plants. *Hilgardia* **17**, 377–409 (1947).

211. Reisenauer, H. M. Cobalt in nitrogen fixation by a legume. *Nature* **186**, 375–376 (1960).

212. Remy, C. N., Richert, D. A., Doisy, R. J., Wells, I. C., and Westerfeld, W. W. Purification and characterization of chicken liver xanthine dehydrogenase. *J. Biol. Chem.* **217**, 293–305 (1955).

213. Richert, D. A., and Westerfeld, W. W. The relationship of iron to xanthine oxidase. *J. Biol. Chem.* **209**, 179–189 (1954).

214. Rickenberg, H. V. The effect of metal ions and proteins on the stability of the β-galactosidase of *Escherichia coli*. *Biochem. et Biophys. Acta* **35**, 122–129 (1959).

215. Riggs, T. R., Walker, L. M., and Christensen, H. N. Potassium migration and amino acid transport. *J. Biol. Chem.* **233**, 1479–1484 (1958).

216. Robbins, P. W., and Lipmann, F. Identification of enzymatically active sulfate as adenosine-3′-phosphate-5′-phosphosulfate. *J. Am. Chem. Soc.* **78**, 2652–2653 (1956).

217. Robbins, P. W., and Lipmann, F. The enzymatic sequence in the biosynthesis of active sulfate. *J. Am. Chem. Soc.* **78**, 6409–6410 (1956).

218. Robinson, W. O., and Edgington, G. Minor elements in plants and some accumulator plants. *Soil Sci.* **60**, 15–28 (1945).

219. Rosenberg, M. A.-J. Action du bore et du *m*-inositol sur *Clostridium saccharobutyricum*. *Compt. rend. acad. sci.* **222**, 1310–1311 (1946).

220. Sadana, J. C., and McElroy, W. D. Nitrate reductase from *Achromobacter fischeri*. Purification and properties: function of flavines and cytochrome. *Arch. Biochem. Biophys.* **67**, 16–33 (1957).

221. Sadasivan, V. Biochemical studies on *Penicillium chrysogenum* Q.176. I. Phosphatase activity and the role of zinc in the production of penicillin. *Arch. Biochem.* **28**, 100–110 (1950).

222. Sadasivan, V. Zinc, ionic, equilibrium and phosphatase activity. *Nature* **170**, 421 (1952).

223. Sands, R. H., and Beinert, H. On the function of iron in DPNH cytochrome *c* reductase. *Biochem. Biophys. Research Communs.* **1**, 171–174 (1959).

224. Sands, R. H., and Beinert, H. On the function of copper in cytochrome oxidase. *Biochem. Biophys. Research Communs.* **1**, 175–178 (1959).

225. Sastry, K., Sivarama, R., and Sarma, P. S. The influence of molybdenum toxicity on sulfur amino acid metabolism in *Neurospora crassa*. *Biochim. et Biophys. Acta* **30**, 438–439 (1958).

226. Schwarz, K. Production of dietary necrotic liver degeneration using American torula yeast. *Proc. Soc. Exptl. Biol. Med.* **77**, 818–823 (1951).

227. Schwarz, K., and Foltz, C. M. Selenium as an integral part of factor 3 against dietary necrotic liver degeneration. *J. Am. Chem. Soc.* **79**, 3292–3293 (1959).

228. Scott, D. A., and Mendive, J. R. Chemical observations on carbonic anhydrase. *J. Biol. Chem.* **140**, 445–451 (1941).

229. Shaukat-Ahmed, and Evans, H. J. Effect of cobalt on the growth of soybeans in the absence of supplied nitrogen. *Biochem. Biophys. Research Communs.* **1**, 271–275 (1959).

230. Shaukat-Ahmed, and Evans, H. J. The essentiality of cobalt for soybean plants grown under symbiotic conditions. *Proc. Natl. Acad. Sci. U.S.* **47**, 24–36 (1961).

231. Shibko, S., and Pinchot, G. B. The effects of magnesium and polyanions on oxidative phosphorylation in bacteria. *Arch. Biochem. Biophys.* **93**, 140–146 (1961).

232. Shrift, A. Sulfur-selenium antagonism. I. Antimetabolite action of selenate on the growth of *Chlorella vulgaris*. *Am. J. Botany* **41**, 223–230 (1954).

233. Shrift, A. Sulfur-selenium antagonism. II. Antimetabolite action of seleno-methionine on the growth of *Chlorella vulgaris*. *Am. J. Botany* **41**, 345–352 (1954).

234. Shrift, A. Biological activities of selenium compounds. *Botan. Rev.* **24**, 550–583 (1958).

235. Shug, A. L., Wilson, P. W., Green, D. E., and Mahler, H. R. The role of molybdenum and flavin in hydrogenase. *J. Am. Chem. Soc.* **76**, 3355–3356 (1954).

236. Sideris, C. P., and Young, H. Y. Growth and chemical composition of *Ananas comosus* (L.), Merr. in solution cultures with different iron-manganese rations. *Plant Physiol.* **24**, 416–440 (1949).

237. Singer, T. P., Kearney, E. B., and Massey, V. Succinic dehydrogenase. *In* "Enzymes: Units of Biological Structure and Function" (O. H. Gaebler, ed.), pp. 417–432. Academic Press, New York, 1955.

238. Singer, T. P., and Massey, V. Experimental foundations of the concept of metal flavoprotein catalysis. *Record Chem. Progr.* (*Kresge-Hooker Sci. Lib.*) **18**, 201–244 (1957).

239. Singer, T. P., Massey, V., and Kearney, E. B. Reversibility of succinic dehydrogenase. *Biochim. et Biophys. Acta* **19**, 200–201 (1956).

240. Skok, J. The role of boron in the plant cell. *In* "Trace Elements" (C. A. Lamb, O. G. Bentley, and J. M. Beattie, eds.), pp. 227–243. Academic Press, New York, 1958.

241. Skoog, F. Relationships between zinc and auxin in the growth of higher plants. *Am. J. Botany* **27**, 939–951 (1940).

242. Smith, E. L., Davis, N. C., Adams, A., and Spackman, D. N. The specificity and mode of action of two metal-peptidases. *In* "Mechanism of Enzyme Action" (W. D. McElroy and H. B. Glass, eds.), pp. 291–312. Johns Hopkins Press, Baltimore, Maryland, 1954.

243. Somers, I. I., and Shive, J. M. The iron-manganese relation in plant metabolism. *Plant. Physiol.* **17**, 582–602 (1942).

244. Sommer, A. L. Copper as an essential for plant growth. *Plant Physiol.* **6**, 339–345 (1931).

245. Sommer, A. L., and Sorokin, H. Effects of the absence of boron and of some other essential elements on the cell and tissue structure of the root tips of *Pisum sativum*. *Plant Physiol.* **3**, 237–261 (1928).

246. Spencer, D. The effect of molybdate on the activity of tomato acid phosphatases. *Australian J. Biol. Sci.* **7**, 151–160 (1954).

247. Stadtman, E. R., Overath, P., Eggerer, H., and Lynen, F. The role of biotin and vitamin B_{12} coenzymes in propionate metabolism. *Biochem. Biophys. Research Communs.* **2**, 1–7 (1960).

248. Stadtman, T. C. Synthesis of adenine-B_{12} coenzyme by *Clostridium sticklandii:* relationship to one-carbon metabolism. *J. Bacteriol.* **79**, 904–905 (1960).

249. Stein, E. A., and Fischer, E. H. The resistance of α-amylases towards proteolytic attack. *J. Biol. Chem.* **232**, 867–879 (1958).

250. Steinberg, R. A. A study of some factors in the chemical stimulation of the growth of *Aspergillus niger. Am. J. Botany* **6**, 330–372 (1919).

251. Steinberg, R. A. Relation of accessory growth substances to heavy metals, including molybdenum, in the nutrition of *Aspergillus niger. J. Agr. Research* **52**, 439–448 (1936).

252. Steinberg, R. A. Role of molybdenum in the utilization of ammonium and nitrate nitrogen by *Aspergillus niger. J. Agr. Research* **55**, 891–902 (1937).

253. Steinberg, R. A. Correlations between biological essentiality and atomic structure of the chemical elements. *J. Agr. Research* **57**, 851–858 (1938).

254. Steinberger, R., and Westheimer, F. N. Metal ion-catalyzed decarboxylation: a model for an enzyme system. *J. Am. Chem. Soc.* **73**, 429–435 (1951).

255. Stern, K. G. *In* "A Symposium on Respiratory Enzymes," 74–103. Univ. of Wisconsin Press, Madison, 1942.

256. Stutz, R. E. The indole-3-acetic acid oxidase of *Lupinus albus* L. *Plant Physiol.* **32**, 31–39 (1957).

257. Symposium on metabolic role of the trace elements in plants and animals: "Trace Elements" (C. A. Lamb, O. G. Bentley, and J. M. Beattie, eds.). Academic Press, New York, 1958.

258. Takemori, S. Studies on cytochrome a. V. Properties of copper in purified cytochrome a. *J. Biochem.* **47**, 382–390 (1960).

259. Tang, Y. W., and Bonner, J. The enzymatic inactivation of indoleacetic acid. I. Some characteristics of the enzyme contained in pea seedlings. *Arch. Biochem.* **13**, 11–25 (1946).

260. Taniguchi, S., and Itagaki, E. Nitrate reductase of nitrate respiration type from *Escherichia coli.* I. Solubilization and purification from the particulate system with molecular characterization as a metalloprotein. *Biochim. et Biophys. Acta* **44**, 263–279 (1960).

261. Taniguchi, S., Sato, R., and Egami, F. The enzymatic mechanism of nitrate and nitrite metabolism in bacteria. *In* "Inorganic Nitrogen Metabolism" (W. D. McElroy and H. B. Glass, eds.), pp. 87–108. Johns Hopkins Press, Baltimore, Maryland, 1956.

262. Thatcher, R. N. A proposed classification of the chemical elements with respect to their function in plant nutrition. *Science* **79**, 463–466 (1934).

263. Theorell, H. Heme-linked groups and mode of action of some hemoproteins. *Advances in Enzymol.* **7**, 265–303 (1947).

264. Thimann, K. V. Studies on the growth and inhibition of isolated plant parts. V. The effects of cobalt and other metals. *Am. J. Botany* **43**, 241–250 (1956).

265. Thomas, M. D., Henricks, R. H., Bryner, L. C., and Hill, G. R. A study of the sulfur metabolism of wheat, barley, and corn using radioactive sulfur. *Plant Physiol.* **19**, 227–244 (1944).

266. Trelease, S. F., and Beath, O. A. "Selenium: Its Geological Occurrence and Its Biological Effects in Relation to Botany, Chemistry, Agriculture, Nutrition, and Medicine." Williams & Wilkins, Baltimore, Maryland, 1949.

267. Tsui, C. The role of zinc in auxin synthesis in the tomato plant. *Am. J. Botany* **35**, 172–179 (1948).

268. Tupper, R., Watts, R. W. E., and Wormall, A. Some observations on the zinc in carbonic anhydrase. *Biochem. J.* **50**, 429–432 (1952).

269. Vallee, B. L., and Neurath, H. Carboxypeptidase, a zinc metalloenzyme. *J. Biol. Chem.* **217**, 253–261 (1955).

270. Vallee, B. L., Ruply, J. A., Coombs, T. L., and Neurath, H. The role of zinc in carboxypeptidase. *J. Biol. Chem.* **235**, 64–69 (1960).

271. Vallee, B. L., Stein, E. A., Summerwell, W. N., and Fischer, E. H. Metal content of α-amylase of various origins. *J. Biol. Chem.* **234**, 2901–2905 (1959).

272. Vander, Wende C., and Wainio, W. W. The state of copper in cytochrome *c* oxidase. *J. Biol. Chem.* **235**, PC 11–12 (1960).

273. Vasington, F. D., Reichard, S. M., and Nason, A. Biochemistry of vitamin E. *Vitamins and Hormones* **18**, 43–87 (1960).

274. Vitamin E and Selenium, Part I and Part II. *Nutrition Revs.* **16**, 149–152, 174–177 (1958).

275. Wagenknecht, A. C., and Burris, R. H. Indoleacetic acid inactivating enzymes from bean roots and pea seedlings. *Arch. Biochem.* **25**, 30–53 (1950).

276. Warburg, O., and Christian, W. Isolierung und Kristallisation des Garungsferments Zymohexase. *Biochem. Z.* **314**, 149–176 (1943).

277. Warrington, K. Some interrelationships between manganese, molybdenum, and vanadium in the nutrition of soybeans, flax, and oats. *Ann. Appl. Biol.* **38**, 624–641 (1951).

278. Webster, G. C. Enzymatic synthesis of gamma-glutamyl-cysteine in higher plants. *Plant Physiol.* **28**, 728–730 (1953).

279. Webster, G. C. Peptide bond synthesis in higher plants. I. *Arch. Biochem. Biophys.* **47**, 241–250 (1953).

280. Webster, G. C., and Varner, J. E. Mechanism of enzymatic synthesis of gamma-glutamyl-cysteine. *Federation Proc.* **13**, 1049 (1954).

281. Webster, G. C. Effect of monovalent ions on the incorporation of amino acids into protein. *Biochim. et Biophys. Acta* **20**, 565–566 (1956).

282. Webster, G. C., and Varner, J. E. Peptide bond synthesis in higher plants. II. *Arch. Biochem. Biophys.* **52**, 22–32 (1956).

283. Weiss, H., Spiegel, H. E., and Titus, E. Isolation of an activator for phospholipase D. *Nature* **183**, 1393–1394 (1959).

284. Weissbach, H., Ladd, J. N., Volcani, B. E., Smyth, R. D., and Barker, H. A. Structure of the adenylcobamide coenzyme: degradation by cyanide, acid, and light. *J. Biol. Chem.* **235**, 1462–1473 (1960).

285. Weissbach, H., Toohey, J. I., and Barker, H. A. Isolation and properties of B₁₂ coenzymes containing benzimidazols or dimethylbenzimidazole. *Proc. Natl. Acad. Sci. U.S.* **45**, 521–525 (1959).

286. Weissberger, A., and LuVallee, J. E. The autoxidation of ascorbic acid in the presence of copper. *J. Am. Chem. Soc.* **66**, 700–705 (1944).

287. Weissberger, A., LuVallee, J. E., and Thomas, D. S. The autoxidation of ascorbic acid. *J. Am. Chem. Soc.* **65**, 1934–1939 (1943).

288. Weissman, G. S., and Trelease, S. F. Influence of sulfur on the toxicity of selenium to *Aspergillus*. *Am. J. Botany* **42**, 489–495 (1955).

289. Wells, A. F. "Structural Inorganic Chemistry," 2nd ed. Oxford Univ. Press, London and New York, 1950.

290. Williams, R. J. P. Metal ions in biological systems. *Biol. Revs. Cambridge Phil. Soc.* **28**, 381–415 (1953).
291. Wills, E. D. The relation of metals and —SH groups to the activity of pancreatic lipase. *Biochim. et Biophys. Acta* **40**, 481–490 (1960).
292. Wilson, L. G., Asahi, T., and Bandurski, R. S. Substrates for yeast sulfate reductase and stimulation by a heat-stable factor. *Federation Proc.* **19**, 2 (1960).
293. Wilson, L. G., and Bandurski, R. S. Enzymatic reactions involving sulfate, sulfite, selenate, and molybdate. *J. Biol. Chem.* **233**, 975–981 (1958).
294. Winfield, M. E. The role of boron in plant metabolism. III. The influence of boron on certain enzyme systems. *Australian J. Exptl. Biol. Med. Sci.* **23**, 267–272 (1945).
295. Wood, J. G., and Sibly, P. M. Carbonic anhydrase activity in plants in relation to zinc content. *Australian J. Sci. Research* **B5**, 244–255 (1952).
296. Yielding, K. L., and Tomkins, G. M. Structural alterations in crystalline glutamic dehydrogenase induced by steroid hormones. *Proc. Natl. Acad. Sci. U.S.* **46**, 1483–1488 (1960).
297. Yonetani, T. Copper in cytochrome oxidase. *Biochem. Biophys. Research Communs.* **3**, 549–553 (1960).
298. Yoshikawa, M. Studien über die Bedeutung des Eisenporphyrins im Zellstoffwechsel. I. *J. Biochem. (Japan)*, **25**, 627–655 (1937).
299. Yudkin, W. H., and Fruton, J. S. The activation of dehydropeptidase by zinc. *J. Biol. Chem.* **170**, 421–422 (1947).

Whereas the ultimate source of carbon for all biological processes is the relatively small concentration of carbon dioxide of the atmosphere, most plants fail to use for their needs even the abundant supplies of elementary nitrogen in the atmosphere but must needs draw this essential element from the usually scanty concentration of nitrate in the aqueous media with which they are in contact. Nevertheless, modern technology does make available to crop plants relatively large amounts of erstwhile atmospheric nitrogen in the form of chemically fixed products. Although the absolute amounts of nitrogen so applied are large in tonnage, they represent, nevertheless, but a small percentage of the total nitrogenous turnover in nature which in fact can only be maintained through the activities of soil microorganisms. The role of microorganisms in plant nutrition, including those that reconvert plant and animal remains to nitrate, receives consideration in Chapter 6, especially from the standpoint of the conditions which prevail in the immediate vicinity of root surfaces, i.e. in the rhizosphere. Chapter 5, however, selects for separate discussion those biological situations in which elementary nitrogen is converted to the organic form. This separate treatment is warranted alike by the impact of biological nitrogen fixation upon the cyclical turnover of nitrogen in nature and by the intrinsic interest which now attaches to the mechanism by which the living cells, or even some cell-free extracts, fix the elementary nitrogen. This chapter, then, is not only pertinent to the over-all study of inorganic plant nutrition, but it contributes also to knowledge of the subsequent fate of nitrogen in plants in general and is thus part of this major topic which will be discussed in Volume IV under nitrogen metabolism of plants.

CHAPTER FIVE

Biological Nitrogen Fixation

Artturi I. Virtanen and Jorma K. Miettinen

I. Introduction

A. The Significance of the Fixation of Molecular Nitrogen in Nature

Biological fixation of molecular nitrogen is considered a fundamental phenomenon in the maintenance of life. However, not long ago it was found by Stevenson (299) that rocks contain variable amounts of ammonium nitrogen and that the total nitrogen in rocks exceeds the molecular nitrogen in the atmosphere. The combined nitrogen in rocks is, however, so firmly fixed in the crystal lattice of the mineral that only when rocks weather may it be utilized by plants. Because this process is very slow, the annually liberated ammonium nitrogen is insignificant for the growth of higher plants. Hence life on earth practically depends on the fixation of atmospheric nitrogen. Apparently only a very small portion of the fixed nitrogen results from the non-biological nitrogen fixation brought about by photochemical reactions or electrical discharges in the atmosphere. In the literature widely varying values are found for the amount of combined nitrogen which is brought to the surface of the earth by precipitation. Until 1950 in seventy investigations from different parts of the world the annual rainfall was found to contain combined nitrogen amounting to from 1 to nearly 30 kg per hectare. In this discussion these results cannot be treated in detail.

In the northern European countries, where settlement is relatively sparse and industry per square kilometer small, the yearly rainfall per hectare contains only small amounts of nitrogen compounds (341). Recent investigations in different parts of Scandinavia have given very variable values for the ammonium and nitrate nitrogen in the annual precipitation. Eriksson (118) reports very low values for both in northern Scandinavia (the lowest values for nitrate nitrogen being 0.23 kg and for ammonium nitrogen 0.15 kg per hectare per year). In southern Scandinavia, where the population density and agricultural and industrial activities are relatively high, much higher values are to be found: in Denmark the highest value for nitrate nitrogen is 2.21 kg, and for ammonium nitrogen 4.94 kg, per hectare per year and the lowest values are 1.74 and 2.50 kg, respectively (118). Since it is probable that the ammonium nitrogen found in rain water originates mainly from the ammonia evaporated from the soil and oceans, and since nitrate nitrogen according to recent investigations is absent from snow collected from regions in New Zealand where no plants or animals exist [Wilson (403)], the nitrogen fixation in the atmosphere seems to be very low—far lower even than was earlier thought. The large amounts of ammonium and nitrate nitrogen (28.2 kg total nitrogen per hectare per year) observed in Central Europe by Scharrer and Fast (287) in the rain water are apparently due mostly to industry, agriculture, and other activities in densely populated areas. Earlier results even from relatively nearby regions often differ greatly [Manshard (220)], in part perhaps owing to the methods used.

The industrial production of nitrogen compounds from atmospheric nitrogen has opened up new possibilities in this century for nitrogen fertilization and thus for improving agricultural production. The fact is, however, that perhaps only 2 or 3% of the nitrogen contained in the annual harvests of the world originates, at present, from nitrogen-ous fertilizers produced by industry. Most of the nitrogen of plants is still a product of biological nitrogen fixation or is derived from the nitrogen reserves of the soil. In the latter case the soil is depleted of its fertility.

Effective against this depletion is the cultivation of legumes. There is no method more effective in preserving the humus and nitrogenous contents of the soil than the cultivation of legume-rich leys,* especially leys of clover (*Trifolium* species) and alfalfa (*Medicago sativa*). Neither is there a more effective or economical way of producing pro-teins for animals. Therefore, the significance of leguminous plants has not yet been diminished by the tremendous development of the manu-facture of nitrogenous fertilizers. From the standpoint of world economy of energy, an effective cultivation of legumes, and thus the utilization of biological nitrogen fixation, is of the greatest importance [Virtanen (342)].

The nitrogen fixation which takes place in the root nodules of legumes is, under favorable conditions, sufficient for the maximal growth of many legumes. In this laboratory greenhouse experiments with red clover (*Trifolium pratense*), grown in pots with quartz sand in the absence of combined nitrogen, have at best given fixation which can be calculated to about 1000 kg of nitrogen per hectare per year. In these experiments clover was cut three times in 6 months [Virtanen (332)]. Under field conditions such high nitrogen fixation cannot of course be obtained since temperature, moisture, nutrients, and other factors which influence growth can be most favorably adjusted during the whole period of growth only in a greenhouse. However, even in a country as far north as Finland, a really good red clover sward (giving yields of from 6000 to 9000 kg of dry matter per hectare in three cuttings per summer) fixes 200–300 kg of nitrogen per hectare in one growing season [Virtanen (333)], and a pea (*Pisum sativum*) crop fixes about 100 kg. In countries where the summer is longer and the weather more favorable, up to 400 kg of nitrogen may be fixed in a very good red clover sward, and in an alfalfa sward even more. These amounts exceed by many times the amounts of nitrogen in the fertiliz-ers used in effective agricultural production. On the average, however, the nitrogen fixed in clover and alfalfa fields is naturally much lower than the maximal values given above [cf. (134), page 218].

In nature many wild leguminous herbs and trees are important as fixers of atmospheric nitrogen and in increasing the nitrogen content of the soil. Also some nonlegumes, such as several species of *Alnus* (on

* The term "leys" relates to cultivated grass for cutting.

the roots of which nitrogen-fixing nodules are formed by specific micro-organisms), are valuable contributors to the formation of a humus rich in nitrogen.

Free-living nitrogen-fixing bacteria, such as anaerobic *Clostridium* and aerobic *Azotobacter*, compete with other microorganisms in the soil for their nutrition, especially for carbon sources. The nitrogen fixed per hectare by these nitrogen fixers is, therefore, much smaller than in symbiotic nitrogen fixation. Accurate information about the amounts of nitrogen thus fixed is lacking, but it is obvious that they vary greatly in different soils, possibly from a few kilograms to 20 kg per hectare per year. Allison (13), on the basis of the highly controversial literature on this point, stated that although as much as 20 pounds per acre probably may be fixed annually on an occasional, well-limed grassland, even the old estimate of 6 pounds per acre per year in the United States [Lipman and Conybeare (211)] may be too high for an average rate. In naturally acid soils *Clostridium* is evidently the most important free-living nitrogen fixer both in forest and cultivated soils. In neutral and slightly alkaline soils *Azotobacter* may be important, but its role is still under debate. Since in the recent years numerous microorganisms have been found to be able to fix nitrogen, our concepts of the role of free-living nitrogen-fixing organisms in nature may in time change.

The most autotrophic microorganisms, which assimilate both carbon dioxide and nitrogen, are the nitrogen-fixing blue-green algae. In marine waters their occurrence is scanty, but from tropical to polar regions they are common in fresh water. Their nitrogen-fixing capacity becomes more clearly distinguishable in nitrogen-deficient surroundings. Information about their importance in nature and agriculture is still very deficient, but their role may be greater than has been supposed hitherto [Calder (89)]. In rice (*Oryza sativa*) fields they even may be of great importance (100, 397), but their role relative to nitrogen-fixing bacteria is still under dispute (95).

B. The History of Biological Nitrogen Fixation

From the beginnings of agriculture symbiotic nitrogen fixation has been unwittingly utilized in the cultivation of legumes. After many contradictory and negative results, in the latter part of the nineteenth century the ability of legumes to grow on poor soils and to improve their fertility was finally explained when, in 1886, Hellriegel and Wilfarth (153) showed experimentally that legumes actually utilize atmospheric nitrogen if their roots bear nodules formed by bacteria. Two years later Beijerinck (35) isolated a bacterium in pure culture which formed nodules on the roots of the host plant. [Beijerinck gave this bacterium the name *Bacillus radicicola*, which Praźmowski (267) changed to *Bacterium radicicola* because it did not form spores. Frank (133) began to use the name *Rhizobium leguminosarum*. In this article *Rhizobium* is used as the name for the genus and rhizobia as the general name for the nodule bacteria of leguminous plants.] The formation of root nodules by specific bacteria thus was conclusively proved.

Of special historical interest is the peculiar fact that the earlier negative results regarding the ability of legumes to utilize atmospheric nitrogen (especially the experiments performed in Rothamsted in 1857–1859) were due to a "too careful" test methodology, in other words the destroying of bacteria indispensable for the fixation. In the excellent monograph of Fred *et al.* (134) and in that of Wilson (407) the dramatic history of the studies on symbiotic nitrogen fixation is thoroughly treated. Especially interesting is a recently published article by Wilson (410).

Beijerinck's original discovery about the inability of rhizobia to fix gaseous nitrogen when growing free on a medium was challenged by many contrary findings. The numerous positive claims were probably influenced by the apparent increase of the *Rhizobium* mass in a nitrogen-free or exceedingly nitrogen-deficient medium. The inoculated bacteria can continue to divide to some extent until their nitrogen content is severely lowered, and they form a voluminous nitrogen-free gum. Cells of *Rhizobium* from a medium containing an excess of a suitable nitrogen source, e.g., asparagine, have a nitrogen content of 8–9% of their dry weight, whereas cells grown on a medium deficient in nitrogen contain only 3.5% of nitrogen [Burris and Wilson (81)]. The dependence of free-living rhizobia on combined nitrogen, and their inability to fix nitrogen, was unequivocally shown in critical experiments in different laboratories during the 1920's and 1930's (cf. 417). More recently this result has been confirmed by Wilson (411) by the sensitive isotope method with N_2^{15}.

The first observations on fixation of atmospheric nitrogen by microorganisms grown in nutrient solution were made in 1862 by Jodin (177), who, soon after Pasteur's discovery of the microbial cause of fermentation, demonstrated that a nutrient solution containing phosphate and a source of carbon such as sugar, glycerol, or tartaric acid, but no combined nitrogen, supports the growth of "mycoderms." By sealing the growing culture into a closed vessel he could prove that both oxygen and nitrogen were utilized, the latter to the extent of about 6–7% of the former.

Berthelot (43), about a quarter of a century later, showed by quantitative determinations an increase of combined nitrogen in soils left in open jars during a summer, whereas no increase took place if the soil was previously sterilized by heating. This pointed to a microbial cause of the fixation. The first to obtain a nitrogen-fixing organism in pure culture was Winogradsky (423). He isolated from soil an anaerobic organism, *Clostridium pasteurianum*, which, growing in a medium containing glucose and phosphate but no combined nitrogen, fixed about 2 mg of gaseous nitrogen per gram of glucose fermented.

A few years later Beijerinck (37) isolated from soil and canal water two aerobic nitrogen-fixing organisms, *Azotobacter chroococcum* and *A. agilis*, respectively. These soon turned out to be highly efficient in fixing nitrogen and became the most commonly used microorganisms in studies of nonsymbiotic nitrogen fixation.

Observations on the nitrogen-fixing capacity of photosynthetic blue-green algae were made as early as in 1889, at which time there was, however, no certainty yet about the purity of algal cultures regarding bacterial contamination. The first observation on nitrogen fixation by a pure culture of a blue-green alga (*Nostoc punctiforme*) was made by Drewes in 1928 (107). In addition to free-living forms, there are many blue-green algae that live in association with other plants. The water fern *Azolla* is, in fact, able to grow without combined nitrogen by means of its symbiotic alga [Bortels (60)]. Bond and Scott (54) recently found that some lichens fix nitrogen with the help of blue-green algae as their algal component.

After $N_2{}^{15}$ came into use in the studies on nitrogen fixation, a number of new microorganisms have been found to possess some capacity to fix molecular nitrogen.

Thus during the last seventy years the gaseous nitrogen of air has been found to be a suitable nitrogen source for numerous microorganisms to a greater or lesser degree. On the other hand, it has never been possible to prove that multicellular green plants fix nitrogen except in symbiosis with specific microorganisms.

II. Nitrogen Fixation by Free-Living Microorganisms

A. DETECTION OF NITROGEN FIXATION

During a half century of research since the earliest investigations, the ability to fix nitrogen has been attributed to numerous species of organisms, mainly bacteria, molds, and yeasts. Many of these claims were evidently at fault owing to uncritical methods. Weak nitrogen fixation is often very difficult to prove with certainty and requires that special attention be paid to the methods used.

Growth without combined nitrogen, so useful in the isolation of nitrogen-fixing organisms and important as evidence for nitrogen fixation, is not an unequivocal proof of it per se. Tiny amounts of combined nitrogen in the inoculum, in the medium, and in the laboratory air may be able to sustain some growth during weeks or months, as already mentioned. Lack of growth of identical cultures incubated in the *absence of* nitrogen is a valuable negative control.

Increase of total nitrogen in the culture, usually determined by the Kjeldahl procedure, is the most widely used and important proof of fixation. If nitrogen fixation is strong or moderate, this method is quite satisfactory, but if the fixation is very small and the organism requires the addition of plant extracts or nitrogenous growth factors to the medium, reliable demonstration of nitrogen fixation by the classic procedures of nitrogen determination becomes difficult. In such cases, when the absolute amount of nitrogen must be determined with high accuracy, it is often advantageous to use reductive substances, like zinc or iron, in the Kjeldahl procedure to ensure the complete reduction of all nitrogenous compounds to ammonia.

Gasometric determination of the consumption of nitrogen (and oxygen) during growth in a closed vessel is the oldest technique; it was used by Jodin (177) as early as 1862, but it is somewhat tedious and it also has its pitfalls. The *Warburg manometrical* technique, though not practical in the detection of new nitrogen-fixing species, is invaluable in chemical and physiological studies of the nitrogen fixation.

In nonsymbiotic organisms like *Azotobacter*, in which it is bound to the growth of the organism, nitrogen fixation as well as growth in physiologically adequate conditions follow the kinetics of a first-order reaction. Therefore, nitrogen fixation can be measured by the velocity constant g of a first-order reaction

$$g = 2.30d \log (a + y)/dt = dy/(a + y) dt \tag{1}$$

where a = initial cell concentration, y = increase in t hours.

In Eq. 1, g can be determined by plotting against time the logarithm of the experimental values of any quantity which is proportional to growth, such as the total number N or the dry material of the cells, or the respiration rate (cubic millimeters of oxygen consumed per hour per milliliter of culture). Of these the rate of respiration (oxygen consumption) is generally used because it can be easily determined by the manometric method of Warburg. Especially Burk [cf., e.g. (72)] has used this technique for studies of the dependence of nitrogen fixation on variable factors like temperature, pH, pN_2, inhibitors, etc.

The *isotope method* with N_2^{15} as a tracer, first introduced to research on nitrogen fixation by Burris and Miller [78, cf. also (76)] at the beginning of the 1940's, is the most sensitive and critical technique so far available. Natural nitrogen contains 0.37% of the heavy isotope N^{15} and an increase of 0.02% above the natural level can be accurately determined by the mass spectrograph. Since N_2^{15} is nowadays available enriched to 60% excess (over the natural concentration), it may be diluted about 3000-fold in the experiment and still be demonstrated with certainty. This means that for 1 mg nitrogen in the organism, fraction, or isolated compound, only 0.35 μg need be derived from fixation. The isotope method has the additional advantage that it is not sensitive to the quantity of nitrogen in the sample, since the size of sample does not appreciably influence the mass spectrographic determination of its isotopic composition.

However, in the studies on nitrogen fixation by the symbiotic system the most critical item of technique is often not the determination of nitrogen, but the use of aseptic culture methods. As will be seen later, the use of open pots in experiments has probably led to more erroneous results than any other technical deficiency.

B. The Species That Fix Nitrogen

A brief summary of the free-living nitrogen-fixing organisms is presented in Table I. Only one member of each of the most typical genera or species is mentioned with a few of its characteristics, the name of the investigator who detected its nitrogen-fixing property, and the year of its detection.

1. Azotobacter and Beijerinckia

As mentioned earlier, Beijerinck in 1901 isolated from soil the type species, *A. chroococcum*, which is ubiquitous in neutral soils, and also the motile species *A. agilis*, which is mainly a water bacterium. Some authorities separate as a third species *A. vinelandii*, which in Bergey's manual is classified as a subspecies of *A. agilis*. *Azotobacter vinelandii* was first isolated by Lipman in 1903 at Vineland, New Jersey. *Azotobacter* species are strongly aerobic, fast growing, and active in nitrogen fixing; they have a pH optimum at about 7 and do not grow with nitrogen gas below pH 6. They get energy for their physiological processes by oxidizing carbohydrates (e.g., mono- and disaccharides and starch), organic acids, and other substances to carbon dioxide. The amount of nitrogen fixed is usually 10–20 mg nitrogen per gram of sugar utilized —at the very highest, 25–30 mg per gram. Nitrogen fixation is most efficient at the time of fastest growth, when an *Azotobacter* culture may

TABLE I

REPRESENTATIVE FREE-LIVING NITROGEN-FIXING MICROORGANISMS

Organism	Growth characteristics	Investigator[a]	Year[b]	Efficiency of fixation (mg N/gm carbohydrate)
Bacteria				
Azotobacter	Heterotrophic, aerobic	Beijerinck	1901	10–30
Beijerinckia	Heterotrophic, aerobic	Starkey and De	1939	10–20
Clostridium	Heterotrophic, anaerobic	Winogradsky	1893	2–12
Aerobacter	Heterotrophic, facultative anaerobic	Hamilton *et al.*	1953	4
Methanobacterium	Chemoautotrophic, anaerobic	Pine and Barker	1954	—
Pseudomonas	Heterotrophic, facultative anaerobic	Anderson	1955	1–15
Achromobacter	Heterotrophic, aerobic	Jensen	1958	1
Bacillus polymyxa	Heterotrophic, aerobic	Hino and Wilson	1958	—
Rhodospirillum	Photoautotrophic, aerobic	Kamen and Gest	1949	—
Chlorobium	Photoautotrophic, aerobic	Lindström *et al.*	1949	—
Chromatium	Photoautotrophic, aerobic	Lindström *et al.*	1950	—
Rhodomicrobium	Photoautotrophic, aerobic	Lindström *et al.*	1950	—
Yeasts				
Saccharomyces, Rhodotorula	Heterotrophic, facultative anaerobic	Metcalfe and Chayen	1954	4
Pullularia	Heteroautotrophic, facultative anaerobic	Brown and Metcalfe	1957	5
Algae				
Nostoc, Anabaena	Photoautotrophic, aerobic	Drewes	1928	10 (in dark)
Cylindrospermum, Aulosira, Calothrix, Tolypothrix, Anabaenopsis, Mastigocladus	Photoautotrophic, aerobic	For references see Fogg (126, 128, 129)	—	—

[a] Investigator who detected nitrogen-fixing property.
[b] Year when nitrogen-fixing property was detected.

fix 10 mg nitrogen per 100 ml per day. With this rate fixation can be determined by the Kjeldahl procedure after only 1–2 hours.

Azotobacter indicus, first isolated by Starkey and De (297) in 1939 and earlier classified as the third species of Azotobacter, is currently, according to Derx (106), classified as the separate genus Beijerinckia (173).* In addition to the type species B. indica, several subspecies are recognized in this new genus [Kluyver and Becking (194)], which is found only in the calcium-deficient tropical laterite soils of Asia, Africa, America, and Australia. The main characteristics of Beijerinckia, which distinguish it from Azotobacter, are its broader pH spectrum (3 to 7, with optimum around 4) and its low calcium ("calcifrige") requirement.

2. Clostridium

This is a large genus of strictly anaerobic, usually motile, gram-positive rods, which typically do not ferment cellulose. Clostridium butyricum, isolated in 1880 by Prażmowski, is the type species; it fixes atmospheric nitrogen moderately. Of the numerous species of Clostridium, the most active in the assimilation of nitrogen is C. pasteurianum, first isolated by Winogradsky (422) in 1893. Numerous other species of the genus also fix nitrogen, though less efficiently. For a list of the nitrogen-fixing species see Bergey's Manual. In a study of 15 species of Clostridium, Rosenblum and Wilson (278) found 12 capable of fixing nitrogen. The nitrogen-fixing efficiency of clostridia is usually 2–3 mg nitrogen per gram of sugar—at the highest 10–12 mg nitrogen per gram of sugar. When serially cultivated in synthetic medium, clostridia gradually lose their ability to grow, but they regain it after one "soil passage," i.e., when cultivated once again in soil. However, when a synthetic nutrient solution contains folic acid, the ability to grow is not lost, according to Virtanen and Lundbom (379).

In nature, clostridia thrive best in association with cellulose-degrading fungi and bacteria, utilize the mono- and disaccharides produced by them [cf. Vartiovaara (329)]. Clostridia cannot use polysaccharides other than starch (cf. Section II,C,3).

Even a small amount of ammonium or nitrate nitrogen inhibits nitrogen-fixation, since the combined forms of nitrogen are used preferentially by Clostridium as well as by Azotobacter.

3. Aerobacter

It was shown by Skinner (294) that Aerobacter aerogenes is able to fix nitrogen, and this observation has been recently confirmed, with the

* Bergey's Manual (7th Edition, 1957) still classifies it as a third species of Azotobacter "until further comparative studies are made."

isotopic N^{15}-technique, by Hamilton et al. (148), Hamilton and Wilson (150), and Jensen (175). Nitrogen fixation by this organism is most intensive if the medium contains traces of nitrate nitrogen (10–20 μg/ml) and a relatively high concentration of glucose or saccharose (2–4%). The strains of Hamilton and co-workers required strictly anaerobic conditions for nitrogen fixation, but the supply of oxygen had no appreciable influence on the growth and nitrogen fixation of the two strains studied by Jensen. Similar results under anaerobic conditions were later reported by Pengra and Wilson (262a) whereas Johnstone and Pfeffer (177a) report results on fermentation of whey by a nitrogen-fixing strain of Aerobacter aerogenes in aerobic conditions. In the isotopic experiment of Hamilton et al. an excess of 17.4 atom per cent was reached in 3 days, which corresponds to a doubling of the original nitrogen or an increase of 30 μg nitrogen per milliliter, an amount which is certainly easily demonstrable by the Kjeldahl method.

Pine and Barker (266) found that the chemautotrophic, anaerobic Methanobacterium omelianskii fixed nitrogen, and they demonstrated this also by the N^{15}-technique. A small amount (5 μg/ml) of ammonium in the medium increased the nitrogen fixation, but a greater amount (30 μg/ml) inhibited it.

Anderson (22) showed that a facultatively anaerobic soil bacterium of the Pseudomonas type, for which he proposed the name P. azotocolligans, fixed atmospheric nitrogen; he demonstrated this both by the N^{15}-technique and by the Kjeldahl method.

Roy and Mukherjee (281) described a nitrogen-fixing microorganism which resembles Anderson's type in some respects but also has distinct differences. Recently Proctor and Wilson (268) have isolated six different species of Pseudomonas, which all possess the ability to fix nitrogen. The nitrogen-fixing enzyme system seemed to be adaptive in these microorganisms.

A number of other genera, mostly anaerobic bacteria, have been shown to possess the power of nitrogen fixation, although the evidence is not always indisputable. Of these may be mentioned Bacillus hydrogenes [Belayaeva (38)], Achromobacter sp. [Jensen (176)], and Bacillus polymyxa [Hino and Wilson (163)]. B. hydrogenes fixes nitrogen both on totally inorganic, nitrogen-free medium in an atmosphere of hydrogen, carbon dioxide, and nitrogen and on glucose-containing medium in the absence of hydrogen; in the latter case the yield is 0.85–2 mg nitrogen per gram of sugar. Quite recently Jensen (176) in Denmark isolated from water a nitrogen-fixing organism which he identified as an Achromobacter species. In a later survey

Proctor and Wilson (268) demonstrated aerobic nitrogen fixation in eight strains of *Achromobacter;* of these only Jensen's strains fixed nitrogen also anaerobically. As in *Pseudomonas* species, the nitrogen-fixing enzyme system seemed to be adaptive. *Bacillus polymyxa* is another species which only quite recently has been shown by Hino and Wilson (163) to be able to fix nitrogen. It contains an active hydrogenase and its nitrogen fixation is sensitive to molecular oxygen. As little as 1% of oxygen significantly reduced nitrogen fixation, competing with nitrogen for the final electrons produced by the cytochrome system. On the contrary, growth of the organism on nitrate nitrogen requires oxygen. Uncertainty still prevails regarding the reported [Sisler and ZoBell (293)] observation that the anaerobic chemautotroph *Desulfovibrio desulfuricans,* which stores energy for its life processes from the reduction of sulfates by hydrogen, is able to fix atmospheric nitrogen. Bach (30) reports that a study, by means of the N^{15}-technique, on the nitrogen-fixing ability of this organism has given a negative result. Bisset (44a) has discussed natural relationships of the nitrogen-fixing bacteria.

4. Soil Yeasts

Metcalfe and Chayen (223) isolated from underneath *Calluna vulgaris,* growing on an acid heath soil at pH 4.5, two yeastlike organisms, one resembling *Saccharomyces,* the other *Rhodotorula.* When cultivated 14 days on nitrogen-free medium, the organisms fixed 1–4 mg nitrogen per gram glucose, that is, having about a tenth of the efficiency of *Azotobacter.* These results also have been confirmed by the N^{15}-technique [Roberts and Wilson (276)]. Somewhat more active is the *Pullularia*-type soil yeast recently isolated by Brown and Metcalfe (65), which is able to fix 4–5 mg nitrogen per gram glucose. On a medium containing combined nitrogen it rapidly loses its nitrogen-fixing power. Nemeth (239, 240) reports the isolation in pure culture, from the root nodules of *Lupinus luteus,* of a yeastlike microorganism which is able to grow rapidly on nitrogen-deficient "rhizobium agar" and to fix nitrogen and which should differ from all previously known free-living nitrogen fixers by containing a red pigment, at first supposed to be hemoglobin but later on (239a) found not to be so.

5. Photosynthetic Bacteria

When studying the photoevolution of hydrogen by *Rhodospirillum rubrum,* Kamen and Gest (184) noticed that nitrogen and ammonia competitively inhibit this process. Wilson and Umbreit (417) had shown in 1937 that hydrogen competitively inhibits nitrogen fixation in the symbiotic system and later in other organisms (see page 560). Kamen and Gest studied whether *Rhodospirillum* might also fix gaseous nitrogen, and with N^{15} found this to be so. Since then, nitrogen-fixing genera have been found in all three families of the suborder Rhodobacteriineae:

Thiorhodaceae: *Chromatium* [Lindström *et al.* (207, 209)]

Athiorhodaceae: *Rhodospirillum rubrum* [Kamen and Gest (184)]; *Rhodopseudomonas* sp. [Lindström *et al.* (208)], *Rhodomicrobium vannielii* [Lindström *et al.* (208, 209)]

Chlorobacteriaceae: *Chlorobium thiosulfatophilum* [Lindström *et al.* (207, 209)]

Lindström *et al.* (208) tested 20 species of *Rhodopseudomonas* for nitrogen fixation, 19 of which gave a positive result; it seems to be the general concensus that this ability is probably possessed by all photosynthetic bacteria. These bacteria usually require organic growth factors (thiamine, biotin, and nicotinic acid), and many of them are able to fix nitrogen also in the dark when growing heterotrophically, though the efficiency of fixation is then low.

6. Blue-Green Algae

Two of the fundamental processes of organic nature—photosynthesis and nitrogen fixation—are united in most species of the widely distributed blue-green algae (Schizophyceae or Myxophyceae).

The first evidence of the nitrogen-fixing ability of these simple organisms, which in their mode of reproduction resemble bacteria, was provided by Frank (132) in 1889. However, since his algal cultures were not free of bacteria and the first pure cultures of microscopic algae (cultures of Chlorophyceae) could not fix nitrogen, the reported nitrogen fixation of earlier algal cultures was suspected to be due to nitrogen-fixing bacteria, which thrive well in the slimy layer covering the algae. Drewes (107) finally showed conclusively, by using pure cultures of *Nostoc punctiforme* and *Anabaena variabilis*, that they are able to fix nitrogen; this result was confirmed by Allison and Morris (15) and others. Since then this ability has been proved in more than 20 species distributed in the genera *Nostoc, Anabaena, Cylindrospermum, Calothrix, Anabaenopsis,* and *Mastigocladus* [for references see Fogg's monographs (126, 128, 129)]. It has been established that the ability to fix nitrogen is common among the blue-greens although some species lack this property [cf. Fogg (128)]. All the blue-green algae that can fix nitrogen seem to have a common peculiarity, namely, they form thick-walled cells, called heterocysts, which appear at regular intervals in the chains of algal cells. The role of heterocysts is not fully understood, but it is generally believed that they are resting cells or organs of perennation. Fogg and Wolfe (130) suspect that the heterocysts and the nitrogen fixation of blue-green algae may have had a common phylogenetic origin.

Nitrogen fixation of the blue-green algae has been confirmed by Williams and Burris (402) by the isotopic tracer technique (N^{15}). The blue-green algae have a special role in the economy of nature, because they, being autotrophic with respect to carbon as well as nitrogen, are able to thrive in places where no other organisms are able to grow, e.g. on humid rocks. They, as well as the photosynthetic bacteria, are believed to belong among the earliest forms of life.* Most of the blue-green algae can also grow heterotrophically in a nitrogen-free medium, but nitrogen fixation is then slower. One strain of *Nostoc muscorum* has been reported to fix 10 mg nitrogen per gram of glucose in darkness.

C. METABOLISM OF NITROGEN-FIXING MICROORGANISMS AND FACTORS THAT INFLUENCE FIXATION

1. General Remarks

Nitrogen fixation in free-living microorganisms is normally inseparably bound with growth. It is not achieved in nongrowing cultures and was not, at first, consistently obtained with cell-free enzyme preparations, although Magee and Burris (218) reported erratic positive results with cell-free *Azotobacter vinelandii* preparations. However, positive results obtained by a dependable method, even occasional ones, mean that the reaction *does* take place. Although all the factors involved are not yet mastered, cell-free nitrogen fixation is expected to be consistently obtained sooner or later.†

* By some—e.g., van Niel—the blue-green algae are regarded as relatively advanced forms among the microorganisms because of their special pigments. Also there is a view that nitrogen fixation came late in the evolution of bacteria, after all the ammonia of the original atmosphere had been used. [Ed.]

† After this manuscript was completed, fixation of nitrogen by cell-free extracts of *Clostridium* was reported by Carnahan *et al.* (90). They obtained from cells of *Clostridium pasteurianum*, dried at 50°C under vacuum and autolyzed at 30°C in anaerobic conditions, soluble preparations capable of reproducible and readily measurable nitrogen fixation in the presence of pyruvate. The techniques applicable to *Clostridium* were not successful for *Azotobacter* and *Nostoc*. However, soon after the above report Wilson and Burris (412a) applied the same method successfully to another blue-green alga, *Mastigocladus laminosus*, and also to a photosynthetic bacterium, *Rhodospirillum rubrum*. At about the same time, Nicholas and Fisher (241b) reported that cell-free extracts from *Azotobacter vinelandii* could fix nitrogen when the cells were disrupted during the early log phase of growth in the culture medium

At this point, however, we must examine the results obtained during the last two decades with growing cultures, even though it is often extremely difficult to decide whether an observed effect was specific to the process of nitrogen fixation itself or to the metabolic processes in the organism in general.

Until quite recently it has been considered that nitrogen-fixing organisms use gaseous nitrogen as a source only of nitrogen, but hardly of energy. The latter possibility has also to be taken into consideration, however. Some years ago, Parker (261a) suggested that nitrogen fixation might well be a form of respiration with nitrogen acting as an alternative to oxygen as a terminal hydrogen acceptor. In a recent paper, Parker and Scutt (261b) emphasize this possibility, based on the competitive inhibition of nitrogen fixation by oxygen in *Azotobacter*, and on the calculations of Bayliss (33a) on the energy changes associated with the reduction of nitrogen to ammonia. Dilworth and Parker (106a) have just found that the inhibition of respiration by oxygen is more severe with the organic acids than with the sugars. When glycerine is the only carbon source, no inhibitory effects of oxygen were observed. No explanation could be offered for the lack of inhibition. Hamilton and Wilson (150) were the first who reported oxygen-inhibited nitrogen fixation by the faculative aerobe *Aerobacter aerogenes*. The specific nature of the inhibition was shown by Pengra and Wilson (262a) for this organism and by Hino and Wilson (163) for another facultative bacterium of the *Bacillus polymyxa* type. The value obtained by Parker and Scutt (261b) for the Michaelis constant was 0.0229 at 20% oxygen concentration, and was in agreement with that obtained by Wilson *et al.* (413).

2. Humidity, Temperature, and pH

Regarding the general conditions of growth, the *Clostridium* species favor a relatively high, *Azotobacter* a moderate, humidity in the soil. The optimum temperature for growth as well as for nitrogen fixation is for *C. pasteurianum* 25°C, for *A. chroococcum* and *A. agilis* 25–28°C, for *Beijerinckia indica* (formerly *A. indicus*) 30°C and, for some tropical strains of the latter, even 33°C.

Both *Clostridium* and *Azotobacter* have the pH optimum of nitrogen fixation slightly on the alkaline side, but the pH evidently does not have

---

in which they were grown. The fixation was shown by them to occur in particle-free extracts provided the "media factors" were present. Thus new possibilities have been opened up for the elucidation of factors necessary for nitrogen fixation and the mechanism of this process.

a direct effect on fixation, since the same optimum (pH 7.6–7.8) is obtained for *Azotobacter* when growing on ammonium nitrogen, as Burk *et al.* (72) showed in 1934. With the exception of *A. indicus*— which currently is classified as a separate genus, *Beijerinckia*—*Azotobacter* does not grow on gaseous nitrogen or fix it below pH 6.0. The cessation of growth at this pH with nitrogen is very abrupt, although growth with ammonium nitrogen diminishes only slowly and ceases somewhere below pH 5 (Fig. 1). In blue-green algae assimilation of nitrogen does not take place below pH 5.7 [Allison *et al.* (14)]. On the

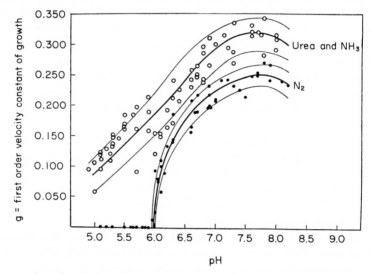

Fig. 1. Growth of *Azotobacter* with urea and ammonia or with nitrogen as a function of pH. From Burk *et al.* (72).

alkaline side the pH dependence of nitrogen fixation for bacteria is similar to that of respiration, being evidently due to the inhibition of the latter.

3. Carbon and Energy Metabolism

It is neither possible nor useful to discuss the carbon metabolism of nitrogen-fixing organisms in great detail here because it does not differ markedly from that of the nonnitrogen-fixing organisms. But brief mention may show, first, which carbon compounds are most readily utilized by a given organism and, second, the efficiency of fixation with a given carbohydrate.

The anaerobic nitrogen-fixing bacteria obtain energy for growth as well as for nitrogen fixation from fermentation of carbohydrates (especially glucose, saccharose, and/or soluble starch) mainly to fatty acids. The nature of the carbohydrates which the organism is able to use has even been adopted as a means of classification [Bredemann (63); Waksman (393)]. Carbohydrates utilized are degraded by the glycolytic mechanism, or by the so-called pentose cycle, to the level of three-carbon compounds, which are then used for building up cell constituents or are further degraded, mainly to acetate. The efficiency of nitrogen fixation by pure cultures of anaerobic nitrogen-fixing bacteria usually has been reported to be about 2–3 mg nitrogen per gram of glucose used. Rosenblum and Wilson (279), however, report an efficiency as high as 10–12 mg nitrogen per gram of sugar used for *Clostridium pasteurianum*. This is nearly the same as the average efficiency of *Azotobacter*. In anaerobic fermentation per mole of glucose only a small amount of energy is released compared with aerobic respiration (total combustion to carbon dioxide and water). Since the low energy production in anaerobic organisms is sufficient for nitrogen fixation, it seems that the extremely high respiration of *Azotobacter* is not directly needed for nitrogen fixation.

Aerobic nitrogen-fixing agents can use a much greater variety of carbon sources than the anaerobic ones. *Azotobacter*, for example, utilizes fatty and hydroxy acids, lower and higher alcohols, and mono-, di-, and polysaccharides. It can also use amino acids, but not peptones, as a source of carbon and energy. Several amino acids are also used as a source of nitrogen (see page 559).

Azotobacter is the fastest-growing organism among the nitrogen-fixing bacteria. In natural conditions its rates of growth and of nitrogen fixation are usually directly dependent on the supply of carbohydrate and oxygen. In a special fermentor with highly efficient aeration and with a high carbohydrate concentration, Alexander and Wilson (4) reported fixation of 0.175 mg nitrogen per milliliter per hour during the exponential period of growth. Such a net increase can be maintained, of course, only for a short time.

Carbon compounds are partially converted to cellular substances, partially oxidized to carbon dioxide and water. When no combined nitrogen is present, *Azotobacter* may fix even 20–30 mg nitrogen per gram of glucose, although an average efficiency is only about 12 mg. Meyerhof and Burk (225) have already shown that a very high respiration rate is typical of the *Azotobacter*: Q_{O_2}-values obtained vary between 2000 and 4000 μl O_2 per hour per milligram dry weight of bacteria. The highest rate is found at an oxygen pressure of 0.10–0.15 atm—somewhat below the atmospheric. In this respect *Azotobacter* differs from the excised, sliced soybean nodules, where fixation increases even at oxygen pressures higher than atmospheric, the maximum lying at about pO_2 0.5 atm (see Section III, K). The high respiration rate seems to have no direct significance for the fixation process. Enzymes for the glycolytic as well as the "direct oxidation" pathway (see Chapter 3, Vol. IA) seem to be present in *Azotobacter* as well as in all the other nitrogen-fixing agents studied. Intermediates of the above "pathways"— pentose, hexose, and sedoheptulose phosphates—as well as the enzymes of the tricarboxylic acid cycle have been shown in *Azotobacter* by Wilson's group [for references see Wilson (411)]. Pyruvate produced by the glycolytic mechanism or "direct oxidation" is further oxidized by the tricarboxylic acid cycle, which is probably the main source of energy for the process of fixation as well as the main source of carbon acceptors for the reduced nitrogen. The nitrogen-fixing blue-green algae normally use atmospheric carbon dioxide as the source of carbon and light as the source of energy, but many of them are also able to fix nitrogen heterotrophically in darkness, using glucose as a source of carbon and energy. Allison *et al.* (14) have reported rather high efficiencies of heterotrophic fixation for *Nostoc muscorum*, 10–12 mg nitrogen per gram of glucose, which are quite comparable to the average efficiency of *Azotobacter* and equal to the highest value reported for *Clostridium* (see above). On the other hand, another strain of *N. muscorum* was an obligate phototroph.

4. Utilization of Molecular and Combined Nitrogen

Burk (68) was the first to study the dependence of nitrogen fixation on the partial pressure of nitrogen (pN_2). He showed that the relationship follows the Michaelis-Menten equation for an enzymatic reaction, but his value for K_m, the pN_2, where the reaction rate of the fixation is half maximal, was too high, because he used molecular hydrogen as a diluent gas. Later, when hydrogen was found by Wilson and Umbreit (417) to be a specific inhibitor of nitrogen fixation, K_m was redetermined in an inert atmosphere; these determinations gave for *Azotobacter* $K_m = 0.02$ atm [Wyss *et al.* (431); Wilson *et al.* (413)], and also for *Nostoc* $K_m = 0.02$ atm, values comparable with those obtained for detached soybean root nodules ($K_m = 0.025$) [Burris *et al.* (77)]. These results show that already half of the maximal rate of fixation is reached by each of these systems at a nitrogen pressure which is only about one-fortieth that of the atmospheric pressure. Gaseous nitrogen, therefore, seldom, if ever, becomes a limiting factor of nitrogen fixation under natural conditions.

In most nitrogen-fixing organisms even low concentrations of NH_4^+ diminish nitrogen fixation markedly, and 5–10 mg ammonium nitrogen per liter suffices to arrest it completely [Burk (68)]. This is about the same concentration, in gram atoms of nitrogen, at which utilization of molecular nitrogen reaches its maximum. Below this concentration both forms of nitrogen are utilized simultaneously, the inhibition by ammonia being "competitive." Above this concentration ammonium nitrogen is usually utilized preferentially. The gram-negative aerobic bacterium recently isolated by Roy and Mukherjee (281) from the soil of Javanese jute (*Corchorus* sp.) fields is the only exception so far reported. This bacterium seems to be an obligate nitrogen fixer.

The enzyme system responsible for ammonium ion assimilation seems to be constitutive, not adaptive, in most nitrogen-fixing organisms because no lag period is usually found in the utilization of ammonium nitrogen when it is added into a nitrogen-fixing culture, but fixation of gaseous nitrogen ceases and utilization of ammonium nitrogen starts immediately. A lag period has been observed in *Azotobacter* only if a relatively high ammonium-ion concentration was used (above $10^{-4} M$; 0.1% w/v of nitrogen as ammonium acetate stops respiration for a period of several hours) [Wilson and Roberts (421); Azim and Roberts (28)], but this may be due to secondary effects, e.g., disturbance of the pH inside the cells because of an excessive assimilation of the ammonium ion.

Nitrate nitrogen is utilized by most nitrogen-fixing organisms also, but, e.g., in an *Azotobacter* culture growing on molecular nitrogen, utilization of nitrate nitrogen begins only after a lag period of about 1 hour [Burk (68)]. This length of time is required for adaptation, i.e., for the formation of a nitrate-reducing enzyme system in the cells. In recent years this enzyme system has been extensively investigated [see Chapter 3 of this volume on inorganic nutrition of microorganisms, by Nicholas; cf. also Nason and Takahashi (238)]. Nitrate is reduced to ammonia in four steps probably by four enzymes, three of which— nitrate reductase, nitrite reductase, and hydroxylamine reductase— have been shown experimentally to exist [Egami *et al.* (110)]. The identity of the third enzyme which leads to the formation of hydroxyl-amine is still not clear [Yamada and Virtanen (432)]. Medina and Nicholas (221, 222) have shown, in *Neurospora* grown on nitrate nitrogen, an enzyme called hyponitrite reductase which may be the missing enzyme. About the same concentration of nitrate nitrogen (5 mg nitrogen per liter), at which nitrogen fixation reaches its maximum is usually sufficient to prevent nitrogen fixation. The blue-green alga *Anabaena cylindrica* is an exception as it utilizes molecular nitrogen also in the presence of high concentrations of nitrate [Allen (7)]. Ammonia, however, stops nitrogen fixation in this case also.

It has been known for some years that nitrous oxide (N_2O) competitively and specifically inhibits nitrogen fixation [Molnar et al. (232)]. Mozen and Burris (234) found N_2O to be slowly assimilated—with a rate of about 5% that of N_2 assimilation. According to Burris (75) utilization of N_2O is competitively inhibited by N_2 and H_2, a fact which suggests that N_2O, N_2, and H_2 are all adsorbed to the same active site of the enzyme surface. According to Roberts (275), however, the observed utilization of N_2O may be due to its decomposition, which leads to highly labeled N_2, N_2O itself being a nonutilizable competitive inhibitor of N_2 fixation.

Hydroxylamine is not utilized by any N_2-fixing organism. After Blom (47) and Endres (115) had presented the idea that it might be an intermediate in nitrogen fixation, it was tested by Burk and Horner (71), who found it nonutilizable and highly toxic to *Azotobacter*. Even in nontoxic concentrations (below 3 mg per liter) it was not utilized, and 5 mg per liter was sufficient to damage the cells. This was confirmed by Novak and Wilson (249) and by Pethica et al. (263), who found even 1.5–2 mg per liter toxic to *Azotobacter*. *Clostridium* is somewhat less sensitive, 5–10 mg per liter being the lower limit of toxicity [Rosenblum and Wilson (280)].

Nonutilization and toxicity of exogenous hydroxylamine have often been cited against its possible role as an intermediate in nitrogen fixation, but these facts are not proof of this. However, there are other findings which suggest that hydroxylamine may not be a probable intermediate in nitrogen fixation. Spencer et al. (296) recently studied soluble nitrate and hydroxylamine reductases of *Azotobacter* and found that these enzymes are adaptive to nitrate but not to molecular nitrogen or to ammonium sulfate. This finding suggests that the enzymes function in nitrate and nitrite assimilation, but not in nitrogen fixation. Derivatives of hydroxylamine with keto acids, oximes, are also nonutilizable [Novak and Wilson (249), Burris (75)].

Hydrazine has been found to be nonutilizable and extremely toxic for *Azotobacter* [Burk and Horner (71)] and for *Clostridium* [Rosenblum and Wilson (280)]. Suzuki and Suzuki (301) noticed that in a heavy, well-aerated suspension of *Azotobacter* hydrazine disappears. Azim and Roberts (29) found that nitrogen fixation is completely inhibited in *Azotobacter* by hydrazine in a concentration of 2×10^{-4} M. Below 2×10^{-5} M, nitrogen fixation is stimulated. Respiration is completely inhibited only in concentrations above 10^{-2} M. According to Roberts (275) hydrazine is, however, nonutilizable and is only "sequestrated" by the cells. Bach (31) showed that with keto acids it forms cyclic derivatives through a chemical reaction. The possible role of such derivatives is discussed below (page 643).

NO_2NH_2 (nitramide) and $(NOH)_2$ (hyponitrite) are two other simple inorganic nitrogenous compounds that have been tested because of their possible role as intermediates in nitrogen fixation. Both are labile compounds, rapidly decomposed in water solution. Kluyver and Verhoeven (195) have shown that the compound used by the earlier workers [Allen and van Niel (9)] really was imidonitric acid ($NHNO_2H$) and not nitramide. Tests by Mozen and Burris [cf. Burris (75)] made in an atmosphere of 20% O_2 + 80% H_2 with N^{15}-labeled nitramide added in successive small aliquots to keep the concentration nontoxic, gave no evidence that it was utilized by *Azotobacter*.

Hyponitrite is still more labile than nitramide. It has been tested by Rosenblum and Wilson (280) using *Clostridium pasteurianum* as test organism and by Chandhary *et al.* (94) using *Azotobacter vinelandii*. These authors have found it to inhibit nitrogen fixation without being utilized itself.

Amino acids and purines in general seem not to be as readily utilized by nitrogen-fixing organisms as by many other microorganisms. Burk and Horner (71) and Horner and Allison (168) have studied the utilization of numerous organic nitrogen compounds by *Azotobacter*, showing that it can utilize urea and several amino acids and purines as sources of nitrogen, although only urea, amino dicarboxylic acids, and adenine are readily utilizable. These compounds do not, however, block nitrogen fixation as ammonium and nitrate nitrogen according to Wilson *et al.* (416). The blue-green alga *Anabaena cylindrica* is also able to utilize several amino acids and other nitrogenous compounds [Fogg and Wolfe (130)] although blue-green algae in general prefer inorganic forms of nitrogen.

5. Excretion of Fixed Nitrogen

Excretion of fixed nitrogen may take place in the case of free-living nitrogen fixers as it does in the case of the symbiotic system (page 598), although it usually is very low. High excretion from *Clostridium pasteurianum*, about 60% of the nitrogen fixed, was reported by Virtanen and Hakala (351). Zelitch *et al.* (435) somewhat later showed by N^{15} that the excreted nitrogen, up to 50% of the fixed nitrogen mainly in the form of asparagine, glutamine, and ammonia, was "juvenile" nitrogen, since its labeling was many times higher than in the same compounds inside the cells. Watanabe (396) studied the excretion of nitrogen by blue-green algae; he found that of several species tested only *Calothrix brevissima* showed a noticeable excretion—40% of fixed nitrogen—in the form of aspartic acid, glutamic acid, and alanine. Fogg (127) made a detailed study of excretion from blue-green algae. He found liberal excretion only from *A. cylindrica;* the excreted nitrogen not being in the form of free amino acids as from *Calothrix brevissima* (396), but in the form of polypeptides containing principally serine and threonine, small amounts of glutamic acid, glycine, and tyrosine, and traces of alanine, valine, and leucine as well. Iron deficiency increased excretion.

It seems that excretion of nitrogenous compounds takes place when the conditions for nitrogen fixation are good but there is a shortage of some other element, e.g., carbon or iron. The significance of the excretion phenomenon from the standpoint of nitrogen fixation is discussed further in connection with the symbiotic system (Section III,G).

6. Inhibition of Nitrogen Fixation by Hydrogen and Carbon Monoxide

It was shown by Wilson and Umbreit (417) that hydrogen competitively inhibits symbiotic nitrogen fixation, but not growth on ammonium or nitrate nitrogen. Later it was shown that the same is true for *Azotobacter* [Wyss *et al.* (431)], *Nostoc* [Wilson (409)], and *Rhodospirillum rubrum* [Kamen and Gest (184)]. In *Clostridium pasteurianum*, in which hydrogen is a normal product of metabolism, it does not inhibit the rate of fixation but only decreases the efficiency of the reaction [Rosenblum and Wilson (279)]. Also in *Rhodospirillum rubrum* hydrogen does not inhibit nitrogen fixation [Gest *et al.* (145)].

It has been established by Wilson and his associates [for references see, e.g., Shug *et al.* (290)] that all free-living nitrogen-fixing microbes possess the enzyme hydrogenase, which activates molecular hydrogen

$$H_2 \rightleftharpoons 2H^+ + 2e^-$$

Quite recently the presence of hydrogenase in the symbiotic system, too, was confirmed [Hoch *et al.* (165)].

All nitrogen-fixing systems hitherto examined thus contain hydrogenase. This enzyme is nonspecific for the oxidant; e.g., methylene blue, cytochrome c, nitrate, pyridine nucleotides, or oxygen may act as electron acceptors [Lee *et al.* (200); Shug *et al.* (289)]. Another interesting feature of hydrogenase is that it is adaptive to nitrogen fixation rather than to the presence of hydrogen; if the nitrogen source of an actively nitrogen-fixing *Azotobacter* culture is changed to ammonium ion, hydrogenase activity is immediately greatly diminished [Lee *et al.* (200); Lee and Wilson (201)]. All the above facts corroborate the hypothesis that the enzyme is connected with nitrogen fixation [Wilson (408, 409)]. The first supposition that the "hydrogenase" and "nitrogenase" were identical, i.e., that each organism possessing hydrogenase was also able to fix nitrogen, was invalidated when it was shown that a number of organisms which have an active hydrogenase (*Hydrogenomonas, Escherichia coli, Proteus vulgaris,* etc.) were not able to fix nitrogen. Wilson then suggested that the hydrogenase system effects reduction of molecular nitrogen adsorbed on the surface of the enzyme nitrogenase. The recent results of Shug *et al.* (289, 290) on purification and characterization of hydrogenase give some experimental support to this hypothesis. The enzyme has been claimed to be a molybdoflavoprotein containing flavin adenine dinucleotide as the prosthetic group. Shug *et al.* (290) further showed a characteristic difference in the absorption spectrum of the enzyme in atmospheres containing mainly either hydrogen or nitrogen. With 0.2 atm of hydrogen and no nitrogen a curve with low absorption maxima is obtained, but with the addition of 0.8 atm of nitrogen a change takes place in the curve, two sharp peaks appearing with maxima at 405 and 425 mμ. This is interpreted to mean that the added nitrogen forms a complex with the nitrogenase present in the preparation, and this enzyme-substrate complex is then immediately reduced by the reduced form of hydrogenase. The latter is simultaneously oxidized, as observed spectrophotometrically. Hamilton *et al.* (149) have found that in extracts of leguminous root nodules the reduced forms of cytochrome b and leghemoglobin in addition to the molybdoflavoprotein are oxidized by nitrogen. The mechanism of the reduction of nitrogen is thus by no means clear (see Section III,M), but Wilson's concept of the role of hydrogenase in nitrogen fixation—to produce activated hydrogen for the reduction of nitrogen absorbed on "nitrogenase"—is acceptable as a plausible working hypothesis.

Hydrogenases prepared from *Aerobacter indologenes* [= *A. cloacae* var.] by Waring and Werkman (1944), from *Proteus vulgaris* by Hoberman and Rittenberg (1943), from *Clostridium butyricum* by Peck and Gest (1954), and from *Desulfovibrio desulfuricans* by Sadana and Jagannathan (1956) appear to be dependent on iron for their activities, and there is little evidence that molybdenum is required. Nicholas and co-workers (241a), from whom the above citations are made, have recently reinvestigated the nature of hydrogenase from *Clostridium pasteurianum*. Results of their metal-deficiency experiments, inhibtor studies, activation of dialyzed preparations of the enzyme, and radioactive tracer assays of purified protein fractions showed that iron is more likely to be the main metal constituent of hydrogenase. They concluded that molybdenum was required for nitrogen fixation.

Carbon monoxide is a well-known inhibitor of respiration, but the fact that the growth of nitrogen-fixing agents is prevented in considerably lower concentrations of carbon monoxide when growing on nitrogen, than when growing on ammonium ion, is usually interpreted to prove that carbon monoxide also has a specific inhibiting effect on nitrogen fixation. The carbon monoxide concentrations required for a strong inhibition of growth were determined for aerobic nitrogen fixation by Lind and Wilson (205, 206): the symbiotic system is markedly inhibited in an atmosphere of 0.01% carbon monoxide and stopped when the percentage of carbon monoxide reaches 0.05. *Azotobacter* is less sensitive, about 0.5% being required before complete cessation of fixation occurs.

Inhibition of the anaerobic fixation by carbon monoxide was studied by Virtanen *et al.* (385) with *Clostridium butyricum* as the experimental organism: 0.3% carbon monoxide in the atmosphere retarded the onset of nitrogen fixation and 1.1% completely prevented the nitrogen fixation without being otherwise harmful to the cells, which started to fix nitrogen again immediately after the removal of carbon monoxide from the gas phase. The efficiency of fixation was also diminished by carbon monoxide from the normal 3.5–7.5 mg nitrogen to 1–2 mg nitrogen fixed per gram of glucose consumed. When the same *Clostridium* was growing on ammonium ion, as much as 5–7% carbon monoxide caused a lag period of only about 24 hours, after which the growth and ammonium assimilation took place with normal speed and efficiency. Similar results have been obtained by Hino (162).

There are two plausible mechanisms for this inhibition. First, it could take place on the supposed "nitrogenase" enzyme itself, carbon monoxide being adsorbed in the place of nitrogen. Both gases have the same molecular weight and very similar physical properties, which would make a physical competition understandable. However, the inhibition in the symbiotic system was found by Lind and Wilson (205) and that in *Azotobacter* by Ebersole *et al.* (109) to be of a noncompetitive nature. Some evidence of a partially competitive inhibition has been found only in *Nostoc* [Burris and Wilson (84)]. A merely physical explanation thus seems improbable.

The second possibility is that the inhibition takes place in another enzyme system upon which nitrogen fixation is closely dependent. It is well known that carbon monoxide has a great affinity for hemochromogen iron, like that in hemoglobins and cytochromes. Indirect evidence exists for an explanation of this kind. Assimilation of ammonium ion is also partly inhibited for about 24 hours, probably because of poisoning of a respiratory cycle, but then becomes practically normal after the organism has been able to build up a carbon monoxide-resistant energy-yielding system. The results of Virtanen *et al.* (385)

show that nitrogen fixation resumes to a small degree after blockage for 3–4 days with carbon monoxide.

In the case of the symbiotic system, which is about 10–100 times more sensitive to carbon monoxide than *Clostridium* or *Azotobacter*, the greater sensitivity is almost surely due to the great affinity of carbon monoxide to hemoglobin. As will be described in detail later, this pigment is somehow linked with the process of nitrogen fixation, although the nature of its action is not yet precisely known. The presence of leghemoglobin in the symbiotic root nodules is the only chemical difference hitherto known in nitrogen fixation between the free-living organisms and the symbiotic system, and it is possible that the higher efficiency of the symbiotic system is due to the presence of this pigment in the root nodules.

7. Microelements Specifically Required for Nitrogen Fixation

Bortels (57) observed that the growth of *Azotobacter* on atmospheric nitrogen in molybdenum-deficient media is greatly stimulated by the addition of minute amounts of molybdenum. Later he showed (58) that vanadium was able to replace molybdenum, although it was somewhat less efficient. He could also confirm a specific molybdenum requirement for other nitrogen-fixing organisms, e.g., the symbiotic system (59) and the blue-green algae (60). Jensen and Spencer (174) confirmed the molybdenum requirement of *Clostridium butyricum*. [For further references see Burk and Burris (70); cf. also Chapters 2, 3, and 4 of this volume.] As is well known, molybdenum is required not solely for nitrogen fixation, but also for growth on nitrate nitrogen; no increase of growth is obtained, however, with the addition of molybdenum if ammonia is available [Burk and Horner (71)]. Wolfe (429) determined the molybdenum requirement of *Anabaena cylindrica* on molecular nitrogen, nitrate, and ammonium nitrogen, finding for the three media molybdenum values of 0.2 ppm, 0.1 ppm, and extremely little if any, respectively. There are also differences between *Azotobacter* species regarding molybdenum requirements: *A. agilis* and *A. vinelandii* showed half-maximal fixation in the most carefully purified molybdenum-deficient medium of Bové *et al.* (61), in which *A. chroococcum* completely failed to grow without added molybdenum.

Vanadium cannot always replace molybdenum. Allen (7) reported a strain of *Anabaena cylindrica* which could not utilize vanadium instead of molybdenum, and Esposito and Wilson (119) report that vanadium could not replace molybdenum for the strain of *A. vinelandii* O. It has been recently observed [Takahashi and Nason (302); Keeler and Varner (186)] that tungstate competitively inhibits the utilization of molybdate but not of vanadate in *Azotobacter*. This suggests that the active sites of these two elements (molybdenum and vanadium) may be different, although their effects are so similar. A little is already known also of the role of molybdenum in nitrogen fixation as well as in nitrate reduction: by Shug *et al.* (289, 290) and by Hamilton *et al.* (149) hydrogenase is characterized as a molybdoflavoprotein although several other workers have found little evidence for a molybdenum requirement in the hydrogenase reaction and emphasize the role of iron as discussed above (page 561). According to a recent paper by Nicholas *et al.* (241a) their results suggest that iron and not molybdenum is the main constituent of hydrogenase. Nitrate reductase has been characterized as a molybdoflavoprotein. In addition to these functions, molybdenum may have additional functions in nitrogen-fixing organisms (see Chapter 2 by Hewitt and Chapter 4 by Nason and McElroy).

A "specific" calcium requirement, partially replaceable only by strontium, was first claimed for nitrogen fixation, but this claim was later withdrawn [Burk and Burris (70)] because no significant difference in the required amount of calcium was found between growths in nitrogen gas or nitrate-containing media. *Beijerinckia*, a nitrogen-fixing bacterium closely related to *Azotobacter*, seems to have no calcium requirement. However, Esposito and Wilson (119) recently reported a specific calcium requirement for nitrogen fixation in *A. vinelandii* O, ammonium ion eliminating the need of calcium. In another paper (120) they presented a hypothesis according to which polymetaphosphate would be the required energy source of nitrogen fixation and calcium would be specifically involved in the synthesis of polymetaphosphate. A specific calcium requirement for the uptake of orthophosphate by pea roots was recently shown by Savioja and Miettinen (285). Norris and Jensen (248a) found calcium to be essential for the growth of *Azotobacter* on all nitrogen sources. They claim that much of the earlier confusion probably arises through the use of unsuitable media and through failure to effect an adequate removal of calcium.

Allen and Arnon (8) have shown that the blue-green algae require calcium for growth on nitrogen gas or nitrate, and this is not replaceable by strontium. It is well known that *Rhizobium* [Albrecht and McCalla (2)] and the leguminous plants have a high calcium requirement, but it has not been possible to show any direct connection between this and nitrogen fixation. McCalla (213) has suggested that it is the three to four times higher calcium content of the leguminous plants compared with the nonlegumes that makes the legumes susceptible to the invasion of *Rhizobium.*

A close connection of iron with nitrogen fixation is also probable. This element forms the prosthetic group of leghemoglobin, which is known to function in symbiotic nitrogen fixation, although its specific role is not known so far (see page 609) and iron also has been reported to have a role in the formation of hydrogenase (see above). Iron is required for so many functions in all living cells that it is not usually possible to show an increased requirement for it for nitrogen-fixing organisms growing on free nitrogen versus combined nitrogen.

Burk (68) compared the iron requirements of *Azotobacter chroococcum* when growing with free nitrogen or nitrate as nitrogen source and found no significant difference. In both cases 4 to 10×10^{-6} M iron was needed for maximum growth. Esposito and Wilson (119) compared the iron requirements of *Azotobacter vinelandii* when growing with free nitrogen or ammonium as nitrogen source. Maximum growth was in both cases obtained at 1 ppm. However, slight differences in stimulation were obtained in lower concentrations: at 0.1 ppm of iron growth on ammonium nitrogen was 77%, but growth on molecular nitrogen only 51%, of the maximal. Higher levels of iron also stimulated oxygen uptake in a hydrogen atmosphere, a finding in accordance with the supposed dependence of hydrogenase on iron. The nature of this dependence was recently discussed by Gest *et al.* (144).

Hitherto it has not been possible to prove a direct connection of iron with nitrogen fixation. Sodium, cobalt, and boron are three microelements that have been shown to be indispensable to the nitrogen-fixing blue-green algae, but they evidently do not have a specific function in the fixation of nitrogen [cf., e.g., Fogg (130)].

III. Symbiotic Nitrogen Fixation in Leguminous Plants

A. CHARACTERISTICS OF THE NODULE BACTERIA

Legume bacteria can best be isolated from crushed legume root nodules. They can be cultivated in synthetic media with inorganic nitrogen. Addition of plant extracts to the medium improves growth [Allen and Allen (6)]. Extracts of green plants, as well as of yeasts and molds, have been successfully used for this purpose. Their effect depends on several different functions: the redox potential may become suitable for the growth of the bacteria, essential or stimulating growth factors (e.g., amino acids, vitamins, trace elements) are added to the medium in this way, and, in some cases at least, increased uptake of trace elements (e.g., molybdenum and iron) which are difficultly assimilated in a neutral or alkaline reaction is facilitated by organic substances in the extract. Biotin has been found by Nilsson *et al.* (245) and West and Wilson (398) to stimulate the growth of most rhizobia. Only a few strains have an absolute requirement for biotin, and some strains give maximum growth even in the absence of it [Wilson and Wilson (404); Jordan (182)]. Thiamine also has a stimulating effect on the growth of certain strains of clover (*Trifolium*) rhizobia [Nilsson *et al.* (245)]. Bergersen (40a) recently reported that the growth of *Rhizobium* is excellent (5 × 10⁹ cells/ml) in a synthetic medium containing sodium glutamate 0.11% as nitrogen source, thiamine 100 μg/l, biotin 125–150 μg/l, and $CaCl_2$ 0.004%, in addition to other mineral salts and mannitol. The ability of rhizobia to synthesize vitamins [Wilson (405); Burton and Lockhead (87)] on their ability to utilize certain growth factors [Jordan (182)] is not correlated with the nitrogen-fixing capacity.

The rhizobia are able to use ammonium salts, nitrate nitrogen, and many amino acids as their nitrogen source. According to Nielsen (243), *R. leguminosarum* assimilated 32 of 39 amino acids tested. With washed cells of *R. meliloti* including genetically similar mutants, Jordan (182) found strain differences in the ability to utilize diverse amino acids. He concluded that an amino nitrogen group is required for the production of metabolically active ammonia and that the amino acids are interrelated by transamination mechanisms.

The deamination of amino acids by rhizobia is in most cases obscure. Generally their demonstrable ability to form ammonia from amino acids, peptides, and proteins is extremely poor. No formation of ammonia could be established even during very long experimental periods with growing alfalfa, pea, and clover rhizobia in milk [Fred *et al.* (134); Virtanen and Laine (366)]; in a yeast extract-glucose medium to which casein or autoclaved cells of the clover organisms were added; or in water suspensions of rhizobial cells or crushed nodules in the presence of toluene (366). Soluble nitrogen and amino nitrogen also increased very slowly. The uptake of amino acids as such may explain the utilization of amino acids by rhizobia.

A great variety of carbon compounds (several carbohydrates, polyhydric alcohols, and organic acids) support growth of the rhizobia. In this respect there are great differences between different *Rhizobium* species. Two broad groups of rhizobia are recognized: the "slow growers" and the "fast growers." Certain organic acids support a much more rapid respiration of the "slow-growing" rhizobia (soybean and cowpea organisms) than do carbohydrates, whereas the "fast-growing" rhizobia oxidize carbohydrates at a rate nearly equivalent to that of the organic acids [Burris and Wilson (81)]. No differences in the fermentation of different carbon compounds have been found by Georgi and Ettlinger (142) between efficient and inefficient strains of rhizobia.

According to Burris *et al.* (79) the rhizobia produce adaptive enzymes for the oxidation of a number of polyhydric alcohols, acetate, and succinate, but their enzymes for the oxidation of carbohydrate are apparently constitutive. All attempts to find such metabolic differences in free-living rhizobial strains in culture, by means of which their effectiveness in symbiotic nitrogen fixation could be predicted, have failed. The decisive role of the host plant in the symbiosis makes it improbable that such attempts will ever be successful, at least until the problem of symbiosis is better understood than at present.

In growing cultures in the presence of oxygen, *Rhizobium* oxidizes the sources of carbon mostly to carbon dioxide and water. In cultures of this kind a very small amount of acid, if any, is found. On the other hand, the carbon sources are also used to form a gum, which is a typical product in rhizobial cultures, by which the cells are surrounded. Hopkins *et al.* (167) established that this gum was nitrogen free and that mainly glucuronic acid and glucose were obtained from it on acid hydrolysis. Later Haworth and Stacey (152) proposed that the chemical structure of the extracellular polysaccharide gum is glucose-1,4-glucuronic acid. About 25–35% of the glucose used by the alfalfa and clover organisms is transformed into gum. Georgi and Wilson (143) even suggested that the gum is an intermediate product in the oxidation of glucose.

Hoover and Allison (166) found that a low gum-forming strain, *R. meliloti*, produced only carbon dioxide, water, and bacterial cells. When corrections were made for basal respiration, the growth rate was proportional to the Q_{O_2} and Q_{CO_2}. The efficiency coefficient (milligrams dry weight of organisms produced per 100 mg of sugar consumed) was 40–50% of the theoretical maximum.

In prolonged respiration experiments (15–20 days) of Georgi and Wilson (143), the respiratory quotients $(CO_2:O_2)$ for the alfalfa and clover organisms in a yeast extract-glucose medium did not differ significantly from the theoretical value of 1.0. Experiments of shorter duration (about 1 day) in a Warburg apparatus with glucose and different nitrogen sources gave in the experiments of Thorne *et al.* (307) values which varied to some extent both with the species of organism and with the sources of nitrogen, but most of these values were not significantly different from unity. When the respiratory quotients were determined, not only for over-all metabolism but also for short periods during the course of the experiment. In both cases greatly differing results, both greater and less than 1.0, were found. The results indicated that the type of compound undergoing oxidation changed during the course of the experiment. When no glucose or other external carbon source was supplied, the respiratory quotients were reasonably close to the theoretical value of 0.8 for the endogenous oxidation of protein.

Using cell suspensions and short-time (30–150 minutes) techniques, Wilson (406) estimated the respiratory activity of different rhizobia. The rates of respiration of the rhizobia were considerably higher than those reported for many species of bacteria, despite the fact that the rhizobia are regarded as slow growers. Dicarboxylic acids, especially succinate and fumarate, are most rapidly metabolized.

When the rate of respiration was determined with suspensions of free-living rhizobia and bacterial material from the nodules, the values did not differ greatly. The rate of respiration of rhizobia, plotted as a function of the pO_2 in the atmosphere, gives typical hyperbolic substrate-activity curves. The maximum rate of respiration was reached with different species and strains of pea and clover rhizobia at a pO_2 of about 0.15 atm, and the partial pressure of oxygen which corresponds to the half-maximum velocity was between 0.01 and 0.02 atm. With suspensions of rhizobia from pea or vetch (*Vicia* sp.) nodules, maximum respiration was attained at a definitely lower pO_2 than with "resting" cells of pea *Rhizobium*. The pO_2 function of soybean bacteria obtained directly from the nodules is similar to that of the same strain grown on a laboratory medium [Burris and Wilson (80)].

The optimum pO_2 for nitrogen fixation in sliced nodules, however, has been found by Burris et al. (77) to be considerably higher—about 0.5 atm.

Rhizobia are obligate aerobes although good growth is obtained at rather low partial pressures of oxygen—less than 0.01 atm [Barthel (33)]. Even though rhizobia do not grow in complete absence of oxygen, the cell suspensions can ferment carbohydrate anaerobically. Virtanen et al. (386) found that a suspension of washed cells of R. trifolii slowly ferments glucose in an oxygen-free atmosphere and produces at first considerable amounts of dl-lactic acid. Later, volatile acids, carbon dioxide, and hydrogen are also formed. Wilson (407) reports the formation of volatile acids and carbon dioxide from glucose in experiments of short duration by rhizobia, grown either in the nodules or in a laboratory medium. No evidence of hydrogen production was secured in his experiments.

The dependence of the growth of different species of rhizobia on the pH of the medium varies somewhat (134). According to experiments of Virtanen (330) most of them have an optimum between pH 6.5 and

7.5 (Fig. 2). In symbiosis with the host plant the dependence of nitrogen fixation on the pH is rather similar. Inoculated red (*Trifolium pratense*), white (*T. repens*), and alsike (*T. hybridum*) clover grow only minimally in quartz sand without combined nitrogen at pH 4.5, and at pH 4.0 not at all, whereas in a parallel experiment with ammonium nitrate growth decreases steadily from pH 6.5 downward without any sharp limit at pH 4.5. Even at pH 4.0 obvious growth can

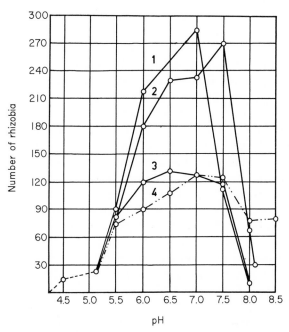

FIG. 2. Growth of different rhizobia on the surface of a gelatin medium of different pH. *Rhizobium 1* from nodules of *Pisum sativum*, *2* from nodules of *Trifolium pratense*, *3* from nodules of *Phaseolus vulgaris*, and *4* from nodules of *Medicago sativa*. From Virtanen (330).

still be observed (330) (Fig. 3). The sensitivity of clover rhizobia to the acidity of the medium is thus greater than that of the host plant.

The optimum growth temperature for most free rhizobia is below 30°C, growth being good, however, even at room temperature (134). In 1921 Jones and Tisdale (178) found that the temperature optimum in soil for nodule formation on soybean was 24°C. For other plants the optimum was about the same. Recently Meyer and Anderson (224) have found that inoculated subterranean clover (*Trifolium subterraneum*) does not fix nitrogen at 30°C although well developed nodules are formed, and the fixation at 20°C is good. With combined nitrogen the growth was good even at 30°C. The temperature limits for growth and nitrogen fixation may then be different. Recent studies of Valle and Virtanen (327) on inoculated pea plants in water cultures in a sterile culture system (see Fig. 12) have led to similar results. At

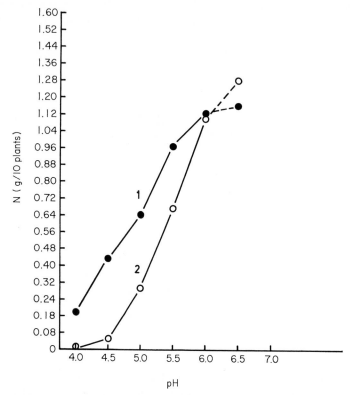

FIG. 3. Nitrogen yields of *Trifolium hybridum* in quartz sand at different pH (roots not included, see Fig. 8). Curve *1*: Uninoculated plants with ammonium nitrate. Curve *2*: Inoculated plants without combined nitrogen. The parallel experiments comprised pH values 4 to 6. Nitrogen yields at pH 6.5 are from another experiment. From Virtanen (330).

a constant temperature of 20 and 24°C red, effective nodules were formed mostly in the upper part of the roots. Nitrogen fixation was strong and growth good. At 27°C the function of nodules was much lower. At 30°C root formation was still good and numerous nodules were formed, but the nodules were smaller, white, and located all over the roots. No nitrogen fixation could be observed. At 35°C root formation was already checked to a great degree and no nodules occurred. Obviously the complicated system which is necessary for nitrogen fixation is no longer formed in pea nodules at so low a temperature (30°C), which is still reasonable for the growth of free rhizobia and favorable for the growth of pea with combined nitrogen. However, inoculated *Phaseolus* grew best at 24 to 27°C and still formed effective nodules at 30°C (327). Accordingly, the nonformation of effective nodules at 30°C on the roots of pea and subterranean clover does not hold for all leguminous plants.

Regarding nitrogen fixation in pea nodules at low temperature, the results of Vartiovaara (328) are to be mentioned. He found in parallel

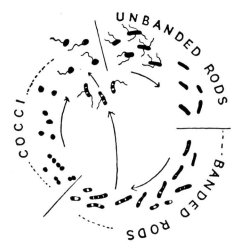

Fig. 4. The life cycle of *Rhizobium*. From Thornton (314).

experiments with different pea rhizobia that strains isolated from soils in the northern countries (Finland or Sweden) produced nodules on pea roots, and fixed more nitrogen at low temperature (mean temperature 11.8°C), than did nodules formed by pea rhizobia isolated from soils from Mediterranean countries. At a higher temperature (about 20°C) there were no differences (331).

The life cycle of the rhizobia has a bearing on their distribution in the soil, and consequently on the infection of the host plant [Thornton (314)]. They may occur as short rods that stain uniformly, as banded rods, or as small coccoid forms which can develop "swarmers" with flagella (Fig. 4). At this stage the organism is able to swim in the soil moisture, and it is probably by such means that it reaches the roots of its host. Thornton and Gangulee (319) have found that the migration through Rothamsted soil is at a rate of about 1 inch in 24 hours.

B. Formation of the Nodules

Ward (394, 395), who in 1887 and 1889 proved nodules to be the result of infection, described even then something of the mode of infection: the appearance of a bright refractive spot on the tip of a root hair, the curvature of the hair at this point, and the growth of an infection filament from the bright spot down the root hair. This observation was confirmed by later investigators. The increased rate of movement of the rhizobia toward the root hairs under the influence of some excreted substance has been established. According to Ludwig and Allison (212), this may be due to the increased proliferation of the rhizobia due to stimulating substances excreted by roots and may generally concern microorganisms living in the rhizosphere, and not specifically the rhizobia. With lucerne (alfalfa) seedlings the stimulating substance has been found by Thornton (317) to be excreted only when the first true leaf expands. By growing a number of plants together or in succession, earlier nodule formation on plants on which nodulation would otherwise be later, may be brought about [Thornton (310); Nutman (256)]. It has been suggested that the effect of the excreted substance is stimulatory at a low concentration and becomes inhibitory at a higher one. The effects are unaffected by the presence of rhizobia. The results of Nutman (260) have recently indicated that root secretions produced from the preplanted species affect both the number of foci and their availability for infection. The rhizosphere populations of rhizobia exceed the nonrhizosphere populations about 100 times, and the maximum values are reached when inoculation is made at the time of sowing, a week before nodulation commences. It seems that a very restricted number of minute rhizobia attack the root hairs and become the infecting agents [Purchase and Nutman (270); Fåhraeus (139)]. It is particularly interesting that according to Hiltner (159) and McCoy (214) the curling of the root hair is caused by a bacterial secretion which is separable by filtration, from the bacterial cell. The substance is thermostable. According to Thimann (306) and Georgi and Beguin (141), there is evidence that the active substance in the bacterial secretion is β-indolylacetic acid, as this compound itself curls root hairs. According to Thornton and Nicol (322), the secreted substance not only causes deformation of the root hairs, but also increases their number and their growth in length. This deformation of root hairs is not specific and can be brought about by rhizobia belonging to a different cross-inoculation group, but only the specific rhizobia can infect the hairs. The point at which the resistance to infection occurs is apparently at the wall of the curled root hair. The basis of the resistance of a given legume to bacteria of a different cross-inoculation group is not known.

The rhizobia of the appropriate sort normally invade the curled tip, but entrance through epidermal and cortical cells is also known [McCoy (215); Schaede (286)]. The mechanism of the infection is not known. No break in the cell wall at the point of entry has been observed. It is possible that the rhizobia are able to effect entry by taking part in some way in the growth processes at the root hair tip (258). Frey-Wyssling (136, 137) has made observations and drawn interesting conclusions in this respect. In the primary wall, at the tip of the root hair, the cellulose fibrillae are thought to be separated by about 0.3 μ, and the looseness of the network of cellulose may thus make the entry possible. Burström (86) suggests that auxin takes part in this process by loosening the cellulose cross linkages. In this connection the electron-microscopic studies of Bergersen and Briggs (41) are of special interest. They found that the cellulose of the infection thread is structurally continuous with the cellulose of the wall of the host, soybean. After invasion the rhizobia grow down inside the root hair owing to the directing influence of the host cell nucleus as many authors suppose (36, 139) in the form of a thread of slime containing bacterial rods. This "infection thread" penetrates to the deeper layers of the root cortex, branches, and enters the host cells in all directions (Fig. 5) [Thornton (314)]. The invaded cells, together with those immediately adjoining, are stimulated to division, and by their growth and differentiation eventually form the nodule tissues. In the nodule, the rhizobia soon escape from the infection thread, and come to lie free in the cytoplasm of the infected plant cells where they rapidly multiply and often fill the entire cell (Fig. 6). According to Thornton (312) the release of the rhizobia from the thread generally takes place from a special vesicle which tends to develop near the host cell nucleus.

The short rod- or coccoid-shaped rhizobia which are found in the infection thread, and at the beginning still in the root cells, soon become swollen, vacuolated, banded, and in the nodules of many plants branched. Probably the first to make observations on the morphology of the organisms responsible for nodule formation was Lachmann in 1858 (198a). He noted that the inner cells of the nodules are filled with small, elongated bodies resembling the so-called vibrios. Some years later Woronin (430) described these "vibrio-like bodies" more fully although he did not definitely state that these bodies were bacteria and were the agents responsible for nodule formation. The "bacteroids" [Brunchorst (66)] in the nodules vary in size and shape with different plant species. In 1888 Beijerinck (35) recognized three different forms of bacteroids: the X- and Y-shaped forms from *Vicia, Pisum,* and *Lathyrus;* the rod-shaped forms from *Phaseolus, Ornithopus,* and *Lotus;* and the pear-shaped or spherical forms from *Trifolium.* These bacteroids constitute the largest portion of the nodule tissue in effective, fully developed nodules. A recent work by Bergersen (39) on clover bacteroids has shown that with effective strains the increase in size of the bacterial cell is accompanied by a division of the nuclear material and by the gradual development of perinuclear

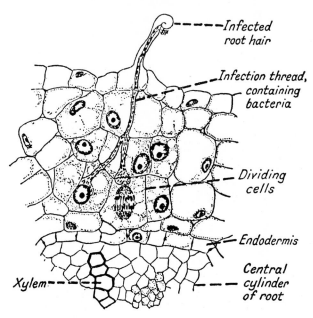

Fig. 5. Infection of lucerne root by *Rhizobium meliloti.* From Thornton (314).

areas. As the nuclear centers become smaller and break up, the perinuclear area enlarges to occupy most of the bacteroid. Nutman (258) has given a detailed report on the formation of root nodules and the factors that influence it.

The significance of bacteroids in nitrogen fixation will be further discussed in Section III, J.

Nodules of the various leguminous species originate from certain definite tissues. In most species they are formed from the inner cortical cells but may sometimes involve pericycle cells within the endodermis of the stele [Thornton (314)]. As the young nodule develops, vascular strands are differentiated in the nodule cortex, and are connected with the vascular system of the host root (see Fig. 6). The vascular system

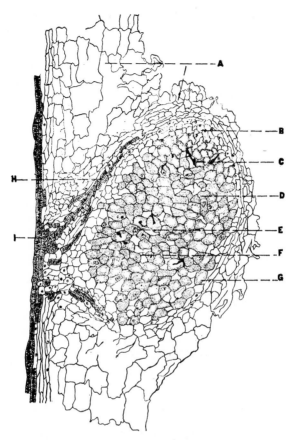

FIG. 6. Longitudinal section of a nodule on 15-day-old clover seedling in sand culture inoculated with *Rhizobium trifolii* strain 205. Fixed in Flemming's solution (medium); section 5 μ thick; stained with Heidenhain's hematoxylin. Camera lucida drawing; magnification approximately $\times$ 175.

A, Cells of the root cortex, stretched and broken by the swelling of the nodule. *B*, Uninfected meristematic cells in the growing end of the nodule. *C*, Fragments of infection threads. *D*, Bacteria free in the host cells; coccoid and red forms in recently infected cells, and progressively more vacuolate and swollen forms in the older infected cells or bacteroid region. *E*, Hypertrophied and deformed nucleus showing conspicuous nucleolus and chromatic granules (chromocenters of Terby). *F*, Uninfected cells. *G*, Hypertrophied plant cell with large vacuole. *H*, Vascular strands lying in the cortex of the nodule and extending to the vascular system of the root stele. *I*, Strands of vascular system of the root showing junction with vascular strands of the nodule. From Fred *et al.* (134, p. 152).

serves for the transport of nutrient to the nodule cells and their bacteria, and for the removal of products of nitrogen fixation from the bacterial cells to the host plant. The gaseous nitrogen diffuses into the nodule from the soil atmosphere and is not transported from the shoot. The system is adequate for a time, but when the nodule grows large and becomes older, irreversible changes occur in the nodule, the result of which is the cessation of nitrogen fixation and degeneration of the nodule cells. The rate of these definite changes apparently depends on many factors which are little known at the present. In this respect the nodules formed by various bacterial strains can differ from each other often very noticeably, but the light conditions, the supply of oxygen, and other external factors are also influential. It is possible that the loss of the function of the vascular system initiates the degeneration and cessation of nitrogen fixation (35). Brenchley and Thornton (64) have demonstrated that a boron deficiency prevents the formation of a vascular system in the root nodules. This is probably due to a general effect of boron deficiency on plants rather than a specific effect on the root nodules. In his recent monograph Schropp (288) has treated the role of boron in the leguminous plants.

The nature of the stimulatory substance (or substances) that cause the rapid cell division and thus nodule formation is not known. The presence of β-indolylacetic acid in the nodules [cf. Thimann (305, 306)] is obviously of no importance in this connection even if Chen (96) has observed that effective strains of *Rhizobium trifolii* form more auxin than ineffective ones. Contradictory observations have been made by Georgi and Beguin (141) with other rhizobial strains. Factors which stimulate the division of cells have not as yet been isolated either from nodules or rhizobia. In connection the observations made by Steward and Shantz (299a) on the cell division factors in coconut milk and the discoveries of Skoog and associates (231, 231a) on the effect of kinetins on cell division should be noticed.

In cytological studies on the nodules of red clover, Wipf and Cooper in 1938 (427) made the remarkable observation that the cells of nodules infected with *Rhizobium* contained a double number of chromosomes ($4n = 28$) compared to ordinary uninfected diploid cells ($2n = 14$). Wipf (426) showed that this rule is valid also for the leguminous species in which polyploidy occurs naturally. *Medicago sativa* is a natural tetraploid. Its normal root tip cells have 32 ($4n$) chromosomes but the infected cells have 64 ($8n$) chromosomes.

These important findings suggested that a doubling of the chromosomes may be associated with invasion of the cell, but a later investigation of Wipf and Cooper (428) with pea and vetch showed that in the root of these species cells with double the $2n$ number of chromosomes were occasionally found among normal cells, and that the invading rhizobia enter only these natural tetraploid cells. The recent investigations by Funke (138) have confirmed these results, and hence it seems to be a general rule that only cells with a double number of chromosomes are involved in nodule formation. This happens in the formation of both effective and ineffective nodules. The cause for this exceptional role of polyploid cells in infection is not known. After the findings of Steward and collaborators (231b,c) that the coconut-milk-cell-division stimulus also causes many cells to become polyploid, there seems to be reason to reinvestigate the question of the possible influence of the rhizobia on polyploid formation in root cells even if Wipf and Cooper seem to have proved convincingly the occurrence of polyploid cells among the normal ones in uninoculated roots of legumes.

Nilsson *et al.* (244) analyzed the amino acid content of $2n$ and $4n$ lines of red clover in order to find the cause of the differences between them in nodulation. With the exception of arginine, which was present only in the $4n$ plants, the same amino acids occurred in all parts of both lines. The important finding of Wipf and Cooper explains at least partly why so few nodules are formed when compared to the large number of infected root hairs. McCoy (214) gives the following data obtained from a lucerne plant 6 weeks old grown on agar:

Total number of hairs on one inch of root	1121
Number of infected hairs in the above section	62
Percentage of hairs infected	5.5
Estimated length of the root system, inches	5.5
Estimated total number of root hairs	6115
Estimated number of infected hairs	341
Number of nodules on the plant	5
Percentage of nodules from infected hairs	1.5

Among species of *Trifolium* the number of root hairs infected is very restricted. Purchase (269) has shown that in red clover the number of infected root hairs closely corresponds to the number of nodules formed.

How the number of inoculated nodule bacteria influences the number of nodules has been the object of many investigations. In early works very contradictory concepts were occasionally presented on this matter, some authors reporting that the number of nodules increases within limits when the number of bacteria in the inoculum is increased, others again considering the number of rhizobial cells unimportant. Thornton (309) fixed attention on the rapid multiplication of bacteria inoculated into the rhizosphere, because the initial inoculum does not represent the number of bacteria available for nodulation. Purchase and Nutman (270) have recently treated this problem thoroughly, as shown on page 572. According to these authors the number of rhizobial cells introduced is not important because the multiplication of rhizobia in the rhizosphere is very rapid.

Evidence of the serological homogeneity of the bacteria isolated from a single nodule suggests that entry may be effected by a single bacterium or by its progeny colonizing a given root hair [Hughes and Vincent (170); Purchase and Nutman (270)]. Rare cases of nodules containing more than one strain of bacteria may be due to a number of infected root hairs providing the initial infection, as reported by Wipf and Cooper (428) and Bond (55) and observed occasionally also by Purchase and Nutman (270).

Generally, effective strains form fewer but larger nodules than ineffective and poor strains. In addition, effective nodules occur primarily on the main roots, whereas ineffective ones tend to be scattered on the lateral roots. In accordance with Golding's (146) earlier observations, Virtanen and von Hausen (354, 355) as well as Bond (49) and Ferguson and Bond (124), who used gas mixtures containing 21, 12, and 5% of oxygen, found that the need for oxygen in nitrogen fixation in the nodules is higher than was earlier thought. In water cultures (sterile system, see Fig. 12) the growth of peas is good with combined nitrogen even when the roots are submerged, but poor without combined nitrogen because the submerged nodules fix relatively little nitrogen or, if deeper in the solution, none at all. Under these conditions even effective strains form numerous small and only weakly reddish or white nodules scattered all over the roots, according to observations made in this laboratory [Virtanen and Linkola (377)]. To explain this observation it was assumed that, under normal growth conditions, the increase in the nitrogen content of the host plant when nitrogen fixation is well under way prevents the formation of numerous nodules. This restriction does not apply to nearly the same extent under conditions unsuitable for nitrogen fixation and is completely lacking when the nodules are ineffective.

An inhibitory action by meristems of earlier-formed effective nodules and root tips was held responsible by Nutman (253) for the limitation of later development of nodule foci and, accordingly, for fewer nodules produced by effective strains. The lack of this inhibitor in meristems of ephemeral, ineffective nodules was proposed as the reason for more profuse and continuing nodulation by ineffective strains [Nutman

(254, 255)]. Recently Radley (271a) suggested that the nodule-inhibiting factor is probably a gibberellin which may diffuse out into the surrounding medium.

After the Compositae, the Leguminosae are the family of angiosperms with the greatest number of species. Although well over 10,000 species of legumes are known, only about 200 of these are cultivated. The formation of root nodules and symbiotic nitrogen fixation is common in this family. However, numerous exceptions are found. According to Allen and Allen (12) only 1196, or about 10–12%, of all species in the Leguminosae have been examined for nodule formation. Of these, 1063 species, or about 89%, form nodules. Most of the plants examined belong to the largest subfamily, the Papilionoideae (Lotoideae). In the subfamily Caesalpinioideae there are actually several genera which are recognized exceptions to the usual pattern of nodule formation [Fred et al. (134)]. Reasons for the absence of nodulation in some genera and species of leguminous plants are not known. The observed lack of nodules need not always be proof of the nonexistence of nodulation, since lack of a suitable *Rhizobium* in the environment may account for the lack of nodules. Allen and Allen (10, 12) have focused attention on the probable lack of spontaneous tetraploidy as an explanation for the consistent lack of nodules among certain leguminous plants.

C. EFFECTIVENESS OF THE NODULES AS NITROGEN FIXERS

1. Effectiveness of Different Rhizobial Strains

The root nodules produced by rhizobia are important for the economy of man and nature only insofar as the nodules fix the gaseous nitrogen of the atmosphere and thus make the growth of the host plant possible. The ability of the root nodules, produced by the inoculated rhizobia, to fix nitrogen determines the effectiveness of rhizobial strains. In this respect rhizobial strains differ enormously one from another. The terms "excellent," "good," "fairly good," and "poor" are used to describe the relative effectiveness of strains (Fig. 7).

Information about root nodules which do not increase the growth or nitrogen content of the host plant began to appear in the literature in the late nineteenth century [Fred et al. (134)]. Whether the nodules really were totally ineffective was not investigated in detail at that time.

In the early 1940's it was concluded in this laboratory, on the basis of experiments performed, that the red pigment, leghemoglobin which is present in the root nodules of legumes (see Section III, I), is an indispensable factor in nitrogen fixation [Virtanen (335, 336)]. Whether the ineffective nodules, in which this hemoprotein could not be established, are completely unable to fix nitrogen then became important. Quantitative nitrogen determinations showed no nitrogen fixation when pea plants were inoculated with the *Rhizobium* H VIII strain of this laboratory, which during many years had proved to be ineffective.

The results presented in Table II show that both uninoculated pea plants and those inoculated with the *Rhizobium* H VIII strain, within the limits of error, contained the same amount of nitrogen, and

Fig. 7. Growth of pea plants in quartz sand inoculated with different strains of pea rhizobia. Extreme right: inoculated with the ineffective strain H VIII. From Virtanen (333).

that this amount corresponded to the combined nitrogen present in the seeds and in the nutrient solution. The results also show that ineffective nodules used about 10% of the nitrogen of the host plant and that they decreased the dry weight and total amount of nitrogen of the roots. It is interesting to note that the nitrogen content of the roots (as per cent of dried roots) was the same (2.0%) in uninoculated and inoculated pea plants.

On the basis of experimental results Virtanen *et al.* (363) came to the conclusion that there are strains which regularly produce quite ineffective nodules. On the other hand, Thornton (316) believed that there are only quantitative differences between effective and ineffective strains. According to his results the active bacterial tissue of "ineffective" nodules has such a short lifetime that the total nitrogen fixation is greatly lowered, although always present to some extent. This concept is undoubtedly valid in regard to "poor" strains, as Thornton's (315) experiments with clover nodules show (Table III).

In the ineffective pea nodules investigated in this laboratory a real symbiosis and active "bacterial tissue" were not developed (see Sections III, I and J). The application of Thornton's explanation to completely

TABLE II
PEA (TORSDAG) INOCULATED WITH THE INEFFECTIVE *Rhizobium* H VIII STRAIN[a,b]

| Inoculation | Shoots | | | Roots | | | Nodules | | | Total dry wt. (mg) | Total N (mg) | Tap water used per plant (ml) |
	Dry wt. (mg)	N (mg)	N (%)	Dry wt. (mg)	N (mg)	N (%)	Dry wt. (mg)	N (mg)	N (%)			
With H VIII	205	5.1	2.5	83	1.6	1.9	18	0.7	4.2	306	7.4 ± 0.77	1308
Uninoculated	188	4.9	2.6	123	2.4	1.9	—	—	—	311	7.3 ± 0.62	1273
With H 6	3430	94.9	2.8	247	5.0	2.0	98	4.6	4.7	3775	104.5	—

[a] From Virtanen *et al.* (363).

[b] Sterile culture system, nutrient solution without combined nitrogen. Period of growth August 31 to October 9, 1943. Nodules appeared on September 17. Nine parallel experiments with inoculated and nine with uninoculated pea plants are compared with one experiment with a pea plant inoculated with the effective H 6 strain. The pea seeds selected for the experiment weighed on the average 191 mg (individual variations 189 to 193 mg) each. On the average the pea seeds of this size contained about 7 mg of nitrogen per seed. The tap water used in the nutrient solution contained 0.28 mg of nitrogen per liter. The results in the table are average values per plant.

ineffective nodules seems thus artificial. Since a strain of *Rhizobium*, which is ineffective in some legume species, may be effective on other species (see Section III, D), it cannot be said with certainty that, for example, the ineffective H VIII strain should be ineffective on all possible host plants. In this laboratory an effective symbiosis of this strain with any pea, vetch, or horse bean (*Vicia faba*) variety used in the experiments has, however, never developed.

The existence of strains producing ineffective nodules is of great importance for the investigation of symbiotic nitrogen fixation. Examination of the differences between effective and ineffective nodules should make it possible to obtain information about the factors necessary for

TABLE III

NODULATION AND NITROGEN FIXATION BY EFFICIENT AND INEFFICIENT
STRAINS OF CLOVER RHIZOBIA[a]

	Strain A	Strain Coryn
Number of replicates	23	12
Nodules per bottle	122	771
Bacterial tissue per bottle (mm^3)	17.39	15.27
Nitrogen fixed per bottle (mg)	6.6	1.5
Nitrogen fixed per 100 mm^3 of bacterial tissue (mg)	37.9	9.8
Duration of healthy bacterial tissue (days)	46	8
Nitrogen fixed per 100 mm^3 bacterial tissue per day (mg)	0.82	1.23

[a] From Thornton (315).

nitrogen fixation. The formation of nodules by the rhizobia does not, as such, mean a development of the system causing nitrogen fixation.

Results reported in the literature which bear on the effectiveness of a rhizobial strain with the same plant variety are inconsistent or variable. Effective strains are claimed to change to ineffective ones and ineffective ones to effective ones by successive passage through a host plant [cf. (134), page 174]. If this were the case, the effectiveness of strains would depend on their relation to the sequence of passages in which the rhizobia were when isolated. Thus we should not speak about the different effectiveness of strains.

In this laboratory attention has been paid to this problem when investigating the occurrence of completely ineffective rhizobial strains. In experiments performed in a sterile system, where external contamination by foreign strains is prevented, it has been found without exception that successive plant passages do not change the ineffective strains to effective ones. The ineffective pea *Rhizobium* H VIII has been systematically investigated in this respect using numerous passages, and shorter experiments have also been performed with some other ineffective strains of pea rhizobia. Also in experiments with two very effective pea rhizobia, the successive passage through the pea plant has not modified the effectiveness of the strains. On the basis of his experiments in a sterile system, Virtanen (336, 374) concluded that the results of the earlier experiments performed in open pots may be due to an infection caused by foreign strains. During investigations in this laboratory on the effectiveness of rhizobial strains carried out in open pots containing quartz sand, it has frequently been noted that, in parallel pots inoculated with the same ineffective strain, some plants unexpectedly began to grow well. On the roots of the pea plants which show the exceptional growth, some red effective nodules are regularly found in addition to the white ineffective ones. Nothing corresponding to this has ever been observed in a sterile system where foreign infections cannot occur. Furthermore, the change of an ineffective rhizobial strain to an effective one has never been observed in our laboratory cultures. On a suitable medium even effective strains have retained their effectiveness fairly well for many years.

Thornton (316) reported that the negative results of Virtanen (i.e., the attempt to change the ineffectiveness of a strain by continued passage through the host) are in general agreement with the results in Rothamsted. On the other hand, it has been found that some rhizobial strains readily produce mutant forms that differ in their effectivity. These mutant forms can be produced by X-rays, ultraviolet radiation, abnormal growth conditions, or treatment with bacteriophage. Cultivation of the bacteria in certain soils will also change an effective into an ineffective strain. It is harder to reverse this process, though it has been accomplished by treatment with phage [cf. Thornton (317)]. Jordan (181) induced mutation in parasitic and effective clover strains with X-rays, ultraviolet radiation, uranium nitrate, and diazomethane. X-Irradiation was the most effective and also produced biochemically deficient rhizobia.

In this connection, Virtanen (330, 337) found the roots of pea and clover plants bearing effective nodules and growing with free nitrogen as the nitrogen source to be coarser in structure and to contain fewer lateral roots than the more bushy roots of a finer structure growing with ammonium nitrate and bearing no nodules (Fig. 8). Roots of pea plants grown in a sterile system with nitrate nitrogen, or ammonium nitrogen or with molecular nitrogen fixed in the nodules are shown in Fig. 9. In agreement with these findings Rudin (282) established that in pea plants nodule formation influenced the form of the root system. Nutman (252) counted lateral roots on inoculated and uninoculated red clover plants and found fewer laterals on the former than on the

(a)

(b)

FIG. 8. Roots of *Trifolium hybridum* grown in quartz sand at different pH (6 to 4). (a) Inoculated plants without combined nitrogen. (b) Uninoculated plants with ammonium nitrate. Nitrogen yields of the shoots of the same plants are presented in Fig. 3. From Virtanen (330).

latter. He thought that the rhizobia in the substrate had an inhibitory effect on the formation of lateral roots.

2. *The Host Plant Specificity of the Rhizobia*

This problem is very complicated. Early workers assumed that a single species was involved in the nodule formation by various leguminous plants. As the technique of bacteriology advanced, this explanation proved to be oversimplified and to be due to inadequate test methods. Workers then went from one extreme to another by explaining that each genus of leguminous plants had a specific

Fig. 9. Roots of pea plants grown in sterile nutrient solution. Comparative experiments (left to right) with nitrate nitrogen, ammonium nitrogen, and molecular nitrogen (inoculated with an effective strain of pea *Rhizobium* without combined nitrogen). The surface of the solution was lowered during the experiment. From Virtanen (337).

nodule bacterium. This theory, however, also proved to be inconsistent with the facts. When more host species were tested, the range of specificity of the rhizobia was often found to be broad, extending to many plant genera and species. If only nodule formation is taken into account and the effectivity of the nodules is not considered, rhizobia can be divided into several groups on the basis of their host plants (cross-inoculation groups). Only six species of rhizobia are now recognized [Allen and Allen (6)] as follows:

1. Alfalfa group (*R. meliloti*)
2. Clover group (*R. trifolii*)
3. Pea group (*R. leguminosarum*)
4. Bean group (*R. phaseoli*)
5. Lupine group (*R. lupini*)
6. Soybean group (*R. japonicum*)

Species designations are lacking for the rhizobial strains which correspond to the other 14 groups of leguminous plants now catalogued in cross-inoculation categories [Fred *et al.* (134); Allen and Allen (6)].

To the six species of rhizobia belong the rhizobia of the most commonly cultivated leguminous plants, which, however, represent only a few of the very numerous species in the Leguminosae.

The division of the rhizobia into groups on the basis of the host plant is dictated by practical considerations. There is still no real explanation for the specificity of the rhizobia to any host plant though some hypotheses will be referred to below. It is probable that specific rhizobia are formed through adaptation [Allen and Allen (6), page 84]. On this hypothesis, the difficulty in classifying the rhizobia, and possibly the absence of nodulation in some leguminous genera, could be easily understood. If the ability of the root nodules to fix nitrogen (effectivity) is also taken into account, it is no longer possible to make any classification whatsoever. There are many examples in which a *Rhizobium* isolated from an effective nodule of a plant in one group produces ineffective nodules on a plant belonging to another genus of the same group, or even on another species of the same genus. Helz *et al.* (154) found strains that were effective on *Pisum* and *Lathyrus* but ineffective on *Vicia faba*, whereas other strains produced an opposite effect. In this laboratory we have not been able to produce effective root nodules on red clover (*Trifolium pratense*) with some rhizobial strains isolated from effective nodules of *T. alexandrinum* [Virtanen (332)]. Likewise a delayed nodulation took place and relatively poor nodules were formed when *T. alexandrinum* was inoculated with our very effective red-clover rhizobia. Strong (300) presents similar results from Australia with red, white, and subterranean clover. Wilson *et al.* (415), in their experiments with various strains of *R. meliloti* in association with different species or strains of *Melilotus*, observed three types of response with respect to nitrogen fixation: (a) The association of certain strains of bacteria with all the species of host plant tested was consistently effective. (b) The association of certain strains was effective with one species of host, but ineffective with another. (c) The association of certain strains of the organism with certain species of plant resulted in erratic responses not only in different experiments, but in a single experiment. These authors consider it possible that this type of response was influenced by the carbohydrate-nitrogen relationship in the plant. Foreign rhizobial infections are, however, also to be considered in open-pot experiments (see page 583).

The observations cited above and many others have shown that symbiotic nitrogen fixation is dependent not only on the effectiveness of the rhizobial strain, but also on the host plant.

Bjälfve (45, 46) concluded from his experiments with field pea and vetch that in leguminous plants some hereditary factor influences the size and position of the nodules on the roots, with consequent effect on the yield of the plant. Nutman (251) has shown that hereditary factors exist in the clover plant which determine the effectiveness of a given strain of rhizobium. Simple recessive genes can produce completely ineffective nodules with a normally effective rhizobial strain. These single genes are highly specific in their action and may operate with only a single rhizobial strain. Nutman (257, 259) has described two independent recessive host genes (i_1 and ie) each of which causes ineffective symbiosis between red clover plants and a normally effective strain of *R. trifolii*. Bergersen and Nutman (42) have found that in type i_1 ineffectiveness is due to the failure of the infecting bacteria to produce bacteroids. In the other type, *ie*, abnormal divisions of the host tissue take place in the vicinity of bacteria which have been released from infection threads. This gives rise to a disorganized tumorlike growth in which no bacteroids are formed.

The specificity of the rhizobia in relation to the host plant, and the dependence of the effectivity of the root nodules on the rhizobial strains as well as on the species and strains of the host plant clearly shows the decisive importance of both parties in nodule formation as well as in the development of the complicated symbiotic system needed in nitrogen fixation.

D. Competition between Rhizobial Strains

When the seed of some leguminous plant is infected simultaneously with many rhizobial strains capable of producing nodules on this plant, all have a chance to produce nodules. Dunham and Baldwin (108) obtained simultaneous nodulation by effective and ineffective strains on the same plant. Using antisera, Thornton and Kleczkowski (320) have identified nodules produced by the inoculation of clover in the field. In addition to nodules produced by the native population of clover rhizobia, nodules produced by the inoculated strain could also be found. Some strains competed more successfully than others with the natural strains in the soil [Nicol and Thornton (242)]. The use of effective rhizobial cultures for inoculation of native legumes in practical agriculture is founded on the supposition that the inoculated bacteria will predominate in the nodule formation. The ability of the inoculated strains to compete with other strains is therefore important. In accordance with the results from Rothamsted, the experiments in this laboratory in a sterile culture system have shown that some effective rhizobia of pea and clover compete more successfully than others with ineffective strains when these are inoculated simultaneously [Virtanen and Linkola (375)].

The situation is, however, quite different if the pea plant is first inoculated with an ineffective strain and, only after the first nodules have formed, with an effective strain. Hiltner (160) noted that a certain degree of immunity is established by the entrance of the first strain and that only bacteria of greater "virulence" can effect secondary invasion. In the literature other contradictory information occurs concerning the immunity against later infections which is produced by the first infection of a rhizobial strain in the host plant. Nicol and Thornton (242) doubt the immunizing effect of the first strain. From experiments with pea and soybean they arrived at the conclusion that the strain having the higher initial growth rate could almost check multiplication of the other strain in the rhizosphere. Chen (97) observed that the limiting number of nodules per gram of root of a given host plant was specific for each strain. This number is formed rapidly by one strain and slowly by another. Far more nodules were produced with ineffective than with effective strains. After the roots have been "saturated" with nodules of a given strain which forms more nodules than the competing strain, the latter is no longer able to form nodules on them. The interval between the first inoculation (at sowing) and the second inoculation was very long in Chen's experiments, 6 weeks in the case of peas.

The experiments in this laboratory in a sterile system and in pot cultures have led to different results [Virtanen and Linkola (375)].

When the roots of young pea plants were first inoculated with the ineffective H VIII strain, and after the formation of the first visible nodules with an effective strain, usually 7–14 days after the first inoculation, no effective nodules were formed during the following month at least. Some differences were noted in this respect between different effective strains. When the pea plant had almost withered, a small group of effective, unusually large nodules could unexpectedly be formed on the roots among the numerous ineffective nodules, with the result that the plant pushed out a new shoot and began to grow (Fig. 10). By following the nodulation of pea plants in the nutrient solution it was found that the ineffective H VIII strain, as well as effective strains, continued to form nodules during the whole growth period for at least a month after the appearance of the first nodules, so that the saturation of the roots was probably not the cause of the "immunity" against the later inoculation with effective strains.

Recent investigations by Purchase and Nutman (270) on the inoculation of mixed cultures of virulent and avirulent clover rhizobia em-

phasize an alternate explanation of the "immunity" suggested already
by Nicol and Thornton (242). Nutman found that the avirulent Bart
A strain strongly inhibited the multiplication of the virulent A strain
in the rhizosphere. The successful suppression of this strain by the
presence of a large excess of the nonvirulent strain was associated

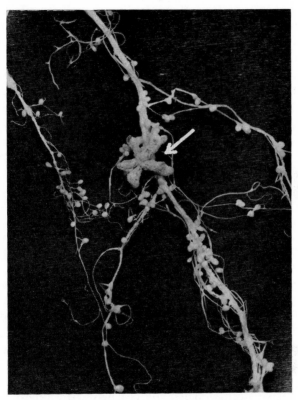

Fig. 10. A cluster of long, red nodules (marked with an arrow) formed by the
effective H 7 strain on roots of pea where the ineffective H VIII strain had previously produced round, white nodules. H 7 nodules appeared only 1½ months after
inoculation when the plant had already withered. From Virtanen and Linkola (375).

with a significant depression of nodulation. Since in our experiments
with pea plants the number of the rhizobia of the H VIII strain had
probably reached its maximum in the rhizosphere when the effective
strain was inoculated (7–14 days later), it is possible that the competition between the strains in the rhizosphere could be the cause of the
"immunity." The appearance of some effective nodules on the roots of
pea bearing ineffective nodules only 1–1½ months after the inoculation

with an effective strain is, however, not easy to understand even on the basis of this hypothesis.

Some observations suggest a harmful effect of ineffective nodules on the growth of the host plant. Chen *et al.* (98) found that a soluble substance, harmful to rhizobial growth *in vitro*, is formed within ineffective nodules and that this substance is localized in, or near, ineffective nodules, since effective nodulation on the same root system is not affected. Sterile, unheated root juice extractions from nonnodulated plants do not contain any adverse growth factor for ineffective strains *in vitro*. Jordan and Garrard (183) suggested that parasitic, or ineffective, strains of rhizobia may produce some phytotoxic substance which has a detrimental effect on plant growth. In this laboratory, addition of combined nitrogen into the nutrient solution of a pea plant nodulated with an ineffective strain of rhizobia leads to normal growth of the plant. The harmful substances possibly formed by the ineffective strain cannot, accordingly, prevent growth with combined nitrogen.

Whatever the explanation for the observed "immunity," its existence has made it possible to determine under normal field conditions what part of the total nitrogen of the pea plant is derived from the combined nitrogen in the soil and what part from molecular nitrogen from the atmosphere. The principle of the method is this: in parallel experiments a group of pea seedlings are inoculated with an ineffective, and another group with an effective, strain of rhizobia. When visible nodules have formed on the roots of the plants, both groups of pea plants are transplanted in parallel plots in the soil in question. If the ineffective strain is able to prevent the infection of the roots by the effective strains found in the soil, the difference between the amount of nitrogen in the two groups of plants represents the nitrogen derived from nitrogen fixation. It is assumed here that both groups of pea plants take up from the soil equal amounts of combined nitrogen. This assumption seems to be valid because the ineffective H VIII strain used in the experiments does not prevent the growth of the pea plants with combined nitrogen. The method developed in this laboratory is described in detail by Virtanen and Saubert-von Hausen (391) and Virtanen and Holmberg (359).

Using this method in pot and field experiments with three different types of soil (light clay, heavy clay, and sandy soil) it was found that the pea plants obtained 70–90% of their nitrogen from the atmosphere. The nitrogen fixation was dependent on the nitrate content of the soil, as might be expected. In mold (formed from fallen leaves) containing 42.5 mg of nitrate nitrogen per 100 gm of dry mold, the fixed nitrogen of the total nitrogen of the pea plant was still 40%. The most surprising thing was that nodules were formed and that large amounts of nitrogen were fixed in the presence of such a high concentration of nitrate. The problem about the influence of combined nitrogen on the nodulation and nitrogen fixation will be reverted to in Section III, H.

In most experiments with different kinds of soil the resistance caused by the H VIII strain usually lasted 1–1½ months in most of the plants, and hence the field method presented above functioned well. In one soil (pot experiment in June) most pea plants inoculated with the H VIII strain were already infected with an effective strain after a couple of weeks, and hence the method could not be used. By following the color and the growth of the plants it is easy to see for how long the formation of effective nodules is prevented by the ineffective nodules.

E. MICROBIAL ANTAGONISM AND PHAGE ACTION IN THE SOIL

Not very much is known about the relations between rhizobia and other soil organisms. There is, however, evidence that some aerobic spore-forming soil bacteria form substances which have an antibiotic effect on rhizobia. It was found in this laboratory that in an autoclaved sample of soil, rich in humus, the inoculation with legume bacteria did not induce growth. A closer examination revealed that a very thermostable, spore-forming bacterium of *B. mesentericus* type isolated from the soil has an antibacterial effect on all tested strains of rhizobia from pea, clover, and bean, as well as on *Azotobacter*. The only exception was a strain of soybean rhizobia which was quite unaffected [Virtanen and Linkola (376)]. The active substances were ether soluble and consisted at least partly of volatile fatty acids which were found in the medium of *B. mesentericus* cultures. In this fatty acid fraction propionic, *n*-butyric, and *i*-valeric acids were found in the relative concentrations 12.5:100:50 in addition to acetic acid. Volatile acids with 6–10 carbon atoms were detected only in traces [Miettinen and Virtanen (227)]. Even in 0.005 M solutions *n*- and *i*-butyric, *n*- and *i*-valeric, and *n*-caproic acids prevent the growth of pea rhizobia.

From a crude filtrate of *Bacillus subtilis*, Casas-Campillo (91, 92) recovered a crystalline water-soluble substance lytic to *R. meliloti*. Allen and Allen [(6), page 92] report a thermostable, highly diffusible, antibiotic substance isolated from a spore former closely resembling *B. cereus*. Preliminary data indicate that fungi and products of their metabolism are important in reducing the rhizobial population in soil [Robinson (277); Thornton *et al.* (318)]. The majority of more than 400 streptomycetes isolated from soils in North America and Japan inhibited strains of *R. japonicum* and *R. lupini* [cf. (6), page 91].

Cowpea rhizobia were among those least frequently inhibited by streptomyces. Among a wide variety of soil bacteria tested, a strain of *R. japonicum* showed the least relative susceptibility to 50 actinomycetes from Canadian soils [cf. (6), page 91].

The examples presented above show that different soil microorganisms can destroy rhizobia in laboratory cultures. This still does not prove that the situation is the same in nature. Abdel-Ghaffar and Allen (1) have found that an antibiotic produced by an aerobic sporeforming bacterium was inactivated by peat particles. The well-known fact that effective strains of native rhizobia exist in many soils for decades and possibly for centuries, even if the leguminous plant in question is not cultivated, demonstrates the resistance of the rhizobia under natural conditions.

Several authors have suggested that the action of phages is much more important in depressing nodulation than is that of microorganisms. Phages specific for the rhizobia appear to be widely distributed, having been isolated from nodules, roots, and soils in which legumes have grown. Resistant as well as sensitive strains of the rhizobia have been isolated. Varying information on the specificity of the phages for strains or species of rhizobia is to be found in the literature [Demolon and Dunez (104); Katznelson (185)]. Almon and Wilson (19) showed that "good" and "poor" strains of clover rhizobia included both phage-sensitive and phage-resistant cultures. The fixation of nitrogen was unaffected by added phage only if the bacterial strain was phage resistant or, if phage sensitive, the bacterial strain was poor with respect to nitrogen fixation. If the strain of rhizobium was both effective and phage sensitive, fixation of nitrogen was decreased and only resistant bacteria were recovered from the nodules. On the basis of laboratory and field experiments Demolon and Dunez (101–103, 105) emphasize the phage as the major cause of "alfalfa fatigue," which is characterized by lack of plant vigor, pale green color, and small ineffective nodules. According to these authors it is an inevitable result of repeated cultivation of alfalfa in phage-infected soils, because the effective rhizobia are lysed by the phage. At the time the phage permeates the entire rhizosphere, the nitrogen fixation is finished. After a time, however, the phage should also disappear since it is sensitive to desiccation, insolation, anaerobiosis, and temperatures below 10°C. When this occurs, alfalfa should develop normally, provided that the seeds are inoculated at the time of planting with an effective strain of rhizobium. On clover-fatigued soils similar observations have been made, but the action of phage seems to be less pronounced here and to proceed at a slower rate. Weak phage effects have been reported also for pea, bean, lupine, and soybean cultures [Demolon and Dunez (104)].

It is a familiar experience that a crop rotation during which legumes alternate with nonlegumes after adequate intervals, gives the best assurance of good crops. This favorable influence of a suitable rotation may partly result from the increasing action of phages in continuous legume cultures. The changing of many factors in soil which influence the nutrition of plants (e.g., deficiency of some macro- or micronutrients, lowering of pH, unfavorable alterations of the microflora) is, however, often the principal cause of subnormal yields in the continuous culture of legumes. On the other hand, there is experimental evidence to show the harmful effect of phages, at least in alfalfa cultures. To restore alfalfa-fatigued soils Demolon and Dunez (101, 103, 105) have recommended the selection of a phage-resistant alfalfa variety or species and the application of inocula consisting of polyvalent resistant rhizobial strains.

Later observations of various workers in different countries have confirmed that phage can influence nodule formation and nitrogen fixation. However, the phage action is complicated, as shown by the investigations at Rothamsted. Kleczkowska (192), a member of this group, writes in a recent paper: "It seems unlikely that phage can directly cause a failure of legume crops by destroying the nodule bacteria. It is possible, however, that phages may increase the proportion of ineffective strains in the soil under certain conditions and this possibility is enhanced by the observation that ineffective phage-resistant mutants are much more readily developed from effective parent strains than *vice versa*."

F. TRANSFER OF THE FIXED NITROGEN FROM THE NODULES TO THE HOST PLANT

Two fundamentally different hypotheses have been proposed to explain the transfer of the fixed nitrogen from the nodules to the host plant: (a) soluble nitrogen compounds are formed through lysis of bacterial cells (either by plant enzymes, by enzymes from dead rhizobia, or by bacteriophages); (b) soluble nitrogen compounds are regularly excreted by the bacteria in the nodules.

All earlier hypotheses according to which fixed nitrogen is first used as a building material for bacterial cells and is then liberated by lysis of the cells are improbable because they do not explain many facts concerning the function of the bacterial mass in the nodule during nitrogen fixation. Considering the large amount of fixed nitrogen which must continuously be transferred from the nodules to the host to enable its growth, and the small amount of nitrogen in the nodules per plant, the multiplication, and decomposition of the rhizobia in the nodules should occur at an enormous rate during nitrogen fixation if the hypothesis of lysis is correct. This is quite inconsistent with the experimental facts related above. First, the bacteroids which form the greatest part of the bacterial mass in effective nodules are incapable of multiplying; secondly, no microscopically detectable disintegration of the bacterial mass in young active nodules has been observed; and, thirdly, the proteolytic activity of the nodules is very low (366). Also the absence of bacteriophage in the nodules does not affect the transfer of the fixed nitrogen to the host plant [Grijns (147)].

The hypothesis that the rhizobia in the nodules excrete soluble nitrogenous products which are passed on to the plant was first advanced by Nobbe and Hiltner (246). For many years, however, this hypothesis lacked experimental support.

In this laboratory attention was given to the excretion of nitrogenous compounds into the substrate (quartz sand) from an inoculated pea plant in the early stages of growth [Virtanen and von Hausen (352); Virtanen et al. (356); Virtanen and Laine (365)]. It was suggested by Virtanen and von Hausen (353) "that the fixation of nitrogen takes place at the surface of the bacterial cells in nodules," and the nitrogenous compounds thus formed (e.g., L-aspartic acid, a quantitatively important factor among the excretion products and a good nitrogen source for legumes) are utilized by the host plant and could also diffuse partly into the medium.

On the other hand, Bond (48) described experiments which were designed to yield quantitative information concerning the uptake of fixed nitrogen by soybean from the nodules. The results led to the conclusion that "from the commencement of fixation and onwards, of the nitrogen fixed by the bacteria a very high proportion, probably in the region of 80 to 90% is regularly liberated without appreciable delay into the host cytoplasm and then undergoes transference to other parts of the plant or the rooting medium. There is no retention or storage to any considerable extent of the fixed nitrogen within the bacteria or the nodules."

From different approaches workers had thus come to a very similar concept of the transfer of fixed nitrogen from the nodules to the host plant. Experimental results similar to those of Bond were obtained earlier with cowpeas (*Vigna catjang*) by Whiting (399) and later with soybeans by Wilson and Umbreit (418), although the latter authors did not consider that the results proved the excretion of nitrogenous compounds from the rhizobial mass into the host cytoplasm.

To give a clear picture of the nodulation, nitrogen fixation, and the transfer of fixed nitrogen to the host plant from the beginning of the nodule formation to the oxidation of leghemoglobin to the green pigment, and the disintegration of the bacteroid mass in the nodules, the results of an experiment with inoculated pea plants by Virtanen and Linkola (377) are presented in Fig. 11. A similar experiment in quartz sand and open pots was described earlier by Virtanen et al. (363).

The analyses of the nitrogenous compounds in root nodules before the "era of chromatography" did not give results from which the nature of the nitrogenous compounds which are transferred from the nodules to the host plant could be concluded [Umbreit and Burris (326)]. Not even the use of chromatographic methods has until now decisively changed the situation. Paper chromatographic analyses of the composition of the nitrogenous compounds of root nodules has not revealed decisive differences between nodules and other parts of the pea plant [Miettinen (226)]. Butler and Bathurst (88) have found that about 80% of the free amino acids of white clover nodules is asparagine, but that, after hydrolysis with 6 N HCl, a ninhydrin-positive compound similar to γ-aminobutyric acid can be detected in very high concentration (about 5 times higher than asparagine found before hydrolysis). The precursor(s) of this ninhydrin-positive compound has a high mobility in phenol-water, but the chemical nature of it is unknown. Miettinen (226) could not find this kind of compound in pea nodules, at least not in higher concentration.

Wieringa and Bakhuis (401) have recently studied the composition of amino acids in the bleeding sap of pea plants (the sap which is transported from the roots to the green parts of the plant) inoculated with effective strains of Rhizobium; they found that it contains mainly aspartic acid, asparagine, glutamine, and smaller amounts of hydroxyproline and threonine. Free glutamic acid was not found. In the bleeding sap of pea plants inoculated with an ineffective strain, or without inoculation, only the spot of aspartic acid was found. Investigations in this laboratory have confirmed these results with some exceptions [Virtanen and Santaoja (389)]. The bleeding sap, taken from a flowering pea plant inoculated with an effective strain, contained asparagine nitrogen plus aspartic acid nitrogen to about 70% of the total nitrogen of the sap. The share of glutamine nitrogen was about 10% and that of homoserine nitrogen about 3%. About 10% of the total nitrogen was found in the "peptide" fraction which passed the Amberlite IR-120 column. In agreement with Wieringa and Bakhuis, glutamic acid was not found. In smaller concentrations (1% or less) some other amino acids were found, but not hydroxyproline. It is probable that the hydroxyproline of Wieringa and Bakhuis was homoserine. It can be said that about 75% of the total nitrogen in the bleeding sap transported during the highest nitrogen fixation to the green part of pea plants from roots bearing effective nodules, belongs to asparagine, aspartic acid, and homoserine. Because homoserine is probably formed from aspartic acid via aspartyl phosphate [Hirsch and Cohen (164)], it also is a derivative of aspartic acid. Aspartic acid is thus on the basis of the amino acid composition of the bleeding sap the central amino acid in the nitrogen nutrition of the inoculated pea plant. The corresponding analyses of the bleeding sap of pea plants grown with ammonium or nitrate nitrogen show that it contains qualitatively the same

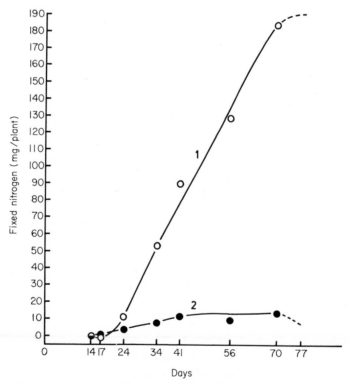

Fig. 11. Curve *1*: Fixed nitrogen in plants. Curve *2*: Nitrogen in nodules. Fixation of nitrogen in root nodules of the pea plant and its transfer to the host plant. Experiment was carried out in sterile nutrient solution without combined nitrogen (see Fig. 12), two plants in each bottle. The whole plants including roots and the excised nodules were analyzed. Every point on the curve is a mean value of a nitrogen determination with 4 plants. The nitrogen of the control (uninoculated) plants was always subtracted from the results.

Fig. 11 (*con't.*)

March 9, 1943: Seeds were sterilized; on March 16, seedlings were transferred in Woulfe bottles and inoculated with the very effective H 2 strain.

March 23: First visible nodules. During the rapid multiplication of rhizobia when nodules are formed, the nitrogen is obtained from the host plant.

March 26: Formation of red pigment and bacteroids is established in the oldest nodules, nitrogen fixation starts, and the pea plant begins to obtain nitrogen compounds from the nodules.

April 2: The rapid formation of nodules has ceased. Nodules above the surface of the liquid are red and contain a bacteroid mass; those in the liquid are slightly reddish or white. The liquid surface was from now on kept low (one-fourth the height of the flask) and at the same level all the time; hence only the nodules on the lowest part of the roots were in the nutrient solution; 398 nodules (63 mg dry weight) per plant

$$\frac{\text{Fixed N in plant 11.4 mg}}{\text{N in nodules 4.3 mg}} = 2.7$$

April 12: The nitrogen content of the plant increases with maximal velocity; 417 nodules (110 mg dry weight) per plant, most nodules red

$$\frac{\text{Fixed N in plant 53.4 mg}}{\text{N in nodules 7.9 mg}} = 6.8$$

April 19: First buds on plants; 492 nodules (165 mg dry weight) per plant; most nodules red, only the lowest nodules in the solution white

$$\frac{\text{Fixed N in plant 90.2 mg}}{\text{N in nodules 11.6 mg}} = 8.5$$

May 4: In full bloom; 537 nodules (157 mg dry weight) per plant; in some nodules greenish color begins to appear in the base of the nodules

$$\frac{\text{Fixed N in plant 129.0 mg}}{\text{N in nodules 10 mg}} = 12.9$$

May 18: Pods have formed; vegetative growth is almost finished; part of the nodules already green, part turning green; 589 nodules (206 mg dry weight) per plant

$$\frac{\text{Fixed N in plant 184.2 mg}}{\text{N in nodules 14 mg}} = 13.2$$

May 25: Most nodules greenish, bacteroids disappeared, rod-shaped rhizobia in the nodules, the nitrogen content of the nodules decreased through decomposition processes.

The number of nodules on the roots of different plants varies to such an extent that the mean values for four plants do not permit a quantitative comparison between individual plants. From Virtanen and Linkola (377).

amino acids as the sap of pea plants getting their nitrogen from the root nodules. Quantitative differences are, however, to be found, the proportion of total amino acids being lower in the sap of plants grown with combined nitrogen.

It appears from these results that the nitrogen metabolism of the roots leads to the same amino acid independently of the source of the nitrogen. It is therefore understandable that leguminous plants grow well both with combined nitrogen and, when bearing effective nodules, with molecular nitrogen. Under favorable conditions of light and temperature, some species give the highest yields with molecular nitrogen. In some experiments with pea and clover in this laboratory, combined nitrogen is required for maximum yields. In the literature there is much information on the favorable effect of combined nitrogen on the yields of nodulated soybeans. In this connection we may refer to Thornton's (308) experiments in which N^{15}-labeled combined nitrogen was used. He found that nodulated soybeans, dependent solely on nitrogen fixation, do not achieve maximum growth. Definite differences in this respect between plant species cannot, however, be presented, because nitrogen fixation depends on genetic factors in the host plants and on the effectivity of the rhizobial strain and in addition on external factors such as light intensity, day length, and temperature.

The literature mentions only one leguminous plant which fails to grow with combined nitrogen. Castelli (93) has found that *Hedysarum coronarium* L. does not use any of the numerous nitrogenous compounds, including nitrate, nitrite, ammonium salts, and urea, added to the soil in pots. The plants wither and die after the exhaustion of the nitrogen in the seeds. Only plants inoculated with the specific rhizobia grow normally. Confirmation of this peculiar finding is needed.

G. EXCRETION OF NITROGENOUS COMPOUNDS FROM THE NODULES INTO THE ROOTING MEDIUM

The state of knowledge in this field is similar to that of nitrogen fixation a century ago.

All the experiments up to 1930 to explain the numerous observations of agriculturists and farmers on the increased growth and nitrogen content of nonlegumes grown in association with legumes were carried out under conditions in which the growth of free-living nitrogen-fixing organisms was also possible. Accordingly, the cause of the benefit to nonlegumes of association with legumes could not be explained. In field experiments and in pot experiments using soil as the medium, other factors also hamper the drawing of binding conclusions. Fred *et al.*

(134) and Wilson (407) have thoroughly reviewed the earlier literature on growth of nonlegumes associated with legumes.

The situation changed when a method for growing plants under
sterile conditions was introduced by Virtanen and von Hausen (352)
in the study of cultures of nonlegumes associated with inoculated
legumes. Because plants do not grow very well in a closed flask, a system was developed by which the roots of the plants are enclosed in a
sterile container, but the shoots are freely exposed to the atmosphere,
which thus makes good growth possible (Fig. 12). With this method

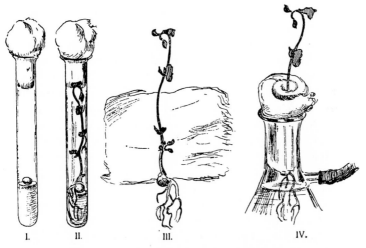

I.   II.   III.   IV.

FIG. 12. The method used for cultivating plants in a sterile system (see also
Fig. 13). From Virtanen (332). For a detailed description of the method see (151).

no microorganisms other than the inoculated strain of rhizobia are
present in the rooting medium [Virtanen *et al.* (356); von Hausen
(151)]. When a leguminous plant inoculated with a pure culture of
rhizobia grew in this system, together with a nonleguminous plant, in
a medium without combined nitrogen, the latter could get nitrogen only
from the rhizobia or from the roots of the legume. Since the free-living
rhizobia have never been found to fix nitrogen, the only possibility was
that the nonlegume obtained organic nitrogen from the legume. In
many experiments with such associated cultures it was found that the
amount of nitrogen in the nonleguminous plant had increased to many
times the small amounts of nitrogenous compounds originally present
in the seed and in the medium. Furthermore, the total nitrogen in the
medium had also increased. It was thus conclusively proved that the

nitrogen fixed in the root nodules had passed from the nodulated root system into the medium (Fig. 13).

In the 1930's many experiments were performed annually in this laboratory to study the excretion of nitrogenous compounds from nodulated pea plants. The experiments were performed using both the sterile culture system and ordinary pot experiments. Since no note-

FIG. 13. Associated cultures of pea and barley in quartz sand without combined nitrogen (sterile system). Left: uninoculated. Right: inoculated (note the three-branched barley; for convenience in photographing the pea was bent down). From Virtanen (332).

worthy excretion occurred when pea plants grew in nutrient solution [Virtanen and von Hausen (354, 355)], quartz sand was generally used as the substrate. With few exceptions the experiments showed an excretion that ranged from 10 to 30% of the total nitrogen fixed, but sometimes it was over 50%. The very high extent of excretion (excreted nitrogen as percentage of total fixed nitrogen) in the latter cases was astonishing because the pea plant itself was then apparently suffering from lack of nitrogen and the growth of the plant was therefore not good [Virtanen *et al.* (358)]. Generally excretion was higher in associated cultures of pea and nonlegumes than when the pea plant grew alone. This can be caused by the uptake of excreted nitrogenous

TABLE IV

Experiment with Pea Plants in Sterile Culture in Quartz Sand[a,b]

Harvested	Dry weight per 2 plants (gm)	Fixed N in 2 plants mg[c]	N%	Excreted N in sand[c] (mg)	Total fixed N (mg)	Excreted N (% of total fixed N)	In the aqueous extract of sand (N/mg)	Foreman precipit. (mainly aminodi-carboxylic acid) (N % of total N)
April 24,	1.319	28.0	3.15	9.1	37.1	24.5		
before	1.648	43.3	3.48	13.0	56.3	23.7	28.8	63.2
flowering	1.449	33.3	3.26	8.2	41.5	19.7		
May 3	3.546	105.4	3.37	35.4	140.8	25.2		
start of	2.947	79.9	3.19	51.8	131.7	39.3	118.3	51.7
flowering	4.011	118.6	3.31	43.7	162.3	27.0		
May 13,	3.438	112.1	3.67	16.3	128.4	12.8		
full bloom	3.449	104.0	3.42	20.6	124.6	16.5	56.1	47.0
	4.460	122.9	3.07	27.4	150.3	18.2		
May 28,	7.904	167.2	2.29	7.7	174.9	4.4		
pods partly	8.453	159.9	2.06	20.2	180.1	11.2	33.1	35.7
developed	8.382	204.8	2.61	11.0	215.8	5.1		
Control un-inoculated	1.009	14.0	1.39	14.0	—	—	—	—

[a] Data from Virtanen (332).
[b] Thirty-one Woulfe bottles each containing 4.8 kg dry quartz sand (3.0 mg nitrogen per kilogram) and 2 liters nitrogen-free nutrient solution, pH 6.5; 2 Torsdag peas in each bottle, inoculated with the effective H X strain. Experiment was started on March 30, 1937, but plants were harvested at different times, in units of three cultures. Roots were removed, and the sand from one bottle at a time was thoroughly extracted at room temperature in an apparatus with water acidified with HCl to pH 3–4.
[c] Control subtracted.

compounds by the pea plant. As an example of this, results of one experiment with inoculated pea plants alone are given in Table IV [Virtanen (332), page 46].

The results presented in Table IV show that part of the nitrogenous compounds excreted into the sand at an early stage of growth had been taken up by the pea plant at a more advanced stage of growth; so much so that when pods were partly developed there remained in the sand only about one-third of the nitrogenous compounds that were present at the beginning of flowering. The results clearly indicate that the rate of excretion is highest before, and at the beginning of, flowering when the nodules are still young and fully active without even a sign of degeneration. The general experience in this laboratory is that unless the excretion appears in young plants soon after the appearance of effective nodules, it does not occur at all. The phenomenon cannot, therefore, be due to autolysis of the root nodules, but is only explained as an excretion process. It can be assumed that the excretion mechanism begins to function when the synthetic processes, primarily protein synthesis, in the host plant are not able to utilize all the soluble nitrogen compounds formed in the nodules.

The nitrogenous compounds that are extracted with cold water from sand in which inoculated pea plants have grown in sterile culture, contain mostly amino nitrogen [Virtanen et al. (358)]. On acid hydrolysis, very little ammonia was formed (356). Later on, dicarboxylic amino acids, principally L-aspartic acid with some glutamic acid, were found to constitute at least half of the excreted amino acids [Virtanen and Laine (371); Virtanen et al. (378)]. Other amino acids could not be conclusively identified by the methods then available. The composition of the excretion products differed from the composition of the nitrogen compounds in the bleeding sap of inoculated pea plants (asparagine, aspartic acid, glutamine, and homoserine) (389) especially with respect to the absence of amides. Nitrogen-free carbon compounds, e.g., fumaric acid, have been found also in a water extract of sand in which nodulated pea plants had grown [Virtanen and Laine (371)].

Virtanen et al. (356) found that uninoculated pea plants grow very well in a sterile system with L-aspartic acid as the only nitrogen source. The fact that the inoculated pea plant had later on taken up most of the nitrogen compounds excreted in the medium, as shown in Table IV, is thus easily understood. Because barley and wheat plants cannot use aminodicarboxylic acids as a nitrogen source, some other amino acids excreted in the medium must have been present. In field and pot experiments the amino acids are deaminated or taken up by microorganisms, and the question of the suitability of the original amino acids to the nonleguminous plants in associated cultures with legumes is no longer important.

In this connection the latest investigations on the uptake and utilization of L- and D-aspartic acids by plants should be mentioned. Valle and Virtanen (327a) found that the pea plant takes up both L-aspartic and L-glutamic acids as well as nitrate and uses them in nitrogen metabolism. The whole amino acid molecules were taken up. The D-form of these amino acids was taken up in small amounts but the dry matter of the plants was lowered by this. Barley and wheat did not take up any L-aspartic acid, and also took up practically no L-glutamic acid.

In an experiment with uninoculated pea plants in sterile quartz sand containing nitrate as the nitrogen source, 3.9 mg of amino nitrogen per two plants could be extracted from the sand. In parallel experiments with pea plants inoculated with an ineffective rhizobium strain and an effective strain, 1.7 mg and 90.0 mg of amino nitrogen per two pea plants were found, respectively [Virtanen et al. (357)]. The occurrence of very small amounts of nitrogen in the medium, such as 1–3 mg per plant, can possibly be ascribed to the extraction of nitrogenous compounds from the roots with water and to sloughed-off portions of the roots and nodules. Findings in this laboratory [Virtanen and Santaoja (390)] have shown that in these cases, independently of whether the pea plant has grown with combined nitrogen or with molecular nitrogen (inoculated plant), only a relatively small part of the increased organic nitrogen in the sand is amino nitrogen, and that the free amino acid fraction contains mostly the amino acids usually to be found in the pea plant. The strong excretion presented above is thus different in principle from the regular occurrence of small amounts of organic nitrogen in the medium of the legumes in a sterile culture system.

When excretion occurred almost regularly in the experiments made in this laboratory in the 1930's, conflicting information also appeared in the literature. After many negative results, Wilson and his collaborators [Wilson and Wyss (420); Wilson and Burton (414)] were able to produce excretion both in a sterile culture system of the type used in our laboratory and in pot experiments. In some unique cases even a very strong excretion (up to 64% of the total fixed nitrogen) was found. Thus the excretion phenomenon was confirmed under bacteriologically controlled conditions in a different part of the world. The results were, however, in many cases erratic, negative results occurring most often in experiments in Madison, Wisconsin. Studies on the effect of temperature, light, day length, etc., on excretion led Wilson (407) to conclude that climatic conditions have a decisive effect on the excretion of nitrogenous compounds, and they explain, at least in part, variable experimental results obtained in different parts of the world. When photosynthesis is low, plants fix and excrete little or no nitrogen. When the rate of photosynthesis is extremely high, fixation is greatly stimulated, but development of the plant rapidly consumes the nitrogen fixed, with the result that again no excretion occurs. Sufficient photosynthesis to insure a fairly high rate of nitrogen fixation but minimal amounts of carbohydrate, which "ties up" the nitrogen as it is fixed, appear to be prerequisites for excretion by the legume [Wilson (407)]. Sironval (291, 292) has recently shown that day length regulates both the chlorophyll and hematin content of the plants. He claims that in lupine on short-day culture some nodules had a hematin content 50% lower than in long-day controls.

Because of the complete dependence of symbiotic nitrogen fixation on the photosynthesis of carbon compounds, the concept by Wilson seems sound. In Helsinki for example, the most suitable season for excretion has been the spring when the temperature is relatively low even in greenhouses, but the light conditions are good and the days long. The very great differences in excretion which appear unexpectedly even among duplicate cultures, cannot, however, be caused by climatic factors alone. There must also be other factors, for the present unknown, which influence the excretion phenomenon. The occasional enormous excretion, when the inoculated pea plant itself has a pale green color and suffers from lack of nitrogen (358), suggests that the transfer of the fixed nitrogen from the nodules to the host plant is disturbed for some reason. The accumulation of nitrogen compounds in the nodules should then cause the excretion.

The further investigation of excretion has been hampered by the fact that, even in this laboratory, for some unknown reason this phenomenon could seldom be reproduced after the 1940's. In associated cultures of pea and barley (*Hordeum vulgare*), it has occurred in a clear, although comparatively weak, form in many experiments in spring, but in pea cultures alone it has occurred only to such an extent that it could not be defined as an excretion phenomenon. When comparing this situation with the high, or very high, excretion obtained almost regularly in the 1930's, it is apparent that some decisive and still unknown factor is now different from what it was then.

As a problem of great practical importance, the excretion of nitrogen compounds in associated cultures of nonlegumes with leguminous plants has naturally been much discussed. The results of field experiments have been contradictory. Under field conditions it is almost impossible to get conclusive proof of excretion, since the soil always contains combined nitrogen and free-living nitrogen-fixing microorganisms. The better growth and increased nitrogen content of nonlegumes in association with leguminous plants may therefore be caused by better utilization of the nitrogenous compounds in soil or by nonsymbiotic nitrogen fixation. There are, however, very positive results from pot and field experiments with associated cultures of legumes and nonlegumes which are difficult to explain without the excretion phenomenon [e.g., Thornton and Nicol (321); Vartiovaara (327b); Jónsson (180)]. Because experiments that utilize as the medium so complicated a system as soil cannot give conclusive proof of excretion, pot and field experiments with associated cultures of legumes and nonlegumes are not treated in this article. In Wilson's monograph (407) a chapter is devoted to this problem.

H. Carbohydrate-Nitrogen Relationships in Symbiotic Nitrogen Fixation, and the Influence of Combined Nitrogen and Other Nutrients on Nodulation and Nitrogen Fixation

A factor that has a strong influence on symbiotic nitrogen fixation is the carbohydrate level in the host plant. This is natural since the formation and the activity of the root nodules presupposes a sufficient supply of carbon compounds from the host plant. Many observations show, however, that the supply of combined nitrogen may be of decisive importance also for the symbiotic nitrogen fixation system. Both the carbohydrate and the nitrogen level in the host plant must therefore be taken into consideration when examining external factors, such as the light intensity or the effect of carbon dioxide and combined nitrogen on the formation and the activity of the nodules.

The Wisconsin group (Fred, Wilson, and their associates) have tried to combine into a single hypothesis (carbohydrate-nitrogen hypothesis) considerations of both the nitrogen and the carbohydrate supply and thus to give a uniform explanation of all the effects due to the factors mentioned (407). The carbohydrate hypothesis followed from observations on the influence of light, pCO_2, and combined nitrogen on the nitrogen fixation process in the nodules. Sunlight of high intensity can bring soybeans into a "nitrogen hunger" stage when they are cultivated in sand, even though numerous, well-developed nodules are to be found on the roots. Plants supplied with ammonium nitrate develop normally under the same conditions. When the nodulated plants in the nitrogen hunger stage are shaded to retard the formation of carbohydrate, nitrogen fixation starts within a few days, according to Orcutt and Fred (261), and the pale leaves of the plants become dark green again. Shading reduces the carbohydrate-nitrogen relationship (as measured by soluble carbohydrate divided by total nitrogen). The same effect can be obtained also when combined nitrogen is added to the sand. On the other hand, a higher ammonium nitrate concentration has inhibitory effects on nodule formation and nitrogen fixation. Wilson and Wagner (419) found that high light intensity or higher pCO_2 in the atmosphere, both of which stimulate carbohydrate production, eliminate to some extent this inhibitory effect of combined nitrogen. Thus the different observations lend support to the hypothesis that an excessive carbohydrate:nitrogen ratio in the plant is the inhibitory factor irrespective of whether this ratio is due to high carbon dioxide or high light intensity. The increase of the carbohydrate:nitrogen ratio has been brought about not only by increasing the supply of carbon dioxide, but also by the addition of sugar to the substrate.

Different findings thus lead to the peculiar result that too low, as well as too high, a carbohydrate:nitrogen ratio may inhibit symbiotic nitrogen fixation. Wilson (407) has dealt exhaustively with this question. For the present there is no real explanation for the carbohydrate-nitrogen hypothesis. It seems as though an excessive carbohydrate: nitrogen ratio in the nodules inhibits the formation of the active bacteroid mass and the synthesis of leghemoglobin, i.e., the formation of the nitrogen-fixing system. The observation made by the Wisconsin group that the nodules remain small, round, and white, and accordingly still ineffective, unless the carbohydrate:nitrogen ratio is reduced, indicates this. However, it is not easy to understand how a high carbohydrate:nitrogen ratio in the plant could prevent the formation of effective nodules. It is possible that an inhibition caused by an excessive carbohydrate:nitrogen ratio might be caused either by the absence of some specific factor required for the formation of effective nodules or by the formation of some inhibiting factor to a disturbing degree. Recent findings on the formation of specific active substances in plants through the influence of light clearly show that light is important not only for the synthesis of carbohydrate, but also for that of some biologically very active substances present in small amounts in plants.

The harmful effect of sunlight of high intensity on nitrogen fixation could also depend on the rise of the temperature in the medium. As mentioned on page 569, it has recently been found that a higher temperature (30°C) prevents nitrogen fixation in nodulated subterranean clover (224) and pea (327). Because the temperature of the medium was not measured in earlier experiments, it is possible that this factor has had an inhibitory effect, at least in some experiments where sunlight of high intensity has been thought to prevent nitrogen fixation.

The influence of combined nitrogen on the formation of nodules and nitrogen fixation has been studied in many laboratories. The literature contains numerous partly contradictory results. It has generally been found that combined nitrogen at higher concentrations reduces the number and the size of nodules [Fred *et al.* (134)]. There are, however, very different pieces of information as to the disturbing concentrations. The different results may be due, in part at least, to factors that influence carbohydrate synthesis, as the hypothesis of a decisive importance of the carbohydrate-nitrogen balance in plants on nodule formation and nitrogen fixation presupposes. The inhibitory effect of combined nitrogen depends also on the nature of the medium. Noticeably smaller amounts of nitrate are injurious in nutrient solutions and in sand than in soil [Fred *et al.* (134)], and there seems also to be a difference between different types of soil. Thornton (313) found that

TABLE V

EFFECT OF NITRATE NITROGEN ON THE NUMBER AND SIZE OF
NODULES FORMED ON ALFALFA BY *Rhizobium meliloti*[a]

NO$_3$–N[b] added (mg)	Number of nodules		Length of nodules (mm)	Volume of bacterial tissue per nodule (mm^3)
	Per 10 plants	Per gram dry weight of roots		
0	496 ± 27	178	2.22 ± 0.057	0.0240
165	508 ± 67	145	1.42 ± 0.095	0.0100
330	333 ± 44	152	1.03 ± 0.13	0.0055
600	204 ± 27	100	0.71 ± 0.039	0.0025
990	69 ± 41	42	0.55 ± 0.057	0.0020
1650	68 ± 22	29	0.59 ± 0.076	0.0020

[a] Data of Thornton and Nicol (321).
[b] All added at start to 12 kg of sand, which held 2:1 of nutrient solution.

sodium nitrate on an agar medium at initial concentrations of 0.1 to 1.0% checks the deformation of root hairs by nodule bacteria and thus prevents infection of the root hairs. Ammonium sulfate had the same effect, and 0.1% of sodium nitrate also checks the stimulation of growth by sterile secretions of the nodule bacteria. These results suggest that nitrate interferes with the carbohydrate supply to the piliferous layer of the root. Thornton and Nicol (321) have shown that the inhibiting effect of nitrate is more noticeable on nodule size than on nodule number. The data of Thornton and Nicol are presented in Table V.

Earlier investigators have found that nitrate nitrogen and ammonium nitrogen have an inhibitory effect on nodulation in about the same concentrations. Only Fred and Graul (135) mention that ammonium sulfate is somewhat less depressing than sodium nitrate. Experiments in this laboratory have shown that nitrate nitrogen suppresses the nitrogen fixation at considerably lower concentrations (about 30 mg per liter) than ammonium nitrogen (over 100 mg per liter) when the pea plant was cultivated in a sterile nutrient culture system [Virtanen et al. (363)]. Nitrate nitrogen may thus have a specific effect on nitrogen fixation too. Richardson et al. (272) also have found that nitrate nitrogen in higher concentration prevented nodule formation of alfalfa more than did ammonium nitrogen.

When the experiment was performed in the branched tube system of Virtanen et al. (363, 375), in which part of the roots (inoculated) grew in a flask containing nutrient solution without combined nitrogen and the other part of the roots (uninoculated) in another flask containing the same nutrient solution but with 119 mg of nitrate nitrogen per liter, effective nodules were formed on the inoculated roots, and about 20% of the total nitrogen of the plant was fixed in the nodules. The experiments of Gäumann et al. (140) have also shown that nitrate supplied to one part of a divided root system has no influence on infection elsewhere. On the basis of these results a local reaction at the root surface is involved. It is tempting to assume that nitrate nitrogen disturbs the symbiotic nitrogen fixation through its reduction products, which in nodules react with the iron of leghemoglobin, forming a stable complex leghemoglobin-NO with it. This compound has so far not been observed in nodules [Virtanen et al. (363)].

Among other factors that influence symbiotic nitrogen fixation is the considerable oxygen requirement previously mentioned. Virtanen and von Hausen (354, 355) were able to enhance growth greatly, and also nitrogen fixation of pea plants in the sterile system, if a current of air was led through the nutrient solution or if the liquid surface was lowered so that the largest part of the roots and the nodules were above the water surface and in air. The size of the nodules was then large, and the red color intense. Bond (49) has confirmed this result. In practical agriculture the functioning of leguminous root nodules depends decisively on a sufficient oxygen supply. Therefore, the physical structure of the soil has a much stronger influence on the thriving of leguminous plants than upon plants that are grown with combined nitrogen.

Regarding the nutritional factors of nodulated plants it is natural that all the elements ordinarily necessary for plant growth are required. Some findings indicate that nodulated plants need larger amounts of some elements than plants supplied with combined nitrogen. This is especially the case with molybdenum. Anderson and Thomas (21), Anderson and Spencer (20), Jensen (172), and Mulder (235, 237) have shown that more molybdenum is needed for symbiotic nitrogen fixation than for the growth of the host plant. The occurrence of vitamin B_{12} in the nodules (203) suggests a cobalt requirement for symbiosis. Quite recently Reisenauer (271b) found that the addition of 0.1 μM of cobalt to the purified cultures of inoculated lucerne plants effects a very strong stimulation on nitrogen fixation (controls 34 mg, cobalt plants 237 mg of nitrogen per pot). According to Hallsworth et al. (147a) addition of cobalt at the rate of 0.006 and 0.06 ppm stimulates nitrogen fixation of subterranean clover. The size of the nodules and the total heme content is increased; the heme concentration per gram of nodular tissue remained unchanged, however. Copper between 0.064 and 0.64 ppm also increased both the percentage of nitrogen and the total nitrogen content.

According to Mulder (237), deficiency of boron affects nodule development by preventing infection in its absence. On page 576 the influence of boron deficiency on the formation of the vascular system in the nodules is mentioned.

Since good growth of the host plant is a condition for symbiotic nitrogen fixation, it is generally difficult to separate the influence of plant nutrients on the growth of the plant from the functioning of the nodules. In this article observations on the influence of other elements are therefore not presented.

I. The Red Pigment, Its Significance in Root Nodules

It may be assumed that the red pigment of the root nodules has been observed by all who have examined root nodules and conducted experiments with legumes, since the red color inside the nodules is often so remarkable. A closer investigation of this pigment, and the discovery of its importance for the nitrogen fixation of the nodules are, however, comparatively recent [cf. Virtanen (338)]. Kubo (198) established the hemoglobin nature of the pigment. This was confirmed both in Keilin's laboratory (190) and in this laboratory (336). A close connection of the pigment with nitrogen fixation was proposed by Virtanen (335, 336) on the basis of the following findings:

1. When the inoculated pea plant grows under such conditions that nitrogen fixation is possible, the root nodules formed by effective bacterial strains always contain red pigment. When the red pigment appears in the first nodules, nitrogen fixation starts. All factors which prevent pigment formation also prevent nitrogen fixation. For example, if gaseous nitrogen is passed through the nutrient solution of a pea plant inoculated with effective rhizobial strains, the red pigment is not formed, and the white nodules do not fix nitrogen. When a current

of air is substituted for gaseous nitrogen, the red pigment begins to appear in the nodules after some days, and nitrogen fixation starts.

2. The nodules formed by ineffective rhizobial strains never contain red pigment, even if the oxygen concentration is sufficient, and they do not fix nitrogen. The occurrence of the red pigment in effective nodules and its absence from ineffective nodules could be observed in all leguminous plants investigated (*Pisum, Vicia, Lathyrus, Phaseolus, Trifolium, Melilotus, Glycine, Caragana*).

3. If cultures of pea plants with effective nodules in full growth are removed for some days into the dark, the red pigment turns greenish. The green nodules are no longer able to fix nitrogen, even if the plants are brought into the light again.

4. Also when growing in light, the red pigment of the effective nodules of pea gradually changes to green with the advance of growth. When the growth of pea is finished, all nodules are changed to green ones.

The change of the color of nodules can best be demonstrated when the inoculated plants are grown in nutrient solution in transparent flasks. Also in pot cultures in quartz sand it is detectable. Under natural soil conditions the green nodules are preserved well enough to be easily visible in dry soil. In wet soil, however, the older nodules which no longer fix nitrogen are rapidly decomposed by foreign microorganisms and it is difficult to discern green nodules [Virtanen (339)]. The absence of the red pigment in ineffective nodules, and its presence, without exception, in the effective ones, has since been confirmed in many laboratories. The experiments of Jordan and Garrard (183) are especially notable in this connection.

Thus a clear chemical difference was found for the first time between effective and ineffective nodules. The red pigment, called leghemo-globin (= hemoglobin of leguminous root nodules) by Virtanen (362), can easily be separated from the nodules by crushing them. Leghemo-globin is then found in solution in the press juice. By washing the crushed nodules with water, the pigment can be isolated quantitatively from the nodules. Even on the basis of this, it was evident that the pigment was not present in the bacteroids in the nodules but around them in the cytoplasm of the nodule cells. The hemoprotein could be determined by the spectrophotometric method in the solution as pyridine hemochromogen (363). Smith (295) successfully used a microspectroscopic means of determining the amount and location of the pigment in nodule slices.

Leghemoglobin can be precipitated from aqueous solution by am-monium sulfate. From a preparation of which the iron content is about

0.27%, leghemoglobin precipitates between 58 and 75% saturation. On electrophoresis this fraction was separated by Ellfolk and Virtanen (113) into two components, of which the faster one has an isoelectric point of 4.4 and the slower one of 4.7. The molecular weight of the former was about 17,000 and the iron content about 0.34%, indicating one heme group per mole. This faster-moving component was considered to be pure ferrileghemoglobin. It has the lowest isoelectric point of all the known hemoglobins and of similar oxygen carriers. Its histidine content is very low, hardly one-fourth of that of myoglobin and blood hemoglobin. In this respect as well as in respect of the isoelectric point, the erythrocruorins are between leghemoglobin and myoglobin [Ellfolk and Virtanen (114)]. According to the estimations of Sternberg and Virtanen (298), the pK value of ferrileghemoglobin is 8.254 ± 0.4. For dog's ferrihemoglobin a pK of 8.12 ± 0.01 [Austin and Drabkin (27)] and for ferrimyoglobin 8.95 [Theorell and Ehrenberg (304)] have been found. Thus ferrileghemoglobin noticeably differs from ferrimyoglobin. It is possible that the linkages between iron and protein are different. The distance in angstrom units of the α-maxima and O_2- and CO-leghemoglobin ("Span") has an unusually high value of 110 [Sternberg and Virtanen (298)]. Keilin and Wang found the value 95.5 (191). The heme group of leghemoglobin seems to be the same as in blood hemoglobin, because the pyridine hemochromogens are identical, but the protein components are different as revealed by the great difference in the amino acid composition, molecular weights, and isoelectric points. The slower-moving component of leghemoglobin had a qualitatively similar spectrum as the faster-moving component, but a somewhat lower iron content and a higher molecular weight [Ellfolk and Virtanen (114)]. Thorogood (322a) has recently studied ferroheme proteins from soybean nodules.

Ellfolk (112, 112a) has obtained both the faster- and the slower-moving components of leghemoglobin in crystalline form. The iron content of the former is 0.320%, and the molecular weight calculated on the basis of it is 17,500. The iron content of the slower-moving component is 0.287% and the molecular weight 19,500. The faster component is not far from spherical in shape, whereas the slower one is somewhat asymmetric or highly hydrated.

In his later work Ellfolk (112b–e) determined the amino acid composition of both ferrileghemoglobin components. They differ only a little from each other. The molecular weight of the faster component, calculated on the basis of the amino acid content, is $16,695 \pm 651$. For the slower component the average molecular weight was found to be $15,429 \pm 548$. New estimations by physical measurements gave the values 16,800 for the faster component and 15,400 for the slower one. The low iron content of the slower component is difficult to explain. The electrophoretic behavior of the two components can be satisfactorily explained on the basis of the amino acid composition. The low histidine content mentioned above and the absence of methionine and cysteine are characteristic of leghemoglobin. The pK value of the faster component was found to be 8.16 and that of the slower 8.34. These values are in good agreement with the values of Sternberg and Virtanen (298) for the unresolved ferrileghemoglobin.

Since hemoglobin does not appear in free-living rhizobia, in the roots of legumes, or even in ineffective nodules, its formation is obviously associated in an essential way with the building of the symbiotic system required for nitrogen fixation. It still is not known what part rhizobia play in the formation of leghemoglobin in nodule cells. Hemoglobin had not previously been found anywhere else in the plant kingdom than in leguminous root nodules [Keilin and Wang (190)], but later on some kind of hemoglobin was detected in occasional samples of bakers' yeast and in cell tissue of *Neurospora crassa* and in *Penicillium notatum* by Keilin (187) and Keilin and Tissières (189).

In very effective root nodules of the pea plant at the flowering stage about 150 μg of hematin per gram of fresh weight corresponding to about 4 mg of leghemoglobin (average molecular weight of the two components $\sim$ 16000), or about 4% leghemoglobin on a dry weight basis, has been found by Virtanen et al. (350). Hence about 10% of the total nitrogen which usually is 6–8% of the dry matter of very effective pea nodules belong to this pigment. The leghemoglobin content of very effective fresh soybean nodules was about twice as high as that of pea nodules. Smith (295) found about 70 μg of hematin corresponding to 2 mg of leghemoglobin per gram of fresh weight in fresh soybean nodules of young plants. On the basis of the high content of leghemoglobin in the root nodules, the synthesis both of the heme part and of the specific protein must be strong.

When the leghemoglobin content of nodules formed by rhizobial strains of different effectivity has been determined in this laboratory, it has been found that the ability of the nodules to fix nitrogen depends to a considerable degree on their leghemoglobin content. There exists a rough parallelism between nitrogen fixation and leghemoglobin concentration in fresh nodules (350). The total amount of leghemoglobin in the nodules per plant is not so important for nitrogen fixation as the concentration of the pigments in the nodules. In other words, a smaller number of intensely red nodules causes a higher nitrogen fixation than a larger number of less red nodules [Virtanen et al.

(350, 363)]. The hematin content of the nodules formed by ten different rhizobial strains, and the increase in nitrogen of the host plant,
are shown in Fig. 14. The small amount of hematin found in ineffective
nodules, which do not contain hemoglobin, is subtracted from the
hematin content of the effective nodules. The hematin found in the
pyridine extract of ineffective nodules is usually 10–15% of the
hematin found in the extracts of very effective nodules and is derived

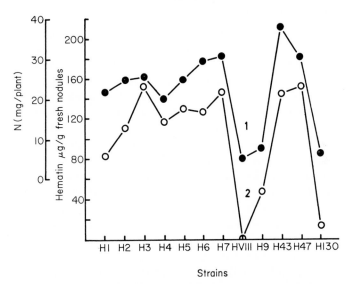

Fig. 14. Nitrogen fixation and hematin content of the nodules of Torsdag pea inoculated with different rhizobial strains. Period of growth: June 28–August 5, 1947.
Harvested before flowering; nodules red. The low hematin content of the ineffective H VIII nodules is subtracted from the hematin content of the effective nodules
produced by other strains used in the experiment. Curve *1*: Nitrogen (milligrams
per plant). Curve *2*: Hematin (micrograms per gram fresh nodules). From Virtanen
et al. (350).

from cytochromes and some unknown hematin compounds or free
hematin [Virtanen *et al.* (350); Smith (295)].

Jordan and Garrard (183) have studied the leghemoglobin content
of many field-grown leguminous species. They have confirmed the
results from this laboratory regarding the effectivity of the nodules and
their leghemoglobin content. They have made interesting observations
on the fluctuation of the concentration of leghemoglobin throughout
the growing season of the host plant and have shown that varietal
differences exist among host plants both in the maximum concentrations of leghemoglobin produced and the rate at which the peak

productions are reached. In field-grown soybeans, alfalfa, alsike clover, and vetch, pigment in excess of 300 μg per gram of nodule tissue was attained prior to blossoming.

The variations in the total iron content of the nodules by no means correspond to the variations in the nitrogen fixation, although the iron content in the ineffective and slightly effective nodules is, as a rule, lower than in very effective ones. Since the major part of the nodule iron does not belong to leghemoglobin (363), a distinct positive correlation can hardly be expected between nitrogen fixation and the

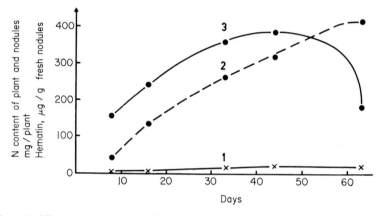

FIG. 15. Nitrogen content of plant and hematin content of nodules at different stages of growth of soybean. (1) N in nodules, milligrams per plant; (2) N, milligrams per total plant minus nodules; (3) hematin, micrograms per gram fresh nodules. From Virtanen et al. (350).

total iron content, even when such a relation exists between nitrogen fixation and the leghemoglobin content.

In experiments on soybean the leghemoglobin content of the nodules was determined at different stages of growth. A clear parallelism was noted between the nitrogen fixed and the leghemoglobin content of the nodules (350) (Fig. 15). Only when flowering begins to come to an end does this parallelism disappear, and the leghemoglobin begins to turn into a green pigment.

The changing of the red pigment of the nodules into a greenish one is mentioned above. Normally this process is practically ended in all the annual leguminous plants investigated in this laboratory at the time when vegetative growth has ceased. The change of color takes place from the base of the nodule toward the tip, i.e., from the older to the younger part. On perennial plants elongated root nodules are often found, the older parts of which are greenish or brown, the tips being red. The roots of *Caragana arborescens* shrubs frequently have older long nodules which may be well over 2 cm in length beside young red nodules, according to Virtanen (336). These nodules, which have the form of a string of pearls, are formed while new bacterial tissue grows at the farther end of the aging nodule. Only the youngest part of the nodule is red.

The turning of leghemoglobin into a green pigment is an irreversible reaction; thus nitrogen fixation cannot take place when all nodules have turned green, unless new red nodules are formed or a new red part is formed on the old ones [Virtanen (336)]. It is interesting that according to Hoch *et al.* (165) the ability of the nodules to evolve molecular hydrogen was lost when hemoglobin disappeared and was replaced by the typical green pigment.

The change of the red pigment to green in the nodules can be followed quantitatively by determining the absorption either between 550 and 560 mμ or 525 and 530 mμ of a pyridine extract of crushed nodules, according to Virtanen *et al.* (350). Since the green pigment has no absorption maximum between 500 and 550 mμ, the lowering of the absorption shows the change of leghemoglobin. Figure 16 illustrates the changes of the absorption spectrum when the red pigment is turning green.

For the isolation of the undenatured green pigment it is necessary to accomplish the color change as fast as possible. Nodulated pea plants are suitable for this purpose. After a pea plant in full growth with red nodules on the roots has been in the dark for some days, the nodules have turned greenish, and the green pigment can be extracted with water from the crushed nodules. Virtanen *et al.* (362) have purified the green pigment by precipitation with ammonium sulfate. When the precipitate which was formed by 50–75% saturation with ammonium sulfate was collected and dialyzed, the best preparation, which is still water soluble, contained 0.29% iron.

The conversion of leghemoglobin into a green pigment is obviously a result of an oxidation reaction. The iron atom and the specific protein are still to be found in the green pigment [Virtanen (338)], but one of the methine bridges in the porphyrin ring is split off, and the ring is either opened or there is an oxygen atom in the place of the methine group, keeping the ring still closed. A full understanding of the structure of the green pigment formed from hemoglobins is still lacking. Virtanen and Miettinen (380) found that iron and globin are split off from the green pigment in glacial acetic acid whereupon biliverdin is formed. The green pigment should thus be an intermediate which corresponds to the green pigment formed as an intermediate when blood hemoglobin is decomposed into bile pigments (202). The name legcholeglobin was therefore proposed for the green pigment of root nodules. According to Lemberg and Legge (201a), a compound with this structure and properties should be called verdohemoglobin rather than choleglobin.

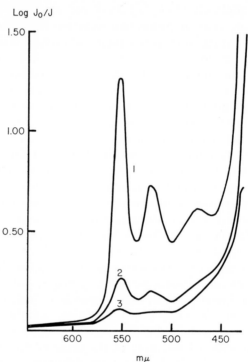

Fig. 16. Absorption spectrum of the pyridine extract from red, partly green, and green nodules of pea. (1) H 7 nodules, red (experiment June 28–August 6, 1947); (2) H 7 nodules, partly green (experiment August 29–October 17, 1947); (3) H 5 nodules, green (experiment August 29–October 17, 1947, plants were kept in the dark for 66 hours after the end of the experiment). From Virtanen et al. (350).

In different legumes the change of red nodules to green takes place at different rates. The soybean, for instance, has to be kept in darkness for several weeks before nodules turn green. When the reaction is slow, the protein is denatured simultaneously. Virtanen and Miettinen (380) could then no longer find any formation of biliverdin from the green pigment.

The red to green change of the nodules during the growth of the host plant depends decisively on the effectiveness of the nodules. Growth conditions, such as light, also have a strong influence on the stability of the red pigment. Nodules formed by very effective strains remain red longer than those formed by less effective strains. For instance the nodules of pea plants inoculated with poorer strains may begin to turn green before the beginning of flowering, while very effective nodules remain red when the plants are still in full bloom, and only then begin to turn green gradually. Morphological and physiological changes in the rhizobia that occur in connection with the formation of leghemoglobin and its turning into green pigment in root nodules are dealt with in Section III, J.

The factors that influence the stability of leghemoglobin in the nodules are mainly unknown. The variations of the redox potential in the nodules may influence the oxidation of leghemoglobin. Pietz (265) has paid special attention to the role of the redox potential in the root nodules and to the significance of the red pigment in the securing and maintenance of a suitable redox potential. Even if this concept of the chemical nature of the red pigment was not true it is obvious that the influence of the redox potential in symbiotic nitrogen fixation is great. It ought to be mentioned here that the ascorbic acid content of the root nodules is 2 to 4 times greater than that of the roots according to Virtanen and Jorma (361). The content of ascorbic acid is lowered in all parts of the plants when they are kept in the dark and the decrease in the reduced form is proportionately greater than that of total ascorbic acid. In the presence of ascorbic acid, hydrogen peroxide causes the formation of the green pigment choleglobin from hemoglobin and also from leghemoglobin *in vitro*. It is a tempting hypothesis that the decrease in catalase activity which is observed when nodules begin to turn green [Virtanen (344)] may be the cause of the oxidation of the porphyrin ring. There is, however, no proof for this hypothesis because the decrease of catalase activity is variable, and direct evidence of the accumulation of hydrogen peroxide in the nodules which turn green is lacking. The easy denaturation of the green pigment in the nodules points to hydrogen peroxide. Lemberg *et al.* (202) are of the opinion that the precursor of bile pigments, choleglobin, is formed in animal tissues from oxyhemoglobin in coupled oxidation with ascorbic acid.

Since the retention of leghemoglobin in the nodules as long as possible is of decisive importance for nitrogen fixation, and thus for the growth of leguminous plants, the decomposition of leghemoglobin to green pigment is not only of theoretical but also of great practical importance. It was recently found in this laboratory (277a) that by cutting the top of a pea plant, several branches are formed, and the greenish nodules formed new red parts at which points they branched. As a result of the cutting, the yield of dry material increased. Nowotny-Mieczyńska (250) has found that addition of CoCl$_2$ and ascorbic acid in suitable concentrations prevents the conversion of the red pigment to a green one without any influence on nitrogen fixation. A close correlation between the amount of red pigment in root nodules and nitrogen fixation was not found. It is difficult to explain these findings because it is not known how these substances influence the nodules. We should bear in mind that other deep-seated changes normally occur in the nodules (Section III, J) when leghemoglobin is oxidized to a green pigment and that leghemoglobin is only one factor in the system responsible for symbiotic nitrogen fixation in leguminous root nodules.

Divalent iron in the red pigment of the nodules is easily oxidized to trivalent. After crushing and centrifugation of the nodules, the solution often contains only ferrihemoglobin. This rapid oxidation of the pigment is largely due to a strong phenoloxidase in the nodules [Keilin and Wang (190); Virtanen (338)]. Divalent iron in electrophoretically purified leghemoglobin is also more easily oxidized than divalent iron in blood hemoglobin, and hence autoxidation also promotes the oxidation of iron. The presence of ferrihemoglobin in intact nodules is difficult to establish because of the rapid oxidation of ferrohemoglobin by crushing of the nodules. However, Virtanen (298, 340) is of the opinion that his results support the concept that leghemoglobin is present in the nodules partly also in the oxidized form. Keilin and Smith (188) disagree with this opinion. The recent findings of the Wilson group (411) on the enzymatic oxidation of leghemoglobin by nitrogen suggest a valency change of the leghemoglobin iron in the nodules, and hence formation of ferrihemoglobin.

The relative affinity of leghemoglobin for oxygen and carbon monoxide is of the same order of magnitude as that of myoglobin. According to Keilin and Wang (190) the equilibrium constant

$$K = \frac{(\mathrm{HbCO})p\mathrm{O}_2}{(\mathrm{HbO})p\mathrm{CO}}$$

for leghemoglobin (about 50% pure preparation) is about 37, and is thus of the same order as that of myoglobin, but much lower than the values found for the hemoglobin of different vertebrates (125 to 550) [Keilin and Wang (191)].

Owing to its hemoglobin nature, the red pigment of the nodules can function as a storer and carrier of oxygen.* The concept that leghemoglobin might contribute to the oxygen uptake of the rhizobial masses

---

* Although the properties of leghemoglobin make it less suited to this function only.

in the nodules, and in this way make the nitrogen fixation possible, seemed therefore probable [Keilin and Wang (190)]. All efforts to confirm this hypothesis have, however, failed. Smith could find no influence (295) of the red pigment on the oxygen uptake of detached root nodules. Carbon monoxide also had no effect on the oxygen uptake of either separated nodules or of nodulated roots when those were attached to the plant. Burris and Wilson (85) found hog hemoglobin to enhance the respiration rate of washed cells of *Rhizobium leguminosarum* supplied with glucose. The percentage increase was greater at a pO_2 of 0.01 atm than at 0.20 atm. Carbon monoxide appeared to inhibit the stimulation by hemoglobin. These authors, however, did not believe that their results proved that hemoglobin acted as a carrier of molecular oxygen in the nodules. In this laboratory no correlation between the oxygen uptake by nodules and their hemoglobin content could be found. The Q_{O_2} was even higher in ineffective nodules than in leghemoglobin-containing effective ones. Also the transfer of the pea plants for 3 days into darkness, when leghemoglobin turns into the green pigment, did not significantly influence the respiration of the nodules in the studies of Virtanen and Tietäväinen (392). All determinations were made at a pO_2 of 0.20 atm. Corresponding determinations at the very low oxygen pressure which obviously prevails in the nodules are still needed.

Virtanen (334), and Virtanen and Laine (373) presented the hypothesis that leghemoglobin could act directly as an oxidation reduction catalyst in nitrogen fixation, either in the primary stage of the reaction with nitrogen or on a later stage in the reduction of some nitrogenous compound formed as an intermediate in nitrogen fixation [Virtanen 338)]. Later direct evidence for the oxidation of leghemoglobin by nitrogen was obtained in P. W. Wilson's laboratory [Hamilton et al. (149)]. When a sonic extract of crushed nodules was exposed to nitrogen, the oxyhemoglobin spectrum peaks were replaced by those of methemoglobin (ferrihemoglobin), indicating that hemoglobin is oxidized by nitrogen. Suitable controls apparently ruled out contamination of the nitrogen by oxygen. Similar experiments indicated that hydrogen can reduce a flavin and a hemoprotein, presumably leghemoglobin, contained in the extract. Bergersen and Wilson (41a) confirmed the oxidation of hemoglobin from the Fe^{2+} to the Fe^{3+} and showed that this effect was not due to undetected traces of oxygen in the gas mixture. In agreement with the observation of Appleby and Bergersen (24) they also found that bacteroids could reduce ferrihemoglobin in the absence of air. On the basis of these findings they (41a) suggested that hemoglobin may function in legume root nodules in a cycle in which it is reduced by the bacteroids and oxidized as a result of the processes of nitrogen fixation. Experimental support exists also for the reduction of some intermediates possibly formed in nitrogen fixation. Hemoglobin of blood [Colter and Quastel (99)], and leghemoglobin [Virtanen et al. (364)], reduce hydroxylamine nearly quantitatively to ammonia in the presence of ascorbic acid or cysteine. Leghemoglobin seems to be the main, or possibly the only, factor in the nodules which causes the reduction of free hydroxylamine in root nodules. Proof of the formation of hydroxylamine as an intermediate in the nitrogen fixation is, however, lacking, since it has been shown that similar hydroxylamine compounds are formed from free nitrogen, nitrate nitrogen, and ammonium nitrogen by Azotobacter [Virtanen and Järvinen (360); Saris and Virtanen (283)]. According to Virtanen and Miettinen (382) the reduction of the more possible intermediate, hydrazine, to ammonia is also catalyzed by hemoglobin. The reaction is, however, much slower than that with hydroxylamine in the concentrations used.

The function of leghemoglobin in the root nodules is thus still unsolved. It is to be observed that this pigment does not occur in free-living nitrogen-fixing bacteria, and hence it is not essential for all biological nitrogen fixation. However, the great difference between the effectiveness of the nodules of legumes and the free-living nitrogen fixers such as the Azotobacter species, cannot in this connection be disregarded. The nitrogen fixation of Azotobacter, as well as that of other free-living nitrogen fixers, is dependent on the multiplication of cells, and a production of about 10 mg of dry bacteria corresponds to about 1 mg of fixed nitrogen; on the other hand, 10 mg of pea nodules (dry weight), containing possibly 5 mg of bacteroid mass, in symbiosis with the host plant can fix 10 mg of nitrogen or even more and give over 90% of this regularly to its host plant (cf. Section III, F). The effectiveness of the nodules of nonlegumes may be of the same order of magnitude as that of the nodules of legumes, but very little is known about this matter. According to Egle and Mundig (111) the hemin content of the nodules of Alnus, as well as that of the nodules of other nonlegumes (Myrica, Hippophaë) is exceptionally high, about five times as high as that in the roots of the plants. The symbiotic system in the nodules of nonleguminous plants is comparatively unknown (cf. Section III, L).

In connection with the formation of leghemoglobin it is interesting that Klüver (193) found metal-free porphyrins, mostly coproporphyrin and traces of some other porphyrin, probably protoporphyrin, in effective root nodules of soybean. In nodules of the red kidney bean (Phaseolus vulgaris) a porphyrin, resembling a coproporphyrin in its spectroscopic properties but a uroporphyrin in its solubility properties, was found in large amounts. Evidence of a porphyrin synthesis in the nodule itself is provided by Richmond and Salomon (273). They have demonstrated the labeling of heme by 2-C^{14}-glycine and by 1-C^{14}- and 2-C^{14}-acetate in homogenates of soybean nodules.

Differences have recently been observed in red, effective leguminous root nodules as compared with white, ineffective nodules with regard to the cytochrome system. Appleby and Bergersen (24) discovered that cytochrome a is lacking in effective nodules but is present in ineffective ones as well as in free-living rhizobia. The low oxygen tension in nodules may be the cause of the loss of cytochrome a, but the presence of this pigment in ineffective nodules makes this explanation unlikely as the pO_2 in effective and ineffective nodules is the same. Cytochromes b and c are found both in effective and ineffective nodules as well as in free-living rhizobia. There is no further information about the function of cytochrome a in the rhizobia. The same authors observed, with a microspectroscope, the reduction of leghemoglobin in fresh homogenates of effective soybean or clover nodules made anaerobic by endogenous respiration; they also found the reduction of bacteroid cytochrome c. It therefore appeared that biological reduction of leghemoglobin and cytochrome c could be closely related.

Bertrand and Wolf (44) have found more cobalt in root nodules of lupines, soybeans, and beans than in the roots or aerial parts. Rhizobia synthesize vitamin B_{12} and excrete a large part of it into the medium. In the assay of the red, leghemoglobin-bearing nodules of alfalfa, clover, and pea plants Levin et al. (203) have revealed that the concentration of vitamin B_{12} is 3 to 34 times higher than that in the root tissue. In the case of alfalfa, the concentration of this vitamin in effective, pink nodules was 400% higher than in ineffective, white nodules. The great quantitative difference between the vitamin B_{12} content of effective and ineffective nodules may, however, be caused by the small rhizobial mass in ineffective nodules (see page 581).

J. THE IMPORTANCE OF BACTEROIDS IN ROOT NODULES

In addition to the formation of the red pigment, which begins a few days after a visible nodule is produced and which clearly shows whether the nodules become effective or not, other biological events occur in the intranodular rhizobia. Since the time of Beijerinck (36), it has been known that the rod-shaped legume bacteria change in the root nodules into swollen and irregular bacteroids which have lost their capacity of multiplying but which function as organized protein bodies. It was believed that they were absorbed by the plant during growth, and that the nitrogen fixed became available to the host plant in this way [cf. Fred *et al.* (134), page 62]. Nobbe and Hiltner (246) stated that the unchanged bacteria are not effective nitrogen fixers and that fixation begins only with bacteroid formation. They arrived at this conclusion from a study of the morphological characteristics of the rhizobia in nodules at different stages of development and with different symbiotic activities. Later this hypothesis was rejected. In experiments with the pea plant Pfeiffer (264) in many cases found no correlation between the transformation of the rods into bacteroids and the accumulation of nitrogen by the plant. According to Bazarewski (34) the bacteroids are involution forms incapable of multiplying and probably unable to fix nitrogen. Almon (18) tested the ability to multiply of 411 single bacteroids in a variety of media used for propagation of the rhizobia. No multiplication was observed. He could likewise secure no nodulation of the proper host plant with bacteroids. Thus the bacteroids seem to be senile and biologically inactive (407).

The inability of bacteroids to multiply does not, however, prove that they could not be the active factors in nitrogen fixation. The very high nitrogen fixation per gram of nodules and the regular transfer of over 90% of the nitrogen fixed in the host plant could not be understood if the nitrogen fixation were dependent on the continuous and regular propagation of rhizobia as is the case with free-living nitrogen-fixing organisms. On the contrary, it is actually to be expected that the "catalyst" which functions in the nodules in nitrogen fixation is unable to multiply. Studies in this laboratory by Virtanen *et al.* (363) have shown without exception that the pea rhizobia in red nodules produced by effective strains appear chiefly as "bacteroids," the branched, swollen form of which is conspicuous. When the nodule has just appeared, the rhizobia are still rod shaped and multiply vigorously using the combined nitrogen of the host plant, but in a few days formation of bacteroids occurs and, concurrently, leghemoglobin is formed and nitrogen fixation begins. When the nodules have reached the stage of maximal nitrogen fixation, only a few rods are to be found among the bacteroids. The simultaneous formation of bacteroids and the leghemoglobin indispensable for nitrogen fixation can hardly be fortuitous. In studies on more than 500 pea nodules Heumann (155, 156) also found that bacteroids are formed only in the cells of nodules where synthesis of leghemoglobin occurs. In the active middle sections of nodules that contained leghemoglobin, about 93% of the rhizobia were swollen bacteroids. In the base of the nodules, where leghemoglobin has already changed to a green pigment, only rods are to be found. This is in full agreement with the findings in this laboratory. Heumann also emphasizes that starch is formed and developed only in nodule cells which contain bacteroids.

On the basis of all known facts, the bacteroids can be regarded as active nitrogen fixers which, without multiplying, function as special "resting cells." As long as the red pigment is retained, no change in the bacteroid mass is to be observed. When nodules turn green, bacteroids disappear and rods appear in abundance in the nodules, according to observations made by Virtanen et al. (363). The lysis of bacteroids is then very rapid. Obviously all these processes are caused initially by the same event. The opinion that degeneration processes in the nodule start when anatomical changes in the vascular system prevent the transport of nutrients to the nodule deserves special attention. Peirce (262) suggested that the necrosis within the nodules of *Medicago hispida* (*M. denticulata*) was due to the inadequacy of the vascular system. The observations made by Brenchley and Thornton (64) on the influence of boron deficiency on the vascular system have been mentioned earlier. Allen and Allen (11) came to the conclusion that in peanut (*Arachis hypogaea*) nodules a suberized cell layer at the nodule base presumably severs the primary vascular strand. Thornton (311) considers that nodule degeneration begins by the multiplication of the rods which have remained in the infection thread and their spread into the interlamellar and intercellular spaces. The cause for the abrupt and rapid multiplication of the rods which have remained unchanged for weeks or months, as well as the lysis of bacteroids and the oxidation of leghemoglobin, are, however, not explained on this hypothesis.

Nodules formed by ineffective strains (observations made in this laboratory with three strains) were found to contain exclusively rods surrounded by a gum such as that found in cultures of free-living rhizobia. Neither formation of bacteroids nor of hemoglobin occurred, and the nodules did not change into nitrogen-fixing ones. Virtanen (338) has discussed the possibility that the gum surrounding the rods may not be decomposed in ineffective nodules but isolates the rods and thus prevents the development of a real symbiosis. Should this be so, the host-plant specificity would depend on the ability of the host-plant enzymes to decompose the gum. This hypothesis provides that the composition of the gum is not identical in all rhizobial species and strains. So far there has been no information on this point. After the present article was written, a paper was, however, published by Humphrey (171) in which 4-O-methylglucuronic acid (identified by paper chromatography) was found to be a component of the gum of six of seven strains of *R. trifolii*, while seven strains of *R. meliloti*, and one of *R. phaseoli* that were tested, lacked this component. In one of two strains of *R. leguminosarum* the compound was found. These results prove conclusively that the chemical composition of the gum is not the same in different rhizobial species and strains. An experimental investigation is now necessary on the enzymatic hydrolysis of the gums in different rhizobial species by the roots and nodules in different leguminous species.

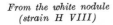

From the white nodule   *From the red nodule*   *From the green nodule*
(strain H VIII)   *(strain H 6)*   *(strain H 6)*

Fig. 17a. Graphical illustration of microscopic preparations of pea *Rhizobium* dyed with Löffler's methylene blue. From Virtanen *et al.* (363).

Fig. 17b. Living bacteroids seen under Professor Wilska's anoptral phase contrast microscope. From Virtanen *et al.* (363).

The drawings in Fig. 17a illustrate the different forms of pea *Rhizobium* in ineffective nodules, in effective red nodules, and in green nodules. Living bacteroids as seen under a phase contrast microscope are shown in Fig. 17b.

The observations that free-living rhizobia can also be changed to bacteroids, e.g., by the addition of caffeine or some other alkaloids to their culture media [Barthel (32)], and that these rhizobia still do not fix nitrogen, does not invalidate their nitrogen-fixing capacity in the nodules. First, it is not known whether the bacteroids formed artificially in the cultures of free-living rhizobia are physiologically similar to those in effective nodules, and second, the symbiotic system is obviously so complicated that all the factors needed must be present, which seems not to be the case in cultures of free-living nodule bacteria.

Bergersen's (40) observation that bacteroids may sometimes persist in nonnitrogen-fixing nodules is a good example of this. Only the presence of leghemoglobin and bacteroids guarantees the effectivity of the nodules.

Since in earlier literature observations are found in which bacteroids are not always characteristic for effective nodules even in the pea plant [cf. Pfeiffer (264)], many authors doubt the general applicability of the observations made in this laboratory [Thornton (316); Smith (295); Allen and Allen (6)]. It must, however, be borne in mind that the determination of the effectivity of the nodules was not established in the earlier observations. No attention was paid to the occurrence of the indispensable red pigment, nor to the fact that on the roots of a leguminous plant both effective and ineffective nodules may be found, and that the form of bacteroids in some leguminous plants can be so similar to normal rods that they are difficult to distinguish. Recently Bergersen (40) strongly emphasized the necessity of bacteroids for nitrogen fixation in the nodules of leguminous plants. He has paid special attention to the fact that the form of bacteroids cannot be distinguished morphologically from rods in all legumes, and that differences in their enzymatic activities are decisive.

K. NITROGEN FIXATION WITH EXCISED ROOT NODULES AND CELL-FREE PREPARATIONS

Connection with the host plant is necessary for a continued effective nitrogen fixation in the root nodules, because only in this way can the nodules obtain carbon compounds and other nutrients. Since the enzymatic machinery needed in nitrogen fixation is, however, located in the nodule, and since some amount of carbon compounds needed in the fixation processes are probably found even in excised nodules, they can be expected to fix nitrogen for some time. In addition it is possible that by adding some suitable carbon compound, nitrogen fixation can be promoted.

For a long time the concept predominated that excised root nodules do not fix nitrogen. In 1937 Virtanen and Laine (368) found such a large increase in nitrogen in many experiments with a system consisting of excised nodules of the pea plant plus added oxalacetic acid solution (pH 7.0) that they were certainly well beyond the limits of experimental error (up to 5 mg nitrogen per 10 gm of fresh nodules). Very effective nodules, the nitrogen content of which was 7–8% of the dry substance (70–80 mg nitrogen per 10 gm of fresh nodules), were used in the experiments. By the help of many persons the nodules were rapidly excised from the roots and immediately used in the experiment. At the beginning of the experiment, and again after 7–24 hours, the nitrogen was determined in the well-mixed nodule mass which, because of the large number of nodules, was quite homogenous when quantities of 10–15 gm were involved. With intact nodules nitrogen fixation could be found, but not with crushed nodules. Using the gasometric method nitrogen fixation could also be observed in some experiments with intact nodules [Virtanen (338)]. Wilson (407) has reported some previously unknown experiments with the gasometric method by Krasheninnikov (197) in 1916, in which a weak nitrogen fixation (about 0.37–1.2 mg nitrogen per 10 gm of nodules) was induced by raising the partial pressure of oxygen. The duration of the experiment (25–93 hours) and the increase in nitrogen fixation when the experimental time was prolonged to 93 hours make it questionable, however, whether or not free-living nitrogen-fixing organisms were responsible for the weak fixation in these experiments. The fact is that excised root nodules loose their activity in a comparatively short time, and in no case do they fix nitrogen after 24 hours.

The nitrogen fixation by excised nodules could not at first be confirmed in Wisconsin although a very sensitive gasometric method was used [Wilson (407)]. For some years also the experiments with N_2^{15} gave erratic results and did not give conclusive proof of nitrogen fixation [Burris et al. (76); Tove et al. (323)]. It seemed probable that deteriorative changes in the machinery required for nitrogen fixation take place in different lots of excised nodules at different speeds, and consequently the results are variable [Virtanen (339)]. After finding that the excised nodules rapidly loose the capacity to fix nitrogen, Aprison and Burris (25) could bring about a regular and powerful nitrogen fixation with very active nodules which were removed from the roots within 3 to 5 minutes and immediately placed under an atmosphere containing N_2^{15}. The method is more sensitive when the nodules are ground with acid after exposure, centrifuged, and only the supernatant is analyzed for N^{15}. Burris's technique has made possible the experimental approach to a number of problems of symbiotic nitrogen fixation with excised nodules.

Some important findings have already been made in Wisconsin by means of this new technique. The optimum temperature for nitrogen fixation by excised soybean nodules is about 25°C [Aprison et al. (26)]. The rate of fixation decreases sharply with time and is weak after only 4 hours. Apparently for a short time after excision the nodules can fix nitrogen at a rate approaching that of unexcised nodules [Aprison and Burris (25)]. A large variety of substrates, including oxalacetate, reducing agents, cofactors, and plant extracts, when added to nodules, regulary decreased their nitrogen fixation rather than enhanced it [Wilson and Burris (412)]. The only substantial stimulation achieved by the Wisconsin group has been with sucrose. It enhanced fixation by 75–80%, whereas glucose was not helpful [Magee (216)]. When visiting this laboratory, Burris, however, found that addition of oxal-acetate considerably enhanced $N_2{}^{15}$ fixation with excised pea nodules [cf. Virtanen (344)]. It is thus possible that the composition of root nodules grown under the light conditions of Finland is somewhat different from the composition of those grown in Wisconsin.

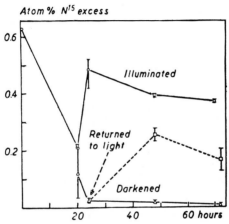

Fig. 18. Influence of illumination of pea plants on fixation by their nodules when excised. Vertical lines define the extreme values of replicate samples. From Virtanen et al. (384a).

The effect of illumination and darkening of pea plants on nitrogen fixation by their excised nodules was studied by the groups of Burris and Virtanen in joint work (384a). When the plants were in darkness for 72 hours practically no fixation was observed; when in darkness for 24 hours and then returned to the light, about half of the effectivity was returned (Fig. 18). It seems most likely that the nitrogen-fixing capacity of nodules from plants kept in the dark for 24 hours arises for the most part from depletion of substrates furnished normally by the photosynthesizing host plant but partly also from the decrease in leghemoglobin in the nodules. Thus it can be understood that the transfer of plants to light causes a partial recovery of the effectivity of the nodules, but far from the whole of it. A longer period in the dark causes an oxidation of the main part of leghemoglobin, as shown in Fig. 16.

Excised nodules have been used to study the influence of the partial pressure of N_2, O_2, and H_2 on the symbiotic nitrogen-fixing system. Burris *et al.* (77) found with slices of excised soybean nodules a half-maximum rate of fixation at pN_2 0.025 ± 0.004 atm which is rather close to the value of 0.02 ± 0.005 atm obtained for *Azotobacter* (cf. page 556). Optimum nitrogen fixation is accomplished by sliced nodules at a pO_2 of about 0.5 atm (77). That the O_2-requirement of the nodules is high was demonstrated years ago with nodulated pea plants in a sterile culture system [Virtanen and von Hausen (354, 355); Ferguson and Bond (124)], but that the optimum is as high as the experiments with sliced nodules have shown is surprising, because the growth of nodulated legumes with nitrogen is extremely good at pO_2 of 0.2 atm. The possibility that the slicing has enhanced the O_2 requirement of the nodules must be considered. Hoch *et al.* (165) have found that liberation of H_2 from soybean nodules was greatly enhanced in the presence of O_2, and that slicing the nodules seriously reduced the evolution of H_2.

During the past two or three years Burris and his associates have had some success in their attempts to produce cell-free preparations of *Azotobacter* that have the ability to fix nitrogen (74). The results, it is true, have been erratic, but they have clearly shown that cell-free preparations can fix nitrogen. The success in consistent demonstration of nitrogen fixation by cell-free preparations should signify a great step forward in deepening our knowledge of this process. The enzyme system needed in nitrogen fixation and the intermediates in it could then be studied in detail (see footnote on page 552).

L. SYMBIOTIC NITROGEN FIXATION IN NONLEGUMINOUS PLANTS

The modern isotopic technique has also confirmed the previous opinion that higher plants cannot use atmospheric nitrogen (412). The symbiotic nitrogen fixation is, however, not restricted to leguminous plants. Nodules of some nonleguminous plants, alder especially, have long been known because of the enormous size of their old nodules. After Woronin [cf. Hiltner (161)] in 1866 had found fungi within alder nodules, Brunchorst (67) suggested that the fungus was not a harmful parasite, but that the formation of nodules was probably a result of symbiosis between the host plant and the fungus. Some years after the final discovery of nitrogen fixation in nodulated legumes, Nobbe *et al.* (248) observed that the growth of *Elaeagnus angustifolia* greatly improved after the formation of nodules and that growth differences between nodulated and nodule-free plants increased with the period of growth. Hiltner (157) made similar observations with

Alnus glutinosa. His continued observations of the growth of nodulated and nodule-free *Alnus* and *Elaeagnus* plants during many years proved that nodules functioned as nitrogen fixers [Hiltner (158); Nobbe and Hiltner (247)]. Hiltner demonstrated conclusively that nitrogen fixation really occurs in root nodules by removing the nodules from the roots of an alder growing in nutrient solution as soon as they appeared. Nitrogen fixation and growth were then negligible. Alders from which the nodules had not been removed grew vigorously, attaining a height of 1.5 m in 4 or 5 years. In modern publications and manuals Hiltner's decisive observations are undervalued. Since the formation of nodules could be achieved by inoculating the seeds or roots of *Alnus* and

TABLE VI

Nitrogen-Fixing Nodules in Trees and Shrubs of Different Families of Dicotyledoneae[a]

Family	Genus	Species in which N$_2$-fixation was first observed
Betulaceae	*Alnus*	*glutinosa*
Elaeagnaceae	*Elaeagnus*	*angustifolia*
	Hippophaë	*rhamnoides*
	Shepherdia	*argentea; canadensis*
Myricaceae	*Myrica*	*cerifera; esculenta (sapida* var. *longifolia)*
Rhamnaceae	*Ceanothus*	*americanus*
Casuarinaceae	*Casuarina*	*equisetifolia (muricata); stricta (quadrivalvis)*
Coriariaceae	*Coriaria*	*japonica*

[a] Adapted from Allen and Allen [(6), page 95].

Elaeagnus plants with a suspension of crushed nodules, the similarity of the symbiotic nitrogen fixation in leguminous and nonleguminous plants was striking.

Root nodules are today reported on 65 species of trees and shrubs within 8 families of Dicotyledoneae. Six are seen in Table VI.

In spite of numerous attempts to isolate the specific microorganisms from the nodules of nonleguminous plants, and to cultivate them in suitable nutrient media, positive results have not been achieved. According to Quispel (271) a definite development of the endophyte of *Alnus glutinosa* in some peat suspensions was measured, but the organism could not be isolated. Many isolated organisms have been considered as the causal factors for nitrogen fixation, but the formation of effective nodules has never been accomplished with any of these. The true causal organism is, therefore, not yet known. Various names such as *Actinomyces alni* and *elaeagni, Mycobacterium, Streptothrix, Rhizo-*

bacterium, Rhizobium, and *Azotobacter,* show the different opinions which have been held on the nature of the active organisms [Allen and Allen (6), page 97].

The reason why it has not been possible to isolate specific organisms which produce the nitrogen-fixing nodules on nonleguminous plants is for the present not known. The lack of some nutrient in the substrates used may be one of the reasons. Since the addition of crushed root nodules to the medium has not made the isolation of the causal organism successful, the possibility exists that the strong enzymatic oxidations which occur in the crushed nodules destroy some factor indispensable for the growth of the microorganism or form some growth-inhibiting substance. Attention has not, as yet, been fixed on these matters. It has also been suggested that two different microorganisms may be necessary to achieve nodulation [Lieske (204); Uemura (325)]. This also is only a hypothesis.

Even though the organisms required for the formation of effective nodules are not known, some information on their specificity already exists. Cross-inoculation tests with crude inocula have shown that plant species of one family are not nodulated by organisms from another family. Using crushed nodules as inocula, no cross-inoculation was obtained by Roberg (274) between *Alnus, Elaeagnus,* and *Hippophaë* and by Bond *et al.* (52) between *Alnus* and *Myrica.* All nine *Casuarina* species investigated were, according to Mowry (233), susceptible to the same organism.

In alder, nodule formation occurs in 1–3 weeks after inoculating the seedlings [Hiltner (158); Virtanen and Saastamoinen (388)]. This has been found to be the case also with *Myrica* and *Hippophaë* seedlings [Bond *et al.* (52)]. In this respect these nonleguminous plants resemble leguminous ones. In the experiments of Virtanen and Saastamoinen (388) nodulated *Alnus glutinosa* plants have grown without combined nitrogen in quartz sand best at a pH of 5 to 6. Compared with most nodulated leguminous plants the pH optimum is thus lower for nodulated alder. Bond *et al.* (52) found that the optimum pH for the growth of nodulated *Alnus* plants in water cultures was between 5.4 and 4.2. For nodulated *Hippophaë* plants the optimum was at pH 6.3. The greatest acid tolerance was shown by the *Myrica* endophyte, followed by *Alnus,* whereas *Hippophaë* showed low tolerance and resembled clover in this respect. Even at very low concentration, ammonium nitrogen has been found to inhibit nodulation strongly in *Hippophaë,* but in *Alnus* and *Myrica* ammonium nitrogen has promoted nodulation (52).

The experiments in which the growth of nodulated plants without combined nitrogen and nonnodulated plants with combined nitrogen has been compared, have shown that in many cases nodulated plants grow better than nonnodulated ones. This has continually been found to be the case with alders in sand cultures [Virtanen and Saastamoinen (387, 388)]. Such a difference has not been found in the experiments in water cultures performed by Bond et al. (52). The difference of the results may depend on the oxygen supply to the solution. According

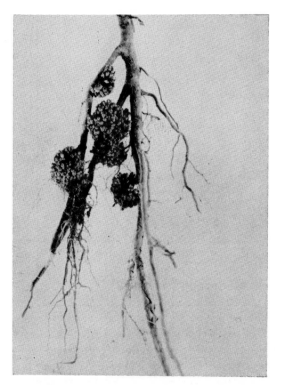

FIG. 19. Nodules of *Alnus glutinosa.*

to Aldrich-Blake (3) growth stimulation among *Casuarina* spp. with inorganic nitrogen has been vastly inferior to the effects obtained from nodulation.

The nodules of nonleguminous plants are initiated on young roots only. In the early stages of development they resemble superficially the elongated nodules of some leguminous plants. Later the nodules become more and more woody and are covered by a brown cork layer, except the apical tips [McLuckie (219)]. By continuous branching of the tips, the perennial nodules are transformed to clusters (Fig. 19) up to 10 cm in diameter in alder.

The air supply of such nodules is improved by lenticel-like gaps in the cork periderm observed in the nodules of *Alnus glutinosa* and *Hippophaë rhamnoides* [Borm (56); Ferguson and Bond (123)]. According to Bond (51), the rootlets growing upward from the nodule clusters in *Myrica* and *Casuarina* act as pneumatophores. Because the endophyte is not known in nonleguminous nodules, the formation of

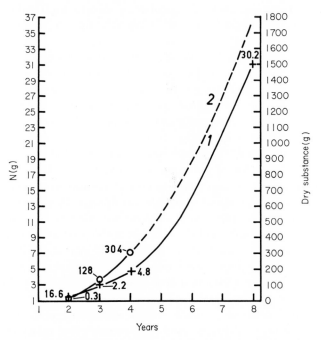

Fig. 20. Eight years' experiment with inoculated *Alnus glutinosa* in quartz sand without combined nitrogen. (*1*) Nitrogen, grams per plant; (*2*) dry substance, grams per plant. From Virtanen (345), and Virtanen and Saastamoinen (388).

these is not further discussed in this article. Most investigations in this field have been made by Fletcher (125) and Taubert (303).

The mode of uptake of the nitrogenous compounds from nodules by the host has not been adequately studied in nonleguminous plants. It can, however, be suggested that the transfer is similar to that in legumes. Hiltner [(161), page 63] already presented this opinion.

The growth and fixation of nitrogen of nodulated *Alnus glutinosa* plants in experiments of long duration performed in the greenhouse of this laboratory in 1931 to 1938 are presented in Fig. 20 (345, 388). About 30 gm of gaseous nitrogen was fixed during eight years in a nodulated alder after the sowing of the seeds. It can thus be estimated that in a grove of *Alnus glutinosa* with 50,000 specimens per hectare, the soil would be enriched through fallen leaves and roots remaining in the soil by a good 1000 kg of nitrogen per hectare from the sowing of the seeds until the plants had reached a height of about 2.5 meters. Nitrogen losses are not taken into account in this calculation. In a report by Virtanen (345) only one alder plant was assumed to grow per square meter. In fact the number of 2–3 m high alder plants in a thick grove of *Alnus glutinosa* is usually five or more per square meter.

As can be seen from Fig. 20, the amount of fixed gaseous nitrogen was small in the first year. During the last two years this amount was about 15 gm per plant. In groves of alders where the trees are 2 and 3 meters high, an amount of nitrogen may thus be fixed during one summer which corresponds to the amount of nitrogen fixed by an average clover-grass field.

Ferguson and Bond (123) estimated, for an alder tree of moderate size, that 0.25–0.5 kg of nitrogen was fixed annually, and that the amount of nitrogen per unit dry weight of nodule tissue exceeded that of legumes grown under comparable conditions. It is clear that trees like these no longer can grow so close together as do young *Alnus* plants 2–3 meters high. While nodules were produced on practically all *Alnus glutinosa* plants after inoculation, only a small percentage of the *Alnus incana* plants were inoculated and thus able to grow with atmospheric nitrogen [Virtanen and Saastamoinen (388)]. Apparently a genetic factor inhibited nodulation in this alder species.

In associated cultures of alder (*Alnus glutinosa*) and spruce (*Picea abies* [*P. excelsa*]) in quartz sand, the spruce grew relatively well although the fallen leaves of the alder were collected on the surface of the sand. A 7-year-old spruce from an associated culture contained 67 gm of dry matter and 590 mg of nitrogen [Virtanen (345)]. The origin of the combined nitrogen which the spruce had used is not adequately known. Part of the nitrogen compounds were possibly derived from the leaves, although these were collected from the surface of the sand once a day at least, part may have come from the watering during the long experimental periods, part from broken roots and nodules, part perhaps also by the functioning of free-living, nitrogen-fixing microorganisms. The papers from this laboratory have stressed that the excretion of nitrogen compounds cannot be established in a non-sterile system [Virtanen and Saastamoinen (388)].

If fallen leaves are left on the surface of the sand, a nitrogen-rich humus is formed which provides good growth conditions for other

trees. For centuries it has been known that the best mold is obtained
under alders. The importance of the alder in nature is thus noticeable.
Bond (50) has called attention to the importance of other nonleguminous plants in fixing nitrogen symbiotically.

Although root nodules could not be produced on nonleguminous
plants with pure cultures of specific microorganisms, the function of
the nodules in nitrogen fixation with these plants can, even on the basis
of Nobbe's and Hiltner's experiments, be considered as conclusively
proved as for leguminous plants on the basis of Hellriegel's decisive
experiments. During more recent years experiments were also performed with nodulated *Alnus* plants, N^{15} being used as indicator.
Bond *et al.* (52) found after 6 days' exposure that the greatest accumulation of N^{15} was in the nodules of 3-month-old *Alnus* plants and
a lesser accumulation in other parts of the plants. Also, excised nodules
of *Alnus* were shown, as a result of joint work of the laboratories in
Wisconsin and Helsinki, to fix gaseous nitrogen by exposure for 30
minutes to 2 hours to molecular oxygen enriched with N_2^{15} [Virtanen
et al. (384)]

In spite of the obvious similarity between the nitrogen fixation in the
root nodules of leguminous and nonleguminous plants, hemoglobin
could not be found in the nodules of *Alnus* (339) and *Myrica* (50).
Davenport (99a) has, however, recently claimed the demonstration
of hemoglobin in the root nodules of *Casuarina*, *Alnus*, and *Myrica*.

In the root nodules of alder, Miettinen and Virtanen (228–230, 381)
found L(+)-citrulline to be the quantitatively dominant amino acid,
whereas asparagine and glutamine, which are typical in leguminous
root nodules, were absent. However, citrulline was also found in roots
of nonnodulated *Alnus*, therefore its direct implication in the nitrogen
fixation was not indicated. The great accumulation of citrulline in the
nodules of alder in autumn (1–2% of the dry weight of nodules) and
its rapid decrease in spring suggests that, in the alder, citrulline plays
a role in the storage and transport of the nitrogen fixed in the nodules.
It may, accordingly, have the same role as asparagine and glutamine
in leguminous plants. Because urea was not found in the nodules, roots,
or leaves of nodulated alder plants, and arginase activity was absent,
it was concluded that citrulline was not utilized through the urea
cycle. Only traces of arginine and ornithine were found in nodules,
but large quantities appeared in those parts of the roots nearest to the
nodules. The metabolic role of citrulline in alder plants is still very
incompletely understood.

Bond *et al.* (53) and Leaf *et al.* (199) estimated the distribution of
N^{15} fixed by root nodules of *Alnus glutinosa*. The highest atom per cent

excess of N^{15} was found in glutamic acid and the next highest in citrulline or aspartic acid. Ammonia contained less N^{15} than these compounds, and arginine contained very little N^{15}. When citrulline was degraded to ammonia and ornithine, the ammonia liberated was even richer in N^{15} than glutamic acid. On the basis of these findings, and assuming that citrulline is formed from carbamyl phosphate and ornithine [cf. Jones et al. (179)] the nitrogen in carbamyl phosphate could be derived from gaseous nitrogen more directly than from the α-amino group in glutamic acid.

M. The Chemical Mechanism of Nitrogen Fixation

The problem is treated in this section supposing that the pathway of nitrogen fixation is identical in symbiotic and nonsymbiotic processes. Although this has not been proved, such a supposition may be justified at the present moment.

For many decades after the discovery of biological nitrogen fixation its mechanism could be dealt with only speculatively. Ammonia was then most frequently considered to be the product of nitrogen fixation, and later some scientists including Kostytschew with associates (196) and Winogradsky (424, 425) considered the presence of ammonia in *Azotobacter* cultures, growing without combined nitrogen, to constitute an experimental proof in support of this concept. Critically examined, their experiments did not, however, confirm the hypothesis since the formation of ammonium nitrogen under the experimental conditions in question is apparently a result of decompositions which occur in cells independently of the type of nitrogen nutrition [Burk (69); Horner and Burk (169); Burk and Burris (70); Burris and Wilson (81)].

Because there was no means, before the use of N^{15}, of proving that some very reactive compound formed in nitrogen fixation, as for instance ammonia, could really arise from molecular nitrogen, the first task was to elucidate whether the same amino acids are formed as a result of nitrogen fixation as in the assimilation of combined nitrogen, or whether decisive differences between them exist. As mentioned before, observations made in this laboratory on the excretion of amino acids into the medium of a nodulated pea plant led to the suggestion that aminodicarboxylic acids, especially L-aspartic acid, which as an amide and free amino acid has a central position in nitrogen metabolism in the pea plant, are primary amino acids in nitrogen fixation in the nodules [Virtanen (331); Virtanen et al. (356, 378); Virtanen and Laine (365)].

Later the transamination reaction was discovered in animal tissues by Braunstein and Kritzmann (62), and subsequently it was also found in green plants and root nodules by Virtanen and Laine (370, 372). The formation of many other amino acids from dicarboxylic amino acids by transamination then became understandable. The occurrence of oxalacetic, α-ketoglutaric, and pyruvic acids in pea plants and many other plants could be experimentally proved in this laboratory [Virtanen and Laine (369); Virtanen et al. (348, 383)]. Later on when keto acids were converted to the corresponding amino acids by reduction of their 2,4-dinitrophenylhydrazones [Virtanen et al. (349); Towers and Steward (324); Fowden and Webb (131); Virtanen and Alfthan (346, 347); Alfthan and Virtanen (5); Virtanen (343)], it became possible to find a great number of different α-keto acids in plants. The importance of transamination as a regulating system of the equilibrium between different amino acids in plants was strongly supported by these findings. Hence the quantitative relations between different amino acids no longer had the same importance as proof of the "primary nature" of special amino acids as it had before the knowledge of the transamination system. Nevertheless the outstanding position of aspartic acid and its derivatives among the excretion products and in the bleeding sap of nodulated pea roots is remarkable.

Since 1940 Burris, Wilson, and their associates have used N^{15} as a powerful weapon in the studies on nitrogen fixation (see page 546). The very sensitive isotopic method made it possible to work on a small scale and at the same time to obtain reliable results on the nitrogen compounds formed in the nitrogen fixation in an atmosphere containing N_2^{15}, since the fixed nitrogen could be distinguished from "old" nitrogen in the organism. Using the tracer technique Burris (73) found that the highest level of N^{15} in the amino acids of *Azotobacter vinelandii* appeared in glutamic acid and the next highest in aspartic acid (see Table VII). In the first experiment of this kind the culture of *A. vinelandii* had grown in natural molecular nitrogen for 18 hours and was then furnished for 90 minutes with nitrogen enriched with N_2^{15}. At the end of this period the cells were immediately harvested, hydrolyzed, and fractionated. The results confirmed the important role of the dicarboxylic amino acids in the nitrogen metabolism of *Azotobacter* and favored the concept of the primary formation of glutamic acid. This result has later been confirmed in numerous short-time experiments by the Wisconsin group with many nitrogen-fixing organisms (see Section II, B). Glutamic acid carried the highest N^{15} concentration also when the organisms were supplied with N^{15}-enriched ammonia. This would be anticipated if the nitrogen were converted to ammonia before assimilation because the enzymatic amination of α-ketoglutaric acid through L-glutamic acid dehydrogenase, detected by Euler, Adler, and their associates, represents the only generally occurring amino acid synthesis in both the plant and animal kingdoms (cf. 344a). The experimental results obtained by the Wisconsin group on the distribution of N^{15} among different nitrogenous fractions with N_2, NH_4^+, and NO_3^- as the source of nitrogen are collected in Table VII. It has to be taken into account that, even when using the isotopic method, rapid transamination reactions may confuse the results considerably. The shorter the experimental times, the more the "primary" nitrogen compounds will become apparent.

There are also many other results from the Wisconsin group which strongly indicate ammonia as the inorganic end product in biological nitrogen fixation (the "key compound" according to Wilson and Burris). Ammonia is preferentially used as a source of nitrogen Azotobacter when there is a choice of nitrogen sources. Only ammonia and urea are capable of completely suppressing nitrogen fixation by the culture. After Azotobacter has grown with molecular nitrogen it can immediately utilize the added ammonia whereas nitrate is used only after adaptation [Burris and Wilson (83)].

More direct evidence for the ammonia hypothesis was obtained in Wisconsin by studying the products excreted from the nitrogen-fixing organisms. Virtanen and Hakala (351) found an unusually high excretion, up to 60% of the total fixed nitrogen in Clostridium cultures, corresponding to about the highest excretion in nodulated pea cultures. The Wisconsin group noted an excretion up to 50% in their C. pasteurianum cultures [Zelitch et al. (435)]. When a culture of this organism actively fixing molecular nitrogen was supplied with N_2^{15} for a short time, the highest N^{15} concentration was found in the free ammonia in the supernatant medium and the next higher in the amide fraction. With a dense suspension of A. vinelandii similar results could be obtained by Newton et al. (241). These experiments constitute direct evidence for the formation of ammonia as the end product of nitrogen fixation.

It is clear that observations on the formation of certain amino acids or even ammonia do not give an explanation for the chemical mechanism of the nitrogen fixation proper. However, they have been of importance when formulating hypotheses of the pathways leading from N_2 to the NH_2-group in amino acids. These will be briefly discussed as follows.

In addition to ammonia, hydroxylamine was presented as early as 1884 as a possible product of nitrogen fixation (23). Blom (47)

TABLE VII

COMPARISON OF THE DISTRIBUTION OF N^{15} IN DIFFERENT NITROGEN FRACTIONS WHEN *Azotobacter vinelandii* AND SOY NODULES WERE SUPPLIED N_2^{15} AND $N^{15}H_4^+$ [a]

Source of N:	*Azotobacter vinelandii* hydrolyzed in 6 N HCl 24 hr							*Nostoc muscorum* [e]			Soy nodules [f] hydrolyzed in 6 N HCl 14 hr
	N_2^{15} [b]	$N^{15}H_4^+$	N_2^{15} [c]	N_2^{15} [d]	$N^{15}H_4^+$ [d]			N_2^{15}	$N^{15}O_3^-$	$N^{15}H_4^+$	N_2^{15}
Time of exposure (minutes):	3	3	30	90	3	8	15	90	90	60	360
Total hydrolyzate	0.035	0.174	0.384	0.275	0.174	0.354	1.049	0.098	0.488	1.055	0.22
Glutamic acid	0.080	0.342	0.584	0.500	0.392	0.909	2.594	0.203	0.618	2.363	0.65
Aspartic acid	0.075	0.187	0.505	0.376	0.187	0.523	0.832	0.118	0.386	0.778	0.19
"Amide" + NH_3	0.053	0.749	0.424	0.325	0.749	1.450	0.981	0.183	0.809	0.446	0.31
Alanine	0.038	—		—	—	—	—	0.058	0.433	0.436	0.39
Glycine	0.015	—		—	—	—	—	0.044	0.441	0.346	0.16
Histidine	0.020	0.034		0.207	0.034	0.153	0.634	0.056	0.431	0.313	0.12
Lysine	0.015	0.052		0.356	0.052	0.097	0.807	—	—	—	0.08
Arginine	0.006	0.026		0.185	0.026	0.165	0.667	0.035	0.299	—	0.11
Phenylalanine	0.030							0.075	0.557	—	0.18

[a] All values are in atom per cent excess N^{15} (Wisconsin experiments).

[b] Allison (16); Allison and Burris (17).

[c] Bach (31).

[d] Burris and Wilson (82).

[e] Magee and Burris (217).

[f] Zelitch *et al.* (436).

found traces of hydroxylamine in *Azotobacter* cultures grown with molecular nitrogen. On the basis of this discovery he advanced the following hypothesis of the chemical mechanism of nitrogen fixation:

$$N \equiv N \xrightarrow{2H_2O} HOHN\!-\!NHOH \xrightarrow{2H} 2NH_2OH$$

Hydroxylamine would thus be the first product in nitrogen fixation which could be identified. Some years later Endres (115–117) found oxime nitrogen but no free hydroxylamine in *Azotobacter* cultures grown with molecular nitrogen, and subsequently also in cultures with nitrate and nitrite but not with ammonia.

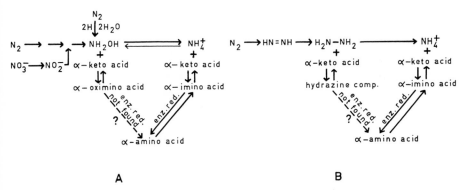

Fig. 21. A. Pathways for nitrogen fixation via hydroxylamine. The first step oxidative or reductive or hydrolytic. B. Pathway for nitrogen fixation via hydrazine. The first step reductive.

After the finding of small amounts of oxime nitrogen among the excretion products of nodulated pea plants, Virtanen and Laine (367) held that a pathway from nitrogen to hydroxylamine was possible also in symbiotic nitrogen fixation. In case hydroxylamine is formed along an oxidative pathway [Virtanen *et al.* (348)] nitrogen fixation and nitrate reduction should have a common intermediate (Fig. 21).

The tempting hypothesis that oximino acids formed spontaneously from hydroxylamine and α-keto acids should be reduced to the corresponding α-amino acids presupposes an enzyme system causing this reduction. It could, however, be established neither in root nodules nor in *Azotobacter* [Virtanen (344)]. The earlier observations on biological reduction of oximino acids may be due at least in part to hydrolysis. As was mentioned earlier, free hydroxylamine is rapidly reduced to ammonia, e.g., in root nodules by leghemoglobin (364).* Thus, ammonia could be considered the probable end product of nitrogen fixation from the experiments of this laboratory, as had become evident from the isotopic experiments of the Wisconsin group. This group also regarded hydroxylamine as a logical intermediate from which ammonia is formed through reduction [Wilson and Burris (412)].

In the cultures of anaerobic *Clostridium*, Virtanen and Hakala (351) found no traces of hydroxylamine even when the atmosphere contained 0.7 volume per cent O_2, a concentration in which *Clostridium* still grew well. The anaerobic nitrogen fixation was therefore suggested to be entirely a reductive process in which hydrazine may be a probable intermediate (340, 351) according to Wieland's theory of dehydrogenation and hydrogenation (400).

Different pathways for aerobic and anaerobic nitrogen fixation did not, however, seem attractive [Virtanen (340)] even though Roberts (275) recently emphasized that there is no objection in principle to envisaging totally different mechanisms for the two types of fixation. New findings in this laboratory on the formation of hydroxylamine compounds in *Azotobacter* cultures and the chemical nature of them no longer compel us to consider hydroxylamine as an intermediate in nitrogen fixation.

In recent studies with *Azotobacter*, Saris and Virtanen (283) found that very small amounts of hydroxylamine compounds (<1 μg/10 ml) were formed during the first hour and disappeared during the following 2 or 3 hours when a vigorous current of air was passed through the water suspension of *Azotobacter chroococcum* both without combined nitrogen and containing nitrate or urea as nitrogen sources (Fig. 22). In nonaerated cultures of *A. chroococcum* growing in flat flasks the formation of bound hydroxylamine was maximal after 3 days and disappeared relatively rapidly thereafter (Table VIII). From the medium of 3-day cultures a fraction could be separated by paper chromatography which, on acid hydrolysis, gave hydroxylamine. This

---

* In this connection it should be mentioned that on the basis of observations with *Neurospora* mutants, Silver and McElroy (290a) have presented an interesting hypothesis about the reduction of hydroxylamine over pyridoxal oxime phosphate to pyridoxamine phosphate which transaminates with keto acids. There is, however, no proof for this hypothesis. In numerous publications Yamafuji (433, 434) considers that he has found an oxime-reducing enzyme (oximase) in silkworms. The most important fact in connection with nitrogen fixation is that no reduction of oximes could be proved with nitrogen-fixing agents, even if the oxime nitrogen formed in small amounts in *Azotobacter* cultures or cell suspensions rapidly disappears, according to new experiments of Saris and Virtanen (283). The mechanism of this disappearance is not known, but possibly it is due to hydrolysis of oximes.

fraction could be separated by electrophoresis into two fractions, which both contained bound hydroxylamine. Most important in this connection is the fact that these fractions were formed regardless of the nitrogen sources used (molecular, nitrate, or ammonium nitrogen) [Saris

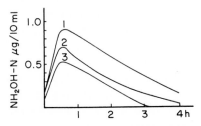

Fig. 22. Bound hydroxylamine in a vigorously aerated suspension of *Azotobacter chroococcum* in nutrient solutions with potassium nitrate (*1*), molecular nitrogen (*2*), and urea (*3*) as nitrogen source. From Saris and Virtanen (283).

and Virtanen (284)]. On the basis of these findings there was no longer any evidence for hydroxylamine as a direct intermediate in nitrogen fixation, and it was suggested that the molecular nitrogen was fixed in aerobic as well as in anaerobic fixation through reductive processes only. Kinetic studies of Allison and Burris (17) with *Azotobacter vinelandii*

TABLE VIII

Effect of the Nitrogen Source on the Enrichment of Bound Hydroxylamine in the Nutrient Solution of *Azotobacter chroococcum*[a,b]

Nitrogen nutrition	NH₂OH—N (μg/10 ml)	Cells (mg/10 ml)	Assimilated N (mg/10 ml)	Excretion total N (mg/10 ml)
N₂	1.46	160	2.15	0.08
KNO₃	1.04	85	1.23	—
(NH₄)₂CO₃	1.80	40	0.52	—
CO(NH₂)₂	1.62	140	2.05	—

[a] From Saris and Virtanen (283).
[b] The medium was analyzed 3 days after inoculation.

(exposure of cultures to N₂¹⁵ for only 1–5 minutes) strongly suggested that molecular nitrogen is fixed in ammonia before the synthesis of dicarboxylic amino acids. Because no oxidized nitrogenous compounds were isolated, the authors postulated that nitrogen fixation is entirely a reductive process. The findings of Nason and his associates (296),

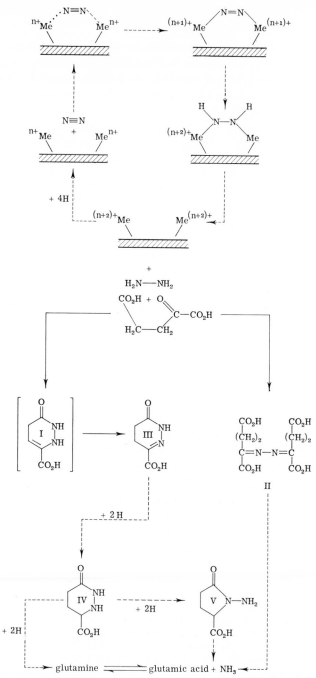

FIG. 23. A suggested mechanism for the biological fixation of molecular nitrogen with hydrazine as an intermediate. The top line represents reactions between nitrogen

which show that the formation of hydroxylamine reductases in *Azotobacter* is stimulated by nitrate but not by free nitrogen, is important in this connection. It ought, however, to be mentioned that there is no binding proof yet against the formation of hydroxylamine as an intermediate in nitrogen fixation. Since there are no longer proofs in support of it, there is no need to maintain the hypothesis.

In 1957 Bach (31) working in Burris' laboratory published most interesting results which give experimental evidence for hydrazine as an intermediate or a by-product in nitrogen fixation by *Azotobacter*. At first sight these results seemed not to be in accordance with the prevailing idea that nitrogen fixation leads to ammonia which is then used for amino acid synthesis.

Bach could show that organic azines, which are formed from hydrazine and α-ketoglutarate without the mediation of biological agents, are also formed in *Azotobacter vinelandii* cells grown on molecular nitrogen and in the nodules of field-grown soybeans. The most important finding was, however, that the fractions from paper chromatograms carrying the azines contained two to six times higher relative and absolute atom per cent N^{15} excess than glutamic acid, aspartic acid, or ammonia when the *Azotobacter* cells were exposed to N_2^{15}, but not when they were supplied with $N^{15}H_4^+$. This was the first recorded instance of the recovery of compounds which yielded N^{15} distributions differing strongly between nitrogen-fixing organisms supplied with N_2^{15} or $N^{15}H_4^+$. It would therefore appear that compounds in these organic fractions lie on the pathway between N_2 and NH_4^+ and are not products of the metabolism of NH_4^+ (Bach). Bach's concept of the mechanism of nitrogen fixation appears from Fig. 23 (31). It is logical to assume that only when the reduction of the nitrogen molecule has reached the hydrazine stage is the reaction product liberated from the enzyme to appear in solution.

The organic hydrazine compounds formed in nitrogen fixation were characterized only by paper chromatography, and far-reaching conclusions from the new findings can therefore be misleading. The high

---

and an enzyme carrying two metal (Me) groups which bind the nitrogen during its initial reduction. In line two the enzyme complex is shown to cleave to yield hydrazine and to regenerate the enzyme. Hydrazine reacts with α-ketoglutarate to form (I), the tautomer of 3,4-dihydropyridazinone-5-carboxylic acid (PCA), or the dimer, α-ketoglutarate azine (II). The tautomer of PCA in turn yields PCA (III) which is reduced to tetrahydropyridazinone-5-carboxylic acid (IV); a reductive cleavage of the N—N bond of this compound would yield glutamine. Alternatively, (IV) could form N-aminopyrrolidonecarboxylic acid (V) reductively and (V) could give glutamic acid plus ammonia. The dimer (II) potentially could form glutamic acid. From Bach (31).

labeling of these compounds with N^{15} is, however, a fact. This can be understood on the basis of the theory that ammonia is the inorganic end product in nitrogen fixation only on the presumption that the hydrazine compounds are not intermediates but by-products in analogy with oximes (see Fig. 21). The main pathway should lead to ammonia. The lower labeling of ammonia compared with that of hydrazine compounds could depend on the dilution of $N^{15}H_3$ with other ammonia in the cells.

Fedorov (121, 122) earlier called attention to the possible role of hydrazine in nitrogen fixation. He introduces the idea that strongly oxidative carbonyl groups in the catalyst oxidize the nitrogen molecule which is simultaneously attached to the oxygen atoms. According to him the structure of the acting enzyme and the first stage in the fixation of molecular nitrogen would be

$$\text{Protein—R—CHNH}_2\text{—}\underset{\underset{O}{\|}}{C}\text{—}\underset{\underset{O}{\|}}{C}\text{—COOH} + N_2 \rightarrow$$

$$\text{Protein—R—CHNH}_2\text{—}\underset{\underset{\underset{\underset{N}{|}}{O}}{|}}{C}\text{=}\underset{\underset{\underset{\underset{N}{|}}{O}}{|}}{C}\text{—COOH}$$

A stepwise reduction of nitrogen with dehydrogenase-H_2 to hydrazine then follows. Amino acids should be formed over hydrazine derivatives of keto acids. It is difficult to get a clear picture of his complicated presentation of evidence from the references accessible.* His methods and conclusions have been subjected to severe criticism by Wilson and Burris (412).

Only when further particulars are obtained regarding the enzyme system regulating the process, can we expect to get definite information on the chemical mechanism of nitrogen fixation. The important observations made in Wisconsin as to hydrogenase and nitrogenase represent a great step forward on this difficult path. Observations on the enzymatic machinery of nitrogen fixation have been briefly treated in Section III, K. The significance of leghemoglobin specific for the root nodules of leguminous plants is reported on at great length in Section III, p. 609. In this connection there is no reason to go into these problems again. A conclusion to which two groups of workers have come

---

* After this manuscript was completed, a book by Fedorow was published in German: Biologische Bindung des atmosphärischen Stickstoffs, VEB Deutscher Verlag der Wissenschaften, Berlin, 1960, 594 pp. Proofs for his hypotheses do not appear in this book either.

independently regarding the localization of nitrogen fixation in the bacterial cell, still ought to be pointed out. As already mentioned the excretion of fixed nitrogen from the bacterial mass of young effective nodules early led Virtanen and von Hausen (353) to the suggestion "that the fixation of N_2 takes place at the surface of the bacterial cells in the nodules." Allison and Burris (17) have recently concluded from their kinetic studies with *Azotobacter vinelandii* that "the rapid excretion of fixed N^{15} into the medium suggested that fixation of N_2 may occur at or near the surface of the cells." It is of special interest that also in free-living *Azotobacter* in which nitrogen fixation is connected with the multiplication of cells and the nitrogen fixed is mainly used by the cells, the excretion of newly fixed nitrogen is so rapid that it justifies this conclusion.

In a paper of Roberts (275) which was published after this manuscript was written, an oxidative pathway in nitrogen fixation is still held to be possible. Roberts, who with his associates has especially studied the stimulation and inhibition of nitrogen fixation by different compounds, believes, on the basis of present evidence, that the first step may be either an oxidative or a reductive or a hydrolytic one. This is a safe position, because it does not bind the author to any concept. In our opinion there is, however, more evidence for a reductive fixation from beginning to end than for any other pathway. Since it is now feasible to get a nitrogen-fixing system into cell-free solution, new results can be expected which may give conclusive evidence of the mechanism of nitrogen fixation.

References

1. Abdel-Ghaffar, A. S., and Allen, O. N. The effects of certain micro-organisms on the growth and function of rhizobia. *Trans. Intern. Congr. Soil Sci. 4th Congr. Amsterdam 1950*, pp. 93–96 (1950).
2. Albrecht, W. A., and McCalla, T. M. A new culture medium for rhizobia. *J. Bacteriol.* **34**, 455–457 (1937).
3. Aldrich-Blake, R. N. On the fixation of atmospheric nitrogen by bacteria living symbiotically in root nodules of *Casuarina equisetifolia. Oxford Forestry Mem.* **14**, 20 pp. (1932). [Secondary source: cf. reference (6), p. 101.]
4. Alexander, M., and Wilson, P. W. Large-scale production of the *Azotobacter* for enzymes. *Appl. Microbiol.* **2**, 135–140 (1954).
5. Alfthan, M., and Virtanen, A. I. Estimation of keto acids in plants. *Acta Chem. Scand.* **9**, 186–187 (1955).
6. Allen, E. K., and Allen, O. N. Biological aspects of symbiotic nitrogen fixation. *In* "Handbuch der Pflanzenphysiologie—Encyclopedia of Plant Physiology" (W. Ruhland, ed.), Vol. 8, pp. 48–118. Springer, Berlin, 1958.
7. Allen, M. B. Photosynthetic nitrogen fixation by blue-green algae. *Sci. Monthly* **83**, 100–106 (1956).

8. Allen, M. B., and Arnon, D. I. Studies on nitrogen-fixing blue-green algae. I. Growth and nitrogen-fixation by *Anabaena cylindrica* Lemm. *Plant Phys.* **30**, 366–372 (1955).

9. Allen, M. B., and van Niel, C. B. Experiments on bacterial denitrification. *J. Bacteriol.* **64**, 397–412 (1952).

10. Allen, O. N., and Allen, E. K. Plants in the sub-family *Caesalpinioideae* observed to be lacking nodules. *Soil Sci.* **42**, 87–91 (1936).

11. Allen, O. N., and Allen, E. K. Response of the peanut plant to inoculation with rhizobia, with special reference to morphological development of the nodules. *Botan. Gaz.* **102**, 121–142 (1940).

12. Allen, O. N., and Allen, E. K. A survey of nodulation among leguminous plants. *Proc. Soil Soc. Am.* **12**, 203–208 (1947).

13. Allison, F. E. The enigma of soil nitrogen balance sheets. *Advances in Agron.* **7**, 213–250 (1955).

14. Allison, F. E., Hoover, S. R., and Morris, H. J. Physiological studies with the nitrogen-fixing alga, *Nostoc muscorum. Botan. Gaz.* **98**, 433–463 (1937).

15. Allison, F. E., and Morris, H. J. Nitrogen fixation by blue-green algae. *Science* **71**, 221–223 (1930).

16. Allison, R. M. Ph.D. thesis, Univ. of Wisconsin, 1955.

17. Allison, R. M., and Burris, R. H. Kinetics of fixation of nitrogen by *Azotobacter vinelandii. J. Biol. Chem.* **224**, 351–364 (1957).

18. Almon, L. Concerning the reproduction of bacteroids. *Zentr. Bakteriol. Parasitenk. Abt. II*, **87**, 289–297 (1933).

19. Almon, L., and Wilson, P. W. Bacteriophage in relation to nitrogen fixation by red clover. *Arch. Mikrobiol.* **4**, 209–219 (1933).

20. Anderson, A. J., and Spencer, D. Molybdenum in nitrogen metabolism of legumes and non-legumes. *Australian J. Sci. Research* **B3**, 414–430 (1950).

21. Anderson, A. J., and Thomas, M. P. Plant responses to molybdenum as a fertilizer. I. Molybdenum and symbiotic nitrogen fixation. *Bull. Council Sci. Ind. Research Australia No.* **198**, 24 pp. (1946).

22. Anderson, G. R. Nitrogen fixation by *Pseudomonas*-like soil bacteria. *J. Bacteriol.* **70**, 129–133 (1955).

23. Anonymous. *Nature* **30**, 548 (1884). [cf. reference (407): monograph by P. W. Wilson, p. 176.]

24. Appleby, C. A., and Bergersen, F. J. Cytochromes of *Rhizobium. Nature* **182**, 1174 (1958).

25. Aprison, M. H., and Burris, R. H. Time course of fixation of N_2 by excised soybean nodules. *Science* **115**, 264–265 (1952).

26. Aprison, M. H., Magee, W. E., and Burris, R. H. Nitrogen fixation by excised soy bean root nodules. *J. Biol. Chem.* **208**, 29–39 (1954).

27. Austin, J. H., and Drabkin, D. L. Spectrophotometric studies. III. Methemoglobin. *J. Biol. Chem.* **112**, 67–88 (1935).

28. Azim, M. A., and Roberts, E. R. Studies in the biological fixation of nitrogen. V. Some observations on the uptake of combined nitrogen by *Azotobacter vinelandii. Biochim. et Biophys. Acta* **18**, 363–369 (1955).

29. Azim, M. A., and Roberts, E. R. Studies in the biological fixation of nitrogen. VII. Inhibition in *Azotobacter vinelandii* by hydrazine. *Biochim. et Biophys. Acta* **21**, 562–568 (1956).

30. Bach, M. K. *In* "Inorganic Nitrogen Metabolism" (W. D. McElroy and B. Glass, eds.), p. 370. Johns Hopkins Press, Baltimore, Maryland, 1956.

31. Bach, M. K. Hydrazine and biological nitrogen fixation. *Biochim. et Biophys. Acta* **26**, 104–113 (1957).

32. Barthel, C. Kunna baljväxtbakterier i renkultur fixera atmosfäriskt kväve? *Medd. No.* **308**. *Centralanstalt. försöksväsendet jordbruks. Bakteriol. avdel. No.* **43**, 16 pp. (1926).

33. Barthel, C. The growth of *Bact. radicicola* under reduced oxygen pressure. *Proc. Intern. Congr. Soil Sci. 2nd Congr. Leningrad 1930*, **3**, 72–73 (1932).

33a. Bayliss, N. S. The thermochemistry of biological nitrogen fixation. *Australian J. Biol. Sci.* **9**, 364–370 (1956).

34. Bazarewski, S. Badania nad bakteroidami. *Roczniki Nauk Rolniczych* **17**, 1–34 (1927).

35. Beijerinck, M. W. Die Bakterien der Papilionaceenknöllchen. *Botan. Ztg.* **46**, 726–735, 741–750, 757–771, 781–790, 797–804 (1888).

36. Beijerinck, M. W. Die Bakterien der Papilionaceenknöllchen. *Botan. Ztg.* **46**, 725, 757 (1888).

37. Beijerinck, M. W. Über oligonitrophile Microben. *Zentr. Bakteriol. Parasitenk. Abt. II*, **7**, 561 (1901).

38. Belayaeva, M. I. The assimilation of molecular nitrogen by hydrogen bacteria. *Uchenye Zapiski Kazan. Gosudarst. Univ.* **114**, (1), 13–18 (1954).

39. Bergersen, F. J. The cytology of bacteroids from root nodules of subterranean clover. *J. Gen. Microbiol.* **13**, 411–419 (1955).

40. Bergersen, F. J. The structure of ineffective root nodules of legumes: an unusual new type of ineffectiveness and an appraisal of present knowledge. *Australian J. Biol. Sci.* **10**, 233–242 (1957).

40a. Bergersen, F. J. The growth of *Rhizobium* in synthetic media. *Australian J. Biol. Sci.* **14**, 349–360 (1961).

41. Bergersen, F. J., and Briggs, M. J. Studies on the bacterial component of soybean root nodules; cytology and organization of the host tissue. *J. Gen. Microbiol.* **19**, 482–490 (1958).

41a. Bergersen, F. J., and Wilson, P. W. Further spectrophotometric studies of soybean nodule extracts. *Proc. Natl. Acad. Sci. U.S.* **45**, 1641–1646 (1959).

42. Bergersen, F. J., and Nutman, P. S. Symbiotic effectiveness in nodulated red clover. IV. *Heredity (London)* **11**, 175–184 (1957).

43. Berthelot, M. Fixation directe de l'azote atmosphérique libre par certains terrains argileux. *Compt. rend. acad. sci.* **101**, 775–784 (1885).

44. Bertrand, D., and Wolf, A. Nickel and cobalt in root nodules of legumes. *Bull. soc. chim. biol.* **36**, 905–906 (1954).

44a. Bisset, K. A. Natural relationships of the nitrogen-fixing bacteria. *Nature* **182**, 405 (1958).

45. Bjälfve, G. The nodules of leguminous plants, their form and effect in different strains. (In Swedish with English summary.) *Medd. No.* **434**. *Centralanstalt. försöksväsendet jordbruks. Bakteriol. avdel. No.* **61**. 43 pp. (cited: p. 85) (1933).

46. Bjälfve, G. The nodules of different varieties, percentage of nitrogen in legumes and their influence on the nitrogen economy of the soil. (In Swedish with English summary.) *Medd. No.* **455**. *Centralanstalt. försöksväsendet jordbruks. Bakteriol. avdel. No.* **65**. 37 pp. (cited: pp. 85, 150, 247) (1935).

47. Blom, J. Ein Versuch, die chemischen Vorgänge bei der Assimilation des molekularen Stickstoffs durch Mikroorganismen zu erklären. *Zentr. Bakteriol. Parasitenk. Abt. II*, **84**, 60–86 (1931).

48. Bond, G. Quantitative observations on the fixation and transfer of nitrogen in the soybean, with especial reference to the mechanism of transfer of fixed nitrogen from bacillus to host. *Ann. Botany (London)* **50**, 559–578 (1936).

49. Bond, G. Symbiosis of leguminous plants and nodule bacteria. IV. The importance of the oxygen factor in nodule formation and function. *Ann. Botany (London)* **15**, 95–108 (1951).

50. Bond, G. The fixation of nitrogen associated with the root nodules of *Myrica gale*, with special reference to its pH relations and ecological significance. *Ann. Botany (London)* **15**, 447–459 (1951).

51. Bond, G. Some features of root growth in nodulated plants of *Myrica gale* (L). *Ann. Botany (London)* **16**, 467–475 (1952).

52. Bond, G., Fletcher, W. W., and Ferguson, T. P. The development and function of the root nodules of *Alnus, Myrica*, and *Hippophaë. Plant and Soil* **5**, 309–323 (1954).

53. Bond, G., Gardner, I. C., and Leaf, G. The distribution of ^{15}N fixed by root nodules of *Alnus glutinosa. Biochem. J.* **69**, 3P (1958).

54. Bond, G., and Scott, G. D. Symbiotic systems for nitrogen fixation. *Ann. Botany (London)* **19**, 65 (1955). [Secondary source: *Nature* **175**, 667 (1955).]

55. Bond, L. Origin and developmental morphology of root nodules of *Pisum sativum. Botan. Gaz.* **109**, 411–434 (1948).

56. Borm, L. Die Wurzelknöllchen von *Hippophaë rhamnoides* und *Alnus glutinosa. Botan. Arch.* **31**, 441–488 (1931).

57. Bortels, H. Molybdän als Katalysator bei der biologischen Stickstoffbindung. *Arch. Mikrobiol.* **1**, 333–342 (1930).

58. Bortels, H. Über die Wirkung von Molybdän- und Vanadiumdüngungen auf *Azotobacter*-Zahl und Stickstoffbindung in Erde. *Arch. Mikrobiol.* **8**, 1–12 (1936).

59. Bortels, H. Über die Wirkung von Molybdän- und Vanadiumdüngungen auf Leguminosen. *Arch. Mikrobiol.* **8**, 13–26 (1936).

60. Bortels, H. Über die Bedeutung des Molybdäns für Stickstoffbindende *Nostacaceen. Arch. Mikrobiol.* **11**, 155–186 (1940).

61. Bové, J., Bové, C., and Arnon, D. I. Molybdenum and vanadium requirements of *Azotobacter* for growth and nitrogen fixation. *Plant Physiol.* **32** (Suppl.), XXIII (1957).

62. Braunstein, A. E., and Kritzmann, M. G. Formation and breakdown of amino acids by intermolecular transfer of the amino group. *Nature* **140**, 503–504 (1937).

63. Bredemann, G. *Bacillus amylobacter* A. M. et Bredemann in morphologischer, physiologischer und systematischer Beziehung. Mit besonderer Berücksichtigung des Stickstoffbindungsvermögens dieses Spezies. *Zentr. Bakteriol. Parasitenk. Abt. II*, **23**, 385–568 (1909).

64. Brenchley, W. E., and Thornton, H. G. The relation between the development, structure, and functioning of the nodules on *Vicia faba*, as influenced by the presence or absence of boron in the nutrient medium. *Proc. Roy. Soc.* **B98**, 373–398 (1925).

65. Brown, M. E., and Metcalfe, G. Nitrogen fixation by a species of *Pullularia. Nature* **180**, 282 (1957).

66. Brunchorst, J. Über die Knöllchen an den Leguminosenwurzeln. *Ber. deut. botan. Ges.* **3**, 241–257 (1885).

67. Brunchorst, J. Über einige Wurzelanschwellungen, besonders diejenigen von

Alnus und den *Elaeagnaceen. Botan. Inst. Tübingen, Untersuch.* **2,** 151–177 (1886).

68. Burk, D. Azotase and nitrogenase in *Azotobacter. Ergeb. Enzymforsch.* **3,** 23–56 (1934).

69. Burk, D. The origin and significance of ammonia formed by *Azotobacter. Soil Sci.* **41,** 81–122 (1936).

70. Burk, D., and Burris, R. H. Biochemical nitrogen fixation. *Ann. Rev. Biochem.* **10,** 587–618 (1941).

71. Burk, D., and Horner, C. K. Über Hydroxylamin, Hydrazin und Amide als Intermediärprodukte bei der N_2-Fixation durch *Azotobacter. Naturwissenschaften* **23,** 259–260 (1935).

72. Burk, D., Lineweaver, H., and Horner, C. K. The specific influence of acidity on the mechanism of nitrogen fixation by *Azotobacter. J. Bacteriol.* **27,** 325–340 (1934).

73. Burris, R. H. Distribution of isotopic nitrogen in *Azotobacter vinelandii. J. Biol. Chem.* **143,** 509–517 (1942).

74. Burris, R. H. Mechanism of biological nitrogen fixation. *In* "Inorganic Nitrogen Metabolism" (W. D. McElroy and B. Glass, eds.), pp. 215–217. Johns Hopkins Press, Baltimore, Maryland, 1956.

75. Burris, R. H. Studies on the mechanism of biological nitrogen fixation. *In* "Inorganic Nitrogen Metabolism" (W. D. McElroy and B. Glass, eds.), p. 316. Johns Hopkins Press, Baltimore, Maryland, 1956.

76. Burris, R. H., Eppling, F. J., Wahlin, H. B., and Wilson, P. W. Detection of nitrogen fixation with isotopic nitrogen. *J. Biol. Chem.* **148,** 349–357 (1943).

77. Burris, R. H., Magee, W. E., and Bach, M. K. The pN_2 and the pO_2 function for nitrogen fixation by excised soybean nodules. *Ann. Acad. Sci. Fennicae Ser. A II No.* **60,** 190–199 (1955).

78. Burris, R. H., and Miller, E. C. Application of N^{15} to the study of biological nitrogen fixation. *Science* **93,** 114–115 (1941).

79. Burris, R. H., Phelps, A. S., and Wilson, J. B. Adaptations of *Rhizobium* and *Azotobacter. Proc. Soil Sci. Soc. Am.* **7,** 272–275 (1942).

80. Burris, R. H., and Wilson, P. W. Respiratory enzyme systems in symbiotic nitrogen fixation. *Cold Spring Harbor Symposia Quant. Biol.* **7,** 349–361 (1939).

81. Burris, R. H., and Wilson, P. W. Biological nitrogen fixation. *Ann. Rev. Biochem.* **14,** 685–708 (1945).

82. Burris, R. H., and Wilson, P. W. Comparison of the metabolism of ammonia and molecular nitrogen in *Azotobacter. J. Biol. Chem.* **165,** 595–598 (1946).

83. Burris, R. H., and Wilson, P. W. Ammonia as an intermediate in nitrogen fixation by *Azotobacter. J. Bacteriol.* **52,** 505–512 (1946).

84. Burris, R. H., and Wilson, P. W. Characteristics of the nitrogen-fixing enzyme system in *Nostoc muscorum. Botan. Gaz.* **108,** 254–262 (1946).

85. Burris, R. H., and Wilson, P. W. Effect of haemoglobin and other nitrogenous compounds on the respiration of the rhizobia. *Biochem. J.* **51,** 90–96 (1952).

86. Burström, H. Mechanisms of cell elongation. *In* "Plant Growth Substances" (F. Skoog, ed.), pp. 36–55. Univ. of Wisconsin Press, Madison, 1951.

87. Burton, M. O., and Lockhead, A. G. Production of vitamin B_{12} by *Rhizobium* species. *Can. J. Botany* **30,** 521–524 (1952).

88. Butler, G. W., and Bathurst, N. O. The underground transference of nitrogen from clover to associated grass. *Proc. Intern. Grassland Congr. 7th Palmerston, New Zealand, 1956,* Paper No. 14 (1956).

89. Calder, E. A. Nitrogen fixation in a Uganda swamp soil. *Nature* **184**, 746 (1959).

90. Carnahan, J. E., Mortenson, L. E., Mower, H. F., and Castle, J. E. Nitrogen fixation in cell-free extracts of *Clostridium pasteurianum*. *Biochim. et Biophys. Acta* **38**, 188–189 (1960).

91. Casas-Campillo, C. Bacterias aerobias esporulades con propiedades antagonistas para *Rhizobium*. *Ciencia (Mex.)* **8**, 108 (1947).

92. Casas-Campillo, C. El antagonismo microbiano en relacion con las bacterias de los nodulos de las plantas leguminosas. *Ciencia (Mex.)* **9**, 193–199 (1949).

93. Castelli, T. Some considerations on the symbiotic microbe of *Hedysarum coronarium* L. *Contrib. Conf. Improv. Pasture Fodder Production in Mediterranean Area, Rome, 1951*, pp. 1–8.

94. Chaudhary, M. T., Wilson, T. G. G., and Roberts, E. R. Studies in the biological fixation of nitrogen. II. Inhibition in *Azotobacter vinelandii* by hypernitrous acid. *Biochim. et Biophys. Acta* **14**, 507–513 (1954).

95. Chaudhuri, H. Nitrogen fixation in the rice-field soils of Bengal. *Nature* **145**, 936–937 (1940).

96. Chen, H. K. Production of growth-substance by clover nodule bacteria. *Nature* **142**, 753–754 (1938).

97. Chen, H. K. The limited numbers of nodules produced on legumes by different strains of *Rhizobium*. *J. Agr. Sci.* **31**, 479–487 (1941).

98. Chen, H. K., Nicol, H., and Thorton, H. G. The growth of nodule bacteria in the expressed juices from legume roots bearing effective and ineffective nodules. *Proc. Roy. Soc.* **B129**, 475–491 (1940).

99. Colter, J. S., and Quastel, J. H. Catalytic decomposition of hydroxylamine by hemoglobin. *Arch. Biochem. Biophys.* **27**, 368–389 (1950).

99a. Davenport, H. E. Haemoglobin in the root nodules of *Casuarina cunninghamiana*. *Nature* **186**, 653–654 (1960).

100. De, P. K., and Mandal, L. N. Fixation of nitrogen by algae in rice soils. *Soil Sci.* **81**, 453–458 (1956).

101. Demolon, A., and Dunez, A. Bactériophage et fatigue des sols cultivés en luzerne. *Compt. rend. acad. sci.* **197**, 1344–1346 (1933).

102. Demolon, A., and Dunez, A. Nouvelles observations sur le bactériophage et la fatigue des sols cultivés en luzerne (2 mémoire). *Ann. agron.* **6**, 434–454 (1956).

103. Demolon, A., and Dunez, A. La fatigue des sols. Causes et remèdes. *Compt. rend. acad. sci.* **202**, 1704–1706 (1936).

104. Demolon, A., and Dunez, A. Symbiose bactérienne et culture des légumineuses. *Ann. agron.* **8**, 220–237 (1938).

105. Demolon, A., and Dunez, A. Observations sur la résistance à la lyse phagique du *Bact. radicicola*. *Compt. rend. acad. sci.* **208**, 1600–1602 (1939).

106. Derx, H. G. *Beijerinckia*, a new genus of nitrogen-fixing bacteria occurring in tropical soils. *Koninkl. Akad. Wetenschap. Amsterdam Proc.* **53**, 140–147 (1950).

106a. Dilworth, M. J., and Parker, C. A. Oxygen inhibition of respiration in *Azotobacter*. *Nature* **191**, 520–521 (1961).

107. Drewes, K. Über die Assimilation des Luftstickstoffs durch Blaualgen. *Zentr. Bakteriol. Parasitenk. Abt. II*, **76**, 88–101 (1928).

108. Dunham, D. H., and Baldwin, I. L. Double infection of leguminous plants with good and poor strains of rhizobia. *Soil Sci.* **32**, 235–249 (1931).

109. Ebersole, E. E. Guttentag, C., and Wilson, P. W. Nature of carbon monoxide inhibition of biological nitrogen fixation. *Arch. Biochem.* **3**, 399–418 (1944).

110. Egami, F., Yamada, T., and Taniguchi, S. Sur la respiration et les enzymes d'oxyde-réduction d'une bactérie sel-résistante. *Congr. intern. biochimie, Paris 1952, Résumé communs.,* pp. 78–79 (1952).

111. Egle, K., and Mundig, H. Über den Gehalt an Häminkörpern in den Wurzelknöllchen von Nicht-Leguminosen. *Naturwissenschaften* **38**, 548–549 (1951).

112. Ellfolk, N. Crystalline leghemoglobin. *Acta Chem. Scand.* **13**, 596–597 (1959).

112a. Ellfolk, N. Crystalline leghemoglobin. I. Purification procedure. *Acta Chem. Scand.* **14**, 609–616 (1960).

112b. Ellfolk, N. Crystalline leghemoglobin. II. The molecular weights and shapes of the two main components. *Acta Chem. Scand.* **14**, 1819–1927 (1960).

112c. Ellfolk, N. Crystalline leghemoglobin. III. Amino acid composition of the two main components. *Acta Chem. Scand.* **15**, 545–554 (1961).

112d. Ellfolk, N. Crystalline leghemoglobin. IV. Spectroscopic studies of the two main metleghemoglobin components and some of their fatty acid complexes. *Acta Chem. Scand.* **15**, 975–984 (1961).

112e. Ellfolk, N., and Levin, K. Crystalline leghemoglobin. V. The N-terminal amino acids of the two main components. *Acta Chem. Scand.* **15**, 444–445 (1961).

113. Ellfolk, N., and Virtanen, A. I. Electrophoresis of leghemoglobin. *Acta Chem. Scand.* **4**, 1014–1019 (1950).

114. Ellfolk, N., and Virtanen, A. I. The molecular weight of leghemoglobin. *Acta Chem. Scand.* **6**, 411–420 (1952).

115. Endres, G. Über ein Zwischenprodukt der N₂-Assimilation. *Naturwissenschaften* **22**, 662 (1934).

116. Endres, G. Zur Kenntnis der Stickstoffassimilierenden Bakterien. II. Über die Bindung des Luftstickstoffes durch *Azotobacter. Ann.* **518**, 109–126 (1935).

117. Endres, G. Beiträge zur Kenntnis der biologischen Bindung des Lufstickstoffes. *Angew. Chem.* **49**, 560 (1936).

118. Eriksson, E. Atmosfärens kemi. *Svensk Kem. Tidskr.* **71**, 15–32 (1959).

119. Esposito, R. G., and Wilson, P. W. Trace metal requirements of *Azotabacter. Proc. Soc. Exptl. Biol. Med.* **93**, 564–567 (1956).

120. Esposito, R. G., and Wilson, P. W. Calcium and polymetaphosphate synthesis in *Azotobacter vinelandii. Biochim. et Biophys. Acta* **22**, 186–187 (1956).

121. Fedorov, M. V. Chemistry of fixation of atmospheric nitrogen by *Azotobacter.* The influence of narcotics (ethylurethan and diphenylurea) on the productivity of nitrogen fixation. (English summary.) *Microbiologiya* **15**, 23–29 (1946).

122. Fedorov, M. V. Significance of carbon-linked hydrogen in fixation of molecular nitrogen by azotobacters. (English summary.) *Microbiologiya* **17**, 208–217 (1948).

123. Ferguson, T. P., and Bond, G. Observations on the formation and function of the root nodules of *Alnus glutinosa* (L.). *Ann. Botany (London)* **17**, 175–188 (1953).

124. Ferguson, T. P., and Bond, G. Symbiosis of leguminous plants. V. The growth of red clover at different oxygen tension. *Ann. Botany (London)* **28**, 385–396 (1954).

125. Fletcher, W. W. The development and structure of the root-nodules of *Myrica gale* L. with special reference to the nature of the endophyte. *Ann. Botany (London)* **19**, 501–513 (1955).

126. Fogg, G. E. Nitrogen fixation by blue-green algae. *Endeavour* **6**, 172–175 (1947).

127. Fogg, G. E. The production of extracellular nitrogenous substances by a blue-green alga. *Proc. Roy. Soc.* **B139**, 372–397 (1952).

128. Fogg, G. E. "The Metabolism of Algae," p. 69. Methuen, London, 1953.

129. Fogg, G. E. Nitrogen fixation by photosynthetic organisms. *Ann. Rev. Plant Physiol.* **7**, 51–70 (1956).

130. Fogg, G. E., and Wolfe, M. The nitrogen metabolism of the blue-green algae (Myxophyceae). *In* "Autotrophic Microorganisms" (B. A. Fry and J. L. Peel, eds.), pp. 99–125. Cambridge Univ. Press, London and New York, 1954.

131. Fowden, L., and Webb, J. A. Evidence for the occurrence of γ-methylene-α-oxoglutaric acid in groundnut plants (*Arachis hypogaea*). *Biochem. J.* **59**, 228–234 (1955).

132. Frank, B. Über den experimentellen Nachweis der Assimilation freien Stickstoffs durch erdbewohnende Algen. *Ber. deut. botan. Ges.* **7**, 34–42 (1889).

133. Frank, B. Über die Pilzsymbiose der Leguminosen. *Landwirtsch. Jahrb.* **19**, 523–640 (1890).

134. Fred, E. B., Baldwin, I. L., and McCoy, E. "Root Nodule Bacteria and Leguminous Plants." Univ. of Wisconsin Press, Madison, 1932.

135. Fred, E. B., and Graul, E. J. The effect of soluble nitrogenous salts on nodule formation. *J. Am. Soc. Agron.* **8**, 316–328 (1916).

136. Frey-Wyssling, A. The growth in surface of the plant cell wall. *Growth Symposium No.* **12**, 151–169 (1948).

137. Frey-Wyssling, A. Growth of plant cell walls. *Symposia Soc. Exptl. Biol. No.* **4**, 320–328 (1952).

138. Funke, C. Über die Chromosomenzahlen der Wurzelknöllchen experimentell erzeugter polyploider Leguminosen. *Naturwissenschaften* **44**, 498 (1957).

139. Fåhraeus, G. The infection of clover root hairs by nodule bacteria studied by a simple glass slide technique. *J. Gen. Microbiol.* **16**, 374–381 (1957).

140. Gäumann, E., Jaag, O., and Roth, S. Über einen Immunisierungsversuch mit Wurzelknöllchenbakterien bei Leguminosen. *Ber. schweiz. botan. Ges.* **55**, 270–277 (1945).

141. Georgi, C. E., and Beguin, A. E. Heteroauxin production by efficient and inefficient strains of rhizobia. *Nature* **143**, 25 (1939).

142. Georgi, C. E., and Ettlinger, J. M. Utilization of carbohydrates and sugar acids by the rhizobia. *J. Bacteriol.* **41**, 323–340 (1941).

143. Georgi, C. E., and Wilson, P. W. The influence of the tension of oxygen on the respiration of rhizobia. *Arch. Mikrobiol.* **4**, 543–564 (1933).

144. Gest, H., Judis, J., and Peck, H. D. Reduction of molecular nitrogen and relationships with photosynthesis and hydrogen metabolism. *In* "Inorganic Nitrogen Metabolism" (W. D. McElroy and B. Glass, eds.), pp. 298–315. Johns Hopkins Press, Baltimore, Maryland, 1956.

145. Gest, H., Kamen, M. D., and Bregoff, H. M. Photoproduction of hydrogen and nitrogen fixation by *Rhodospirillum rubrum*. *J. Biol. Chem.* **182**, 153–170 (1950).

146. Golding, J. Experiments on peas in water culture. *Zentr. Bakteriol. Parasitenk. Abt. II*, **11**, 1–7 (1904).

147. Grijns, A. Clover plants in sterile cultivation do not produce a bacteriophage of *B. radicicola*. *Zentr. Bakteriol. Parasitenk. Abt. II*, **71**, 248–251 (1927).

147a. Hallsworth, E. G., Wilson, S. B., and Greenwood, E. A. N. Copper and cobalt in nitrogen fixation. *Nature* **187**, 79–80 (1960).

148. Hamilton, P. B., Magee, W. E., and Mortenson, L. E. Nitrogen fixation by *Aerobacter aerogenes* and cell-free extracts of the *Azotobacter vinelandii*. *Bacteriol. Proc. (Soc. Am. Bacteriologists)* **53**, 82 (1953).

149. Hamilton, P. B., Shug, A. L., and Wilson, P. W. Spectrophotometric examination of hydrogenase and nitrogenase in soybean nodules and *Azotobacter. Proc. Natl. Acad. Sci. U.S.* **43**, 297–304 (1957).

150. Hamilton, P. B., and Wilson, P. W. Nitrogen fixation by *Aerobacter aerogenes. Ann. Acad. Sci. Fennicae Ser. A II No.* **60**, 139–150 (1955).

151. von Hausen, S. The role of vitamin C in the growth of higher plants. (Doctoral thesis.) *Ann. Acad. Sci. Fennicae Ser. A* **46**, (3) (1936).

152. Haworth, N., and Stacey, M. The chemistry of the immunopolysaccharides. *Ann. Rev. Biochem.* **17**, 97–114 (1948).

153. Hellriegel, H., and Wilfarth, H. Untersuchungen über die Stickstoffnahrung der Gramineen und Leguminosen. *Beilageheft Z. ver. Rübenzucker-Industrie deut. Reichs* (1888).

154. Helz, G. E., Baldwin, I. L., and Fred, E. B. Strain variations and host specificity of the root-nodule bacteria of the pea group. *J. Agr. Research* **35**, 1039–1055 (1927).

155. Heumann, W. Über Wesen und Bedeutung der Bakteroide in den Wurzelknöllchen der Erbse. *Naturwissenschaften* **39**, 66 (1952).

156. Heumann, W. Über das Abhängigkeitsverhältnis zwischen Hämoglobin-, Stärke-, Bakteroidvorkommen und Stickstoffbindung in den Wurzelknöllchen der Erbse. *Naturwissenschaften* **39**, 66–67 (1952).

157. Hiltner, L. Über die Bedeutung der Wurzelknöllchen von *Alnus glutinosa* für die Stickstoffernährung dieser Pflanze. *Landwirtsch. Vers. Sta.* **46**, 153–161 (1896).

158. Hiltner, L. Über Entstehung und physiologische Bedeutung der Wurzelknöllchen. B. Die Wurzelknöllchen der Erbsen und Elaeagnaceen. *Forstl. Naturw. Z.* **7**, 415–423 (1898).

159. Hiltner, L. Über die Ursachen welche die Grösse, Zahl, Stellung und Wirkung der Wurzelknöllchen der Leguminosen bedingen. *Arb. kaiserl. Gesundh. Biol. Abt.* **1**, 177–222 (1900).

160. Hiltner, L. Über die Impfung der Leguminosen mit Reinkulturen. *Deut. landwirtsch. Presse* **29**, 119–120 (1902).

161. Hiltner, L. Die Bindung von freiem Stickstoff durch das Zusammenwirken von Schizomyceten und von Eumyceten mit höheren Pflanzen. *In* "Handbuch der Technischen Mykologie" (F. Lafar, ed.), Vol. III, pp. 24–70. Fischer, Jena, 1904–1906.

162. Hino, S. Studies on the inhibition by carbon monoxide and nitrous oxide of anaerobic nitrogen fixation. *J. Biochem. (Tokyo)* **42**, 775–784 (1955).

163. Hino, S., and Wilson, P. W. Nitrogen fixation by a facultative bacillus. *J. Bacteriol.* **75**, 403–408 (1958).

164. Hirsch, M. L., and Cohen, G. N. Mise en évidence d'un systéme synthétisant la L-homosérine à partir de l'acide L-aspartique. *Biochim. et Biophys. Acta* **15**, 560–567 (1954).

165. Hoch, G. E., Little, H. N., and Burris, R. H. Hydrogen evolution from soybean root nodules. *Nature* **179**, 430–431 (1957).

166. Hoover, S. R., and Allison, F. E. The growth metabolism of *Rhizobium* with evidence of the interrelations between respiration and synthesis. *J. Biol. Chem.* **134**, 181–192 (1940).

654 A. I. VIRTANEN AND J. K. MIETTINEN

167. Hopkins, E. W., Peterson, W. H., and Fred, E. B. Glucuronic acid, a constituent of the gum of root nodule bacteria. *J. Am. Chem. Soc.* **53**, 306–309 (1931).

168. Horner, C. K., and Allison, F. E. Utilization of fixed nitrogen by *Azotobacter* and influence on nitrogen fixation. *J. Bacteriol.* **47**, 1–14 (1944).

169. Horner, C. K., and Burk, D. The nature and amount of extracellular nitrogen in *Azotobacter* cultures. *Trans. Third Comm. Intern. Soc. Soil Sci., New Brunswick, N.J. 1939 A*, pp. 168–174 (1939).

170. Hughes, D. Q., and Vincent, J. M. Serological studies of the root-nodule bacteria. III. Tests of neighbouring strains of the same species. *Proc. Linnean Soc. N. S. Wales* **67**, 142–152 (1942).

171. Humphrey, B. A. Occurrence of 4-O-methyl glucuronic acid in *Rhizobium* gums. *Nature* **184**, 1802 (1959).

172. Jensen, H. L. Nitrogen fixation in leguminous plants. VII. The nitrogen fixing activity of root nodule tissue in *Medicago* and *Trifolium*. *Proc. Linnean Soc. N. S. Wales* **72**, 265–291 (1948).

173. Jensen, H. L. The Azotobacteriaceae. *Bacteriol. Revs.* **18**, 195–214 (1954).

174. Jensen, H. L., and Spencer, D. The influence of molybdenum and vanadium on nitrogen fixation by *Clostridium butyricum* and related organisms. *Proc. Linnean Soc. N. S. Wales* **72**, 73–86 (1947).

175. Jensen, V. Nitrogen fixation by strains of *Aerobacter aerogenes*. *Physiol. Plantarum* **9**, 130–136 (1956).

176. Jensen, V. A new nitrogen fixing bacterium from a Danish watercourse. *Arch. Mikrobiol.* **29**, 348–353 (1958).

177. Jodin, C. R. Du rôle physiologique de l'azote faisant suite à un précédant travail présenté à l'Académie dans la séance du 28 avril 1862. *Acad. sci. Paris* **55**, 612–615 (1862).

177a. Johnstone, D. B., and Pfeffer, M. Aerobic fermentation of whey by a nitrogen-fixing strain of *Aerobacter aerogenes*. *Nature* **183**, 992–993 (1959).

178. Jones, F. R., and Tisdale, W. B. Effect of soil temperature upon the development of nodules on the roots of certain legumes. *J. Agr. Research* **22**, 17–31 (1921).

179. Jones, M. E., Spector, L., and Lipmann, F. Carbamyl phosphate, the carbamyl donor in enzymatic citrulline synthesis. *J. Am. Chem. Soc.* **77**, 819–820 (1955).

180. Jónsson, Ó. Belgjurtir. II (Die Ergebnisse neunjähriger Versuche mit Leguminosen). (Icelandic with German summary.) Aburdarsala rikisins. *Smarit No.* **11**, cited pp. 229, 230, 237 (1939).

181. Jordan, D. C. Studies on the legume root nodule bacteria. II. The production and behaviour of colonial mutants produced by x-ray irradiation. *Can. J. Botany* **30**, 125–130 (1952).

182. Jordan, D. C. Studies on the legume root nodule bacteria. III. Growth factor requirements for effective, ineffective, and parasitic strains. *Can. J. Botany* **30**, 693–700 (1952).

183. Jordan, D. C., and Garrard, E. H. Studies on the legume root nodule bacteria. I. Detection of effective and ineffective strains. *Can. J. Botany* **29**, 360–372 (1951).

184. Kamen, M. D., and Gest, H. Evidence for a nitrogenase system in the photosynthetic bacterium *Rhodospirillum rubrum*. *Science* **109**, 560 (1949).

185. Katznelson, H. Bacteriophage and the legume bacteria. *Trans. Third Comm. Intern. Soc. Soil Sci., New Brunswick, N.J. 1939 A*, pp. 43–48 (1939).

186. Keeler, R. F., and Varner, J. E. Tungstate as an antagonist of molybdate in *Azotobacter vinelandii. Arch. Biochem. Biophys.* **70**, 585–590 (1957).
187. Keilin, D. Haemoglobin in fungi. Occurrence of haemoglobin in yeast and the supposed stabilization of the oxygenated cytochrome oxidase. *Nature* **172**, 390–393 (1953).
188. Keilin, D., and Smith, J. D. Haemoglobin and nitrogen fixation in the root nodules of leguminous plants. *Nature* **159**, 692–694 (1947).
189. Keilin, D., and Tissières, A. Haemoglobin in mould: *Neurospora crassa* and *Penicillium notatum. Nature* **172**, 393–394 (1953).
190. Keilin, D., and Wang, Y. L. Haemoglobin in the root nodules of leguminous plants. *Nature* **155**, 227–229 (1945).
191. Keilin, D., and Wang, Y. L. Haemoglobin of gastrophilus larvae. Purification and properties. *Biochem. J.* **40**, 855–866 (1946).
192. Kleczkowska, J. A study of phage-resistant mutants of *Rhizobium trifolii. J. Gen. Microbiol.* **4**, 298–310 (1950).
193. Klüver, H. On a possible use of the root nodules of leguminous plants for research in neurology and psychiatry (preliminary report on a free porphyrin-hemoglobin system). *J. Psychol.* **25**, 331–356 (1948).
194. Kluyver, A. J., and Becking, J. H. Some observations on the nitrogen fixing bacteria of the genus *Beijerinckia* Derx. *Ann. Acad. Sci. Fennicae Ser. A II No.* **60**, 367–380 (1955).
195. Kluyver, A. J., and Verhoeven, W. Studies on true dissimilatory nitrate reduction. *Antonie van Leeuwenhoek J. Microbiol. Serol.* **20**, 241–262 (1954).
196. Kostytschew, S., Ryskaltschuk, A., and Schwezowa, O. Biochemische Untersuchungen über *Azotobacter agile. Z. physiol. Chem. Hoppe-Seyler's* **154**, 1–17 (1926).
197. Krasheninnikov, T. Assimilation of nitrogen gas by the root nodules of leguminous plants. (In Russian.) *Rec. d'articles sci.* dédié au Prof. C. Timirazeff, pp. 307–324, Moscow, 1916. Abstracted in *Physiol. Abstr.* **4**, 424 (1919).
198. Kubo, H. Über das Hämoprotein aus den Wurzelknöllchen von Leguminosen. *Acta Phytochim. (Japan)* **11**, 195–200 (1939).
198a. Lachmann, J. Über Knöllchen der Leguminosen. *Landwirtsch. Mitt. Z. kaiserl. Lehranst. Vers. Sta. Poppelsdorf (Bonn)* **37** (1858). [Secondary source: Fred, E. B., Baldwin, I. L., and McCoy, E. "Root Nodule Bacteria and Leguminous Plants," p. 52. Univ. of Wisconsin Press, Madison, 1932.]
199. Leaf, G., Gardner, I. C., and Bond, G. Observations on the composition and metabolism of the nitrogen-fixing root nodules of *Alnus. J. Exptl. Botany* **9**, 320–331 (1958).
200. Lee, S. B., Wilson, J. B., and Wilson, P. W. Mechanism of biological nitrogen fixation. X. Hydrogenase in cell-free extracts and intact cells of *Azotobacter. J. Biol. Chem.* **144**, 273–281 (1942).
201. Lee, S. B., and Wilson, P. W. Hydrogenase and nitrogen fixation by *Azotobacter. J. Biol. Chem.* **151**, 377–385 (1943).
201a. Lemberg, R., and Legge, J. W. "Hematin Compounds and Bile Pigments," Chapter X, p. 465. Interscience, New York, 1949.
202. Lemberg, R., Legge, J. W., and Lockwood, W. H. Coupled oxidation of ascorbic acid and haemoglobin. II–V. *Biochem. J.* **36**, 328–338, 339–352, 353–362, 363–379 (1941).
203. Levin, A. P., Funk, H. B., and Tendler, M. D. Vitamin B_{12}, rhizobia, and leguminous plants. *Science* **120**, 784 (1954).

204. Lieske, R. "Morphologie und Biologie der Strahlenpilze (Actinomyceten)." Borntraeger, Leipzig, 1921.
205. Lind, C. J., and Wilson, P. W. Mechanism of biological nitrogen fixation. VIII. Carbon monoxide as an inhibitor for nitrogen fixation by red clover. *J. Am. Chem. Soc.* **63**, 3511–3514 (1941).
206. Lind, C. J., and Wilson, P. W. Nitrogen fixation by *Azotobacter* in association with other bacteria. *Soil Sci.* **54**, 105–111 (1942).
207. Lindström, E. S., Burris, R. H., and Wilson, P. W. Nitrogen fixation by photosynthetic bacteria. *J. Bacteriol.* **58**, 313–316 (1949).
208. Lindström, E. S., Lewis, S. M., and Pinsky, M. J. Nitrogen fixation and hydrogenase in various bacterial species. *J. Bacteriol.* **61**, 481–487 (1951).
209. Lindström, E. S., Tove, S. R., and Wilson, P. W. Nitrogen fixation by the green and purple sulfur bacteria. *Science* **112**, 197–198 (1950).
210. Lipman, J. G. Experiments on the transformation and fixation of nitrogen by bacteria. *New Jersey Agr. Expt. Sta. Bull. No.* **24**, 217–285 (1903). Cf. reference (411).
211. Lipman, J. G., and Conybeare, A. B. Preliminary note on the balance sheet of plant nutrients in the United States. *New Jersey Agr. Expt. Sta. Bull. No.* **607**, 3–23 (1936).
212. Ludwig, C. A., and Allison, F. E. Some factors affecting nodule formation on seedlings of leguminous plants. *J. Am. Soc. Agron.* **27**, 895–902 (1935).
213. McCalla, T. M. Behaviour of legume bacteria in relation to exchangeable calcium and hydrogen ion concentration of the colloidal fraction of the soil. *Missouri Agr. Expt. Sta. Research Bull. No.* **256**, 1–44 (1937). [Secondary source: Allen, E. K., and Allen, O. N. Biochemical and symbiotic properties of the *Rhizobia. Bacteriol. Revs.* **14**, 273–330 (see p. 309) (1950).]
214. McCoy, E. Infection by *Bac. radicicola* in relation to the microchemistry of the host's cell walls. *Proc. Roy. Soc.* **B110**, 514–533 (1932).
215. McCoy, E. A cytological and histological study of the root nodules of the bean, *Phaseolus vulgaris* L. *Zentr. Bakteriol. Parasitenk. Abt. II*, **79**, 394–412 (1929).
216. Magee, W. E. Ph.D. thesis, University of Wisconsin, 1955. Cf. reference (75), p. 318.
217. Magee, W. E., and Burris, R. H. Fixation of nitrogen and utilization of combined nitrogen by *Nostoc muscorum. Am. J. Botany*, **41**, 777–782 (1954).
218. Magee, W. E., and Burris, R. H. Oxidative activity and nitrogen fixation in cell-free preparations from *Azotobacter vinelandii. J. Bacteriol.* **71**, 635–643 (1956).
219. McLuckie, J. Studies in symbiosis. IV. The root-nodules of *Casuarina cunninghamiana* and their physiological significance. *Proc. Linnean Soc. N. S. Wales* **48**, 194–205 (1923).
220. Manshard, E. Herkunft und Vorkommen von gebundenem Stickstoff in Boden und Gewässern. *In* "Handbuch der Pflanzenphysiologie—Encyclopedia of Plant Physiology" (W. Ruhland, ed.), Vol. 8, pp. 119–149. Springer, Berlin, 1958.
221. Medina, A., and Nicholas, D. J. D. Hyponitrite reductase in *Neurospora. Nature* **179**, 533–534 (1957).
222. Medina, A., and Nicholas, D. J. D. Metallo-enzymes in the reduction of nitrite to ammonia in *Neurospora. Biochim. et Biophys. Acta* **25**, 138–141 (1957).

223. Metcalfe, G., and Chayen, S. Nitrogen fixation by soil yeasts. *Nature* **174**, 841–842 (1954).

224. Meyer, D. R., and Anderson, A. J. Temperature and symbiotic nitrogen fixation. *Nature* **183**, 61 (1959).

225. Meyerhof, O., and Burk, D. Über die Fixation des Lufsticksoffs durch *Azotobacter*. *Z. physik. Chem. Leipzig* **A139**, 117–142 (1928).

226. Miettinen, J. K. Free amino acids in the pea plant (*Pisum sativum*). *Ann. Acad. Sci. Fennicae Ser. A II No.* **60**, 520–535 (1955).

227. Miettinen, J. K., and Virtanen, A. I. Kemiantutkimus-Säätiön vuosikertomus toimintavuodelta 1950. (In Finnish.) (Annual report of the Foundation for Chemical Research for the year 1950; see p. 5.)

228. Miettinen, J. K., and Virtanen, A. I. The free amino acids in the leaves, roots, and root nodules of the alder (*Alnus*). *Physiol. Plantarum* **5**, 540–557 (1952).

229. Miettinen, J. K., and Virtanen, A. I. Nitrogen metabolism of the alder (*Alnus*). The absence of arginase and presence of glutamic acid decarboxylase. *Acta Chem. Scand.* **7**, 289–296 (1953).

230. Miettinen, J. K., and Virtanen, A. I. Nitrogen metabolism of pea and alder. Transaminations of γ-aminobutyric acid and L(+)-citrulline with α-ketoglutaric acid. *Acta Chem. Scand.* **7**, 1243–1246 (1953).

231. Miller, C. O., Skoog, F., Okumura, F. S., Saltza, M. H. von, and Strong, F. M. Structure and synthesis of kinetin. *J. Am. Chem. Soc.* **77**, 2662–2663 (1955).

231a. Miller, C. O., Skoog, F., Saltza, M. H. von, and Strong, F. M. Kinetin, a cell division factor from DNA. *J. Am. Chem. Soc.* **77**, 1392–1393 (1955).

231b. Mitra, J., Mapes, M. O., and Steward, F. C. Growth and organized development of cultured cells. IV. The behavior of the nucleus. *Am. J. Bot.* **47**, 357–368 (1960).

231c. Mitra, J., and Steward, F. C. Growth induction in cultures of *Haplopappus gracilis*. II. The behavior of the nucleus. *Am. J. Bot.* **48**, 358–368 (1961).

232. Molnar, D. M., Burris, R. H., and Wilson, P. W. The effect of various gases on nitrogen fixation by *Azotobacter*. *J. Am. Chem. Soc.* **70**, 1713–1716 (1948).

233. Mowry, H. Symbiotic nitrogen fixation in the genus *Casuarina*. *Soil Sci.* **36**, 409–425 (1933).

234. Mozen, M. M., and Burris, R. H. The incorporation of N^{15}-labelled nitrous oxide by nitrogen-fixing agents. *Biochim. et Biophys. Acta* **14**, 577–578 (1954).

235. Mulder, E. G. Importance of molybdenum in the nitrogen metabolism of microorganisms and higher plants. *Plant and Soil* **1**, 94–119 (1948).

236. Mulder, E. G. Investigations on the nitrogen nutrition of pea plants. *Plant and Soil* **1**, 179–212 (1948).

237. Mulder, E. G. Molybdenum in relation to nitrogen fixation of leguminous crops. *Trans. Intern. Congr. Soil Sci. 4th Congr. Amsterdam 1950* **2**, 124–127 (1950).

238. Nason, A., and Takahashi, H. Inorganic nitrogen metabolism. *Ann. Rev. Microbiol.* **12**, 203–246 (1958).

239. Nemeth, G. A new nitrogen-fixing micro-organism producing a red pigment. *Nature* **183**, 1460–1461 (1959).

239a. Nemeth, G., Uresch, F., Fodor, G., and Láng, L. Chemical character of the pigments in a new nitrogen-fixing micro-organism. *Nature* **191**, 1413–1414 (1961).

240. Nemeth, G., and Matkovics, B. Ein neuer, ein rotes Pigment erzeugender und den atmosphärischen Stickstoff bindender Mikro-organismus. *Naturwissenschaften* **44**, 621 (1957).

241. Newton, J. W., Wilson, P. W., and Burris, R. H. Direct demonstration of ammonia as an intermediate in nitrogen fixation by *Azotobacter*. *J. Biol. Chem.* **204**, 445–451 (1953).

241a. Nicholas, D. J. D., Fisher, D. J., Redmond, W. J., and Wright, M. A. Some aspects of hydrogenase activity and nitrogen fixation in *Azotobacter* spp. and in *Clostridium pasteurianum*. *J. Gen. Microbiol.* **22**, 191–205 (1960).

241b. Nicholas, D. J. D., and Fisher, D. J. Nitrogen fixation in extracts of *Azotobacter vinelandii*. *Nature* **186**, 735–736 (1960).

242. Nicol, H., and Thornton, H. G. Competition between related strains of nodule bacteria and its influence on infection of the legume host. *Proc. Roy. Soc.* **B130**, 32–59 (1941).

243. Nielsen, N. Untersuchungen über biologische Stickstoffbindung. I. Der Wert verschiedener Aminosäuren als Stickstoffquelle für *Bacterium radicicola*. *Compt. rend. trav. lab. Carlsberg, Sér. physiol.* **23**, 115–134 (1940).

244. Nilsson, P. E., Korsan-Bengtsen, K., and Mellander, O. Amino acid content of leguminous proteins as affected by genetic and nutritional factors. I. *Arch. Mikrobiol.* **20**, 404–409 (1954).

245. Nilsson, R., Bjälfve, G., and Burström, D. Vitamin B₁ als Zuwachsfaktor für *Bact. radicicola*. I. and II. *Naturwissenschaften* **26**, 284, 661 (1938).

246. Nobbe, F., and Hiltner, L. Wodurch werden die knöllchenbesitzenden Leguminosen befähigt, den freien atmosphärischen Stickstoff für sich zu verwerten? *Landwirtsch. Vers. Sta.* **42**, 459–478 (1893).

247. Nobbe, F., and Hiltner, L. Über das Stickstoffsammlungsvermögen der Erlen und *Elaeagnaceen*. *Naturw. Z. Forst-u. Landwirtsch.* **2**, 366–369 (1904).

248. Nobbe, F., Schmid, E., Hiltner, L., and Hotter, E. Über die physiologische Bedeutung der Wurzelknöllchen von *Elaeagnus angustifolius*. *Landwirtsch. Vers. Sta.* **41**, 138–140 (1892).

248a. Norris, J. R., and Jensen, H. L. Calcium requirements of *Azotobacter*. *Nature* **180**, 1493–1494 (1957).

249. Novak, R., and Wilson, P. W. The utilization of nitrogen in hydroxylamine and oximes by *Azotobacter vinelandii*. *J. Bacteriol.* **55**, 517–524 (1948).

250. Nowotny-Mieczyńska, A. Some factors influencing the pigmentation of nodules of leguminous plants. (In Polish with English summary.) *Acta Microbiol. Polon.* **1**, 43–52 (1952).

251. Nutman, P. S. Genetical factors concerned in the symbiosis of clover and nodule bacteria. *Nature* **157**, 463–465 (1946).

252. Nutman, P. S. Physiological studies on nodule formation. I. The relation between nodulation and lateral root formation in red clover. *Ann. Botany (London)* **12**, 81–96 (1948).

253. Nutman, P. S. Physiological studies on nodule formation. II. The influence of delayed inoculation on the rate of nodulation in red clover. *Ann. Botany (London)* **13**, 261–283 (1949).

254. Nutman, P. S. A discussion on symbiosis involving microorganism. Host factors influencing infection and nodule development in leguminous plants. *Proc. Roy. Soc.* **B139**, 176–185 (1952).

255. Nutman, P. S. Studies on the physiology of nodule formation. III. Experiments on the excision of root-tips and nodules. *Ann. Botany (London)* **16**, 79–101 (1952).

256. Nutman, P. S. Studies on the physiology of nodule formation. IV. The mutual inhibitory effects on nodule production of plants grown in association. *Ann. Botany (London)* 17, 95–126 (1953).

257. Nutman, P. S. Symbiotic effectiveness in nodulated red clover. II. A major gene for ineffectiveness in the host. *Heredity (London)* 8, 47–60 (1954).

258. Nutman, P. S. The influence of the legume in root-nodule symbiosis. A comparative study of host determinants and functions. *Biol. Revs. Cambridge Phil. Soc.* 31, 109–151 (1956).

259. Nutman, P. S. Symbiotic effectiveness in nodulated red clover. III. *Heredity (London)* 11, 157–173 (1957).

260. Nutman, P. S. Studies on the physiology of nodule formation. V. Further experiments on the stimulating and inhibitory effects of root secretions. *Ann. Botany (London)* 21, 321–337 (1957).

261. Orcutt, F. S., and Fred, E. B. Light intensity as an inhibiting factor in the fixation of atmospheric nitrogen by Manchu soybeans. *J. Am. Soc. Agron.* 27, 550–558 (1935).

261a. Parker, C. A. Effect of oxygen on the fixation of nitrogen by *Azotobacter*. *Nature* 173, 780–781 (1954).

261b. Parker, C. A., and Scutt, P. B. The effect of oxygen on nitrogen fixation by *Azotobacter*. *Biochim. et Biophys. Acta* 38, 230–238 (1960).

262. Peirce, G. J. The root-tubercles of bur clover (*Medicago denticulata* Willd.) and some other leguminous plants. *Proc. Calif. Acad. Sci.* [3] *Bot.* 2, 295–328 (1902).

262a. Pengra, R. M., and Wilson, P. W. Physiology of nitrogen fixation by *Aerobacter aerogenes*. *J. Bacteriol.* 75, 21–25 (1958).

263. Pethica, B. A., Roberts, E. R., and Winter, E. R. S. Studies in the biological fixation of nitrogen. I. Inhibition in *Azotobacter vinelandii* by hydroxylamine. *Biochim. et Biophys. Acta* 14, 85–99 (1954).

264. Pfeiffer, H. Die Stickstoffsammlung und die aus ihr zu ziehenden Rückschlüsse auf die Formumgestaltung der Knöllchenbakterien. *Zentr. Bakteriol. Parasitenk. Abt. II*, 73, 28–57 (1928).

265. Pietz, J. Beitrag zur Physiologie des Wurzelknöllchenbakteriums. *Zentr. Bakteriol. Parasitenk. Abt. II*, 99, 1–32 (1938).

266. Pine, M. J., and Barker, H. A. Studies on the methane bacteria. XI. Fixation of atmospheric nitrogen by *Methanobacterium omelianskii*. *J. Bacteriol.* 68, 589–591 (1954).

267. Praźmowski, A. Die Wurzelknöllchen der Erbse. *Landwirtsch. Vers. Sta.* 37, 161–238 (1890).

268. Proctor, M. H., and Wilson, P. W. Nitrogen fixation by gram-negative bacteria. *Nature* 182, 891 (1958).

269. Purchase, H. F. Nodule bacteria in the rhizosphere. *Rept. Rothamsted Exptl. Sta.* 66–67 (1953).

270. Purchase, H. F., and Nutman, P. S. Studies on the physiology of nodule formation. VI. The influence of bacterial numbers in the rhizosphere on nodule initiation. *Ann. Botany (London)* 21, 439–454 (1957).

271. Quispel, A. Symbiotic nitrogen fixation in non-leguminous plants. III. Experiments on the growth *in vitro* of the endophyte of *Alnus glutinosa*. *Acta Botan. Neerl.* 4, 671–689 (1955).

271a. Radley, M. Gibberellin-like substances in plants. *Nature* 191, 684–685 (1961).

271b. Reisenauer, H. M. Cobalt in nitrogen fixation by a legume. *Nature* 186, 375–376 (1960).

272. Richardson, D. A., Jordan, D. C., and Garrard, E. H. Influence of combined nitrogen on nodulation and nitrogen fixation by *Rhizobium meliloti*. *Can. J. Plant Sci.* **37**, 205–214 (1957).

273. Richmond, J. E., and Salomon, K. Biosynthesis of hemin in soybean nodules. *Biochim. et Biophys. Acta* **17**, 48–55 (1955).

274. Roberg, M. Weitere Untersuchungen über die Stickstoffernährung der Erle. *Ber. deut. botan. Ges.* **52**, 54–64 (1934).

275. Roberts, E. R. Some observations on the chemistry of biological nitrogen fixation. *Symposia Soc. Exptl. Biol. No.* **13**, 24–41 (1959).

276. Roberts, E. R., and Wilson, T. G. G. Nitrogen fixation by soil yeasts. *Nature* **174**, 841–842 (1954).

277. Robinson, R. S. The antagonistic action of the by-products of several soil microorganisms on the activities of the legume bacteria. *Proc. Soil Sci. Soc. Am.* **10**, 206–210 (1945).

277a. Roponen, I., and Virtanen, A. I. Unpublished data.

278. Rosenblum, E. D., and Wilson, P. W. Fixation of isotopic nitrogen by *Clostridium*. *J. Bacteriol.* **57**, 413–414 (1949).

279. Rosenblum, E. D., and Wilson, P. W. Molecular hydrogen and nitrogen fixation by *Clostridium*. *J. Bacteriol.* **59**, 83–91 (1950).

280. Rosenblum, E. D., and Wilson, P. W. The utilization of nitrogen in various compounds by *Clostridium pasteurianum*. *J. Bacteriol.* **61**, 475–480 (1951).

281. Roy, A. B., and Mukherjee, M. K. A new type of nitrogen-fixing bacterium. *Nature* **180**, 236 (1957).

282. Rudin, P. E. Versuche zur Physiologie der Knöllchenbildung bei *Pisum sativum* L. Ph.D. thesis, University of Basle, 1956.

283. Saris, N.-E., and Virtanen, A. I. On hydroxylamine compounds in *Azotobacter* cultures. I. Formation of hydroxylamine compounds. *Acta Chem. Scand.* **11**, 1438–1440 (1957).

284. Saris, N.-E., and Virtanen, A. I. On hydroxylamine compounds in *Azotobacter* cultures. II. On the chemical nature of the bound hydroxylamine fraction in *Azotobacter* cultures. *Acta Chem. Scand.* **11**, 1440–1442 (1957).

285. Savioja, T., and Miettinen, J. K. Influence of calcium upon the uptake of orthophosphate by pea roots. *Suomen Kemistilehti* **B33**, 78–80 (1960).

286. Schaede, R. Die Knöllchen der advertiven Wasserwurzeln von *Neptunia oleracea* und ihre Bakteriensymbiose. *Planta* **31**, 1–21 (1940).

287. Scharrer, K., and Fast, H. Untersuchungen über die dem Boden durch die Niederschläge zugeführten Pflanzennährstoffe. *Z. Pflanzenernähr. Düng. u. Bodenk.* **55** (**100**), 97–106 (1951).

288. Schropp, W. Bor und Leguminosen. *Arb. u. Ber. Süddeut. Vers.-u. Forschungsanstalt Milchwirtsch.*, Band **II**, 83–186 (1957).

289. Shug, A. L., Hamilton, P. B., and Wilson, P. W. The role of molybdenum and flavine in hydrogenase. *J. Am. Chem. Soc.* **76**, 3355–3356 (1954).

290. Shug, A. L., Hamilton, P. B., and Wilson, P. W. Hydrogenase and nitrogen fixation. *In* "Inorganic Nitrogen Metabolism" (W. D. McElroy and B. Glass, eds.), pp. 344–360. Johns Hopkins Press, Baltimore, Maryland, 1956.

290a. Silver, W. S., and McElroy, W. D. Enzyme studies on nitrate and nitrite mutants of *Neurospora*. *Arch. Biochem. Biophys.* **51**, 379–394 (1954).

291. Sironval, C. Relation between chlorophyll metabolism and nodule formation in soya bean. *Nature* **181**, 1272–1273 (1958).

292. Sironval, C. Day-length and hematin compounds in plants. *Nature* **182**, 1170–1171 (1958).

293. Sisler, F. D., and ZoBell, C. E. Hydrogen utilization by some marine sulfate-reducing bacteria. *J. Bacteriol.* **62**, 117–127 (1951).

294. Skinner, C. E. The fixation of nitrogen by *Bacterium aerogenes* and related species. *Soil Sci.* **25**, 195–205 (1928).

295. Smith, J. D. The concentration and distribution of haemoglobin in the root nodules of leguminous plants. *Biochem. J.* **44**, 585–591 (1949).

296. Spencer, D., Takahashi, H., and Nason, A. Relationship of nitrite and hydroxyl-amine reductases to nitrate assimilation and nitrogen fixation in *Azotobacter agile. J. Bacteriol.* **73**, 553–562 (1957).

297. Starkey, R. L., and De, P. K. A new species of *Azotobacter. Soil Sci.* **47**, 329–343 (1939).

298. Sternberg, H., and Virtanen, A. I. Studies on the absorption spectrum of leghemoglobin, especially of leghemiglobin. *Acta Chem. Scand.* **6**, 1342–1352 (1952).

299. Stevenson, F. J. On the presence of fixed ammonium in rocks. *Science* **130**, 221–222 (1959).

299a. Steward, F. C., and Shantz, E. M. The chemical induction of growth in plant tissue cultures. *In* "The Chemistry and Mode of Action of Plant Growth Substances" (R. L. Wain and F. Wightman, eds.), pp. 165–186. Academic Press, New York, 1956.

300. Strong, T. H. The influence of host plant species in relation to the effectiveness of the *Rhizobium* of clovers. *J. Council Sci. Ind. Research* **10**, 12–16 (1937).

301. Suzuki, N., and Suzuki, S. Hydroxylamine reduction and hydrazine oxidation by *Azotobacter vinelandii. Sci. Repts. Tôhoku Univ. Fourth Ser.* **20**, 195–201 (1945).

302. Takahashi, H., and Nason, A. Tungstate as a competitive inhibitor of molybdate in nitrate assimilation and in N_2 fixation by *Azotobacter. Biochim. et Biophys. Acta* **23**, 433–435 (1957).

303. Taubert, H. Über den Infektionsvorgang und die Entwicklung der Knöllchen bei *Alnus glutinosa* Gaertn. *Planta* **48**, 135–156 (1956).

304. Theorell, H., and Ehrenberg, A. Spectrophotometric, magnetic and titrimetric studies on the heme-linked groups in myoglobin. *Acta Chem. Scand.* **5**, 823–848 (1951).

305. Thimann, K. V. On the physiology of the formation of nodules on legume roots. *Proc. Natl. Acad. Sci. U.S.* **22**, 511–514 (1936).

306. Thimann, K. V. The physiology of nodule formation. *Trans. Third Comm. Intern. Soc. Soil Sci. New Brunswick, N.J. 1939 A*, pp. 24–28 (1939).

307. Thorne, D. W., Neal, O. R., and Walker, R. H. Physiological studies on *Rhizobium*. VIII. The respiratory quotient. *Arch. Mikrobiol.* **7**, 477–487 (1936).

308. Thornton, G. D. The effect of nitrogen fertilization on the nitrogen nutrition of legumes. *Iowa State Coll. J. Sci.* **22**, 84–86 (1948).

309. Thornton, H. G. The influence of the number of nodule bacteria applied to the seed upon nodule formation in legumes. *J. Agr. Sci.* **19**, 373–381 (1929).

310. Thornton, H. G. Role of the young lucerne plant in determining the infection of the root by the nodule-forming bacteria. *Proc. Roy. Soc.* **B104**, 481–492 (1929).

311. Thornton, H. G. The influence of the host plant in inducing parasites in luzerne and clover nodules. *Proc. Roy. Soc.* **B106**, 110–122 (1930).

312. Thornton, H. G. The early development of the root nodule of lucerne (*Medicago sativa* L.). *Ann. Botany (London)* **44**, 385–392 (1930).

313. Thornton, H. G. The action of sodium nitrate upon the infection of lucerne root-hairs by nodule bacteria. *Proc. Roy. Soc.* **B119**, 474–492 (1936).

314. Thornton, H. G. The present state of our ignorance concerning the nodules of leguminous plants. *Sci. Progr.* **31**, 236–249 (1936).

315. Thornton, H. G. A suggested explanation of the "inefficiency" of certain strains of *Rhizobia. Trans. Third Comm. Intern. Soc. Soil Sci. New Brunswick, N.J. 1939 A*, pp. 20–23 (1939).

316. Thornton, H. G. Effective and ineffective strains of legume nodule bacteria. *Nature* **156**, 654–655 (1945).

317. Thornton, H. G. Problems presented by nodule bacteria and legume host. *Agr. Progr.* **24**, Part II, 102–107 (1949).

318. Thornton, H. G., de Alencar, J., and Smith, F. B. Some effects of *Streptomyces albus* and *Penicillium* spp. on *Rhizobium meliloti. Soil Sci. Soc. Am. Proc.* **14**, 188–191 (1949).

319. Thornton, H. G., and Gangulee, N. Life-cycle of the nodule organism. *Bacillus radicicola* (Beij.) in soil and its relation to the infection of the host plant. *Proc. Roy. Soc.* **B99**, 427–451 (1926).

320. Thornton, H. G., and Kleczkowski, J. Use of antisera to identify nodules produced by the inoculation of legumes in the field. *Nature* **166**, 1118–1119, (1950).

321. Thornton, H. G., and Nicol, H. Further evidence upon the nitrogen uptake of grass grown with lucerne. *J. Agr. Sci.* **24**, 540–543 (1934).

322. Thornton, H. G., and Nicol, H. Stimulation of root-hair growth in legumes by sterile secretions of nodule bacteria. *Nature* **137**, 494–495 (1936).

322a. Thorogood, E. Oxygenated ferroheme proteins from soybean nodules. *Science* **126**, 1011–1012 (1957).

323. Tove, S. R., Niss, H. F., and Wilson, P. W. Fixation of N_2^{15} by excised nodules of leguminous plants. *J. Biol. Chem.* **184**, 77–82 (1950).

324. Towers, G. H. N., and Steward, F. C. The keto acids of the tulip (*Tulipa gesneriana*) with special reference to the keto analog of γ-methyleneglutamic acid. *J. Am. Chem. Soc.* **76**, 1959–1961 (1954).

325. Uemura, S. Studies on the root nodules of alders (*Alnus* spp.). IV. Experiment on the isolation of actinomycetes from alder nodules. *Bull. Govt. Forestry Expt. Sta.* (*Japan*) **52**, 1–18 (1952). (English summary.) [Secondary source: cf. reference (6).]

326. Umbreit, W. W., and Burris, R. H. Composition of soybean nodules and root nodule bacteria. *Soil Sci.* **45**, 111–126 (1938).

327. Valle, E., and Virtanen, A. I. Unpublished.

327a. Valle, E., and Virtanen, A. I. On the uptake and assimilation of D- and L-amino acids by pea and barley plants. *Suomen Kemistilehti* **B33**, 201–204 (1960).

327b. Vartiovaara, U. Untersuchungen über die Leguminosen-Bakterien und -Pflanzen. XII. Über die Stickstoff-haushalt des Hafers bei feldmässigen Mischkulturen zusammen mit der Erbse. *Z. Pflanzenernähr. Düng. u. Bodenk.* **A31**, 253–259 (1933).

328. Vartiovaara, U. Investigations on the root-nodule bacteria of leguminous plants. XXI. The growth of the root-nodule organisms and inoculated peas at low temperatures. *J. Agr. Sci.* **27**, Part IV, 626–637 (1937).

329. Vartiovaara, U. The associative growth of cellulose-decomposing fungi and nitrogen-fixing bacteria. *Maataloustieteellinen Aikakauskirja* **10**, 241–264 (1938).

330. Virtanen, A. I. Über die Einwirkung der Bodenazidität auf das Wachstum und die Zusammensetzung der Leguminosepflanzen. *Biochem. Z.* **193**, 300–312 (1928).

331. Virtanen, A. I. Om växternas kvävenäring. *Nordiske Kjemikermøte 4th Meeting Oslo 1932*, pp. 137–151 (1933).

332. Virtanen, A. I. "Cattle Fodder and Human Nutrition." Cambridge Univ. Press, London and New York, 1938.

333. Virtanen, A. I. "AIV-Järjestelmä karjanruokinnan perustana." (AIV System as the Basis of Cattle Feeding.) Pellervo-Seura, Helsinki, 1943.

334. Virtanen, A. I. Significance of haemoglobin ⇌ methaemoglobin in the N-fixation by leguminous root nodules. *Suomen Kemistilehti* **B18**, 38 (1945).

335. Virtanen, A. I. Roter Farbstoff in den Wurzelknöllchen von Hülsenpflanzen. *Sitzber. finn. Akad. Wiss.*, 12 Jan., 1945.

336. Virtanen, A. I. Symbiotic nitrogen fixation. *Nature* **155**, 747–748 (1945).

337. Virtanen. A. I. Kemiantutkimus-Säätiön vuosikertomus toimintavuodelta 1946. (In Finish.) (Annual report of the Foundation for Chemical Research for the year 1946; see pp. 1–13.)

338. Virtanen, A. I. The biology and chemistry of nitrogen fixation by legume bacteria. *Biol. Revs. Cambridge Phil. Soc.* **22**, 239–269 (1947).

339. Virtanen, A. I. Biological nitrogen fixation. *Ann. Rev. Microbiol.* **2**, 485–506 (1948).

340. Virtanen, A. I. Some aspects of biological nitrogen fixation. *Ann. Acad. Sci. Fennicae Ser. A II No. 43* (1952).

341. Virtanen, A. I. Molecular nitrogen fixation and nitrogen cycle in nature. *Tellus* **4**, 304–306 (1952).

342. Virtanen, A. I. Atmosphärischer Stickstoff als Aufrechthalter des Lebens auf der Erde. *Angew. Chem.* **65**, 1–11 (1953).

343. Virtanen, A. I. Neue Amino- und Ketosäuren in grünen Pflanzen und die Biosynthese der Aminosäuren. *Angew. Chem.* **67**, 381–388 (1955).

344. Virtanen, A. I. Biological nitrogen fixation. *Proc. Intern. Congr. Biochem. 3rd Congr. Brussels 1955*, pp. 425–433 (1956).

344a. Virtanen, A. I. Some aspects of amino acid synthesis in plants and related subjects. *Ann. Rev. Plant Physiol.* **12**, 1–12 (1961).

345. Virtanen, A. I. Investigations on nitrogen fixation by the alder. II. Associated culture of spruce and inoculated alder without combined nitrogen. *Physiol. Plantarum* **10**, 164–169 (1957).

346. Virtanen, A. I., and Alfthan, M. New α-keto acids in green plants. α-Ketopimelic acid, γ-hydroxy-α-ketopimelic acid, and hydroxypyruvic acid in *Asplenium septentrionale*, α-ketoadipic acid in germinating pea seeds. *Acta Chem. Scand.* **8**, 1720–1721 (1954).

347. Virtanen, A. I., and Alfthan, M. New α-keto acids in green plants. II. β-Hydroxy- and γ-hydroxy-α-ketobutyric acid in cowberries. *Acta Chem. Scand.* **9**, 188–190 (1955).

348. Virtanen, A. I., Arhimo, A. A., Sundman, J., and Jännes, L. Vorkommen und Bedeutung der Oxalessigsäure in grünen Pflanzen. *J. prakt. Chem.* **162**, 71–90 (1943).

349. Virtanen, A. I., Arhimo, A. A., and Suomalainen, H. Estimation and occurrence of keto acids in green plants. *Nature* **144**, 597 (1939).

350. Virtanen, A. I., Erkama, J., and Linkola, H. On the relation between nitrogen fixation and leghaemoglobin content of leguminous root nodules. II. *Acta Chem. Scand.* **1**, 861–870 (1947).

351. Virtanen, A. I., and Hakala, M. Anaerobic nitrogen fixation and formation of oxime nitrogen. *Acta Chem. Scand.* **3**, 1044–1049 (1949).
352. Virtanen, A. I., and von Hausen, S. Untersuchungen über die Leguminose-Bakterien und -Pflanzen. IX. Die Ausnutzung verschiedener Stickstoffverbindungen sowie des in Wurzelknöllchen gesammelten Stickstoffs durch Leguminospflanzen. *Biochem. Z.* **232**, 1–14 (1931).
353. Virtanen, A. I., and von Hausen, S. Excretion of nitrogenous compounds from the root nodules of leguminous plants. *Nature* **135**, 184 (1935).
354. Virtanen, A. I., and von Hausen, S. Investigations on the root nodule bacteria of leguminous plants. XVI. Effect of air-content of the medium on the function of the nodule and on the excretion of nitrogen. *J. Agr. Sci.* **25**, 278–289 (1935).
355. Virtanen, A. I., and von Hausen, S. Investigations on the root nodule bacteria of leguminous plants. XVII. Continued investigations on the effect of air content of the medium on the development and function of the nodule. *J. Agr. Sci.* **26**, Part II, 281–287 (1936).
356. Virtanen, A. I., von Hausen, S., and Karström, H. Untersuchungen über die Leguminose-Bakterien und -Pflanzen. XII. Die Ausnutzung der aus den Wurzelknöllchen der Leguminosen herausdiffundierten Stickstoffverbindungen durch Nichtleguminosen. *Biochem. Z.* **258**, 106–117 (1933).
357. Virtanen, A. I., von Hausen, S., and Laine, T. Investigations on the root nodule bacteria of leguminous plants. XIX. Influence of various factors on the excretion of nitrogenous compounds from the nodules. *J. Agr. Sci.* **27**, 332–348 (1937).
358. Virtanen, A. I., von Hausen, S., and Laine, T. Investigations on the root nodule bacteria of leguminous plants. XX. Excretion of nitrogen in associated cultures of legumes. *J. Agr. Sci.* **27**, 584–610 (1937).
359. Virtanen, A. I., and Holmberg, A.-M. The quantitative determination of molecular nitrogen fixed by pea plants in pot cultures and in field experiments. *Suomen Kemistilehti* **B31**, 98–102 (1958).
360. Virtanen, A. I., and Järvinen, H. On the formation of bound hydroxylamine in *Azotobacter. Acta Chem. Scand.* **5**, 220–226 (1951).
361. Virtanen, A. I., and Jorma, J. Changes in the ascorbic acid content of green plants in the dark. *Suomen Kemistilehti* **B18**, 50–52 (1945).
362. Virtanen, A. I., Jorma, J., and Laine, T. The iron and haemin content of leghaemoglobin. *Suomen Kemistilehti* **B18**, 49 (1945).
363. Virtanen, A. I., Jorma, J., Linkola, H., and Linnasalmi, A. On the relation between nitrogen fixation and leghaemoglobin content of leguminous root nodules. *Acta Chem. Scand.* **1**, 90–111 (1947).
364. Virtanen, A. I., Kemppi, A., and Salmenoja, E.-L. Reduction of hydroxylamine in the root nodules of leguminous plants. *Acta Chem. Scand.* **8**, 1729–1730 (1954).
365. Virtanen, A. I., and Laine, T. Chemical nature of the amino acids excreted by leguminous root nodules. *Nature* **136**, 756 (1935).
366. Virtanen, A. I., and Laine, T. Investigations on the root nodule bacteria of leguminous plants. XVIII. Breakdown of proteins by the root nodule bacteria. *Biochem. J.* **30**, 377–381 (1936).
367. Virtanen, A. I., and Laine, T. Fixation of nitrogen in the root nodules. *Suomen Kemistilehti* **B9**, 5 (1936).
368. Virtanen, A. I., and Laine, T. N-Fixation by excised root nodules. *Suomen Kemistilehti* **B10**, 24 (1937).

369. Virtanen, A. I., and Laine, T. Oxalacetic acid in leguminous plants. *Suomen Kemistilehti* **B10**, 35 (1937).

370. Virtanen, A. I., and Laine, T. Biological synthesis of amino acids from atmospheric nitrogen. *Nature* **141**, 748–749 (1938).

371. Virtanen, A. I., and Laine, T. Investigations on the root nodule bacteria of leguminous plants. XXII. The excretion products of root nodules. The mechanism of N-fixation. *Biochem. J.* **33**, 412–427 (1939).

372. Virtanen, A. I., and Laine, T. Über die Umaminierung in grünen Pflanzen. *Biochem. Z.* **308**, 213–215 (1941).

373. Virtanen, A. I., and Laine, T. N-Fixation by free-living legume bacteria. *Suomen Kemistilehti* **B18**, 39 (1945).

374. Virtanen, A. I., and Linkola, H. Über die Aktivität verschiedener Stämme der Leguminosebakterien. *Suomen Kemistilehti* **B17**, 22 (1944).

375. Virtanen, A. I., and Linkola, H. Competition of *Rhizobium* strains in nodule-formation. *Antonie van Leeuwenhoek J. Microbiol. Serol.* **12**, 65–77 (1947).

376. Virtanen, A. I., and Linkola, H. On the antibacterial effect of spore-forming soil bacteria on the legume bacteria. *Suomen Kemistilehti* **B21**, 12–13 (1948).

377. Virtanen, A. I., and Linkola, H. Unpublished.

378. Virtanen, A. I., Linkola, H., Hakala, M., and Rautanen, N. Glutamic acid among the excretion products of leguminous root nodules. *Suomen Kemistilehti* **B19**, 83 (1946).

379. Virtanen, A. I., and Lundbom, S. The growth of *Clostridium pasteurianum* in synthetic nutrient solution. *Acta Chem. Scand.* **8**, 870–871 (1954).

380. Virtanen, A. I., and Miettinen, J. K. Formation of biliverdin from legcholeglobin, the green pigment in leguminous root nodules. *Acta Chem. Scand.* **3**, 17–21 (1949).

381. Virtanen, A. I., and Miettinen, J. K. Free amino-acids in the leaves, roots and root nodules of the alder (*Alnus*). *Nature* **170**, 283 (1952).

382. Virtanen, A. I., and Miettinen, J. K. The effect of hemoglobin on the formation of ammonia from hydrazine. *Suomen Kemistilehti* **B31**, 192 (1958).

383. Virtanen, A. I., Miettinen, J. K., and Kunttu, H. α-Ketoacids in green plants. *Acta Chem. Scand.* **7**, 38–44 (1953).

384. Virtanen, A. I., Moisio, T., Allison, R. M., and Burris, R. H. Fixation of molecular nitrogen by excised nodules of the alder. *Acta Chem. Scand.* **8**, 1730–1731 (1954).

384a. Virtanen, A. I., Moisio, T., and Burris, R. H. Fixation of nitrogen by nodules excised from illuminated and darkened pea plants. *Acta Chem. Scand.* **9**, 184–186 (1955).

385. Virtanen, A. I., Mustakallio, H., and Strandström, H. Einwirkung von Kohlenmonoxyd auf die anaerobe Stickstoffbindung. *Suomen Kemistilehti* **B26**, 6–9 (1953).

386. Virtanen, A. I., Nordlund, M., and Hollo, E. Fermentation of sugar by the root nodule bacteria. *Biochem. J.* **28**, 796–802 (1934).

387. Virtanen, A. I., and Saastamoinen, S. Über die Stickstoffbindung bei Erlen (*Alnus*). *Acta Chem. Fennica* **B6**, 57 (1933).

388. Virtanen, A. I., and Saastamoinen, S. Untersuchungen über die Stickstoffbindung bei der Erle. *Biochem. Z.* **284**, 72–85 (1936).

389. Virtanen, A. I., and Santaoja, I.-M. Kemiantutkimus-Säätiön vuosikertomus toimintavuodelta 1959. (In Finnish.) (Annual report of the Foundation for Chemical Research for the year 1959.)

390. Virtanen, A. I., and Santaoja, I.-M. Unpublished.
391. Virtanen, A. I., and Saubert-von Hausen, S. A method for determining in pea cultures the amount of molecular nitrogen fixed and the amount of combined nitrogen taken up from the soil. *Plant and Soil* **4**, 171–177 (1952).
392. Virtanen, A. I., and Tietäväinen, A. Die Atmung der Leguminosen Wurzelknöllchen in Beziehung zu deren Hämoglobingehalt. *Suomen Kemistilehti* **B26**, 1–5 (1953).
393. Waksman, S. A. "Soil Microbiology." Wiley, New York, 1952.
394. Ward, H. M. On the tubercular swellings on the roots of *Vicia faba*. *Phil. Trans. Roy. Soc. (London)* **B178**, 539–562 (1887).
395. Ward, H. M. On the tubercles on the roots of leguminous plants with special reference to the pea and bean. *Proc. Roy. Soc.* **46**, 431–443 (1889).
396. Watanabe, A. Production in cultural solution of some amino acids by the atmospheric nitrogen-fixing blue-green algae. *Arch. Biochem. Biophys.* **34**, 50–55 (1951).
397. Watanabe, A., Nishigaki, S., and Konishi, C. Effect of nitrogen fixing blue-green algae on the growth of rice plants. *Nature* **168**, 748–749 (1951).
398. West, P. M., and Wilson, P. W. Biotin as a growth stimulant for the nodule bacteria. *Enzymologia* **8**, 152–162 (1940).
399. Whiting, A. L. A biochemical study of nitrogen in certain legumes. *Illinois Univ. Agr. Expt. Sta. Bull. No.* **179**, 471–542 (1915).
400. Wieland, H. Über den Verlauf der Oxydationsvorgänge. *Ber.* **55**, 3639–3648 (1922).
401. Wieringa, K. T., and Bakhuis, J. A. Chromatography as a means of selecting effective strains of *Rhizobia*. *Plant and Soil* **8**, 254–262 (1957).
402. Williams, A. E., and Burris, R. H. Nitrogen fixation by blue-green algae and their nitrogenous composition. *Am. J. Botany* **39**, 340–342 (1952).
403. Wilson, A. T. Surface of the ocean as a source of air-borne nitrogenous material and other plant nutrients. *Nature* **184**, 99–101 (1959).
404. Wilson, J. B., and Wilson, P. W. Biotin as a growth factor for rhizobia. *J. Bacteriol.* **43**, 329–341 (1942).
405. Wilson, P. W. Symbiotic nitrogen-fixation by the Leguminosae. *Botan. Rev.* **3**, 365–399 (1937).
406. Wilson, P. W. Respiratory enzyme systems in symbiotic nitrogen fixation. I. The "resting cell" technique as a method for study of bacterial metabolism. *J. Bacteriol.* **35**, 601–623 (1938).
407. Wilson, P. W. "The Biochemistry of Symbiotic Nitrogen Fixation." Univ. of Wisconsin Press, Madison, 1940.
408. Wilson, P. W. Biological nitrogen fixation. *In* "Bacterial Physiology" (C. H. Werkman and P. W. Wilson, eds.), pp. 467–499. Academic Press, New York, 1951.
409. Wilson, P. W. The comparative biochemistry of nitrogen fixation. *Advances in Enzymol.* **13**, 345–375 (1952).
410. Wilson, P. W. On the sources of nitrogen of vegetation, etc. *Bacteriol. Revs.* **21**, 215–226 (1957).
411. Wilson, P. W. Asymbiotic nitrogen fixation. In "Handbuch der Pflanzenphysiologie—Encyclopedia of Plant Physiology" (W. Ruhland, ed.), Vol. 8, pp. 9–47. Springer, Berlin, 1958.
412. Wilson, P. W., and Burris, R. H. Biological nitrogen fixation—a reappraisal. *Ann. Rev. Microbiol.* **7**, 415–432 (1953).

412a. Wilson, P. W., and Burris, R. H. Fixation of nitrogen by cell-free extracts of micro-organisms. *Science* **131**, 1321 (1960).

413. Wilson, P. W., Burris, R. H., and Lind, C. J. The dissociation constant in nitrogen fixation by *Azotobacter*. *Proc. Natl. Acad. Sci. U.S.* **28**, 243–250 (1942).

414. Wilson, P. W., and Burton, J. C. Excretion of nitrogen by leguminous plants. *J. Agr. Sci.* **28**, 307–323 (1938).

415. Wilson, P. W., Burton, J. C., and Bond, V. S. Effect of species of host plant on nitrogen fixation in *Melilotus*. *J. Agr. Research* **55**, 619–629 (1937).

416. Wilson, P. W., Hull, J. F., and Burris, R. H. Competition between free and combined nitrogen in nutrition of *Azotobacter*. *Proc. Natl. Acad. Sci. U.S.* **29**, 289–294 (1943).

417. Wilson, P. W., and Umbreit, W. W. Mechanism of symbiotic nitrogen fixation. III. Hydrogen as a specific inhibitor. *Arch. Mikrobiol.* **8**, 440–457 (1937).

418. Wilson, P. W., and Umbreit, W. W. Fixation and transfer of nitrogen in the soybean. *Zentr. Bakteriol. Parasitenk. Abt. II*, **96**, 402–411 (1937).

419. Wilson, P. W., and Wagner, F. C. Combined nitrogen and the nitrogen fixation process in leguminous plants. *Trans. Wisconsin Acad. Sci.* **30**, 43–50 (1935).

420. Wilson, P. W., and Wyss, O. Mixed cropping and the excretion of nitrogen by leguminous plants. *Contrib. Dept. Agr. Bacteriol. and Agr. Chem. Univ. Wisconsin No.* **147** (1937).

421. Wilson, T. G. G., and Roberts, E. R. Studies in the biological fixation of nitrogen. IV. Inhibition in *Azotobacter vinelandii* by nitrous oxide. *Biochim. et Biophys. Acta* **15**, 568–577 (1954).

422. Winogradsky, S. Sur l'assimilation de l'azote atmosphéric par les microbes. *Compt. rend. acad. sci.* **116**, 1385–1388 (1893).

423. Winogradsky, S. Sur l'assimilation de l'azote gazeux de l'atmosphère par les microbes. *Compt. rend. acad. sci.* **118**, 353–355 (1894).

424. Winogradsky, S. Sur la synthèse de l'ammoniac par les *Azotobacter* du sol. *Compt. rend. acad. sci.* **190**, 661–665 (1930).

425. Winogradsky, S. Sur le dégagement de l'ammoniac par les nodosités des racines des légumineuses. *Compt. rend. acad. sci.* **197**, 909–912 (1933).

426. Wipf, L. Chromosome numbers in root nodules and root tips of certain *Leguminosae*. *Botan. Gaz.* **101**, 51–67 (1939).

427. Wipf, L., and Cooper, D. C. Chromosome numbers in nodules and roots of red clover, common vetch and garden peas. *Proc. Natl. Acad. Sci. U.S.* **24**, 87–91 (1938).

428. Wipf, L., and Cooper, D. C. Somatic doubling of chromosomes and nodular infection in certain *Leguminosae*. *Am. J. Botany* **27**, 821–824 (1940).

429. Wolfe, M. The effect of molybdenum upon the nitrogen metabolism of *Anabaena cylindrica*. *Ann. Botany (London)* **18**, 299–325 (1954).

430. Woronin, M. Über die bei der Schwarzerle (*Alnus glutinosa*) und der gewöhnlichen Gartenlupine (*Lupinus mutabilis*) auftretenden Wurzelanschwellungen. *Mém. acad. imp. sci. St. Petersbourgh* [7] **10** (6), 1–13 (1866). [Secondary source: cf. reference (134), p. 52.]

431. Wyss, O., Lind, C. J., Wilson, J. B., and Wilson, P. W. Mechanism of biological nitrogen fixation. VII. Molecular H_2 and the pN_2 function of *Azotobacter*. *Biochem. J.* **35**, 845–854 (1941).

432. Yamada, T., and Virtanen, A. I. Enzymatic formation of nitrous oxide from nitrite. *Acta Chem. Scand.* **10**, 20–25 (1956).

433. Yamafuji, K. Existence of an enzyme catalysing the hydrogenation of oximes in silkworms. *Nature* **167,** 770–771 (1951).
434. Yamafuji, K., and Omura, H. On the oximase. *Enzymologia* **15,** 296–302 (1952).
435. Zelitch, I., Rosenblum, E. D., Burris, R. H., and Wilson, P. W. Isolation of the key intermediate in biological nitrogen fixation by *Clostridium*. *J. Biol. Chem.* **191,** 295–298 (1951).
436. Zelitch, I., Wilson, P. W., and Burris, R. H. The amino acid composition and distribution of N^{15} in soybean root nodules supplied N^{15}-enriched N_2. *Plant Physiol.* **27,** 1–8 (1952).

ADDENDUM. Since this chapter, and also Chapter 3, were written and even since the footnote on p. 552 was inserted, further important advances have been made in the understanding of the biochemistry of cell-free nitrogen fixation, particularly by *Clostridium pasteurianum*. This is mainly due to workers in the Central Research Department of E. I. du Pont de Nemours & Co., and a summary of this work by J. E. Carnahan and J. E. Castle is to appear in the *Annual Review of Plant Physiology* for 1963. The following brief abstract is based on the authors' manuscript of this paper.

Fifty to 100 molecules of pyruvate are metabolized per molecule of nitrogen fixed. Seeking an understanding of the pyruvate metabolism in this cell-free system, a new electron transport mechanism has been uncovered. This depends on a non-heme protein (mol. wt. of the order of 12,000) which is called "ferredoxin." Ferredoxin has been prepared from various microorganisms.

Pyruvate is decarboxylated to give an enzyme-bound "active-acetyl" group. From this complex the acetyl radical passes via CoA into the formation of acetyl phosphate by steps which are mediated by transacetylase. Concomitantly, as the acetyl group combines first with CoA and later with inorganic phosphate, electrons are liberated and accepted by ferredoxin in its oxidized form. Ferredoxin oxidized is thereby reduced, and the resultant reduced ferredoxin may be re-oxidized by hydrogenase with the production of molecular hydrogen from hydrogen ions.

The importance of all this is that the molecular hydrogen so produced can reduce nitrite or hydroxylamine to ammonia and, inasmuch as the operation of the whole system consumes pyruvate, it also promotes the fixation of nitrogen. Thus this work opens the door to a biochemical explanation of the reduction of nitrogen which is based upon the properties of ferredoxin, a novel electron transport system. As this system becomes more widely implicated in electron transport mechanisms, its biochemical significance will also increase. Already there are indications that similar, although not identical, "ferredoxins" occur in green leaves. Relations, if any, of the ferredoxin system to the role of leghemoglobin in symbiotic nitrogen fixation are, however, still obscure, especially as the symbiotic system has not yet yielded a cell-free nitrogen fixing preparation even by the methods that suffice for *Clostridium*.

ED.

PREAMBLE TO CHAPTER 6

Although the theme of this volume is the role of inorganic substances in the nutrition of higher plants, it has been neither possible nor desirable to confine attention narrowly to this topic. Soil is the chief medium through which roots are nourished, and its properties as a physicochemical system were presented in Chapter 1. The role of microorganisms in the over-all economy of nature justifies the separate discussion of their inorganic nutrition in Chapter 3, and because of the special role of microorganisms in the economy of nitrogen through its fixation, this topic was selected for separate discussion in Chapter 5. These special chapters, however, do not exhaust the soil as a complex biological system or its implication for the interpretation of the nutrition of higher plants. This concluding chapter, therefore, provides a further opportunity to consider the soil in this way, to describe it as a complex system which itself carries out metabolic transformations through its microbial activities, for these in turn make nutritional demands on the constituents of soil. This chapter also provides the opportunity to consider both the organic constituents of soil and that immediate vicinity, or intimate environment, of roots which is termed the rhizosphere. Although this might well have been an appropriate point of departure from which to begin the study of inorganic plant nutrition, it is nevertheless a suitable way to end it; namely on the note that inorganic plant nutrition is the resultant of many complex interactions, including those between plants and soils, which need to be both appreciated and understood.

CHAPTER SIX

Microbial Activities of Soil As They Affect Plant Nutrition

J. H. Quastel

I. Microbial Activities of Soil and Soil Structure

A. ORGANIC MATTER IN SOIL

The organic matter of soil is primarily derived from the decomposition products of plants and from the products of autolysis of the microbiological population which develop at the expense of substances of plant origin. A dynamic equilibrium exists in the soil between the large numbers of bacteria, protozoa, yeasts, fungi, etc., that inhabit the soil and the organic matter continually being supplied by the decaying animal and vegetable tissues. This equilibrium is such that the ratio of carbon to nitrogen in soil organic matter is remarkably constant, approximately 10. Autotrophic bacteria, which obtain their carbon from atmospheric carbon dioxide, and the nitrogen fixers, such as species of *Azotobacter*, play a fundamental part in withdrawing carbon dioxide and nitrogen from the air into the organic matter of soil.

Soil normally contains a variety of substances commonly classed as metabolites of plants and animals. The speed of change of these substances may be very great, the rate depending on the temperature, hydrogen ion concentration, aeration, water availability, and mineral content of soil. A number of substances, derived from animals, plants, or microorganisms, are, however, relatively resistant to breakdown, and such substances make up for the most part what is commonly known as soil organic matter. Such substances have physical and chemical properties which together help to determine the structure of a soil. These substances are also in a continuous state of change, but an equilibrium is achieved so that their total quantity remains fairly constant in any one locale, the amount being largely dependent on climate and geographical conditions and the types of plant being supplied.

1. Humus

Among the most characteristic of the products which compose soil organic matter is the black colloidal material, having high hydrophilic power, known as humus, whose presence helps to make possible the crumb structure of soil so necessary for its fertility. Humus is a complex mixture of which humic acid is an important constituent. It is apparently formed in at least the following ways: (a) by bacterial attack on cellulose, (b) by chemical transformations of lignin, (c) from fungal mycelia. Humic acid from soil is stated to contain about 5% nitrogen; it cannot be wholly, therefore, a lignin or cellulose condensation product. Oden (179) believed it to be a tetrabasic acid with an equivalent weight of about 300.

Many of the characteristics of soil organic matter are consistent with the view that lignin, or lignin derivatives, represents a major constituent. This is made more likely by the fact that lignin is very resistant to microbiological attack. Lignins from various sources vary in composition; thus, the lignin from grass roots is not identical with the lignin of oak leaves or of pine needles.

Various views have been advanced to account for the formation of humus. It was originally thought that humus is derived from cellulose in the soil. Thus Beckley (18) found that sugars on treatment with acids give rise to hydroxymethylfurfuraldehyde, which readily condenses to form a substance closely resembling humus. He found indications of the presence of this aldehyde in a dunged soil and in rotting straw in which humus was being formed. An alternative view (53) was advanced that humus was derived from the oxidation of quinones.

Fischer (57) suggested that lignin is the parent substance of humic acid. It was already known that, during the bacterial decay of wood, cellulose disappears within three years whereas the lignin suffers but little diminution in that period. Lignin and humic acid have, chemically, much in common (58), and studies of the fractionation of organic matter in mineral soils (4) indicated that lignin was a source of humic matter of soil. Moreover, there was a correlation between the formation of humic acid and loss of lignin, but not that of cellulose or pentosan. Humic acid of soil is a true acid and may be obtained from diverse soils such as peat and agricultural soil (179). It readily gives rise to colloidal solutions. Its salts with alkali metals are soluble and behave as colloidal electrolytes. The salts with other metals are insoluble.

Waksman (255–257, 261) has emphasized the lack of satisfactory methods of characterizing humic matter and has pointed out that many of the products referred to as humus and humic acid are not homogeneous. He uses the term humus to designate "organic residues which have undergone extensive decomposition by microorganisms whether in peat bog or in compost, in forest soil or in mineral soils . . . . The chemical composition of humus varies considerably, depending on the nature of the plant residues, on the conditions of decomposition, on the extent of decomposition and the microorganisms active in the decomposition process. Humus is not in a static condition but undergoes continuous change, the range of change depending upon the above conditions. Humus is, therefore, not constant in chemical composition."

Waksman has published (255) the figures given in Table I, showing analyses of soil humus derived from a variety of sources. The results given in Table I show that, with certain exceptions, natural humus formations tend to be low in carbohydrate and to have a high lignin and protein content. The sphagnum peats are exceptional because (a) the carbohydrates of the sphagnum plant are more resistant to decomposition than those of the grasses; this in turn produces a low protein accumulation because insufficient carbon is released to build up the protein of the microorganisms, and (b) the highly acid conditions of sphagnum bogs reduce the rate of decomposition by microorganisms. Constituents of the carbohydrate group, e.g., hemicelluloses of the uronic acid type, are also contained in the resistant fraction of the humus. Soil humus, after a variety of transformations proceeding at different

TABLE I

Chemical Nature of Soil Humus[a]

Nature of humus	Per cent of total humus in ash-free material		
	Carbohydrates	Lignins and lignin-like derivatives	Proteins
Hardwood-spruce forest, F layer	27.16	43.18	9.11
Hardwood-spruce forest, H layer	17.00	57.00	8.49
Lowmoor peat, Newton	11.85	44.08	25.84
Lowmoor peat, Florida	7.43	51.24	25.62
Highmoor peat, young sphagnum	37.04	34.72	5.33
Highmoor peat, old sphagnum	21.76	53.25	5.85
Alpine humus	17.95	35.18	35.77
Chernozem soil, Kansas	13.88	40.81	34.74
Prairie soil (Carrington loam)	11.85	49.29	30.38

[a] From Waksman (255).

rates on the various plant products, tends to have the following composition: (a) lignin-protein complexes, 60–80%; (b) certain resistant hemicellulose and waxy substances, 5–12%; (c) cellulose and other products in an active state of transformation, 5–25%. When the humus is treated with alkali, a large part of groups (a) and (b) are brought into solution leaving group (c) undissolved, the latter being "humin." When the alkali extract is acidified, the major part of (a) and some of (b) are precipitated giving the "humic acids," while a part of group (b) and possibly a part of (c) are left in solution to be termed the "fulvic acid" fraction. Tenney and Waksman (244, 245) have shown that the decomposition of plant products in the soil proceeds much more slowly under anaerobic conditions than under aerobic. This is true especially of the lignins and organic nitrogenous complexes when compared with the decomposition of celluloses and hemicelluloses.

Although in fresh plant residues the ratio of carbon to nitrogen varies from 200:1 to 50:1, the humus in the soil shows a narrow ratio of C:N approximating 10:1, with variations depending on factors including the nature of organic residues and extent of decomposition. It is unlikely that the organic nitrogenous complexes in the humus are free proteins; they are often regarded as lignoproteinates. They are accompanied by pectins, uronic acids, fats, waxes, etc. Organic matter of the soil may be divided (260) into two groups:

1. The humus nucleus, consisting of lignoproteins often combined with bases, e.g., calcium, iron, aluminum, and probably also with silicates and phosphates. These lignoproteinates, possibly forming complexes with the hemicelluloses, form the fraction designated as humic acid and are responsible for the characteristic color and organic colloidal properties of soil.

2. The remaining constituents of humus, consisting of cellulose, hemicelluloses, waxes, fats, starches, etc., in various amounts and proportions according to the location, e.g., forest soils, highland peats. These together form the fraction known as "humin."

The lignoprotein complexes are not completely resistant to decomposition and may be broken down by a variety of fungi including the mycorhiza associated with the roots of trees.

2. Lignin

According to Hibbert (92, 93), the older ideas of Klason that lignin is a coniferyl type (e.g., coniferyl alcohol, coniferaldehyde, or oxyconiferyl alcohol) of condensation polymer have been largely confirmed. Investigations have shown (a) that a large yield of vanillin is formed from spruce (*Picea*) wood (around 25%) and a still larger combined yield of vanillin (I) and syringaldehyde (II) (around 45%) is formed from

Vanillin	Syringaldehyde
(I)	(II)

maple (*Acer*) wood; (b) that spruce lignin is a mixture of condensation polymers formed from simple units containing an aromatic ring having a three-carbon side chain (in support of this view, such products as α-hydroxypropiovanillone and vanilloyl methyl ketone have been isolated); and (c) that hydrogenation of wood and of extracted lignins produces a high yield of cyclohexane derivatives having a three-carbon side chain.

The lignins of all softwoods seem to be identical, consisting of guaiacylpropane units connected to each other through ether and carbon-carbon linkages. Those of the hardwoods differ by the presence of derivatives containing the syringyl radical in addition to the guaiacyl radical.

Freudenberg and his colleagues (63c, e, f, g, i), using a lignin obtained by alternate extraction of spruce wood meal with cupric ammonium hydroxide and hot dilute sulfuric acid with subsequent methylations and oxidations of the methylated products, were able to isolate veratric acid (III), isohemipinic acid (IV), and dehydrodiveratric acid (V). Freudenberg concluded, from these and other studies, that lignin

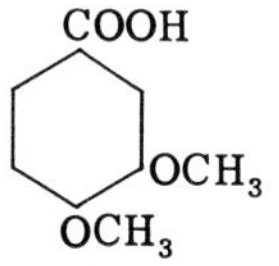

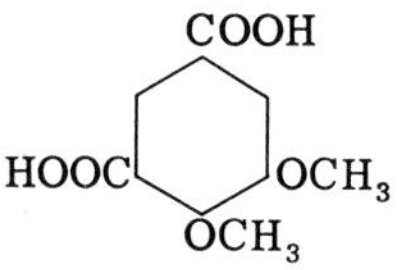

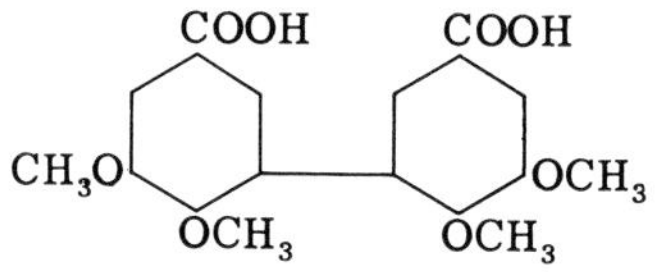

is formed as a result of a preliminary condensation between the side chains of one molecule and the aromatic nucleus of another, thus:

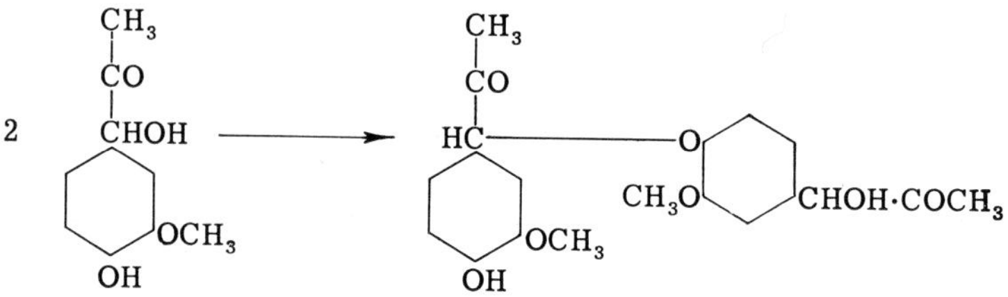

All or most of the reactive groups are located at the alpha carbon atoms of the side chains. Hibbert (92, 93) impressed by the fact that the principal water-soluble ethanolysis products isolated from spruce and maple wood represent ene-diol and 1,2-diketone oxidation systems (VI,

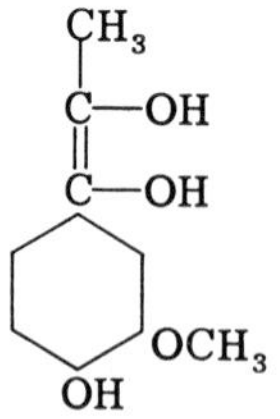

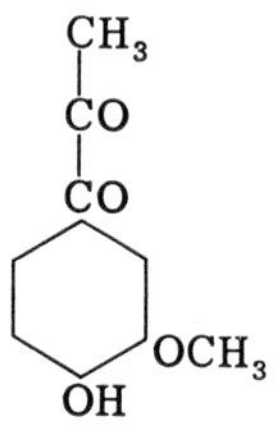

VII) and that these substituted phenylpropane compounds are apparently the building units from which lignin is formed, suggests that the latter "is derived from a series of monomolecular hydrogen transporting plant catalysts, which, during the life of the plant and in the subsequent post-mortal stage, undergo conversion into more complex condensation polymer products." The plant catalysts in question are $R \cdot CO \cdot CHOH \cdot CH_3$, $R \cdot CO \cdot CO \cdot CH_3$, $R \cdot CHOH \cdot CO \cdot CH_3$, $R \cdot CH_2 \cdot CO \cdot CH_2 \cdot OH$, and molecules of similar nature where $R =$ guaiacyl or syringyl.

These substances probably play an important role in plant metabolism, but their mode of action is at present obscure.

There seems to be agreement that in the plant lignin is attached to carbohydrates, possibly polyuronic acids. Presumably such complexes exist in the soil, for they are only very slowly broken down by microorganisms.

a. Biosynthesis of lignin. Freudenberg (63a) and his colleagues have studied biosynthesis of lignin by introducing radioactive substances into spruce saplings (63h). They found that radioactive lignin is formed from D-coniferin, but not from L-coniferin, and from radioactive phenylalanine, the latter being converted first into radioactive coniferin. There is rapid transformation of phenylalanine into coniferyl alcohol and of the latter into its glucoside.

Lignin may be formed *in vitro* by bubbling air through a dilute (<0.5%) solution of coniferyl alcohol in presence of laccase (mushroom) at 20°C at pH 5.5–6.5. Cambium laccase may be used instead of mushroom (63d). Moreover lignin can also be formed from coniferyl alcohol by using horseradish (*Armoracia lapathifolia*) peroxidase and dilute hydrogen peroxide. Biosynthetic and natural lignins seem to be identical, with molecular weights about 10,000 (63b). Laccase and peroxidase cannot attack coniferin; only coniferyl alcohol is attacked to form lignin. During the vegetative period the tissues of the cambium and adjacent cells contain much coniferin. This is split by a β-glucosidase present in these cells to form coniferyl alcohol which is then transformed into lignin. The cell dries as soon as the hollow spaces of the cell wall are filled with lignin.

Intermediates between coniferyl alcohol and lignin are numerous and complex; they include: dehydrodiconiferyl alcohol, *dl*-pinoresinol, guaiacylglycerol-β-coniferyl ether, and coniferyl aldehyde. All these intermediates as well as lignin itself are optically inactive. This is due to the fact that enzymatic attack on coniferyl alcohol causes the removal of a phenolic hydrogen atom, leaving a radical which exists in a variety of mesomeric forms and which are optically inactive. These on combining with each other form various arrangements, e.g. (VIII), which may combine (IX) with methanol or cane sugar.

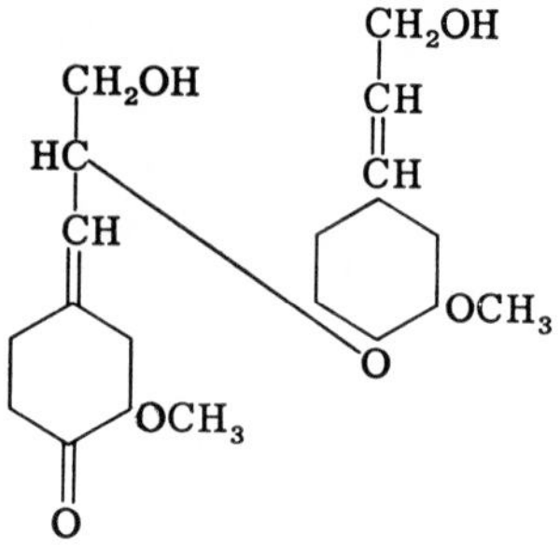

Dehydrodiconiferyl
alcohol

(VIII)

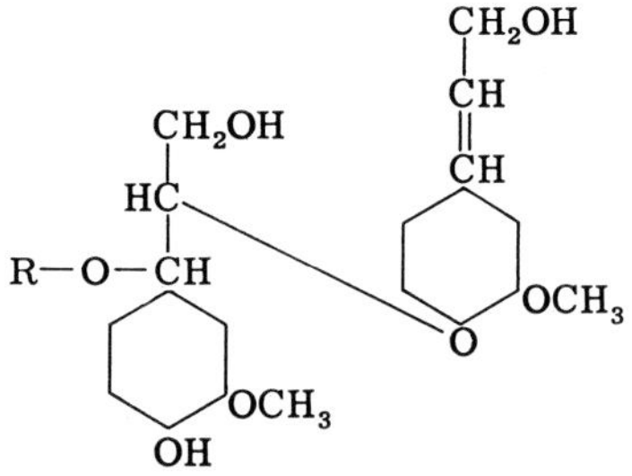

where R = CH_3 or $C_{12}C_{21}O_{10}$

(IX)

Lignin can undergo further dehydrogenations in presence of laccase or peroxidase. In the plant lignin synthesis takes place, but no further reactions occur when the cell walls are fully lignified.

In soil, however, lignin is attacked by laccases or peroxidases from wood-rotting fungi and breakdown takes place. The presence of these enzymes in the fungi enables the organisms to obtain breakdown products, presumably for their nourishment. The breakdown of lignins in this manner is analogous to the breakdown of phenols and is part of the humification process of soils.

A review of the methods of humus analysis, including the lignin fractions, is given by Waksman (258).

3. Carbohydrate Decomposition in Soil

Carbohydrates represent a major constituent of that part of soil organic matter which undergoes relatively rapid transformation. They are quickly broken down, but they are also continually being resynthesized by the great variety of organisms that are nourished by soil organic matter. At the same time, decaying plant material enriches the soil with a constant supply of a variety of carbohydrates.

The continued presence of carbohydrates in the soil stimulates the proliferation of those organisms that can attack these substances and derive from them the energy and the carbon for their growth. Soil, therefore, normally contains many types of carbohydrate-splitting organisms.

Various factors influence the numbers and types of organisms that respond to carbohydrates. Such factors are the availability of nitrogen, the presence or absence of oxygen, the hydrogen ion concentration, and the moisture content of the soil.

Carbohydrate metabolism in a soil, therefore, under field conditions depends very much on the type of soil, on its structure and its location. Forest soils, which are usually acidic in nature, show a great preponderance of fungi whereas limed, manured soils of neutral or alkaline pH show a preponderance of bacteria. The forms of metabolism of carbohydrate will vary according to the site of the soil and its previous treatment. Anaerobic soils, such as those presented by bogs and fens, show a different metabolic behavior, the type of carbohydrate breakdown associated with anaerobic life being dominant. The main product of carbohydrate breakdown in the soil is bacterial or fungal matter. It has been estimated that between 40 and 70% of the carbon of cellulose that is decomposed in soil is transformed into microbial cells. The main carbohydrates in soil are represented by cellulose, hemicellulose, starches including lichenin, dextrans, and levans, and the simple sugars. The rates of attack of these substances in soil vary very considerably; the simpler sugars are broken down relatively quickly whereas certain hemicelluloses, including the polyuronides, are more resistant to attack.

a. Cellulose breakdown. A large variety of organisms attack cellulose, including anaerobic and aerobic bacteria and fungi. Actinomycetes and the filamentous fungi, including *Fusarium, Aspergillus, Penicillium,* and *Trichoderma,* are all involved. According to Waksman, in the breakdown of wood by fungi, three stages may be distinguished: (a) attack by Uredineae and Ustilagineae that decompose sugars and starches, (b) attack by fungi belonging to the genera *Mucor, Penicillium,* and *Aspergillus* that bring about the destruction of sugars and starches and decompose hemicellulose and polyuronides, and (c) development of the true wood-destroying fungi belonging to the Polyporaceae and Agaricaceae that attack both cellulose and lignin. Protozoa and a variety of wood-boring insects (termites, cockroaches, etc.) are also involved in cellulose decomposition in soil. The products of cellulose decomposition may be, besides carbon dioxide, organic acids (chiefly acetic, butyric, and valeric acids), alcohols, hydrocarbons (e.g., methane) and hydrogen. These are usually produced by anaerobic organisms. Aerobic bacteria and fungi seem to bring about the complete destruction of cellulose.

Cellulose is insoluble in water, and presumably organisms that can break down and flourish on cellulose must have the means of producing from it some soluble product that can pass into the cell. The conventional view is that an exoenzyme brings about hydrolysis of the cellulose molecule with subsequent liberation of glucose, which is destroyed within the cell—the products formed varying with the nature of the organism. It is not known whether cellulose dextrins are produced in the enzymatic attack on cellulose, but the evidence indicates that two types of hydrolytic attack take place, one accomplishing the initial attack, possibly rupturing cross linkages or securing considerable chain shortening, and the other bringing about hydrolysis of the fragments. The evidence for this is the observation that insoluble dextrans prepared by cold acid hydrolysis of cellulose are apparently utilized more readily and by more varieties of organisms than untreated cellulose itself. Pringsheim (189) postulated the existence of two hydrolytic enzyme systems, cellulase and cellobiase, the former producing cellubiose from cellulose and the latter breaking down the disaccharide to glucose. Simola (220), in a study of two aerobic spore-forming organisms named *Cellulobacillus myxogenes* and *Cellulobacillus mucosus*, obtained results supporting Pringsheim's view. Both glucose and cellobiose were identified among the products of breakdown.

Cellulases are now known to be widely distributed in plant products, particularly in seeds, in the digestive secretions of invertebrates, and in extracts of various molds and bacteria. They appear to be produced by the normal intestinal flora of insects. Termites can exist for long periods on a diet of pure cellulose when the normal flora representatives of two orders of flagellates are present. Cellulases develop in fungi and bacteria when these are grown with cellulose as substrate, and it is possible that they are to be regarded as adaptive enzymes. Cellulases of invertebrates are obtained from the gut; snails represent a rich source.

Enzymatic hydrolysis of cellulose leads almost wholly to *d*-glucose, but cellobiose is probably an intermediate in the process.

The variable resistance of cellulose to enzymatic attack has been ascribed to chain length (degree of polymerization), but there is strong evidence that the principal factor is the degree of crystallinity. A comparison of the equilibrium moisture contents of cellulose of widely different reactivities showed a direct correlation with the extent of enzymatic hydrolysis. Highly variable results have been recorded concerning the degradation of cellulose by microorganisms, this being doubtless due to variations in the physical state of the cellulose. It is well known that native cotton (*Gossypium*) cellulose and wood are much more resistant to enzymatic hydrolysis than regenerated cellulose.

There is, unfortunately, little evidence as to the nature of the initial attacks by enzymes on cellulose, beyond the fact that they are primarily hydrolytic. Winogradsky (276) put forward the view that an oxidation took place, the terminal alcohol groups being oxidized to aldehydes which were then oxidized to carboxyl groups. Cellulose attacked by bacteria was observed to have acid properties. In support of this view, Walker and Warren (263) isolated a gum from cellulose suspensions decomposed by *Cytophaga* and showed it to be an acid, yielding furfuraldehyde and carbon dioxide on treatment with 12% hydrochloric acid, a property common to polyuronides. Because of its low reducing power, they considered the gum to be an acidic type of oxycellulose and stated that it was an intermediate stage in cellulose breakdown. This interpretation, however, according to Norman and his colleagues (176, 177), is not justified, as oxidation would not, itself, cause immediate chain splitting to such an extent that all the oxidized fragments would be water soluble. There was no evidence that the residual cellulose was more oxidized than the original sample, and uronic acid groupings, previously introduced by chemical means, were actually preferentially removed by the organism.

The latter stages of cellulose decomposition are not much more satisfactorily understood than the earlier stages. In general, the aerobic organisms effect extensive oxidations, the major product being carbon dioxide. Two-thirds of the carbon removed from cellulose decomposed by *Cytophaga* is removed as carbon dioxide, and almost all the remainder can be accounted for in the gum synthesized by the organism (263). None of the species of *Vibrio* apparently produces acid from cellulose. The two aerobic sporeformers, studied by Simola (220), yield about 10% volatile acids acetic and formic from cellulose, the acetic acid being in considerable excess. Anaerobic organisms give larger yields of acid products and even alcohol from cellulose—so much so that attempts have been made to develop large-scale fermentation processes involving cellulose, but so far with little success. Over fifty years ago, Omelianski showed that certain anaerobes will decompose cellulose to give high yields of fatty acids, chiefly acetic and butyric, together with carbon dioxide and either hydrogen or methane, but it is now considered unlikely that methane is a product of cellulose decomposition. It is more likely that it is produced by the action of the methane organisms that bring about a reduction of carbon dioxide by hydrogen or by hydrogenation. The products of anaerobic breakdown of cellulose are those that might be expected from the anaerobic decomposition of glucose, namely, acetic, butyric, and lactic acids, ethyl alcohol, carbon dioxide, and hydrogen.

Although celluloses are vigorously attacked by fungi, little is known of the intermediate products. As is well known, fungi produce from sugars a variety of acids, such as citric, oxalic, fumaric, succinic, and gluconic—but none of these acids is reported during the fungal attack of cellulose, although of course they may be formed and rapidly broken down. Much work, with selective inhibitors, is required to throw light on the action of cellulose degradation by fungi. The most obvious product of cellulose metabolism is synthesized microbial substance. As much as 50% of the carbon of cellulose finds its way into the mycelium of fungi. Available nitrogen is required for this process, and it is calculated that the ratio between cellulose decomposed and nitrogen immobilized is about 35 to 1.

Thermophilic bacteria have been studied chiefly with a view to the development of an industrial fermentation process to obtain acids or alcohol from cellulose. Vigorous and rapid decomposition of cellulose at 65° will take place in the presence of these organisms which are easily obtained from highly manured soils. Thus, in the presence of a thermophilic organism, 42 gm of cellulose gave rise to 21.6 gm of acetic acid, 10.3 gm of ethyl alcohol, 11.9 gm of carbon dioxide, and an undetermined quantity of hydrogen.

A fact of importance in the breakdown of carbohydrates in soils is that association of organisms of different metabolic character, such as bacteria and fungi, may be more effective than the organisms taken separately. Thus, a pure culture of a variety of *Aspergillus* brought about a smaller rate of breakdown (28% in 48 days) of oat (*Avena*) straw cellulose than when it was present in a mixed culture (39% decomposition in the same time). Apparently, the presence of carbohydrates more easily available than cellulose, and permitting the development of a vigorous flora, seems to pave the way for an attack on cellulose (175).

The nature of breakdown of an organic substance in soil is clearly determined by competitive, as well as by adaptive and symbiotic, factors in the soil population.

b. Hemicelluloses and polyuronic acids. This group contains hexosans, as mannans and galactans, pentosans of formula $(C_5H_8O_4)_x$, pectins, and polyuronides. They are present in considerable amounts in higher green plants whence they find their way to the soil. The largest group of the hemicelluloses are the pentosans which may be present to the extent of 7% in pine needles and 32% in corn cobs. Precise knowledge of the constitution of the ill-defined polyuronide hemicelluloses is practically nonexistent owing to the difficulty of isolating homogeneous products. In many cases the uronic acid constituent has not been identified with certainty.

Polyuronides and uronic groupings are widely distributed in soils and their content has a direct relation to soil fertility, as they contribute greatly to the water retention and crumb structure of soil. Such polyuronides are pectic acid and alginic acid as well as a variety of bacterial polysaccharides. Pectic acid, which is the main constituent of the pectins, is composed of D-galactopyruronic acid units mutually united by 1,4-α-linkages. Alginic acid, on the other hand, is represented as a chain of D-mannopyruronic acid residues joined by 1,4-β-linkages. A polyuronide representing the highly important group of specific bacterial polysaccharides, which must form a significant proportion of soil carbohydrates, is built of cellobiuronic acid residues joined by β-linkages in the 1,3 position. These yield glucose and glucuronic acids on hydrolysis.

Many mucilaginous polysaccharides contain uronic acid units (94a). Seed mucilages of the plantains may have a high proportion of xylopyranose end groups and a smaller proportion of galactopyranose end groups. The work of Hirst and of others (e.g., 94b, 221a, 44a) has given information on the complex polyuronides present in gum arabic and other plant gums that may be found in soils that contain decaying vegetable matter. There seems to be little doubt that the metabolism of both microorganisms and plants contributes greatly to the store of polyuronic acids in soil.

The products of hydrolysis of the hemicellulose of Iceland moss (*Cetraria islandica*) gave rise to glucose, mannose, galactose, and glucuronic acids.

Mucilaginous polysaccharides contain uronic acid units, and such compounds have very complex structures. The mucilage of the seed of the plantain has a high proportion of xylopyranose end groups, galactopyranose units, galactouronic acid, and a methyl pentose, as yet unidentified. Glucuronic acid is incorporated with galactopyranose units in gum arabic, and plant gums contain structures of this kind associated with rhamnofuranoses, arabofuranoses, etc.

Hemicelluloses, especially the pentosans or xylans, are readily decomposed by soil fungi, actinomycetes, and bacteria. The decomposition may take place more rapidly than that of cellulose but, as has been pointed out by Waksman and Starkey (260a), the organic matter in certain peats and mineral soils may be free from cellulose under conditions where there is still much hemicellulose present. This is due to the greater resistance of certain hemicelluloses to decomposition and through the synthetic activities of a number of microorganisms that give rise to gums and slimes.

Hydrolysis of this group of substances may take place by hemicellulases which are widely distributed as extracellular enzymes of microorganisms, and in seeds and in the digestive systems of invertebrates. Fungi, such as *Aspergillus oryzae,* are rich in such hydrolytic enzymes which exert their optimal activity at pH 4–5, but fungal hydrolysis of the xylans is rarely complete. Mannogalactans, found in soil through the breakdown of plant seeds, are hydrolyzed to mannose or galactose by fungi or by snail enzymes whereas mannan is hydrolyzed to mannose by various anaerobic bacteria.

The pectic acids, which consist of colloidal polygalacturonic acids, undergo hydrolysis by enzymes existing in plants and microorganisms. Pectinase, now known as pectin polygalacturonase, causes a fission of glycosidic linkages between neighboring anhydrogalacturonic acid units. Another enzyme, once known as pectase, but now known as pectin methylesterase or pectin esterase, accelerates the removal of ester groups in pectinic acids. These enzymes are present in bacteria and in molds and are of obvious importance in controlling the initial breakdown of the pectins in soil. Another enzyme, provisionally termed a depolymerase, exists in yeasts and plants and presumably plays its part in soil metabolism. This enzyme hydrolyzes polygalacturonic acids of larger molecular weight only, and the hydrolysis does not proceed beyond the point where the degree of polymerization is about 5.

c. Estimation of polyuronic acids. Methods of estimation depend on the fact, first shown by Lefevre and Tollens (131), that prolonged boiling with 12% HCl liberates carbon dioxide from uronic acids. Bartholomew and Norman (17) have worked out a method of estimation of uronic acids in soils based on this observation. Some of their results are given in Table II. There is some error due to CO_2 evolution from hexosan groups.

The polyuronides, whose content in soil seems to have a direct relation to the fertility of soil, contribute greatly to the water retention or crumb structure of soil. Quastel and Webley (203), using a manometric technique, have shown that the addition of sodium alginate to a soil greatly improves its structure as shown by increased crumb stability at high water contents. It was suggested that alginate confers its soil-improving properties by its combination as an ion with one or more constituents of the soil particles.

d. Lichenin. This carbohydrate, of Iceland moss and other plants, is broken down by lichenases found in many fungi and certain bacteria (*Cytophaga*) and in many invertebrates. The distribution of these enzymes is similar to that of cellulose. They are extracellular, diffusible enzymes that may be extracted directly from the organisms used as sources; they may be separated from cellulase and other enzymes by fractional precipitation of aqueous solutions by ethanol and ethyl ether. Lichenase hydrolyzes lichenin quantitatively to *d*-glucose

TABLE II

URONIC CONTENT OF VARIOUS SOILS EXPRESSED AS CARBON DIOXIDE YIELD[a]

Soil type	Depth (inches)	CO_2 yield per 100 gm air dry cell (gm)
Edina silt loam	0–4	0.082; 0.084
Edina silt loam	16–19	0.016; 0.016
Weller silt loam	0–1½	0.114; 0.118
Weller silt loam	10–13	0.028; 0.030
Ames very fine sandy loam	0–2½	0.232; 0.238
Webster silty clay loam	0–6	0.162; 0.162
Leon fine sand	0–1½	0.108; 0.110
Leon fine sand	1–1⅔	0.019; 0.021

[a] Data from Bartholomew and Norman (17).

The relationship between cellulase and lichenase is not clear; they seem to be different but further work on this question is required.

e. Polymeric conversion of sucrose. Among the sugars that enter the soil and are swiftly metabolized, sucrose has special importance not only because of the quantities concerned, but because of the special reactions in which it is enzymatically involved.

Sucrose, like other disaccharides, is rapidly hydrolyzed to the constituent hexoses by many soil microorganisms, and thenceforward the metabolism of the sugars follows the familiar lines that occur in aerobic and anaerobic bacteria or fungi. Sucrose, however, gives rise to two products of considerable importance in soil metabolism. They, together with the polyuronides, greatly affect soil structure and stability. These products are the polymers, dextrans and levans.

When sucrose is perfused through a neutral soil under aerobic conditions, a considerable portion of it is converted to a levan polysaccharide. This reaction is not brought about by glucose or fructose or by

a mixture of these monosaccharides. The synthesis of the levan is secured by specific microorganisms of soil, e.g., *Bacillus subtilis*. A soluble cell-free enzyme which brings about levan production from sucrose has been isolated from *B. subtilis* and *Aerobacter levanicum* by
Hestrin and his colleagues (91). On the other hand, cells of *Leuconostoc mesenteroides* and related organisms have yielded a soluble enzyme, forming dextran from sucrose. In both cases the polymerization
of one component of the sucrose molecule is accompanied by an accumulation of an equivalent amount of the other component in the form
of free hexose, e.g., fructose in dextran production and glucose in levan
production.

Nord and Vitucci (174) investigated the carbohydrate metabolism of
the wood-destroying fungi, all of which are basidiomycetes. Acetic acid
had been previously shown to be the last identifiable metabolite of
these organisms, but Nord and Vitucci, by starting with sodium acetate instead of cellulose, found that the oxalic acid salt was the last product. From results based on trapping procedures and the use of identified intermediates as sole carbon sources, they concluded that the two
pathways of degradation shown in Scheme A may take place with the
fungi under investigation.

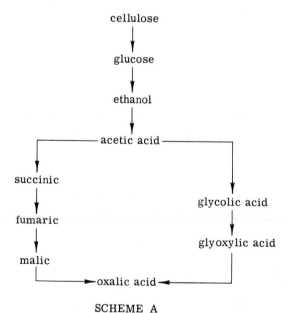

SCHEME A

Further work by Nord and Vitucci demonstrated that although the
over-all chemical result of the action of many wood-destroying fungi

is the same, the modes of metabolism of the organisms may differ considerably. *Lentinus lepideus*, one of the known root fungi, growing on wood or in a glucose or xylose medium produces an oily substance which was found to be a mixture of esters of cinnamic acid and anisic acid. Methyl *p*-methoxycinnamate was also produced by a mechanism depending on the carbohydrate portion of the wood (Scheme B).

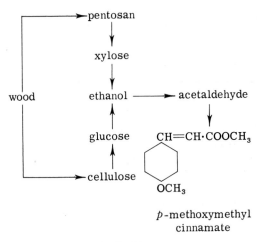

p-methoxymethyl
cinnamate

SCHEME B

Soil has enormous potentialities for the digestion or breakdown of organic matter. It is unlikely that any form of carbohydrate would long withstand the action of the soil organisms that develop under soil conditions. The preliminary steps in the decomposition of complex carbohydrates consist of hydrolysis to the simple sugars; a variety of enzymes accomplishing such changes are known.

B. SOIL AS A BIOLOGICAL SYSTEM

Soil may be considered as a complex biological system in which hosts of organisms are competing with each other, often for a limited supply of nutritional material. They exercise profound effects on each other's development and chemical activities and establish between themselves a dynamic equilibrium which is constantly changing with changes in the physical and chemical environment of the soil.

Some conception of the enormous population of microorganisms in soil is provided by the fact that there may be as many as 5000 millions of bacteria per gram of soil. This corresponds to a weight of over 4 tons of bacterial substance per acre of soil. The numbers fluctuate greatly, depending on the availability of the food supply, moisture, aeration conditions, temperature, hydrogen ion concentration of the soil, the types of plants growing in the soil, etc. Results, given in Table III, are taken from the standard work by S. A. Waksman, "Principles of Soil Microbiology" (Williams & Wilkins, Baltimore, Maryland,

TABLE III

NUMBER OF MICROORGANISMS IN SOIL IN RESPONSE TO TREATMENTS[a]

Treatment of the soil	Hydrogen ion concentration of the soil	Microorganisms found[b]		
		Bacteria	Actinomycetes	Fungi
Unfertilized and unlimed	4.6	3000	1150	60
Lime only added	6.4	5410	2410	23
Salts and ammonium sulfate added	4.1	2690	370	112
Salts, ammonium sulfate and lime added	5.8	6990	2520	39
Stable manure and salts added	5.4	8800	2920	73

[a] From S. A. Waksman (see text).
[b] In thousands per gram of soil, determined by plate method.

TABLE IV

NUMBER OF MICROORGANISMS IN SOIL AS AFFECTED BY PROXIMITY TO ROOTS[a]

Plant	Sample of soil taken	Microorganisms found[b]		
		Bacteria	Actinomycetes	Fungi
Rye	Near roots	28,600	4,400	216
	Away from roots	13,200	3,200	162
Sugar beet	Near roots	57,800	15,000	222
	Away from roots	32,100	12,200	176
Alfalfa	Near roots	93,800	9,000	268
	Away from roots	17,800	3,300	254

[a] From Starkey (229).
[b] In thousands per gram soil.

1932); they show how the microorganisms of soil vary in number according to the treatment of the soil.

Results given in Table IV, taken from Starkey (229), show how the proportions of microorganisms in soil vary according to their proximity to plants.

The bacteria range in number, usually from a few hundred thousand to several hundred million per gram of soil, though many species do not develop under the ordinary plating technique. Gray and Thornton (77) obtained direct counts of the order of 4000 millions bacteria in a gram of manured arable soil. Such figures were over a hundred times greater than those obtained by a plating technique. Protozoa may reach figures of the order of one million per gram of soil (amoebae 280,000; flagellates 770,000; ciliates 1000—estimated on a neutral manured arable soil at Rothamsted). Algae may exceed 100,000 per gram of soil. According to Waksman and Starkey (260a) the numbers of actinomycetes range from a few thousand to many millions per gram of soil, and the numbers of fungi may exceed one hundred thousand per gram.

In such a complex microbiological population there exist numerous chemical interrelationships that affect metabolic behavior and cell proliferation. Symbiotic associations take place and antibiotic developments occur. Thus Waksman and Woodruff (262) have shown that, by the use of a proper extractant (e.g., ether), it is possible to demonstrate that soils contain substances of the actinomycin type which inhibit the growth of certain bacteria in culture media. Such substances may be both bacteriostatic and bacteriocidal; their effects may be considerably modified by soil constituents (259).

Cell adaptation occurs and the enzyme equipment of the soil microorganisms undergoes changes in response to changes in their environment. Kluyver (114) commented, in a recent lecture, that the amount of microbial protoplasm in earth surpasses that of animal protoplasm by almost twenty times. It is obvious that in dealing with the subject of metabolic activities of the soil we are dealing with the metabolism of vast numbers of living cells, which greatly exceed the number of cells found in animals.

Considerations such as these, together with increasing knowledge of the phenomena of cell adaptations as a function of the environment, make it necessary to investigate soil as an integral biological whole (192). Its organic matter may be, according to the circumstances, largely that of living organisms, similar in many fundamental respects to that of plants or of animals, or it may be largely that of the lignoprotein-polyuronide system of complexes with relatively little living material present. The study of all such material—living and nonliving—is proper to the topic of soil organic matter.

C. ORGANIC MATTER AND SOIL AERATION AND STRUCTURE

It is now well known that organic matter plays an essential role in securing in soil the structure, or tilth, that is conducive to high fertility.

In fact, maintenance of the supply of organic matter to arable soils is of the greatest practical importance, for productive capacity is largely dependent upon it.

Aggregating substances are uniformly distributed in soil crumbs. They consist, according to Kroth and Page (118), of polar organic substances, resulting from the decomposition of fresh organic matter, and of a group of substances, including iron and aluminum oxides, fats, waxes, and resins, that are less efficient as soil aggregators. Bacterial slimes and fungal mycelia, it is well known, play an important role in soil aggregation and resistance of soils to erosion (71, 166).

Following work (154) on the binding action of mycelia and organic matter on soil particles, Martin (153) showed that addition of cultures of *Bacillus subtilis* to soil produces aggregations of soil particles owing to the organic substances formed by the growth of the organism from a molecule such as sucrose. He demonstrated that addition of bacterial polysaccharides, such as the levans and dextrans, will affect soil structure to a greater degree than addition of casein or of lignin. Geoghegan and Brian (68a, b) have found that bacterial and other polysaccharides aggregate soils. They reported that bacterial levans and dextrans have marked aggregating effects on soil particles, the levans being formed by a wide variety of aerobic organisms, and the dextrans being formed by various species of *Leuconostoc*. Soil crumbs containing small quantities of levans are very stable but are eventually broken down by bacterial action. The aggregating action of the products derived from microorganisms is much greater than the direct binding effect of the microbial cells themselves. As soil aggregators, dextrans produced from sucrose by the metabolic action of *Leuconostoc* are apparently superior to the levans derived from sucrose by the action of *B. subtilis*. A polysaccharide formed by *Rhizobium* and containing 67% glucose and 20% uronic acid residues (44) is a less efficent soil aggregator than either the levans or the dextrans. Undoubtedly, the structure of the polysaccharide or polyuronide fraction has a strong influence on the aggregating properties of soil. Hydrogen bonding is considered a major mechanism whereby polysaccharides are bound to the soil particle.

Haworth, Pinkard, and Stacey (89) have shown that poor soils with a low total organic content have only traces of polysaccharides; those with higher total organic content have 0.5–1.5 gm polysaccharide per kilogram moisture-free soil and possess a greater moisture-retaining capacity. Polysaccharide fractions containing levans were isolated from such soils. Swaby (237) finds that a variety of substances, including proteins and polyuronides, affect soil aggregation.

There is now an extensive literature on the formation of soil organic matter by various cropping systems and incorporation of crop residues, and its bearing on soil structure and soil fertility. A brief summary has been given recently (191).

1. Soil Aggregation

The structure of a soil is largely determined by its crumb or aggregate formation. This greatly influences water movement, aeration, and heat transfer. Many of the biochemical and chemical changes that affect soil fertility take place at the large surface areas presented by soil aggregates. Substances that stabilize crumbs, or aid in soil aggregation, are uniformly distributed in the crumbs of soil of good structure.

a. *Polyuronides, polysaccharides, and related substances as soil aggregators.* Polyuronides and uronic groupings are present among humus constituents and these are widely distributed in plants, composts, and soils. The uronic acid content varies with the soil type (17), and is apparently related to its fertility. The polyuronides present include pectic acid, alginic acid, and various bacterial polysaccharides. Many mucilaginous saccharides contain uronic acid units, and it is known that complex polyuronides compose the plant gums found in soils containing decaying vegetable matter.

The aggregating effect of lignins, or lignin-like substances, in humus has been investigated by McCalla (148) and Alderfer *et al.* (1). Straw composts in various stages of decomposition aggregate soils. Material containing more than 11% hemicellulose and 18% cellulose increases crumb formation. It seems that conditions favorable for microbial activity facilitate the improving action of the organic material on crumb formation, but they also hasten the destruction of the formed aggregates.

The marked effect of a polyuronide, alginic acid, in increasing soil aeration by improving crumb stability and apparent water retention was first shown by Quastel and Webley (203) [see also Quastel (190)]. Using a manometric technique (54) that measures directly the availability of oxygen to living cells in soil, they were able to demonstrate that the presence of alginates greatly affects the air-water relationship of soil. The amount of water that may be added to a soil before the availability of oxygen to the soil organisms falls through waterlogging and aggregate breakdown is much increased by the addition of sodium alginate. The addition of 1% sodium alginate increases the aeration capacity of a poor soil to that found for a fertile garden soil. The effect of the alginate rapidly increases with increase of concentration to a maximum. Even a garden soil with a fairly high content of organic matter, showing good aeration at a high water content, is affected favorably by addition of alginate.

2. Effects of Cellulose Products on Soil Aeration

Using their manometric method, Quastel and Webley (203) showed that not only a polyuronide, such as alginate, is effective in improving soil structure, but that cellulose esters, such as cellulose acetate, ethyl cellulose, and carboxymethyl cellulose, will improve air-water relationships of a soil. These substances at concentrations of 1% (per dry weight of soil) exercise effects similar to those due to about 0.5% sodium alginate. The results are consistent with those of Felber and Gardner (55, 56), who found that addition of methyl cellulose to soil secures considerable retention of moisture.

Addition of farmyard manure and horse dung greatly improves the air-water relationships and crumb stability of a soil. Quastel and Webley (203) point out that the effects of addition of these substances are twofold: (a) physical, due to the presence of fine straw which has a binding effect on the soil crumbs—the effect here is reversible, as washing the soil results in removal of the straw and the soil reverts largely to its original condition; (b) chemical, or physicochemical, due probably to the presence of polyuronides, or polysaccharides, affecting the soil particles—here the effect is irreversible as washing the soil causes no immediate diminution in crumb stability.

Addition of sewage sludges, composts, and refuses to soil improves the air-water relationships, usually in proportion to the amounts of organic matter present. Alkaline extracts of soils and peats, after subsequent neutralization, may also be effective.

D. Soil Improvers (Conditioners)

The conclusion reached by the writer in 1945 as a result of experiments with alginate, etc., was that it is unlikely that polyuronides, or polysaccharides, will be successful as soil improvers on a wide scale, though they may be of importance in glasshouses where immediate improvements in soil structure may be very beneficial. For field work, especially, substances must be sought that are less vulnerable to attack in the soil than the polyuronides and polysaccharides. These substances are metabolites of the cell, subject to breakdown by a variety of soil organisms. Their speed of decomposition in the soil, with consequent breakdown of the crumbs stabilized by such substances, is determined, among other factors, by availability of nitrogenous compounds whose mobilization by the organisms attacking the polyuronides, etc., would also be deleterious to the plant. Moreover, the relatively large amounts of polyuronide salts required for structure improvement (5–10 tons per acre) would cause harmful effects to the soil due to the release of large quantities of cations present in the salts.

It became clear that the ideal soil conditioner should be a substance having perhaps a mechanism similar to that of the polyuronides or polysaccharides in aggregating soil particles but which would undergo a relatively slow rate of destruction in soil. It should, like the naturally occurring soil conditioners, be devoid of toxic effects on plant or animal. It should not interfere with the soil microbiological equilibria, involving, for example, the growth of nitrogen-fixing organisms. Nor should it inhibit processes of soil nitrification; on the contrary, by improving soil aeration, it might accelerate them. It should not remove, at any rate irreversibly, the trace elements that are important for plant nutrition.

This ideal has been achieved to a great extent by the introduction of the synthetic polyelectrolytes.*

1. Effects of Synthetic Polyelectrolytes on Aggregation, Aeration, and Water Relationships of the Soil (191)

Hedrick and Mowry (90) found that only certain water-soluble polymeric electrolytes of high molecular weight are effective as soil aggregators at the very low concentrations required by practical considerations. One of the most active substances was made by the hydrolysis of polyacrylonitrile. Other polymers of nearly related structure also showed great improving effects on soil aeration and soil aggregation. The two materials on which most work was reported were the sodium salt of hydrolyzed polyacrylonitriles and another carboxylated polymer used as a partial calcium salt. Both polymers are polyanions. Hedrick and Mowry showed that these substances, at concentrations of 0.1% (per dry weight soil) give better aeration values, in a sandy loam, than any other materials tested (e.g., sodium alginate, sodium carboxymethyl cellulose, pectin, lignin) at 1%. The aggregate stability is greatly increased, the effect being observed with many different soils. Very pronounced improvement in the workability of all soils treated with the polymers takes place. They are crumbly and friable at high water contents. While the primary effect of the polyelectrolyte on the soil is on crumb stability, the percolation rate through treated soil often shows a hundredfold increase over the rate in untreated soil. The moisture equivalent is stated to be improved, and evidence from experiments on the wilting of plants indicates that all the increase in water held by the soil is available for plant growth. In addition to the more rapid infiltration and percolation of water, and increased moisture storage, a Miami silt loam treated with the synthetic

* By the Monsanto Chemical Company, with whose scientific staff the writer was associated in the search for a synthetic soil improver.

conditioners showed decreased surface evaporation, an effect apparently due to the increased stability of the soil aggregates.

Allison (3) found from both laboratory and field studies that alkali soils from the western United States, which are low in permeability, on treatment with the polymer,* give marked increases in permeability in proportion to the rate of treatment. High water-stable aggregation in several saline and alkali soils is obtained after application of the conditioners at rates of 0.025 and 0.1%. The aggregates prove to be water stable, the structural improvement persisting through a second growing season (157).

Vallance (247) finds that treatment of poorly aggregated soil with Krilium, at rates of 0.015–0.075%, increases water-stable aggregates up to 53–70%, but there is little effect in well-aggregated (55%) soils.

It cannot be overemphasized that the soil conditioners, such as polyuronides or synthetic polyelectrolytes, stabilize soil crumbs, and that, for their effective use, soils must be worked into a good structure before, or at the time of, application of the conditioners.

Krilium produces a large increase in permeability of all soils, but the increases vary greatly with the different soils. Swanson (239) has also shown that Krilium administration improves aggregation, porosity, and permeability and prevents slaking; it stabilizes existing structure and facilitates drying. Improvements of soil structure of a cultivated loess by Krilium application have been noted, but there is apparently no improving effect on the surface layer of an acid and degraded forest soil. Increases of porosity and permeabilities of Ohio clays and silts after application of Krilium have been reported by Martin and Volk (158). It appears that the amount of clay in the soil is a dominating factor in determining the aggregating power of the polyelectrolyte. As determined by permeability measurements, the polyelectrolyte treatment, at both 0.025 and 0.100% levels, seems to overcome the dispersive effect of a high content of exchangeable sodium (3). In a comparison of aggregating effects of the Krilium polymers on nine western soils, varying widely in a number of chemical and physical characteristics, it was found that regardless of pH, salinity, exchangeable-sodium percentage, or clay content of the various soils tested, there seems to be no significant difference between the abilities of the polymer conditioners to produce water-stable aggregates.

Administration of the polyelectrolyte to alkaline and saline soils facilitates removal of salt and exchangeable sodium after soil irrigation, a property of considerable importance in soil reclamation.

* Now known as Krilium, which is the trademark of the Monsanto Chemical Company for substances such as hydrolyzed polyacrylonitrile sold as soil conditioners.

2. Kinds of Soil Conditioners and Formulations

Gardner (66) presents a useful list of the trade names, physical form, and percentage of active conditioning material in various substances sold as conditioners. Most of the legitimate soil-conditioning materials have as their basis some form of hydrolyzed polyacrilonitrile or a modified vinylacetate-maleic acid compound. The Krilium formulations contain one or other of these products. In addition to these materials, there are other chemical, mineral, organic, and biological products claimed to have properties similar to those of the synthetic polyelectrolytes.

Various silicates and silicones, resistant to attack by microorganisms, have been investigated as soil aggregators. These have facilitated soil aggregations, but they give rise to waterproofing effects (and high alkalinity in the case of sodium silicate) or are impracticable, as with the volatile silicones. Perhaps they are worthy of more extensive field testing in view of certain beneficial effects of sodium silicate on grass yield on a calcareous Houston clay. The acid salts of iron and aluminum have been used as soil conditioners, apparently with some success in Italy. A flocculating action of these trivalent ions, together with acidity, cause increased friability and permeability in dense clays.

3. Stability of Synthetic Soil Conditioners in Soils

Hedrick and Mowry (90) pointed out that the synthetic polyelectrolytes are highly resistant to attack by microorganisms. Using the soil perfusion apparatus of Lees and Quastel (126), as modified (Fig. 1) by Audus (7), they showed persistence of conditioner-stabilized aggregates after treatment with 0.1% Krilium for 32 months at 76°F, a far longer period than was obtained after treatment with 1% sodium alginate and with a dried compost. They showed, too, that little or no loss of conditioner took place after thorough leaching of the treated crumbs for 6 weeks. Martin (156) reports that preliminary tests with C^{14}-labeled polymers indicate that the polymers combine with the soil particles very quickly in solution and do not move appreciably afterward. When dry mixed and then leached, movement of the polymer occurs, probably during the solution process. Radioactive carbon was not detected in the material leached from a 16-inch column of soil through which passed 39 inches of water. Incubation of a Brookston silty clay loam with C^{14}-labeled polyelectrolyte at 27°C with optimum moisture, resulted in the production after 39 days of $C^{14}O_2$ equivalent to 0.97% of the conditioner, 13% of this being in the first 24 hours of incubation. Field tests indicate the marked persistence of the aggregations caused by the synthetic polyelectrolytes, but plowing and cultivation result ultimately in crumb breakdown. In tests where synthetic polyelectrolytes at the rate of 0.05% were added annually for 3 years to Brookston clay loam in a plow layer application, appreciable breakdown of aggregates occurred each year over the levels attained at the time of application. Aggregation at the end of the third season, however, was greater than at the commencement, i.e., 46% in 1950, 54% in 1951, and 65% in 1952, the controls being 50%, 26%, and 32% for the same dates, respectively.

4. Effects of Synthetic Soil Conditioners on Nutrient Availability

Bould and Tolhurst (23) find that application of the sodium salt of hydrolyzed polyacrylonitrile has no effect on exchangeable potassium or exchangeable magnesium of a soil when used over the range 0.05–2% on a dry-weight basis. The polymer has no effect either on available soil potassium, but it increases available soil phosphate, the latter effect increasing with increase of rate of application. The polymer also has no significant over-all effect on the uptake of potassium and phosphate from soil by rye (*Secale cereale*) seedlings grown in plots in the presence and absence of added potassium and phosphate fertilizers. Spectroscopic evidence derived from analysis of kidney beans (*Phaseolus vulgaris*), wheat (*Triticum* sp.), and radish (*Raphanus sativus*) showed that nutrients and trace elements are not rendered unavailable by conditioner treatment. Plant tissue analyses show that so far as nitrogen, phosphorus, and potassium are concerned, soil conditioners do not influence nutrient uptake. Sherwood and Engibous (219) report, however, that availability of mineral elements may be increased by application of soil conditioners. In one case, corn (*Zea mays*) growing on treated soils absorbed more phosphorus than on untreated soil, but rye grass (*Lolium* sp.) did not. This was reversed with respect to the absorption of nitrogen. Neither species showed increased potassium absorption.

5. Soil Erosion

Equal in importance to the experiments that show the effects of soil conditioners on the improvements of crop yields in various soils are those that demonstrate the effects of conditioners in the control of soil erosion. Weeks and Colter (268) have shown that surface soil can be satisfactorily stabilized against the erosive action or rainfall by treating the surface with the soil conditioner. The permeable film produced by the conditioners not only stabilizes the soil but prevents "runoff." The effect is much the same as that due to the application of straw mulch at a high rate. Addition of half to one pound of polyelectrolyte to 100 square feet may provide satisfactory protection to the soil. One set of results on the effects of artificial rainfall on experimental plots showed that erosion equal to a loss of 50 tons of soil per acre was reduced to a loss of 3 tons per acre by application of the soil conditioner.

II. Nitrogen Metabolism in Soil

A. Main Steps in the Nitrogen Cycle in Soil

Nitrogen metabolism in soil covers the sequence of chemical changes undergone by nitrogen in the biological processes that take place in soil until its final liberation into the atmosphere. The main processes comprising this cycle of changes are as follows:

1. The first such process is the transformation of atmospheric nitrogen by soil microorganisms into substances that nourish both microbes and plants. The process is generally known as biological nitrogen fixation and is accomplished by organisms living in symbiosis with leguminous plants (*Rhizobium*) and by other organisms, both aerobic (*Azotobacter*) and anaerobic (*Clostridium pasteurianum*), that proliferate in soil independently of the plant. Other organisms are also implicated in nitrogen fixation, e.g., the blue-green algae, certain photosynthetic bacteria, and some molds and yeasts. Biological nitrogen fixation is the subject of Chapter 5 in this volume.

Azotobacter and *Clostridium* are apparently the most widely distributed nitrogen fixers in soil. They are found also in salt and fresh water, often in association with algae. Winogradsky in 1893 found that *Clostridium* will fix free nitrogen when supplied with glucose, the amount of nitrogen fixed being proportional to the amount of glucose broken down. The fixation of nitrogen is inhibited by the presence of ammonium salts and this inhibition may be counteracted by an increase in the glucose concentration. Thus the ratio of carbohydrate to combined nitrogen determines the rate of nitrogen fixation. An interesting feature of this organism is that it loses its power of nitrogen fixation on prolonged cultivation on artificial media but the power is restored by culture of the organism once again in soil. *Azotobacter* (which was isolated by Beijerinck in 1901 from soil and mud) does not lose its power of fixing nitrogen on prolonged culture on synthetic laboratory media and it requires traces of molybdenum or vanadium for its metabolism (see also Chapters 4 and 5).

In arid soils relatively poor in organic matter, microorganisms form more than their usual proportion (about 5%) of the organic matter, and this is chiefly due to the marked development of *Azotobacter* under the alkaline or saline conditions of such soils. In the chestnut soils of southeast Russia, where almost all of the organic matter is in the form of microorganisms, there are up to 900,000,000 *Azotobacter* cells per gram of soil.

The most important single factor which influences nitrogen fixation in soils is the presence of nitrate. With both *Clostridium* and *Azotobacter* the presence of utilizable combined nitrogen diminishes the rate of nitrogen fixation, ammonium or nitrate nitrogen being effective in this way. Inhibition of fixation by *Azotobacter* is complete in the presence of ammonium nitrogen at a concentration of 0.5 mg of nitrogen per 100 ml. The presence of nitrate or of ammonium salts in the soil also makes legumes resistant to attack by *Rhizobium*, fewer root hairs and nodules being formed. The net result is that, when excess combined nitrogen is available in the soil, little or no fixation of atmospheric nitrogen takes place. The presence of carbohydrates diminishes the effect due to the combined nitrogen.

2. The second process in the cycle of changes in the soil that concern nitrogen is the transformation into ammonium ions of organic nitrogen compounds which arise from autolysis of all forms of biological material, or from the excreta of animals, or from the products of metabolism of living soil organisms. These processes are accomplished by a great variety of soil microorganisms which, while proliferating either aerobically or anaerobically on organic nitrogen compounds, produce ammonium ions in the course of their metabolism. They may also be brought about by the operation of hydrolytic or oxidizing enzymes present in soil microorganisms whether they are proliferating or are in a resting state.

3. The third process is the conversion of ammonium cations into nitrite and nitrate anions. This process is usually referred to as soil nitrification and is accomplished largely by two groups of organisms: *Nitrosomonas* (also *Nitrosocystis* and *Nitrosospira*), which forms nitrite from ammonium ions, and *Nitrobacter* (also *Nitrocystis* and *Bactoderma*), which converts nitrite ions into nitrate ions. The conversion of certain organic nitrogenous substances into nitrite, without prior breakdown to ammonium ions, by the action of a number of heterotrophic organisms may also occur in the soil.

4. The reduction of nitrate into nitrite and finally into ammonium ions or into free nitrogen is also part of the nitrogen cycle in soil. The process whereby reduction of nitrate (or nitrite) takes place to form gaseous nitrogen (or oxides of nitrogen) is known usually as denitrification. Reduction of nitrate into nitrite and ammonia is accomplished by many microorganisms by the operation of enzymes whose properties are the subjects of many present-day investigations. The

process of liberation of nitrogen and nitrous oxide is less well understood.

Nitrates form the main source of nitrogen for higher plants that grow in soil, although ammonium ions are assimilated by many plants (e.g., certain grasses and forest trees) which grow in soils that do not readily support nitrification.

B. Formation of Ammonia in Soil

It is known that nitrogen compounds in plant residues are decomposed in soil to form ammonia so long as the ratio of carbon to nitrogen in the organic matter does not greatly exceed 10:1.

Proteins and other nitrogenous compounds are broken down in soil by a variety of organisms, the ultimate nitrogenous product being ammonia. Whether the ammonia appears, or not, depends upon the rate of proliferation of organisms in the soil requiring the ammonia nitrogen for their own synthetic operations. If ample utilizable nonnitrogenous material, such as carbohydrate, is present, the ammonia nitrogen will not appear, as it is entirely used for building up fresh bacterial or fungal matter. The amount of nitrogen liberated as ammonia in protein decomposition may be generally represented as follows:

$$\begin{array}{c}\text{nitrogen of}\\\text{substance}\\\text{decomposed}\end{array} - \left[\begin{array}{c}\text{nitrogen synthesized}\\\text{by microorganisms}\\\text{for growth}\end{array} + \begin{array}{c}\text{unassimilable}\\\text{nitrogen}\end{array}\right] = \begin{array}{c}\text{ammonium}\\\text{nitrogen}\end{array}$$

Proteins, being rich in nitrogen in the form of amino acids, yield ammonia in relatively large amounts. Many organisms are involved in ammonia formation, the mechanisms of which may vary from organism to organism. The amino acids yield ammonia by the exercise of oxidizing or reducing systems in either resting or proliferating organisms, the amounts being greatly dependent on the aerobic or anaerobic conditions of the soil. The process of ammonia production, followed by nitrification, occurs also in muds and in sea water. Observations made in the English Channel (16) indicate that the concentrations of ammonium, nitrite, and nitrate ions undergo seasonal changes during their metabolic transformations.

C. Amino Acids in Soil

Although amino acids are known to exist in soils, their amounts fluctuate very widely. Bremner (24) and Sowden and Parker (222) could find no free amino acids in the soils they studied, but Dadd, Fowden, and Pearsall (45) and Payne, Rowatt, and Katznelson (182) have reported their presence in a variety of soils. Payne and co-workers point out that the air drying of a moist soil greatly increases its free amino acid content.

It is to be expected that the breakdown products of organic matter in soil will contain amino acids but much attention has been given recently to the excretion into the soil of amino acids from roots. Rovira (211) showed that considerable amounts of organic matter are excreted from the roots of seedlings, and Kandler (104) has found that a number of amino acids and amides, including asparagine, glutamine, alanine, serine, valine, leucine, aspartate, and glutamate, are excreted from the excised roots of corn grown in the absence of microorganisms. Amino acids have been found in leachings from the nonsterile sand substrata of a number of plants (108, 109), larger quantities being found when the plants had wilted; they have also been detected among the products excreted from the roots of germinating rice (*Oryza sativa*) (6). It is now well known (250) that aspartic acid and β-alanine are excreted by nodulated legumes (cf. Chapter 5).

The presence of amino acids in the soil stimulates the growth of microorganisms whose products, especially in the rhizosphere, doubtless exercise specific influences on root growth.

The most important product, however, for plant nutrition, obtained by metabolism of amino acids by soil organisms, is the ammonium ion,* whose conversion to nitrate represents a major metabolic process in the soil.

The rapid breakdown of amino acids in the soil is indispensable for normal crop growth. It has been shown (10) that a large number of amino acids and amines (derived by bacterial decarboxylation of amino acids) have a toxic action on plant growth. Of these tryptophan, tryptamine, glycine, and *p*-aminobenzoic acid have the largest effects. Urea and nicotinic acid are also strongly inhibitive. Were these substances allowed to accumulate in the soil, they would undoubtedly exercise a large influence on the development of plants. It is of interest that alanine, glutamic acid, and aspartic acid are without toxic effects —possibly because they represent substances that are more normally involved in plant root metabolism.

D. NITRIFICATION IN SOIL

The metabolic process whereby ammonia and organic nitrogenous substances are converted to nitrate in soil was shown by Schloesing and

---

* Under strictly anaerobic conditions in soil, amino acids are slowly reduced to ammonia and the corresponding fatty acids (80). Some amino acids, e.g., proline, hydroxyproline, methionine, tryptophan, leucine, valine, are very resistant to such attack.

Müntz (214–217), from a study of the purification of sewage waters by land filters, to be a biological process. Warington found that soil nitrification is inhibited by the application of chloroform and carbon disulfide, and both he and the Franklands (59, 267) established the fact that nitrification proceeds in two stages, ammonia being oxidized to nitrite and the nitrite to nitrate. Winogradsky (275) succeeded in isolating the responsible organisms in pure culture, an achievement of considerable importance for the study of autotrophic organisms. Organic matter was shown to be unnecessary for their metabolism and, in fact, it was stated to be injurious to their development. Warington concluded that the final fate of nitrogen in the soil is the formation of nitrate. Much important work on the behavior of nitrifying organisms in pure culture has been carried out by Meyerhof (161–163) and others; details of the early history of this subject will be found in articles by Quastel and Scholefield (196) and Delwiche (47).

1. Autotrophic Nitrification

The autotrophic nitrifying organisms, belonging to the *Nitrosomonas* and *Nitrobacter* groups, are mainly responsible for the conversion of ammonium ions into nitrite and nitrate in soil. These organisms have requirements for calcium and magnesium ions (22, 113) and probably also for copper (121, 170). A need for iron by *Nitrosomonas* has been demonstrated (159, 277).

The development of a soil perfusion, or percolation, technique by Lees and Quastel (128a–c) made it possible to study nitrification in soil in a more satisfactory manner than hitherto, and a variety of models for the study of soil metabolism by this technique is now available (7, 78, 120b, 122). The modification due to Audus (7) has been found to be very convenient. The perfusion technique is now being used extensively for soil metabolism studies.

The technique permits the soil to be treated as a biological whole and the metabolic events that take place in the soil may be studied by this technique with considerable accuracy. Emphasis is placed on the changes brought about by soil under defined experimental conditions, care being taken that the soil itself is not interfered with throughout the experimental period. The principle is recognized that "the *biological* changes taking place in soil are a direct result of the initial chemical stimulus applied to the soil, and are as much a part of the over-all chemical change as the more easily identified metabolic changes themselves" [Lees and Quastel (128a–c)].

An apparatus is used in the perfusion technique whereby a column of soil (in the form of sieved air-dried crumbs) is perfused with oxygenated or aerated fluid by a circulatory system. This same soil solution is made to percolate through the soil for an indefinite period. The soil perfusate is adequately mixed and aerated and the perfusion is intermittent, so that waterlogging of the soil does not occur. The process is automatic and may be maintained for an indefinite period. The substance whose metabolism is being investigated is dissolved in the perfusion fluid or mixed with the column of soil. Analysis is confined to the constituents of the perfusate, but the soil may be examined after any arbitrary time for analysis of the ions which are adsorbed upon it. The apparatus has many advantages for the biochemical study of soil, and with it many aspects of metabolism are as amenable to study in soil as they are in plant or animal tissues. The soil is, in fact, treated as though it were a living system, every effort being made to ensure constancy of the environment in which the soil is exercising its metabolic functions.

The first studies on the process of nitrification (128a–c), using the soil perfusion technique, confirmed it as a comparatively slow process accomplished entirely by microorganisms. Further experiments gave rise to the conclusion that the rate of nitrification of a given quantity of ammonium sulfate in soil is a function of the degree to which the ammonium ions are adsorbed on, or combined in, the soil in the form of the soil's base-exchange complexes. The greater the amount of adsorption, the faster was the nitrification.

The interpretation of these results was that *under soil conditions* the nitrifying bacteria grow on the surfaces of the soil crumbs, at the sites where ammonium ions are held in base-exchange combination, and they proliferate at the expense of such adsorbed ammonium ions. It has been confirmed by Jansson (97), using N^{15} in his studies of soil nitrogen transformation, that nitrifying flora metabolize adsorbed ammonium ions and that exchangeable ammonium ions are nitrified before the release of fixed ammonium. These facts do not imply, of course, that *Nitrosomonas* cannot proliferate except in the presence of particulate matter or of solid surfaces. It is known that the organisms can grow under optimal nutritional conditions in the absence of particulate matter (76, 132). The facts, however, indicate that under field conditions, nitrification takes place largely at the expense of base-exchangeable ammonium ions.

Lees and Quastel (128a–c) concluded that, when all the relevant sites on soil crumb surfaces have been occupied, further growth of the organisms will not occur except to replace cells which have died and disintegrated. Remarkably few living nitrifying cells enter into the soil solution. There arose, therefore, the conception of a bacteria-saturated soil; that is to say, a soil in which the area of proliferation is limited and cannot be extended owing to full occupancy of the available sites for proliferation. Such a bacteria-saturated soil may be made to yield information as to whether any given substance is broken down by the cells which saturate the soil. If an organic nitrogen compound, for example, is broken down and is oxidized to nitrate by nitrifying cells, then the course of nitrate formation in a soil saturated with such cells should be linear and should show no initial lag period. If a lag phase does take place, the inference is that the compound in question needs attack by organisms other than the nitrifiers before nitrification can take place. In this way it has been proved that aliphatic amines, which are nitrified in soil, require organisms other than the nitrifiers to effect their initial decomposition.

Another phenomenon that has been observed is the remarkable bacteriostatic effect of potassium chlorate on the organisms that convert nitrite to nitrate (127). Small concentrations of chlorates, e.g., $10^{-6}M$, have the power of preventing the proliferation of *Nitrobacter*, whereas that of *Nitrosomonas* proceeds unchecked. The result is that when nitrogenous substances are nitrified in soil in the presence of small quantities of chlorates, nitrites but not nitrates accumulate. Potassium chlorate acts as a typical bacteriostatic agent. It does not poison or interfere with the bacterial oxidation of nitrite to nitrate, for with a bacteria-enriched soil the conversion of nitrite to nitrate proceeds at a constant rate uninfluenced by concentrations of chlorate which inhibit proliferation of the organisms involved. Chlorate bacteriostasis may be reversed by the presence of nitrates.

2. Effects of Changes of Hydrogen Ion Concentration on Soil Nitrification

The buffering power of a soil plays an important part in determining the rate of nitrification of ammonium salts. The optimum rate of nitrification by *Nitrosomonas* in pure culture takes place at pH 8.5, the lower limit being pH 4. Since the oxidation of ammonium ions brings about the formation of nitric acid it is obvious that the pH will fall during nitrification unless there is good buffering. One of the most important of the factors that control soil buffering is the amount of calcium carbonate present. In fact the addition of sodium bicarbonate to acid, or slightly acid soils, will improve the rate of nitrification, but the action is not so well sustained as in the presence of chalk. Admixture of sodium salts of organic acids, such as pyruvic, succinic, or acetic acids, will also improve the rates of nitrification in acid soils, in much the same manner as sodium bicarbonate. The accelerating action of these salts of organic acids is due to their conversion by soil heterotrophic organisms into sodium bicarbonate, which then increases the soil pH. Addition of glycerol, or of glucose, to soil does not increase the rate of nitrification of ammonium ions, there being no increase of the pH of the soil, and it usually depresses the rate. This effect of glycerol (or glucose) is partly due to the mobilization of nitrogen, either from ammonia or from nitrate, by the heterotrophic organisms which assimilate the carbon of these compounds.

When an amino acid is added to the soil, the rate of nitrate formation may differ from that obtained with an equivalent quantity of ammonium ions. For example with a soil of pH 6.5, the rate of nitrate formation from glycine exceeds that from ammonium chloride. A neutral or slightly alkaline soil, however, favors the nitrification of ammonium chloride rather than that of glycine, whereas an acid soil (pH 4.5) fails to nitrify either substance satisfactorily. The reason for the preferential nitrification of glycine over ammonium chloride in slightly acid soils (pH 6.5)—a phenomenon which must be of importance in connection with fertilizer problems—is easy to perceive.

When nitrification of one ammonium ion takes place, two hydrogen ions are liberated, thus:

$$NH_4^+ + 2O_2 \rightarrow 2H^+ + NO_3^- + H_2O$$

When glycine is nitrified, the following is the end result:

$$^+NH_3 \cdot CH_2 \cdot COO^- + 7(O) \rightarrow 2CO_2 + 2H_2O + H^+ + NO_3^-$$

In this case one hydrogen ion is liberated per molecule of glycine, apart from the production of carbon dioxide, and hence the production of acidity will not be as great as during the nitrification of an ammonium salt of a mineral acid. Unless, therefore, the soil is well buffered, the fall of pH per equivalent of nitrogen will be greater when ammonium chloride (or sulfate) is nitrified than when glycine (or any other amino acid) is nitrified. Doubtless the buffering action of the amino acid itself may play, initially, some role in maintaining the pH of the soil, but this cannot be of long duration as the attack of heterotrophs on the amino acids in soil and the liberation of ammonia are very rapid.

3. Rates of Nitrate Formation, and Recovery of Organic Nitrogen as Nitrate, from Amino Acids in Soil

The rates of nitrate formation from such amino acids as glycine, alanine, and glutamic acid on continuous perfusion through a well-buffered garden soil (pH 7.2) do not markedly differ from that from ammonium chloride used at equivalent concentrations (73, 194, 196).

The results indicate that, in spite of the development of heterotrophic organisms which capture part of the available nitrogen, sufficient ammonia is produced to encourage the proliferation of nitrifying organisms at nearly optimal rates. Such a result proves that, under soil conditions, the presence of organic matter in the form of the simple amino acids quoted is no hindrance to the process of nitrification. The initial lag period that takes place between the addition of the amino acid and the start of nitrate formation is of the same order as that obtained with ammonium chloride itself.

A striking exception, however, presents itself with *dl*-methionine, which has a marked inhibitory action on soil nitrification (194). Another amino acid whose presence in soil affects the rate of nitrification of ammonium salts is cysteine. Its depressing effect is in no way comparable with that of methionine (180, 195). Although neutral cysteine retards the nitrification of ammonium chloride, the effect is that of a general slowing down, as would be expected from a fall of pH. With *dl*-methionine however, there is a long lag period during which there is neither nitrification of methionine itself, nor of ammonium chloride added to it. Eventually the lag ceases, doubtless when the methionine is completely decomposed, and then there is a rapid rate of nitrification both of the nitrogen of methionine alone and of the nitrogen of a mixture of methionine and ammonium chloride.

During cysteine perfusion through soil, free sulfate ions are formed and there is little doubt that the initial retardation of the rate of nitrification secured by cysteine is due to the fall of pH consequent upon the acidity produced on the liberation of sulfuric acid from cysteine oxidation. The retarding action of cysteine on nitrite oxidation in soil, may also be partly ascribed to the fall of pH due to sulfuric acid formation (180, 194).

The recovery as nitrate of the nitrogen of the ammonium salt of a mineral acid during the continuous perfusion through soil is very nearly 100%, but this is not the case with the nitrogen of α-amino acids. Typical results (194) shown in Table V indicate that the recovery decreases with increase in the C:N ratio of the amino acid. This conclusion is to be expected as the heterotrophic organisms which proliferate at the expense of the amino acid must use part of the nitrogen for their own development. The greater the quantity of carbon available for proliferation purposes, the greater will be the quantity of nitrogen which will be used to support this proliferation. Hence the smaller will be the quantity of nitrogen which will be available as ammonia at the disposal of the nitrifying organisms. This is an illustration of the well-known fact that the presence of assimilable carbon in

TABLE V

PERCENTAGE RECOVERY OF PERFUSED ORGANIC NITROGEN AS NITRATE NITROGEN
ON CONTINUOUS PERFUSION OF AMINO ACIDS THROUGH
SOIL AT 70° FOR 15 DAYS[a]

Source of nitrogen	Recovered as nitrate nitrogen[b] (μg/ml)	Percentage recovery
Ammonium chloride	138	98.5
Glycine	135	96.5
DL-Alanine	118	84.0
DL-Sodium glutamate	95	68.0

[a] From Quastel and Scholefield (194).
[b] Maximum absolute recovery possible = 140 μg/ml.

the soil diminishes the availability of ammonia, or of nitrate, nitrogen
to the plant.

E. EFFECTS OF ORGANIC SUBSTANCES ON NITRIFICATION OF AMMONIUM IONS

1. Methionine and Analogous Sulfur Compounds

dl-Methionine, as already mentioned, has a highly inhibitory effect
on nitrification of ammonium ions in soil. It greatly retards the rates of
nitrite, or of nitrate, formation from ammonia or from glycine (194).
Nevertheless, according to Lees (123), methionine has no inhibitory
effect on the activities of isolated nitrifying organisms. Under soil conditions, not only is methionine inhibitory to soil nitrification, but so is a
series of substances of analogous constitution. The results given in
Table VI (28) show how all the mercaptoamino acids mentioned bring
about a diminution of the rate of soil nitrification. The mercapto compounds cause a far greater inhibition than the sulfoxides, which in turn
are rather more effective than the sulfones. The highest activity in the
mercapto series lies between S-methyl- and S-hexylhomocysteine. The
increase in the lag period before nitrification begins, brought about by
the addition of methionine, is equal to the time during which any of
the methionine remains undecomposed in the soil solution. It is probable, as pointed out by Frederick, Starkey, and Segal (61), that the
inhibition is partly due to the effects of products of breakdown in soil
of the sulfur compounds, volatile mercaptans and sulfides being formed.
Mercaptans are definitely inhibitory to soil nitrification. Nevertheless,
it has been shown (28) that benzylmercaptan is less inhibitory to soil

nitrification than benzylmercaptopropionic acid, that ethylmercaptan is less inhibitory than ethylmercaptopropionic acid, and that ethylmercaptoacetic acid, which does not give rise to ethyl mercaptan, has an inhibitory effect on soil nitrification. It appears, therefore, that apart from the alkyl mercaptans, certain sulfur-containing organic substances may produce inhibitory effects on the nitrification of ammonia in soils. The mercapto acids (e.g., alkylmercapto derivatives of propionic and acetic acids) affect mainly the process of proliferation of the nitrifying organisms (28). Jensen and Sörensen (103) list the following organic

TABLE VI

Effects of $R \cdot SO_x \cdot CH_2 \cdot CH_2 \cdot CH(NH_2)COOH$ on Soil Nitrification[a]

R: Form of sulfur present		x	Time in days for soil nitrification of 50% of the amino acid (in absence of added NH_4^+)	Increase in length of lag period in days preceding soil nitrification (in presence of added NH_4^+)
Methyl	Mercapto	0	14	11.5
	Sulfoxide	1	12	9
	Sulfone	2	10.5	5
Ethyl	Mercapto	0	>20	>30
	Sulfoxide	1	15	13.5
	Sulfone	2	6	10
Propyl	Mercapto	0	>20	>30
	Sulfone	2	3	5.5
Butyl	Mercapto	0	>20	>30
	Sulfoxide	1	4	7
	Sulfone	2	4	4

[a] From Brown et al. (28).

substances in order of increasing toxicity to *Nitrosomonas europaea:* taurine, ammonium thiocyanate, methionine, cysteine, sodium diethyl dithiocarbamate, thiourea (124, 196).

2. Urethanes

Many urethanes are very inhibitory to the process of nitrification in soil. Indeed ethyl urethane is more inhibitory to the proliferation of the ammonia-oxidizing soil organisms than to any other biological process so far investigated. It will inhibit markedly at a concentration of 0.3 mM; far higher concentrations are needed to bring about narcotic effects in the higher animals.

Meyerhof (161–163) showed that alkyl urethanes inhibit the respiration of nitrite-oxidizing organisms, the inhibitory power increasing with increasing size of the aliphatic radical. Ethyl urethane inhibits the respiration of an isolated pure culture of *Nitrosomonas* by 42% at a concentration of 16 m*M*. Lees and Quastel (128a–c) found a higher sensitivity of the process of nitrification to ethyl urethane under soil conditions and showed that the effect is reversible. It was subsequently pointed out (194) that although 10 m*M* ethyl urethane completely suppresses nitrification of 10 m*M* ammonium chloride in garden soil for about 20 days, the final rate of nitrification proceeds normally. The nitrate recovered accounts for 80% of the total nitrogen of the ammonium chloride and ethyl urethane. The ethyl urethane is ultimately, itself, converted to nitrate. It was concluded (196) that nitrification of an ammonium chloride-urethane mixture takes place only when organisms capable of breaking down the urethane have developed in the soil and that the urethane, at low concentrations, interferes with an aspect of ammonia metabolism which is essential for the development of the nitrifying organisms (194). Studies of the mode of breakdown of ethyl urethane in soil showed (197) that it is first broken down to ethanol, ammonia, and carbon dioxide with subsequent formation of acetic and nitric acids.

3. Herbicidal Activity and Inhibition of Nitrification

Urethanes, such as isopropyl carbanilate and ethyl carbanilate, having high herbicidal activities, have marked inhibitory effects on the nitrification of ammonium ions in soil. On the other hand, ethyl urethane, a powerful inhibitor of soil nitrification, has but little herbicidal activity. There is, therefore, no complete parallel between the inhibition of nitrification and the herbicidal action of the urethanes. Nevertheless, there is some connection between these two properties, for the most active herbicidal urethanes tend to be the most active inhibitors of nitrification. Some typical results are shown in Table VII. The substituted ureide known as CMU [$Cl \cdot C_6H_4 \cdot NH \cdot CO \cdot N(CH_3)_2$], which is a powerful herbicide, is also a powerful inhibitor of soil nitrification (197). It is of interest that the presence of various urethanes in soils greatly inhibits the rate of nitrate formation from ethyl urethane itself, and there is evidence that specific enzymes are formed by adaptation in the nitrifying organisms that are capable of attacking various urethanes.

The mode of action of urethanes, either as herbicides or as inhibitors of nitrification, is unknown; it seems possible that the urethane may inhibit a reaction which is common to both processes—perhaps a reaction involving an early metabolic step in the utilization of the ammonium ion both in the plant or in the nitrifying organism.

4. Other Organic Inhibitors of Soil Nitrification

Work with pure cultures of nitrifying organisms (161–163) and the soil perfusion technique (128a–c) has shown that guanidine is a highly effective inhibitor of nitrification of ammonium ions. The effect of guanidine is to produce a long lag, extending to about 20 days, before nitrification commences. The rate of nitrification then proceeds normally (196).

Thiourea and allylthiourea inhibit soil nitrification at low concentrations (e.g., 0.3 mM) (196). Thiourea is toxic to higher plants (173) and

TABLE VII

EFFECTS OF VARIOUS URETHANES (3.3 mM) ON RATES OF SOIL NITRIFICATION AT 70°F OF 10 mM AMMONIUM CHLORIDE[a]

Urethane used in presence of 10 mM ammonium chloride	Time in days to produce 70 μg/ml nitrate nitrogen	Estimated lag period before nitrification begins
None	9	0
Isopropyl carbanilate $C_6H_5 \cdot NH \cdot CO \cdot O \cdot CH(CH_3)_2$	41	32
Ethyl-N-butyl carbamate $C_4H_9 \cdot NH \cdot CO \cdot O \cdot C_2H_5$	38	29
Ethyl carbamate (urethane) $NH_2 \cdot CO \cdot O \cdot C_2H_5$	20	11
Ethyl carbanilate $C_6H_5 \cdot NH \cdot CO \cdot O \cdot C_2H_5$	15.5	6.5
Ethyl-N-isopropyl carbamate $(CH_3)_2CH \cdot NH \cdot CO \cdot O \cdot C_2H_5$	15	6

[a] From Quastel and Scholefield (197).

inhibits *Nitrosomonas* in pure culture (103, 124). Conceivably its effect may be due to combination at low concentrations with metallic ions, e.g., copper, which may play a role in the process of soil nitrification (120a, 121, 170). Jensen (100) has found that thiourea, which is not an available source of nitrogen to higher plants, will support the growth of fungi.

It is of interest to note the effects on ammonia oxidation in soil by a variety of organic-nitrogen compounds. Using the Warburg manometric technique, it is possible to estimate the rates of oxygen consumption of soils enriched with nitrifying organisms both in the absence and presence of ammonium ions and other substances. In this way Quastel and Scholefield (194) were able to demonstrate the highly inhibitory effect of thiourea on the process of ammonia oxidation by nitrifying cells in soil. Since that time the manometric technique has become increasingly used for the study of soil microbial metabolism (30, 39a, b, 72, 112a, b, 196, 198, 210). Some results which show qualitatively the effects of a number of organic nitrogen compounds on the oxygen consumption of soils which are oxidizing ammonium ions are given in Table VIII (196).

TABLE VIII

The Effects of Various Compounds on the Oxygen Consumption of Soils[a]

Substance	Inhibition of respiration of enriched nitrifying soils in presence of NH_4Cl
Methylamine	+
Ethylamine	0
Ethanolamine	0
Ethylurethane	+
N-Methylurethane	+
Guanidine	+
N-Methylguanidine	+
Arginine, creatine, glycine	0
Methionine sulfoxide	+
Urea, acetamide	0
Thiourea	+

[a] From Quastel and Scholefield (196).

No doubt these effects are brought about by the inhibition of one or more of the processes involved in the nitrification of ammonium ions, the details of which are still obscure.

F. Oxidation of Nitrite in Soil

Since the discovery and isolation of the organisms responsible for nitrite oxidation in soil by Winogradsky (275) and the early studies of Meyerhof (161–163), little was known about the process of nitrite conversion to nitrate in soil until the advent of the soil perfusion technique. By this method, the rate of oxidation of nitrite in soil was followed (128a–c) and the fact that increasing concentrations of nitrite in soil give rise to increasing lag periods before nitrite metabolism commences was established. Moreover, it was shown that soils that have been exposed to high concentrations of nitrite acquire the ability to oxidize nitrite at higher rates than soils that have been exposed to low concentrations of nitrite (196). A process of adaptation in *Nitrobacter* seems to occur whereby it is able not only to oxidize nitrite at relatively high rates, but also to proliferate in what would normally be toxic concentrations of nitrite. It has been suggested, as a result of studies with suspensions of *Nitrobacter* (129), that nitrite oxidation involves the participation of cytochrome components. Possibly the cells' content of these components is increased in the adaptation process.

Inhibitors of Nitrite Oxidation in Soil

a. Chlorate. The bacteriostatic action of chlorate at low concentrations (10^{-5} to $10^{-6}M$) on the development of *Nitrobacter* was first observed with the perfusion technique (127). Such concentrations suppress the proliferation of nitrite-oxidizing organisms, but that of the ammonia oxidizers proceeds unchecked. The result is that when nitrogenous substances are added to soil in the presence of small quantities of chlorates, nitrites (but not nitrates) accumulate. Chlorate does not poison or interfere with the bacterial oxidation of nitrite to nitrate, except at relatively high concentrations, for with a soil enriched with *Nitrobacter* cells the conversion of nitrite to nitrate proceeds at a constant rate uninfluenced by the low concentrations of chlorate that inhibit the proliferation of the organisms involved (196). However, chlorate at $10^{-3}M$ inhibits oxidation of nitrite by an enriched soil. The chlorate inhibition of *Nitrobacter* growth may be alleviated by the presence of nitrate (127). It has been pointed out (129) that the kinetics of the inhibition of nitrite oxidation by chlorate may be explained on the basis of the destruction, by chlorate, of a cytochrome component in *Nitrobacter* whose concentration determines the rate of oxidation of nitrite. Chlorate, however, does not inhibit nitrite oxidation directly but is converted, during the course of nitrite oxidation, into a substance, presumably chlorite, which is inhibitory. It is well known that chlorite is highly inhibitory to bacterial growth and that chlorite may be derived from chlorate by certain microorganisms (202). The alleviating action of nitrate is held to be due to its retardation of chlorite formation (129).

b. Methionine. This amino acid has a highly inhibitory action on nitrite oxidation in soil (196), the effect being confined to the proliferating cells. The oxidation of nitrite by resting *Nitrobacter* cells, in an enriched soil, is not affected by methyl-, or ethyl-, mercaptacetate or mercaptopropionate at concentrations that are inhibitory to the growing organisms in soil (28).

c. Other inhibitors of nitrite oxidation in soil. Nitrourea is highly inhibitory to *Nitrobacter* oxidation of nitrite in soil (196). Possibly the effect is due to the formation of cyanate, which is also an effective inhibitor of nitrite oxidation by *Nitrobacter* (129). The antibiotic chloromycetin is highly inhibitory to soil oxidation of nitrite (196) at concentrations that seem not to affect appreciably the oxidation of ammonium ions. Thiourea is highly inhibitory. Ethyl urethane has no effect on nitrite oxidation in soil, or *Nitrobacter* proliferation, at concentrations that markedly affect the activities of *Nitrosomonas*.

The Role of Oxidation of Hydroxylamine

Kluyver and Donker (115) considered that the oxidation of ammonia to nitrite in *Nitrosomonas* takes place with the intermediate formation of hydroxylamine hyponitrite. Hofman and Lees (96) claim that the oxidation of ammonia by *Nitrosomonas* can proceed, in the presence of hydrazine as an inhibitor, with accumulation of hydroxylamine. Hydroxylamine is highly inhibitory to soil nitrification, but in the presence of pyruvate full nitrification of the nitrogen of hydroxylamine takes place. This is accomplished by heterotrophic organisms by the oxidation of pyruvic oxime formed as an intermediate (128a–c, 200, 201). It has been shown, however, that at low concentrations hydroxylamine may itself be oxidized by washed *Nitrosomonas* cells as rapidly as the ammonium ion (125).

G. CONVERSION OF OTHER NITROGEN COMPOUNDS TO NITRATE

1. Oximes

Certain oximes, notably pyruvic oxime and oxalacetic oxime, undergo conversion to nitrite in soils by heterotrophic organisms which have been isolated and studied in pure culture (98, 101, 130, 200, 201). At least three species of organisms that attack pyruvic oxime are involved; two fall into the genera *Achromobacter* and a third is identified as a *Corynebacterium* (200, 201). Apparently pyruvic oxime is oxidized directly to pyruvic acid and nitrous acid by an enzyme (pyruvic oxime oxidase) which is present in the heterotrophic organisms mentioned. The oxidase is inhibited by certain oximes, e.g., those of phenylpyruvic acid and of α-ketoglutaric acid, which are not attacked by the enzyme in question. This heterotrophic formation of nitrite in soil from oximes is not affected by chlorate, nitrourea, thiourea, methionine, or ethyl urethane (98, 101, 130, 194, 196). It is, however, inhibited by sulfadiazine, chloromycetin, hydrazine, azide, or cyanide (98, 101, 130, 200, 201).

2. Amines (196)

Amines (methylamine, ethylamine, ethanolamine) are converted to nitrate in soil after preliminary conversion to ammonium ions. Methylamine inhibits nitrification of ammonium ions, the inhibition being a logarithmic function of the concentration. Organisms that develop in soil in response to the presence of ethylamine can oxidize this amine but can only feebly oxidize ethanolamine; organisms that develop in soil in response to the presence of ethanolamine can attack this amine but they cannot oxidize ethylamine. Thus organic substances in soil stimulate therein the development, by adaptation, of organisms (or of enzymes) that may specifically attack the substances in question.

3. Amino Acids

Amino acids, as already mentioned, are converted to ammonia prior to nitrification and, apart from cysteine and methionine, they have little effect on the nitrification of ammonium ions. The recovery of amino nitrogen as nitrate decreases with increase of the C:N ratio of the amino acid (194). The amino acids tend to retard the disappearance of admixed nitrite, probably as they themselves give rise to nitrite. Cysteine and methionine, as pointed out earlier, have highly inhibitory effects on nitrite utilization.

Arginine, when admixed with nitrite, gives rise in soil to nitrite and, only after a lengthy period, to nitrate. This phenomenon is due to the gradual liberation from arginine of urea, which is then hydrolyzed by soil organisms to ammonium carbonate, thus raising the soil pH. This in turn facilitates the conversion of ammonium ions to nitrite, the optimum pH for which is 8.6, and, by making available ammonia at a high pH, brings about an inhibition of nitrite oxidation by *Nitrobacter* (196).

Most of the common amino acids (with the exception of threonine and methionine) decompose in soil in a similar manner, a rapid deamination taking place. Some of the carbon and nitrogen of the amino acids are retained in the soil, possibly in a protein form (78, 181, 194). Threonine decomposes very slowly (78), and methionine decomposition depends on the presence of other organic constituents in the soil, e.g., glucose (233).

4. Chitin

According to Veldkamp (248), the addition of chitin to soil results in the development of organisms that attack chitin, with the ultimate production of nitrate. The percentage of chitin nitrogen which can be recovered as nitrate depends on the type of soil and on the soil conditions, but as much as 60% of the nitrogen originally present in chitin has been recovered as nitrate nitrogen.

H. DENITRIFICATION IN SOIL

The problems concerned with nitrate and nitrite reduction in microorganisms have been discussed at length by Verhoeven; Taniguchi, Sato, and Egami; Nason; McElroy and Spencer; Delwiche; and others in a symposium devoted to the subject (149). They will be discussed, here, only as they are relevant to soil problems.

The loss of nitrogen, in a gaseous form, from soils is usually referred to as denitrification. The conditions under which this process occurs are not well understood, but it seems that the loss of nitrogen from the soil is greatly increased by poor drainage and lack of aeration. It may be of considerable magnitude, however, even in well-managed cropped soils and possibly also in lands still in a virgin condition.

Gayon and Dupetit (67a–c) showed that nitrous oxide as well as nitrogen are formed by denitrifying bacteria and pointed out that nitrate undergoes reduction at the expense of organic substrates by the microflora concerned. They reported upon the culture and behavior of some of the microorganisms which are capable of denitrification, two of which they called *Bacterium denitrificans* A and B. Strain A produced N_2O and N_2, strain B formed N_2, on synthetic media. There is probably a universal distribution in soil and water of denitrifying organisms. Very many microorganisms are capable of reducing nitrate to nitrite, the former molecule acting as a hydrogen acceptor to a variety of facultative anaerobes (202) and competing with oxygen as a source of energy for these organisms. Denitrifiers, which were studied by such authors as Gayon and Dupetit, Winogradsky, Burris and Stutzer and others, belong to the genera *Pseudomonas*, *Micrococcus*, and *Spirillum*. Beijerinck (19) demonstrated denitrification with concomitant oxidation of sulfur by *Thiobacillus denitrificans* and *Thiobacillus thioparus*. Kluyver and Verhoeven (116a, b) found that *Micrococcus denitrificans* will bring about oxidation of hydrogen at the expense of nitrate.

As pointed out by Delwiche (149), soils have unique properties that make them very efficient as denitrifying systems. Ammonium ions, derived from organic matter in the surface layers of the soil, are held by the soil colloids by base exchange and there undergo nitrification by the nitrifying organisms. The nitrate formed is no longer held by base exchange and is leached to lower levels of the soil where there are diminished tensions of oxygen. Here the nitrate is reduced to nitrite and finally to nitrogen or is lost by leaching into lower water strata. Chapman, Broadbent, and others (25, 26, 36, 88, 271) have made lysimetric studies of losses of salts in this way, and they have studied the soil nitrogen-loss problem in its various aspects. Using an electrolytic respirometer to study soil denitrification, McGarity, Gilmour, and Bollen (150) have concluded that the criterion for denitrification in well-drained field soils depends, not only on the availability of nitrate in excess of that needed for assimilation by the microflora, but on a critical rate of oxygen consumption whose magnitude depends on such soil characteristics as structure and permeability. It is already known (221) that active denitrification of nitrate occurs only when the oxygen supply is depleted. Thus the oxygen tension in the soil will influence the process of denitrification. This tension will depend on a number of factors, namely, the microflora present, the organic substrates available, the permeability to air, which in turn depends on soil structure and water content, and on the depth of the soil. Wijler and Delwiche (271) found, in soil systems which simulated field conditions, that even less than 1% of oxygen was sufficient to suppress denitrification to about 12% of that obtained under anaerobic conditions.

The evidence indicates that oxygen and nitrate compete as hydrogen acceptors in the denitrifying cells, the affinity for oxygen exceeding that for nitrate. It is of interest that cells which are grown aerobically show a lag period in the utilization of nitrate, thus pointing perhaps to an adaptive mechanism operating for nitrate breakdown.

The denitrification of nitrate to nitrogen or to nitrous oxide leads to a rise in pH. Wijler and Delwiche (271) found that at different hydrogen ion concentrations the gaseous nitrogenous products differ in their amounts; the evolution of nitrous oxide is favored at a neutral or alkaline condition, that of nitric oxide is favored under acid conditions amounting to as much as 20% of the total nitrogen evolved at pH 5. Thus the buffering power of a soil may markedly affect the nature of the nitrogenous gases evolved in denitrification. A fact of importance is that nitrous oxide may itself act as a hydrogen acceptor with many denitrifying organisms, e.g., *Pseudomonas denitrificans, P. (Bacterium) stutzeri* (36, 26, 25, 48, 88, 271).

1. Nitrate Reduction to Nitrite

This process, taking place under biological conditions, involves the operation of an enzyme (202) which is cyanide sensitive (5, 204, 235). The enzyme, now termed nitrate reductase, is a flavoprotein linked with triphosphopyridine nucleotide (169, 172), molybdenum also being involved in the activity of the flavin adenine dinucleotide (cf. Chapter 4). The following general pathway has been suggested (169, 172):

$$\text{substrate} \rightarrow \text{triphosphopyridine nucleotide} \rightarrow \text{flavin adenine nucleotide} \rightarrow \text{Mo} \rightarrow \text{NO}_3^-$$

2. Nitrite Reduction

This process is not well understood. Najjar and Chung (149) conclude that the reduction of nitrite to nitric oxide requires the presence of the pyridine and the flavin nucleotides as electron carriers with possible participation of copper and iron. They consider that the cyto-chromes may be involved in the process. Reduction of nitric oxide to nitrogen seems to involve the same components. Evans and McAuliffe (149) have shown that reduced diphosphopyridine nucleotide and ascorbic acid at pH 3–6 can reduce nitrite to NO, N_2O, and N_2, nitric oxide being the main product. McElroy and Spencer (149) conclude that pyridoxine, or some derivative of it, is directly involved in nitrite reduction and assimilation.

The steps shown in Eqs. 1–4 occur in the reduction of nitrate to N_2 [Delwiche (47)]. This scheme (Eqs. 1–4), however, does

$$NO_3^- \xrightarrow[\text{nitrate reductase}]{2H} NO_2^- + H_2O \tag{1}$$

$$NO_2^- \xrightarrow{2H} NO^- \text{ (nitroxyl)} + H_2O \tag{2}$$

$$2NO^- \longrightarrow N_2O_2^{--} \text{ (hyponitrite)} \tag{3}$$

$$N_2O_2^{--} \begin{array}{c} \xrightarrow{2H} N_2O + H_2O \\ \xrightarrow{4H} N_2 + 2H_2O \end{array} \tag{4}$$

not indicate the mode of formation of nitric oxide, unless this results from the dissociation of nitrous acid thus: $2\,HNO_2 \rightarrow NO_2 + NO + H_2O$. This suggestion is tentative and there is currently much discussion as to the possible role of nitric oxide, nitroxyl, and nitrous oxide as intermediates in the process of denitrification. Sacks and Barker (213) have observed that under some conditions the utilization of nitrous oxide by nitrate-adapted cells of *Pseudomonas denitrificans* show a lag which indicates that adaptation to nitrate does not neces-sarily include adaptation to nitrous oxide; they have also concluded that, in this organism, nitrous oxide is not a necessary intermediate. Allen and van Niel (2) suggest that nitrous oxide is not an inter-mediate in the formation of nitrogen gas from nitrite, but that it is reversibly derived from an intermediate product in the denitrifica-tion process. Kluyver and Verhoeven (116a, b) conclude that nitrous oxide is normally an intermediate in the denitrification process, but they suggest that there are two possible paths of denitrification and that there occurs hydrogenation of an intermediate $N_2O_2H_2$. Using isotopically labeled nitrate or nitrite, Delwiche (48) has observed the conversion of these anions to nitrous oxide (or nitrogen) and the utiliza-tion of nitrous oxide by *P. denitrificans*. With low levels of nitrate these cells quickly adapt to utilization of nitrous oxide, but with high levels of nitrate, adaptation to nitrous oxide occurs after a long lag period. Delwiche concludes that when the supply of nitrate or nitrite is limited the nitrous oxide formed is reabsorbed and reduced to nitrogen gas.

III. Sulfur Metabolism in Soil

Sulfur transformations in soil, involving the metabolism of inorganic sulfur compounds, such as sulfate, sulfide, and polythionates, and of organic sulfur compounds, are of profound importance in the nutrition of plants. Not only does the plant need for its development the sulfur compounds which are obtained only from the soil, but the processes of germination and plant growth are markedly influenced by the presence of sulfur compounds such as hydrogen sulfide or thiosulfate.

A. Forms of Sulfur in Soil

The sulfur of soil exists in various forms, including inorganic sulfates and sulfides and elementary sulfur and also organic compounds which are mostly of biological origin. It has been calculated that from 80 to 90% of the sulfur in soil is present in organic combination and that only about 10–20% is present as sulfate. Plant residues contain organic sulfur compounds; alfalfa (*Medicago sativa*), for example, contains 0.29% sulfur, turnip (*Brassica rapa*) tops 0.9%; and wheat (*Triticum aestivum*) straw 0.12%; this sulfur is eventually transformed into sulfate in the soil.

Much is now becoming known of the biological transformations of sulfur in soil [see reviews by Starkey (231), Bunker (29), and Butlin (31)]. Guittoneau (81) and Roach (206) have shown that sulfur may undergo biological attack with the formation of thiosulfate, and Guittoneau and Keilling (82) have found that heterotrophic organisms can transform sulfur into thiosulfate and tetrathionate. The autotrophs *Thiobacillus thiooxidans* and *Thiobacillus thioparus* accomplish the oxidation of thiosulfate to sulfate and sulfur, and a variety of heterotrophs oxidize thiosulfate to tetrathionate (227). Many years ago Lockett (145) demonstrated that when thiosulfates and other polythionates (except dithionate) are passed through sewage sludge they are oxidized, microbiologically, to sulfate. The polythionates undergo both biological and nonbiological transformations into sulfur and sulfate. Vishniac (251) has shown that the oxidation of thiosulfate by *Thiobacillus thioparus* is accompanied by the formation of tetrathionate and trithionate. Moreover, elemental sulfur may arise in cultures of *T. thioparus* by a nonbiological mechanism, excess thiosulfate catalyzing the dismutation of tetrathionate to trithionate and pentathionate, the latter breaking down to tetrathionate and sulfur (251). It had been suggested earlier by Tamiya *et al.* (241) that spontaneous decomposition of tetrathionate gives rise to sulfur and trithionate. Vishniac and

Santer (252) have proposed a comprehensive scheme to cover the oxidation of thiosulfate, tetrathionate, and sulfur. This scheme envisages that sulfur enters the cell by reversible combination with protein thiol groups, and then it condenses with intracellular sulfite to form thiosulfate, which becomes oxidized by way of tetrathionate to sulfate.

Sulfate reduction is effected largely by a specific group of anaerobic organisms generally referred to as members of the genus *Desulfovibrio*. The culture first described by Beijerinck (19a), and the one to which reference is usually made, is *Desulfovibrio desulfuricans*. The sulfate-reducing bacteria are widely distributed as they are able to grow on various organic substances and also in the presence of elementary hydrogen and they can also tolerate wide ranges of temperature and salt content and high concentrations of sulfide (165). They are readily obtained from soil, mud, fresh and salt water sediments, and sewages. They are responsible for most of the sulfide occurring as ferrous sulfide in marine sediments and in waterlogged soils. It should be recalled in this connection that sulfate is one of the most abundant ions in sea water. Redfield (205) has pointed out that the quantities of oxygen in the sea may have been regulated by the activities of sulfate-reducing organisms, which have the ability to use sulfate as an oxidizing source. The over-all reaction

$$SO_4^{--} \rightarrow S^{--} + 2 O_2$$

is made up of two main reactions which occur in different locations:

$$SO_4^{--} + 2 C \text{ (carbon compound)} \rightarrow 2 CO_2 + S^{--}$$
$$2 CO_2 \rightarrow 2 C + 2 O_2 \text{ (photosynthesis)}$$

Thus microbiological sulfate reduction is an indirect, but important, source of atmospheric oxygen. Presumably much of the sulfide so formed has been laid down in sedimentary rocks.

Apart from the necessity of the presence of inorganic sulfur in the form of sulfate for plant nutrition, there is reason to believe that organic sulfur compounds are also necessary, e.g., for optimal root development and growth. Thiamine is already known to be of importance in this connection. Possibly other sulfur-containing substances, such as biotin, thioethanolamine, lipoic acid, methionine, taurine, may also be implicated.

B. OXIDATION OF SULFUR IN SOIL

Sulfur oxidation in soil takes place usually by the operations of the thiobacilli, but it is also brought about by the photosynthetic purple and green sulfur bacteria. A brief description of the physiology of thiobacilli is given by Baalsrud (13).

Thiobacillus thiooxidans, described by Waksman and Joffe in 1922, converts sulfur into sulfuric acid and is able to withstand considerable acidity, e.g., pH values between 0 and 1, and it may survive for long periods in this acid condition. This group of organisms is economically important because it can cause rapid corrosion of concrete (33). It is of obvious importance in soils as it brings about a lowered pH, with consequent increased availability to the plant of phosphates and certain metallic ions, and possibly also a more favorable pH and improved soil structure for plant growth. Sulfur has been used, in this manner, to combat manganese deficiency, a condition often encountered in soils subjected to excessive liming, or with increased pH, or with a high content of organic matter. However, some of the remedial effects of sulfur in counteracting manganese deficiency may be due to the liberation of thiosulfate (193) as well as to that of acid. *Thiobacillus thiooxidans* is a strict autotroph which oxidizes sulfur, thiosulfate, or tetrathionate to sulfate. Its optimum pH for these oxidations is 2.0 to 3.0, and it fails to grow appreciably above pH 6.0. It is encountered in all soil environments that have become acid by oxidations of sulfur or its compounds.

Thiobacillus thioparus, the first of this group to be described (by Nathanson in 1902 and named by Beijerinck) is a strict autotroph, oxidizes sulfur slowly and polythionates such as thiosulfate with greater rapidity. The reactions involved are as follows:

$$5\,Na_2S_2O_3 + 4\,O_2 + H_2O \rightarrow 5\,Na_2SO_4 + H_2SO_4 + 4\,S$$
$$2\,S + 3\,O_2 + 2\,H_2O \rightarrow 2\,H_2SO_4$$

The organism, which is widely distributed in soils and waters, grows well near neutrality, causing somewhat acid conditions (between pH 4 and 5) which when maintained cause the death of the organism.

Thiobacillus denitrificans, which may be a variant of *T. thioparus,* was described by Beijerinck as an autotrophic organism which oxidizes thiosulfate with reduction of nitrate. It has been established (14) that although nitrate is utilized by the organism, it cannot supply the nitrogen for assimilation; ammoniacal nitrogen suffices for this purpose. The organism can grow aerobically without nitrate, but it needs both nitrate and ammonia for anaerobic growth. It develops best near neutrality and oxidizes sulfur, and thiosulfate more rapidly, in accordance with the following reactions:

$$Na_2S_2O_3 + 2\,O_2 + H_2O \rightarrow Na_2SO_4 + H_2SO_4$$
$$2\,S + 3\,O_2 + 2\,H_2O \rightarrow 2\,H_2SO_4$$
$$5\,Na_2S_2O_3 + 8\,KNO_3 + H_2O \rightarrow 5\,Na_2SO_4 + 4\,K_2SO_4 + H_2SO_4 + 4\,N_2$$
$$5\,S + 6\,KNO_3 + 2\,H_2O \rightarrow 3\,K_2SO_4 + 2\,H_2SO_4 + 3\,N_2$$

Some sulfur is usually formed during the thiosulfate oxidation.

Other organisms placed, for the time being, in the *Thiobacillus* family are *Thiobacillus novellus* (228), a facultative anaerobe that oxidizes thiosulfate to sulfate; *Thiobacillus ferrooxidans* (43, 243) an autotroph that oxidizes not only thiosulfate, but also ferrous ions under acid conditions; and *Thiobacillus thiocyanoxidans* (85, 86, 279) a strict autotroph that oxidizes thiocyanate, thiosulfate, and sulfur. Many of the thiobacilli oxidize sulfides at low concentrations, but there exists a group of sulfur bacteria that are apparently adapted to the aerobic oxidation of sulfide or hydrogen sulfide in solution. These are the filamentous bacteria *Beggiatoa* and *Thiothrix* (21). They are able to deposit sulfur in granules within their cells, oxidizing it to sulfate when the supply of sulfide is depleted. Winogradsky (272, 273) reported that they can oxidize two to four times their weight of hydrogen sulfide daily.

A group of sulfur bacteria resembles green plants in that its members require light for growth (119) and contain pigments of the carotene and chlorophyll class. These organisms may be red (*Chromatium, Thiopedia*), owing to high carotene content, or green (*Chlorobium*), owing to the chlorophyll present. The colored sulfur bacteria carry out a reaction, analogous to that in plants, namely:

$$CO_2 + H_2S \xrightarrow{\text{light}} \text{carbon complexes} + H_2O + S$$

They can oxidize the sulfur further to sulfuric acid. They are strict anaerobes and are plentiful (e.g., in certain lakes in Cyrenaica) where sulfur is being produced naturally, and they may there contribute to the sulfur formation. The green bacterium *Chlorobium thiosulfatophilum* oxidizes sulfur, sulfide, thiosulfate, and tetrathionate to sulfate, but *C. limicola* oxidizes only sulfur and sulfide. All the purple and green bacteria are able to develop in the absence of organic matter, using carbon dioxide as their source of carbon and reduced sulfur compounds, the oxidation of which provides energy for growth. They are capable also of nitrogen fixation (134, 135, 266).

1. Oxidation of Polythionates in Soil

Gleen and Quastel (75) used a soil perfusion technique which made it possible to study the transformations of sulfur compounds in soil under conditions which approximated to those in the field; they found that, under aerobic conditions, thiosulfate is transformed in soil to sulfate and tetrathionate, or to sulfate and sulfur, the former products being the more commonly occurring. The presence of relatively high concentrations of phosphate, or of thiosulfate, tends to favor the production of sulfur and sulfate. Soils, exposed to thiosulfate, become enriched with thiosulfate-oxidizing organisms, and such soils will retain their oxidizing activities for several months if they are dried and stored at 0°C. Tetrathionate is oxidized in the soil to sulfate during perfusion at room temperature, the organisms responsible being also capable of oxidizing thiosulfate. Tetrathionate is a normal intermediate in the conversion of thiosulfate to sulfate in soil. The kinetics of thiosulfate and tetrathionate oxidation in soil point to the presence of adaptive enzymes, which oxidize these sulfur compounds, in the organisms involved. Trithionate is oxidized to sulfate in soils, but dithionate is very resistant to breakdown.

2. Effects of Biological Inhibitors on Thiosulfate Oxidation in Soil

Sodium azide (0.01%) and sulfanilamide (0.1%) inhibit thiosulfate oxidation in soil, but the latter acts only by retarding the proliferation of the organisms responsible (75). Chloretone, a narcotic that inhibits nitrification, also inhibits thiosulfate oxidation in soil. The presence of 2,4-dinitro-o-cresol and 2,4-dinitro-o-phenol at low concentrations suppresses thiosulfate oxidation in soil. This indicates that phosphorylation mechanisms may be involved in microbiological thiosulfate oxidations, a fact to be correlated with the observations of Vogler and Umbreit (253) on the esterification of inorganic phosphate during the oxidation of sulfur by *Thiobacillus thiooxidans*. Arsenites, selenites, and tellurites inhibit thiosulfate oxidation in soil, but arsenates, selenates, and tellurates are without effect. Sodium pyruvate is also highly inhibitory, but glucose is without effect (75).

3. Effects of the Presence of Sugars and Amino Acids

In view of the fact that soil, at any time, may contain transient quantities of sugars and amino acids, it is of interest to know the effect of such substances on sulfur metabolism in soil.

Perfusion studies (75) show that the presence of amino acids increases the rate of oxidation of thiosulfate to tetrathionate, possibly by favoring the growth of heterotrophs which are capable of this oxidation (e.g., *Pseudomonas fluorescens*). The presence of glucose, sucrose, or mannitol favors the reduction of tetrathionate to thiosulfate in soil. It is evident that tetrathionate can undergo both oxidation to sulfate and reduction to thiosulfate according to the conditions in soil, the presence of sugars favoring the reductive process. The reduction of tetrathionate to thiosulfate by intestinal organisms is a well-known phenomenon sometimes used for diagnostic purposes (117, 183).

C. Metabolism of Sulfur Amino Acids in Soil

Much of the sulfur in agricultural soils in humid or semiarid regions is organic in character (50, 264). Relatively little is known of the manner in which this sulfur is converted to sulfate in soil.

Using the soil perfusion technique, Freney (62) has shown that cysteine is oxidized to sulfate in soil, the steps in the process being as follows: cysteine → cystine → cystine disulfoxide → cysteine-sulfinic acid → sulfate. The first step is nonbiological, the remainder are biological and in the soil perfusion apparatus exhibit the kinetics characteristic of effects attributable to proliferating organisms. Cystine disulfoxide was observed, as an intermediate, by chromatography of the soil perfusate. Taurine was not detected; nor is it an intermediate in cysteine oxidation.

Although these steps represent the over-all mode of breakdown of cysteine in soil, it must be borne in mind that a variety of soil organisms, when examined separately, will oxidize cysteine to different products. Thus cystine is broken down by *Achromobacter cystinovorum* to sulfur as a final product (15); by *Microsporum gypseum* to sulfite and sulfate (223); by other soil organisms to sulfur, polythionates, and sulfate (233).

Methionine is known to be broken down to mercaptans by the anaerobe *Clostridium tetanomorphum* (278) and to methyl mercaptan and dimethyl sulfide by *Scopulariopsis brevicaulis* (151) and by *M. gypseum* and *Aspergillus niger* (35). It will form mercaptans and sulfides in soil (192). Methionine decomposition, however, takes place very slowly, in soils, compared with that of other amino acids, and no nitrate appears until the methionine has been fully decomposed. Methionine doubtless produces a variety of substances, besides the mercaptans, that can exercise a suppressing effect on soil nitrification. The presence of other forms of organic matter stimulates breakdown of methionine in soil (233).

Using the soil perfusion technique, Frederick, Starkey, and Segal (61) have found that cystine, taurine, and taurocholate readily form sulfate in soils, thiamine is less easily broken down, and such substances as methionine, thiourea, phenylthiourea, ethylxanthate, sulfathiazole, or sulfonemethane show almost no breakdown during a period of 6 weeks' perfusion. Methionine forms, to some extent, methylmercaptan and its oxidized form dimethyl disulfide. Thiourea, which is highly inhibitory to soil nitrification and which is broken down very slowly in an agricultural soil, can be attacked by *Aspergillus* and *Penicillium* with sulfate formation (100).

D. Sulfate Reduction in Soil

The sulfate-reducing bacteria, of which *Desulfovibrio desulfuricans* is a typical example, are strictly anaerobic and use sulfate as the hydrogen acceptor. Sulfite, thiosulfate, and tetrathionate may, however, be used instead of sulfate. Hydrogen donors may be formate, lactate, amino acids, carbohydrates, and hydrogen itself. When it utilizes hydrogen, the organism behaves as an autotroph (32), the energy for growth being derived from the reaction:

$$4 H_2 + CaSO_4 \rightarrow H_2S + Ca(OH)_2 + 2 H_2O$$

Microbiological sulfate reduction may occur at moderate and high temperatures (55–60°C), the cultures showing the characteristics of mesophils or thermophils, the latter of which produce spores. The sporing and nonsporing forms are apparently different groups of bacteria. They are widely distributed and are of great importance in modifying plant fertility in waterlogged or semianaerobic soils. They are also of economic importance as bacterial reduction of sulfate is concerned in the disintegration of concrete, in the corrosion of metals, and in lethal effects on fish in the oceans and in lakes. Oxygen is a strong inhibitor of the metabolism of *Desulfovibrio desulfuricans* (64a).

The process of sulfate reduction involves the participation of cytochrome c_3 (186). This was an unexpected observation, as the cytochromes were not believed to exist in anaerobic bacteria. All the mesophilic (30°) strains of *Desulfovibrio desulfuricans* contain cytochrome c_3 and desulfoviridin, but these pigments are not detectable in the strains of the thermophilic *D. thermodesulfuricans* grown at 50–55°. These organisms do not reduce selenate, but selenate acts as a competitive inhibitor to sulfate (184). Monofluorphosphate, which has a structural analogy to sulfate, is also a competitive inhibitor, but substituted sulfates do not affect the reaction (185). A study by Butlin, Selwyn, and Wakerley (34) of the microbiological reduction of sulfate in sewage sludge has shown that sterilized sludge, fortified with sulfate and inoculated with *D. desulfuricans* yields but little sulfide. The unsterilized sludge, supplemented with sulfate, and inoculated with crude cultures of sulfate-reducing bacteria obtained from sewage, produces appreciable quantities of sulfide. Thus, only when mixed populations of sulfate-reducing bacteria and other microorganisms derived from sewage are used is considerable sulfate reduction obtained. Doubtless increased rates of formation of the organisms which metabolize sewage sludge components are necessary for the production of the hydrogen donors that are required for the reduction of sulfate by the proliferating sulfate reducers. Presumably, similar conditions exist in soils where rapid sulfide formation takes place. Studies of the microbial metabolism in paddy soils (240) have shown that after the initial stages of iron reduction and nitrate disappearance, there is active sulfide formation. Moreover, in the final stage, following initial carbon dioxide production, hydrogen and then methane are evolved. Such soils are rich in sulfate-reducing organisms (65).

E. The Cycle of Sulfur Transformations in Soil

As already mentioned, the interconversions of thiosulfate and tetrathionate in soils involves the activities of both autotrophic and heterotrophic organisms. In fact the conversion of thiosulfate to sulfate may be suppressed if sufficient organic matter (e.g., carbohydrate) is present to stimulate the reduction of tetrathionate to thiosulfate. Another product of thiosulfate breakdown is sulfur itself, which undergoes oxidation by appropriate organisms to thiosulfate and thence to tetrathionate and sulfate. So a cycle of operations takes place in soil, this cycle being extended under anaerobic or semianaerobic conditions, as sulfate, then, undergoes biological reduction to hydrogen sulfide which in turn is oxidized to sulfur [see Butlin (31) or Butlin and Postgate (33) for a description of the sulfur cycle in soils].

The study of sulfur metabolism in soil shows how varied species of organisms may arise that are capable of attacking both the initial substrate and the products derived from it. These dependent organisms develop almost simultaneously, forming a biological complex that accomplishes a cycle of events. In this cycle the sulfur may act in a catalytic role because, by its varied transformations, it secures the growth of the groups of organisms which obtain energy for development from oxidations and reductions of specific sulfur-containing substances. If the cycle is blocked at any point, accumulation of a sulfur product at the blocked point will progress until no further change occurs. Proliferation of the responsible organisms will then cease, for the sulfur is no longer available for energy-yielding purposes and the majority of organisms involved in the cycle will then cease to multiply and will disintegrate, leaving only a few hardy members to carry on operations again when favorable conditions return (192).

F. Influence of Manganese Dioxide

It is well established that under optimal aerobic conditions the transformations of sulfur compounds in soil lead to maximum yields of sulfate. It is noteworthy that the properties of manganese dioxide, which can accomplish the oxidation of sulfides and thiol compounds, ferrous ions, polyphenols, etc. (95), have important consequences in soil chemistry. It is well known that thiol compounds act in a harmful manner in soil either by depriving soil microflora of oxygen or by encouraging the development of anaerobes or by accomplishing specific toxic effects on the plant. The presence of manganese dioxide in a soil, will, so long as it is in excess, render the soil relatively free from thiol compounds. When the anaerobic conditions are replaced by aerobic, the manganese ions are reconverted to manganese dioxide and the soil store of this substance is replenished. Thus the manganese dioxide-manganese cycle acts as an oxidation buffer system protecting the soil organisms, including the higher plants, against deleterious agents such as a variety of sulfur compounds and a variety of other reducing bodies. It may well be that an indispensable constituent of a fertile soil is the presence in it of such a substance as manganese dioxide that will accomplish the oxidation of toxic compounds formed when the oxygen supply becomes limited or when it disappears altogether.

G. Herbicidal Effects of Thiosulfates

The herbicidal effects of thiosulfates are relevant to the subject of sulfur metabolism in soil in relation to plant nutrition. Table IX indi-

TABLE IX
Effects of Sodium Thiosulfate on Plant Growth[a]

Plant	Concentrations (mM) producing 50% inhibition	
	Of root growth	Of germination
Garden pea	4.0	31.0
Cress	4.7	26.0
Cabbage	6.0	20.0
Rape	10.0	25.0
Maize	11.0	31.0
Flax	20.0	33.0
Radish	25.0	80.0
Mustard	27.0	15.0
Carrot	41.0	38.0

[a] From Audus and Quastel (11).

cates the concentrations of thiosulfate required to bring about 50% inhibition of the normal rates of germination and of root growth of various plants in water culture (11). It is obvious that there are selective herbicidal effects, the root growth of the garden pea (*Pisum sativum*) being far more sensitive to thiosulfate than that of carrot

(*Daucus carota* var. *sativa*). The reason for the toxicity of thiosulfate to root growth of certain plants is unknown. Dithionate and trithionate are ten times less effective than thiosulfate under the identical experimental conditions.

IV. The Rhizosphere and Plant Nutrition*

Hiltner (93) proposed the term "rhizosphere" to denote a region of soil in the immediate environment of plant roots, that is, a place where the soil is greatly influenced by the roots. He considered that the many microorganisms which are present in the rhizosphere play an important role in plant growth. The dimensions of the rhizosphere are variable and depend on the soil and the plant, the largest effects of the plant appearing at the root surface and in the soil in contact with the root "but effects may extend for several millimetres beyond the root where fungus mycelium penetrates the soil from the rhizosphere which is the food base" [Starkey (232)].

A. Microorganisms in the Rhizosphere

Evidence indicates that the rhizosphere microflora differs qualitatively and quantitatively from that in the soil more distant from the roots. This applies to a large variety of organisms including ammonifying and denitrifying bacteria, clostridia, etc. (46, 105, 142, 254). Results obtained by Katznelson, Rouatt, and Payne (110) of a microbiological analysis of the rhizosphere of wheat roots and of neighboring control soils are shown in Table X. Not only is it obvious that the rhizosphere is very favorable for microbiological proliferation, but there are striking increases in the numbers of ammonifying and denitrifying bacteria and of aerobic cellulose-decomposing organisms compared with those in the control soils. There is no increase in *Azotobacter* and nitrifying bacteria and there is a decrease in the number of algae.

Bacteria are more abundant in the rhizosphere than in more distant soils and many studies (e.g., 226) serve to indicate that the soils in the immediate neighborhood of plant roots are very favorable for microbiological development. The microbiological population of the rhizosphere is affected by the species of plant and its stage of growth; the largest effects are obtained when the plant is actively developing and the effects disappear when the plant dies. Thus the population of the rhizosphere is dependent on the growth of the plant involved.

Although the largest effects are seen in bacterial numbers, significant increases in the rhizosphere of actinomycetes and fungi also occur.

---

* For reviews of this subject see Starkey (224, 225), Katznelson *et al.* (106), Clark (41).

Where mycorhizae are formed, fungi are the dominant root organisms and they affect favorably the growth of a variety of plants, particularly the Coniferae.

B. Nutrients, Vitamins and Cofactors, and Other Organic Substances in the Rhizosphere

1. General

It has been suggested that the microflora at the root surface arises chiefly from the seed coat (83, 211) and that the rhizosphere microorganisms are derived from both the seed coat and the soil. There seems

TABLE X

Numbers[a] of Soil Microorganisms in the Rhizosphere[a,b]

Groups or organisms	Numbers in control soil	Numbers in rhizosphere soil
Total bacteria	52.7×10^6	1121×10^6
Fungi	1.2×10^5	11.6×10^5
Protozoa	990	2410
Algae	26.9×10^3	4.5×10^3
Ammonifying bacteria	1.8×10^6	$>100 \times 10^6$
Denitrifying bacteria	1.4×10^5	126×10^5
Nitrifying bacteria	10^5	10^5
Bacterial spores	5.7×10^5	9.3×10^5
Aerobic cellulose-decomposing bacteria	2.7×10^3	720×10^3
Anaerobic cellulose-decomposing bacteria	1.2×10^5	9.1×10^3
Anaerobic bacteria	6.5×10^6	11.8×10^6

[a] Average of five samples.
[b] From Katznelson et al. (110).

to be little doubt, however, that the determining factors which control the rhizosphere population are the nutrients and cofactors which are made available by the plant roots.

Two groups of substances are involved as nutrients in the rhizosphere—the cellular debris derived from roots and substances excreted from the roots. These include sugars, amino acids, vitamins or cofactors such as thiamine, biotin, p-aminobenzoate, meso-inositol, and also a variety of compounds such as alkaloids and tannins.

2. Vitamins and Growth Factors

Lochhead and Burton (139) have pointed out that soil normally contains vitamins and growth factors which are essential for the growth of many soil microorganisms. It was shown (141) that organisms exist that depend on a variety of substances to be found in soil extract, including vitamin B_{12} (143) and other factors (138). They calculated (139) that of 499 bacteria isolated on a nonselective basis from soil extract agar plates, 28.4% (representing 14.9 millions bacteria per gram of the soil studied) require one or more vitamins for their growth. The vitamins, either singly or collectively, required by the greatest numbers of bacteria are, in order of requirement: thiamine, biotin, vitamin B_{12}, pantothenic acid, folic acid, nicotinic acid, and riboflavin (140). It is evident, as already pointed out (209), that the vitamin content of the

TABLE XI

INCIDENCE IN SOIL AND CROP RHIZOSPHERES OF BACTERIA CAPABLE OF SYNTHESIZING VARIOUS GROWTH FACTORS[a]

Growth factor produced	Control soil		Rye rhizosphere		Barley rhizosphere	
	Percentage of total isolates	Number (10^6/gm)	Percentage of total isolates	Number (10^6/gm)	Percentage of total isolates	Number (10^6/gm)
Thiamine	35.5	41	32.4	375	56.7	1487
Biotin	19.6	23	15.2	176	32.7	858
Riboflavin	39.2	45	35.2	407	67.3	1765
Vitamin B_{12}	29.9	35	33.3	385	34.6	907
Terregens factor	22.4	26	19.0	219	25.0	656

[a] From Lochhead (136, 137).

soil is an important determinant of the types and numbers of microorganisms in soil; this obviously applies in marked degree to the rhizosphere.

Schmidt and Starkey (218) in studies of the decomposition of added riboflavin or pantothenic acid in soil, showed that these vitamins are rapidly broken down by soil microorganisms. They are formed during the decomposition of plant residues in the soil, microbial activity resulting initially in marked increases, followed by decreases, in the vitamin content. Thus the concentration of a growth factor in the soil at any time depends on the relative velocities of liberation or synthesis of the factor and of its destruction.

Results obtained by Lochhead (136, 137), given in Table XI, show that bacteria isolated from the rhizosphere, as well as from the control soil, are capable of synthesis of vitamins and cofactors. The absolute numbers of bacteria which are capable of producing growth factors are much higher in the rhizosphere than those in more distant soil. Although such data indicate the potentialities of soil bacteria (especially those in the rhizosphere) for the formation of vitamins that are important for plant growth, they do not establish that such vitamins are in fact formed in soil. It is reasonable, however, to conclude that they are formed during bacterial proliferation in soil but that their amounts (free) in the soil, as extracellular available vitamins, will depend on the rates at which they are being assimilated and decomposed by soil organisms, including the plant roots themselves. Lochhead (136, 137) emphasizes the fact that growth-promoting factors in soil should be considered in all problems concerning the influence of microbes in soil, particularly so in problems of plant growth and health where the growth promoter aspects of the rhizosphere may assume considerable practical importance.

3. Amino Acids

Various reports (104, 107, 143, 208, 265, 269) have indicated that there is a preponderance in the rhizosphere of those bacteria which require amino acids for their optimal growth, and it is now clear that plant roots excrete amino acids into the rhizosphere (cf. Chapter 5).

According to Kandler (104), the following amino acids are excreted from the excised roots of corn (*Zea mays*) grown in the absence of microorganisms: alanine, aspartic acid, asparagine, glutamic acid, glutamine, leucine, serine, and valine. The amounts excreted depend on the concentration in the roots. As early as 1920 Lyon and Wilson (147) showed that plants grown in sterile media excrete nitrogenous substances, and Virtanen and Laine (250) demonstrated that nodulated legumes secrete aspartic acid and β-alanine, no excretion being obtained with uninoculated legumes. Katznelson *et al.* (109, 182) have shown that when roots in sand or in sandy soils are dried and remoistened, appreciable amounts of amino acids, and some reducing compounds, are liberated. It seems probable, therefore, that in field soils, where there is frequent drying and remoistening, this effect takes place, amino acids thus being liberated into the rhizosphere; the following amino acids have been identified: alanine, aspartic acid, cysteine, glutamic acid, glycine, leucine, lysine, phenylalanine, proline. Sterile sand, in which seedlings of peas (*Pisum sativum*) and oats (*Avena sativa*) have been grown for 10 or 21 days, when extracted with water, yields many amino acids, more with peas than with oats [Rovira (212)]. Roots of germinating rice (*Oryza sativa*) excrete aspartic acid, glutamic acid, lysine, and tryptophan; with some varieties (resistant to root rot by *Fusarium moniliforme*) the amino acids asparagine, cystine, methionine, and tyrosine are also released (6).

The amounts of amino acids in the rhizosphere depend on their rates of excretion from plant roots (or formation from decomposing plant and microbial proteins in the soil) and their rates of assimilation and decomposition by ammonifying, denitrifying, and nitrifying bacteria [Quastel and Scholefield (196)]. Conditions may arise when the amino acids are broken down anaerobically in the soil, ammonia and volatile fatty acids being formed [Greenwood and Lees (80)]. However, the speed of anaerobic breakdown of amino acids in soil is much less than that which occurs aerobically, deamination under anaerobic conditions being five to ten times slower than under aerobic conditions.

It should be noted that amino acids are also taken up by plant roots and that this uptake can be suppressed by plant growth inhibitors such as 2:4 dichlorophenoxyacetic acid (Wright, 278a).

4. Other Substances Formed in the Rhizosphere

Tartaric acid, oxalic acid, D-xylose, and D-fructose have been found in exudates of roots of sorghum (*Sorghum vulgare*) and mustard (*Brassica juncea*) (20); malic acid, citric acid, glucose, and maltose have also been found in exudates of mustard roots. Glucose and fructose have been detected among the products released to sand by seedlings of peas and oats (211). Purines and pyrimidines as well as amino acids are excreted by the cotyledons of pea seeds during germination (64). Scopoletin (6-methoxy-7-oxycoumarin) is excreted by roots of germinating oats (52, 155). Stolp (236) has claimed that mucoid materials are liberated by young roots; possibly these influence considerably the bacterial proliferation in the rhizosphere. Nucleotides and flavanones, as well as reducing substances, are formed by roots of peas and wheat (146). The active substance in exudates from seedling roots of sorghum, which produces extension growth of root segments of peas and maize, is considered to be a pentose, or a closely allied compound (27); acetaldehyde is a product of excised wheat roots (168).

When some substances are placed on the stems or leaves of plants they may find their way into the rhizosphere and thence to other plants. Thus α-methoxyphenylacetate has been found in the root exudate of plants after treating the shoots with the substance (187) and similar results have been obtained with 2,3,6-trichlorobenzoic acid and 2,3,5,6-tetrachlorobenzoic acid (133).

C. The Microflora of the Rhizosphere and Plant Growth

While it is evident that the microflora in the rhizosphere will be greatly affected by the various organic substances which are excreted by plant roots, or formed by decomposing root cells, other conditions that obtain during plant growth will also have their influence. For example, the tensions of carbon dioxide, oxygen, water vapor, hydrogen ions, and other inorganic ions, which will vary in the close vicinity of the root, according to the nature and amount of root tissue, will all affect the rates of proliferations of microorganisms and their complex interrelationships. For these reasons, it is to be expected, and indeed it is found, that root microfloras will differ according to plant and location.

It seems astonishing that plant roots, in a healthy condition, can withstand the presence of hosts of organisms in the rhizosphere. Their resistance is presumably due partly to the existence in the roots of antimicrobial agents. Virtanen *et al.* (249) have found antifungal agents, in seedlings of rye (*Secale cereale*) and other plants, which doubtless contribute to the resistance of this plant to the fungi. Two of these agents were identified as 2(3)-benzoxazolinone and 6-methoxy-2(3)-benzoxazolinone.

The extent to which microflora of the rhizosphere affects plant growth depends very much on local conditions. Both beneficial and harmful effects may result. Gerretsen (70) has demonstrated that a solubilizing effect of root microflora on the otherwise insoluble phosphates occurs and that solvent effects of rhizosphere microflora occur upon calcium carbonate, this being doubtless due to the local action of carbon dioxide of microbial origin (60, 160). Differences in nutrient uptake are also known to occur between mycorhizal and nonmycorhizal seedlings (41).

A harmful feature, due to the presence of large numbers of microorganisms in the rhizosphere, is the reduction of available nitrogen to the plant resulting from competition by the rhizosphere microflora with the plant for this substance. This, however, is marked only where the percentage of nitrogen in the organic matter is low. This subject is fully discussed by Harmsen and Van Schreven (87).

D. RELATIONS OF AMINO ACIDS, AUXINS, AND HERBICIDES IN THE
   RHIZOSPHERE TO PLANT GROWTH

The extent to which growth substances such as the auxins, that greatly affect plant development, are influenced by the rhizosphere is still largely unknown.

Nutman, Thornton, and Quastel (178) found that β-indolylacetic acid and α-naphthylacetic acid produce marked root hair deformation in agar cultures of red clover and that both substances are toxic to the germination and to subsequent growth of red clover (*Trifolium pratense*) at dilutions of 1 part in 10^7. It has been further shown (178) that, in a sterile agar medium, tryptophan exerts a toxic action on red clover at concentrations which exceed 10 parts per million, but that when *Rhizobium* is present the limit of toxicity is lowered to 1 part per million. These results support the conclusion, from Thimann's (246) and Chen's (40) evidence, that this organism is able to produce β-indolylacetic acid from tryptophan.

It thus appears evident that a growth factor, which affects root development, may be formed by appropriate organisms in the rhizosphere.

TABLE XII

NITROGENOUS COMPOUNDS THAT INHIBIT ROOT GROWTH[a]

Substance	Concentration at which inhibitor of growth of roots of cress seedlings in water culture is detectable (in parts per million)	Percentage inhibition of root growth (cress) at a concentration of 1000 ppm
DL-Alanine	>1000	0
L-Glutamic acid	>1000	0
Glycine	100	50
L-Aspartic acid	100	15
L-Proline	100–1000	30
D-Arginine	100	30
p-Aminobenzoic acid	100	65
o-Aminobenzoic acid	10	94
L-Tryptophan	<10	80
Tryptamine	10	51
Nicotinic acid	10	40
Nicotinamide	10–100	35
Urea	100	75

[a] From Audus and Quastel (10).

Both amino acids and amines may markedly affect seedling growth in water culture. Some typical results, which were obtained by Audus and Quastel (10), are shown in Table XII. In fact, out of a series of compounds so tested only alanine and glutamic acid showed no inhibitive effects on root growth. Tryptophan and tryptamine were highly inhibitory, possibly owing to their conversion in the plant roots to inhibitory auxins. p-, and o-Aminobenzoic acids were also inhibitory to root growth [see also (12)]. It is, therefore, evident that the breakdown of amino acids and related substances by microorganisms in the rhizosphere is an important aspect of the conditions that control plant development in soil.

The common plant metabolite, coumarin, has high phytocidal activity, its effect disappearing in soil (9) like that of β-indolylacetic acid (178). Both substances are broken down by soil microorganisms (178, 246). The rhizosphere can thus be regarded not only as a region in which substances that are beneficial for plants may be formed, but also where substances that are inhibitory to plant development may be destroyed.

It may be pointed out, in this connection, that the selective herbicide 2,4-dichlorophenoxyacetic acid (2,4-D) was discovered (178) in an effort to find a substance analogous in structure to β-indolylacetic acid and with similar growth-inhibiting effects on plant roots, but which would resist attack by soil microorganisms for an appreciable period of time. In view of the considerable agricultural importance of 2,4-D as a selective herbicide, much work has been carried out on its decomposition (as well as on that of related substances) in soil (8a, b, 99, 102, 171, 207). There seems now to be little doubt that such chloro-substituted aromatic acids, applied as herbicides, are removed in soil by biological decomposition rather than simply by leaching or by physical means, and that their persistence in soil depends on the development of microorganisms that become adapted to these substances.

The remarkable effects of gibberellic acid on plant growth and development has led to much discussion concerning its possible application in agriculture. However, its application to most crops that have been studied gave disappointing results (167) since the increased growth of stems and leaves was not accompanied by increased crop yield in terms of dry matter. Grasses gave consistent yield increases, but yields of root crops were reduced. How far microbiological attack in the soil on gibberellic acid is responsible for these results is still undetermined.

V. Studies of Soil Metabolism

A. The Perfusion Technique

The perfusion technique (7, 120b, 122, 126, 128a–c) was primarily designed for the study of metabolic patterns in soils. It has the advantage over techniques which involve the use of pure cultures of organisms in that it enables studies to be made of soil metabolic processes, and of the factors which influence the proliferation of the responsible organisms, under conditions which approximate to those in the field. Investigations are confined to studies of organisms proliferating in contact with the many species of microorganisms normally present in soil. Thus, it may be shown that a compound (e.g., methionine) which normally has but little effect on an organism grown in a pure culture, is highly inhibitory to the development of the organism in soil. This result is due to the compound giving rise in soil to other substances that are highly inhibitory to the organism under investigation. It also happens that a substance highly inhibitory to an organism grown in pure culture (e.g., certain antibiotics) has but little effect on the same organisms as they develop in soil. This results from the rapid decomposition of the substance in soil or from the development of resistant or adapted strains of the organisms under study. Problems of adaptation of mutation may be conveniently investigated with the soil perfusion technique.

1. Perfusion Apparatus

The apparatus used at present [Audus (7)] is a modification of that used by Lees and Quastel (126), as the latter is somewhat complicated and involves the use of a continuous stream of water to produce the intermittent perfusion. The modification (7) is shown in Fig. 1; the technique is described below in some detail.

The soil, 30 gm of air-dried sieved crumbs (2–4 mm in diameter), is contained in a glass tube between pads of glass wool. The perfusing solution is in the separating funnel, F. A constant small suction is applied at A. This suction is transmitted back through the lengths of thermometer tubing, R_1 and R_2 (or other suitable resistances), and the soil column in P to the perfusing solution in tube T. This causes air to be drawn in at the bottom of the side tube, S, thereby detaching a column of solution which is drawn up tube T and falls on the top of the soil column. This discharge releases the partial vacuum, and the solution again rises above the base of S until it reaches the level of the solution in F. More air is then drawn in, through S, and the whole process is repeated. The liquid discharged from tube T perfuses through the column of soil, which thus becomes saturated with fluid and is intermittently aerated. The apparatus may be insulated against aerial organisms by a cotton plug, but this has not been found to be necessary. It may be linked with any source of gas (oxygen, nitrogen, helium, carbon dioxide, or mixtures of these gases) by connecting with an appropriate gas cylinder. For analysis, the suction is stopped and fluid is allowed to rise in S, whence aliquots are removed. After such removal, the suction is restored and perfusion recommences. This may proceed indefinitely. The soil is not handled until the end of the experiment, so as not to interfere with the equilibria established in the soil. The soil may of course be removed at any time for analysis of adsorbed constitutents. Experiments are run in a thermostatically controlled room (21°C) in the dark. As the apparatus is inexpensive and

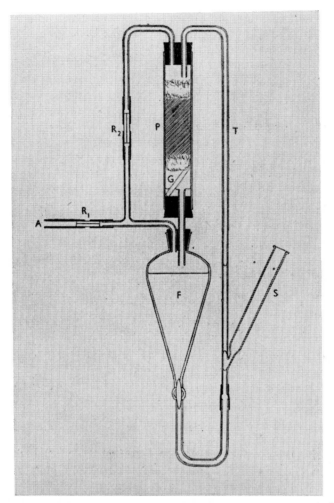

Fig. 1. Apparatus for intermittent perfusion of soil. See text for description of the technique. From Audus (7).

easy to handle, experiments may be run in duplicate or triplicate and many such perfusion units may be assembled into a bank.

A substance whose metabolism in the soil is being investigated is dissolved in the perfusion fluid or mixed with the column of soil. The volume of perfusate is kept constant by periodic additions of water to replace the amount lost by evaporation.

This technique for investigating soil metabolism has a variety of advantages, including the following:

1. The water content of the soil is kept constant and it is homogeneously distributed in the soil throughout the experiment.

2. Maximal aeration of the soil is effected.

3. Gases entering the apparatus can be controlled, and metabolic events in any defined atmosphere may be studied.

4. Substances such as biological poisons or inhibitors may be added to the soil solution (or perfusate) during the course of the experiment, at any period corresponding to a known metabolic activity of the soil.

5. The soil solution can be replaced at any time by a solution of any metabolite whose transformations by a soil with known metabolic activity are the subject of study.

6. Ionic equilibria between soil and solution are quickly established and are not further affected except insofar as the equilibria are disturbed by the products of metabolism in soil.

7. The soil is not handled in any way during the experiment, analysis being confined to the constituents of the perfusate. The soil may be sampled after any arbitrary time for analysis of ions and other substances adsorbed onto the soil.

8. Gases leaving the apparatus may be analyzed for CO_2, etc.

9. The apparatus minimizes biological variation between one sample of soil and another and lends itself to quantitative kinetic studies which may be reproduced with considerable accuracy.

The perfusion unit has been modified by Lees (78, 120b, 122), by Temple (242), and by Collins and Sims (42).

2. The Soil and the Perfusate

Experience has shown that the ideal soil for the perfusion apparatus is one that has been air dried for a week at room temperature and which consists of particles 2–4 mm in diameter. A garden soil or agricultural soil of good structure is to be preferred. Details of the handling of soils from various sources are given by Quastel and Scholefield (199).

In most experiments in which the soil perfusion technique is utilized, no nutrients other than the substrate under consideration are added. Soils do not seem to require the addition of minerals, vitamins, essential amino acids, or any accessory growth factors for metabolism to take place. For example, to obtain good proliferation of the nitrifying organisms in soil it is necessary only to perfuse ammonium chloride solution.

The concentration of a substrate may be varied within wide limits, while ensuring good rates of metabolism. High concentrations produce only an increase in the lag period preceding proliferation, and low concentrations suffer only from the drawback that most of the substrate is oxidized or metabolized before the proliferating stage is reached. In general, a concentration of $10^{-2}M$ substrate has been found convenient.

3. Enriched Soils

When a metabolizable substrate, e.g., ammonium ions, nitrite or thiosulfate ions, manganese or arsenite ions, is perfused through soil, there occurs an initial lag period before metabolism commences. Its duration varies with the type of soil, concentration of substrate, etc. It diminishes with subsequent perfusions. Eventually, after repeated perfusions a constant rate of breakdown of substrate or other metabolite occurs. With each perfusion an increased enrichment of the soil with those microorganisms that attack the substrate takes place, and finally a state of saturation of the soil occurs after which no further increase in the velocity of breakdown of the metabolite takes place. Such a soil is often referred to as an enriched or bacterially saturated soil. With many forms of metabolism in soil, and especially those involving the autotrophs, the entire metabolism seems to occur at the surfaces of the soil particles. When the soil is removed, no further changes take place in the soil perfusate, which is usually water clear and shows remarkably few organisms under the microscope. The organisms are adsorbed by, and probably proliferate at, the soil crumb surfaces.

Such an enriched, or saturated, soil may be used for a variety of experimental purposes (196). It may be used for the metabolic events under study, or it may be used directly for kinetic and stoichiometric studies. Experiments show that such an enriched soil acts in every way as though it were a preparation of resting cells of the responsible organisms. The fact that the soil organisms are not proliferating under these conditions is shown by the absence of any inhibitory effect of such a growth inhibitor as sulfanilamide. Many other properties of the resting organisms in soil may be studied in a similar manner.

Enriched soil crumbs may be used to inoculate fresh samples of soil and so diminish, or avoid, lag periods.

It is known now that a soil may become enriched at the same time with at least two different sets of organisms (198), it being apparent that specific organisms adhere to, or proliferate at, specific sites on the soil crumb surfaces.

When wet "enriched" soils (e.g., those capable of oxidizing thiosulfate) are quickly dried in a current of cold air, they may retain their high oxidizing activities for several months if they are stored between 0° and 4°C. However, if the soils are kept at room temperature, this rapid oxidizing power may be lost in a few days. The retention of oxidizing ability of stored "enriched" soils depends on the efficiency, and temperature, of drying and on the nature of the organisms involved.

B. METABOLIC STUDIES AND MANOMETRIC STUDIES OF SOIL

1. Metabolic Studies

The following are some of the metabolic studies in soil, many of which have a bearing on plant nutrition, that have been carried out by the perfusion technique:

1. Nitrification in soil and nitrate formation from organic nitrogen compounds (37, 38, 78, 128a–c, 194, 196).
2. Effects of chlorates on soil nitrification (127).
3. Effects of alkylthio compounds on soil nitrification (28).
4. Effects of urethanes on soil nitrification and metabolism of urethanes (197).
5. Conversion of oximes to nitrites (200, 201).
6. Manganese metabolism (151).
7. Thiosulfate and tetrathionate metabolism (75).
8. Arsenite conversion to arsenate (198).
9. Iron metabolism (73).
10. Breakdown of indoleacetic acid, coumarin, and herbicides such as 2,4-dichlorophenoxyacetic acid (8a,b, 9).
11. Metabolism of bile acids in soil (84).
12. Thiocyanate oxidation in soil (74).

2. Rocking Percolation Technique

A rocking percolation, or perfusion, technique for soil studies has been devised by Greenwood and Lees (78); this technique allows for measurements of oxygen consumption. It has been modified (79, 238, 270) in such a way that automatically metered and electrolytic generated oxygen within the apparatus replaces the oxygen consumed by metabolic processes. This electrolytic, rocking, percolation unit retains the advantages of the original manometric, rocking, percolating apparatus and allows measurements to be made of oxygen uptake during the breakdown of any substance in a soil at a given partial pressure of oxygen.

3. Manometric Studies of Soils

Samples of soil taken either directly from the field, or from the perfusion apparatus after soil has been enriched with organisms that attack a particular substrate, may be placed in a conventional Warburg manometric apparatus and their rates of oxygen consumption in the presence or absence of the substrates or of other substances may be measured (75, 194, 196). In this way, for example, it is easily shown that for every molecule of thiosulfate added to a suitably enriched soil four atoms of oxygen corresponding to the complete oxidation of thiosulfate to sulfate are taken up (75). The process is affected by respiratory inhibitors and by substances which uncouple phosphorylation and oxidation, so that it becomes possible to make observations on the mechanisms involved in the respiratory process by investigations only on the enriched soils. Again manometric studies of suitably enriched soils show that the theoretical oxygen consumption occurs in the oxidation in soil of arsenite to arsenate (198) and that certain oxides of arsenic and antimony can inhibit this process. Another pertinent example is the manometric study (197) of soils enriched with organisms that decompose ethyl urethane. The oxygen consumed by such soils in the oxidation of ethyl urethane is in accordance with the conclusion that acetic acid is the end product. Acetic acid is, apparently, not further oxidized or is oxidized only very slowly. The kinetic and stoichiometric evidence leads to the conclusion that ethyl urethane is first broken down by soil organisms to ethanol, ammonia, and carbon dioxide with the subsequent formation of acetic and nitric acids [see also (234)].

Katznelson and Rouatt (111) have pointed out, on the basis of manometric studies, that the oxygen consumption of the soil in the rhizosphere is greater than that of nonrhizosphere soils, both with and without added substrates. Manometric studies of soils have been carried out to study the effects of the admixture of soils with straw and straw extracts, with nitrates and ammonium salts on soil respiration (72). Various studies of microbial metabolism in soil, using the manometric method, have been made (30, 39a,b, 51, 112a,b, 210) and these indicate the potentialities of this technique for soil studies in relation to plant nutrition. The use of the manometric method for studies of soil aeration has long been advocated (54, 203) and was of considerable service in the study of synthetic soil conditioners.

C. ROLE OF MANGANESE AND OF IRON

It is known (cf. Chapter 4) that for the healthy growth of plants traces of a variety of elements such as iron, copper, boron, zinc, manganese, and molybdenum are necessary, and probably also of cobalt, vanadium and sodium. The amounts of some of these elements which are required for the healthy development of a given plant may be exceedingly small. Deficiencies of these substances, however, lead to a great variety of plant diseases. It does not follow that, if an essential element is present in the soil, it is necessarily available to the plant.

1. Manganese Metabolism

A deficiency of manganese in soil—and soils rich in organic matter and lime are prone to this deficiency—leads to plant diseases, such as gray speck of oats or marsh spot of peas, and to a substantial reduction in the yield of a potato (Solanum tuberosum) crop or to the complete failure of an oat crop. But many of these deficient soils—as diagnosed by inspection and analysis of the crop—often contain relatively large quantities of manganese. Thus it is apparent that manganese exists in the soil in at least two forms, of which only one is available for the plant. So far as is known it is only the base-exchangeable form of manganese (probably the divalent manganous ions) which is available for the plant. The question now arises why certain soils, which contain ample quantities of manganese, are "manganese deficient" and why other soils, which may contain much less manganese, are "manganese available." This problem is intimately connected with the metabolic transformations to which manganese is subjected in soil.

It is now known (151) that when manganese sulfate is perfused through soil, oxidation of the manganese takes place. In neutral or slightly alkaline soil this oxidation is almost entirely accomplished by the microorganisms which are present. This is so because the rate of oxidation of manganese in soil at 21°C follows the logarithmic course expected if proliferating organisms are responsible for the oxidation, and by the fact that sterilization of a soil, or its treatment with cell poisons and narcotics, may result in a complete cessation of manganese oxidation. It was already known (69, 70a, 188) that soil contains organisms which are capable of oxidizing bivalent manganese, but quantitative studies with the perfusion apparatus have established how much of the oxidation which takes place in the soil is in fact due to microorganisms. Nonbiological autoxidation of manganese in soil had been thought to be a dominant process. Not only is bivalent manganese oxidized to states of higher valency by soil microorganisms, but similar agencies are responsible for the reduction of tervalent and quadrivalent manganese to the bivalent form. Many substances in soil will reduce manganese dioxide, e.g., polyphenols, thiol compounds, and ferrous ions, but bacterial suspensions will also accomplish the reduction so long as there are present traces of such hydrogen carriers as bacterial pigments or hematins. Normally, biological reduction of the higher valency forms of manganese takes place in the soil at the expense of the organic substances present which are themselves oxidized. The presence of glucose, and other carbohydrates, in a soil containing manganese dioxide brings about an increased production of manganese ions, for the glucose stimulates the growth of organisms which accomplish the reduction of the higher valency states of manganese. This phenomenon is seen in the curves shown in Fig. 2.

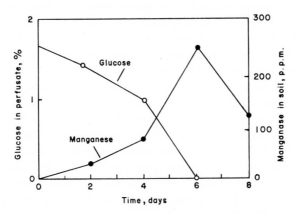

FIG. 2. Effects of perfusing glucose at 21°C on exchangeable (bivalent) manganese of Rothamsted soil. From Mann and Quastel (151).

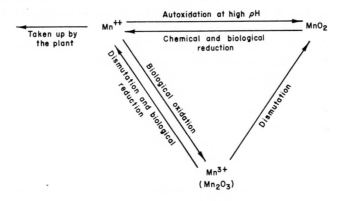

FIG. 3. Manganese cycle in soil under aerobic conditions. From Mann and Quastel (151).

The facts point to the existence in soil of a cycle of biological changes which involve manganese oxidation and reduction, such as that shown in Fig. 3. The kinetics of the processes in this cycle determine the amount of bivalent manganese available in soil at any moment. To prevent manganese deficiency in the field, so long as some form of manganese is present, it is necessary to bring about a suitable shift in the equilibrium. This may be accomplished by sulfur [and possibly thiosulfate (193)] treatment, but it is usually accomplished by spraying with manganese sulfate (for fruits, peas, and oats). Dion and Mann (49) have shown that the first product of biological oxidation of divalent manganese in soil is the trivalent ion which, under acid conditions, gives rise to a mixture of divalent manganese ion and manganese dioxide. This dismutation apparently goes on in soil so that it is clear that the biological oxidation of bivalent manganese in neutral or slightly acid soils eventually leads wholly to manganese dioxide.

Under anaerobic conditions, or in the presence of respiratory poisons such as sodium azide, the manganese equilibrium shifts markedly toward divalent manganese, and ultimately all the manganese would appear in that form if oxidative conditions were completely suppressed.

Manganese dioxide can act as an oxidant, or terminal hydrogen acceptor, in a variety of biological systems (95), and its biological oxidizing properties may have important consequences in soil chemistry. It is well known that thiol compounds act in a harmful manner in the soil either by depriving soil microflora of oxygen, or by encouraging the development of anaerobes, or by accomplishing specific toxic effects. The presence of manganese dioxide in a soil will, so long as it is in some excess, render the soil relatively free from thiol compounds. When the anaerobic conditions are replaced by the aerobic, the manganese ions are reconverted to manganese dioxide and the soil store of this substance is replenished. Thus the manganese dioxide-manganese cycle acts as an oxidant buffer system protecting the soil organisms, including plants, against deleterious agents, such as a variety of sulfur compounds and other reducing bodies.

2. Ferrous Oxidation

Just as biological oxidation of divalent manganese takes place in soil so does a biological oxidation of ferrous ions occur (73). Specific iron-oxidizing organisms are abundant in soil. Any ferric ions, that are formed, can also undergo biological reduction, so it is apparent that, as with manganese, a cycle of oxidation-reduction takes place with iron.

Such cyclic processes involve the proliferation both of autotrophic organisms, which accomplish, for example, the oxidation of divalent iron, and of heterotrophic organisms that bring about the reduction of these substances to lower valency states.

VI. Concluding Remarks

Thus, in this chapter, many of the main features of the soil as a biological system have been described insofar as these considerations bear upon plant nutrition. Considerable attention has been directed to the immediate vicinity of roots, namely the rhizosphere. Without unduly recapitulating what has already been said, it is clear that the relation of the soil to the nutrition of plants is not simple and cannot be explained alone in terms of its physical and chemical properties; for soil is also a dynamic system in which the elements of a complex microflora are interdependent with each other, with the roots of plants, and with many environmental soil factors. It is shown here that these interactions convey to a soil its unique biological and biochemical individuality.

REFERENCES

1. Alderfer, R. B. Gribbins, M. F., and Haley, D. E. Effect of waste sulfite liquor on aggregation of soil particles. *Ind. Eng. Chem.* **36**, 272–274 (1944).
2. Allen, M. B., and van Niel, C. B. Experiments on bacterial denitrification. *J. Bacteriol.* **64**, 397–412 (1952).
3. Allison, L. E. Effect of synthetic polyelectrolytes on the structure of saline and alkali soils. *Soil Sci.* **73**, 443–454 (1952).
4. Arnold, C. W. B. *Ann. Repts. Chem. Soc.* (*Biochem.*), pp. 173–183 (1924).
5. Aubel, E., and Glaser, M. Sur la réduction des nitrites par le Bacille Coli. *Compt. rend. soc. biol.* **128**, 45–49 (1938).
6. Audal, R., Bhuvaneswari, K., and Subba Rao, N. S. Root exudates of paddy. *Nature* **178**, 1063 (1956).
7. Audus, L. J. A new soil perfusion apparatus. *Nature* **158**, 419 (1946).
8a. Audus, L. J. Biological detoxication of 2,4-dichlorophenoxyacetic acid in soil. *Plant and Soil* **2**, 31–36 (1949).
8b. Audus, L. J. The biological detoxication of hormone herbicides in soil. *Plant and Soil* **3**, 170–192 (1951).
9. Audus, L. J., and Quastel, J. H. Coumarin as a selective phytocidal agent. *Nature* **159**, 320 (1947).
10. Audus, L. J., and Quastel, J. H. Toxic effects of amino-acids and amines on seedling growth. *Nature* **160**, 222–223 (1947).
11. Audus, L. J., and Quastel, J. H. Selective toxic action of thiosulfate on plants. *Nature* **160**, 263–264 (1947).
12. Audus, L. J., and Quastel, J. H. The growth-inhibitory activity of the sulphonamides and plant growth substances, and the effects thereon of *p*-aminobenzoic acid. *Ann. Botany* (*London*) **12**, 27–34 (1948).
13. Baalsrud, K. Some aspects of the physiology of *Thiobacilli*. *Symposium Soc. Gen. Microbiol. 4th*, 54–67 (1954).
14. Baalsrud, K., and Baalsrud, K. S. Studies on *Thiobacillus denitrificans*. *Arch. Mikrobiol.* **20**, 34–62 (1954).
15. Barber, H. H., and Burrows, R. B. The production of free sulfur from L-cystine by soil bacterium. *Biochem. J.* **30**, 599–603 (1936).
16. Barnes, H. "Chemical Aspects of Oceanography." Royal Institute of Chemistry, Lecture 4 (1955).
17. Bartholomew, W. V., and Norman, A. G. Determination of uronic groups in soils and plant materials. *Iowa State Coll. J. Sci.* **15**, 253–260 (1941).
18. Beckley, V. A. The formation of humus. *J. Agr. Sci.* **11**, 69–77 (1921).

19. Beijerinck, M. W. Phénomènes de réduction produits par les microbes. *Arch. néerl. sci. II* **9**, 131–141 (1904).

19a. Beijerinck, M. W. Uber *Spirillum desulphuricans* als ursache von sulfareduktion. *Centr. Bakteriol. Abt. II* **1**, 1–9, 49–59, 104–114, (1895).

20. Bhuvaneswari, K., and Subba Roa, N. S. Root exudates in relation to the rhizosphere effect. *Proc. Indian Acad. Sci.* **45**, 299–301 (1957).

21. Bisset, K. A., and Grace, J. B. The nature and relationships of autotrophic bacteria. *Symposium Soc. Gen. Microbiol. 4th*, 28–53 (1954).

22. Bömeke, H. Über die Ernährungs- und Wachstumsfactoren der Nitrifikationsbacterien. *Arch. Mikrobiol.* **14**, 63–98 (1949).

23. Bould, C., and Tolhurst, J. Nutrient placement in relation to fruit tree nutrition. *Ann. Rept. Agr. Hort. Research Station, Long Ashton Bristol*, pp. 49–59 (1952).

24. Bremner, J. M. The amino acid composition of the protein material in soil. *Biochem. J.* **47**, 538–542 (1950).

25. Broadbent, F. E. Denitrification in some California soils. *Soil Sci.* **72**, 129–137 (1951).

26. Broadbent, F. E., and Chapman, H. D. Lysimeter investigation of gains, losses, and balance of salts and plant nutrients in irrigated soil. *Soil Sci. Soc. Am. Proc.* **14**, 261–269 (1950).

27. Brown, R., Robinson, E., and Johnson, A. W. The effects of D-xyloketose and certain root exudates in extension growth. *Proc. Roy. Soc.* **B136**, 577–591 (1949).

28. Brown, W. T., Quastel, J. H., and Scholefield, P. G. Effects of mercapto compounds on soil nitrification. *Appl. Microbiol.* **2**, 235–239 (1954).

29. Bunker, H. G. A review of the physiology and biochemistry of the sulphur bacteria. *Gt. Brit. Dept. Sci. Ind. Research Spec. Rept. No.* **3** (1936).

30. Bunt, J. S., and Rovira, A. D. The effect of temperature and heat treatment on soil metabolism. *J. Soil Sci.* **6**, 129–136 (1955).

31. Butlin, K. R. The bacterial sulphur cycle. *Research* **6**, 184 (1953).

32. Butlin, K. R., and Adams, M. E. Autotrophic growth of sulphate-reducing bacteria. *Nature* **160**, 154–155 (1947).

33. Butlin, K. R., and Postgate, J. R. The economic importance of autotrophic microorganisms. *Symposium Soc. Gen. Microbiol. 4th*, 271–305 (1954).

34. Butlin, K. R., Selwyn, S. C., and Wakerley, D. S. Sulphide production from sulphate-enriched sewage sludges. *J. Appl. Bacteriol.* **19**, 3–15 (1956).

35. Challenger, F., and Charlton, P. J. Studies on biological methylation. X. *J. Chem. Soc.* 424–429 (1947).

36. Chapman, H. D., Liebig, G. F., and Rayner, D. S. Lysimeter investigation of nitrogen gains and losses under various systems of covercropping and fertilization, and a discussion of error sources. *Hilgardia* **19**, 57–128 (1949).

37. Chase, F. E. A preliminary report on the use of the Lees and Quastel soil perfusion technique in determining the nitrifying capacity of field soils. *Sci. Agr.* **28**, 315–320 (1948).

38. Chase, F. E., and Barker, G. A comparison of microbial activity in an Ontario forest soil under pine, hemlock and maple cover. *Can. J. Microbiol.* **1**, 45–54 (1954).

39a. Chase, F. E., and Gray, P. H. Use of the Warburg respirometer to study microbial activity in soils. *Nature* **171**, 481 (1953).

39b. Chase, F. E., and Gray, P. H. Application of the Warburg respirometer in studying respiratory activity in soil. *Can. J. Microbiol.* **3**, 335–349 (1957).

40. Chen, H. K. Production of growth-substance by clover nodule bacteria. *Nature* **142**, 753–754 (1938).

41. Clark, F. E. Soil microorganisms and plant roots. *Advances in Agron.* **1**, 241–288 (1949).

42. Collins, F. M., and Sims, C. M. A compact soil perfusion apparatus. *Nature* **178**, 1073–1074 (1956).

43. Colmer, A. R., Temple, K. L., and Hinkle, M. E. An iron-oxidizing bacterium from the drainage of some bituminous coal mines. *J. Bacteriol.* **59**, 317–328 (1949).

44. Cooper, E. A., Daker, W. D., and Stacey, M. Enzyme formation and polysaccharide synthesis by bacteria. *Biochem. J.* **32**, 1752–1758 (1938).

44a. Cunneen, J. I., and Smith, F. Constitution of mesquite gum. *J. Chem. Soc.*, 1141–1146 (1948).

45. Dadd, C. C., Fowden, L., and Pearsall, W. H. An investigation of the free amino-acids in organic soil types using paper partition chromatography. *J. Soil Sci.* **4**, 69–71 (1953).

46. Daste, P. L'effet "Rhizosphère" chez le *Triticum Sphaerococcum. Rev. gén. botan.* **57**, 685–688 (1950).

47. Delwiche, C. C. "Nitrification" and "Denitrification." *In* "Inorganic Nitrogen Metabolism" (W. D. McElroy and B. Glass, eds.), pp. 218–232, 233–259. Johns Hopkins Press, Baltimore, Maryland, 1956.

48. Delwiche, C. C. Production and utilization of nitrous oxide by *Pseudomonas denitrificans. J. Bacteriol.* **77**, 55–59 (1959).

49. Dion, H. G., and Mann, P. J. G. Three-valent manganese in soils. *J. Agr. Sci.* **36**, 239–245 (1946).

50. Donald, C. M., and Williams, C. H. Fertility and productivity of a podzolic soil as influenced by subterranean clover (*Trifolium subterraneum* L.) and superphosphate. *Australian J. Agr. Research* **5**, 664–687 (1954).

51. Drobník, J. The use of respirometry in the microbiology of soil. *Českoslov. mikcrobiol.* **3**, 5 (1958).

52. Eberhardt, F. Ein Beitrag zum Problem der Wurzelausscheidungen. *Z. Botan.* **43**, 405–422 (1955).

53. Eller, W., and Koch, K. Studien über Huminsäuren. *Ber.* **53B**, 1469 (1920).

54. Ellinger, G., and Quastel, J. H. Preliminary experiments in the study of the respiratory activity of microorganisms suspended in thin films of fluid adhering to solid surfaces. *Biochem. J.* **42**, 214–218 (1948).

55. Felber, I. M. Persistence of the moisture covering effect of methyl cellulose in soil. *Proc. Soc. Hort. Sci.* **45**, 331–337 (1944).

56. Felber, I. M., and Gardner, V. R. Effect of a hydrophilic colloid of high viscosity on water loss from soils and plants. *Agr. Expt. Sta. Tech. Bull. Mich. State Coll. No.* **189**, 3–30 (1944).

57. Fischer, F. The decay of cellulose and lignin. *Brennstoff-Chem.* **5**, 132–137 (1924).

58. Fischer, F., and Tropsch, H. Vergleichende Untersuchungen über Lignin und Cellulose. *Ber.* **56B**, 2418–2428 (1923).

59. Frankland, P. F., and Frankland, G. The nitrifying process and its specific ferment. *Trans. Roy. Soc. London* **B181**, 107–128 (1890).

60. Fred, E. B., and Haas, A. R. C. The etching of marble by roots in the presence and absence of bacteria. *J. Gen. Physiol.* **1**, 631–638 (1919).

61. Frederick, L. R., Starkey, R. L., and Segal, W. Decomposibility of some organic sulfur compounds in soil. *Soil. Sci. Soc. Am. Proc.* **21**, 287–292 (1957).

62. Freney, J. R. Aerobic transformation of cysteine to sulphate in soil. *Nature* **182**, 1318–1319 (1958).

63a. Freudenberg, K. Biosynthesis and constitution of lignin. *Nature* **183**, 1152–1155 (1959).

63b. Freudenberg, K. Structure and formation of lignin. *Ind. Eng. Chem.* **49**, 1384 (1957).

63c. Freudenberg, K., Harder, M., and Markert, L. Bemerkungen zur Chemie des Lignins. *Ber.* **61**, 1760–1765 (1928).

63d. Freudenberg, K., Harkin, J. M., Reichert, M., and Fukuzumi, T. Enzymes participating in lignification. *Chem. Ber.* **91**, 581–590 (1958).

63e. Freudenberg, K., Janson, A., Knopf, E., and Haag, A. Zur Kenntnis des Lignins. *Ber.* **69**, 1415–1425 (1936).

63f. Freudenberg, K., Klinck, F., Flickinger, E., and Sobek, A. Die Bindung des Formaldehyde in Lignin. *Ber.* **72**, 217–226 (1937).

63g. Freudenberg, K., Meister, M., and Flickinger, E. Fichtenlignin. *Ber.* **70**, 500–513 (1937).

63h. Freudenberg, K., Reznik, H., Fuchs, W., and Reichert, M. Formation of lignin and of wood. *Naturwissenschaften* **42**, 29–35 (1955).

63i. Freudenberg, K., Zocher, H., and Dürr, W. Weitere Versuche mit Lignin. *Ber.* **62**, 1814–1823 (1929).

64. Fries, N., and Forsman, B. Quantitative determination of certain nucleic acid derivatives in pea root exudate. *Physiol. Plantarum* **4**, 410–420 (1951).

64a. Furusaka, C. Sulphate metabolism by *Desulfovibrio desulfuricans*. *Nature* **192**, 427–429 (1961).

65. Furusaka, C., and Hatton, T. Microbial metabolism in Paddy soils. *Bull Inst. Agr. Research (Tohoku Univ.)* **8**, 35 (1956).

66. Gardner, W. H. Synthetic soil conditioners and some of their uses. *Proc. Wash. State Hort. Assoc.* **48**, 115–122 (1952).

67a. Gayon, U., and Dupetit, G. Sur la fermentation des nitrates. *Compt. rend. acad. sci.* **95**, 644–646 (1882).

67b. Gayon, U., and Dupetit, G. Sur la transformation des nitrates en nitrites. *Compt. rend. acad. sci.* **95**, 1365–1367 (1882).

67c. Gayon, U., and Dupetit, G. Recherches sur la réduction des nitrates par les infiniment petits. *Mém. soc. sci. phys. nat. Bordeaux [Sér. 3]* **2**, 201–307 (1886).

68a. Geoghegan, M. J., and Brian, R. C. Influence of bacterial polysaccharides on aggregate formation in soils. *Nature* **158**, 837 (1946).

68b. Geoghegan, M. J., and Brian, R. C. Aggregate formation in soil. *Biochem. J.* **43**, 5–13 (1948).

69. Gerretsen, F. C. Manganese deficiency of oats and its relation to soil bacteria. *Ann. Bot. [N.S.]* **1**, 207–230 (1937).

70. Gerretsen, F. C. The influence of microorganisms on the phosphate intake by the plant. *Plant and Soil* **1**, 51–81 (1948).

70a. Gerretsen, F. C. Manganese in relation to photosynthesis. II. Redox potentials of illuminated crude chloroplast suspensions. *Plant and Soil* **2**, 159–193 (1950).

71. Gilmour, C. M., Allen, O. N., and Truog, E. Soil aggregates as influenced by the growth of mold species, kind of soil and organic matter. *Soil Sci. Soc. Am. Proc.* **13**, 292–296 (1948).

72. Gilmour, C. M., Daimsky, L., and Bollen, W. B. Manometric gas analysis as an index of microbial oxidations and reductions in soil. *Can. J. Microbiol.* **4**, 287–293 (1958).

73. Gleen, H. Biological oxidation of iron in the soil. *Nature* **166**, 871–872 (1950).
74. Gleen, H. Microbial oxidation of ammonium and thiocyanate ions in soil. *Nature* **168**, 117–118 (1951).
75. Gleen, H., and Quastel, J. H. Sulfur metabolism in soil. *Appl. Microbiol.* **1**, 70–77 (1953).
76. Goldberg, S. S., and Gainey, P. L. Role of surface phenomena in nitrification. *Soil Sci.* **80**, 43–53 (1955).
77. Gray, P. H., and Thornton, H. G. The estimation of bacterial numbers in soil by direct counts from stained films. *Nature* **122**, 400–401 (1928).
78. Greenwood, D. J., and Lees, H. Studies on the decomposition of amino acids in soils. I. A preliminary survey of techniques. *Plant and Soil* **7**, 253–268 (1956).
79. Greenwood, D. J., and Lees, H. An electrolytic rocking percolator. *Plant and Soil* **11**, 87–91 (1959).
80. Greenwood, D. J., and Lees, H. Studies on the decomposition of amino acids in soils. II. The anaerobic metabolism. *Plant and Soil* **12**, 69–80 (1960).
81. Guittoneau, G. Sur l'oxydation microbienne du soufre au cours de l'ammonisation. *Compt. rend. acad. sci.* **184**, 45–46 (1927).
82. Guittoneau, G., and Keilling, J. L'évolution et la solubilisation du soufre élémentaire dans la terre arable. *Ann. agron.* (N.S.) **2**, 690–725 (1932).
83. Gyllenberg, H. G. Seasonal variation in the composition of the bacterial soil flora in relation to plant development. *Can. J. Microbiol.* **3**, 131–134 (1957).
84. Halperin, A. H., Quastel, J. H., and Scholefield, P. G. Bacterial oxidation of cholic acid. *Arch. Biochem. Biophys.* **52**, 5–17 (1954).
85. Happold, F. C., Johnstone, K. I., Rogers, H. J., and Youatt, J. B. The isolation and characteristics of an organism oxidizing thiocyanate. *J. Gen. Microbiol.* **10**, 261–266 (1954).
86. Happold, F. C., and Key, A. The bacterial purification of gas-works liquors. II. The biological oxidation of ammonium thiocyanate. *Biochem. J.* **31**, 1323–1329 (1937).
87. Harmsen, G. W., and Van Schreven, D. A. Mineralization of organic nitrogen in soil. *Advances in Agron.* **7**, 299–398 (1955).
88. Hauck, R. D., and Melsted, S. W. Some aspects of the problem of evaluating denitrification in soils. *Soil Sci. Soc. Am. Proc.* **20**, 361–364 (1056).
89. Haworth, W. N., Pinkard, F. W., and Stacey, M. Function of bacterial polysaccharides in the soil. *Nature* **158**, 836–837 (1946).
90. Hedrick, R. M., and Mowry, D. T. Effect of synthetic polyelectrolyes on aggregation, aeration and water relationships of soil. *Soil Sci.* **73**, 427–441 (1952).
91. Hestrin, S., and Avineri-Shapiro, S. Mechanism of polysaccharides production from sucrose. *Biochem. J.* **38**, 2–10 (1944).
92. Hibbert, H. Status of the lignin problem. *Paper Trade J.* July 24 (1941).
93. Hibbert, H. Lignin. *Ann. Rev. Biochem.* **11**, 183–202 (1942).
94. Hiltner, L. Über neuere Erfahrungen und Probleme auf dem Gebiet der Bodenbakteriologie und unter besonderer Berücksichtigung der Gründüngung und Bruche. *Arb. deut. Landwirtsch. Ges.* **98**, 59–78 (1904).
94a. Hinton, C. L. The polyuronides. *Ann. Rev. Biochem.* **20**, 67–86 (1951).
94b. Hirst, E. L. and Jones, J. K. N. Constitution of Damson gum, *J. Chem. Soc.* 506–512 (1946). Chemistry of some plant gums and mucilages, *J. Soc. Dyers Colorists* **63**, 249–254 (1947). Constitution of egg-plum gum, *J. Chem. Soc.* 1064–1068 (1947).

95. Hochster, R. M., and Quastel, J. H. Manganese dioxide as a terminal hydrogen acceptor in the study of respiratory systems. *Arch. Biochem. Biophys.* **36**, 132–146 (1952).

96. Hofman, T., and Lees, H. The biochemistry of the nitrifying organisms. 4. The respiration and intermediary metabolism of *Nitrosomonas*. *Biochem. J.* **54**, 579–583 (1953).

97. Jansson, S. L. Tracer studies in nitrogen transformations in soil with special attention to mineralization-immobilization relationships. *Ann. Roy. Agr. Coll. Sweden* **24**, 101–121 (1958).

98. Jensen, H. L. Nitrification of oxime compounds by heterotrophic bacteria. *J. Gen. Microbiol.* **5**, 360–368 (1951).

99. Jensen, H. L. Decomposition of chloro-substituted aliphatic acids by soil bacteria. *Can. J. Microbiol.* **3**, 151–164 (1956).

100. Jensen, H. L. Biological transformation of thiourea. *Arch. Mikrobiol.* **28**, 145–152 (1957).

101. Jensen, H. L., and Gundersen, K. Biological decomposition of aromatic nitro compounds. *Nature* **175**, 341 (1954).

102. Jensen, H. L., and Petersen, H. I. Decomposition of hormone herbicides by bacteria. *Acta Agr. Scand.* **2**, 215–231 (1952).

103. Jensen, H. L., and Sörensen, H. The influence of some organic sulfur compounds and enzyme inhibitors on *Nitrosomonas europaea*. *Acta. Agr. Scand.* **2**, 295–304 (1952).

104. Kandler, O. Papierchromatographischer Nachweis der Aminosäureausscheidung *in vitro* kultivierter Mainswurzeln. *Z. Naturforsch.* **6b**, 437–445 (1951).

105. Katznelson, H. The "rhizosphere effect" of mangles on certain groups of soil microorganisms. *Soil Sci.* **62**, 343–354 (1946).

106. Katznelson, H., Lochhead, A. G., and Timonin, M. I. Soil microorganisms and the rhizosphere. *Botan. Rev.* **14**, 543–587 (1948).

107. Katznelson, H., and Richardson, L. T. The microflora of the rhizosphere of tomato plants in relation to soil sterilization. *Can. J. Research* **C21**, 249–255 (1943).

108. Katznelson, H., Rouatt, J. W., and Payne, T. M. B. Liberation of amino-acids by plant roots in relation to desiccation. *Nature* **174**, 1110–1111 (1954).

109. Katznelson, H., Rouatt, J. W., and Payne, T. M. B. The liberation of amino acids and reducing compounds by plant roots. *Plant and Soil* **7**, 35–42 (1955).

110. Katznelson, H., Rouatt, J. W., and Payne, T. M. B. Recent studies on the microflora of the rhizosphere. *Proc. 6th Cong. Soil Sci. Paris* **3**, 151–156 (1956).

111. Katznelson, H., Rouatt, J. W., and Payne, T. M. B. Manometric studies with rhizosphere and non-rhizosphere soil. *Can. J. Microbiol.* **3**, 673–678 (1957).

112a. Katznelson, H., and Stevenson, L. L. Metabolic activity of soil microorganisms. *Bacteriol. Proc. (Soc. Am. Bacteriologists)* **56**, 24 (1956).

112b. Katznelson, H., and Stevenson, L. L. Observations on the metabolic activity of the soil microflora. *Can. J. Microbiol.* **2**, 611–622 (1956).

113. Kingma Boltjes, T. Y. Untersuchungen über die nitrifizierenden Bakterien. *Arch. Mikrobiol.* **6**, 79–138 (1935).

114. Kluyver, A. J. The changing appraisal of the microbe. Leeuwenhoek lecture. *Proc. Roy. Soc.* **B141**, 147–161 (1953).

115. Kluyver, A. J., and Donker, H. J. C. Die Einheit in der Biochemie. *Chem. Zelle u. Gewebe* **13**, 134–190 (1926).

116a. Kluyver, A. J., and Verhoeven, W. Studies on true dissimilatory nitrate reduction. II. The mechanism of denitrification. *Antonie van Leeuwenhoek J. Microbiol. Serol.* **20**, 242–262 (1954).

116b. Kluyver, A. J., and Verhoeven, W. True dissimilary nitrate reduction; adaptation in *Micrococcus denitrificans. Antonie van Leeuwenhoek J. Microbiol. Serol.* **20**, 337–347 (1954).

117. Knox, R., Gell, P. G. H., and Pollock, M. R. The selective action of tetrathionate in bacteriological media. A report to the Medical Research Council. *J. Hyg.* **43**, 147–159 (1943).

118. Kroth, E. M., and Page, J. B. Aggregate formation in soils with special reference to cementing substances. *Soil. Sci. Soc. Am. Proc.* **11**, 27–34 (1946).

119. Larsen, H. The photolitho-autotrophic bacteria and their energy relations. *Symposium Soc. Gen. Microbiol.* **4th**, 186–201 (1954).

120a. Lees, H. Effect of copper-enzyme poisons on soil nitrification. *Nature* **158**, 97 (1946).

120b. Lees, H. A simple automatic percolator. *J. Agr. Sci.* **37**, 27–28 (1947).

121. Lees, H. The effects of zinc and copper on soil nitrification. *Biochem. J.* **42**, 534–538 (1948).

122. Lees, H. The soil percolation technique. *Plant and Soil* **1**, 221–239 (1949).

123. Lees, H. Studies on the nitrifying organisms. *J. Gen. Microbiol.* **5**, xvii–xviii (1951).

124. Lees, H. The biochemistry of the nitrifying organisms. 1. The ammonia-oxidizing systems of *Nitrosomonas. Biochem. J.* **52**, 134–139 (1952).

125. Lees, H. The biochemistry of the nitrifying bacteria. *Symposium Soc. Gen. Microbiol.* **4th**, 84–98 (1954).

126. Lees, H., and Quastel, J. H. New technique for the study of soil sterilization. *Chem. & Ind. (London)* **26**, 238–239 (1944).

127. Lees, H., and Quastel, J. H. Bacteriostatic effects of potassium chlorate on soil nitrification. *Nature* **155**, 276–278 (1945).

128a. Lees, H., and Quastel, J. H. Biochemistry of nitrification in soil. 1. Kinetics of, and the effects of poisons on, soil nitrification as studied by soil perfusion technique. *Biochem. J.* **40**, 803–815 (1946).

128b. Lees, H., and Quastel, J. H. Biochemistry of nitrification in soil. 2. The site of soil nitrification. *Biochem. J.* **40**, 815–823 (1946).

128c. Lees, H., and Quastel, J. H. Biochemistry of nitrification in soil. 3. Nitrification of various organic nitrogen compounds. *Biochem. J.* **40**, 824–828 (1946).

129. Lees, H., and Simpson, J. R. The biochemistry of nitrifying organisms. 5. Nitrite oxidation by *Nitrobacter. Biochem. J.* **65**, 297–305 (1957).

130. Lees, H., Simpson, J. R., Jensen, H. L., and Sörensen, H. Formation of nitrite from oximes and hydroxylamine by micro-organisms. *Nature* **173**, 358 (1954).

131. Lefevre, K. N., and Tollens, B. Untersuchungen über die Glucuronsäure; ihre quantitative Bestimmung und ihre Farbe Reactionen. *Ber.* **80**, 4513 (1907).

132. Lewis, R. F., and Pramer, D. Isolation of *Nitrosomonas* in pure culture. *J. Bacteriol.* **76**, 524–528 (1958).

133. Linder, P., Craig, J. C., Cooper, F. E., and Mitchell, J. W. Movement of 2,3,6-trichlorobenzoic acid from one plant to another through their root systems. *J. Agr. Food Chem.* **6**, 356–357 (1958).

134. Lindstrom, E. S., Burris, R. H., and Wilson, P. W. Nitrogen fixation by photosynthetic bacteria. *J. Bacteriol.* **58**, 313–316 (1949).

135. Lindstrom, E. S., Tove, S. R., and Wilson, P. W. Nitrogen fixation by the green and purple sulfur bacteria. *Science* **112**, 197–198 (1950).

136. Lochhead, A. G. Qualitative studies of soil microorganisms. XV. Capability of the predominant bacterial flora for synthesis of various growth factors. *Soil Sci.* **84**, 395–403 (1957).

137. Lochhead, A. G. Soil bacteria and growth-promoting substances. *Bacteriol. Revs.* **22**, 145–153 (1958).

138. Lochhead, A. G., and Burton, M. O. An essential bacterial growth factor produced by microbial synthesis. *Can. J. Botany* **31**, 7–22 (1953).

139. Lochhead, A. G., and Burton, M. O. Importance of soil extract in the enumeration and study of soil bacteria. *Proc. 6th Congr. Soil Sci. Paris* **3**, 157–161 (1956).

140. Lochhead, A. G., and Burton, M. O. Qualitative studies of soil microorganisms. XIV. Specific vitamin requirements of the predominant bacterial flora. *Can. J. Microbiol.* **3**, 35–42 (1957).

141. Lochhead, A. G., and Chase, F. E. Qualitative studies of soil microorganisms. V. Nutritional requirements of the predominant bacterial flora. *Soil Sci.* **55**, 185–195 (1943).

142. Lochhead, A. G., and Rouatt, J. W. The "rhizosphere effect" on the nutritional groups of soil bacteria. *Soil Sci. Soc. Am. Proc.* **19**, 48–49 (1955).

143. Lochhead, A. G., and Thexton, R. H. Qualitative studies of soil microorganisms. VII. The "rhizosphere effect" in relation to the amino acid nutrition of bacteria. *Can. J. Research* **C25**, 20–26 (1947).

144a. Lochhead, A. G., and Thexton, R. H. Vitamin B_{12} as a growth factor for soil bacteria. *Nature* **167**, 1034 (1951).

144b. Lochhead, A. G., and Thexton, R. H. Qualitative studies of soil microorganisms. X. Bacteria requiring vitamin B_{12} as a growth factor. *J. Bacteriol.* **63**, 219–226 (1952).

145. Lockett, W. T. Oxidation of thiosulfate by certain bacteria in pure culture. *Proc. Roy. Soc.* **B87**, 441–444 (1914).

146. Lundegårdh, H., and Stenlid, G. *Arch. Botanik* **31A**, 1 (1944); see Harley, J. L. Mycorrhiza and soil ecology. *Biol. Revs. Cambridge Phil. Soc.* **23**, 127–158 (1952).

147. Lyon, T. L., and Wilson, J. K. Liberation of organic matter by roots of growing plants. *Cornell Univ. Agr. Expt. Sta. Mem.* **40**, 1–44 (1921).

148. McCalla, T. M. Influence of microorganisms and some organic substances on soil structure. *Soil Sci.* **59**, 287–297 (1945).

149. McElroy, W. D., and Glass, B., eds. "Inorganic Nitrogen Metabolism." Johns Hopkins Press, Baltimore, Maryland, 1956.

150. McGarity, J. W., Gilmour, C. M., and Bollen, N. B. Use of an electrolytic respirometer to study denitrification in soil. *Can. J. Microbiol.* **4**, 303–316 (1958).

151. Mann, P. J. G., and Quastel, J. H. Manganese metabolism in soils. *Nature* **158**, 154–156 (1946).

152. Martin, J. P. Microorganisms and soil aggregation. *Soil Sci.* **59**, 163–174 (1945).

153. Martin, J. P. Microorganisms and soil aggregation. 11. Influence of bacterial polysaccharides on soil structure. *Soil Sci.* **61**, 157–166 (1946).

154. Martin, J. P., and Waksman, S. A. Influence on microorganisms on soil aggregation and erosion. *Soil Sci.* **50**, 29–47 (1940).

155. Martin, P. Einfluss der Kulturfiltrate von Mikroorganismen auf die Abgabe von Scopoletin aus den Keimwurzeln des Hafers (*Avena sativa* L.). *Arch. Mikrobiol.* **29**, 154–168 (1958).

156. Martin, W. P. Status report on soil conditioning chemicals. *Soil Sci. Soc. Am. Proc.* **17**, 1–9 (1953).
157. Martin, W. P., Taylor, G. S., Engibous, J. C., and Burnett, E. Soil and crop responses from field applications of soil conditioners. *Soil Sci.* **73**, 455–471 (1952).
158. Martin, W. P., and Volk, G. W. Soil conditioners and fertilizers. *Natl. Fertilizer Rev.* **27** (4), 11–13 (1952).
159. Meiklejohn, J. Iron and the nitrifying bacteria. *J. Gen. Microbiol.* **8**, 58–65 (1953).
160. Metzger, W. H. The effect of growing plants on solubility of soil nutrients. *Soil Sci.* **25**, 273–280 (1928).
161. Meyerhof, O. Untersuchungen über den Atmungsvorgang nitrifizierender Bakterien. I. Die Atmung des Nitratbildners durch chemische Substanzen. *Arch. ges. Physiol. Pflüger's* **164**, 353–427 (1916).
162. Meyerhof, O. Untersuchungen über den Atmungsvorgang nitrifizierender Bakterien. II. Beeinflussung der Atmung des Nitratbildners durch chemische Substanzen. *Arch. ges. Physiol. Pflüger's* **165**, 229–284 (1916).
163. Meyerhof, O. Untersuchungen über den Atmungsvorgang nitrifizierender Bakterien. III. Die Atmung des Nitritbildners und ihre Beeinflussung durch chemische Substanzen. *Arch. ges. Physiol. Pflüger's* **166**, 240–280 (1916–1917).
164. Miller, L. D. Rapid formation of high concentrations of hydrogen sulfide by sulfate-reducing bacteria. *Contribs. Boyce Thompson Inst.* **15**, 437–465 (1949).
165. Miller, L. D. Tolerance of sulfate-reducing bacteria to hydrogen sulfide. *Contribs. Boyce Thompson Inst.* **16**, 73–83 (1950).
166. Mishustin, E. N., and Gromyko, E. P. Stability of soil macroaggregate formed by microorganisms. *Mikrobiologiya* **15**, 169–175 (1946).
167. Morgan, D. G., and Mees, G. C. Gibberellic acid and the growth of crop plants. *Nature* **178**, 1356–1357 (1956).
168. Nance, J., and Cunningham, L. W. Evolution of acetaldehyde by excised wheat roots in solutions of nitrate and nitrite salts. *Am. J. Botany* **38**, 604–609 (1951).
169. Nason, A., and Evans, H. J. Triphosphopyridine nucleotide-nitrate reductase in *Neurospora*. *J. Biol. Chem.* **202**, 655–673 (1953).
170. Nelson, D. H. Isolation and characterization of *Nitrosomonas* and *Nitrobacter*. *Zbl. Bakteriol. Parasitenk. Abt. II.* **83**, 280–311 (1931).
171. Newman, A. S., and Thomas, J. R. Decomposition of 2,4-dichlorophenoxyacetic acid in soil and liquid media. *Soil Sci. Soc. Am. Proc.* **14**, 160–164 (1949).
172. Nicholas, D. J. D., and Nason, A. Mechanism of action of nitrate reductase from *Neurospora*. *J. Biol. Chem.* **211**, 183–197 (1954).
173. Nicolas, E., and Nicolas, G. Observations sur l'influence de l'urée, de la sulfo-urée et de l'allylsulfo-urée sur les végétaux supérieurs. *Compt. rend. acad. sci.* **180**, 1286–1289 (1925).
174. Nord, F. F., and Vitucci, J. C. On the mechanism of enzyme action; acetate metabolism of certain wood destroying molds and mechanisms of decay. *Arch. Biochem.* **14**, 229–242, 243–255 (1947).
175. Norman, A. G. The biological decomposition of plant materials. II. The role of the furfuraldehyde-yielding substances in the decomposition of straws. *Biochem. J.* **23**, 1367–1384 (1939).
176. Norman, A. G., and Bartholomew, W. V. The action of some mesophilic bacteria on cellulose. *Soil Sci. Soc. Am. Proc.* **5**, 243–247 (1940).

177. Norman, A. G., and Fulley, W. H. Cellulose decomposition by microorganisms. *Advances in Enzymol.* **2**, 239–264 (1942).
178. Nutman, P. S., Thornton, H. G., and Quastel, J. H. Inhibition of plant growth by 2,4-dichlorophenoxyacetic acid and other plant substances. *Nature* **155**, 498–500 (1945).
179. Oden, S. The application of physico-chemical methods to the study of humus. *Trans. Faraday Soc.* **7**, 288–294 (1922).
180. Owen, O., and Windsor, G. W. Nitrification of amino acids. *Nature* **166**, 239 (1950).
181. Owen, O., Windsor, G. W., and Long, M. I. E. Effect of carbon nitrogen ratio upon the formation of nitrate and ammonia from amino-acids in soil. *Nature* **166**, 152 (1950).
182. Payne, T. M. B., Rouatt, J. W., and Katznelson, H. Detection of free amino acids in soil. *Soil Sci.* **82**, 521–524 (1956).
183. Pollock, M. R., and Knox, R. Bacterial reduction of tetrathionate. *Biochem. J.* **37**, 476–481 (1943).
184. Postgate, J. R. Competitive inhibition of sulphate reduction by selenate. *Nature* **164**, 670 (1949).
185. Postgate, J. R. Competitive and non-competitive inhibitors of bacterial sulphate reduction. *J. Gen. Microbiol.* **6**, 128–141 (1952).
186. Postgate, J. R. Cytochrome c₃ and desulphoviridin: pigments of the anaerobe *Desulphovibrio desulphuricans*. *J. Gen. Microbiol.* **14**, 545–572 (1956).
187. Preston, W. H., Jr., Mitchell, J. W., and Reeve, W. Movement of α-methoxyphenylacetic acid from one plant to another through their root systems. *Science* **119**, 437–438 (1954).
188. Pringsheim, E. G. On iron flagellates. *Phil. Trans. Roy. Soc. London* **B232**, 311–342 (1947).
189. Pringsheim, H. Über den fermentativen Abbau der Cellulose. *Z. physiol. Chem. Hoppe-Seyler's* **78**, 266–291 (1912).
190. Quastel, J. H. Influence of organic matter on aeration and structure of soil. *Soil Sci.* **73**, 419–426 (1952).
191. Quastel, J. H. Soil Conditioners. *Ann. Rev. Plant Physiol.* **5**, 75–92 (1954).
192. Quastel, J. H. Leeuwenhoek lecture "Soil metabolism." *Proc. Roy. Soc.* **B143**, 159–175 (1955).
193. Quastel, J. H., Hewitt, E. J., and Nicholas, D. J. D. The control of manganese deficiency in soils. 1. The effects of sulphur and thiosulphates on crops growing on manganese-deficient soils. *J. Agr. Sci.* **38**, 315–322 (1948).
194. Quastel, J. H., and Scholefield, P. G. Influence of organic compounds on nitrification in soil. *Nature* **164**, 1068–1072 (1949).
195. Quastel, J. H., and Scholefield, P. G. Nitrification of amino acids. *Nature* **166**, 239 (1950).
196. Quastel, J. H., and Scholefield, P. G. Biochemistry of nitrification in soil. *Bacteriol. Revs.* **15**, 1–53 (1951).
197. Quastel, J. H., and Scholefield, P. G. Urethanes and soil nitrification. *Appl. Microbiol.* **1**, 282–287 (1953).
198. Quastel, J. H., and Scholefield, P. G. Arsenite oxidation in soil. *Soil Sci.* **75**, 279–285 (1953).
199. Quastel, J. H., and Scholefield, P. G. *In* "Methods in Enzymology" (S. P. Colowick, and N. O. Kaplan, eds.), Vol. 4, pp. 336–342. Academic Press, New York, 1957.

200. Quastel, J. H., Scholefield, P. G., and Stevenson, J. W. Oxidation of pyruvic-oxime by soil organisms. *Nature* **166,** 940–942 (1950).

201. Quastel, J. H., Scholefield, P. G., and Stevenson, J. W. Oxidation of pyruvic acid oxime by soil organisms. *Biochem. J.* **51,** 278–284 (1952).

202. Quastel, J. H., Stephenson, M., and Whetham, M. D. Some reactions of resting bacteria in relation to anaerobic growth. *Biochem. J.* **19,** 304–317 (1925).

203. Quastel, J. H., and Webley, D. M. Effects of the addition to soil of alginic acid and of other forms of organic matters on soil aeration. *J. Agr. Sci.* **37,** 257–266 (1947).

204. Quastel, J. H., and Wooldridge, W. R. Experiments on bacteria in relation to the mechanism of enzyme action. *Biochem. J.* **21,** 1224–1251 (1927).

205. Redfield, A. C. The biological control of the chemical factors in the environment. *Am. Scientist* **46,** 205–221 (1958).

206. Roach, W. A. Sulphur as a soil fungicide against the potato wart disease organism. *J. Agr. Sci.* **20,** 74–96 (1930).

207. Rogoff, M. H., and Reid, J. J. Bacterial decomposition of 2,4-dichlorophen-oxyacetic acid. *J. Bacteriol.* **71,** 303–307 (1956).

208. Rouatt, J. W., and Atkinson, R. G. The effect of the incorporation of certain cover crops on the microbiological balance of potato scab infested soil. *Can. J. Research* **C28,** 140–152 (1950).

209. Roulet, M. A. Recherches sur les vitamines du sol. *Experientia* **4,** 149–150 (1948).

210. Rovira, A. D. Use of the Warburg apparatus in soil metabolism studies. *Nature* **172,** 29–30 (1953).

211. Rovira, A. D. Plant root excretions in relation to the rhizosphere effect. I. The nature of root exudate from oats and peas. *Plant and Soil* **7,** 178–194 (1956).

212. Rovira, A. D. Plant root excretions in relation to the rhizosphere effect. II. A study of the properties of root exudate and its effects on the growth of microorganisms isolated from the rhizosphere and control soil. *Plant and Soil* **7,** 195–208 (1956).

213. Sacks, L. E., and Barker, H. A. Substrate oxidation and nitrous oxide utilization in denitrification. *J. Bacteriol.* **64,** 247–252 (1952).

214. Schloesing, T., and Müntz, C. A. Sur la nitrification par les ferments organisés. *Compt. rend. acad. sci.* **84,** 301–303 (1877).

215. Schloesing, T., and Müntz, C. A. Sur la nitrification par les ferments organisés. *Compt. rend. acad. sci.* **85,** 1018–1020 (1877).

216. Schloesing, T., and Müntz, C. A. Recherches sur la nitrification par les ferments organisés. *Compt. rend. acad. sci.* **86,** 892–895 (1878).

217. Schloesing, T., and Müntz, C. A. Recherches sur la nitrification. *Compt. rend. acad. sci.* **89,** 1074–1077 (1879).

218. Schmidt, E. L., and Starkey, R. L. Soil microorganisms and plant growth substances. II. Transformations of certain B-vitamins in soil. *Soil Sci.* **71,** 221–231 (1951).

219. Sherwood, L. V., and Engibous, J. C. Status report on soil conditioning chemicals. II. *Soil Sci. Soc. Am. Proc.* **17,** 9–16 (1952).

220. Simola, P. E. Über den Abbau der Cellulose durch Microorganismen. *Ann. Acad Sci. Fennicae Ser. A. No.* **34** (6), 1–115 (1931).

221. Skirman, V. B. D., and MacRae, I. C. The influence of oxygen on the reduction of nitrate by adapted cells of *Pseudomonas denitrificans. Can J. Microbiol.* **3,** 215–230 (1957).

221a. Smith, F. Constitution of carob gum. *J. Am. Chem. Soc.* **70**, 3249–3253 (1948).
222. Sowden, F. J., and Parker, D. I. Amino nitrogen of soils and of certain fractions isolated from them. *Soil Sci.* **76**, 201–208 (1953).
223. Stahl, W. H., McQue, B., Mandels, G. R., and Siu, R. G. Studies on the microbiological degradation of wool: I. Sulfur metabolism. *Arch. Biochem.* **20**, 422–432 (1949).
224. Starkey, R. L. Some influences of the development of higher plants upon the microorganisms in the soil. I. Historical and introductory. *Soil Sci.* **27**, 319–334 (1929).
225. Starkey, R. L. Some influences of the development of higher plants upon the microorganisms in the soil. II. Influence of the stage of plant growth upon abundance of organisms. *Soil Sci.* **27**, 355–378 (1929).
226. Starkey, R. L. Some influences of the development of higher plants upon the microorganisms in the soil. IV. Influence of proximity to root on abundance and activity of microorganisms. *Soil Sci.* **32**, 367–393 (1931).
227. Starkey, R. L. The production of polythionates from thiosulfate by microorganisms. *J. Bacteriol.* **28**, 387–400 (1934).
228. Starkey, R. L. Isolation of some bacteria which oxidize thiosulfate. *Soil Sci.* **39**, 197–215 (1935).
229. Starkey, R. L. Some influences of the development of higher plants upon the microorganisms in the soil. VI. Microscopic examination of the rhizosphere. *Soil Sci.* **45**, 207–249 (1938).
230. Starkey, R. L. Relations of microorganisms to transformations of sulfur in soils. *Soil Sci.* **70**, 55–65 (1950).
231. Starkey, R. L. Transformations of sulfur by microorganisms. *Ind. Eng. Chem.* **48**, 1429–1437 (1956).
232. Starkey, R. L. Interrelations between microorganisms and plant roots in the rhizosphere. *Bacteriol. Revs.* **22**, 154–172 (1958).
233. Starkey, R. L., Segal, W., and Manaker, R. A. Sulfur products of the decomposition of methionine and cystine by microorganisms. *Proc. Intern. Congr. Microbiol. 6th Congr. Rome 1953* **1**, 256–257 (1953).
234. Stevenson, I. L., and Katznelson, H. The oxidation of ethanol and acetate in soils. *Can. J. Microbiol.* **4**, 73–79 (1958).
235. Stickland, L. H. The reduction of nitrates by *Bact. coli. Biochem. J.* **25**, 1543–1554 (1931).
236. Stolp, H. Beiträge zur Frage der Beziehungen zwischen Microorganismen und höheren Pflanzen. *Arch. Mikrobiol.* **17**, 1–30 (1952).
237. Swaby, R. J. Influence of humus on soil aggregation. *J. Soil Sci.* **1**, 182–194 (1950).
238. Swaby, R. J., and Passay, B. I. A simple macrorespirometer for studies in soil microbiology. *Australian J. Agr. Research* **4**, 334–339 (1953).
239. Swanson, C. L. W. Soil conditioners awaken new interest in soils. *Frontiers of Plant Sci.* **5**, (1) 4–5 (1952).
240. Takai, Y., Koyama, T., and Kamura, T. *Soil and Plant Food (Tokyo)* **2**, 63 (1956).
241. Tamiya, H., Haga, K., and Huizisige, H. Zur Physiologie der chemoautotrophen Schwefelbakterien 1. *Acta Phytochim. (Japan)* **12**, 173–225 (1941).
242. Temple, K. L. A modified design of the Lees soil percolation apparatus. *Soil Sci.* **71**, 209–210 (1951).
243. Temple, K. L. The autotrophic oxidation of iron by a new bacterium: *Thiobacillus ferrooxidans. J. Bacteriol.* **62**, 605–611 (1951).

244. Tenney, F. G., and Waksman, S. A. Composition of natural organic materials and their decomposition in the soil. IV. The nature and rapidity of decomposition of the various organic complexes in different plant materials, under aerobic conditions. *Soil Sci.* **28**, 55–84 (1929).

245. Tenney, F. G., and Waksman, S. A. Composition of natural organic materials and their decomposition in the soil. V. Decomposition of various chemical constituents in plant materials under anaerobic conditions. *Soil Sci.* **30**, 143–160 (1930).

246. Thimann, K. V. On the physiology of the formation of nodules on legume roots. *Proc. Natl. Acad. Sci. U.S.* **22**, 511–514 (1936).

247. Vallance, L. G. *Proc. Queensland Soc. Sugar Cane Technologists* **20**, 123 (1953).

248. Veldkamp, H. A study of the aerobic decomposition of chitin by microorganisms. *Med. Landbouwhogeschool Wageningen* **55**, (3) 127–174 (1955).

249. Virtanen, A. I., Hietala, P. K., and Wahlroos, O. Antimicrobial substances in cereals and fodder plants. *Arch. Biochem. Biophys.* **69**, 486–500 (1957).

250. Virtanen, A. I., and Laine, T. Investigations on the root nodule bacteria of leguminous plants. XXII. The excretion products of root nodules. The mechanism of N-fixation. *Biochem. J.* **33**, 412–427 (1939).

251. Vishniac, W. The metabolism of *Thiobacillus thioparus*. I. The oxidation of thiosulfate. *J. Bacteriol.* **64**, 363–373 (1952).

252. Vishniac, W., and Santer, M. The Thiobacilli. *Bacteriol. Revs.* **21**, 195–213 (1957).

253. Vogler, K. G., and Umbreit, W. W. Studies on the metabolism of the autotrophic bacteria. III. The nature of the energy storage material active in the chemosynthetic process. *J. Gen. Physiol.* **26**, 157–167 (1943).

254. Vozniakovskaia, Y. M. Influence of wheat root systems on soil microflora. *Mikrobiologiya* **17**, 458 (1948).

255. Waksman, S. A. The origin and nature of the soil organic matter or soil "humus." I. Introductory and historical. *Soil Sci.* **22**, 123–162 (1926).

256. Waksman, S. A. The origin and nature of the soil organic matter or soil "humus." III. The nature of the substances contributing to the formation of humus. *Soil Sci.* **22**, 323-333 (1926).

257. Waksman, S. A. The origin and nature of the soil organic matter or soil "humus." V. The role of microorganisms in the formation of "humus" in the soil. *Soil Sci.* **22**, 421–436 (1926).

258. Waksman, S. A. The method of proximate analysis and its application to the study of plant residues, composts, and humus formations. *Trans. Third Comm. Intern. Soc. Soil Sci. New Brunswick, N.J. 1939 A*, 101–119 (1939).

259. Waksman, S. A. "Microbial Antagonisms and Antibiotic Substances." The Commonwealth Fund, New York, 1945.

260. Waksman, S. A., and Iyer, K. R. N. Synthesis of humus nucleus, an important constituent of humus soils, peats and composts. *J. Wash. Acad. Sci.* **22**, 41–50 (1932).

260a. Waksman, S. A., and Starkey, R. L. "Soil and the Microbe," pp. 67, 110, 157. Wiley, New York, 1931.

261. Waksman, S. A., and Tenney, F. G. On the origin and nature of the soil organic matter or soil "humus." IV. The decomposition of the various ingredients of straw and of alfalfa meal by mixed and pure cultures of microorganisms. *Soil Sci.* **22**, 395–406 (1926).

262. Waksman, S. A., and Woodruff, H. B. The occurrence of bacteriostatic and bactericidal substances in the soil. *Soil Sci.* **53**, 233–239 (1942).
263. Walker, E., and Warren, F. L. Decomposition of cellulose by *Cytophaga*. I. *Biochem. J.* **32**, 31–43 (1938).
264. Walker, T. W. The sulphur cycle in grassland soils. *J. Brit. Grassland Soc.* **12**, 10–18 (1957).
265. Wallace, R. H., and Lochhead, A. G. Qualitative studies of soil microorganisms. IX. Amino acid requirements of rhizosphere bacteria. *Can. J. Research* **C28**, 1–6 (1950).
266. Walls, J. S., Wagenknecht, A. C., Newton, J. W., and Burris, R. H. Comparison of the metabolism of ammonia and molecular nitrogen in photosynthesizing bacteria. *J. Bacteriol.* **63**, 563–573 (1952).
267. Warington, R. On nitrification (part 4). *J. Chem. Soc.* **59**, 484–497 (1891).
268. Weeks, L. E., and Colter, W. G. Effect of synthetic soil conditioners on erosion control. *Soil Sci.* **73**, 473–484 (1952).
269. West, P. M., and Lochhead, A. G. Qualitative studies of soil microorganisms. IV. The rhizosphere in relation to the nutritive requirements of soil bacteria. *Can. J. Research* **C18**, 129–135 (1940).
270. Wieringa, K. T., and Kerkhof Magot, M. F. An apparatus for the determination of the respiration process in soil samples. *Plant and Soil* **8**, 395–396 (1957).
271. Wijler, J., and Delwiche, C. C. Investigations on the denitrifying process in soil. *Plant and Soil* **5**, 155–169 (1954).
272. Winogradsky, S. Über Schwefelbakterien. *Z. Botan.* **45**, 489 (1887).
273. Winogradsky, S. Recherches physiologiques sur les sulfobactéries. *Am. inst. Pasteur* **3**, 50 (1889).
274. Winogradsky, S. Recherches sur les organismes de la nitrification. *Ann. inst. Pasteur* **4**, 213–231; 257–275; 760–771 (1890).
275. Winogradsky, S. *Ann. inst. Pasteur* **5**, 92, 577 (1890–1891).
276. Winogradsky, S. Sur la dégradation de la cellulose dans le sol. *Ann. inst. Pasteur* **43**, 549–633 (1929).
277. Winogradsky, S., and Omeliansky, V. Über den Einfluss der organischen Substanzen auf die Arbeit der nitritizierenden Bakterien. *Centr. Bakteriol. Abt.* *II* **5**, 329, 429 (1899).
278. Woods, D. D., and Clifton, C. E. Studies in the metabolism of strict anaerobes (genus *Clostridium*). VI. Hydrogen production and amino acid utilization by *Clostridium tetanomorphum*. *Biochem. J.* **31**, 1774–1788 (1937).
278a. Wright, D. E. Effect of plant growth inhibition on uptake of amino acids by plant roots. *Nature* **192**, 1044–1045 (1961).
279. Youatt, J. B. Studies on the metabolism of *Thiobacillus thiocyanoxidans*. *J. Gen. Microbiol.* **11**, 139–149 (1954).

AUTHOR INDEX

Numbers in boldface refer to pages on which the complete reference is listed at the end of a chapter. Numbers in lightface indicate the pages in the text on which the references are cited. Numbers in parentheses are reference numbers.

A

Abdel-Ghaffar, A. S., 592, **645**

Abraham, R. G., 387(200), **440**, 495(176), **530**

Adams, A., 452(242), **533**

Adams, M. E., 723(32), **744**

Addoms, R. M., 159(383), **349**

Adelstein, S. J., 469(1), **522**

Afridi, M. M. R. K., 283(210), 290(210), 291, **340**

Aghulon, H., 35, 102, **120**, 499, **522**

Ahmed, M. B., 210, 328(5), **330**

Ahmed, S., 83(2), 105(2, 3, 3a), 109(2), 110(3), 112(2, 3), **120**, 325(6, 7, 7a), **330**, 364(1, 2, 156), 423(1, 2, 156), 424(156), **431, 432, 439**

Akazawa, T., 499(4), **522**

Albaum, H. G., 509(5), **522**

Albers, M., 175(593), **360**

Albert, L. S., 249, 251, 252, 263, 265, **330**

Albrecht, W. A., 52(4), **120**, 312(469), 315(470), **354**, 564, **645**

Alderfer, R. B., 691, **743**

Aldrich-Blake, R. N., 631, **645**

Aleem, M. I. H., 397, 398(5), 412(3), 413(5), **431**

Alexander, M., 396, 397(75, 76), 412(3), **431, 435**, 555, **645**

Alexander, T. R., 250, 261(8), **330**

Alfthan, M., 636, **645**

Allen, E. K., 565, 579, 585, 586, 591, 592(6), 623, 625, 629, 630, **645, 646**

Allen, M. B., 93, 104, **120**, 285(20, 21), **331**, 387(198), 389, 391, 402, 413(6, 7), **431, 440**, 485, 503, **522**, 557, 559, 563, 564, **645, 646**, 690(71), 716, **743**

Allen, O. N., 565, 579, 585, 586, 591, 592(1, 6), 623, 625, 629, 630, **645, 646, 746**

Allison, F. E., 364(113), 418(113), **437**, 503(108), **527**, 542, 551, 554, 556, 559, 567, 572, **646, 653, 654, 656**

Allison, L. E., 694, **743**

Allison, R. M., 634(384), 638, 641, 645, **665**

Alm, F., 318(385a), **349**

Almon, L., 592, 622, **646**

Anderson, A. J., 155(10, 11), 270, 273 (8a, 9, 10, 12), 274(10, 12), **330**, 484, **522**, 569, 606(224), 608, **646, 657**

Anderson, G. R., 425, **437**, 549, **646**

Anderson, I., 212, **330**

Anderson, M. S., 72(7), 76, **120**

Anderssen, F. G., 222(14), **330**

Andreae, W. A., 220(15), 221, **330**, 510(8), **522**

Angrist, A. A., 398(121), **437**

Appelby, C. A., 481(9), **522**, 619, 621, **646**

Appleman, L. O., 267(465), **353**

Aprison, M. H., 626, **646**

Argawala, S. C., 275(1, 4), 276(1, 2, 3, 4, 211), 281, 283, 284(2, 4, 213), 286, 287, 289, 290(4), 291(4), 300 (214), **329, 330, 340**, 492, **522**

Arhimo, A. A., 636(348, 349), 639(348), **663**

Arnold, C. W. B., 673(4), **743**

Arnon, D. I., 52, 99(11a, 12), 100, 102 (9, 10), 103(10, 16, 239), 104, 105, 106(11, 15, 17), 107, 108(17, 114, 239), 109(13, 17, 114, 239), 110 (239), 111, 112(16, 17), 115, 116 (17), **120, 125, 131**, 176(17), 226, 270, 285(20, 21), 292(18a, 236a), 297, **330, 331, 342**, 364(10, 35), 365, 366(11, 119), 375(9, 12), 402, 418(11, 35), 421, **431, 432, 433, 437,**

INDEX TO PLANT NAMES

Numbers in this index designate the pages on which reference is made, in the text, to the plant in question. No reference is made in the index to plant names included in the titles that appear in the reference lists. In general, where a plant has been referred to in the text sometimes by common name, sometimes by its scientific name, all such references are listed in the index after the scientific name; cross reference is made, under the common name, to this scientific name. However, in a few instances when a common name as used cannot be referred with certainty to a particular species, the page numbers follow the common name.

A

SUBJECT INDEX

A

Absorption, *see* Foliar absorption, Roots
Activation analysis,
  for cobalt and vanadium, 115
Adaptation,
  of rhizobia, 586
  to unfavorable conditions, 118–120
Adsorption,
  of ions by roots, 65
Alcohol dehydrogenase, 468–469
Aldehyde oxidase,
  role of molybdenum in, 483, 493
  role of nitrate in, 493
  reactivation by silicomolybdates, 493
Aldolase,
  iron content of, 482
Alginic acid,
  composition of, 683
  effect on soil aeration, 691
Alkali metals, 318–322
  biochemical functions of, 321–322
  see also individual metals
Allylthiourea,
  inhibitor of soil nitrification, 709
Aluminum, 3, 52, 326–328
  general effects of, 326–328
  toxicity in soil, 52
Amines in soil,
  conversion to nitrate, 712–713
  toxicity to plants, 700
Amino acids, *see also* names of specific
    amino acids
  as nitrogen sources, 55, 559
  in bleeding sap, 595–596
  effects of nutrient status on, 299–318
  excretion from nodules, 602
  for deficiency effects on, *see* individual
    nutrients, 305
  in nitrogen fixation, 635
  in nodules of nonleguminous plants,
    634
  in soil, 27, 699–700
  inhibition of root uptake of, 730
  leaching from plants, 96

metabolism of in soil, 713
nitrogen sources for rhizobia, 566
toxic effects on plants, 700
Amino acid synthesis,
  in plants and animals, 637
Amino sugars,
  in soil, 27
Ammonia,
  formation by rhizobia, 566
  inhibitor of nitrogen fixation, 556–557
  occurrence in soil, 49, 699
  product of nitrogen fixation, 635, 637
  role in nitrate assimilation, 393–394
  utilization by microorganisms, 376–379
Ammonium
  inhibitory effect on nodulation, 607–608
Ammonium ion,
  product of amino acid metabolism, 700
Ammonium nitrogen,
  in rain water, 540
Ammonium sulfate,
  rate of nitrification of, 702
Amylase,
  calcium ions in, 511
Apical meristems,
  boron deficiency effects, 241
Arginase,
  activating ions, 454
Arginine,
  conversion in soil, 713
Arsenic,
  in soils, 37
Ascorbic acid,
  effects of molybdenum on, 284–285
  in root nodules, 617
  non-enzymatic autoxidation, 455–456
Ascorbic acid oxidase,
  catalytic activity of, 474–475
  reaction in activation of, 475
  reactions of, 472
  role of metal ions in, 456, 475
L-Aspartic acid,
  as nitrogen source in aseptic cultures,
    602
  in nutrition of peas, 596

797